# Shooter's Bible

## 105TH EDITION

# Shooter's Bible
## 105TH EDITION

SKYHORSE PUBLISHING

10 9 8 7 6 5 4 3 2 1

ISBN: 978-1-62636-066-2
ISSN: 0080-9365

Printed in Canada

Note: Every effort has been made to record specifications and descriptions of guns, ammunition, and accessories accurately, but the Publisher can take no responsibility for errors or omissions. The prices shown for guns, ammunition, and accessories are manufacturers' suggested retail prices (unless otherwise noted) and are furnished for information only. These were in effect at press time and are subject to change without notice. Purchasers of the book have complete freedom of choice in pricing for resale.

# CONTENTS

# INTRODUCTION

*I*t's hard to believe that another year has gone by and here we are, publishing the 105th edition of the *Shooter's Bible*. It goes without saying that it has been a tumultuous year for gun owners. Despite this, the gun industry itself saw unprecedented sales in 2012, with a 40 percent increase in sales of firearms and ammunition in 2012 over 2011 (based on excise tax data). This, in turn, has lead to increased industry contributions to the Federal Aid in Wildlife Restoration Fund (aka the Pittman-Robertson Act).

By all accounts, the coming year should be just as prosperous, and arms manufacturers everywhere are ramping up their production to meet the insatiable demands of the gun-buying public. Many companies have come out with new and exciting firearms this year. Doubletap's titanium two-barrel derringer, Chiappa Firearms' triple-barrel shotgun, and the ZiP gun from U.S. Fire Arms are just a few examples of the high-tech manufacturing techniques that are changing firearms design throughout the industry.

As you pore over the more than one hundred pages in the New Products section, you'll be amazed at the wide array of new firearms that is now available. You'll also be pleased to see Remington coming out with the fiftieth anniversary edition of the revered Model 1100, while Winchester Repeating Arms is relaunching the Winchester 1873, one hundred forty years after the Gun That Won The West was introduced.

As you move on to the meat of the *Shooter's Bible*, the existing products section, starting on page 107, you'll find practically every gun in production on the planet, with totally up-to-date prices and specs. I'm

**EDITORIAL DIRECTOR JAY CASSELL TRACKS AN INCOMING CANADA GOOSE FROM A LAYOUT BLIND IN NORTHERN MANITOBA. HE WAS USING A 12-GAUGE BROWNING MAXUS ON THIS HUNT. BROWNING HAS ADDED A SPORTING GOLDEN CLAYS MODEL TO THE MAXUS LINE OF GAS-OPERATED SEMIAUTO SHOTGUNS THIS YEAR.**

## Return of "The Gun That Won the West"

The Model 1873 lever-action rifle (MSRP: $1,300)—the real thing, the genuine article—is again being produced by Winchester Repeating Arms. The '73 rifle is the stuff of legends with some 720,610 rifles, carbines, and muskets produced from 1873 up until 1919 by the original Winchester factory located in New Haven, Connecticut. Along with the rifle, Winchester also debuted a new cartridge named the .44 Winchester or .44 WCF (Winchester Center Fire), but the cartridge is more commonly known as the .44-40; a .44 caliber bullet atop 40 grains of black powder. Later it was chambered in .38-40 and .32-20. Lawmen, settlers, outlaws, hunters, and renegades used the 1873 with efficiency. It was the first truly strong repeating rifle that offered rapid rifle when muzzleloaders and single shots were common. Many paired the rifle with a pistol in the same caliber. Since then the company has gone through numerous reorganizations and Italian-manufactured 1873 clones have been imported to the U.S. The new Winchester 1873 has an oil-finished walnut stock with a classic blued-steel crescent buttplate and a 20-inch round barrel. It is chambered in .357 Mag./.38 Spl.

—Robert A. Sadowski

**WINCHESTER MODEL 1873 SHORT RIFLE**

*Shooter's Bible* was published in 1925; it has been published annually, and in some cases bi-annually, ever since. More than seven million copies have been sold in that time, and it continues to be the ultimate reference book for millions of people who want information on new guns, ammunition, optics, and accessories, as well as up-to-date prices and specs for thousands of in-production firearms.

The Skyhorse staff—including head researcher Lindsey Breuer (below) as well as intern Ryan Gerhardt—is proud of this newest edition of the *Shooter's Bible*, a book that has been continually updated and fact-checked for the past twelve months. Not content to rest on our laurels, however, we have also continued to produce more and more

**RESEARCHER LINDSEY BREUER HOLDING HER NEW BENELLI ULTRA LIGHT 28-GAUGE.**

guessing that everyone reading this book owns some firearms that are in this section. (If you own a gun that isn't in this section, it is probably out of production, in which case you need to pick up a copy of another Skyhorse Publication, the 35th edition of the *Gun Trader's Guide*.) Optics, ammunition, and accessories are also covered in this year's edition of the *Shooter's Bible*, as they are every year.

If this is first time you have picked up a copy of the *Shooter's Bible*, you should know that it has a long and storied past. The first numbered edition of the

## A Classic Shotgun 50 Years in the Making and Still Going Strong

The Remington Model 1100 is America's favorite semiauto shotgun. Back in 1963 it debuted to compete against recoil-operated shotgun designs. The 1100 uses a gas system to cycle the semiautomatic action. This system not only quickly and reliably cycled the action; it also greatly reduced recoil. It's also lightweight and points naturally. Hunters have used the 1100 for duck, pheasant, turkey, grouse, rabbit, and deer—to name just a few. Over the years more than four million 1100s have been manufactured in a variety of finishes, barrel lengths, and types. It has been chambered in the tiny .410 and 28-gauge to 20-, 16- and 12-gauge. Visit a trap, skeet, or sporting clays field and you will no doubt see an 1100 in action. The military and LE have also specified certain features on the 1100 for tactical use. A special 12-gauge Model 1100 50th Anniversary collectors' edition (MSRP: $1,999) features a machine-cut engraved receiver with gold fill, B-grade walnut stock with a white-diamond grip cap and white line spacer, and 28-inch vent rib barrel with Rem. chokes. —Robert A. Sadowski

**REMINGTON 1100 50TH ANNIVERSARY EDITION**

*Shooter's Bible* guidebooks. In the past year, we have added a number of new volumes to our growing lineup, including the *Shooter's Bible Guide to Gun Assembly, Disassembly, and Cleaning*, by Robert A. Sadowski; the *Shooter's Bible Guide to Planting Food Plots*, by Peter Fiduccia; the *Shooter's Bible Guide to Bowhunting*, by Todd A. Kuhn; the *Shooter's Bible Guide to Concealed Carry*, by Brad Fitzpatrick, and the *Shooter's Bible Guide to the Hunting Rifle and Its Ammunition*, by Thomas C. Tabor.

Other guidebooks include the *Shooter's Bible Guide to Cartridges*, the *Shooter's Bible Guide to Rifle Ballistics*, the *Shooter's Bible Guide to Optics*, the *Shooter's Bible Guide to AR-15s*, the *Shooter's Bible Guide to Combat Handguns*, the *Shooter's Bible Guide to Knives*, and the *Shooter's Bible Guide to Whitetail Strategies*. All of these must-have books include useful, up-to-date information on topics that shooters and outdoorsmen value.

What does the future hold? How about the *Shooter's Bible Guide to Extreme Iron*, the *Shooter's Bible Guide to Long-Range Tactical Rifles*, and the *Shooter's Bible Guide to Home Defense*?

As you can see, we're trying to cover all of your specialized needs, needs that merit guidebooks of their own. And in the meantime, we hope you enjoy this, the 105th edition of the *Shooter's Bible*. It's got something for everyone.

**Jay Cassell**
*Editorial Director*
Skyhorse Publishing

ADVANCED ARMAMENT CORP. MULTI PURPOSE WEAPON (MPW)

ANSCHÜTZ 1416 D HB WALNUT THUMBHOLE

ANSCHUTZ 1727F IMAGE

ARMALITE AR-30A1 STANDARD RIFLE

## ADVANCED ARMAMENT CORP. MULTI PURPOSE WEAPON (MPW)
**Action**: Bolt
**Stock**: Magpul CTR
**Barrel**: 9 in., 12.5 in., 16 in.
**Sights**: None
**Weight**: N/A
**Caliber**: 7.62x35mm (300 AAC Blackout)
**Magazine**: 30 rounds
**Features**: Bolt carrier features a proprietary design with a modified cam path and nickel-boron finish to enhance reliability and ease of cleaning; bolt machined from Carpenter 158 steel; freefloating forearm; lower receiver features a Geissele two-stage trigger; six-position Mil-Spec collapsing stock
**MSRP**. . . . . . . . . . . . . . . . . **$1599.95**

## ANSCHÜTZ 1416 D HB WALNUT THUMBHOLE
**Action**: Bolt
**Stock**: Walnut
**Barrel**: 23 in.
**Sights**: None
**Weight**: 6 lb. 8 oz.
**Caliber**: .22 LR
**Magazine**: 5 rounds
**Features**: Luxus repeating rifle; single-stage trigger; black buttplate; carved German checkering on the pistol grip; sling swivel studs; wave-style V-block dovetail rail for telescopic sight
**MSRP**. . . . . . . . . . . . . . . . . . .**$1517**

## ANSCHÜTZ 1727F
**Action**: Lever
**Stock**: Walnut German stock
**Barrel**: 22 in.
**Sights**: None
**Weight**: 7 lb. 10 oz.
**Caliber**: .17 HMR

**Magazine**: None
**Features**: Two-stage trigger; precision barrel; rubber buttplate
**MSRP**. . . . . . . . . . . . . . . . . . .**$3409**

## ARMALITE AR-30A1 STANDARD RIFLE
**Action**: Bolt
**Stock**: Aluminum
**Barrel**: 24 in., 26 in.
**Sights**: None
**Weight**: 12 lb. 13 oz.–13 lb. 6 oz.
**Caliber**: .300 Win. Mag., .338 Lapua
**Magazine**: 5 rounds
**Features**: Cheekpiece is at the optimum height for viewing through a telescopic sight; buttstock is ergonomically correct; steel magazine; ambidestrous magazine catch; fixed stock; detachable sight rail, hard case, and sling included
**MSRP**. . . . . . . . . . . . . . **$3264–$3404**

## ARMALITE AR-30A1 TARGET RIFLE

*Action*: Bolt
*Stock*: Aluminum
*Barrel*: 24 in., 26 in.
*Sights*: None
*Weight*: 14 lb. 8 oz.–15 lb. 5 oz.
*Caliber*: .300 Win. Mag., .338 Lapua
*Magazine*: 5 rounds
*Features*: MOA Picatinny rail over receiver and barrel; cheekpiece vertically adjustable; adjustable buttstock; 1913 accessory rail at the bottom of the buttstock; buttpad is adjustable for height
**MSRP** . . . . . . . . . . . . . $3460–$3599

## ARSENAL, INC. SAM7R

*Action*: Semiautomatic
*Stock*: Polymer
*Barrel*: 16.25 in.
*Sights*: Scope rail
*Weight*: 8 lb.
*Caliber*: 7.62x39mm
*Magazine*: 10 rounds
*Features*: Milled receiver; chrome-lined, hammer-forged barrel; muzzle brake; cleaning rod; intermediate length US-made 10 in. trapdoor buttstock
**MSRP** . . . . . . . . . . . . . . . . . .$1299

## ARSENAL, INC. SLR-106F

*Action*: Semiautomatic
*Stock*: Synthetic
*Barrel*: 16.25 in.
*Sights*: Scope rail

*Weight*: 7 lb. 5 oz.
*Caliber*: 5.56 NATO
*Magazine*: 5 rounds
*Features*: Stamped receiver; chrome-lined, hammer-forged barrel; bayonet lug; stainless steel heat shield handguards; left-side folding buttstock; also available in desert sand color
**MSRP** . . . . . . . . . . . . . . . . . .$1080

## BERETTA USA ARX100

*Action*: Semiautomatic
*Stock*: Telescopic folding
*Barrel*: 12 in., 16 in.
*Sights*: Removable back-up sights
*Weight*: 6 lb. 13 oz.
*Caliber*: 5.56 NATO (other barrels available)
*Magazine*: 30 rounds
*Features*: Cold hammer forged barrel can be replaced with barrels in different lengths and calibers; case injections switch from right to left at a button push; completely ambidextrous; technopolymer receiver; contains no pins and can be disassembled without the use of tools; optional .300 Black Out kit available
**MSRP** . . . . . . . . . . . . . . . . . .$1950

ARMALITE AR-30A1 TARGET RIFLE

ARSENAL, INC. SAM7R

ARSENAL, INC. SLR-106F

BERETTA USA ARX100

# NEW Products: **Rifles**

BLASER USA R8 PROFESSIONAL SUCCESS

BROWNING AB3 (A-BOLT III) COMPOSITE STALKER

BROWNING BAR SHORTRAC HOG STALKER REALTREE MAX-1

BROWNING BLR LIGHTWEIGHT '81 HOG STALKER TAKEDOWN GREEN

## BLASER USA R8 PROFESSIONAL SUCCESS

*Action*: Bolt
*Stock*: Synthetic
*Barrel*: 22.8 in., 25.6 in.
*Sights*: Open
*Weight*: 7 lb.
*Caliber*: .222 Rem., .204 Ruger, .223 Rem., .22-250, .243 Win., 6XC, 6.5x55 SE, 6.5x57, 6.5x65 RWS, .270 Win., 7x64, .308 Win., .30-06, 8x57 IS, 8.5x63, 9.3x57, 9.3x62, 6.5x68, 7.5x55 Suisse, 8x68 S, .257 Wby. Mag., .270 Wby. Mag., .270 WSM, 7mm Blaser Mag., 7mm Rem. Mag., .300 Blaser Mag., .300 Win. Mag., .300 Wby. Mag., .300 WSM, .338 Blaser Mag., .338 Win. Mag., .375 Blaser Mag., .375 H&H
*Magazine*: 3+1, 4+1, 5+1 rounds
*Features*: Blaser precision trigger; radial locking system; ergonomically optimized stock in dark green or dark brown and elastomer grips; double loading option; leather model available
**MSRP**. . . . . . . . . . . . . . . . . . .**$4148**
**Leather:**. . . . . . . . . . . . . . . . . .**$5198**

## BROWNING AB3 (A-BOLT III) COMPOSITE STALKER

*Action*: Bolt
*Stock*: Composite
*Barrel*: 22 in., 26 in.
*Sights*: None
*Weight*: 6 lb. 10 oz.–7 lb. 3 oz.
*Caliber*: .270 Win., .30-06 Spfd., 7mm Rem. Mag., .300 Win. Mag.
*Magazine*: 3 rounds (magnum), 4 rounds (standard)
*Features*: Matte blued barreled action; matte black synthetic stock; barrel is individulally finished with a hand-reamed chamber; free-floating barrel; receiver drilled and tapped for scope mounts; generous trigger guard; top-tang safety; sling swivel studs
**MSRP**. . . . . . . . . . . . . . . . . . .**$599.99**

## BROWNING BAR SHORTRAC HOG STALKER REALTREE MAX-1

*Action*: Gas-operated autoloader
*Stock*: Composite Realtree Max-1
*Barrel*: 20 in.
*Sights*: None
*Weight*: 9 lb. 5 oz.
*Caliber*: .308 Win.

*Magazine*: 10 rounds
*Features*: Aircraft-grade alloy receiver; drilled and tapped for scope mount; three interchangeable cheekpieces and recoil pads for different fit options; ambidextrous magazine release
**MSRP**. . . . . . . . . . . . . . . . .**$1669.99**

## BROWNING BLR LIGHTWEIGHT '81 HOG STALKER TAKEDOWN GREEN

*Action*: Lever
*Stock*: Green laminate wood
*Barrel*: 18 in.
*Sights*: TruGlo/Marble fiber optic fron
*Weight*: 6 lb. 11 oz.
*Caliber*: .223 Rem., .308 Win.
*Magazine*: Detachable box
*Features*: Satin nickel finish on receiver; matte finish on barrel; receiver drilled and tapped for scope mounts; checkered straight grip on stock; separates for storage or transportation; sling swivel studs; Picatinny rail scope base; Hog Stalker soft case included
**MSRP**. . . . . . . . . . . . . . . . .**$1339.99**

## BUSHMASTER 300 AAC BLACKOUT

*Action*: Semiautomatic
*Stock*: Magpul ACS stock
*Barrel*: 16 in.
*Sights*: None
*Weight*: 6 lb. 9 oz.
*Caliber*: .300 AAC Blackout
*Magazine*: Accepts all AR-types
*Features*: A compact 30-caliber solution for the AR platform; sound and flash suppression; use existing AR magazines; low-profile milled gas block; Magpul MOW grip; quad rail; Magpul enhanced trigger guard
**MSRP . . . . . . . . . . . . . . . . $1471.39**

**BUSHMASTER 300 AAC BLACKOUT**

## CENTURY INTERNATIONAL ARMS CENTURION 39 SPORTER

*Action*: Semiautomatic
*Stock*: Synthetic
*Barrel*: 16.5 in.
*Sights*: Front post, adjustable rear
*Weight*: 8 lb. 3 oz.
*Caliber*: 7.62x39mm
*Magazine*: 30 rounds
*Features*: Milled receiver machined from an 11-pound block of 4140 ordnance quality steel; rear sight adjustable for windage and elevation; high visibiliy from sight postl buttstock 1 in. longer than military-style stocks; upper and lower handguard have four Picatinny rails; two 30 round magazines included; 100 percent American made
**MSRP . . . . . . . . . . . . . . . . . $999.95**

**CENTURY INTERNATIONAL ARMS CENTURION 39 SPORTER**

## CHIAPPA FIREARMS LITTLE BADGER

*Action*: Single shot
*Stock*: Metal foldable
*Barrel*: 16.5 in.
*Sights*: Adjustable rear
*Weight*: 3 lb. 8 oz.
*Caliber*: .22LR
*Magazine*: None
*Features*: Single barrel; foldable rifle; extremely light for comfortable carry; folds to 16.5 in. total length; nylon carry bad and special cartridge holder available
**MSRP . . . . . . . . . . .$179.95–$189.95**

## CHIAPPA FIREARMS M1-22

*Action*: Semiautomatic
*Stock*: Wood or black synthetic
*Barrel*: 18 in.
*Sights*: Adjustable rear
*Weight*: 5 lb. 8 oz.
*Caliber*: .22LR
*Magazine*: 10 rounds
*Features*: The M1 carbine is a lightweight, easy-to-use semiautomatic carbine that became a standard firearm for the U.S. military during World War II, the Korean War, and the Vietnam War, and was produced in several variants.
**Synthetic: . . . . . . . . . . . . . . . $349**
**Wood: . . . . . . . . . . . . . . . . . . $399**

**CHIAPPA FIREARMS LITTLE BADGER**

**CHIAPPA FIREARMS M1-22**

# NEW Products: **Rifles**

CIMARRON 1886 BOAR BUSTER

CIMARRON 1886 CLASSIC

## CIMARRON 1886 BOAR BUSTER
*Action*: Lever
*Stock*: Walnut
*Barrel*: 19 in.
*Sights*: Fiber optic
*Weight*: N/A
*Caliber*: .45-70
*Magazine*: Fixed tube
*Features*: Carbine model; scout rail; pistol grip stock
MSRP . . . . . . . . . . . . . . . . $1792.70

## CIMARRON 1886 CLASSIC
*Action*: Lever
*Stock*: Walnut
*Barrel*: 26 in.
*Sights*: Open
*Weight*: N/A

*Caliber*: .45-70
*Magazine*: Fixed tube
*Features*: Blued receiver; pistol grip stock
MSRP . . . . . . . . . . . . . . . . $1792.70

## CIMARRON 1886 PREMIUM
*Action*: Lever
*Stock*: Premium Walnut
*Barrel*: 26 in.
*Sights*: Open
*Weight*: N/A
*Caliber*: .45-70
*Magazine*: Fixed tube
*Features*: Case colored receiver
MSRP . . . . . . . . . . . . . . . . $1883.70

## CIMARRON SADDLE SHORTY
*Action*: Lever
*Stock*: Wood
*Barrel*: 18 in.
*Sights*: Open
*Weight*: N/A
*Caliber*: .357 Mag./.38 Spl., .45 Colt, .44 WCF
*Magazine*: Fixed tube
*Features*: Full octagon barrel; straight stock with checkered forearm and stock
MSRP . . . . . . . . . . . . . . . . .$1059

CIMARRON 1886 PREMIUM

CIMARRON SADDLE SHORTY

## COLT COMPETITION MARKSMAN CRX-16

**Action**: Semiautomatic
**Stock**: M4 carbine-style
**Barrel**: 16 in.
**Sights**: None
**Weight**: 6 lb. 7 oz.
**Caliber**: .223 Rem.
**Magazine**: 30 rounds
**Features**: Match-grade chrome-moly steel barrel; twin-port muzzle brake; vented modular float-tube handguard; low profile gas block; charging handle with extended tactical latch; match-target trigger coated with nickel-Teflon
**MSRP**.....................$1399

**COLT COMPETITION CRX-16**

## COLT COMPETITION PRO CRP-18

**Action**: Semiautomatic
**Stock**: Magpul CTR adjustable
**Barrel**: 18 in.
**Sights**: None
**Weight**: 7 lb. 3 oz.
**Caliber**: .223 Rem.
**Magazine**: 30 rounds
**Features**: Match-grade, polished 416 stainless steel barrel; gas-operated, original direct-impingement system; triple port muzzle brake; Picatinny top handguard rail and accessory rail; Magpul MOE grip with extended backstrap; low profile adjustable gas block
**MSRP**....................$2019

**COLT COMPETITION CRP-18**

**COOPER FIREARMS MODEL 51**

## COOPER FIREARMS MODEL 51

**Action**: Bolt
**Stock**: Classic, Custom Classic, Western Classic, Schnabel, Mannlicher, Jackson Game, Jackson Hunter, Excaliber, Varminter, Montana Varminter, Varmint Extreme, Varmint Laminate, Phoenix
**Barrel**: 22 in., 24 in.
**Sights**: None
**Weight**: 6 lb. 4 oz.–7 lb. 4 oz.
**Caliber**: .17 Rem., .19-223, Tactical .20, .204 Ruger, .222 Rem., .222 Rem. Mag., .223 Rem., .223 Rem. AI, 6x45, 6x47, .300 Blackout
**Magazine**: None
**Features**: Longer barrel standard on all varmint models; fully adjustable single-stage trigger; Sako style extraction machined from solid bar stock
**MSRP**.............. $2225–$5095

**CZ-USA 455 AMERICAN**

### CZ-USA 455 AMERICAN
*Action*: Bolt
*Stock*: Black polymer
*Barrel*: 20.5 in.
*Sights*: None
*Weight*: 5 lb. 13 oz.

*Caliber*: .22LR
*Magazine*: Detachable box, 5 rounds
*Features*: New black synthetic stock; cold hammer-forged barrel; interchangeable barrel system; adjustable trigger
**MSRP** . . . . . . . . . . . . . . . . . . . . **$374**

**CZ-USA 455 VARMINT TACTICOOL**

### CZ-USA 455 VARMINT TACTICOOL
*Action*: Bolt
*Stock*: Black laminate
*Barrel*: 20.5 in.
*Sights*: None
*Weight*: 7 lb. 6 oz.
*Caliber*: .22LR
*Magazine*: Detachable box, 5 rounds
*Features*: Built as a tactical trainer with

a number of ergonomic features; stock has ambidextrous palm swells on its pistol grip and an especially high Monte Carlo to accommodate larger scopes; beavertail forend is great for riding bags or affixing bipod; cold hammer-forged barrel; interchangeable barrel system; adjustable trigger
**MSRP** . . . . . . . . . . . . . . . . . . . . **$522**

**CZ-USA 455 VARMINT THUMBHOLE SST FLUTED**

### CZ-USA 455 VARMINT THUMBHOLE SST FLUTED
*Action*: Bolt
*Stock*: Forest camo laminate
*Barrel*: 20.5 in.
*Sights*: Integrated 11mm dovetail
*Weight*: 7 lb.
*Caliber*: .17 HMR
*Magazine*: Detachable box, 5 rounds

*Features*: Fitted into a vented thumbhole stock in forest camo laminate; barrel is fluted to cut down on weight and speed cooling; CZ's new SST for the 455 platform
**MSRP** . . . . . . . . . . . . . . . . . . . . **$615**

DAKOTA ARMS MODEL 76 PH

DEL-TON DTI EVOLUTION

DEL-TON DT SPORT OR

DEL-TON ECHO 316H OR

## DAKOTA ARMS MODEL 76 PH

*Action*: Bolt
*Stock*: Fiberglass
*Barrel*: 23 in.
*Sights*: Fixed blade banded front, fiber optic bead
*Weight*: 9 lb.
*Caliber*: .375 H&H, .404 Jeffrey, .416 Rem., .416 Rigby, .458 Lott, .450 Dakota, .450 Rigby
*Magazine*: None
*Features*: Custom fiberglass stock; Douglas premium stainless steel barrel; barrel band; CeraKote matte black, black decelrator pad; right- and left-hand models available
**MSRP**. . . . . . . . . . . . . . . . . . .**$7995**

## DEL-TON DTI EVOLUTION

*Action*: Semiautomatic
*Stock*: Magpul CTR Mil-Spec
*Barrel*: 16 in.
*Sights*: Folding front, flip rear
*Weight*: 7 lb. 3 oz.
*Caliber*: 5.56x45mm
*Magazine*: 30 rounds
*Features*: Chrome-lined barrel; Samson Evolution free-float rail; Quick Flip Dual Aperture rear sight; Magpul MOE+ grip
**MSRP**. . . . . . . . . . . . . . . . . . .**$1300**

## DEL-TON DT SPORT OR

*Action*: Semiautomatic
*Stock*: M4 six-position
*Barrel*: 16 in.
*Sights*: None
*Weight*: 5 lb. 13 oz.
*Caliber*: 5.56x45mm
*Magazine*: 30 rounds

*Features*: Low profile gas block; six-position M4 stock; CAR handguards with single heat shields; A2 flash hider; anodized receiver; gun lock included
**MSRP**. . . . . . . . . . . . . . . . . . .**$699**

## DEL-TON ECHO 316H OR

*Action*: Semiautomatic
*Stock*: M4 five-position
*Barrel*: 16 in.
*Sights*: None
*Weight*: 6 lb. 10 oz.
*Caliber*: 5.56x45mm
*Magazine*: 30 rounds
*Features*: Single rail gas block; CAR handguards with single heat shields; A2 flash hider; forged 7075 T6 aluminum upper and lower receivers
**MSRP**. . . . . . . . . . . . . . . . . . .**$864**

## DPMS PANTHER ARMS DPMS 3G2

**Action**: Semiautomatic
**Stock**: Synthetic
**Barrel**: 16 in.
**Sights**: Magpu Gen 2 BUS
**Weight**: 7 lb. 1.6 oz.
**Caliber**: 5.56x45mm
**Magazine**: Detachable box, 30 rounds
**Features**: Stainless lightweight barrel with Miculek compensator; full length M111 handguard allows for the placement of back-up sights either on the top rail or on a 45-degree angle for rapid close-range target acquisition; Ergo grip and Magpul STR stock round out this range-ready carbine; pistol grip stock
**MSRP**....................$1239

## DPMS PANTHER ARMS 300 PERSONAL DEFENSE

**Action**: Semiautomatic
**Stock**: AP4 com. tube
**Barrel**: 23.75 in.
**Sights**: Magpul vertical
**Weight**: 5 lb. 8 oz.
**Caliber**: 5.56 NATO
**Magazine**: 30 rounds
**Features**: The DPMS Personal Defense Weapon, or PDW, is designed to bring maximum firepower into a small package. Features forged 7075 T6 A3 flattop upper receiver; chromoly barrel standard AR-15 fire control; PDW free float handguard with vertical grip
**MSRP**....................$1289

## DPMS PANTHER ARMS DPMS 6.8 HUNTER

**Action**: Semiautomatic
**Stock**: A2-style
**Barrel**: 20 in.
**Sights**: N/A, optics ready
**Weight**: 7 lb. 2 oz.
**Caliber**: 6.8 SPC
**Magazine**: 25 rounds
**Features**: Carbon-fiber free-float tube handguard; flattop upper; fluted teflon coated barrel; two-stage match fire control
**MSRP**....................$1269

## DPMS PANTHER ARMS DPSM .22 BULL BARREL

**Action**: Semiautomatic
**Stock**: Fixed A2 synthetic
**Barrel**: 16 in.

DPMS 3G2

DPMS PDW

DPMS 6.8 HUNTER

DPMS .22 BULL BARREL

**Sights**: None
**Weight**: 7 lb. 5 oz.
**Caliber**: .22LR
**Magazine**: 10 rounds

**Features**: Capable of accepting aftermarket stocks, grips, fire control components; integral feed ramp; fixed ejector
**MSRP**....................$1029

## FNH FN/UNIQUE ALPINE BALLISTA

**Action**: Bolt
**Stock**: Collapsible
**Barrel**: 26 in.
**Sights**: N/A, scope compatible
**Weight**: 15 lb.
**Caliber**: .308 Win., .300 Win. Mag., .338 Lapua Mag.
**Magazine**: 8 or 15 rounds (.308 Win.), 6 or 10 rounds (.300 Win. Mag.), 5 or 8 rounds (.338 Lapua)
**Features**: Modular, multi-caliber designed for long-range precision work; aluminum alloy receiver; adjustable trigger; ambidextrous stock; vibration-isolated aluminum alloy receiver; Mil-Std 1913 rail
**MSRP** . . . . . . . . . . . . . . . . . . . .**$9995**

FNH FN-UNIQUE ALPINE BALLISTA

FNH FN SPR A5 XP

## FNH FN SPR A5 XP

**Action**: Bolt
**Stock**: McMillan fiberglass
**Barrel**: 20 in., 24 in.
**Sights**: None
**Weight**: 11 lb. 5 oz.-11 lb. 13 oz.
**Caliber**: .300 WSM, .308 Win.
**Magazine**: 4 or 5 rounds
**Features**: Threaded tactical bolt knob; barrel threaded muzzle; Mil-Std 1913 rail; external claw extractor with controlled round feeding; integral recoil lug; three-position safety; knurled bolt handle
**MSRP** . . . . . . . . . . . . . . . . . . . .**$2899**

## HECKLER & KOCH MR762A1 (LRP)

**Action**: Semiautomatic
**Stock**: Synthetic
**Barrel**: 16.5 in.
**Sights**: 3-9x40mm scope
**Weight**: 9 lb. 15 oz.
**Caliber**: 7.62x51mm
**Magazine**: 10, 20 rounds
**Features**: Rifle; Leupold 3-9 VX-R Patrol scope and mount; HK G28 buttstock; LaRue Tactical BRM-S bipod; ERGO Pistol Grip; Blue Force Gear sling; Manta rail covers; OTIS cleaning kit; a 10- and 20-round magazine; Model 1720 Pelican case
**MSRP** . . . . . . . . . . . . . . . . . . .**$6895**

HECKLER & KOCH MR762A1 (LRP)

HENRY REPEATING ARMS THE ORIGINAL HENRY RIFLE

## HENRY REPEATING ARMS THE ORIGINAL HENRY RIFLE

**Action**: Lever
**Stock**: Walnut
**Barrel**: 24.5
**Sights**: Folding ladder rear
**Weight**: 9 lb.
**Caliber**: .44-40
**Magazine**: 13+1 rounds
**Features**: True to original specifications; first time the Original Henry has been offered in the U.S. by an American manufacturer in 150 years
**MSRP** . . . . . . . . . . . . . . . . . . . .**$2300**

## HOWA BY LEGACY SPORTS WHITETAIL PACKAGE

*Action*: Bolt
*Stock*: Synthetic
*Barrel*: 20 in.
*Sights*: 2.5-10x42mm scope
*Weight*: 9 lb.
*Caliber*: .204, .223, .22-250, .243, .308, 7mm-08
*Magazine*: 5 round detachable
*Features*: Contour barrel; shaved receiver and hollowed bolt handle; two-stage trigger; three-position safety; forged bolt with two locking lugs; three MoonShine Camo patterns: Muddy Girl, Harvest Moon, and Outshine; Nikko Stirling Nighteater 2.5-10x42 scope with #4 duplex reticle; Buffalo River bipod also included
**MSRP** . . . . . . . . . . . . . . . . . . . **$762**

**HOWA WHITETAIL OUTSHINE**

**J. P. SAUER & SOHN SAUER 101**

## J. P. SAUER & SOHN SAUER 101

*Action*: Bolt
*Stock*: Walnut
*Barrel*: 22 in., 24 in.
*Sights*: Adjustable open sights optional
*Weight*: 6 lb. 12 oz.
*Caliber*: .22-250 Rem., .243 Win., .270 Win., .308 Win., .30-06, 6.5x55, 7x64, 8x57IS, 9.3x62, 7mm Rem. Mag., .300 Win. Mag., .338 Win. Mag.
*Magazine*: 5+1 rounds (standard), 4+1 rounds (magnum)
*Features*: 60-degree bolt lift; six locking lugs; available in standard and magnum calibers; matte black finish; DURA SAFE firing pin safety; EVER REST action bedding; ambidextrous stock
**MSRP** . . . . . . . . . . . . . **$1499–$1699**

## KRISS VECTOR SBR

*Action*: Semiautomatic
*Stock*: Polymer
*Barrel*: 5.5 in.
*Sights*: Custom flip-up iron
*Weight*: 5 lb. 10 oz.
*Caliber*: .45 ACP
*Magazine*: 13 rounds
*Features*: Also available in Carbine and Special Duty Pistol configurations; adjustable folding stock; picatinny rails; ambidextrous F/S controls; foregrip; cable lock
**MSRP** . . . . . . . . . . . . . . . . . . .**$1995**

**KRISS VECTOR SBR**

K-VAR SGL 31-95

### K-VAR SGL 31-95

*Action*: Semiautomatic
*Stock*: Mil-Spec black polymer
*Barrel*: 16.3 in.
*Sights*: Rear leaf
*Weight*: 7 lb. 5 oz.
*Caliber*: 5.45x39.5mm
*Magazine*: 30, 45 rounds
*Features*: Manufactured at the Izhmash Factry in Russia; authentic Russian polymer side-folding buttstock; chrome-lined, hammer-forged barrel; scope rail; accessory lug
**MSRP**...................**$1299**

### MAGNUM RESEARCH MAGNUM LITE MLR22 WIN MAG

*Action*: Semiautomatic
*Stock*: Hogue Overmolded; Barracuda
*Barrel*: 18 in.
*Sights*: Rail for Weaver style rings
*Weight*: 7 lb. 5 oz.
*Caliber*: .22 Win. Mag
*Magazine*: 9 rounds
*Features*: Barrel features an 11 degree crown; patented gas system and block under barrel; available in nutmeg, pepper, forest camo, stainless steel, or matte
**MSRP**...............**$727–$819**

### MASTERPIECE ARMS MPAR 556 RIFLE

*Action*: Semiautomatic
*Stock*: Synthetic
*Barrel*: 16 in.
*Sights*: None
*Weight*: 7 lb. 13 oz.
*Caliber*: 5.56mm NATO (.223 Rem.)
*Magazine*: N/A
*Features*: Short stroke piston design; lightweight, free-floating, two-piece aluminum handguard; user located Picatinny rails; side-folding collapsible stock; full length top rail
**MSRP**...................**$999**

MAGNUM RESEARCH MAGNUM LITE
MLR22 WIN MAG BARRACUDA

MASTERPIECE ARMS
MPAR 556 RIFLE

### MAUSER M12 HUNTING RIFLE

*Action*: Bolt
*Stock*: Wood, Synthetic
*Barrel*: 22 in., 24.5 in.
*Sights*: None
*Weight*: 7 lb.
*Caliber*: .22-250 Rem., .243 Win., 6.5x55 SE, .270 Win., 7x64, .308 Win., .30-06 Spfd., 8x57 IS, 9.3x62, 7mm Rem., .300 Win. Mag., .338 Win. Mag.
*Magazine*: 5+1 rounds
*Features*: 60-degree bolt lift; detachable magazine; open sights available; drilled and tapped for scopes; stock extension available
**MSRP**...................**$1799**
**Extreme:**.................**$1499**

### MCMILLAN FIREARMS EOL MOUNTAIN EXTREME ALPINE

*Action*: Bolt, McMillan G30 Long Action
*Stock*: Composite, khaki and gray
*Barrel*: 26 in.
*Sights*: 20 MOA Picatinny style scope bases
*Weight*: 7 lb. 4 oz.
*Caliber*: 6.5x284 Norma
*Magazine*: N/A
*Features*: Jewell trigger; metal black finish; NP3 muzzle brake; EDGE graphite technology
**MSRP**...................**$6775**

### MCMILLAN FIREARMS EOL MOUNTAIN EXTREME DENALI

*Action*: Bolt, McMillan G30 Long Action
*Stock*: EDGE A3-5 composite, khaki and gray
*Barrel*: 28 in.
*Sights*: 40 MOA Picatinny style scope bases
*Weight*: 9 lb. 8 oz.
*Caliber*: 7mm EOL Mag./7mm Rem. Ultra Mag., .300 EOL Mag./.300 Rem. Ultra Mag., .338 Lapua
*Magazine*: N/A
*Features*: Jewell trigger; metal black finish; NP3 muzzle brake; EDGE graphite technology; hand-lapped match grade barrel
**MSRP**...................**$6895**

**MAUSER M12 HUNTING RIFLE**

**MCMILLAN EOL MOUNTAIN EXTREME ALPINE**

**MCMILLAN EOL MOUNTAIN EXTREME DENALI**

**MCMILLAN FIREARMS EOL MOUNTAIN EXTREME YUKON**

## MCMILLAN FIREARMS EOL MOUNTAIN EXTREME YUKON

**Action**: Bolt, McMillan G30 Long Action
**Stock**: EDGE Outdoorsman composite, khaki and gray
**Barrel**: 27 in.
**Sights**: 20 MOA Picatinny style scope bases

**Weight**: 8 lb. 4 oz.
**Caliber**: 7mm EOL Mag./7mm Rem. Ultra Mag., .300 EOL Mag./.300 Rem. Ultra Mag., .338 EOL Mag./.338 Lapua
**Magazine**: N/A
**Features**: Jewell trigger; metal black finish; NP3 muzzle brake; EDGE graphite technology; hand-lapped match grade barrel
**MSRP** . . . . . . . . . . . . . . . . . . . .**$6775**

**MONTANA RIFLES AMERICAN VANTAGE RIFLE (AVR)**

## MONTANA RIFLES AMERICAN VANTAGE RIFLE (AVR)

**Action**: Bolt
**Stock**: Walnut, Synthetic
**Barrel**: 24 in.
**Sights**: Marble replaceable front and rear
**Weight**: 9 lb.

**Caliber**: .35 Whelen, .375 H&H, .375 Ruger, .416 Rem. Mag., .416 Ruger, .458 Lott, .458 Win. Mag.
**Magazine**: N/A
**Features**: Matte blued chrome moly steel or stainless steel barreled actions; available in right or left hand configurations
**MSRP** . . . . . . . . . . . . . . . . . .**$1279**

**MOSSBERG MVP PATROL RIFLE**

## MOSSBERG MVP PATROL RIFLE

**Action**: Bolt
**Stock**: Birch, black textured
**Barrel**: 16.25 in.
**Sights**: Front fiber optic, adjustable rear; optional 3-9x32mm scope

**Weight**: 7 lb.
**Caliber**: 5.56mm NATO/.223 Rem.
**Magazine**: 10 rounds
**Features**: MVP Drop-Push bolt design; A2 flash suppressor; Lightning Bolt Action Trigger System; matte blue finish; picatinny rails; spiral fluted bolts; front and rear swivel studs; available threaded barrel
**MSRP** . . . . . . . . . . . . . . . . $681–$829

### REMINGTON MODEL 700 SPS WOOD TECH

*Action*: Bolt
*Stock*: Synthetic walnut finish
*Barrel*: 22 in., 24 in.
*Sights*: None
*Weight*: 7 lb. 6 oz.–7 lb. 10 oz.
*Caliber*: .270 Win., 30-06 Spfd., .300 Win., 7mm Rem. Mag.
*Magazine*: 4 rounds
*Features*: Hammer-forged barrel; X-Mark Pro externally adjustable trigger ensures peak shot control; over-molded grip panels on stock; SuperCell recoil pad
**MSRP** . . . . . . . . . . . . . . . . . . . **$800**

### REMINGTON MODEL 783

*Action*: Bolt
*Stock*: Black synthetic
*Barrel*: 22 in., 24 in.
*Sights*: None
*Weight*: 7 lb.–7 lb. 4 oz.
*Caliber*: .270 Win., 30-06 Spfd., .308 Win., 7mm Rem. Mag.
*Magazine*: 4 rounds
*Features*: CrossFire trigger system; carbon steel magnum contour button rifled barrel; pillar-bedded stock and free-floated barrel; SuperCell recoil pad
**MSRP** . . . . . . . . . . . . . . . . . . . **$451**

REMINGTON MODEL 700 SPS WOOD TECH

REMINGTON MODEL 783

## ROCK RIVER ARMS LAR-15 DELTA CAR/DELTA MID-LENGTH

*Action*: Semiautomatic
*Stock*: Synthetic
*Barrel*: 16 in.
*Sights*: None
*Weight*: 7 lb.-7 lb. 4.8 oz.
*Caliber*: 5.56mm NATO, .223

*Magazine*: 30 rounds
*Features*: Delta Quad Rail two piece drop-in and gas system, available in CAR or Mid-length; low profile gas block; Ergo SureGrip; two stage trigger
**MSRP** . . . . . . . . . . . . . . . . . . . .**$1085**

**ROCK RIVER ARMS LAR-15 DELTA CAR/
DELTA MID-LENGTH**

## ROCK RIVER ARMS LAR-15LH LEF-T COYOTE RIFLE & CARBINE

*Action*: Semiautomatic
*Stock*: Synthetic A2
*Barrel*: 16 in., 20 in.
*Sights*: None
*Weight*: 7 lb.-8 lb. 6.4 oz.
*Caliber*: 5.56mm NATO, .223

*Magazine*: 20 rounds
*Features*: Smith Vortex Flash Hider; Hogue free float tube; Hogue grip; two stage trigger
**Carbine:** . . . . . . . . . . . . . . . . .**$1400**
**Rifle:** . . . . . . . . . . . . . . . . . . . .**$1450**

**ROCK RIVER ARMS LAR-15LH LEF-T
COYOTE RIFLE & CARBINE**

## ROCK RIVER ARMS LAR-15 R3 COMPETITION RIFLE

*Action*: Semiautomatic
*Stock*: Synthetic A2 or CAR
*Barrel*: 18 in.
*Sights*: None
*Weight*: 7 lb. 9.6 oz.
*Caliber*: 5.56mm NATO, .223
*Magazine*: 30 rounds
*Features*: RRA tuned and ported

muzzle brake; low profile gas block; two stage trigger; Hogue Rubber grip
**MSRP** . . . . . . . . . . . . . . . . . . . .**$1310**

**ROCK RIVER ARMS LAR-15 R3
COMPETITION RIFLE**

### ROSSI CIRCUIT JUDGE .44 MAG.

*Action*: SA/DA
*Stock*: Hardwood
*Barrel*: 18.5 in.
*Sights*: Red fiber optic front
*Weight*: 5 lb. 3 oz.
*Caliber*: .44 Mag.
*Magazine*: 6 rounds
*Features*: Yoke detent; transfer bar; Taurus Security System
**MSRP** . . . . . . . . . . . . . . . . . . . . **$684**

### ROSSI CIRCUIT JUDGE CONVERTIBLE

*Action*: SA/DA
*Stock*: Synthetic
*Barrel*: 18.5 in.
*Sights*: Red fiber optic front
*Weight*: N/A
*Caliber*: .22LR, .22 Mag.
*Magazine*: 6 rounds
*Features*: Removable cylinder to change easily from .22LR to .22 Mag.; blued finish
**MSRP** . . . . . . . . . . . . . . . . . . . . **$732**

### RUGER 10/22 TAKEDOWN

*Action*: Autoloading
*Stock*: Black synthetic
*Barrel*: 16.6 in.
*Sights*: Gold bead front, adjustable rear
*Weight*: 4 lb. 10.7 oz.
*Caliber*: .22LR
*Magazine*: 10 rounds
*Features*: Built of alloy steel with satin black finish; threaded barrel with flash suppressor; easy takedown and reassembly; detachable rotary magazine; extended magazine release; combination scope base adapter; push-button manual safety
**MSRP** . . . . . . . . . . . . . . . . . . . . **$419**

**ROSSI CIRCUIT JUDGE .44 MAG.**

**ROSSI CIRCUIT JUDGE CONVERTIBLE**

**RUGER 10/22 TAKEDOWN**

RUGER GUIDE GUN

RUGER GUNSITE SCOUT RIFLE STAINLESS

RUGER M77 HAWKEYE MAGNUM HUNTER

RUGER SR-556VT

## RUGER GUIDE GUN WITH MUZZLE BRAKE SYSTEM

**Action**: Bolt
**Stock**: Green Mountain laminate
**Barrel**: 20 in.
**Sights**: Bead front, adjustable rear
**Weight**: 8 lb.-8 lb. 2 oz.
**Caliber**: .300 RCM, .300 Win. Mag., .30-06 Spfd., .338 RCM, .338 Win. Mag., .375 Ruger
**Magazine**: 3 rounds (4 rounds in .30-06 Spfd.)
**Features**: LC6 Trigger; Mauser-type extractor; muzzle brake system; three-position safety; manner-forged barrel; integral scope mounts; stainless steel bolt; swivel studs;
**MSRP** . . . . . . . . . . . . . . . . . . . .$1199

## RUGER GUNSITE SCOUT RIFLE STAINLESS

**Action**: Bolt
**Stock**: Black laminate
**Barrel**: 18 in.

**Sights**: Post front, adjustable rear
**Weight**: 7 lb. 2 oz.
**Caliber**: .308 Win.
**Magazine**: 10 rounds
**Features**: Flash suppressor; picatinny rail; detachable box magazine; recoil pad; integral scope mounts; Mauser-type extractor; "Gunsite Approved"; stainless steel bolt; muzzle thread protector; available in both left and right hand
**MSRP** . . . . . . . . . . . . . . . . . . . .$1099

## RUGER M77 HAWKEYE MAGNUM HUNTER WITH MUZZLE BRAKE SYSTEM

**Action**: Bolt
**Stock**: Green Hogue
**Barrel**: 24 in.
**Sights**: None
**Weight**: 8 lb.
**Caliber**: .300 Win. Mag.
**Magazine**: 3 rounds

**Features**: Hawkeye matte stainless finish; LC6 trigger; Mauser-type controlled extractor; steel floorplate; muzzle brake system; integral scope mounts; three-position safety; stainless steel bolt
**MSRP** . . . . . . . . . . . . . . . . . . .$1099

## RUGER SR-556VT

**Action**: Autoloading
**Stock**: Black synthetic
**Barrel**: 20 in.
**Sights**: None
**Weight**: 8 lb. 8 oz.
**Caliber**: 5.56mm NATO
**Magazine**: 5 rounds
**Features**: Two-stage piston with adjustable regulator; handguard; target-style trigger; hammer-forged barrel; pistol grip; charging handle; chrome-plated bolt
**MSRP** . . . . . . . . . . . . . . . . . . . .$1995

# NEW Products: **Rifles**

## SAVAGE ARMS AXIS XP YOUTH CAMO

*Action*: Bolt
*Stock*: Synthetic
*Barrel*: 20 in.
*Sights*: Scope included
*Weight*: 6 lb. 13 oz.
*Caliber*: .223 Rem., .243 Win., 7mm-08 Rem.
*Magazine*: 4 rounds, detachable box
*Features*: Made with cooperation from the Youth Shooting Sports Alliance; carbon steel barrel with matte black finish; stock comes in camo or muddy girl
**MSRP** . . . . . . . . . . . . . . . . . . . . **$475**

## SAVAGE ARMS LAW ENFORCEMENT SERIES 110 BA LEFT HAND MODEL

*Action*: Bolt
*Stock*: Aluminum
*Barrel*: 26 in.
*Sights*: Drilled and tapped for scope
*Weight*: 15 lb. 12 oz.
*Caliber*: .300 Win. Mag., .338 Lapua Mag.
*Magazine*: 5 rounds, detachable box
*Features*: Also available in right hand model; AccuTrigger; matte black carbon steel barrel; 20 MOA scope rail
**MSRP** . . . . . . . . . . . . . . . . . . . .**$2465**

## SAVAGE ARMS SPECIALTY SERIES MODEL 42

*Action*: Break-action
*Stock*: Synthetic
*Barrel*: 20 in.
*Sights*: Adjustable
*Weight*: 6 lb. 2 oz.
*Caliber*: .22LR, .22 WMR
*Magazine*: None
*Features*: Rifle-shotgun combo; break-open combination gun over 410 bore; carbon steel matte black barrel; matte black synthetic stock;
**MSRP** . . . . . . . . . . . . . . . . . . . . **$480**

**SAVAGE ARMS AXIS XP YOUTH CAMO**

**SAVAGE ARMS LAW ENFORCEMENT SERIES 110 BA LEFT HAND MODEL**

**SAVAGE ARMS SPECIALTY SERIES MODEL 42**

**SIG SAUER SIG716 PRECISION**

## SIG SAUER SIG716 PRECISION

***Action***: Semiautomatic
***Stock***: Magpul UBR
***Barrel***: 18 in.
***Sights***: None
***Weight***: 11 lb.
***Caliber***: 7.62x51mm NATO
***Magazine***: 20 rounds
***Features***: Short-stroke push rod operating system; 1913 Mil-Std rail; free-floating barrel; telescoping stock; Magpul PMAG; Match grade trigger group
**MSRP** . . . . . . . . . . . . . . . . . . .**$2666**

## STAG ARMS MODEL 8T

***Action***: Gas-operated piston
***Stock***: 6 position collapsible
***Barrel***: 16 in.
***Sights***: Diamondhead premium flip up sight set
***Weight***: N/A
***Caliber***: 5.56 NATO
***Magazine***: 30 rounds
***Features***: Short-stroke piston system; left or right-handed versions; ergonomic modular free-floating VRS-T handguard; chrome-lined barrel; Mil-spec trigger; lifetime warranty
**MSRP** . . . . . . . . . . . . . . . . . . .**$1275**

**STAG ARMS MODEL 8T**

### TURNBULL MFG. CO TAR-15

*Action*: Semiautomatic
*Stock*: Black Walnut
*Barrel*: 16 in.
*Sights*: None
*Weight*: 8 lb. 8 oz.
*Caliber*: .223
*Magazine*: 5 and 10 rounds
*Features*: AR-15 gas impingement system; 8620 carbon steel receivers; color case hardened steel; oversized integral trigger guard; picatinny rail; screw on muzzle brake; also available in 7.62x39 and .300 AAC Blackout
**MSRP** . . . . . . . . . . . . . . . . . . .$2750

### WEATHERBY MARK V ACCUMARK RC RIFLE

*Action*: Bolt
*Stock*: Monte Carlo composite
*Barrel*: 24 in., 26 in., 28 in.
*Sights*: None
*Weight*: 7 lb. 4 oz.–9lb.
*Caliber*: .240 Wby. Mag., .270 Win., .308 Win., .30-06 Spfd., .257 Wby. Mag., .270 Wby. Mag., 7mm Rem. Mag., 7mm Wby. Mag., .300 Win. Mag., .300 Wby. Mag., .30-378 Wby. Mag., .338-378 Wby. Mag., .340 Wby. Mag., .338 Lapua
*Magazine*: 5+1, 3+1, or 2+1 rounds
*Features*: "Range Certified" model comes with a SUB-MOA guarantee; button-rifled stainless steel barrel; free floated barrel with a recessed target crown; Pachmayr Decelerator pad
**MSRP** . . . . . . . . . . . . $2400–$2700

### WEATHERBY VANGUARD 2 BACK COUNTRY

*Action*: Bolt
*Stock*: Monte Carlo composite
*Barrel*: 24 in.
*Sights*: None
*Weight*: 6 lb. 12 oz.
*Caliber*: .240 Wby. Mag., .270 Win., .257 Wby. Mag., .30-06 Spfd., .300 Win. Mag., .300 Wby. Mag.
*Magazine*: 5+1 or 3+1 rounds
*Features*: SUB-MOA guarantee; chrome moly metalwork with Cerakote Tactical Grey finish; pillar-bedded stock; two-stage trigger; 3-position safety; auxiliary trigger sear; Pachmayr Decelerator pad
**MSRP** . . . . . . . . . . . . . . . . . . . .$1399

TURNBULL MFG. CO TAR-15

WEATHERBY MARK V ACCUMARK RC RIFLE

WEATHERBY VANGUARD 2 BACK COUNTRY

**WEATHERBY VANGUARD 2 SYNTHETIC PACKAGE**

WINCHESTER REPEATING ARMS
MODEL 70 FEATHERWEIGHT GRADE III

WINCHESTER REPEATING ARMS MODEL 70
ULTIMATE SHADOW HUNTER SS

## WEATHERBY VANGUARD 2 SYNTHETIC PACKAGE

*Action*: Bolt
*Stock*: Synthetic
*Barrel*: 24 in.
*Sights*: 3-9x42mm Redfield Revenge scope
*Weight*: 8 lb. 4 oz.–8 lb. 8 oz.
*Caliber*: .223 Rem., .22-250 Rem., .243 Win., .25-06 Rem., .270 Win., 7mm-08 Rem., .308 Win., .30-06 Spfd., .257 Wby. Mag., 7mm Rem. Mag., .300 Win. Mag., .300 Wby. Mag., .338 Win. Mag.
*Magazine*: 5+1 or 3+1 rounds
*Features*: SUB-MOA guarantee; mounted and boresighted Redfield scope with matte finish and 4-plex reticle; Talley-designed mounts; adjustable nylon sling; injection-molded scoped rifle case
**MSRP . . . . . . . . . . . . . . . . . . . $999**

## WINCHESTER REPEATING ARMS MODEL 70 FEATHERWEIGHT GRADE III

*Action*: Bolt
*Stock*: Walnut
*Barrel*: 22 in.
*Sights*: None
*Weight*: 7 lb.
*Caliber*: .270 Win.
*Magazine*: 5 rounds
*Features*: Polished blued steel; free-floating barrel with target crown; adjustable M.O.A. Trigger System; three-position safety; controlled round feed and ejection; hinged floorplate; jeweled bolt body; Pachmayr Decelerator pad
**MSRP . . . . . . . . . . . . . . . . $1019.99**

## WINCHESTER REPEATING ARMS MODEL 70 ULTIMATE SHADOW HUNTER SS

*Action*: Bolt
*Stock*: Synthetic MO Break-Up Infinity Camo
*Barrel*: 22 in., 24 in., 26 in.
*Sights*: None
*Weight*: 6 lb. 12 oz.–7 lb. 4 oz.
*Caliber*: .243 Win., 7mm-08 Rem., .308 Win., .270 Win., 30-06 Spfd., .300 Win. Mag., .338 Win. Mag., .300 WSM, .270 WSM, .325 WSM
*Magazine*: 3 rounds
*Features*: Gray overmolded rubberized gripping surfaces; matte metal; alloy one-piece bottom metal; pre-'64 style controlled round feed with claw extractor; three-position safety; free-floating stainless steel barrel; recessed target crown; blade-type ejector; M.O.A. Trigger System; available in blued and stainless steel
**Blued: . . . . . . . . . . $829.99–$869.99**
**SS: . . . . . . . . . . . . .$1039.99–$1079.99**

# NEW Products: **Rifles**

## WINCHESTER REPEATING ARMS MODEL 94 CARBINE

*Action*: Lever
*Stock*: Walnut
*Barrel*: 20 in.
*Sights*: Adjustable semi-buckhorn rear, Marble Arms front
*Weight*: 6 lb. 8 oz.
*Caliber*: 30-30 Win., 38-55 Win.
*Magazine*: N/A
*Features*: Triple-checked button rifled barrel; round locking bolt trunnions; top-tang safety; rebounding hammer; bolt relief cut; steel loading gate; articulated cartridge stop; available knurled hammer spur extension
**MSRP** . . . . . . . . . . . . . . . . **$1199.99**

## WINCHESTER REPEATING ARMS MODEL 1873 SHORT RIFLE

*Action*: Lever
*Stock*: Walnut
*Barrel*: 20 in.
*Sights*: Semi-buckhorn rear, Marble Arms gold bead front
*Weight*: 7 lb. 4 oz.
*Caliber*: 357 Mag.
*Magazine*: 10 rounds (357 Mag.) or 11 rounds (38 Spl.)
*Features*: Blued steel crescent buttplate; steel loading gate; receiver rear tang; round barrel; based off the original Model 73
**MSRP** . . . . . . . . . . . . . . . . **$1299.99**

## WINCHESTER REPEATING ARMS MODEL 1885 LOW WALL HUNTER RIMFIRE OCTAGON

*Action*: Lever
*Stock*: Walnut
*Barrel*: 24 in.
*Sights*: Semi-buckhorn rear, gold bead front
*Weight*: 7 lb. 8 oz.
*Caliber*: .22LR, .22 WMR, .17 HMR, .17 WSM
*Magazine*: Single shot
*Features*: Gloss blued steel receiver; octagon barrel; pistol grip buttstock; Pachmayr rubber butt pad; sling swivel studs
**MSRP** . . . . . . . . . . . . . . . . **$1469.99**

**WINCHESTER REPEATING ARMS MODEL 94 CARBINE**

**WINCHESTER REPEATING ARMS MODEL 1873 SHORT RIFLE**

**WINCHESTER REPEATING ARMS MODEL 1885 LOW WALL HUNTER RIMFIRE OCTAGON**

AIRFORCE AIRGUNS CONDOR SS

BEEMAN PRECISION AIRGUNS RAM DELUXE

BEEMAN PRECISION AIRGUNS
SILVER KODIAK X2 DC

### AIRFORCE AIRGUNS CONDOR SS

**Power**: Compressed air
**Stock**: Composite
**Overall Length**: 38.125 in.
**Sights**: Open or optical may be installed
**Weight**: 6 lb. 2 oz.
**Caliber**: .177, .20, .22, .25
**Features**: CondorSS combines the major attributes of the TalonSS's quiet operation and the Condor's high power levels; new sound reduction technology; 18-inch barrel blue, red, or original black; 600-1300 fps; two-stage trigger; single shot
**Quick-Detach**: . . . . . . . . . . . . . **$717**
**Spin-Loc**: . . . . . . . . . . . . . . . . **$737**

### BEEMAN PRECISION AIRGUNS RAM DELUXE

**Power**: Break action, spring piston
**Stock**: Hardwood
**Overall Length**: 47.5 in.
**Sights**: 4x32 scope
**Weight**: 9 lb.
**Caliber**: .177, .22
**Features**: Checkered European hardwood stock; ported muzzle brake; 1000 fps max velocity
**MSRP**. . . . . . . . . . . . . . . . . . **$239**

### BEEMAN PRECISION AIRGUNS SILVER KODIAK X2 DC

**Power**: Break action, spring piston
**Stock**: All-weather synthetic
**Overall Length**: 47.5 in.
**Sights**: 3-9x32 scope
**Weight**: 8 lb. 12 oz.
**Caliber**: .177, .22
**Features**: Two airguns in one; satin nickel plated barrel and receiver; ported muzzle brake; 1000 fps max velocity
**MSRP**. . . . . . . . . . . . . . . **$245–$249**

## BEEMAN PRECISION AIRGUNS SILVER PANTHER

*Power*: Break action, spring piston
*Stock*: All-weather synthetic
*Overall Length*: 47.5 in.
*Sights*: 4x32 scope
*Weight*: 8 lb. 12 oz.
*Caliber*: .177, .22
*Features*: Satin nickel plated barrel and receiver; ported muzzle brake; 1000 fps max velocity
**MSRP** . . . . . . . . . . . . . . . . . . **$189**

## CROSMAN BENJAMIN LEGACY JIM SHOCKEY SIGNATURE SERIES

*Power*: Break action Nitro Piston
*Stock*: Synthetic
*Overall Length*: 43 in.
*Sights*: 3-9x40mm scope
*Weight*: 6 lb. 11 oz.
*Caliber*: .22
*Features*: Nitro Piston technology delivers smooth cocking, reduced vibration and shoots with 70% less noise; over-molded barrel with soft-touch inserts; adjustable comb; 800-950 fps max velocity
**MSRP** . . . . . . . . . . . . . . . . . . **$349.99**

## CROSMAN FURY NP

*Power*: Break action Nitro Piston
*Stock*: Synthetic all-weather
*Overall Length*: 45 in.
*Sights*: 4x32mm scope
*Weight*: 6 lb. 6 oz.
*Caliber*: .177
*Features*: Velocities up to 1200 fps; rifled steel barrel; adjustable two-stage trigger; Nitro Piston technology delivers smooth cocking, reduced vibration and shoots with 70% less noise
**MSRP** . . . . . . . . . . . . . . . . . . **$139.99**

**BEEMAN PRECISION AIRGUNS SILVER PANTHER**

**CROSMAN BENJAMIN LEGACY JIM SHOCKEY SIGNATURE SERIES**

**CROSMAN FURY NP**

CROSMAN MTR77NP

## CROSMAN MTR77NP

**Power**: Break action Nitro Piston
**Stock**: Synthetic all-weather
**Overall Length**: 40 in.
**Sights**: 4x32mm scope
**Weight**: 6 lb. 2 oz.
**Caliber**: .177
**Features**: Nitro Piston technology delivers smooth cocking, reduced vibration and shoots with 70% less noise; sling mounts; storage in false magazine; up to 1200 fps; carry handle available
**MSRP** . . . . . . . . . . . . . . . . . . . . **$300**

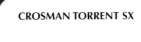

CROSMAN TORRENT SX

## CROSMAN TORRENT SX

**Power**: Variable pump
**Stock**: Synthetic
**Overall Length**: 36.75 in.
**Sights**: Fiber optic front, adjustable rear
**Weight**: 2 lb. 15 oz.
**Caliber**: .177
**Features**: Lightweight, variable pump BB/pellet rifle; adjustable stock; customized length of pull; up to 695 fps; five-shot clip; olive-drab stock and forearm
**MSRP** . . . . . . . . . . . . . . . . . . . .**$49.95**

# NEW Products: **Air Rifles**

DAISY WINCHESTER MODEL 1100SS

DAISY WINCHESTER MODEL 1250WS

GAMO USA BIG CAT 1400

## DAISY WINCHESTER MODEL 1100SS
*Power*: Break action/spring piston
*Stock*: Composite
*Overall Length*: 46.25 in.
*Sights*: Blade front, micro-adjustable rear
*Weight*: 6 lb. 10 oz.
*Caliber*: .177
*Features*: Rifled steel barrel; 1100 fps with alloy pellets; single shot; thumb safety engages when rifle is cocked
**MSRP** . . . . . . . . . . . . . . . . . **$129.99**

## DAISY WINCHESTER MODEL 1250WS
*Power*: Break action/spring piston
*Stock*: Hardwood
*Overall Length*: 46.25 in.
*Sights*: Fiber optic front, 3–9x32mm scope
*Weight*: 6 lb. 10 oz.
*Caliber*: .177
*Features*: Rifled steel barrel; 1250 fps with alloy pellets; folding bipod; single shot; thumb safety engages when rifle is cocked
**MSRP** . . . . . . . . . . . . . . . . . **$149.99**

## GAMO USA BIG CAT 1400
*Power*: Break action/spring piston
*Stock*: Synthetic
*Overall Length*: 43.3 in.
*Sights*: 4x32 scope
*Weight*: 6 lb. 2 oz.
*Caliber*: .177
*Features*: 33mm power plant enabling it to shoot at up to 1,400 fps with PBA Platinum Ammo; Smooth Action Trigger to maximize pinpoint accuracy; all-weather synthetic stock with rubberized grips; Shock Wave Absorber recoil pad
**MSRP** . . . . . . . . . . . . . . . . . **$229.95**

GAMO USA LITTLE CAT

GAMO USA WHISPER FUSION PRO

STOEGER AIRGUNS ATAC SUPPRESSOR

## GAMO USA LITTLE CAT

*Power*: Break action/spring piston
*Stock*: Beechwood
*Overall Length*: 36 in.
*Sights*: Front, rear fiber optics
*Weight*: 5 lb. 10 oz.
*Caliber*: .177
*Features*: Newest addition to the Youth Precision Airguns family from Gamo; 525 fps with Match Lead Pellets and up to 750 fps with PBA Platinum; metal barrel; grooved cylinder for optional scope mounting
**MSRP . . . . . . . . . . . . . . . . . $139.95**

## GAMO USA WHISPER FUSION PRO

*Power*: Break action/spring piston
*Stock*: Synthetic
*Overall Length*: 43 in.
*Sights*: 3–9x40 adjustable objective scope
*Weight*: 8 lb.
*Caliber*: .177
*Features*: Includes the latest noise dampening technology developed exclusively by Gamo that is integrated in the barrel; noise is reduced by up to 89.5%; Smooth Action Trigger; new recoil pad Shock Wave Absorber that is able to absorb the recoil up to 74%; rubberized grips; all-weather black stock with adjustable cheekpiece; max velocity 1400 fps
**MSRP . . . . . . . . . . . . . . . . . $329.95**

## STOEGER AIRGUNS ATAC SUPPRESSOR

*Power*: Break action/gas-operated
*Stock*: Synthetic
*Overall Length*: 42.5 in.
*Sights*: 4–16x40 scope
*Weight*: 8 lb. 14 oz.
*Caliber*: .177, .22
*Features*: Airflow control technology and dual-stage noise reduction system; automatic ambidextrous safety; black tactical stock; up to 1200 fps with alloy pellets (.177); adjustable length of pull; integral Picatinny rails
**MSRP . . . . . . . . . . . . . . . . . . $299**

# NEW Products: **Shotguns**

AYA ADARRA

BENELLI M2 FIELD COMPACT

BENELLI MONTEFELTRO BLACK SYNTHETIC

BENELLI VINCI SPEEDBOLT

### AYA (AGUIRRE Y ARANZABAL) ADARRA

*Action*: Side-by-side hammerless boxlock ejector shotgun
*Stock*: Walnut
*Barrel*: 28 in., with other lengths to order
*Chokes*: Screw-in tubes
*Weight*: 6 lb. 10 oz.
*Bore/ Gauge*: 12, 16, 20, 28, .410
*Magazine*: None
*Features*: Double locking mechanism with replaceable hinge pin; disc set firing pins; double trigger;
MSRP. . . . . . . . . . . . . . . . . . $4800

### BENELLI M2 FIELD COMPACT

*Action*: Inertia operated semiautomatic
*Stock*: Black synthetic
*Barrel*: 24 in., 26 in.

*Chokes*: C, IC, M, IM, F
*Weight*: 5 lb. 10 oz.–7 lb.
*Bore/ Gauge*: 12, 20
*Magazine*: 3+1 rounds
*Features*: M2 Field now in compact model; ComforTech gel recoil pad and comb insert; ComforTech shim kit; red bar front sight
MSRP. . . . . . . . . . . . . $1359–$1409

### BENELLI MONTEFELTRO BLACK SYNTHETIC

*Action*: Semiautomatic
*Stock*: Black synthetic
*Barrel*: 26 in.
*Chokes*: IC, M, F
*Weight*: 6 lb. 14 oz.
*Bore/ Gauge*: 12
*Magazine*: 4 +1 rounds
*Features*: Now with a black synthetic stock; red bar front sight; black rubber

ventilated recoil pad; hard case included
MSRP. . . . . . . . . . . . . . . . . . $1139

### BENELLI VINCI SPEEDBOLT

*Action*: Inertia operated semiautomatic
*Stock*: Black synthetic
*Barrel*: 24 in.
*Chokes*: C, IC, M, IM, F
*6 lb. 13 oz.*
*Bore/ Gauge*: 12
*Magazine*: 3+1 rounds
*Features*: Practical Speed Performance with new Speed-Bolt, a bolt inset with tungsten that is designed for faster cycling and loads as weighing one ounce or greater; QuadraFit buttstock; vent rib; drilled and tapped for scope mounting; red bar front sight and metal bead mid-sight
MSRP. . . . . . . . . . . . . . . . . . $1599

## BERETTA 692 SPORTING

**Action**: Over/under
**Stock**: Walnut
**Barrel**: 30 in., 32 in.
**Chokes**: 5 OCHP
**Weight**: 7 lb. 11 oz.
**Bore/ Gauge**: 12
**Magazine**: None
**Features**: Steelium Plus barrels; longer forcing cone; Beretta Fast Adjustment System Technology; Adjustable Balance System; adjustable trigger
**MSRP** . . . . . . . . . . . . . . . . . . $4755

## BERETTA DT11 SPORTING

**Action**: Over/under
**Stock**: Walnut
**Barrel**: 30 in., 32 in.
**Chokes**: OCHPe
**Weight**: 9 lb.
**Bore/ Gauge**: 12
**Magazine**: None
**Features**: Steelium Pro barrel; top rib with hollowed bridges; ergonomic top lever; safety selector switch; increased receiver side wall thickness; select high-quality walnut wood finished in oil; stock and forend can be fitted to customer's measurement; pistol grip and forend are hand-checkered; B-Fast adjustable stock available
**MSRP** . . . . . . . . . . . . . . . . . . $8999

## BERNARDELLI MEGA

**Action**: Semiautomatic
**Stock**: Walnut, synthetic
**Barrel**: 24 in., 26 in., 28 in., 30 in.
**Chokes**: 5 tubes
**Weight**: 5 lb. 14 oz.
**Bore/ Gauge**: 12, 20
**Magazine**: 5+1 rounds
**Features**: Gas-operated system with partial autocompensator for a more uniform action bar speed; plasma technology to increase corrosion resistance; Made in Italy and steel proof tested; four shims to adjust drop; also available in silver, sporting, and synthetic
**MSRP** . . . . . **Available upon request**

BERETTA 692 SPORTING

BERETTA DT11 SPORTING

BERNARDELLI MEGA

BROWNING BPS MICRO MIDAS

BROWNING BT-99 MICRO MIDAS

## BROWNING BPS MICRO MIDAS

**Action**: Bottom ejection pump
**Stock**: Walnut
**Barrel**: 24 in., 26 in.
**Chokes**: 3 Invector-Plus (12, 20 Ga.), 3 Standard Invector (28, .410 Ga.)
**Weight**: 6 lb. 15 oz.-7 lb. 10 oz.
**Bore/ Gauge**: 12, 20, 28, .410
**Magazine**: None
**Features**: Ventilated rib barrel; dual steel action bars; top-tang safety; scaled down for smaller shooters; Inflex Technology recoil; silver colored front bead sight; stock spacers
**MSRP** . . . . . . . . . . **$649.99–$689.99**

## BROWNING BT-99 MICRO MIDAS

**Action**: Pump, extractor only
**Stock**: Walnut
**Barrel**: 28 in., 30 in.
**Chokes**: 1 Invector-Plus
**Weight**: 7 lb. 11 oz

**Bore/ Gauge**: 12
**Magazine**: None
**Features**: Blued finish; high-post ventilated rib barrel; beavertail forearm; scaled down for smaller shooters; Vector-Pro lengthed forcing cone; recoil pad; ivory front and mid-bead sights
**MSRP** . . . . . . . . . . . . . . . . **$1429.99**

## BROWNING CITORI 725 FEATHER

**Action**: Over/under
**Stock**: Walnut
**Barrel**: 26 in., 28 in.
**Chokes**: 3 Invector-DS
**Weight**: 6 lb. 7 oz.
**Bore/ Gauge**: 12
**Magazine**: None
**Features**: Lightweight alloy receiver; low-profile; silver nitride finish; ventilated top rib barrel; Fire Lite Mechanical Trigger system; hammer ejectors; ivory front and mid-bead sights
**MSRP** . . . . . . . . . . . . . . . . **$2649.99**

## BROWNING MAXUS SPORTING GOLDEN CLAYS

**Action**: Autoloader, gas operated
**Stock**: Walnut
**Barrel**: 28 in., 30 in.
**Chokes**: 5 Invector-Plus
**Weight**: 7 lb. 3 oz.
**Bore/ Gauge**: 12
**Magazine**: None
**Features**: Gold-enhanced engraving; lightweight aluminum alloy; flat, ventilated rib; 3 in. chamber; Power Drive Gas System; Speed Lock Forearm; Vector Pro lengthened forcing cone; HiViz Pro-Comp fiber optic front sight
**MSRP** . . . . . . . . . . . . . . . . **$1999.99**

BROWNING CITORI 725 FEATHER

BROWNING MAXUS SPORTING GOLDEN CLAYS

## CAESAR GUERINI CHALLENGER ASCENT

*Action*: Over/under
*Stock*: Hand rubbed oil
*Barrel*: 30 in., 32 in.
*Chokes*: 6 MAXIS competition chokes
*Weight*: 8 lb. 6 oz.–8 lb. 8 oz.
*Bore/ Gauge*: 12
*Magazine*: None
*Features*: 10mm high tapered top rib is designed to shoot at 50/50% point-of-impact; White Bradley style front sight, with brass center bead; DTS trigger system; manual safety
**MSRP. . . . . . . . . . . . . . . . . . $5995**

## CAESAR GUERINI ELLIPSE

*Action*: Round body
*Stock*: Hand rubbed oil on walnut
*Barrel*: 28 in., 30 in.
*Chokes*: 5 nickel plated, flush fitting
*Weight*: 6 lb. 1 oz.–7 lb. 4 oz.
*Bore/ Gauge*: 12, 20, 28
*Magazine*: None
*Features*: Engraving pattern coated with Invisalloy; brass front bead sight; single (selective optional) trigger; manual safety; tapered, solid top rib
**MSRP. . . . . . . . . . . . . $4195–$5995**

## CAESAR GUERINI MAGNUS SPORTING

*Action*: Over/under
*Stock*: Hand rubbed oil on walnut
*Barrel*: 30 in., 32 in., 34 in.
*Chokes*: 6 CCP competition chokes (6 MAXIS for 12 Ga. models)
*Weight*: 7 lb. 2 oz.–8 lb. 2 oz.
*Bore/ Gauge*: 12, 20, 28, .410
*Magazine*: None
*Features*: Single selective trigger; manual safety; ventilated center rib; available 20/28 gauge combo and 20/28/.410 gauge combo
**MSRP. . . . . . . . . . . . . . . . . . $4995**
**Combo gauges: . . . . . . $6795–$8770**

CAESAR GUERINI CHALLENGER ASCENT

CAESAR GUERINI ELLIPSE

CAESAR GUERINI MAGNUS SPORTING

CHIAPPA TRIPLE CROWN

CHIAPPA TRIPLE THREAT

## CHIAPPA TRIPLE CROWN

*Action*: Break-action
*Stock*: Wood
*Barrel*: 28 in.
*Chokes*: Rem-choke in all barrels
*Weight*: 8 lb. 11 oz.
*Bore/ Gauge*: 12
*Magazine*: None
*Features*: Side-by-side and middle arrangement sporting model with three shotgun barrels; chokes in all three barrels; sling swivel studs
**MSRP** . . . . . . . . . . . . . . . . . . **$1629**

## CHIAPPA TRIPLE THREAT

*Action*: Break-action
*Stock*: Wood
*Barrel*: 18.5 in.
*Chokes*: Rem Choke in all barrels

*Weight*: 8 lb.
*Bore/ Gauge*: 12
*Magazine*: None
*Features*: Side-by-side and middle arrangement defense model with three shotgun barrels; chokes in all three barrels; sling swivel studs; wooden stock can be partly disassembled
**MSRP** . . . . . . . . . . . . . . . . . . **$1629**

## CIMARRON 1878 COACH GUN

*Action*: Side-by-Side
*Stock*: Wood
*Barrel*: 20 in., 26 in.
*Chokes*: Open
*Weight*: 8 lb.–8 lb. 15 oz.
*Bore/ Gauge*: 12
*Magazine*: None

*Features*: 3 in. blue steel real working hammers; available in standard blue, original finish, or USA finish
**MSRP** . . . . . . . . . . **$574.60–$851.10**

## CIMARRON WYATT EARP SHOTGUN

*Action*: Side-by-Side
*Stock*: Walnut
*Barrel*: 20 in.
*Chokes*: Open
*Weight*: N/A
*Bore/ Gauge*: 12
*Magazine*: None
*Features*: Built on the Doc Holliday model with "Wyatt Earp" engraved on the receiver; case hardened steel frame with standard blue finish
**MSRP** . . . . . . . . . . . . . . . . . **$1558.70**

CIMARRON 1878 COACH GUN

CIMARRON WYATT EARP SHOTGUN

## CZ-USA 612 HC-P

*Action*: Pump
*Stock*: Black polymer
*Barrel*: 20 in.
*Chokes*: Removable cylinder
*Weight*: 6 lb. 8 oz.
*Bore/ Gauge*: 12
*Magazine*: None
*Features*: Full-length pistol grip stock; ghost ring sights with glow fiber dots for fast zombie target acquisition; full-length pump forend; barrel accepts CZ choke tubes and ships with one cylinder choke
**MSRP** . . . . . . . . . . . . . . . . . . . **$349**

## CZ-USA 612 HOME DEFENSE

*Action*: Semiautomatic
*Stock*: Polymer
*Barrel*: 18.5 in.
*Chokes*: Fixed cylinder
*Weight*: 6 lb.
*Bore/ Gauge*: 12
*Magazine*: 5+1
*Features*: Cylinder-bore barrel; a 26-inch vent-rib barrel is available for purchase that easily converts the 612 Home Defense into a field gun
**MSRP** . . . . . . . . . . . . . . . . . . . **$290**

## CZ-USA SPORTER STANDARD GRADE

*Action*: Over/under
*Stock*: Grade 2 Turkish walnut
*Barrel*: 30 in.
*Chokes*: 6 Kicks extended SS
*Weight*: 8 lb. 8 oz.
*Bore/ Gauge*: 12
*Magazine*: None
*Features*: Designed specifically with the sporting clay enthusiast in mind; single selectable trigger system; Grade 2 Monte Carlo sporting stock with adjustable comb and right-hand palm swell; ships with a set of 6 Kicks stainless steel extended choke tubes
**MSRP** . . . . . . . . . . . . . . . . . . . **$1799**

## CZ-USA SUPER SCROLL COMBO SET

*Action*: Over/under
*Stock*: Grade 5 Turkish walnut
*Barrel*: 30 in.
*Chokes*: 5 per gauge
*Weight*: 6 lb. 11 oz.
*Bore/ Gauge*: 20, 28
*Magazine*: None

CZ-USA 612 HC-P

CZ-USA 612 HOME DEFENSE

CZ-USA SPORTER STANDARD GRADE

CZ-USA SUPER SCROLL COMBO SET

CZ-USA UPLAND STERLING

*Features*: Intended for the hunter or sporting clays shooter who wants to carry an absolutely gorgeous shotgun; ornate hand-engraved scrollwork on receiver, faux sideplates, trigger guard and mono-block; both barrel sets are equipped with ejectors; five chokes per gauge and a full grip, making it an excellent crossover gun between clay and feather
**MSRP** . . . . . . . . . . . . . . . . . . . **$3899**

## CZ-USA UPLAND STERLING

*Action*: Over/under
*Stock*: Turkish walnut

*Barrel*: 28 in.
*Chokes*: 5 screw-in
*Weight*: 7 lb. 8 oz.
*Bore/ Gauge*: 12
*Magazine*: None
*Features*: Built on a new platform featuring a CNC-milled steel receiver, resulting in mechanical components that operate with clockwork precision and consistency; Turkish walnut stock features a stippled grip area on the wrist and forend rather than the traditional checkering
**MSRP** . . . . . . . . . . . . . . . . . . . **$979**

# NEW Products: **Shotguns**

**ESCORT BY LEGACY SPORTS EXTREME AND SUPREME LEFT HANDED ACTIONS**

### ESCORT BY LEGACY SPORTS EXTREME AND SUPREME LEFT HANDED ACTIONS

*Action*: Semiautomatic
*Stock*: Black synthetic, Realtree camo (Supreme model only), or Wood
*Barrel*: 26 in., 28 in.
*Chokes*: F, M, IM, IC, Skeet (Extreme Camo models also come with MR Waterfowl)
*Weight*: 6 lb. 8 oz.–7 lb. 10 oz.
*Bore/ Gauge*: 12, 20
*Magazine*: Tubular, 5+1 rounds
*Features*: Available in Magnum and Supreme Magnum models; cycle rate of 3 shots/second with 7/8oz. loads; true left-handed action and receiver; SMART valve cycling for blowback; nickel chrome moly lined barrel; ventilated rib and fiber optic front sight; magazine cut-off for quick load changes
**MSRP . . . . . . . . . . . . . . . $549–$799**

### ESCORT BY LEGACY SPORTS YOUTH 20 GAUGE

*Action*: Semiautomatic
*Stock*: Wood, Black Synthetic, Realtree Max4 and AP camo, and Moon Shine Muddy Girl camo
*Barrel*: 22 in., 26 in. (Ladies Muddy Girl)
*Chokes*: Multi-3
*Weight*: 6 lb. 6 oz.
*Bore/ Gauge*: 20
*Magazine*: Cut-off for single round loading
*Features*: TRIO recoil pad; top of receiver milled with 3/8 in. dovetail for sights; raised, ventilated sight rib with fiber optic sight; nickel chrome moly lined barrel
**Synthetic . . . . . . . . . . . . . . . . . $499**
**Wood . . . . . . . . . . . . . . . . . . . . $525**
**Camo . . . . . . . . . . . . . . . . . . . . $549**

### FABARM ELOS DELUXE

*Action*: Over/under
*Stock*: European walnut
*Barrel*: 28 in.
*Chokes*: 5 Inner HP
*Weight*: 5 lb. 14 oz.–7 lb. 1 oz.
*Bore/ Gauge*: 20
*Magazine*: None
*Features*: Round action and trim stock provide speed in keeping up with wild birds; Fabarm Tribore HP tapered bore; steel or aluminum frame
**MSRP . . . . . . . . . . . . . . $2895–$2995**

**ESCORT BY LEGACY SPORTS YOUTH 20 GAUGE**

**FABARM ELOS DELUXE**

**FRANCHI ASPIRE**

**FRANCHI INTENSITY**

## FRANCHI ASPIRE

**Action**: Over/under
**Stock**: Walnut
**Barrel**: 28 in.
**Chokes**: IC, M, F
**Weight**: 5 lb. 13 oz.
**Bore/ Gauge**: 28, .410
**Magazine**: None
**Features**: Slim, round-action receiver; color-case hardened receiver; automatic safety with built-in barrel selector;
**MSRP** . . . . . . . . . . . . . . . . . . $2299

## FRANCHI INTENSITY

**Action**: Semiautomatic, inertia driven
**Stock**: Black synthetic, Realtree Max4, Realtree APG, Bottomlands
**Barrel**: 26 in., 28 in., 30 in.
**Chokes**: IC, M, F
**Weight**: 6 lb. 11 oz.
**Bore/ Gauge**: 12
**Magazine**: 4+1 rounds
**Features**: Inertia Driven system; recoil spring encircles the magazine tube forward the receiver; stepped, ventilated-rib, red fiber optic front sight; three extended choke tubes
**MSRP** . . . . . . . . . . . . . . $1099–$1199

## ITHACA GUN COMPANY MODEL 37 WATERFOWL

**Action**: Bottom ejection
**Stock**: Camo, synthetic black
**Barrel**: 28 in., 30 in.
**Chokes**: Briley choke tubes
**Weight**: 7 lb. 3 oz.-7 lb. 6 oz.
**Bore/ Gauge**: 12, 20
**Magazine**: 4+1 rounds
**Features**: 3 in. chamber; gold plated trigger; gamescene engraving; perma-guard protection
**MSRP** . . . . . . . . . . . . . . . . . . . . $759

**ITHACA GUN COMPANY MODEL 37 WATERFOWL**

### KRIEGHOFF MODEL KX-6

*Action*: Single-shot trap
*Stock*: Walnut
*Barrel*: 34 in.
*Chokes*: IM, LIM, F
*Weight*: 8 lb. 12 oz.
*Bore/ Gauge*: 12
*Magazine*: None
*Features*: White pearl front sight and metal center bead; case hardened, long lasting black nitro carbonized finish; semi-automatic ejector; adjustable tapered rib; available choke tubes: CY, SK, IC, M, SF
MSRP . . . . . . . . . . . . . . . . . $5490

KRIEGHOFF MODEL KX-6

MAROCCHI FINNCLASSIC 612

### MAROCCHI FINNCLASSIC 612

*Action*: Over/under
*Stock*: Wood
*Barrel*: 24 in., 28 in., 30 in.
*Chokes*: 5 choke tube Maxi 70 plus key
*Weight*: 6 lb. 8 oz.
*Bore/ Gauge*: 12
*Magazine*: None
*Features*: 3 in. chamber; available Maxi 90 choke tubes; special steel, proof tested by the Italian National Proof House; scroll work
MSRP . . . . . . . . . . . . . . . . . $1375

### MOSSBERG 835 ULTI-MAG-RECOIL REDUCTION SYSTEM

*Action*: Pump
*Stock*: Recoil Reduction System/ Mathews
*Barrel*: 24 in., 28 in.
*Chokes*: Accu-Mag set, Modified tube, or Ulti-full tube
*Weight*: 8 lb. 8 oz.
*Bore/ Gauge*: 12
*Magazine*: 6 rounds
*Features*: Exclusive stock incorporating Mathews Harmonic Damper Technology; two interchangeable low and high profile combs; 3.5 in. chamber; ported barrels; free gun lock and 10-year limited warranty
MSRP . . . . . . . . . . . . . . . . . $630

### MOSSBERG SILVER RESERVE II FIELD

*Action*: Over/under
*Stock*: Walnut, satin
*Barrel*: 26 in., 28 in.
*Chokes*: 5, Field set
*Weight*: 7 lb. 8 oz.
*Bore/ Gauge*: 12, 20, 28, .410
*Magazine*: 2 rounds
*Features*: Bead front sight; 3 in. chamber; blued barrels with silver receiver and scroll engraving; 12 Ga. model features shell ejectors
MSRP . . . . . . . . . . . . . . . . . $799

MOSSBERG 835 ULTI-MAG-RECOIL REDUCTION SYSTEM

MOSSBERG SILVER RESERVE II FIELD

REMINGTON MODEL 1100 50TH
ANNIVERSARY LIMITED EDITION

REMINGTON VERSA MAX SPORTSMAN

REMINGTON VERSA MAX ZOMBIE

### REMINGTON MODEL 1100 50TH ANNIVERSARY LIMITED EDITION

*Action*: Autoloading
*Stock*: Walnut
*Barrel*: 28 in.
*Chokes*: N/A
*Weight*: 8 lb. 4 oz.
*Bore/ Gauge*: 12
*Magazine*: 4+1 rounds
*Features*: After 50 years the Model 1100 has cemented its name as the most famous autoloading shotgun of all time. Featuring a machine-cut engraved receiver with a commemorative 1963 serial number prefix; B-Grade walnut stock with white diamond grip cap; vent rib barrel with Rem Choke tube; shipped in green Remington hard case
**MSRP**. . . . . . . . . . . . . . . . . . **$1999**

### REMINGTON VERSA MAX SPORTSMAN

*Action*: Autoloading
*Stock*: Synthetic
*Barrel*: 22 in., 26 in., 28 in.
*Chokes*: Modified Pro Bore Flush Mount; Pro Bore Wingmaster Turkey TXF Extended
*Weight*: 7 lb. 8 oz.
*Bore/ Gauge*: 12
*Magazine*: 3+1, 2+1 rounds
*Features*: VersaPort Gas System; 4140 Hammer-Forged barrel; available in Mossy Oak Camo, Realtree AP Camo, and black oxide; SuperCell Recoil Pad; ivory front bead sights, steel mid bead
**MSRP**. . . . . . . . . . . . . **$1025–$1175**

### REMINGTON VERSA MAX ZOMBIE

*Action*: Autoloading
*Stock*: Synthetic
*Barrel*: 22 in.
*Chokes*: IC and Tactical Extended Choke Tubes
*Weight*: 7 lb. 12 oz.
*Bore/ Gauge*: 12
*Magazine*: 8+1 rounds
*Features*: Oversized bolt release button and bolt release; oversized trigger guard; Picatinny rail on receiver; HiViz front sight; vent rib barrel; synthetic stock available in gargoyle green or pink explosion
**MSRP**. . . . . . . . . . . . . . . . . . . **$1599**

NEW PRODUCTS

STOEGER MODEL 3000

### STOEGER MODEL 3000

*Action*: Semiautomatic
*Stock*: Black synthetic, Realtree APG, Realtree APG SteadyGrip
*Barrel*: 24 in.
*Chokes*: IC, M, XFT, wrench
*Weight*: 7 lb. 5 oz.
*Bore/ Gauge*: 12
*Magazine*: 4+1 rounds
*Features*: Intertia Driven; red-bar front sight; drilled and tapped; shim kit; 3 in. loads
**MSRP** . . . . . . . . . . . . . . . **$529–$629**

### TAYLOR'S & CO. WYATT EARP SHOTGUN

*Action*: Side-by-side
*Stock*: Walnut checkered pistol grip
*Barrel*: 20.06 in.
*Chokes*: N/A
*Weight*: 7 lb. 1 oz.
*Bore/ Gauge*: 12
*Magazine*: 2 rounds
*Features*: Easily opened with one hand for fast shell loading; case-hardened frame stamped with 'Wyatt Earp'; chromed barrel bores with blued finish
**MSRP** . . . . . . . . . . . . . . . . . . **$1738**

TAYLOR'S & CO. WYATT EARP SHOTGUN

**TRISTAR SPORTING ARMS HUNTER EX LT**

**TRISTAR SPORTING ARMS RAPTOR A-TAC**

## TRISTAR SPORTING ARMS HUNTER EX LT

*Action*: Over/under
*Stock*: Wood
*Barrel*: 26 in.
*Chokes*: SK, IC, M, IM, F
*Weight*: 5 lb. 6.4 oz.
*Bore/ Gauge*: 20
*Magazine*: N/A
*Features*: Aluminum alloy receiver; steel hinge and firing pins; chambered for 3 in.; fiber optic sight
**MSRP** . . . . . . . . . . . . . . . . . . . **$659**

## TRISTAR SPORTING ARMS RAPTOR A-TAC

*Action*: Semiautomatic
*Stock*: Synthetic, fixed pistol grip
*Barrel*: 20 in.
*Chokes*: Extended Tactical Beretta/ Benelli/Style choke
*Weight*: 6 lb. 8 oz.
*Bore/ Gauge*: 12
*Magazine*: N/A
*Features*: 3 in. chamber; bridge-front sight with fiber optic bead; picatinni rail; ghost ring sight; swivel studs; 5-year warranty
**MSRP** . . . . . . . . . . . . . . . . . . . **$449**

## TRISTAR SPORTING ARMS TEC 12

*Action*: Pump/Auto
*Stock*: Black synthetic
*Barrel*: 20 in.
*Chokes*: External Ported Cylinder choke
*Weight*: 7 lb. 6.4 oz.
*Bore/ Gauge*: 12
*Magazine*: N/A
*Features*: Capable of operating in Pump or Semi-Auto mode; 3 in. chamber; picatinny rail; ghost ring sight; raised front bridge sight with fiber optic bead; fixed rubber pistol grip; military sling swivels and swivel studs
**MSRP** . . . . . . . . . . . . . . . . . . . **$689**

**TRISTAR SPORTING ARMS TEC 12**

# NEW Products: **Shotguns**

**TRISTAR SPORTING ARMS VIPER G2 LH**

**UTAS UTS-15 NAVY**

**WEATHERBY PA-459 TR 20 GAUGE**

## TRISTAR SPORTING ARMS VIPER G2 LH

*Action*: Semiautomatic
*Stock*: Synthetic
*Barrel*: 28 in.
*Chokes*: IC, M, F
*Weight*: 6 lb. 14.4 oz.
*Bore/ Gauge*: 12
*Magazine*: N/A
*Features*: Chrome lined chambers; barrels threaded for Beretta/Benelli style choke tubes; 3 in. chambers
**MSRP** . . . . . . . . . . . . . . . $549–$629

## UTAS UTS-15 NAVY

*Action*: Pump
*Stock*: Polymer
*Barrel*: 18.5 in.
*Chokes*: N/A
*Weight*: 6 lb. 15 oz.
*Bore/ Gauge*: 12
*Magazine*: 15 rounds
*Features*: Corrosion-resistant, satin-nickel plating that is black-chromed
**MSRP** . . . . . . . . . . . . . . . . . . $1200

## WEATHERBY PA-459 TR 20 GAUGE

*Action*: Pump
*Stock*: Synthetic
*Barrel*: 18.5 in.
*Chokes*: Extended Ported Cylinder
*Weight*: 5 lb. 12 oz.
*Bore/ Gauge*: 20
*Magazine*: 5+1 or 4+1 rounds
*Features*: Short length of pull (13.5 in.) and ergonomic buttstock; chrome-lined barrel; adjustable rear LPA-style ghost ring sight; matte black metalwork; swivel studs; also available in 12 gauge
**MSRP** . . . . . . . . . . . . . . . . . . . $499

### WINCHESTER REPEATING ARMS SUPER X PUMP MARINE DEFENDER

*Action*: Pump
*Stock*: Synthetic
*Barrel*: 18 in.
*Chokes*: Invector-Plus cylinder
*Weight*: 7 lb. 5 oz.
*Bore/ Gauge*: 12
*Magazine*: 6 rounds
*Features*: Matte hard chrome plating; alloy receiver; tactical ribbed forearm; brass bead front sight; rotary bolt; crossbolt safety; Inflex technology recoil pad
**MSRP. . . . . . . . . . . . . . . . .$399.99**

### WINCHESTER REPEATING ARMS SUPER X3 WATERFOWL HUNTER

*Action*: Autoloader
*Stock*: Synthetic
*Barrel*: 26 in., 28 in.
*Chokes*: Invector-Plus tube
*Weight*: 6 lb. 10 oz.–7 lb. 2 oz.
*Bore/Gauge*: 12, 20
*Magazine*: None
*Features*: Mossy Oak Shadow Grass Blades; .742 Back-Bored technology; hard chrome chamber and bore; vent rib; TruGlo Long Bead fiber optic front sight; Active Valve Gas System; Quadra-Vent Ports; ambidextrous crossbolt safety
**MSRP. . . . . . . . . . . $1139.99–$1199**

### WINCHESTER REPEATING ARMS SXP COMPACT FIELD

*Action*: Pump
*Stock*: Satin finish
*Barrel*: 26 in., 28 in.
*Chokes*: Three Invector-Plus chokes
*Weight*: 6 lb. 8 oz.–6 lb. 10 oz.
*Bore/ Gauge*: 12
*Magazine*: None
*Features*: Aluminum alloy receiver; matte black finish; hard chrome chamber and bore; Speed plug system; brass bead front sight; Inflex technology recoil pad
**MSRP. . . . . . . . . . . . . . . . .$399.99**

**WINCHESTER REPEATING ARMS SUPER X PUMP MARINE DEFENDER**

**WINCHESTER REPEATING ARMS SUPER X3 WATERFOWL HUNTER**

**WINCHESTER REPEATING ARMS SXP COMPACT FIELD**

# NEW Products: **Handguns**

## ACCU-TEK FIREARMS
## LT-380

*Action*: SA semiautomatic
*Grips*: Composite
*Barrel*: 2.8 in.
*Sights*: Adjustable rear sight
*Weight*: 15 oz.
*Caliber*: .380 ACP
*Capacity*: 6 rounds
*Features*: Aluminum frame; stainless steel slide; exposed hammer; manual safety; European type magazine release
**MSRP** . . . . . . . . . . . . . . . . . . . **$308**

**ACCU-TEK
FIREARMS
LT-380**

**AMERICAN DERRINGER LM4
SIMMERLING**

## AMERICAN DERRINGER
## LM4 SIMMERLING

*Action*: Hinged breech
*Grips*: Mesquite, Rosewood, custom
*Barrel*: 3.85 in.
*Sights*: Open, fixed
*Weight*: 24 oz.
*Caliber*: .45 ACP
*Capacity*: 5 rounds
*Features*: Vest pocket pistol; first round carried in the chamber; only 1in. thick; stainless steel
**MSRP** . . . . . . . . . . . . . . . . . . **$4250**

## AMERICAN DERRINGER
## LM5

*Action*: Hinged breech
*Grips*: Rosewood
*Barrel*: 2 in.
*Sights*: Open, fixed
*Weight*: 15 oz.
*Caliber*: .25 Auto, .32 Mag.
*Capacity*: 4 (.32) or 5 (.25) rounds
*Features*: Stainless steel; cam lock safety
**MSRP** . . . . . . . . . . . . . . . . . . . **$715**

**AMERICAN DERRINGER LM5**

**AMERICAN TACTICAL IMPORTS FX45 FATBOY LIGHTWEIGHT**

**ARSENAL INC. SAM7K**

**AMERICAN TACTICAL IMPORTS FX45 TITAN LIGHTWEIGHT**

**AUTO-ORDNANCE 1911TC THOMPSON CUSTOM 1911 STAINLESS**

## AMERICAN TACTICAL IMPORTS FX45 FATBOY LIGHTWEIGHT

*Action*: Semiautomatic
*Grips*: Alloy, no panels
*Barrel*: 3.2 in.
*Sights*: Black post, white dot front, Novak-style rear
*Weight*: 27 oz.
*Caliber*: .45 ACP
*Capacity*: 12+1 rounds
*Features*: Alloy frame; 1911-style slide and controsl; wide-body, high-capacity frame; cone barrel with no bushing; blued finish
**MSRP**. . . . . . . . . . . . . . . . . **$699.95**

## AMERICAN TACTICAL IMPORTS FX45 TITAN LIGHTWEIGHT

*Action*: Semiautomatic
*Grips*: Wood
*Barrel*: 3.13 in.
*Sights*: Black post, white dot front, Novak-style rear
*Weight*: 27.9 oz.
*Caliber*: .45 ACP
*Capacity*: 7 rounds
*Features*: Alloy frame; 1911-style slide and controsl; ambidextrous safety; target trigger; blued finish
**MSRP**. . . . . . . . . . . . . . . . . **$597.95**

## ARSENAL INC. SAM7K

*Action*: Semiautomatic
*Grips*: Black Polymer
*Barrel*: 10.5 in.
*Sights*: Peep rear
*Weight*: 129.5 oz.
*Caliber*: 7.62x39mm
*Capacity*: 5 rounds
*Features*: Milled receiver; short gas system; front sight block; gas block system; chrome-lined hammer-forged barrel; ambidextrous safety lever; scope rail; sling included
**MSRP**. . . . . . . . . . . . . . . . . . **$1235**

## AUTO-ORDNANCE 1911TC THOMPSON CUSTOM 1911 STAINLESS

*Action*: Semiautomatic
*Grips*: Checkered laminate
*Barrel*: 5 in.
*Sights*: Low-profile iron sights
*Weight*: 39 oz.
*Caliber*: .45 ACP
*Capacity*: 7+1 rounds
*Features*: Frames machined on high precision computerized machinery from a 420 stainless steel casting; slide is machined from a solid stainless steel billet utilizing specialized tooling to reduce set-up and refixturing; matte finish on slide and frame; front and rear sights are black with serrations; extended beavertail grip safety; extended magazine release
**MSRP**. . . . . . . . . . . . . . . . . . **$813**

## BERETTA PICO .380

**Action**: Semiautomatic
**Grips**: Technopolymer
**Barrel**: 2.7 in.
**Sights**: Front and rear adjustable
**Weight**: 11.5 oz.
**Caliber**: .380 ACP
**Capacity**: 6+1 rounds
**Features**: Stainless steel sub-chassis engraved with serial number; snag-free slide and frame; barrel can be replaced with a .32 ACP barrel; dovetail quick-change sights; frames available in flat dark earth, white, or purple
**MSRP** . . . . . . . . . . . . . . . . . . . . **$399**

BERETTA PICO .380

## BROWNING BUCK MARK CAMPER UFX

**Action**: Blowback
**Grips**: Overmolded Ultragrip FX
**Barrel**: 5.5 in.
**Sights**: Pro-Target adjustable
**Weight**: 34 oz.
**Caliber**: .22LR
**Capacity**: 10+1 rounds
**Features**: Built from aircraft-grade aluminum alloy; single-action trigger; target-crowned; large manual thumb safety; ambidextrous grip and slide release; available in blued or stainless finish
**MSRP** . . . . . . . . . . **$379.99–$419.99**

BROWNING BUCK MARK
CAMPER UFX

## CABOT GUN COMPANY AMERICAN JOE 1911

**Action**: Semiautomatic
**Grips**: Aluminum
**Barrel**: 5 in.
**Sights**: Adjustable 2-dot rear
**Weight**: 40 oz.
**Caliber**: .45 ACP
**Capacity**: 8+1 rounds
**Features**: For this art gun crossing the rubicon between firearms and art, Cabot commissioned rock star designer Joe Faris to design art that represents Detroit and Americana, and the result is a limited edition run of a new iconic 1911, the American Joe. Features top slide serrations; 420 stainless steel frame and slide; 20 LPI front strap checkering; tristar trigger
**MSRP** . . . . . . . . . . . . . . . . . . . **$7450**

CABOT GUN COMPANY
AMERICAN JOE 1911

**CENTURY INTERNATIONAL
ARMS, INC. TP-9**

### CENTURY INTERNATIONAL ARMS, INC. TP-9
*Action*: DA semiautomatic
*Grips*: Polymer, interchangeable backstraps
*Barrel*: 4 in.
*Sights*: Adjustable 3-dot
*Weight*: 26.4 oz.
*Caliber*: 9mm
*Capacity*: 17+1 rounds
*Features*: Double-action striker-fired mechanism with de-cocking button; polymer frame and steel slide; modeled after S&W 99; available titanium, OD green, and desert finish
**MSRP** . . . . . . . . . . . . . . . . .**$425.95**

**CHIAPPA FIREARMS M9-22**

### CHIAPPA FIREARMS M9-22
*Action*: Semiautomatic
*Grips*: Wood or plastic
*Barrel*: 5 in.
*Sights*: Fixed front, adjustable rear; Novak-style fiber optic (tactical)
*Weight*: 37 oz.
*Caliber*: .22LR
*Capacity*: 10 rounds
*Features*: A replica of the U.S. Military sidearm chambered in .22 rimfire and is available in two versions, the Standard model featuring fixed front sight and windage adjustable rear sight, and the Tactical model with Novak style fiber optic sights.
**MSRP** . . . . . . . . . . . . . . .**$329–$369**

**CHIAPPA FIREARMS
RHINO REVOLVER**

### CHIAPPA FIREARMS RHINO REVOLVER
*Action*: Revolver
*Grips*: Wood
*Barrel*: 6 in.
*Sights*: Front blade; adjustable rear
*Weight*: 37 oz.
*Caliber*: .357, .40 S&W, 9x19, 9x21
*Capacity*: 6 rounds
*Features*: Rhino barrel is aligned with the bottom most chamber, which lowers the center of gravity and yields a centerline of the bore more in line with the shooter's arm allowing for the most natural "point ability" while engaging a target; reduces both recoil and muzzle flip which insures subsequent shots are on target faster; frame available in chrome, black, or gold finish
**MSRP** . . . . . . . . . . . . . .**$849–$1079**

# NEW Products: **Handguns**

**CIMARRON 1911 WILD BUNCH COMBO**

**COLT MARINE PISTOL**

**COONAN COMPENSATED CLASSIC**

## CIMARRON 1911 WILD BUNCH COMBO

*Action*: Semiautomatic
*Grips*: Diamond checkered walnut
*Barrel*: 5 in.
*Sights*: Fixed
*Weight*: 39.52 oz.
*Caliber*: .45 ACP
*Capacity*: 8+1 rounds
*Features*: Correct historical markings; the original 1911 frame with a Type 1 smooth mainspring housing; combo includes the 1911 in polished blue finish and the Tanker shoulder holster, a reproduction of the rig used by William Holden in the movie The Wild Bunch
**MSRP** . . . . . . . . . . . . . . . . . **$817.70**

## COLT MARINE PISTOL

*Action*: Semiautomatic
*Grips*: Composite
*Barrel*: 5 in.
*Sights*: Novak 3-dot night sights
*Weight*: 40 oz.
*Caliber*: .45 ACP
*Capacity*: 7 rounds
*Features*: Desert Tan Cerakoted stainless steel receiver and slide; serrated mainspring housing with lanyard loop; enhanced hammer; Colt tactical ambidextrous safety lock; National Match barrel; 1913 accessory rail
**MSRP** . . . . . . . . . . . . . . . . . . . **$1995**

## COONAN COMPENSATED CLASSIC

*Action*: Semiautomatic
*Grips*: Smooth black walnut
*Barrel*: 5 in.
*Sights*: Dovetail front and rear
*Weight*: 42 oz.
*Caliber*: .357 Mag.
*Capacity*: 7+1 rounds
*Features*: Coonan Classic with compensator barrel; recoil operated; extended slide catch and thumb lock; custom carry case
**MSRP** . . . . . . . . . . . . . . . . . . **$1375**
**Compensator:** . . . . . . . . . . . . **$1625**

**CZ-USA 75 SHADOW SAO**

**CZ-USA 75 SP-01 ACCU-SHADOW**

**CZ-USA P-09 DUTY**

### CZ-USA 75 SHADOW SAO

*Action*: SAO semiautomatic
*Grips*: Plastic
*Barrel*: 4.6 in.
*Sights*: Fiber optic front
*Weight*: 35.2 oz.
*Caliber*: 9mm
*Capacity*: 16+1
*Features*: Fitted with a redesigned unit originally used in the CZ 75 Champion, the hammer of the SAO is slightly wider with modified sear engagement, resulting in smoother release and more positive ignition. The CZ single action aluminum trigger has an overtravel adjustment screw; to further smooth the trigger pull and improve trigger reset distance, the CZ 85 Combat-style slide without a firing pin block is used; ships with three 16-round magazines
**MSRP** . . . . . . . . . . . . . . . . . . . **$979**

### CZ-USA 75 SP-01 ACCU-SHADOW

*Action*: SA/DA semiautomatic
*Grips*: Thin aluminum
*Barrel*: 4.6 in.
*Sights*: Fiber optic front, HAJO rear
*Weight*: 38.4 oz.
*Caliber*: 9mm
*Capacity*: 18+1
*Features*: The Accu-Bushing system holds the barrel with much more precision; pistols returned test groups substantially less than 3" at 50 yards (using Fiocci 124 JHP); competition hammer; lighter springs; stainless steel guide rod and polished internals; short-reset disconnector is used to greatly reduce trigger reset between shots; fiber optic front and HAJO serrated target rear (adjustable for height, also drift adjustable for windage)
**MSRP** . . . . . . . . . . . . . . . . . . . **$1665**

### CZ-USA P-09 DUTY

*Action*: DA/SA semiautomatic
*Grips*: Three interchangeable backstraps
*Barrel*: 4.39 in.
*Sights*: Dovetailed, low profile front post, drift-adjustable, dovetailed rear notch
*Weight*: 30.39 oz.
*Caliber*: .40 S&W, 9mm
*Capacity*: 19+1
*Features*: This full-size version of the P-07 boasts an impressive 19+1 capacity in its flush-fitting magazine that is unsurpassed by any other 9mm service pistol; Omega trigger system; shipped with decockers installed but can easily be converted to a manual safety with the supplied parts and instructions; three interchangeable backstraps; integrated 1913 Picatinny rail
**9mm:** . . . . . . . . . . . . . . . . . . . . **$514**
**.40 S&W:** . . . . . . . . . . . . . . . . **$528**

# NEW Products: **Handguns**

## DOUBLETAP DEFENSE LLC DOUBLETAP

**Action**: DAO semiautomatic
**Grips**: Synthetic
**Barrel**: 3 in.
**Sights**: Front blade
**Weight**: 12 oz.–14 oz.
**Caliber**: .45 ACP, 9mm
**Capacity**: 2+2 rounds
**Features**: Titanium frame with a MIL-STD finish that resists corrosion; integral grips house additional two spare rounds; ported barrel reduces muzzle flip and recoil; ambidextrous thumb latch to eject spent rounds; quick-change interchangable barrels; comes with one barrel and you can purchase extra conversion kits

**Aluminum:** . . . . . . . . . . . **$499–$569**
**Titanium:** . . . . . . . . . . . . . **$729–$799**
**Conversion kits:** . . . . . . . **$199–$269**

**DOUBLETAP DEFENSE LLC DOUBLETAP**

## EAGLE IMPORTS MAC 1911 BOBCUT

**Action**: SA semiautomatic
**Grips**: Hardwood
**Barrel**: 4.25 in.
**Sights**: Adjustable rear, dovetail front
**Weight**: 34.58 oz.
**Caliber**: .45 ACP
**Capacity**: 8+1 rounds
**Features**: 4140 steel frame and hammer forged slide; fully adjustable Novak-type rear sight; dovetail front sight with fiber optic; flared and lowered ejection port; enhanced beavertail grip safety; skeletal hammer; combat trigger; stippled front strap serration; throated forged steel barrel

**Deep Blue:** . . . . . . . . . . . . . . . **$902**
**Hard Chrome:** . . . . . . . . . . . . **$978**

**EAGLE IMPORTS MAC 1911 BOBCUT**

**EAGLE IMPORTS MAC 1911 BULLSEYE**

## EAGLE IMPORTS MAC 1911 BULLSEYE

**Action**: SA semiautomatic
**Grips**: Hardwood
**Barrel**: 6 in.
**Sights**: Adjustable rear, dovetail front
**Weight**: 46.91 oz.
**Caliber**: .45 ACP
**Capacity**: 8+1 rounds
**Features**: The largest of the MAC 1911 pistol line; 4140 steel frame and hammer forged slide; fully adjustable Bomar-type rear sight; dovetail front sight; flared and lowered ejection port; enhanced beavertail grip safety; skeletal hammer; combat trigger; checkered front strap serration; ramped match grade bull barrel

**Deep Blue:** . . . . . . . . . . . . . . **$1204**
**Hard Chrome:** . . . . . . . . . . . **$1279**

## EAGLE IMPORTS MAC 1911 CLASSIC

*Action*: SA semiautomatic
*Grips*: Hardwood
*Barrel*: 5 in.
*Sights*: Adjustable rear, dovetail front
*Weight*: 40.56 oz.
*Caliber*: .45 ACP
*Capacity*: 8+1 rounds
*Features*: 4140 steel frame and hammer forged slide; fully adjustable bomar-type rear sight; dovetail front sight with fiber optic; flared and lowered ejection port; enhanced beavertail grip safety; skeletal hammer; combat trigger; checkered front strap serrations; ramped match grade bull barrel
**Deep Blue:** . . . . . . . . . . . . . . **$1038**
**Hard Chrome:** . . . . . . . . . . . **$1112**

**EAGLE IMPORTS MAC
1911 CLASSIC**

## EAGLE IMPORTS SPS PANTERA

*Action*: SA semiautomatic
*Grips*: Glass-filled nylon polymer
*Barrel*: 5 in.
*Sights*: Adjustable rear, dovetail front
*Weight*: 36.68 oz.
*Caliber*: .45 ACP
*Capacity*: 12+1 rounds
*Features*: IPSC Standard or Open Competition ready; fully adjustable Bomar-type rear sight, dovetail front sight with fiber optic; light weight polymer trigger; wide front and rear slide serrations; ambidextrous thumb safety; black chrome finish
**MSRP** . . . . . . . . . . . . . . . . . **$1895**

**EAGLE IMPORTS SPS
PANTERA**

## EAGLE IMPORTS SPS VISTA LONG AND SHORT

*Action*: SA semiautomatic
*Grips*: Glass-filled nylon polymer
*Barrel*: 5 in., 5.5 in.
*Sights*: Sight mount included
*Weight*: 41.62 oz.–43.38 oz.
*Caliber*: 9mm (Short), .38 Super (Long)
*Capacity*: 21 rounds
*Features*: Hammer forged steel slide; scope mount for C-MORE optical sight included; checkered front strap serration; ramped match grade threaded barrel; wide magwell; black chrome finish
**MSRP** . . . . . . . . . . . . . . . . . **$2450**

**EAGLE IMPORTS SPS VISTA
LONG AND SHORT**

# NEW Products: **Handguns**

**ED BROWN SPECIAL FORCES CARRY**

## ED BROWN SPECIAL FORCES CARRY

*Action*: Autoloader
*Grips*: Double diamond checkered Cocobolo wood
*Barrel*: 4.25 in.
*Sights*: Fixed dovetail 3-dot night sights
*Weight*: 35 oz.
*Caliber*: .45 ACP
*Capacity*: 7 rounds
*Features*: Commander model slide, single stack Bobtail frame; chainlink treatment on forestrap; Bobtail housing; slide coated with Gen III low glare protection; high visibility white outlines for sights; available stainless finish
**MSRP** . . . . . . . . . . . . . . . . . . **$2795**

## E.M.F. COMPANY, INC. GREAT WESTERN II ALL BLUE "PALADIN"

*Action*: Revolver
*Grips*: Ultra Ivory
*Barrel*: 3.5 in., 5.5 in., 7.5 in.
*Sights*: Fixed
*Weight*: N/A
*Caliber*: 45 LC
*Capacity*: 6 rounds
*Features*: Single action; all blued barrel, cylinder, and frames as seen in Hollywood westerns
**MSRP** . . . . . . . . . . . . . . . . . . **$560**

**EMF COMPANY, INC. GREAT WESTERN II ALL BLUE "PALADIN**

**EMF COMPANY, INC. GREAT WESTERN II BUNTLINE**

## E.M.F. COMPANY, INC. GREAT WESTERN II BUNTLINE

*Action*: Revolver
*Grips*: Walnut or Ultra Stag
*Barrel*: 12 in.
*Sights*: Fixed
*Weight*: N/A
*Caliber*: 45 LC
*Capacity*: 6 rounds
*Features*: Deep color case hardened finish; first version was designed by Colt for Ned Buntline
**MSRP** . . . . . . . . . . . . . . . . . . **$580**

### E.M.F. COMPANY, INC. GREAT WESTERN II DELUXE SHERIFF

*Action*: Revolver
*Grips*: Ultra Ivory
*Barrel*: 3 in.
*Sights*: Fixed
*Weight*: N/A
*Caliber*: .357 Mag., 45 LC
*Capacity*: 6 rounds
*Features*: Manufactured in Italy; stainless steel with factory laser engraving
**MSRP . . . . . . . . . . . . . . . . . . . $800**

### E.M.F. COMPANY, INC. GREAT WESTERN II "LIBERTY"

*Action*: Revolver
*Grips*: Ultra Ivory
*Barrel*: 4.75 in., 5.5 in.
*Sights*: Fixed
*Weight*: N/A
*Caliber*: .357 Mag., 45 LC
*Capacity*: 6 rounds
*Features*: Manufactured in Italy; all blued barrel, cylinder, and frame; factory laser engraved
**MSRP . . . . . . . . . . . . . . . . . . . $630**

### EUROPEAN AMERICAN ARMORY SARSILMAZ ST10

*Action*: Autoloader
*Grips*: Polymer
*Barrel*: 4.4 in.
*Sights*: 3-dot, low-profile
*Weight*: 34 oz.
*Caliber*: 9mm
*Capacity*: 16 rounds
*Features*: Steel frame and slide; adjustable sight; accessory rail; manual safety; low barrel axis; slide serrations; upper and lower barrel lockup; external hammer; available in blue steel or two-tone
**MSRP . . . . . . . . . . . . . . . $712–$776**

**EMF COMPANY, INC. GREAT WESTERN II DELUXE SHERIFF**

**EMF COMPANY, INC. GREAT WESTERN II "LIBERTY"**

**EUROPEAN AMERICAN ARMORY SARSILMAZ ST10**

# NEW Products: **Handguns**

**FNH FNX-45**

## FNH FNX-45

*Action*: DA/SA Autoloader
*Grips*: Interchangeable backstraps with lanyard eyelets
*Barrel*: 4.5 in.
*Sights*: Fixed 3-dot
*Weight*: 33.2 oz.
*Caliber*: .45 ACP
*Capacity*: 15 rounds
*Features*: Polymer frame with stainless steel barrel; external extractor with loaded chamber indicator; front and rear cocking serrations; 1913 accessory rail; manual, ambidextrous safety; available in black or flat dark earth
**MSRP** . . . . . . . . . . . . . . . . . . . **$824**

## GLOCK G20 GEN4

*Action*: Autoloader
*Grips*: Textured polymer
*Barrel*: 4.61 in.
*Sights*: 3-dot fixed sights
*Weight*: 27.51 oz.
*Caliber*: 10mm
*Capacity*: 15 rounds
*Features*: Full-size polymer frame; multiple backstrap frame with reduced short-frame trigger mechanism housing; three grip options; Rough Textured Frame; reversible magazine release catch; dual recoil spring
**MSRP** . . . . . . . . . . . . . . . . . . . **$637**

**GLOCK G20 GEN4**

**GLOCK G29 GEN4**

## GLOCK G29 GEN4

*Action*: Autoloader
*Grips*: Textured polymer
*Barrel*: 3.78 in.
*Sights*: 3-dot fixed sights
*Weight*: 24.34 oz.
*Caliber*: 10mm
*Capacity*: 10 rounds
*Features*: Subcompact polymer frame; trigger safety; multiple backstrap frame with reduced short-frame trigger mechanism housing; three grip options; Rough Textured Frame; reversible magazine release catch; dual recoil spring
**MSRP** . . . . . . . . . . . . . . . . . . . **$637**

**GLOCK G33 GEN4**

### GLOCK G33 GEN4

*Action*: Autoloader
*Grips*: Textured polymer
*Barrel*: 3.43 in.
*Sights*: 3-dot fixed sights
*Weight*: 19.75 oz.
*Caliber*: .357 SIG
*Capacity*: 9 rounds
*Features*: Subcompact polymer frame; trigger safety; multiple backstrap frame with reduced short-frame trigger mechanism housing; three grip options; Rough Textured Frame; reversible magazine release catch; dual recoil spring
**MSRP . . . . . . . . . . . . . . . . . . . . $599**

### GLOCK G30S

*Action*: Autoloader
*Grips*: Textured polymer
*Barrel*: 3.78 in.
*Sights*: White-dot front, white-outlines rear
*Weight*: 20.28 oz.
*Caliber*: .45 Auto
*Capacity*: 10 rounds
*Features*: "Slim"model built with the "Short Frame" Glock 30SF; polymer frame; dual recoil spring assembly; accessory rail; cold-hammer-forged barrel with octagonal rifling
**MSRP . . . . . . . . . . . . . . . . . . . . $637**

**GLOCK G30S**

### HECKLER & KOCH HK45 TACTICAL

*Action*: Autoloader
*Grips*: Polymer with finger grooves
*Barrel*: 5.16 in.
*Sights*: 3-dot tritium night sights
*Weight*: 31.7 oz.
*Caliber*: .45 ACP
*Capacity*: 10 rounds
*Features*: Polymer frame; recoil-operated with modified Browning locking system; threaded barrel; 1913 Picatinny rail; key-based HK Lock-Out system; nine different trigger firing modes; available in black, tan, and green
**MSRP . . . . . . . . . . . . . . $1392–$1461**

**HECKLER & KOCH HK45 TACTICAL**

**ISSC BY LEGACY SPORTS ISSC M22 MOONSHINE SERIES**

**KAHR ARMS CW380**

**KIMBER MASTER CARRY**

## ISSC BY LEGACY SPORTS ISSC M22 MOONSHINE SERIES

**Action**: Semiautomatic
**Grips**: Polymer
**Barrel**: 4 in.
**Sights**: White dot front, adjustable rear
**Weight**: 21.4 oz.
**Caliber**: .22LR
**Capacity**: 10 rounds
**Features**: Five safety features: hammer drop-down, loaded chamber indicator, external key lock, trigger safety tab, and magazine disconnect; windage-adjustable rear sight; white dot front sight; polymer frame; MoonShine Attitude Attire series features new camo patterns Harvest Moon, Outshine, and Muddy Girl
**MSRP** . . . . . . . . . . . . . . . . . . . . **$469**

## KAHR ARMS CW380

**Action**: DAO
**Grips**: Black polymer
**Barrel**: 2.58 in.
**Sights**: Adjustable white bar-dot combat rear, pinned in polymer front
**Weight**: 10.2 oz.
**Caliber**: .380 ACP
**Capacity**: 6+1 rounds
**Features**: Lock breech; modified Browning type recoil lug; "safe cam" action; conventional rifled barrel; metal-injection-molded slide stop lever; slide lock after last round; black and stainless matte finish
**MSRP** . . . . . . . . . . . . . . . . . . . . **$419**

## KIMBER MASTER CARRY

**Action**: Autoloader
**Grips**: Crimson Trace Lasergrips
**Barrel**: 3in. (Ultra), 5 in.
**Sights**: Fixed low profile
**Weight**: 25 oz.–31 oz.
**Caliber**: .45 ACP
**Capacity**: 7 or 8 rounds
**Features**: Aluminum, round-heel frame; satin silver finish; dovetailed night sights; recessed slide-stop pin; serrated mainspring housing; stainless steel slide; available in a Custom model, Pro, or Ultra
**MSRP** . . . . . . . . . . . . . . . . . . . **$1568**

## KIMBER MICRO CARRY

**Action**: Autoloader
**Grips**: Black synthetic or Rosewood, double diamond
**Barrel**: 2.75 in.
**Sights**: Fixed low profile
**Weight**: 13.4 oz.
**Caliber**: .380 ACP
**Capacity**: 6 rounds
**Features**: Aluminum frame; stainless steel barrel; dovetailed sights; single-side thumb safety; available in black, stainless, CDP, and CDP with Crimson Trace Lasergrips
**MSRP**. . . . . . . . . . . . . . . . . . . . **$651**
**Stainless:**. . . . . . . . . . . . . . . . **$679**
**CDP:** . . . . . . . . . . . . . . . . . . **$1121**
**CDP Lasergrips:**. . . . . . . . . . **$1406**

## KIMBER WARRIOR SOC

**Action**: Autoloader
**Grips**: Kimber G10
**Barrel**: 5 in.
**Sights**: Fixed tactical wedge tritium night sights, desert tan Crimson Trace Rail Master laser sight
**Weight**: 39 oz.
**Caliber**: .45 ACP
**Capacity**: 7 rounds
**Features**: Steel frame; front and rear slide serrations; 1913 Picatinny rail; ambidextrous thumb safety; checkered front strap; stainless steel barrel and bushing; beavertail grip; KimPro II dark green finish
**MSRP**. . . . . . . . . . . . . . . . . . **$1665**

## MG ARMS WRAITHE

**Action**: Semiautomatic
**Grips**: Custom G10
**Barrel**: 4.5 in.
**Sights**: Night or fixed
**Weight**: 18 oz.–20 oz.
**Caliber**: .45, 9mm
**Capacity**: 8+1, 9+1 rounds
**Features**: Aluminum alloy bobtail frame, custom grip panels, high ride beavertail safety, two Wilson magazines included, available in olive drab, black, desert tan, or limited edition 2011 Ti titanium frame
**MSRP**. . . . . . . . . . . . . . . . . . . **$2595**
**Titanium:**. . . . . . . . . . . . . . . . **$2995**

MG ARMS WRAITHE

KIMBER MICRO CARRY

KIMBER WARRIOR SOC

NIGHTHAWK CUSTOM T4

## NIGHTHAWK CUSTOM T4

**Action**: Autoloader
**Grips**: Slim
**Barrel**: 3.8 in.
**Sights**: Fixed
**Weight**: 34.3 oz.
**Caliber**: 9mm
**Capacity**: 9 or 10 rounds
**Features**: Thinned aluminum frame and mainspring housing
**MSRP**. . . . . . . . . . . . . . . . . . . **$3350**

# NEW Products: **Handguns**

## NORTH AMERICAN ARMS SIDEWINDER

*Action*: Revolver
*Grips*: Laminated rosewood
*Barrel*: 1 in.
*Sights*: Stainless steel post
*Weight*: 6.7 oz.
*Caliber*: .22 Mag.
*Capacity*: 5 rounds
*Features*: Features NAA's safety cylinder; stainless steel frame; available .22LR conversion
**MSRP** . . . . . . . . . . . . . . . . . . . . **$349**

**NORTH AMERICAN ARMS SIDEWINDER**

## OLYMPIC ARMS WHITNEY WOLVERINE

*Action*: Autoloader
*Grips*: Black checkered
*Barrel*: 4.625 in.
*Sights*: Blade type front sight, dovetail rear sight
*Weight*: 19.2 oz.
*Caliber*: .22LR
*Capacity*: 10+1 rounds
*Features*: Revival of ray-gun style semiauto pistol; polymer frame; ventilated rib; thumb safety; available in black, pink, coyote brown, and desert tan
**MSRP** . . . . . . . . . . . . . . . . . . . . **$294**

**OLYMPIC ARMS WHITNEY WOLVERINE**

## PARA BLACK OPS 14.45

*Action*: Autoloader
*Grips*: Beavertail
*Barrel*: 5 in.
*Sights*: Trijicon 3-dot night sights
*Weight*: 41 oz.
*Caliber*: .45 ACP
*Capacity*: 14+1 rounds
*Features*: Stainless steel frame; oversized flared ejection port; ramped barrel; adjustable skeletonized trigger; black IonBond finish
**MSRP** . . . . . . . . . . . . . . . . . . . . **$1299**

**PARA BLACK OPS 14.45**

PARA ELITE

PARA EXECUTIVE CARRY

PARA EXPERT

## PARA ELITE

**Action**: Autoloader
**Grips**: Beavertail
**Barrel**: 5 in.
**Sights**: 2-dot dovetail rear, green fiber optic front
**Weight**: 39 oz.
**Caliber**: .45 ACP
**Capacity**: 8+1 rounds
**Features**: Stainless steel frame; oversized flared ejection port; ramped barrel; adjustable skeletonized trigger; black IonBond PVD slide and frame
**MSRP**. . . . . . . . . . . . . . . . . . **$949**

## PARA EXECUTIVE CARRY

**Action**: Autoloader
**Grips**: VZ G10
**Barrel**: 3 in.
**Sights**: Trijicon night sights
**Weight**: 26 oz.
**Caliber**: .45 ACP
**Capacity**: 8+1 rounds
**Features**: Ed Brown Bobtail mainspring housing; lightweight aluminum frame; adjustable skeletonized trigger; two magazines included
**MSRP**. . . . . . . . . . . . . . . . . . **$1449**

## PARA EXPERT

**Action**: Autoloader
**Grips**: Polymer
**Barrel**: 5 in.
**Sights**: Green fiber optic front; 2-dot combat rear
**Weight**: 39 oz.
**Caliber**: .45 ACP
**Capacity**: 8+1 rounds
**Features**: Double-stack stainless steel frame; stainless match-grade barrel; adjustable skeletonized trigger; two magazines included
**MSRP**. . . . . . . . . . . . . . . . . . . **$949**

# NEW Products: **Handguns**

## PARA LDA CARRY

*Action*: Autoloader
*Grips*: Polymer
*Barrel*: 3 in.
*Sights*: 2-dot combat rear, green fiber optic front
*Weight*: 30 oz.
*Caliber*: .45 ACP, 9mm
*Capacity*: 6+1, 8+1 rounds
*Features*: Oversized, flared ejection port; steel frame and slide; beavertail grip safety; adjustable skeletonized trigger; black nitride finish available
**MSRP** . . . . . . . . . . . . . . . . . . **$1025**

## REMINGTON MODEL 1911 R1 CARRY

*Action*: Autoloader
*Grips*: Cocobolo wood
*Barrel*: 5 in.
*Sights*: Novak sights with tritium front night sight
*Weight*: 38.5 oz.
*Caliber*: .45 Auto
*Capacity*: 7 or 8 rounds
*Features*: De-horned forged carbon steel frame and de-horned carbon steel slide; beavertail grip safety with checkered memory bump; checkered front strap and mainspring housing; ambidextrous safety; satin black oxide finish
**MSRP** . . . . . . . . . . . . . . . . . . **$1299**

**PARA LDA CARRY**

**REMINGTON MODEL 1911 R1 CARRY**

**ROSSI MODEL R981 "PLINKER"**

**RUGER 22-45 LITE RIMFIRE**

*Caliber*: .22LR
*Capacity*: 8 rounds
*Features*: Alloy steel frame; key-based Taurus security system; transfer bar/hammer block safety; yoke detent system; blued finish
**MSRP** . . . . . . . . . . . . . . . . . . . **$431**

## RUGER 22/45 LITE RIMFIRE PISTOL

*Action*: SA autoloader
*Grips*: Black laminate
*Barrel*: 4.4 in.
*Sights*: Fixed front, adjustable rear
*Weight*: 23 oz.
*Caliber*: .22LR
*Capacity*: 10 rounds
*Features*: Aluminum upper, black anodized finish; stainless barrel sleeve; polymer grip frame; manual safety; loaded chamber indicator; magazine disconnect
**MSRP** . . . . . . . . . . . . . . . . . . . **$499**

**RUGER LC380**

## RUGER LC380

*Action*: Autoloader
*Grips*: Black, glass-filled nylon
*Barrel*: 3.12 in.
*Sights*: Adjustable 3-dot
*Weight*: 17.2 oz.
*Caliber*: .380 Auto
*Capacity*: 7+1 rounds
*Features*: Hardened alloy steel slide; checkered grip frame; finger grip extension floorplate; three safeties and loaded chamber indicator; blued finish
**MSRP** . . . . . . . . . . . . . . . . . . . **$449**

## ROSSI MODEL R981 "PLINKER"

*Action*: DA/SA revolver
*Grips*: Ribber
*Barrel*: 4 in.
*Sights*: Fixed red fiber optic front, adjustable rear
*Weight*: 29 oz.

## RUGER SR45

*Action*: Autoloader
*Grips*: Black, glass-filled nylon
*Barrel*: 4.5 in.
*Sights*: Adjustable 3-dot
*Weight*: 30.15 oz.
*Caliber*: .45 ACP
*Capacity*: 10+1 rounds
*Features*: Reversible backstrap; ambidextrous safety and magazine release; mouting rail; loaded chamber indicator; black nitride or brushed stainless finish
**MSRP** . . . . . . . . . . . . . . . . . . . **$529**

RUGER SR45

## RUGER SR1911

*Action*: Autoloader
*Grips*: Hardwood
*Barrel*: 4.25in., 5 in.
*Sights*: Windage adjustable Novak 3-dot
*Weight*: 36.4 oz.–39 oz.
*Caliber*: .45 ACP
*Capacity*: 7+1, 8+1 rounds
*Features*: Checkered backstrap; stainless steel barrel and bushing; positive barrel lock-up; lightweight, aluminum, skeletonized trigger and hammer; beavertail grip safety; low-glare stainless finish
**MSRP** . . . . . . . . . . . . . . . . . . . **$829**

RUGER SR1911

## SIG SAUER 1911 .22LR CAMO

*Action*: SAO
*Grips*: Polymer Camo
*Barrel*: 5 in.
*Sights*: Contrast sights
*Weight*: 34 oz.
*Caliber*: .22LR
*Capacity*: 10 rounds
*Features*: Lightweight metal frame and slide; low-profile sights; ambidextrous thumb safety; camo coating
**MSRP** . . . . . . . . . . . . . . . . . . . **$518**

SIG SAUER 1911 .22LR CAMO

## SIG SAUER 1911 SPARTAN

*Action*: SAO
*Grips*: Hogue Spartan
*Barrel*: 5 in.
*Sights*: Low profile night sights
*Weight*: 41.6 oz.
*Caliber*: .45 ACP
*Capacity*: 8 rounds
*Features*: Oil-rubbed bronze Nitron finish; gold inlay engraving; 1911 design and ergonomic feel; ancient Greek inscription on slide and grip supposedly spoken by Spartan King Leonidas: "Molon labe," or "Come and take it"
**MSRP** . . . . . . . . . . . . . . . . . . **$1356**

SIG SAUER 1911 SPARTAN

SIG SAUER M11-A1

## SIG SAUER M11-A1

*Action*: DA/SA
*Grips*: Polymer
*Barrel*: 3.9 in.
*Sights*: Siglite night sights
*Weight*: 32 oz.
*Caliber*: 9mm
*Capacity*: 15 rounds
*Features*: Stainless steel slide; Short Reset Trigger; flush fit magazines; phosphate coated internals; Nitron slide finish; black hard anodized
**MSRP** . . . . . . . . . . . . . . . . . . **$1125**

## SIG SAUER P227

*Action*: DA/SA
*Grips*: One-piece polymer
*Barrel*: 4.4 in.
*Sights*: Contrast or Siglite night sights
*Weight*: 32 oz.
*Caliber*: .45 ACP
*Capacity*: 10 rounds
*Features*: Full-size and carry lengths; double stack magazines; integral accessory rail; black hard anodized; Nitron slide finish
**MSRP** . . . . . . . . . . . . . . . . . . **$993**
**w/Night Sights:** . . . . . . . . . . . **$1085**

SIG SAUER P227

# NEW Products: **Handguns**

## SMITH & WESSON M&P PRO SERIES C.O.R.E. PISTOL

*Action*: Striker Fire Double Action
*Grips*: Polymer
*Barrel*: 4.25 in., 5 in.
*Sights*: White dot dovetail front, fixed 2-dot rear
*Weight*: 24 oz.–26 oz.
*Caliber*: 9mm, .40 S&W
*Capacity*: 17+1 and 15+1 rounds
*Features*: Competition Optics Ready Equipment; mounting platform on slide; engineered as a competition platform; polymer frame; ambidextrous operating controls; interchangeable back strap; Performance Center sear; Melonite finish
**MSRP** . . . . . . . . . . . . . . . . . . . **$729**

## SMITH & WESSON M&P SHIELD PISTOL

*Action*: Striker Fired
*Grips*: Polymer
*Barrel*: 3.1 in.
*Sights*: White dot front, white 2-dot rear
*Weight*: 19 oz.
*Caliber*: 9mm, .40 S&W
*Capacity*: 6, 7, and 8 round
*Features*: Slim, concealable, and lightweight defense firearm; high-strength polymer frame; Melonite coated; consistent 6.5 lb. trigger pull; loaded chamber indicator
**MSRP** . . . . . . . . . . . . . . . . . . . **$449**

## SMITH & WESSON SD9 VE AND SD40 VE

*Action*: Striker Fired
*Grips*: Textured polymer
*Barrel*: 4 in.
*Sights*: White dot front, fixed 2-dot rear
*Weight*: 22.7 oz.
*Caliber*: 9mm, .40 S&W
*Capacity*: 10+1, 14+1, and 16+1 rounds
*Features*: Lightweight polymer frame; front and rear slide serrations; Self Defense Trigger; ergonomic grip; Picatinny rail; two-tone finish
**MSRP** . . . . . . . . . . . . . . . . . . . **$379**

SMITH & WESSON M&P PRO SERIES C.O.R.E. PISTOL

SMITH & WESSON M&P SHIELD PISTOL

SMITH & WESSON SD9 VE

SPRINGFIELD
ARMORY XD-S

STI INTERNATIONAL
DUTY ONE SERIES

STEYR L-A1

STI INTERNATIONAL
TACTICAL SS FAMILY

## SPRINGFIELD ARMORY XD-S

*Action*: DAO autoloader
*Grips*: Polymer
*Barrel*: 3.3 in.
*Sights*: Steel dovetail rear, fiber optic front
*Weight*: 21.5 oz.
*Caliber*: .45 ACP
*Capacity*: 5+1 rounds
*Features*: Slim contour, single stack frame; Ultra Safety Assurance Trigger System; loaded chamber indicator; fail-safe disassembly; Picatinny rail system; Mould-Tru backstraps; Melonite finish
**MSRP**. . . . . . . . . . . . . . . . **$599–$669**

## STEYR L-A1

*Action*: Autoloader
*Grips*: Synthetic
*Barrel*: 4.5 in.
*Sights*: Fixed triangular/trapezoid

*Weight*: 28.6 oz.
*Caliber*: 9mm, .40 S&W
*Capacity*: 12 or 15 rounds
*Features*: Rectangular sights with or without Trilux, match sights; full size service pistol; matte finish
**From** . . . . . . . . . . . . . . . . . **$549.99**

## STI INTERNATIONAL DUTY ONE SERIES

*Action*: Autoloader
*Grips*: STI patented modular polymer
*Barrel*: 3 in., 4.37 in., 5.11 in.
*Sights*: STI Ramped front, Tactical Adjustable Rear Sight
*Weight*: 31.6 oz.–37.2 oz.
*Caliber*: 9mm, .40 S&W, .45 ACP
*Capacity*: 8, 9 rounds
*Features*: STI government frame; integral tactical rail; ambidextrous thumb safeties and beavertail grip safety; lowered and flared ejection port; STI RecoilMaster guide rod

system; front and rear serrations; blued matte finish
**MSRP**. . . . . . . . . . . . . . . . . . **$1330**

## STI INTERNATIONAL TACTICAL SS FAMILY

*Action*: Autoloader
*Grips*: STI patented modular polymer
*Barrel*: 3.76 in., 4.26 in., 5 in.
*Sights*: STI Ramped front, STI Fixed Ledge Style Rear
*Weight*: 34.4 oz.–41.1 oz.
*Caliber*: 9mm, .40 S&W, .45 ACP
*Capacity*: 8+1 rounds
*Features*: Tactical line features in a traditional 1911 package; fully forged frames with Picatinny rail system; flat top slide with front and rear serrations; ambidextrous thumb safety and beavertail grip safety; blued matte finish
**MSRP**. . . . . . . . . . . . . . . . . . **$2030**

**TRADITIONS FIREARMS
FRONTIER**

## TRADITIONS FIREARMS FRONTIER SERIES

*Action*: SA revolver
*Grips*: Simulated ivory or walnut
*Barrel*: 4.75 in., 5.5 in., 7.5 in.
*Sights*: Front blade
*Weight*: N/A
*Caliber*: .357, .44 Mag., .45 LC, .44/40
*Capacity*: 6 rounds
*Features*: 1873 single action revolvers; deep bluing and nickel frames and barrel or color case hardened frame, all polished to perfection; transfer bar safety system provides the highest lever of safety offered in an 1873 single action firearm
**MSRP . . . . . . . . . . . . . . . $515–$609**

**TRADITIONS FIREARMS
RAWHIDE**

## TRADITIONS FIREARMS RAWHIDE SERIES

*Action*: SA revolver
*Grips*: Walnut
*Barrel*: 4.75 in., 5.5 in., 7.5 in.
*Sights*: Front blade
*Weight*: N/A
*Caliber*: .45 LC, .357, .22LR, and .22LR/.22 Mag.
*Capacity*: 6 rounds
*Features*: Quality single action shooter features at an affordable price; matte black finish that provides excellent corrosion resistance; transfer bar system provides the highest level of safety offered in an 1873 single action
**MSRP . . . . . . . . . . . . . . . $440–$485**

## TRISTAR ARMS C-100

*Action*: DA/SA semiautomatic
*Grips*: Polymer
*Barrel*: 3.9 in.
*Sights*: Rear dovetail, fixed front
*Weight*: 24.48 oz.–26.08 oz.
*Caliber*: 9mm, .40 S&W
*Capacity*: 11, 15 rounds
*Features*: Produced to NATO specs;
rear snag-free dovetail sights; fixed
blade front sight; black polycoat finish;
black polymer checkered grips;
includes two magazines and a hard
plastic case
**MSRP . . . . . . . . . . . . . . . $429–$439**

TRISTAR ARMS C-100
CHROME

## TRISTAR ARMS P-120

*Action*: DA/SA semiautomatic
*Grips*: Polymer
*Barrel*: 4.7 in.
*Sights*: Rear dovetail, fixed front
*Weight*: 29.9 oz.
*Caliber*: 9mm
*Capacity*: 17 rounds
*Features*: Originally created for
military use; constructed from steel
alloy; blued or chrome finish; rear
snag-free dovetail sights; fixed blade
front sight; includes two magazines,
cleaning kit, gun lock, and a black
carrying case
**MSRP . . . . . . . . . . . . . . . $429–$439**

TRISTAR ARMS P-120

## TRISTAR ARMS T-100

*Action*: DA/SA semiautomatic
*Grips*: Polymer
*Barrel*: 3.7 in.
*Sights*: Rear dovetail, fixed front
*Weight*: 26.24 oz.
*Caliber*: 9mm
*Capacity*: 15 rounds
*Features*: Compact pistol perfect for
concealed carry; constructed from
steel alloy; blued or chrome finish;
rear snag-free dovetail sights; fixed
blade front sight; includes two
magazines, cleaning kit, gun lock, and
a black carrying case
**MSRP . . . . . . . . . . . . . . . $429–$439**

TRISTAR ARMS
T-100 BLUED

UBERTI 1873 CATTLEMAN .22LR

## UBERTI 1873 CATTLEMAN .22LR

*Action*: SA revolver
*Grips*: Walnut
*Barrel*: 4.75 in., 5.5 in., 7.5in.
*Sights*: Fixed, open
*Weight*: 36.8 oz.
*Caliber*: .22LR
*Capacity*: 6 and 12 round models
*Features*: Ideal for cowboy-action shooting practice; light recoil; six-shot comes with brass or steel backstrap and trigger guard; available in six- or twelve-shot; case-hardened frame; blued finish
**MSRP** . . . . . . . . . . . . . . **$509–$559**

UBERTI 1873 HORSEMAN

## UBERTI 1873 HORSEMAN

*Action*: SA revolver
*Grips*: Walnut
*Barrel*: 4.75 in., 5.5 in., 7.5in.
*Sights*: Fixed, open
*Weight*: 36.8 oz.
*Caliber*: .45 Colt, .357 Mag.
*Capacity*: 6 rounds
*Features*: Transfer-bar safety system; coil main spring; wider trigger; case-hardened frame; blued finish
**MSRP** . . . . . . . . . . . . . . . . . . . **$559**

U.S. FIREARMS ZIP

## U.S. FIREARMS ZIP

*Action*: SA striker fired
*Grips*: Polymer, checkered
*Barrel*: 5.25 in.
*Sights*: Fixed, open
*Weight*: 15.2 oz.
*Caliber*: .22LR
*Capacity*: N/A
*Features*: Modular firearm system built on a polymer frame; configurations include striker-fired gun as a pistol or short barreled rifle; features an accessory rail; accepts Ruger 10/22-style magazines; available in black, gray, coyote tan, and blue
**MSRP** . . . . . . . . . . **$199.99–$219.99**

## WALTHER PPK/S .22

*Action*: DA/SA autoloader
*Grips*: Polymer
*Barrel*: 3.3 in.
*Sights*: Fixed, open
*Weight*: 24 oz.
*Caliber*: .22LR
*Capacity*: 10 rounds
*Features*: Manual safety; top strap waved to reduce glare; internal slide stop; iconic PPK/S frame; beaver tail extension; nickel plated or black finish
**MSRP . . . . . . . . . . . . . . . $399–$429**

WALTHER PPK/S .22

## WALTHER PPQ M2

*Action*: Striker fire action autoloader
*Grips*: Polymer
*Barrel*: 4 in., 4.1 in., 4.6 in., 5 in.
*Sights*: 3-dot adjustable low-profile
*Weight*: 24 oz. (9mm), 25.6 oz. (.40 S&W)
*Caliber*: 9mm, 9mm (Navy SD), .40 S&W
*Capacity*: 15 rounds (9mm), 15/17 rounds (9mm Navy SD), 11 rounds (.40 S&W)
*Features*: Quick defense trigger; three safeties; ergonomic grip with checkered trigger guard; ambidextrous slide stop and magazine release button; Tenifer coated slide and barrel with matte finish
**MSRP . . . . . . . . . . . . . . . $599–$699**

WALTHER PPQ M2

WALTHER PPX

## WALTHER PPX

*Action*: Hammer fire action autoloader
*Grips*: Polymer
*Barrel*: 4 in., 4.6 in. (9MM SD)
*Sights*: 3-dot adjustable low-profile
*Weight*: 27.2 oz.
*Caliber*: 9mm, 9mm (SD), .40 S&W
*Capacity*: 16 rounds (9mm), 14 rounds (.40 S&W)
*Features*: Constant 6.5 lb. trigger pull; three safeties; ergonomic grip; ambidextrous slide stop and reversible push button magazine release; loaded chamber viewport; Mil-Std-1913 Picatinny accessory mounting rail; Tenifer coated slide and barrel; available in black and stainless
**MSRP . . . . . . . . . . . . . . . $449–$499**

# NEW Products: **Black Powder**

**CONNECTICUT VALLEY ARMS (CVA) OPTIMA V2**

**LYMAN PRODUCTS MODEL OF 1878 SIDE-HAMMER SHARPS BY PEDERSOLI**

## CONNECTICUT VALLEY ARMS (CVA) OPTIMA V2

*Lock*: Break-action muzzleloading
*Stock*: Realtree Xtra Green or black
*Barrel*: 26 in.
*Sights*: Fiber optic sights or mount
*Weight*: 6 lb. 10 oz.
*Bore/Caliber*: .50
*Features*: Modeled on the Accura V2; stainless steel barrel; quick release breech plug; 100% ambidextrous stock; includes DuraSight Dead-On scope mount and ramrod
**Realtree:** . . . . . . . . $391.95–$425.95
**SS/Black:** . . . . . . . . $338.95–$348.95
**Blued/Black:** . . . . . $307.95–$317.95

## LYMAN PRODUCTS MODEL OF 1878 SIDE-HAMMER SHARPS BY PEDERSOLI

*Lock*: Centerfire
*Stock*: Walnut
*Barrel*: 30 in.
*Sights*: Lyman's tang and globe sights
*Weight*: 9 lb.
*Bore/Caliber*: .45-70
*Features*: Reproduced for today's single shot enthusiast, Sharps' final iconic side-hammer design and Lyman's sights combine to create Lyman's "Model of 1878" .45/70 barrel; double-set triggers; shotgun-style butt; forend finished with premium ebony tip; laser engraved; black powder cartridge optional
**MSRP** . . . . . . . . . . . . . . . . . . **$1995**

## PEDERSOLI BOUTET 1ER EMPIRE

*Lock*: Flintlock
*Stock*: Hardwood
*Barrel*: 10 in.
*Sights*: Fixed
*Weight*: 2 lb. 14 oz.
*Bore/Caliber*: .45
*Features*: Napoleon often wrote with flattering appreciation about the style and prestige of the Boutet guns, which Pedersoli now proudly introduces with fine checkering on the sides; metal buttplate; ramrod has a horn tip; single set trigger; on the lock two lines are engraved with MANUF RE/a Versailles.
**MSRP** . . . . . . . . . . . . . . . . . . **$2200**

**PEDERSOLI BOUTET 1ER EMPIRE**

## PEDERSOLI KODIAK EXPRESS MK VI

*Lock*: Breechloading
*Stock*: Hardwood
*Barrel*: 24.25 in.
*Sights*: Creedmore
*Weight*: 10 lb. 2 oz.
*Bore/Caliber*: .50, .54, .58
*Features*: A very manageable gun, perfectly balanced; particularly suitable for wild boar hunting; practical rubber buttplate; half pistol grip stock; equipped with ghost sights
**MSRP** . . . . . . . . . . . . . . . . . **$1388**

## PEDERSOLI MAMELOUK

*Lock*: Flintlock
*Stock*: Hardwood
*Barrel*: 7.6 in.
*Sights*: Fixed
*Weight*: 1 lb. 10 oz.
*Bore/Caliber*: 14.5mm
*Features*: Like all the firearms equipping Napoleon's Imperial Guards, the Mameluke pistols were made at the Manufacture of Versailles under the technical management of Nicolas-Noël Boutet; the trigger guard, buttcap, screw washers of the lock, and ramrod tip are brass
**MSRP** . . . . . . . . . . . . . . . . . **$978**

## PEDERSOLI ZOUAVE U.S. MODEL 1863

*Lock*: Caplock
*Stock*: Hardwood
*Barrel*: 33 in.
*Sights*: Front, rear
*Weight*: 9 lb. 4 oz.
*Bore/Caliber*: .58
*Features*: Intended for the U.S. Artillery Department and never distributed to any Civil War army division; features brass furnitures; ramrod with a tulip tip; three-leaf rear sight; two sling swivels; the lock shows the Eagle stamp and the U.S. letters in front of the hammer
**MSRP** . . . . . . . . . . . . . . . . . **$1241**

## TRADITIONS FIREARMS VORTEK STRIKERFIRE

*Lock*: Break-action muzzleloading
*Stock*: Soft Touch synthetic
*Barrel*: 28 in.
*Sights*: Fiber optic
*Weight*: N/A
*Bore/Caliber*: .50

PEDERSOLI KODIAK EXPRESS MK VI

PEDERSOLI MAMELOUK

PEDERSOLI ZOUAVE U.S. MODEL 1863

TRADITIONS FIREARMS VORTEK STRIKERFIRE

*Features*: This patent-pending rifle takes in-line muzzleloaders to the next level by taking away the external hammer and using an internal StrikerFire™ System. To cock the gun, simply slide the striker button forward until it locks and fire. The recessed de-cocking buttons allows for quick and quiet de-cocking of the firearm and the gun is also equipped with an automatic de-cocking mechanism - when the gun is opened, it is automatically de-cocked. Also includes: two-stage trigger; CeraKote finish; Realtree Xtra or black stock
**MSRP:** . . . . . . . . . . . . . . . **$489–$649**

## SCOPES

### ALPEN APEX XP 6-24X50MM RIFLESCOPE MODEL 4058

**Weight**: 24 oz.
**Length**: 15.5 in.
**Power**: 6-24x
**Obj. Dia.**: 50mm
**Main Dia.**: 30mm
**Exit Pupil**: 8-2mm
**Field of View**: 16-4ft @ 100yds
**Twilight Factor**: 17.3-34.6
**Eye Relief**: 3.5 in.
**Features**: WBDC-TACT reticle; shock tested to 1,000 g's magnum load; fully multi-coated lenses; waterproof; fogproof; shockproof; zero-set low profile windage and elevation adjustments; black matte finish; Alpen's No-Fault, No Problem Lifetime Warranty
**MSRP** . . . . . . . . . . . . . . . . . . . **$653**

### BRUNTON ECHO 3.5-10X50MM RIFLESCOPE

**Weight**: 17.6 oz.
**Length**: 13 in.
**Power**: 3.5-10x
**Obj. Dia.**: 50mm
**Main Dia.**: 1 in.
**Exit Pupil**: N/A
**Field of View**: 28.3ft @ 3.5x @ 100yds
**Twilight Factor**: 13.2-22.4
**Eye Relief**: 3.34–2.95 in.
**Features**: Fast focus eyepiece; fully multi-coated optics; waterproof; fogproof; shockproof; glass etched reticle; precision finger turrets; also available in 1.5-5x20 Duplex Reticle, 1.5-6x40 Duplex Reticle, 1.5-6x40 Crossbow Reticle, 3-9x40 BDC Reticle, 3.5-10x50 BDC Reticle, and 6-24x50 Mil-Dot Reticle; matte finish
**MSRP** . . . . . . . . . . . . . . . . . . . **$265**

### BURRIS 2X-7X SCOUT SCOPE

**Weight**: 13 oz.
**Length**: 9.7 in.
**Power**: 2-7x
**Obj. Dia.**: 32mm
**Main Dia.**: 1 in.
**Exit Pupil**: 16-4.6mm
**Field of View**: 21-7ft @ 100yds
**Twilight Factor**: 8-15
**Eye Relief**: 11–21 in.
**Features**: Ballistic Plex reticle; fully multi-coated; variable power; low mounting capabilities; black matte finish
**MSRP** . . . . . . . . . . . . . . . . . . . . . **$399**

ALPEN APEX XP 6-24X50MM RIFLESCOPE MODEL 4058

BRUNTON ECHO 3.5-10X50MM RIFLESCOPE

BURRIS 2X-7X SCOUT SCOPE

BURRIS C4 RIFLESCOPE
4.5X-14X42MM

BURRIS ELIMINATOR 3.5X-10X40MM

BURRIS ELIMINATOR II 4X-12X42MM

## BURRIS C4 RIFLESCOPE 4.5X-14X42MM

*Weight*: 18 oz.
*Length*: 12.2 in.
*Power*: 4.5-14x
*Obj. Dia.*: 42mm
*Main Dia.*: 1 in.
*Exit Pupil*: 9-3mm
*Field of View*: 23-8ft @ 100yds
*Twilight Factor*: 13.7-24.2
*Eye Relief*: 3.2–3.9 in.
*Features*: Custom knob to match elevation adjustment and a specified catridge and bullet; index matched Hi-Lume multi-coatings; ergonomic power rings; black matte finish; available in 3x-9x-40mm and 4.5x-14x-42mm in both 1 in. and 30 mm tubes
**MSRP** . . . . . . . . . . . . . . . . . $449–749

## BURRIS ELIMINATOR 3.5X-10X40MM

*Weight*: 26 oz.
*Length*: 13 in.
*Power*: 3.5-10x
*Obj. Dia.*: 40mm
*Main Dia.*: 39mm
*Exit Pupil*: 11.4-4.0mm
*Field of View*: 25.4-9.6ft @ 100yds
*Twilight Factor*: 11.8-20
*Eye Relief*: 3.5–4 in.
*Features*: Laser rangefinder; range of 800 yards; aiming dot with storable programming; black matte finish
**MSRP** . . . . . . . . . . . . . . . . . . $1235

## BURRIS ELIMINATOR II 4X-12X42MM

*Weight*: 26 oz.
*Length*: 13 in.
*Power*: 4-12x
*Obj. Dia.*: 42mm
*Main Dia.*: 39mm
*Exit Pupil*: 10.5-3.5mm
*Field of View*: 25-9ft @ 100yds
*Twilight Factor*: 13-22.4
*Eye Relief*: 3–3.5 in.
*Features*: Laser rangefinder; range of 999 yards; accurate at any magnification; ergonomic activation buttons; enhanced extreme range ballistic programming; black matte finish
**MSRP** . . . . . . . . . . . . . . . . . . $1584

## BURRIS ELIMINATOR III 4X-16X50MM

**Weight**: 26 oz.
**Length**: 15.75 in.
**Power**: 4-16x
**Obj. Dia.**: 50mm
**Main Dia.**: 39mm
**Exit Pupil**: 12.5-3.1mm
**Field of View**: 25-7ft @ 100yds
**Twilight Factor**: 14.1-28.3
**Eye Relief**: 3.5–4 in.
**Features**: Laser rangefinder with wind compensation; range of 1,200+ yards; accurate at any magnification; ergonomic activation buttons; parallax adjustment 50 yards-infinity; black matte finish; fully multi-coated
**MSRP** . . . . . . . . . . . . . . . . . . **$2413**

BURRIS ELIMINATOR III 4X-16X50MM

## BUSHNELL AR OPTICS 1-4X24MM THROW DOWN PCL

**Weight**: 17.3 oz.
**Length**: 3.6 in.
**Power**: 1-4x
**Obj. Dia.**: 24mm
**Main Dia.**: 30mm
**Exit Pupil**: 13-6mm
**Field of View**: 110-36ft @ 100yds
**Twilight Factor**: 4.9-9.8
**Eye Relief**: 3.6 in.
**Features**: Illuminated BTR-1 reticle; first focal plane; Throw Down PCL lever for power changes; fully multi-coated optics; holdovers out to 500 yds; target turrets; matte finish
**MSRP** . . . . . . . . . . . . . . . . . . **$280.95**

BUSHNELL AR OPTICS 1-4X24MM THROW DOWN PCL

## BUSHNELL AR OPTICS 2-7X32MM RIMFIRE

**Weight**: 19.6 oz.
**Length**: 11.3 in.
**Power**: 2-7x
**Obj. Dia.**: 32mm
**Main Dia.**: 1 in.
**Exit Pupil**: 13.5-4.6mm
**Field of View**: 50-17ft @ 100yds
**Twilight Factor**: 8-15
**Eye Relief**: 3.7 in.
**Features**: Target turrets; Drop Zone 22 LR BDC reticle; fully multi-coated optics; matte finish
**MSRP** . . . . . . . . . . . . . . . . . . **$209.95**

BUSHNELL AR OPTICS 2-7X32MM RIMFIRE

### BUSHNELL AR OPTICS 3-12X40MM

**Weight**: 21.3 oz.
**Length**: 12 in.
**Power**: 3-12x
**Obj. Dia.**: 40mm
**Main Dia.**: 1 in.
**Exit Pupil**: 13.7-3.7mm
**Field of View**: 33-11ft @ 100yds
**Twilight Factor**: 11-21.9
**Eye Relief**: 3.7 in.
**Features**: Target turrets; side parallax adjustment; Drop Zone 223 BDC reticle; second focal plane; fully multi-coated optics; 600 yard range; matte finish
**MSRP** . . . . . . . . . . . . . . . . .$280.95

### BUSHNELL AR OPTICS 4.5-18X40MM

**Weight**: 21.5 oz.
**Length**: 12.4 in.
**Power**: 4.5-18x
**Obj. Dia.**: 40mm
**Main Dia.**: 1 in.
**Exit Pupil**: 8.6-2.3mm
**Field of View**: 22-7.3ft @ 100yds
**Twilight Factor**: 13.4-26.8
**Eye Relief**: 3.7 in.
**Features**: Target turrets; side parallax adjustment; Drop Zone 223 BDC reticle; second focal plane; fully multi-coated optics; 600 yard range; matte finish
**MSRP** . . . . . . . . . . . . . . . . .$349.95

### BUSHNELL ELITE TACTICAL 1-8.5X24MM

**Weight**: 23 oz.
**Length**: 10.2 in.
**Power**: 1-8.5x
**Obj. Dia.**: 24mm
**Main Dia.**: 34mm
**Exit Pupil**: 13.2-3.2mm
**Field of View**: 105-14ft @ 100yds
**Twilight Factor**: 4.9-14.3
**Eye Relief**: 3.5 in.
**Features**: Illuminated BTR-2 reticle; first focal plane; .1 Mil click value; eleven brightness settings; T-Lok turrets; black matte finish
**MSRP** . . . . . . . . . . . . . . . . .$2149.95

**BUSHNELL AR OPTICS 3-12X40MM**

**BUSHNELL AR OPTICS 4.5-18X40MM**

**BUSHNELL ELITE TACTICAL 1-8.5X24MM**

## BUSHNELL ELITE TACTICAL 4.5-30X50MM XRS

**Weight**: 37 oz.
**Length**: 10.2 in.
**Power**: 4.5-30x
**Obj. Dia.**: 50mm
**Main Dia.**: 34mm
**Exit Pupil**: 9-1.7mm
**Field of View**: 24-3.6ft @ 100yds
**Twilight Factor**: 15-38.7
**Eye Relief**: 3.7 in.
**Features**: T-Lok locking target turrets; Z-Lok zero stop; G2 reticle; first focal plane; side parallax adjustment; 1. Mil Clicks, 10 Mils/rev; blacked-out finish
**MSRP**. . . . . . . . . . . . . . . . . **$3252.95**

BUSHNELL ELITE TACTICAL
4.5-30X50MM XRS

## BUSHNELL ELITE TACTICAL ERS 3.5-21X50MM

**Weight**: 35 oz.
**Length**: 13 in.
**Power**: 3.5-21x
**Obj. Dia.**: 50mm
**Main Dia.**: 34mm
**Exit Pupil**: 10-2.4mm
**Field of View**: 26-5ft @ 100yds
**Twilight Factor**: 13.2-32.4
**Eye Relief**: 3.7 in.
**Features**: T-Lok locking turrets; Z-Lok zero stop; G2 reticle; first focal plane; side parallax adjustment; 1. Mil Clicks, 10 rev; available in matte black or flat dark earth finishes
**MSRP**. . . . . . . . . . . . . . . . . **$2975.95**

BUSHNELL ELITE TACTICAL ERS
3.5-21X50MM

## CARL ZEISS SPORTS OPTICS CONQUEST HD5 2-10X42MM

**Weight**: 17.5 oz.
**Length**: 13.19 in.
**Power**: 2-10x
**Obj. Dia.**: 50mm
**Main Dia.**: 25.4mm
**Exit Pupil**: 10.6-4.2mm
**Field of View**: 52-10ft @ 100yds
**Twilight Factor**: 6.5-20.5
**Eye Relief**: 3.5 in.
**Features**: Versatile in close encounters from cover to mid-range; parallax free to 100yds; available in z-Plex reticle, Rapid-Z 600, or standard hunting turrets; matte finish
**MSRP**. . . . . . . . . . . . . . . . . **$889–$972**

CARL ZEISS SPORTS OPTICS
CONQUEST HD5 2-10X42MM

CARL ZEISS SPORTS OPTICS
CONQUEST HD5 5-25X50MM

## CARL ZEISS SPORTS OPTICS CONQUEST HD5 3-15X42MM

**Weight**: 18.4 oz.
**Length**: 13.8 in.
**Power**: 3-15x
**Obj. Dia.**: 50mm
**Main Dia.**: 25.4mm
**Exit Pupil**: 10-2.8mm
**Field of View**: 35-7ft @ 100yds
**Twilight Factor**: 9.5-25.1
**Eye Relief**: 3.5 in.
**Features**: Mid- to long-range; low profile; parallax adjustment; Z-Plex reticle; hunting turret or lockable target turret; available Rapid-Z 600 or 800 reticle for hunting turret; most versatile of HD5 line; matte finish
**MSRP** . . . . . . . . . . . . . . $999–$1111

## CARL ZEISS SPORTS OPTICS CONQUEST HD5 5-25X50MM

**Weight**: 26.6 oz.
**Length**: 14 in.
**Power**: 5-25x
**Obj. Dia.**: 60mm
**Main Dia.**: 25.4mm
**Exit Pupil**: 8.5-2mm
**Field of View**: 21-4.2ft @ 100yds
**Twilight Factor**: 14.5-35.4
**Eye Relief**: 3.5 in.
**Features**: Mid- to extra-long range; wide magnification range provide flexibility; side parallax adjustment; Z-Plex reticle with lockable target turret, Rapid-Z 800 with hunting turret, Rapid-Z 1000 with lockable target turret, or Rapid-Z Varmint reticle and hunting turret; matte finish
**MSRP** . . . . . . . . . . . . . . $1111–$1194

CARL ZEISS SPORTS OPTICS
CONQUEST HD5 3-15X42MM

CARL ZEISS SPORTS
OPTICS TERRA 3X
3-9X42MM

## CARL ZEISS SPORTS OPTICS TERRA 3X 3-9X42MM

**Weight**: 14.8 oz.
**Length**: 12.4 in.
**Power**: 3-9x
**Obj. Dia.**: 42mm
**Main Dia.**: 25.4mm
**Exit Pupil**: 13.8-4.6mm
**Field of View**: 35.9-12.3ft @ 100yds
**Twilight Factor**: 11.2-19.4
**Eye Relief**: 3.5 in.
**Features**: MC anti-reflective coatings; standard Z-Plex or RZ 600 and 800 ballistic reticles available; all-purpose scope; larger objective for better low light situations; waterproof; matte finish
**MSRP** . . . . . . . . . . . . . . . $444–$499

## LEICA ERI 3-12X50MM RIFLESCOPE

**Weight**: 21.9 oz.
**Length**: 13.4 in.
**Power**: 3-12x
**Obj. Dia.**: 50mm
**Main Dia.**: 30mm
**Exit Pupil**: 14.9-4.1mm
**Field of View**: 35-10ft @ 100yds
**Twilight Factor**: 12.2-24.5
**Eye Relief**: 4 in.
**Features**: Illuminated reticle; four reticle options; optional rapid reticle adjustment; matte finish
**MSRP** . . . . . . . . . . . . . . . . . . **$1979**

**LEICA ERI 3-12X50MM RIFLESCOPE**

**LEUPOLD MARK 6
1-6X20MM**

## LEUPOLD MARK 6 1-6X20MM

**Weight**: 17 oz.
**Length**: 10.3 in.
**Power**: 1-6x
**Obj. Dia.**: 20mm
**Main Dia.**: 1.34 in.
**Exit Pupil**: 10.2-3.3mm
**Field of View**: 103.2-17.4ft @ 100yds
**Twilight Factor**: 4.5-11
**Eye Relief**: 3.7 in.
**Features**: Xtended Twilight Lens System with Diamond Coat 2; illuminated front focal plane reticles; zerolock adjustments with available BDC; waterproof; fogproof; matte finish
**MSRP** . . . . . . . . . . . . . . . . **$2439.99**

## LEUPOLD MARK 6 3-18X44MM

**Weight**: 23.6 oz.
**Length**: 11.9 in.
**Power**: 3-18x
**Obj. Dia.**: 44mm
**Main Dia.**: 1.34 in.
**Exit Pupil**: 10.3-2.4mm
**Field of View**: 36.8-6.3ft @ 100yds
**Twilight Factor**: 11.5-28.1
**Eye Relief**: 3.8–3.9 in.
**Features**: Xtended Twilight Lens System with Diamond Coat 2; M5B2 Autolocking Pinch & Turn; Elevation Zero Stop with Revolution Indicator; factory or custom quick change BDC rings available; waterproof; matte finish
**MSRP** . . . . . . . . . . . . . . . . **$2749.99**

**LEUPOLD MARK 6
3-18X44MM**

LEUPOLD VX6 2-12X42MM IR

## LEUPOLD VX6 2-12X42MM IR

**Weight**: 17.8 oz.
**Length**: 12.5 in.
**Power**: 2-12x
**Obj. Dia.**: 42mm
**Main Dia.**: 1.18 in.
**Exit Pupil**: 10-3.5mm
**Field of View**: 57.5-10.2ft @ 100yds
**Twilight Factor**: 9.2-22.4
**Eye Relief**: 3.8 in.
**Features**: Xtended Twilight lens;
Diamond Coat 2 and Edge Blackened Lenses; lead-free optical design; FIREDOT illumination; waterproof; fogproof; matte finish
**MSRP**.................$1249.99

## LEUPOLD VX6 3-18X50MM

**Weight**: 20.7 oz.
**Length**: 13.5 in.
**Power**: 3-18x
**Obj. Dia.**: 50mm
**Main Dia.**: 1.18 in.
**Exit Pupil**: 10-2.4mm
**Field of View**: 75.9-13.7ft @ 100yds
**Twilight Factor**: 12.2-30
**Eye Relief**: 3.7 in.
**Features**: Xtended Twilight lens; Diamond Coat 2 and Edge Blackened Lenses; lead-free optical design; Motion Sensor Technology (MST); FIREDOT illumination; waterproof; fogproof; matte finish
**From:**.................$1374.99

LEUPOLD VX6 3-18X50MM

## MINOX ZE 5I 1-5X24MM

**Weight**: 16.9 oz.
**Length**: 11.2 in.
**Power**: 1-5x
**Obj. Dia.**: 24mm
**Main Dia.**: 30mm
**Exit Pupil**: 11.4-4.8mm
**Field of View**: 110.6-23.1ft @ 100yds
**Twilight Factor**: 4.9-11
**Eye Relief**: 3.94 in.
**Features**: Illuminated central red-dot with eleven brightness settings; automatic shut down to conserve battery; German A4, BDC, and Dot reticles available; finished with Minox's M* coating; waterproof; shockproof; Z-rail mount
**MSRP**...................$1649

MINOX ZE 5I 1-5X24MM

# NEW Products: Optics

## MINOX ZE 5I 2-10X50MM

**Weight**: 22.9 oz.
**Length**: 13.2 in.
**Power**: 2-10x
**Obj. Dia.**: 50mm
**Main Dia.**: 30mm
**Exit Pupil**: 11.4-5.1mm
**Field of View**: 55.2-11.5ft @ 100yds
**Twilight Factor**: 10-22.4
**Eye Relief**: 3.94 in.
**Features**: Illuminated central red-dot with eleven brightness settings; automatic shut down to conserve battery; German A4, BDC, and Dot reticles available; finished with Minox's M* coating; waterproof; shockproof; Z-rail mount
**MSRP** . . . . . . . . . . . . . . . . . . **$1849**

MINOX ZE 5I 2-10X50MM

MINOX ZE 5I 3-15X56MM

MINOX ZE 5I 5-25X56MM

## MINOX ZE 5I 3-15X56MM

**Weight**: 26.1 oz.
**Length**: 14.6 in.
**Power**: 3-15x
**Obj. Dia.**: 56mm
**Main Dia.**: 30mm
**Exit Pupil**: 11.4-3.8mm
**Field of View**: 36.3-7.6ft @ 100yds
**Twilight Factor**: 13-29
**Eye Relief**: 3.94 in.
**Features**: Illuminated central red-dot with eleven brightness settings; automatic shut down to conserve battery; German A4, BDC, and Dot reticles available; finished with Minox's M* coating; waterproof; shockproof; Z-rail mount
**MSRP** . . . . . . . . . . . . . . . . . . **$1949**

## MINOX ZE 5I 5-25X56MM

**Weight**: 27.9 oz.
**Length**: 16.9 in.
**Power**: 5-25x
**Obj. Dia.**: 56mm
**Main Dia.**: 30mm
**Exit Pupil**: 10.9-2.5mm
**Field of View**: 21.6-4.5ft @100yds
**Twilight Factor**: 16.7-37.4
**Eye Relief**: 3.94 in.
**Features**: Illuminated central red-dot with eleven brightness settings; automatic shut down to conserve battery; German A4, BDC, and Dot reticles available; finished with Minox's M* coating; waterproof; shockproof; Z-rail mount
**MSRP** . . . . . . . . . . . . . . . . . . **$2049**

## NIGHTFORCE OPTICS, INC. 5-25X56MM ADVANCED TACTICAL RIFLESCOPE (ATACR)

**Weight**: 38 oz.
**Length**: 14.3 in.
**Power**: 5-25x
**Obj. Dia.**: 56mm
**Main Dia.**: 34mm
**Exit Pupil**: 10.52-2.28mm
**Field of View**: 17.96-4.92ft @ 100yds
**Twilight Factor**: 16.7-37.4
**Eye Relief**: 3.54 in.
**Features**: Fully multi-coated ED glass; ZeroStop comes standard; available in MOAR and MIL-R reticles; 120 MOA/34.9Mils elevation adjustment; matte finish
**From:** . . . . . . . . . . . . . . . . . . **$2328**

**NIGHTFORCE OPTICS, INC. 5-25X56MM ADVANCED TACTICAL RIFLESCOPE (ATACR)**

## NIGHTFORCE OPTICS, INC. 5-25X56MM B.E.A.S.T.

**Weight**: 39 oz.
**Length**: 15.37 in.
**Power**: 5-25x
**Obj. Dia.**: 56mm
**Main Dia.**: 34mm
**Exit Pupil**: 8.3-2.3mm
**Field of View**: 18.7-4.92ft @ 100yds
**Twilight Factor**: 16.7-37.4
**Eye Relief**: 3.35–3.54 in.
**Features**: First focal plane precision; Nightforce Digillum illumination; 90%+ light transmission; i4F intelligent four-function elevation control, ZeroStop system; XtremeSpeed adjustments; available with MIL-R, MOAR, MD2.0, TReMoR, and H59 reticles; matte finish
**From:** . . . . . . . . . . . . . . **$3298–$3783**

**NIGHTFORCE OPTICS, INC. 5-25X56MM B.E.A.S.T.**

## NIGHTFORCE OPTICS, INC. 15-55X52MM COMPETITION

**Weight**: 27.87 oz.
**Length**: 16.2 in.
**Power**: 15-55x
**Obj. Dia.**: 52mm
**Main Dia.**: 30mm
**Exit Pupil**: 3.54-.93mm
**Field of View**: 6.91-1.83ft @ 100yds
**Twilight Factor**: 27.9-53.5
**Eye Relief**: 3.15 in.
**Features**: ED glass; 92% light transmission; fast-focus European-style eyepiece; side parallax adjustment; available with CTR-1 or DDR reticles; available in matte and silver
**From:** . . . . . . . . . . . . . . . . . . **$2231**

**NIGHTFORCE OPTICS, INC. 15-55X52MM COMPETITION**

## NIKON INLINE XR 3-9X40MM BDC 300

**Weight**: 13.8 oz.
**Length**: 11.3 in.
**Power**: 3-9x
**Obj. Dia.**: 40mm
**Main Dia.**: 1 in.
**Exit Pupil**: 4.4-13.3mm
**Field of View**: 8.4-25.2ft @ 100yds
**Twilight Factor**: 11-19
**Eye Relief**: 5 in.
**Features**: Long range muzzleloader; BDC 300 reticle; ¼-MOA adjustments; Spring-Loaded Zero-Reset Turrets; silver finish; waterproof; fogproof; shockproof
**From:**.................**$199.95**

## NIKON MONARCH 3 1-4X20MM BDC

**Weight**: 12.2 oz.
**Length**: 10.35 in.
**Power**: 1-4x
**Obj. Dia.**: 20mm
**Main Dia.**: 1 in.
**Exit Pupil**: 5-20mm
**Field of View**: 23.1-92.9ft @ 100yds
**Twilight Factor**: 4.5-8.9
**Eye Relief**: 4 in.
**Features**: BDC reticle; designed for big game hunting; Spot On Ballistic Match technology; Spring Loaded Instant Zero-Reset Turrets; quick-focus eyepiece; enhanced mount ring spacing; waterproof; fogproof
**MSRP**.................**$279.95**

## NIKON MONARCH 3 4-16X42MM SIDE FOCUS MILDOT

**Weight**: 19 oz.
**Length**: 13.5 in.
**Power**: 4-16x
**Obj. Dia.**: 42mm
**Main Dia.**: 1 in.
**Exit Pupil**: 2.6-10.5mm
**Field of View**: 6.3-25.2ft @ 100yds
**Twilight Factor**: 13-25.9
**Eye Relief**: 4 in.
**Features**: Mildot reticle; Max Adj. 40 MOA; waterproof; fogproof; Spring Loaded Instant Zero-Reset Turrets; Spot On Ballistic Match technology; Monarch 3 Eyebox technology; matte finish
**MSRP**.................**$469.95**

NIKON INLINE XR 3-9X40MM BDC 300

NIKON MONARCH 3 1-4X20MM BDC

NIKON MONARCH 3 4-16X42MM SIDE FOCUS MILDOT

**NIKON P-300 BLK 2-7X32MM BDC SUPERSUB**

**NIKON PROSTAFF 5 2.5-10X50MM MATTE BDC**

**NIKON PROSTAFF 5 3.5-14X50MM ILLUMINATED NIKOPLEX**

### NIKON P-300 BLK 2-7X32MM BDC SUPERSUB

*Weight*: 16.1 oz.
*Length*: 11.5 in.
*Power*: 2-7x
*Obj. Dia.*: 32mm
*Main Dia.*: 1 in.
*Exit Pupil*: 4.6-16mm
*Field of View*: 12.7-44.5ft @ 100yds
*Twilight Factor*: 8-15
*Eye Relief*: 3.8 in.
*Features*: BDC SuperSub reticle; optimized for use with supersonic and subsonic ammo; Max Adj. 80 MOA; waterproof; fogproof; matte black
**MSRP** . . . . . . . . . . . . . . . . . .**$199.95**

### NIKON PROSTAFF 5 2.5-10X50MM MATTE BDC

*Weight*: 18 oz.
*Length*: 13.7 in.
*Power*: 2.5-10x
*Obj. Dia.*: 50mm
*Main Dia.*: 1 in.
*Exit Pupil*: 5-20mm
*Field of View*: 9.9-40.4ft @ 100yds
*Twilight Factor*: 11.2-22.4
*Eye Relief*: 4 in.
*Features*: Hand-turn reticle adjustments with Spring-Loaded Zero-Reset turrets; BDC reticle; multi-coated optics; Max Adj. 70 MOA; waterproof; fogproof; parallax setting
**MSRP** . . . . . . . . . . . . . . . . . .**$379.95**

### NIKON PROSTAFF 5 3.5-14X50MM ILLUMINATED NIKOPLEX

*Weight*: 19.9 oz.
*Length*: 14.3 in.
*Power*: 3.5-14x
*Obj. Dia.*: 50mm
*Main Dia.*: 1 in.
*Exit Pupil*: 2.9-14.3mm
*Field of View*: 7.2-28.6ft @ 100yds
*Twilight Factor*: 13.2-26.5
*Eye Relief*: 4 in.
*Features*: Illuminated reticle; hand-turn reticle adjustments with Spring-Loaded Zero-Reset turrets; waterproof; fogproof; parallax adjustment; matte finish
**MSRP** . . . . . . . . . . . . . . . . . .**$569.95**

# NEW Products: Optics

## REDFIELD (LEUPOLD) BATTLEZONE 3-9X42MM

**Weight**: 14.8 oz.
**Length**: 12.4 in.
**Power**: 3-8.6x
**Obj. Dia.**: 42mm
**Main Dia.**: 1 in.
**Exit Pupil**: 14.2-14.9mm
**Field of View**: 32.9-11.4ft @ 100yds
**Twilight Factor**: 11.2-19
**Eye Relief**: 3.5 in.
**Features**: Pop-up resettable ¼ MOA finger-click adjustments; BDC dials; TAC-MOA Reticle Matches Adjustments; waterproof; fogproof; shockproof; Redfield Lifetime Warranty; matte finish
**From**:. . . . . . . . . . . . . . . . .**$199.99**

REDFIELD (LEUPOLD) BATTLEZONE 3-9X42MM

SIMMONS .22 MAG
3-9X32MM

## SIMMONS .22 MAG 3-9X32MM

**Weight**: 10 oz.
**Length**: 12 in.
**Power**: 3-9x
**Obj. Dia.**: 32mm
**Main Dia.**: 1 in.
**Exit Pupil**: 10.7-3.6mm
**Field of View**: 31.4-10.5ft @ 100yds
**Twilight Factor**: 9.8-17
**Eye Relief**: 3.75 in.
**Features**: One piece tube construction; fully coated optics; waterproof; fogproof; shockproof; Truplex reticle; RF Rings with available Adjustable Objective; also available in 4x32; matte or silver finish
**From**:. . . . . . . . . . . . **$70.95–$106.95**

## SIMMONS 8-POINT 3-9X40MM

**Weight**: 10 oz.
**Length**: 13.125 in.
**Power**: 3-9x
**Obj. Dia.**: 40mm
**Main Dia.**: 1 in.
**Exit Pupil**: 10.7-3.6mm
**Field of View**: 31.4-10.5ft @ 100yds
**Twilight Factor**: 11-19
**Eye Relief**: 3.75 in.
**Features**: TrueZero fingertip adjustments; Quick Target Acquisition; fully coated optics; waterproof; fogproof; recoilproof; Truplex reticle; also available in 4x32, 3-9x32, and 3-9x50; matte finish
**From**:. . . . . . . . . . . . . . . . . .**$70.95**

SIMMONS 8-POINT 3-9X40MM

## SIMMONS PROSPORT 4-12X50MM

**Weight**: 14 oz.
**Length**: 13 in.
**Power**: 4-12x
**Obj. Dia.**: 50mm
**Main Dia.**: 1 in.
**Exit Pupil**: 12.5-4.2mm
**Field of View**: 23.8-8.2ft @ 100yds
**Twilight Factor**: 14.1-24.5
**Eye Relief**: 3.75 in.
**Features**: Adjustable Objective (AO); fully coated optics; TrueZero fingertip adjustments; Quick Target Acquisition eyepiece with Fast Focus; waterproof; fogproof; recoilproof; Truplex reticle; also available in 3-9x40, 3-9x50, 4-12x40 (AO), and 6-18x50 (AO); matte finish with silver or Realtree available for the 3-9x40 model
**From:** . . . . . . . . . . . . . . . . . **$158.95**

**SIMMONS PROSPORT 4-12X50MM**

### TRIJICON 3X30MM ACOG WITH 300 AAC BLACKOUT RETICLE

**Weight**: 11.64 oz.
**Length**: 6.1 in.
**Power**: 3x
**Obj. Dia.**: 30mm
**Main Dia.**: N/A
**Exit Pupil**: 10mm
**Field of View**: 19.3ft @ 100yds
**Twilight Factor**: 9.5
**Eye Relief**: 1.9 in.
**Features**: TA60 Mount; designed for law enforcement and military applications; 300 AAC Blackout Ballistic Reticle for subsonic and supersonic rounds; bullet drop compensator; Bindon Aiming Concept (BAC), fiber optics & tritium illuminated; available with amber, green, or red crosshair reticle
**MSRP** . . . . . . . . . . . . . . . . . . **$1257**

**TRIJICON 3X30MM ACOG WITH 300 AAC BLACKOUT RETICLE**

### TRIJICON 3.5X35MM ACOG NICKEL BORON DUAL ILLUMINATED .223 BALLISTIC RETICLE

**Weight**: 14 oz.
**Length**: 8 in.
**Power**: 3.5x
**Obj. Dia.**: 35mm
**Main Dia.**: N/A
**Exit Pupil**: 10mm
**Field of View**: 28.9ft @ 100yds
**Twilight Factor**: 11.1
**Eye Relief**: 2.39 in.
**Features**: Nickel Boron plating; red or green Chevron BAC reticle; Flat Top Adapter; range up to 800 meters; 5.53 MOA; fiber optics & tritium illumination; bullet drop compensator; available in 4x32, and with Horseshoe or Crosshair reticle
**MSRP** . . . . . . . . . . . . . . . . . . **$1476**

**TRIJICON 3.5X35MM ACOG NICKEL BORON DUAL ILLUMINATED .223 BALLISTIC RETICLE**

## TRIJICON VCOG 1-6X24MM RIFLESCOPE

*Weight*: 23.2 oz.
*Length*: 10.05 in.
*Power*: 1-6x
*Obj. Dia.*: 24mm
*Main Dia.*: N/A
*Exit Pupil*: 10.4-3.8mm
*Field of View*: 95-15.9ft @ 100yds
*Twilight Factor*: 12
*Eye Relief*: 4 in.
*Features*: Designed and built in the U.S.; Mil Spec, hard-coat finish; 90 MOA of windage and elevation adjustment; fully multi-coated lenses; waterproof; seven different reticle choices, between centered crosshair and horseshoe/dot reticle; red illuminated reticle; six brightness settings; matte finish
**MSRP** . . . . . . . . . . . . . . . . . . **$2270**

**TRIJICON VCOG 1-6X24MM RIFLESCOPE**

## WEAVER GRAND SLAM 3-12X50MM

*Weight*: 16.6 oz.
*Length*: 12.6 in.
*Power*: 3-12x
*Obj. Dia.*: 50mm
*Main Dia.*: 1 in.
*Exit Pupil*: 13.6-4.2mm
*Field of View*: 32.7-8.4ft @ 100yds
*Twilight Factor*: 12.2-24.5
*Eye Relief*: 3.19–3.46 in.
*Features*: 4x magnification ranges; ground, fully multi-coated lenses; fogproof; side focus parallax adjustments on select models; multiple reticle options; available in 2-8x36, 3-12x42, and 4-16x44; matte finish
**MSRP** . . . . . . . . . . **$518.95–$530.95**

**WEAVER GRAND SLAM 3-12X50MM**

## WEAVER KASPA TACTICAL 1-4X24MM

*Weight*: N/A
*Length*: 10.5 in.
*Power*: 1-4x
*Obj. Dia.*: 24mm
*Main Dia.*: 30mm
*Exit Pupil*: 6-13mm
*Field of View*: 27-109ft @ 100yds
*Twilight Factor*: 4.9-9.8
*Eye Relief*: 3.54–4 in.
*Features*: Illuminated Dual-X reticle; tactical 30 mm tube; ¼" MOA adjustments; fully multi-coated lenses; fogproof; matte finish
**MSRP** . . . . . . . . . . . . . . . . . . **$329.99**

**WEAVER KASPA TACTICAL 1-4X24MM**

## SIGHTS

### AIMPOINT 9000SC

*Weight*: 7.4 oz.
*Length*: 6.3 in.
*Obj. Dia.*: 38mm
*Features*: Ideal for short length action rifles, semi-automatic firearms, and magnum handguns; ACET technology for longer battery life; available in 2 or 4 MOA dot sizes; two-ring configuration for mounting; waterproof; matte finish
**From:** . . . . . . . . . . . . . . . . . . . . **$419**

**AIMPOINT 9000SC**

### BURRIS AR-536

*Weight*: 18.75 oz.
*Length*: 5.75 in.
*Power*: 5x
*Obj. Dia.*: 36mm
*Field of View*: 20ft @ 100yds
*Eye Relief*: 2.5–3.5 in.
*Features*: Ballistic/CQTM lighted reticle; 600 yard range; multi-coated lenses; adjutable diopter; three Picatinny rail mounting points; black matte finish; Max Adj. 60 MOA; one-year warranty
**MSRP** . . . . . . . . . . . . . . . . . . . . **$602**

**BURRIS AR-536**

**BUSHNELL FIRST STRIKE RED DOT**

### BROWNING 2-1 HUNTING SIGHTS

*Features*: Magnetic base attaches to shotgun rib; features both red and green LitePipes; comes with both round and triangular LitePipe systems; designed for guns with narrow ribs
**MSRP** . . . . . . . . . . . . . . . . . . . . **$39**

**BROWNING 2-1 HUNTING SIGHTS**

### BUSHNELL 1X MP ZOMBIE ASSAULT SIGHT

*Power*: 1x
*Features*: Illuminated T-Dot reticle; five brightness settings; red or green reticle display; multi-coated optics for transition and glare; waterproof; fogproof; shockproof
**MSRP** . . . . . . . . . . . . . . . . . . **$199.99**

**BUSHNELL 1X MP ZOMBIE ASSAULT SIGHT**

### BUSHNELL FIRST STRIKE RED DOT

*Weight*: 2.1 oz.
*Length*: 2.4 in.
*Field of View*: unlimited
*Eye Relief*: unlimited
*Features*: 5 MOA red dot reticle; multi-coated optics; self-regulating brightness; integrated mount; waterproof; fogproof; shockproof; matte finish
**MSRP** . . . . . . . . . . . . . . . . . . **$149.99**

### BURRIS AR-132

*Weight*: 11.5 oz.
*Length*: 5.25 in.
*Power*: 1x
*Obj. Dia.*: 32mm
*Field of View*: 50ft @ 100yds
*Eye Relief*: 2.5 in.
*Features*: 4 MOA red dot sight; integrated lens covers; three Picatinny rail mounting brackets; tethered windage and elevation caps; black matte finish; Max Adj. 60 MOA; one-year warranty
**MSRP** . . . . . . . . . . . . . . . . . . . . **$422**

**BURRIS AR-132**

### BUSHNELL AR OPTICS 1X28MM RED DOT

*Weight*: 6 oz.
*Length*: 5.5 in.
*Power*: 1x
*Obj. Dia.*: 28mm
*Exit Pupil*: 28mm
*Field of View*: 68ft @ 100yds
*Eye Relief*: unlimited
*Features*: 6 MOA red dot sight; eleven brightness settings; tactical rings for variably mounts and heights; matte finish
**MSRP**     **$116.95**

**BUSHNELL AR OPTICS 1X28MM RED DOT**

## BUSHNELL SCOUT DX 1000

**Weight**: 6.6 oz.
**Power**: 6x
**Features**: Built-in inclinometer; ARC Bow and Rifle Modes; Variable Sight-in; range up to 1,000yds; diopter adjustment; waterproof; compatible with magnetic attachment system; available in black or RealTree AP
**MSRP** . . . . . . . . . . . . . . . . . **$476.95**

## BUSHNELL TRS-25 HIRISE

**Weight**: 6.3 oz.
**Length**: 2.4 in.
**Power**: 1x
**Obj. Dia.**: 25mm
**Exit Pupil**: 22mm
**Field of View**: unlimited
**Eye Relief**: unlimited
**Features**: 3 MOA red dot reticle; eleven brightness settings; multi-coated; waterproof; fogproof; shockproof; riser block; matte finish
**MSRP** . . . . . . . . . . . . . . . . . **$129.99**

## CABELA'S TACTICAL RED DOT SIGHT

**Features**: Bullet-drop-compensating reticle; reticle features three selectable colors; five adjustable brightness settings; multi-coated optics for low-light shooting; waterproof; shockproof; runs up to 300 hours on one battery
**MSRP** . . . . . . . . . . . . . . . . . **$299.99**

**BUSHNELL SCOUT DX 1000**

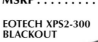

## CABELA'S TACTICAL REFLEX SIGHT

**Features**: Automatically turns on when cap is lifted; automatic reticle-brightness control; multi-coated optics with 5-MOA center-dot reticle; waterproof; shockproof; mounts to any MIL-STD-1913 rail; runs for up to 300 hours on one battery
**MSRP** . . . . . . . . . . . . . . . . . **$149.99**

## EOTECH XPS2-300 BLACKOUT

**Weight**: 8 oz.
**Length**: 3.5 in.
**Power**: 1x
**Field of View**: 90ft @100yds
**Eye Relief**: unlimited
**Features**: 2-dot ballistic drop reticle for either subsonic or supersonic rounds; mounts to 1 in. Weaver on MIL-

**BUSHNELL TRS-25 HIRISE**

STD-1913 rail; repeatable to within 1 MOA when remounting; runs 600 continuous hours; 65 MOA Ring with (2) 1 MOA aiming dots; waterproof to 10ft; fogproof; 20 brightness settings; anti-glare coating
**MSRP** . . . . . . . . . . . . . . . . . . . **$549**

**CABELA'S TACTICAL RED DOT SIGHT**

**CABELA'S TACTICAL REFLEX SIGHT**

**EOTECH XPS2-300 BLACKOUT**

## LEICA RANGEMASTER CRF 1000-R

**Weight**: 7.8 oz.
**Length**: 4.4 in.
**Power**: 7x
**Obj. Dia.**: 24mm
**Field of View**: 345ft @ 100yds
**Features**: Starter model; basic ballistic funtionality; measures linear and horizontal distance; integrated diopter compensation; automatic brightness control; LED display; angle-of-inclination display
**MSRP** . . . . . . . . . . . . . . . . . $599

LEICA RANGEMASTER CRF 1000-R

## MILLETT OPTICS SCOPES (BUSHNELL) SP SERIES RED DOT

**Features**: Precision-click adjustments; dot intensity control with eleven settings; waterproof; shockproof; available with 1 in. or 30mm tube; available 3Min Dot, 5Min Dot, and 3, 5, 8, 10 Min Multi Dot; available in matte or silver
**MSRP** . . . . . . . . . . . $86.95–$118.95

MILLETT OPTICS SCOPES (BUSHNELL) SP SERIES RED DOT

## LEICA RANGEMASTER CRF 1600-B

**Weight**: 8.1 oz.
**Length**: 4.4 in.
**Power**: 7x
**Obj. Dia.**: 24mm
**Field of View**: 345ft @ 100yds
**Features**: Point-of-aim correction, angle, temperature, and barometric pressure readings; ABC intelligent ballistics program; LED display; range up to 1600 yds; waterproof
**MSRP** . . . . . . . . . . . . . . . . . . $799

LEICA RANGEMASTER CRF 1600-B

## NIKON PROSTAFF 7 LASER RANGEFINDER

**Weight**: 5.8 oz.
**Length**: 4.4 in.
**Power**: 6x
**Obj. Dia.**: 21mm
**Exit Pupil**: 3.5mm
**Field of View**: 11-600yds
**Eye Relief**: 0.7 in.
**Features**: Multi-coated optics; waterproof; fogproof; Tru Target Technology; switchable display; Nikon's ID Technology; angle compensation
**MSRP** . . . . . . . . . . . . . . . . . $299.95

NIKON PROSTAFF 7 LASER RANGEFINDER

## LUCID M7 MICRO RED DOT

**Weight**: 4.6 oz.
**Obj. Dia.**: 21mm
**Field of View**: 48ft @ 100yds
**Eye Relief**: unlimited
**Features**: 2MOA dot 25MOA circle reticle; auto brightness sensor; auto shut off; seven brightness levels; capped and leashed turrets; ½ MOA adjustments; parallax free; waterproof; fogproof; shockproof; cast aluminum; Limited Lifetime Warranty
**MSRP** . . . . . . . . . . . . . . . . . $229

LUCID M7 MICRO RED DOT

## PENTAX RD MINI WATERPROOF DOT SIGHT

**Weight**: 4.4 oz.
**Field of View**: 41.8ft @ 100yds
**Features**: 5 MOA dot size; waterproof and nitrogen filled; seven brightness settings; parallax-free; black matte finish
**From:** . . . . . . . . . . . . . . . . . $98.49

PENTAX RD MINI WATERPROOF DOT SIGHT

## PEDERSOLI FOLDING FRONT SIGHT

**Features**: Globe sight for long-range when raised, or fold down for built-in blade for close range; ball/detent locking mechanism; 3/8 in. dovetail base; 1/2 in. high
**From**: . . . . . . . . . . . . . . . . . . $69.35

PEDERSOLI FOLDING
FRONT SIGHT

## REDFIELD BY LEUPOLD COUNTERSTRIKE 1X30MM TACTICAL RED DOT

**Weight**: 14.8 oz.
**Length**: 5.9 in.
**Power**: 1x
**Obj. Dia.**: 30mm
**Exit Pupil**: 30mm
**Eye Relief**: unlimited
**Features**: Coin-click ½ MOA adjustments; tethered adjustment covers; 4 MOA red/green dot; auto shut off; up to 5,000 hour battery life; waterproof; fogproof; shockproof; Redfield "No Excuses" Warranty
**From**: . . . . . . . . . . . . . . . . $179.99

REDFIELD BY LEUPOLD COUNTERSTRIKE
1X30MM TACTICAL RED DOT

## TRIJICON GLOCK SUPPRESSOR BRIGHT & TOUGH NIGHT SIGHTS

**Features**: Three-dot iron sights; shock-resistant design; increase night-fire accuracy by as much as 5x; fits the 17, 17L, 19, 22, 23, 24, 26, 27, 33, 34, 35, 38, and 39 Glock Models; available in black or white outline, with a green, orange, or yellow tritium lamp
**MSRP**. . . . . . . . . . . . . . . . . . . $145

TRIJICON GLOCK SUPPRESSOR
BRIGHT & TOUGH NIGHT SIGHTS

## TRIJICON RMR 3.25MOA NICKEL BORON SIGHT

**Weight**: 1.2 oz.
**Length**: 45mm
**Power**: 1x
**Features**: LED illuminated; up to 2 years of typical battery use; aluminum housing; nickel boron plating; easy-to-use adjusters with audible clicks; also available in 7MOA Dual-Illuminated Amber Dot, 9MOA Dual-Illuminated Green Dot, and 12.9MOA Dual-Illuminated Green Triangle
**MSRP**. . . . . . . . . . . . . . . . . . . $644

TRIJICON RMR 3.25MOA
NICKEL BORON SIGHT

## WEAVER MICRO DOT SIGHT

**Weight**: 2.8 oz.
**Length**: 1.9 in.
**Power**: 1x
**Eye Relief**: unlimited
**Features**: 4 MOA red dot reticle; matte finish; mounts to most firearms; adjustable brightness
**MSRP**. . . . . . . . . . . . . . . . . $108.45

WEAVER MICRO
DOT SIGHT

## BARNES BULLETS TAC-XPD AMMUNITION

*Features*: Loaded with Barnes TAC-XP bullets, the all-copper construction and very large, deep hollow-point cavity expand, penetrate, and perform consistently and optimally for personal and home defense.
*Available in*: .380 Auto; 9mm Luger +P; .40 S&W; .45 Auto +P
**Box 20:. . . . . . . . . . . . $24.99–$29.99**

BARNES BULLETS TAC-XPD AMMUNITION

## BRENNEKE USA MAGNUM CRUSH

*Features*: Delivers a force of more than 3.800ft/lbs, weighs a full 1 ½ ounce / 666 grains, and the flat trajectory is ideal for bigger game. Special coating to reduce lead fouling and broad ribs for optimum groove engagement.
*Available in*: 12 Ga. (3 in.)
**Box 5:. . . . . . . . . . . . . . . . . .$12.37**

BRENNEKE USA MAGNUM CRUSH

## CCI AMMUNITION TROY LANDRY SIGNATURE SERIES

*Features*: Gator-tested performance endorsed by Troy Landry, clean-burning propellants, reliable cycling, and sure-fire CCI priming. The Mini-Mag is 36-grain, copper-plated hollow point; 1,260 fps. The Maxi-Mag is 40-grain, jacketed hollow point; 1,875 fps.
*Available in*: .22 LR Mini-Mag; .22 WMR Maxi-Mag
**.22 LR Box 375:. . . . . . . $23.99–29.99**
**.22 WMR Box 250:  . . . $46.99–$52.99**

CCI AMMUNITION TROY LANDRY SIGNATURE SERIES

## COR-BON AMMUNITION DPX THUNDER RANCH AMMUNITION

*Features*: Teamed up with Thunder Ranch Training Center for exclusive ammunition package. Solid Copper X Bullet, deep penetrating, barrier blind, impressive expansion, and environmentally friendly.
*Available in*: .38 Special +P 110GR; 9mm Luger 1115GR; .357 Mag. 125 GR; .40 S&W 140 GR; .45 Auto +P 185 GR
**Box 20:. . . . . . . . . . . . $33.53–$41.09**

COR-BON AMMUNITION DPX THUNDER RANCH AMMUNITION

## ENVIRON-METAL HEVI DUTY HOME DEFENSE

**Features**: Frangible, non-toxic, low recoil home defense load. 00 buckshot loads coming soon.
**Available in**: 12 Ga. (2 ¾ in.) Shot sizes: 4
**Box 5:**. . . . . . . . . . . . . . . . . . . .$8.99

## FEDERAL PREMIUM HST (HANDGUN AMMUNITION)

**Features**: Provides near 100% weight retention through most barriers. Consistent expansion, optimum penetration, and superior terminal performance, it's specially designed hollow point won't plug while passing through a variety of barriers.
**Available in**: 9mm Luger, .40 S&W, .45 Auto
**Box 20:**. . . . . . . . . . . $23.99–$25.99

## FEDERAL PREMIUM WOODLEIGH HYDRO SOLID (RIFLE AMMUNITION)

**Features**: Provides safari hunters superb accuracy, consistent performance, and tremendous impact. Special heavy jackets provide excellent weight retention, up to 100% for solids.
**Available in**: 9.3x62 Mauser, 9.3x74 R, .370 Sako Mag. (Cape-Shok), .375 H&H Mag., .416 Rigby, .416 Rem. Mag., .458 Win. Mag., 458 Lott, .470 Nitro Express, .500 Nitro Express 3
**Box 20:**. . . . . . . . . $114.99–$212.99

**ENVIRON-METAL HEVI DUTY HOME DEFENSE**

**FEDERAL PREMIUM HST (HANDGUN AMMUNITION)**

**FEDERAL PREMIUM WOODLEIGH HYDRO SOLID (RIFLE AMMUNITION)**

## FEDERAL FUSION FUSION MSR

*Features*: Modern sporting rifles (MSRs) represent a very versatile class of firearms, handling a wide range of ammo and game. Shooters often build these rifles from the ground up and trick them out with accessories to match their specific needs. All-new Fusion® MSR loads provide that same degree of customization in ammunition.
*Available in*: .223 Rem., .308 Win., .338 Fed., 6.8 SPC
**Box 20:. . . . . . . . . . . . $20.99-$28.99**

FEDERAL FUSION
FUSION MSR

## FEDERAL FUSION FUSION SP

*Features*: Real-world recoil can translate to inaccurate shooting and missed trophies. For this reason, bullet weights and velocities have been developed to be lethal on whitetails, without pounding the shooter.
*Available in*: .357 Mag., .41 Rem. Mag., .44 Rem. Mag., .454 Casull, .460 S&W, .500 S&W, 50 Action Express
**Box 20:. . . . . . . . . . . $16.99–$38.49**

FEDERAL FUSION
FUSION SP

## HORNADY AMERICAN WHITETAIL

*Features*: Loaded with Hornady InterLock Bullets, optimized loads specifically for deer hunting, and select propellants for greater consistency.
*Available in*: .243 Win.; 25-06 Rem.; .270 Win.; 7mm-08 Rem.; 7mm Rem. Mag; 30-30 Win.; .308 Win.; 30-06 Spfd.; .300 Win. Mag
**Box 20:. . . . . . . . . . . $26.65–$38.33**

HORNADY AMERICAN
WHITETAIL

## HORNADY HEAVY MAGNUM COYOTE

*Features*: Loaded with 1 ½ oz. of nickel plated lead shot in either a BB or 00 buckshot for close range predators. Features Hornady Versatite wad for more impact on target; 1,300 fps.
*Available in*: 12 Ga. (3 in., 00 buckshot or BB)
**Box 10:. . . . . . . . . . . . . . . . $17.08**

HORNADY HEAVY
MAGNUM COYOTE

## NORMA AMERICAN PH

*Features*: In the "American" style, this line of ammunition features lighter bullets, higher muzzle velocity, and longer average ranges.
*Available in*: .222 Rem.; .223 Rem.; .243 Win.; .257 Roberts; 6.5 Jap; 6.5 Carcano; 6.5x55; 6.5-284; .270 Win.; .270 WSM; 7mm-08; .280 Rem.; 7mm Rem. Mag; .308 Win.; .30-06; .308 Norma Magnum; .300 Win. Mag; .300 WSM; .300 RUM; 7.65 Arg; 7.7 Jap; .338 Win. Mag; 9.3*62; 9.3*74R; .375 H&H Mag; .338 Lapua Mag; .257 Wby.; .270 Wby.; 7mm Wby.; .300 Wby.; .30-378 Wby.; .340 Wby.
**From:** . . . . . . . . . . . **$38.34–$129.60**

NORMA AMERICAN PH

## NOSLER DEFENSE HANDGUN AMMUNITION

*Features*: Bonded 'Performance' bullets for higher weight retention and maximum barrier penetration; either jacketed hollow point or polymer tipped configuration.
*Available in*: 9mm Luger +P; .40 S&W; 45 ACP +P
**MSRP** . . . . . . . . . . . . . . . . . . . .**N/A**

NOSLER DEFENSE HANDGUN AMMUNITION

## PMC AMMUNITION X-TAC MATCH

*Features*: X-TAC ammo performance comined with Sierra Bullets' ballistics, with a match grade .50 caliber bullet.
*Available in*: .223 Rem., .308 Win.
**Box 20:** . . . . . . . . . . . **$27.99–$39.99**

PMC AMMUNITION X-TAC MATCH

## REMINGTON AMMUNITION 300 AAC BLACKOUT

*Features*: A great 30-cal solution for the R-15 platform. It matches the ballistic power of the 7.62x39mm AK, but at 300 meters has 16.7% more energy. Optimal for sound and flash-suppressed fire, all in a low-recoiling package. Featuring waterproofed primers, crimped and cannelured open-tip match bullets, and a low-drag design.
*Available in*: .300 AAC Blackout
**Box 20:** . . . . . . . . . . . **$15.29–$29.49**

REMINGTON AMMUNITION 300 AAC BLACKOUT

## REMINGTON AMMUNITION HD ULTIMATE HOME DEFENSE

***Features***: Loaded with high-performance Brass Jacket Hollow Point (BJHP), these new rounds deliver massive expansion and deep penetration for ultimate stopping power. Premium nickel-plated cases resist corrosion and cycle dependably through extended storage.
***Available in***: .380 Auto, 9mm Luger, .38 Spl. +P, .40 S&W, .45 Auto
**Box 20:** . . . . . . . . . . . . . . . . . **$21.99**

## REMINGTON AMMUNITION HOG HAMMER

***Features***: Penetrating even the thickest-skinned pigs with a Barnes TSX® Bullet at its heart, the all copper construction provides for 28% deeper penetration than standard lead-core bullets. One of the toughest expanding bullets on the market, it offers near 100% weight-retention on-hog, while expanding rapidly to deliver devastating wound channels. Hog Hammer utilizes a flash-suppressed propellant for nighttime or low light hunts, and uses nickel-plated cases for reliable feeding in today's hog rifles.
***Available in***: .300 AAC Blackout, .223 Rem., .30 Rem. AR, .30-30 Win., .30-06 Spfd., .308 Win., .450 Bushmaster
**Box 20:** . . . . . . . . . . . . **$28.99–$43.99**

## RWS EVOLUTION GREEN

***Features***: New lead-free Evolution Green bullets made of food-safe metal. Features a specially pre-fragmented front core and RWS Speed Tip bullet points for shock effect. Maximum knock-down power with a flat trajectory, for humane and successful hunting.
***Available in***: .30 R Blaser; .300 Win. Mag; .30-06; .308 Win.; 7mm Rem. Mag; 7x57 R; 7x64; 7x65 R; 8x57 JRS; 8x57 JS; 9,3x62; 9,3x74 R
**MSRP** . . . . . . . . . . . . . . . . . . . . **N/A**

## WINCHESTER AMMUNITION VARMINT X

***Features***: Polymer tip, alloy jacket, lead core, and rapid fragmentation.
***Available in***: .204 Ruger; .22-250 Rem.; .223 Rem.; .243 Win.
**From:** . . . . . . . . . . . . . **$18.99–$25.99**

**REMINGTON AMMUNITION HD ULTIMATE HOME DEFENSE**

**REMINGTON AMMUNITION HOG HAMMER**

**RWS EVOLUTION GREEN**

**WINCHESTER AMMUNITION VARMINT X**

# NEW Products: MZ Ammunition

## MUZZLELOADING BULLETS

HORNADY MONOFLEX ML

### HORNADY MONOFLEX ML
**Features**: Constructed with the Hornady Flex Tip and retaining 95% of its original weight, it's available in both a High Speed/Low Drag sabot and Lock-N-Load Speed Sabot.
**Available in**: .50 cal. sabot with .45 cal. (250 gr.) bullet
**Box 20**: . . . . . . . . . . . $24.84–$26.71

### KNIGHT RIFLES BLOODLINE BULLETS
**Features**: Individually machined, double knurled bullets for increased visual blood trails.
**Available in**: .45 (185, 200 gr.); .50 (220, 250, 275, 300 gr.); .52 (220, 275, 300 gr.); .54 (325 gr.)
**Box 20**: . . . . . . . . . . . $25.99–$31.49

KNIGHT RIFLES BLOODLINE BULLETS

THOMPSON/CENTER
SUPER 45 XR SABOTS

### THOMPSON/CENTER SUPER 45 XR SABOTS
**Features**: Centerfire weight performance without the recoil, Super 45 XR sabots have a flatter trajectory, provide deep penetration, and nearly 2 times the expansion of its original diameter.
**Available in**: .45 (155, 180 gr.)
**Box 30**: . . . . . . . . . . . $25.36–$27.39

## POWDERS

### ALLIANT POWDER RELODER 33

***Features***: Specifically designed for the .338 Lapua, this powder is also suited to a variety of large magnum rifle cartridges. Double base formulation provides consistency, and it meters well.

**1lb:**. . . . . . . . . . . . . . . . . . . .**$19.15**
**8lb:**. . . . . . . . . . . . . . . . . . .**$137.50**

### ALLIANT POWDER POWER PRO 1200-R

***Features***: Specifically formulated for high-volume .223 progressive loadings. Double base formulation provides consistency, it meters well, and is made in the U.S.

**1lb:**. . . . . . . . . . . . . . . . . . .**$18.10**
**8lb:**. . . . . . . . . . . . . . . . . . .**$129.25**

ALLIANT POWDER
POWER PRO 1200-R

ALLIANT POWDER
RELODER 33

**HORNADY HOT TUB SONIC CLEANER**

HORNADY BALANCE
BEAM SCALE

## RELOADING TOOLS

### HORNADY HOT TUB SONIC CLEANER

***Features***: Featuring a 9 liter capacity, the Hot Tub is long enough to clean a 16 inch AR-15 upper. It has 4 transducers as well as a heating element for cleaning action. The microjet action removes carbon residue and other debris, and can clean internal and external surfaces. Available inner tanks for separating batches and solutions. 110V.

**MSRP**. . . . . . . . . . . . . . . . . .**$658.33**

### HORNADY BALANCE BEAM SCALE

***Features***: A traditional analog scale for powder measurement, this high tolerance scale is consistent to .1 of a grain. East to read laser etched beam.

**MSRP**. . . . . . . . . . . . . . . . . . . .**$82.17**

# NEW Products: Handloading Equipment

## LYMAN E-ZEE PRIME HAND PRIMING TOOL

**Features**: Provides an ergonomic shape to minimize hand fatigue, accepts popular brands of standard shell holders like Hornady, RCBS, and Redding, and plenty of leverage. Features integral primer tray and primer punch assembly with built-in shut-off gate.

**MSRP** . . . . . . . . . . . . . . . . . . **$47.50**

**LYMAN E-ZEE PRIME HAND PRIMING TOOL**

## LYMAN GEN5 TOUCH SCREEN POWDER SYSTEM

**Features**: New touch-screen controls with extra large, easy-to-read LCD display. An auto repeat function, quick-drain, and fast operation all make the Gen5 efficient and easy to use. Accurate to .1 grain, anti-static/anti-drift technologies and electronic interferences shields all improve performance. 115V and 230V.

**MSRP** . . . . . . . . . . . . . . . . . . **$349.95**

**LYMAN GEN5 TOUCH SCREEN POWDER SYSTEM**

**LYMAN GEN6 COMPACT TOUCH SCREEN POWDER SYSTEM**

## LYMAN GEN6 COMPACT TOUCH SCREEN POWDER SYSTEM

**Features**: New touch-screen controls and compact size maximize efficiency and space use. Auto repeat, quick-drain, fast operation, and easy access for right and left hand users make the Gen6 effective and user friendly. Anti-static/anti-drift technologies and electronic interferences shields all improve performance. 115V and 230V.

**MSRP** . . . . . . . . . . . . . . . . . . **$289.95**

## LYMAN POWER PRO ULTRASONIC CLEANER

***Features***: Designed for high volume cleaning, the 34 ¾ inch heated stainless steel tank can handle most barreled actions and upper receivers. Ten powerful industrial transducers clean the parts inside and out, and also accomodates quick changing from cleaning to lubrication. Has both a timer and adjustable heat control. 115V.

**LYMAN POWER PRO
ULTRASONIC CLEANER**

**MEC RELOADERS
600 SLUGGER**

MSRP . . . . . . . . . . . . . . . . . $1395

## MEC RELOADERS 600 SLUGGER

***Features***: Self-inclusive device; folds plastic into shell like a roll crimp; available in 12 and 20 gauges; available primer feed upgrade.
**MSRP. . . . . . . . . . . . . . . . . $275**

## MEC RELOADERS SIZEMASTER ZOMBIE RELOADER

***Features***: "Power Ring" collet resizer returns every base back to factory specification. Resizing station handles brass or steel heads. E-Z Prime auto primer is standard. 12 and 20 Ga., adjustable for 3 in. shells.
**MSRP . . . . . . . . . . . . . . . . . $283.50**

**MEC RELOADERS SIZEMASTER
ZOMBIE RELOADER**

# NEW Products: Handloading Equipment

**RCBS EXPLORER AND EXPLORER PLUS RELOADING KITS**

**RCBS SUMMIT SINGLE STAGE RELOADING PRESS**

## RCBS EXPLORER AND EXPLORER PLUS RELOADING KITS

*Features*: Explorer includes: Reloader Special-5 press, Uniflow Powder Measure, 1,500-grain Digital Pocket Scale, Nosler 7th Edition Reloading Manual, Hand Priming Tool, Universal Case Loading Block, Debur Tool, Powder Funnel, Case Slick Spray Lube, and Powder Trickler-2. Explorer Plus includes all Explorer items plus: Advanced Powder Measure Stand, Pow'r Pull Kit, Stainless Steel Dial Caliper, Measure Cylinder, six die lock rings, and No. 2, 3, 4, 10, and 43 shell holders.

**Explorer From:** . . . . . . . . . . $279.99
**Explorer Plus From:** . . . . . . . $369.99

## RCBS SUMMIT SINGLE STAGE RELOADING PRESS

*Features*: The ambidextrous Summit Single Stage Reloading Press provides for bench-top operation and full frontal access. With a 2 inch diameter ram, press adapter bushing, and quick die change, convenience and efficiency are maximized.

**From:** . . . . . . . . . . . . . . . . . $209.99

**RCBS ULTRASONIC CASE CLEANER**

## RCBS ULTRASONIC CASE CLEANER

*Features*: 3.2 quart stainless steel tank, powerful 60W transducer and 100W ceramic heater, and 36kHz ultrasonic frequency. User-friendly keypad and display, sensor to indicate when to change out solution, de-gas function, and convenient drain valve.

**From:** . . . . . . . . . . . . . . . . . $139.99

**RCBS UNIVERSAL CASE PREP CENTER**

## RCBS UNIVERSAL CASE PREP CENTER

*Features*: With an ambidextrous design, powerful 24-VDC motor, and ability to accommodate case head diameters from .25–.625 inches and lengths from .72-3.375 inches, the Universal Case Prep Center provides for a quick trim and prep for high volumes of cases. Carries a two-year limited warranty.
**From:**................... **$399.99**

## REDDING RELOADING .17 HORNET DIE SETS

*Features*: The 17 Hornet provides an exciting low noise, low recoil cartridge for varmint hunting. Available in Standard Die Sets, Type-S Die Sets, and as a Competition Seating Die.
**MSRP** .....................**N/A**

**REDDING RELOADING .17 HORNET DIE SETS**

**REDDING RELOADING MICRO ADJUSTABLE TAPER CRIMP DIES**

## REDDING RELOADING MICRO ADJUSTABLE TAPER CRIMP DIES

*Features*: Being top adjusting, these dies avoid the need to remove the die and reposition the lock ring like traditional taper crimp dies. Uses a knurled, micrometer type head for quicker and more precise adjustments. Available in .17 Hornet, 9mm/38 Super, 45 Acp/45Cap, and 40 S&W/10mm.
**From:**...................**$59.99**

# Advanced Armament Corp.

ADVANCED ARMAMENT MODEL 7

## MODEL 7

**Action**: Bolt
**Stock**: Synthetic
**Barrel**: 16 in.
**Sights**: None
**Weight**: 6 lb. 8 oz.

**Caliber**: 7.62x35mm
**Magazine**: None
**Features**: Factory-threaded barrel; receiver mounted Picatinny rail; externally adjustable X-Mark Pro trigger;

sling swivels; weatherproof synthetic stock with AAC adjustable cheekpiece
**MSRP** . . . . . . . . . . . . . . . . . . . . $899

# J. G. Anschütz

ANSCHÜTZ 1416 D HB NUSS CLASSIC

ANSCHÜTZ 1416 D KL

ANSCHÜTZ 1517 D HB NUSS CLASSIC

## 1416 D HB

**Action**: Bolt
**Stock**: Walnut
**Barrel**: 23 in.
**Sights**: None
**Weight**: 6 lb. 6 oz.
**Caliber**: .22LR, .17 Mach 2, .17 HMR
**Magazine**: Detachable box, 5 rounds
**Features**: Heavy barrel; lacquered walnut wood stock (optional beavertail); pistol grip; black buttplate; studs for sling swivel; lateral sliding safety
**MSRP** . . . . . . . . . . . . . . . . . . . $1099

## 1416 D KL

**Action**: Bolt
**Stock**: Walnut
**Barrel**: 22 in.
**Sights**: Open
**Weight**: 5 lb. 15 oz.
**Caliber**: .22LR
**Magazine**: Detachable box, 5 rounds
**Features**: Folding leaf adjustable sights; lacquered walnut wood stock; pistol grip; black buttplate; studs for sling swivel; lateral sliding safety
**MSRP** . . . . . . . . . . . . . . . . . . . $1099

## 1517

**Action**: Bolt
**Stock**: Walnut, hardwood
**Barrel**: 22 in.
**Sights**: None
**Weight**: 6 lb. 2 oz.–8 lb. 9 oz.
**Caliber**: .17 HMR
**Magazine**: 4 rounds
**Features**: Single- or two-stage adjustable trigger; optional beavertail stock
**MSRP** . . . . . . . . . . . . . . $1079–$1429

RIFLES

ANSCHÜTZ 1710 D HB NUSS CLASSIC

ANSCHÜTZ 1780 CLASSIC

## 1710
**Action**: Bolt
**Stock**: Walnut
**Barrel**: 22 in.
**Sights**: Open
**Weight**: 7 lb. 8 oz.
**Caliber**: .22LR
**Magazine**: 5 rounds
**Features**: Drilled and tapped for scope mounts; sliding safety catch; two-stage or single-stage trigger; adjustable folding leaf sights and pear front adjustable ramp; Meistergrade has engraved forestock and trigger guard; black plastic buttplate
**Classic:** . . . . . . . . . . . . $1899–$2159
**Monte Carlo:** . . . . . . . . $2039–$2269

## 1770
**Action**: Bolt
**Stock**: Walnut
**Barrel**: 22 in.
**Sights**: Drilled and tapped for scopes
**Weight**: 7 lb. 11 oz.
**Caliber**: .223 Rem.
**Magazine**: Detachable, 3-shot, in-line
**Features**: Six locking lug action for strength and reliability; adjustable, single-stage match trigger; hand checkered stock with oval cheekpiece and rubber buttpad; detachable sling swivel studs
**MSRP** . . . . . . . . . . . . . . . . . $2499

## 1780
**Action**: Bolt
**Stock**: Walnut
**Barrel**: 22 in.
**Sights**: Drilled and tapped for scopes
**Weight**: 7 lb.
**Caliber**: .308 Win., .30-06, 8x57 IS, 9.3x62
**Magazine**: 5 rounds
**Features**: Single-stage trigger; fast acquisition sight; sliding safety catch; stock made of walnut heartwood, thumbhole optional
**Classic:** . . . . . . . . . . . . . . . . $2757
**German:** . . . . . . . . . . . . . . . $3077
**Thumbhole:** . . . . . . . . . . . . . $3398
**Monte Carlo:** . . . . . . . . . . . . $3495

ANSCHÜTZ 1827 FORTNER SPRINT

## 1827 FORTNER SPRINT
**Action**: Bolt
**Stock**: Biathlon, walnut
**Barrel**: 22 in.
**Sights**: None
**Weight**: 8 lb. 2 oz.
**Caliber**: .22LR
**Magazine**: Detachable box, 5 rounds
**Features**: Combination of an extra light 1827 Fortner barreled action with the stock of the 1827 model; lacquered walnut stock with stippled checkering; heavy, cylindrical match barrel; match stage two or single trigger
**MSRP** . . . . . . . . . . . . . . . . . $3398

# J. G. Anschütz

ANSCHÜTZ 1903 TARGET
SMALL BORE RIFLE

ANSCHÜTZ 1907 IN 1914 STOCK

## 1903 TARGET SMALL BORE RIFLE
**Action**: Bolt
**Stock**: Hardwood
**Barrel**: 26 in., heavy
**Sights**: None
**Weight**: 9 lb. 11 oz.
**Caliber**: .22LR
**Magazine**: None
**Features**: A match rifle for small bore shooters; anatomically perfect walnut stock with vertically adjustable cheek piece; optional aluminum, hook, or rubber buttplate; aluminum accessories rail
**MSRP** . . . . . . . . . . . . . . . . . . $1282

## 1907 IN 1914 STOCK
**Action**: Bolt
**Stock**: Walnut
**Barrel**: 32.28 in.

**Sights**: None
**Weight**: 10 lb. 12 oz.
**Caliber**: .22LR
**Magazine**: None
**Features**: Match 54 action; heavy, cylindrical barrel; match two-stage or single-stage trigger; safety signal pin
**MSRP** . . . . . . . . . . . . . . . . . . $3013

## 2007/660, 2013/690 WITH 2018 PRECISE STOCK
**Action**: Bolt
**Stock**: Aluminum
**Barrel**: 32 in., 33 in.
**Sights**: None
**Weight**: 13 lb., 13 lb. 10 oz.
**Caliber**: .22LR
**Magazine**: None
**Features**: Single loader; two-stage trigger; optional buttplate; new backend

offers large range of adjustment for small shooters
**MSRP** . . . . . . . . . . . . . . . . . . $4296

## MSR RX 22
**Action**: Semiautomatic
**Stock**: Laminated wood, plastic
**Barrel**: 16.5 in.
**Sights**: None
**Weight**: 7 lb.
**Caliber**: .22LR
**Magazine**: 10 rounds
**Features**: Folding stock; aluminum grooved Picatinny rail for accessories; 6 possible positions for cocking lever; optional buttplate and sight set; black, desert, aluminum colors available
**Precision, Precision Black**: . . . $995
**Black Hawk, Desert**: . . . . . . . . $895

ANSCHÜTZ 2007/660 WITH
2018 PRECISE STOCK

ANSCHÜTZ MSR RX 22 BLACK

ARMALITE AR-10 A4
CARBINE

ARMALITE AR-10A2CF CARBINE

## AR-10 A4 CARBINE

**Action**: Semiautomatic
**Stock**: Synthetic
**Barrel**: 16 in.
**Sights**: Front
**Weight**: 7 lb. 14 oz.
**Caliber**: 7.62/.308
**Magazine**: Detachable box, 20 rounds
**Features**: Functionally identical to the AR-10B family, the AR-10A family is designed to accept early ArmaLite AR-10 "Waffle" magazines and good quality magazines copied from them, including Magpul PMAG 20LR, Knight's Armament, and DPMS. Gas block with Picatinny rail; black synthetic stock; sling, hard case, and sling swivel mounts included
**MSRP** . . . . . . . . . . . . . . . . . . **$1571**

## AR-10A2CF CARBINE

**Action**: Semiautomatic
**Stock**: Synthetic
**Barrel**: 16 in.
**Sights**: Open
**Weight**: 9 lb.
**Caliber**: .308
**Magazine**: Detachable box, 10, 20 rounds
**Features**: Chrome-lined barrel; forged A2 receiver; sling; black case; flash suppressor; tactical two-stage trigger; black or green stock; stage trigger
**MSRP** . . . . . . . . . . . . . . . . . . **$1583**

## AR-10 SUPER SASS

**Action**: Semiautomatic
**Stock**: Synthetic
**Barrel**: 20 in.
**Sights**: Adjustable front
**Weight**: 11 lb. 13 oz.
**Caliber**: 7.62/.308
**Magazine**: Detachable box, 20 rounds
**Features**: Functionally identical to the AR-10B family, the AR-10A family is designed to accept early ArmaLite AR-10 "Waffle" magazines and good quality magazines copied from them, including Magpul PMAG 20LR, Knight's Armament, and DPMS. Adjustable gas block front sight; black synthetic stock; sling, hard case, and sling swivel mounts included
**MSRP** . . . . . . . . . . . . . . . . . . **$3100**

## AR-10 TBNF

**Action**: Semiautomatic
**Stock**: Synthetic
**Barrel**: 20 in.
**Sights**: None
**Weight**: 10 lb. 2 oz.
**Caliber**: .308
**Magazine**: Detachable box, 10-round
**Features**: Free-float handguard in black; two-stage NM trigger; black case; triple-lapped barrel; black or green stock
**MSRP** . . . . . . . . . . . . . . . . . . **$1914**

## AR-10T CARBINE

**Action**: Semiautomatic
**Stock**: Synthetic
**Barrel**: 16 in.
**Sights**: Open
**Weight**: 8 lb. 10 oz.
**Caliber**: .308
**Magazine**: Detachable box, 10, 20 round
**Features**: Free-float handguard in black; two-stage NM trigger; flash suppressor; black case; black stock
**MSRP** . . . . . . . . . . . . . . . . . . **$1914**

RIFLES

ARMALITE
AR-10
SUPER SASS

ARMALITE AR-10T
CARBINE

ARMALITE
AR-10 TBNF

# ArmaLite

**ARMALITE M-15 A2**

**ARMALITE M-15 A2 CARBINE**

## RIFLES

### AR-50A1 NM
**Action**: Bolt
**Stock**: Synthetic
**Barrel**: 33 in.
**Sights**: None
**Weight**: 33 lb. 3 oz.
**Caliber**: .50 BMG
**Magazine**: None
**Features**: Chromoly barrel; muzzle-brake; 15minute rail; single-stage trigger
**MSRP** . . . . . . . . . . . . . . . . . $4230

### M-15 A2
**Action**: Semiautomatic
**Stock**: Synthetic
**Barrel**: 20 in.
**Sights**: Open
**Weight**: 8 lb. 1 oz.
**Caliber**: .223
**Magazine**: Detachable box, 30 rounds
**Features**: Double-lapped, chrome-lined barrel; flash suppressor; forged A2 Receiver; tactical two-stage trigger;

sling; black case; black or green synthetic stock
**MSRP** . . . . . . . . . . . . . . . . . $1174

### M-15 A2 CARBINE
**Action**: Semiautomatic
**Stock**: Synthetic
**Barrel**: 16 in.
**Sights**: Open
**Weight**: 6 lb. 13 oz.
**Caliber**: .223
**Magazine**: Detachable box, 30 rounds
**Features**: Forged A2 receiver; double-lapped, chrome-lined barrel; sling; handguards; black or green synthetic stock; black case; tactical two-stage trigger; flash suppressor
**MSRP** . . . . . . . . . . . . . . . . . $1174

### M-15 A2 NATIONAL MATCH RIFLE
**Action**: Semiautomatic
**Stock**: Synthetic
**Barrel**: 20 in.

**Sights**: Open
**Weight**: 9 lb. 3 oz.
**Caliber**: .223
**Magazine**: Detachable box, 30 rounds
**Features**: Forged A2 receiver with NM hooded rear sight; triple-lapped, stainless steel barrel with NM sleeve; A2 front sight assembly; two-stage NM trigger; black or green stock
**MSRP** . . . . . . . . . . . . . . . . . $1422

### M-15 A4 CARBINE
**Action**: Semiautomatic
**Stock**: Synthetic
**Barrel**: 16 in.
**Sights**: None
**Weight**: 6 lb. 7 oz.
**Caliber**: 7.62x39mm
**Magazine**: Detachable box, 10 rounds
**Features**: Forged flattop with Picatinny rail; forged aluminum receiver; tactical two-stage trigger; A2 flash suppressor; sling; black case; black or green stock
**MSRP** . . . . . . . . . . . . . . . . . $1115

**ARMALITE AR-50A1 NM**

**ARMALITE M-15 A2 NM RIFLE**

**ARMALITE M-15 A4 CARBINE**

## M-15 A4 CBK WITHOUT CARRY HANDLE

**Action**: Semiautomatic
**Stock**: Synthetic
**Barrel**: 16 in.
**Sights**: None
**Weight**: 6 lb. 3 oz.
**Caliber**: .223
**Magazine**: Detachable box, 30 rounds
**Features**: Chrome-lined barrel; muzzle flash suppressor; forged flattop; Picatinny rail; tactical two-stage trigger; no carry handle; black stock; sling; black case
**MSRP** . . . . . . . . . . . . . . . . . . . . **$989**

ARMALITE M-15 A4 CBK
WITHOUT CARRY HANDLE

ARMALITE SPR MOD
1 LE CARBINE

## SPR MOD 1 LE CARBINE

**Action**: Semiautomatic, short gas system
**Stock**: Synthetic
**Barrel**: 16 in.
**Sights**: 3 detachable rails
**Weight**: 6 lb. 8 oz.

**Caliber**: .223, 6.8mm SPC, 7.62x39mm
**Magazine**: Detachable box, 30 rounds
**Features**: Muzzle flash suppressor; black synthetic tactical stock; aluminum handguard; tactical two-stage trigger, sling; black case
**MSRP** . . . . . . . . . . . . . . . . . . . **$1554**

# Arsenal, Inc.

ARSENAL SA RPK-3R

ARSENAL SAM7R-61C (CALIFORNIA
COMPLIANT)

## SAM7R-61C (CALIFORNIA COMPLIANT)

**Action**: Gas-operated autoloader
**Stock**: Black polymer
**Barrel**: 16.3 in.
**Sights**: Open
**Weight**: 8 lb. 2 oz.
**Caliber**: 7.62x39mm
**Magazine**: 10-round U.S.-made

**Features**: Milled receiver; non-detachable magazine; includes muzzle nut, cleaning rod, and bayonet lug
**MSRP** . . . . . . . . . . . . . . . . . . **$1349**

## SA RPK-3R

**Action**: Gas-operated autoloader
**Stock**: Black polymer or blond wood
**Barrel**: 23.2 in.
**Sights**: Open

**Weight**: 10 lb. 8 oz.
**Caliber**: 5.45x39.5mm
**Magazine**: 45-round
**Features**: RPK heavy barrel; milled receiver; U.S.-made; paddle style buttstock and scope rail; includes sling, oil bottle, and cleaning kit
**MSRP** . . . . . . . . . . . . . . **$2500–$2750**

# Auto-Ordnance

## AOM150

**Action**: Semiautomatic
**Stock**: Walnut; handguard
**Barrel**: 18 in.
**Sights**: Blade front; flip style rear
**Weight**: 5 lb. 6 oz.
**Caliber**: .30
**Magazine**: 15-shot stick
**Features**: Folding stock; Parkerized finish
**MSRP** . . . . . . . . . . . . . . . . . . . . . $903

**AUTO-ORDNANCE AOM150**

## M1SB THOMPSON M1 SBR

**Action**: Semiautomatic
**Stock**: Walnut, vertical foregrip
**Barrel**: 10.5 in.
**Sights**: Blade front, fixed battle rear
**Weight**: 10 lb. 8 oz.
**Caliber**: .45 ACP
**Magazine**: 30-shot stick
**Features**: Will not accept drum magazines; frame and receiver made from solid steel
**MSRP** . . . . . . . . . . . . . . . . . . . . $1970

**AUTO-ORDNANCE T1
THOMPSON 1927 A-1**

**AUTO-ORDNANCE
M1SB THOMPSON
M1 SBR**

## T1 THOMPSON 1927 A-1

**Action**: Semiautomatic
**Stock**: Walnut, vertical foregrip
**Barrel**: 16.5 in.
**Sights**: Blade front, open rear adjustable
**Weight**: 13 lb.
**Caliber**: .45 ACP
**Magazine**: 30-shot stick
**Features**: Frame and receiver made from solid steel; compensator; optional 50-round drum magazine
**MSRP** . . . . . . . . . . . . . . . . . . . . $1420
**With 50rd drum:** . . . . . . . . . . $1668

RIFLES

**AUTO-ORDNANCE T1-C
THOMPSON 1927 A-1
COMMANDO**

### T1-C THOMPSON 1927 A-1 COMMANDO

*Action*: Semiautomatic
*Stock*: Black finish stock and forend
*Barrel*: 16.5 in.
*Sights*: Blade front, open rear adjustable
*Weight*: 13 lb.
*Caliber*: .45 ACP
*Magazine*: 30-shot stick
*Features*: Frame and receiver made from solid steel; compensator; black nylon sling
**MSRP . . . . . . . . . . . . . . . . . . $1393**

### T1SB THOMPSON 1927 A-1 SBR SHORT BARREL RIFLE

*Action*: Semiautomatic
*Stock*: Walnut, vertical foregrip
*Barrel*: 10.5 in.
*Sights*: Blade front, open rear adjustable
*Weight*: 12 lb.
*Caliber*: .45 ACP
*Magazine*: 30-shot stick
*Features*: Frame and receiver made from solid steel; blued steel finish
**MSRP . . . . . . . . . . . . . . . . . . $2053**
**Detachable butt stock: . . . . . $2554**

**AUTO-ORDNANCE T1SB THOMPSON
1927 A-1 SBR SHORT BARREL RIFLE**

### TM1 THOMPSON M1

*Action*: Semiautomatic
*Stock*: Walnut, vertical foregrip
*Barrel*: 16.5 in.
*Sights*: Blade front, fixed battle rear
*Weight*: 8 lb., 11 lb. 8 oz.
*Caliber*: .45 ACP
*Magazine*: 30-shot stick
*Features*: Side bolt action; frame and receiver made from solid steel; lightweight model features a frame and receiver made from solid aluminum
**MSRP . . . . . . . . . . . . . . . . . . $1334**

**AUTO-ORDNANCE TM1
THOMPSON M1 CARBINE**

# Barrett

**BARRETT 82A1**

**BARRETT 98B**

## MODEL 82A1

**Action**: Semiautomatic
**Stock**: Synthetic
**Barrel**: 20 in., 29 in.
**Sights**: Flip-up iron sights or Leupold scope
**Weight**: 30 lb. 14 oz.
**Caliber**: .416, .50 BMG
**Magazine**: Detachable box, 10 rounds
**Features**: Pelican case; detachable adjustable bipod legs; cleaning kit; carry handle; muzzlebrake; M1913 optics rail; chrome-lined barrel
**MSRP** . . . . . . . . . . . . . $8900–$9100

## MODEL 95

**Action**: Semiautomatic
**Stock**: Synthetic
**Barrel**: 29 in.
**Sights**: Flip-up iron sights
**Weight**: 25 lb.
**Caliber**: .50 BMG
**Magazine**: Detachable box, 5 rounds
**Features**: Pelican case; detachable adjustable bipod legs; cleaning kit; M1913 optics rail
**MSRP** . . . . . . . . . . . . . . . . . $6500

## MODEL 98B

**Action**: Bolt
**Stock**: Synthetic
**Barrel**: 20 in., 26 in.
**Sights**: None
**Weight**: 13 lb. 8 oz.
**Caliber**: .338 Lapua Mag.
**Magazine**: Detachable box, 10 rounds
**Features**: Ergonomic pistol grip; muzzlebrake; heavy or fluted barrel; Harris bipod; monopod; cleaning kit; side accessory rail; Air/watertight hard case; black stock
**MSRP** . . . . . . . . . . . . . $4699–$4849

**BARRETT 95**

BARRETT 99

BARRETT M107A1

BARRETT MRAD

## MODEL 99
*Action*: Bolt
*Stock*: Synthetic
*Barrel*: 29 in., 32 in.
*Sights*: None
*Weight*: 25 lb.
*Caliber*: .416, .50 BMG
*Magazine*: None
*Features*: M1913 optics rail; pelican case; detachable adjustable bipod; cleaning kit
**MSRP . . . . . . . . . . . . . $3849–$4099**

## M107A1
*Action*: Semiautomatic
*Stock*: Synthetic
*Barrel*: 20 in., 29 in.
*Sights*: Flip-up iron sights
*Weight*: 30 lb. 14 oz.
*Caliber*: .50 BMG
*Magazine*: Detachable box, 10 rounds
*Features*: Chrome-lined barrel, Flat Dark Earth stock finish; suppressor-ready muzzlebrake; pelican case; M1913 optics rail; detachable adjustable lightweight bipod legs; lightweight monopod
**MSRP . . . . . . . . . . . . . . . . $12000**

## MRAD
*Action*: Bolt action repeater
*Stock*: Synthetic
*Barrel*: 20 in., 24.5 in., 27 in.
*Sights*: None
*Weight*: 14 lb. 13 oz.
*Caliber*: .338 Lapua Mag.
*Magazine*: Detachable box, 10 rounds
*Features*: Fluted barrel; multi-role brown finish stock; folding stock; adjustable cheekpiece and buttplate; includes two 10-round magazines, two sling loops, and three adjustable accessory rails
**MSRP . . . . . . . . . . . . . $5850–$6000**

# Benelli USA

BENELLI MR1

## MR1
*Action*: A.R.G.O (Auto-Regulating-Gas-Operated)
*Stock*: Synthetic tactical pistol grip (ComforTech optional)
*Barrel*: 16 in.
*Sights*: Military-style aperture sights with Picatinny rail
*Weight*: 7 lb. 14 oz.

*Caliber*: .223 Rem.
*Magazine*: Detachable box, 5 shot
*Features*: Self-cleaning stainless piston system with gas port forward of chamber; accepts high-capacity M-16 magazines; hard chrome-lined barrel
**Pistol Grip: . . . . . . . . . . . . . . $1339**
**ComforTech: . . . . . . . . . . . . . $1461**

# Benelli USA

**BENELLI R1 AA-GRADE SATIN WALNUT**

## R1
*Action*: Semiautomatic
*Stock*: AA-grade satin walnut, synthetic or Realtree APG
*Barrel*: 22 in., 24 in.
*Sights*: None
*Weight*: 7 lb. 2 oz.–7 lb. 5 oz.
*Caliber*: .30-06 Spfd., .300 Win. Mag., .338 Win. Mag.

*Magazine*: Detachable box, 3+1, 4+1 rounds
*Features*: Picatinny rail; synthetic and APG finish come with GripTight coating; raised comb; auto-regulating gas-operated system
**Walnut:** . . . . . . . . . . . . . . . . . **$1019**
**ComforTech:** . . . . . . . . **$1039–$1249**

# Beretta USA

**BERETTA CX4 STORM**

## CX4 STORM
*Action*: Single-action
*Stock*: Synthetic
*Barrel*: 16.6 in.
*Sights*: Front sight post
*Weight*: 5 lb. 12 oz.
*Caliber*: 9mm, .40 S&W, .45 ACP
*Magazine*: Detachable box, 10,15,17,20 (9mm); 10, 11, 12, 14, 17 (40 S&W); 8 (.45 ACP) rounds

*Features*: Picatinny rail; allows for reverse ejection and extraction; ideal for left-handed shooters; adjustable length-of-pull; easy to accessorize
**MSRP** . . . . . . . . . . . . . . . . . . . . **$915**

# Blaser USA

**BLASER K95 BARONESSE STUTZEN**

## K95 BARONESSE STUTZEN
*Action*: Single shot
*Stock*: Walnut
*Barrel*: 19.75 in.
*Sights*: None
*Weight*: 5 lb. 11 oz.
*Caliber*: .222 Rem., 5.6xR Mag., 5.6xR, .243 Win., 6.5x57R, 7x57 R, .308 Win., .30-06, 8x57 IRS

*Magazine*: None
*Features*: Octagonal barrel standard, barrels are interchangeable; available from grade Lexus; split forearm for continuous precision even in extreme weather; black forearm tip; range of ornamentation and game engravings
**MSRP** . . . . . . . . . . . . . . . . . **$16931**

BLASER R8 JAEGER

BLASER R8 PROFESSIONAL

BLASER R93 PROFESSIONAL

## R8 JAEGER

**Action**: Straight-pull bolt-action
**Stock**: Walnut, pistol grip
**Barrel**: 20.5 in., 23 in., 25.75 in.
**Sights**: None
**Weight**: 6 lb. 6 oz.
**Caliber**: .222 Rem. to .338 Win. Mag.
**Magazine**: Detachable box, 3 rounds with lock
**Features**: Cold-hammer-forged barrels and chambers; black forearm tip; synthetic stock in dark green or walnut, straight comb; manual cocking system; integrated trigger/magazine unit; original Blaser saddle mount
**MSRP** . . . . . . . . . . . . . . . . . . $4195

## R8 PROFESSIONAL

**Action**: Straight-pull bolt-action
**Stock**: Matte dark green synthetic stock, pistol grip
**Barrel**: 20.5 in., 23 in., 25.75 in.
**Sights**: None
**Weight**: 6 lb. 6 oz.
**Caliber**: .222 Rem. to .338 Win. Mag.
**Magazine**: Detachable box, 3 rounds with lock

**Features**: Shatter-proof, synthetic dark green stock; detachable magazine/trigger unit; single-stage trigger; quick-release scope mount; ergonomically optimized pistol grip; kickstop optional; precision trigger; black forearm tip; integrated receiver
**MSRP** . . . . . . . . . . . . . . . . . $3623

## R93 PROFESSIONAL

**Action**: Straight-pull bolt-action
**Stock**: Synthetic
**Barrel**: 25.50 in. (Magnum), 25.59 (Ultra Magnum); 27.56 in. (Swiss Kaliber)
**Sights**: None
**Weight**: 6 lb. 6 oz.–6 lb. 13 oz.
**Caliber**: .222 Rem., .223 Rem., .22-250, .243 Win., 6x62 Freres, .25-06, 6.5x5.5, 6.5x57, 6.5-284 Norma, 6.5x65 RWS, .270 Win., .280 Rem., 7x57, 7mm-08, 7x64, .308 Win., .30-06, 8x57IS, 8x64 S, 8.5x63, 9.3x62, 6.5x68, 7.5x55, 8x68 S, .257 Wby. Mag., .270 Wby. Mag., 7mm Rem. Mag., .300 Win. Mag., .300 Wby.

Mag., .338 Win. Mag., .375 H&H Mag., 7mm STW, .300 Rem. Ultra Mag., 1.3x60 R
**Magazine**: In-line box, 2, 3, 4 rounds
**Features**: Anodized barrel; quick-release scope mount; shatter-proof stock comes in natural stone, slate gray, dark green, Mossy Oak camo; left-handed version optional
**MSRP** . . . . . . . . . . . . . . . . . . $3145
**Left-hand versions add** . . . . . . . $459

## S2 SAFARI DOUBLE RIFLE

**Action**: Tilting block, double-barrel
**Stock**: Grained walnut
**Barrel**: 24.4 in.
**Sights**: None
**Weight**: 11 lb. 11 oz.
**Caliber**: .375 H&H Mag., .470 NE, .500/.416 NE, .500 NE
**Magazine**: None
**Features**: Straight Safari stock with Monte Carlo cheekpiece; kickstop; rubber recoil pad; half-beavertail forend
**MSRP** . . . . . . . . . . . . . . . . . $11060

# Browning

**BROWNING A-BOLT M-1000 ECLIPSE**

**BROWNING A-BOLT STAINLESS STALKER**

## A-BOLT M-1000 ECLIPSE

*Action*: Bolt
*Stock*: Gray Laminated
*Barrel*: 26 in.
*Sights*: None
*Weight*: 9 lb. 14 oz.–10 lb.
*Caliber*: .22-250 Rem., 7mm-08 Rem., .308 Win., .300 WSM, .270 WSM, 7mm WSM
*Magazine*: Detachable box
*Features*: Steel, matte blued finish receiver; drilled and tapped for scope mounts; hinged floor plate; top-tang safety; thumbhole grip; Monte Carlo cheekpiece
**MSRP . . . . . . . . .$1339.99–$1469.99**

## A-BOLT STAINLESS STALKER

*Action*: Bolt
*Stock*: Composite
*Barrel*: 22 in., 23 in., 24 in., 26 in.
*Sights*: None
*Weight*: 6 lb. 4 oz.–6 lb. 11 oz.
*Caliber*: .243 Win., 7mm-08 Rem., .308 Win., .270 Win., .30-06 Spfd., 7mm Rem. Mag., .388 Win. Mag., .300 WSM, .270 WSM, 7mm WSM, .325 WSM
*Magazine*: Detachable box
*Features*: Composite stock comes in matte black, checkered; stainless steel, matte finish receiver; drilled and tapped for scope mounts; adjustable stainless steel trigger; hinged floor plate; top-tang safety; recoil pad; BOSS and BOSS-CR option; left-hand version available
**MSRP . . . . . . . . .$1239.99–$1269.99**

## BAR LIGHTWEIGHT STALKER

*Action*: Gas-operated autoloader
*Stock*: Composite
*Barrel*: 23 in.
*Sights*: None
*Weight*: 7 lb. 4 oz.
*Caliber*: 7mm WSM
*Magazine*: Detachable box
*Features*: Composite stock in matte black; aircraft-grade alloy receiver in matte blued finish; drilled and tapped for scope mounts; recoil pad; cross-bolt safety
**MSRP . . . . . . . . . . . . . . . .$1339.99**

## BAR LONGTRAC, BREAK-UP INFINITY

*Action*: Gas-operated autoloader
*Stock*: Composite
*Barrel*: 22 in., 24 in.
*Sights*: None
*Weight*: 6 lb. 15 oz.–7 lb. 8 oz.
*Caliber*: .270 Win., .30-06 Spfd., 7mm Rem. Mag., .300 Win. Mag.
*Magazine*: Detachable box
*Features*: Aircraft-grade alloy receiver; drilled and tapped for scope mounts; hammer-forged barrel; multi-lug rotary bolt; composite trigger guard and floor plate; cross-bolt safety; Dura-Touch Armor coating; composite stock comes in Mossy Oak camo finishes; interchangeable recoil pad
**MSRP . . . . . . . . .$1359.99–$1459.99**

**BROWNING BAR LIGHTWEIGHT STALKER**

**BROWNING BAR LONGTRAC, BREAK-UP INFINITY**

# Browning

BROWNING BAR LONGTRAC STALKER

BROWNING BAR SAFARI

BROWNING BAR SHORTTRAC

BROWNING BAR
SHORTTRAC, LEFT-HAND

## BAR LONGTRAC STALKER

**Action**: Gas-operated autoloader
**Stock**: Composite
**Barrel**: 22 in., 24 in.
**Sights**: None
**Weight**: 6 lb. 15 oz.–7 lb. 8 oz.
**Caliber**: .270 Win., .30-06 Spfd., 7mm
Rem. Mag., .300 Win. Mag.
**Magazine**: Detachable box
**Features**: Aircraft-grade alloy receiver
with matte blued finish; drilled and
tapped for scope mounts; hammer-
forged; multi-lug rotary bolt; compos-
ite stock in matte black finish; gripping
panels; recoil pad; composite trigger
guard and floor plate
**MSRP** . . . . . . . . . .$1259.99–$1339.99

## BAR SAFARI

**Action**: Gas-operated autoloader
**Stock**: Walnut
**Barrel**: 22 in., 23 in., 24 in.
**Sights**: None
**Weight**: 7 lb. 6 oz.–8 lb. 6 oz.
**Caliber**: .243 Win., .308 Win., .25-06
Rem., .270 Win., .30-06 Spfd., 7mm

Rem. Mag., .300 Win. Mag., .338 Win.
Mag., .270 Win. (BOSS), 7mm Rem.
Mag. (BOSS), .300 Win. Mag. (BOSS),
.338 Win. Mag. (BOSS), .300 WSM
(BOSS), .270 WSM (BOSS), 7mm WSM
(BOSS)
**Magazine**: Detachable box
**Features**: Checkered, select gloss finish
walnut stock; steel receiver with blued
finish and scroll engraving; drilled and
tapped for scope mounts; multi-lug
rotary bolt; recoil pad BOSS and
BOSS-CR option; sling swivel studs
installed
**MSRP** . . . . . . . . . .$1229.99–$1499.99

## BAR SHORTTRAC

**Action**: Gas-operated autoloader
**Stock**: Walnut
**Barrel**: 23 in.
**Sights**: None
**Weight**: 6 lb. 10 oz.–7 lb. 4 oz.
**Caliber**: .243 Win., 7mm-08 Rem.,
.308 Win., .300 WSM, .270 WSM,
7mm WSM, .325 WSM
**Magazine**: Detachable box

**Features**: Oil finish walnut stock with
stylized forearm; aircraft-grade alloy
receiver with blued finish; drilled and
tapped for scope mounts; interchangeable recoil pad
**MSRP** . . . . . . . . . .$1229.99–$1339.99

## BAR SHORTTRAC, LEFT-HAND

**Action**: Gas-operated autoloader
**Stock**: Walnut
**Barrel**: 22 in., 23 in.
**Sights**: None
**Weight**: 6 lb. 10 oz.–7 lb. 4 oz.
**Caliber**: .243 Win., 7mm-08 Rem.,
.308 Win., .300 WSM, .270 WSM,
7mm WSM, .325 WSM
**Magazine**: Detachable box
**Features**: Aircraft-grade alloy receiver;
drilled and tapped for scope mounts;
hammer-forged barrel; grade II walnut
stock with oil finish; stylized,
checkered forearm; sling swivel studs
installed; interchangeable recoil pad
**MSRP** . . . . . . . . . .$1269.99–$1359.99

# Browning

BROWNING BLR LIGHTWEIGHT '81

BROWNING BLR LIGHTWEIGHT STAINLESS

BROWNING BLR LIGHTWEIGHT '81 STAINLESS TAKEDOWN

BROWNING BLR WHITE GOLD MEDALLION

### BLR WHITE GOLD MEDALLION

**Action**: Lever-action
**Stock**: Walnut, pistol grip
**Barrel**: 20 in., 22 in.
**Sights**: Open
**Weight**: 6 lb. 8 oz.–6 lb. 12 oz.
**Caliber**: .243 Win., 7mm-08 Rem., .308 Win., .300 WSM, .270 WSM
**Magazine**: Detachable box
**Features**: Aircraft-grade aluminum receiver with nickel finish; high-relief engraving on receiver; drilled and tapped for scope mounts; crowned muzzle; stainless steel barrel; stock comes in grade IV/ V walnut with a checkered pistol grip and forearm; rosewood forend cap; silver pistol grip cap; adjustable sights; recoil pad; sling swivel studs installed
**MSRP** . . . . . . . . . .$1469.99–$1549.99

### BLR LIGHTWEIGHT '81

**Action**: Lever-action
**Stock**: Walnut, straight grip
**Barrel**: 20 in., 22 in., 24 in.
**Sights**: None
**Weight**: 6 lb. 8 oz.–7 lb. 12 oz.
**Caliber**: .223 Rem., .22-250 Rem., .243 Win., 7mm-08 Rem., .308 Win., .358 Win., .270 Win., .30-06 Spfd., 7mm Rem. Mag., .300 Win. Mag., .300 WSM, .270 WSM, 7mm WSM, .450 Marlin, .325 WSM
**Magazine**: Detachable box
**Features**: Aircraft-grade alloy receiver; drilled and tapped for scope mounts; crowned muzzle; adjustable sights; gloss finish walnut stock; recoil pad
**MSRP** . . . . . . . . . $959.99–$1039.99

### BLR LIGHTWEIGHT '81 STAINLESS TAKEDOWN

**Action**: Lever-action
**Stock**: Laminate, straight grip
**Barrel**: 20 in., 22 in., 24 in.
**Sights**: Open
**Weight**: 6 lb. 8 oz.–7 lb. 12 oz.
**Caliber**: .223 Rem., .22-250 Rem., .243 Win., 7mm-08 Rem., .308 Win., .358 Win., .270 Win., .30-06 Spfd., 7mm Rem. Mag., .300 Win. Mag., .300 WSM, .270 WSM, 7mm WSM, .450 Marlin, .325 WSM
**Magazine**: Detachable box
**Features**: Aircraft-grade alloy receiver; drilled and tapped for scope mounts; stainless steel barrel with matte finish; gray laminate wood stock in satin finish; recoil pad; separates for storage or transportation; optional Scout-style scope mount; TRUGLO/Marble's fiber optic front sight
**MSRP** . . . . . . . . .$1229.99–$1299.99

### BLR LIGHTWEIGHT STAINLESS

**Action**: Lever-action
**Stock**: Walnut, pistol grip
**Barrel**: 20 in., 22 in., 24 in.
**Sights**: None
**Weight**: 6 lb. 8 oz.–7 lb. 12 oz.
**Caliber**: .223 Rem., .22-250 Rem., .243 Win., 7mm-08 Rem., .308 Win., .358 Win., .270 Win., .30-06 Spfd., .300 Win. Mag., .300 WSM, .270 WSM, 7mm WSM, .450 Marlin, .325 WSM
**Magazine**: Detachable box
**Features**: Aircraft-grade alloy receiver; drilled and tapped for scope mounts; steel barrel with matte finish; crowned muzzle; adjustable sights; gloss finish walnut stock with pistol grip; sling swivel studs installed; recoil pad
**MSRP** . . . . . . . . . .$1019.99–$1099.99

**BROWNING RMEF X-BOLT WHITE GOLD**

**BROWNING X-BOLT HUNTER**

## RMEF X-BOLT WHITE GOLD

**Action**: Bolt
**Stock**: Walnut
**Barrel**: 23 in.
**Sights**: None
**Weight**: 7 lb. 3 oz.
**Caliber**: .325 WSM
**Magazine**: Detachable rotary box
**Features**: Monte Carlo stock; stainless steel barrel and receiver, receiver etched in gold; raised cheekpiece; Inflex technology recoil pad; adjustable feather trigger; top-tang safety with bolt unlock button
**MSRP** . . . . . . . . . . . . . . . . . $1499.99

## X-BOLT HUNTER

**Action**: Bolt
**Stock**: Satin finish walnut stock
**Barrel**: 22 in., 23 in., 24 in., 26 in.
**Sights**: None
**Weight**: 6 lb. 13 oz.–7 lb.
**Caliber**: .243 Win., 7mm-08 Rem., .308 Win., .25-06 Rem., .270 Win., .280 Rem., .30-06 Spfd., 7mm Rem. Mag., .388 Win. Mag., .300 WSM,

.270 WSM, 7mm WSM, .325 WSM, .223 Rem., .22-250 Rem.
**Magazine**: Detachable rotary box
**Features**: Adjustable feather trigger; top-tang safety with bolt unlock button; sling swivel studs installed; Inflex technology recoil pad
**MSRP** . . . . . . . . . . $899.99–$939.99

## X-BOLT MEDALLION

**Action**: Bolt
**Stock**: Walnut
**Barrel**: 22 in., 23 in., 24 in., 26 in.
**Sights**: Open
**Weight**: 6 lb. 6 oz.–7 lb.
**Caliber**: .223 Rem., .22-250 Rem., .243 Win., .308 Win., .25-06 Rem., .270 Win., .280 Rem., .30-06 Spfd., 7mm Rem. Mag., .300 Win. Mag., .338 Win. Mag., .300 WSM, .270 WSM, 7mm WSM, .325 WSM
**Magazine**: Detachable rotary box
**Features**: Gloss finish walnut stock, rosewood forend grip and pistol cap; Inflex technology recoil pad; adjustable feather trigger; drilled and tapped for scope mounts; left-hand option
**MSRP** . . . . . . . . . . $1029.99–$1069.99
**Left-hand**: . . . . . . $1069.99–$1099.99

## X-BOLT MICRO MIDAS

**Action**: Bolt
**Stock**: Walnut
**Barrel**: 20 in.

**Sights**: None
**Weight**: 6 lb. 1 oz.
**Caliber**: .243 Win., 7mm-08 Rem., .308 Win., .22-250 Rem.
**Magazine**: Detachable rotary magazine
**Features**: Drilled and tapped for scope mounts, low-luster blued finish, free-floating barrel; adjustable feather trigger; top-tang safety; left-hand option
**MSRP** . . . . . . . . . . . . . . . . . $839.99

## X-BOLT STAINLESS STALKER

**Action**: Bolt
**Stock**: Composite
**Barrel**: 22 in., 23 in., 24 in., 26 in.
**Sights**: None
**Weight**: 6 lb. 3 oz.–6 lb. 13 oz.
**Caliber**: .243 Win., 7mm-08 Rem., .308 Win., .25-06 Rem., .270 Win., .280 Rem., .30-06 Spfd., 7mm Rem. Mag., .300 Win. Mag., .388 Win. Mag., .300 WSM, .270 WSM, 7mm WSM, .325 WSM, .223 Rem., .22-250 Rem.
**Magazine**: Detachable rotary box
**Features**: Composite stock in matte black with textured gripping surfaces; Dura-Touch armor coating; adjustable feather trigger; top-tang safety; bolt unlock button; palm swell
**MSRP** . . . . . . . . . . $1119.99–$1159.99

**BROWNING X-BOLT MEDALLION**

**BROWNING X-BOLT MICRO MIDAS**

**BROWNING X-BOLT STAINLESS STALKER**

# Browning

**BROWNING X-BOLT STALKER
CARBON FIBER FLUTED**

**BROWNING X-BOLT
VARMINT SPECIAL STAINLESS**

RIFLES

## X-BOLT STALKER CARBON FIBER FLUTED

*Action*: Bolt
*Stock*: Composite
*Barrel*: 22 in., 23 in., 26 in.
*Sights*: None
*Weight*: 6 lb. 3 oz.–6 lb. 11 oz.
*Caliber*: .308 Win., .270 Win., .30-06 Spfd., .300 Win. Mag., .300 WSM, .270 WSM
*Magazine*: Detachable rotary
*Features*: Matte blued receiver glass bedded; drilled and tapped for scope mounts; matte blued barrel; hand chambered; target crown; eight flutes to reduce weight and increase cooling; adjustable feather trigger; top-tang safety; bolt unlock button; Dura-Touch® armor coating; Inflex technology recoil pad; sling swivel studs installed
**MSRP . . . . . . . . . $1269.99–$1329.99**

## X-BOLT VARMINT SPECIAL STAINLESS

*Action*: Bolt
*Stock*: Altamont Paladin, black laminated
*Barrel*: 24 in., 26 in.
*Sights*: None
*Weight*: 8 lb. 8 oz.–8 lb. 11 oz.
*Caliber*: .223 Rem., .22-250 Rem., .308 Win., .300 WSM
*Magazine*: Detachable rotary box
*Features*: Stainless steel, free-floating barrel; adjustable feather trigger; top-tang safety; bolt unlock button; Inflex technology recoil pads; sling swivel studs installed
**MSRP . . . . . . . . . . . . . . . . $1069.99**

# Bushmaster Firearms Internat'l

## .308 HUNTER

*Action*: Semiautomatic
*Stock*: Synthetic
*Barrel*: 20 in.
*Sights*: None
*Weight*: 8 lb. 6 oz.
*Caliber*: .308 Win., 7.62 NATO
*Magazine*: Detachable box, 5 rounds
*Features*: Two riser blocks, A2 grip on Vista; free-floating, vented aluminum forend; MOE trigger guard for gloved finger
**Hunter: . . . . . . . . . . . . . . $1685.32**

**BUSHMASTER .308 HUNTER**

**BUSHMASTER .308 ORC**

**BUSHMASTER .450 RIFLE & CARBINE**

## .308 ORC

*Action*: Semiautomatic
*Stock*: Synthetic
*Barrel*: 16 in. (carbine), 20 in. (rifle)
*Sights*: None
*Weight*: 7 lb. 12 oz.
*Caliber*: .308 Win. 7.62 NATO
*Magazine*: Detachable box, 20 rounds
*Features*: Milled gas block; heavy, chrome-lined barrel; A2 Birdcage flash hider; receiver-length Picatinny optics rail with two .5-in. optic raisers; heavy oval hand guards; six-position tele-scoping stock; shipped in lockable hard case with yellow safety block; black web sling included
**MSRP . . . . . . . . . . . . . . . . $1476.99**

## .450 RIFLE & CARBINE

*Action*: Semiautomatic
*Stock*: Synthetic, A2 pistol grip
*Barrel*: 16 in. (carbine), 20 in. (rifle)
*Sights*: None
*Weight*: 8 lb. 2 oz. (carbine), 8 lb. 8 oz. (rifle)
*Caliber*: .450 Bushmaster
*Magazine*: Detachable box, 5 rounds
*Features*: Chromoly steel barrels; free-floating aluminum forends; forged aluminum receivers; solid A2 buttstock with trapdoor storage compartment; Pictatinny rail; black web sling included; shipped in lockable hard plastic case with orange safety block
**Rifle: . . . . . . . . . . . . . . . . $1484.76**
**Carbine: . . . . . . . . . . . . . $1500.31**

## ACR BASIC FOLDER COMBINATION

*Action*: Semiautomatic
*Stock*: Synthetic
*Barrel*: 10.5 in., 14.5 in., 16.5 in.
*Sights*: None
*Weight*: N/A
*Caliber*: .223/5.56mm NATO to 6.8mm Rem. SPC
*Magazine*: 30-round PMAG
*Features*: Cold-hammer-forged barrel with melonite coating; A2 birdcage-type hider; toolless quick-change bar-rel system; quick and easy multi-cali-ber bolt carrier assembly; free-floating MIL-STD 1913 monolithic top rail for optic mounting; high-impact compos-ite hand guard with heat shield; ambi-dextrous controls; composite stock comes in black or coyote
**MSRP . . . . . . . . . . . . . . . . . $2490**

**BUSHMASTER ACR BASIC FOLDER COMBINATION**

# Bushmaster Firearms Internat'l

**BUSHMASTER A-TACS PREDATOR**

**BUSHMASTER A-TACS VARMINTER**

## A-TACS PREDATOR
**Action**: Semiautomatic
**Stock**: Synthetic
**Barrel**: 20 in.
**Sights**: None
**Weight**: 8 lb.
**Caliber**: 5.56mm or .223 Rem.
**Magazine**: Detachable box, 5 rounds
**Features**: Coated in A-Tacs digital camouflage; fluted extra-heavy barrel with competition muzzle crown; two-stage competition trigger
**MSRP** . . . . . . . . . . . . . . . **$1518.97**

## A-TACS VARMINTER
**Action**: Semiautomatic
**Stock**: Synthetic
**Barrel**: 24 in.
**Sights**: None
**Weight**: 8 lb. 6 oz.
**Caliber**: 5.56mm or .223 Rem.
**Magazine**: Detachable box, 5 rounds
**Features**: Coated in A-Tacs digital camouflage; free-floated barrel with a vented aluminum forend; two-stage competition trigger
**MSRP** . . . . . . . . . . . . . . . **$1534.51**

## BA50 RIFLES
**Action**: Bolt
**Stock**: Synthetic
**Barrel**: 30 in.
**Sights**: None
**Weight**: 30 lb.
**Caliber**: .50 BMG
**Magazine**: Detachable box, 10 rounds
**Features**: MIL-STD1913 rail; steel bipod with folding legs; ErgoGrip deluxe tactical pistol grip; LimbSaver Butt Pad; Magpul PRS adjustable buttstock; aluminum receiver; recoil reducing brake
**MSRP** . . . . . . . . . . . . . . . **$5519.27**

## CARBON 15 9MM CARBINE
**Action**: Semiautomatic
**Stock**: Composite

**Barrel**: 16 in.
**Sights**: None
**Weight**: 5 lb. 11 oz.
**Caliber**: 9mm NATO
**Magazine**: Detachable box, 30 rounds
**Features**: Carbon fiber composite receivers; birdcage flash hider; chromoly steel barrel; manganese phosphate bolt carrier; Picatinny rail mounted on upper receiver; six-position telescoping buttstock; shipped in lockable Bushmaster carrying case
**MSRP** . . . . . . . . . . . . . . . **$932.99**

## DCM-XR
**Action**: Semiautomatic
**Stock**: Synthetic
**Barrel**: 20 in.
**Sights**: Open, adjustable
**Weight**: 13 lb. 1 oz.
**Caliber**: 5.56mm, .223 Rem.
**Magazine**: Detachable box, 10 rounds (accepts all M16/AR15 type)
**Features**: M16A2 Dual aperture rear sight with interchangeable apertures; competition front sight; extra heavy competition barrel; barrel is lead lapped and hardened to Rockwell C26 to 32; two-stage competition trigger; competition free-floater tube handguard; shipped in lockable hard case
**MSRP** . . . . . . . . . . . . . . . **$1360.39**

**BUSHMASTER BA50 RIFLE**

**BUSHMASTER DCM-XR**

RIFLES

# Bushmaster Firearms Internat'l

**BUSHMASTER M4 TYPE CARBINE**

**BUSHMASTER MOE 308 MID-LENGTH**

## M4 TYPE CARBINES

*Action*: Semiautomatic
*Stock*: Synthetic
*Barrel*: 16 in.
*Sights*: Open
*Weight*: 6 lb. 3 oz.
*Caliber*: 5.56mm, .223 Rem.
*Magazine*: Detachable box, 30 rounds (accepts all M16/ AR15 type)
*Features*: Six-position telestock; "Izzy" flash suppressor; hard chrome-lined barrels are designed to accept M203 grenade launcher; upper receivers available in A2 or A3 configurations; A2 receiver has 300-800 meter rear sight system; A3 receiver is mounted with Pictatinny rail, 300-600 meter rear sight system and removable carry handle; shipped in lockable hard case with orange safety block
**A2:** . . . . . . . . . . . **$1197.14–$1274.88**
**A3:** . . . . . . . . . . . . . . . . . . **$1391.48**

## MOE 308 MID-LENGTH

*Action*: Semiautomatic
*Stock*: Synthetic
*Barrel*: 16 in.
*Sights*: Magpul MSBUS rear flip sight
*Weight*: 6 lb. 2 oz.
*Caliber*: .308 Win., 7.62 NATO
*Magazine*: Detachable box, 20 rounds
*Features*: Receiver length Picatinny optics rail; Magpul MOE polymer mid-length handguard; Magpul MOE adjustable buttstock with strong A-frame design; rubber buttplate; Magpul MOE vertical grip; MOE enhanced trigger guards; shipped in lockable hard case with yellow safety block; stock comes in black, Flat Dark Earth, or OD green
**MSRP** . . . . . . . . . . . . . . . . **$1508.08**

## O.R.C. (OPTICS READY CARBINE)

*Action*: Semiautomatic
*Stock*: Synthetic
*Barrel*: 16 in.
*Sights*: None
*Weight*: 6 lb.
*Caliber*: 5.56mm, .223 Rem.
*Magazine*: Detachable box, 30 rounds (accepts any AR type mag)
*Features*: Flat-top upper receiver made for easy optic attachment; chrome-lined barrel; A2 birdcage suppressor; receiver length Picatinny optics rail with .5-inch optics risers; milled gas block; heavy oval M4 type handguards; telestock
**MSRP** . . . . . . . . . . . . . . . . **$1391.48**

## PREDATOR

*Action*: Semiautomatic
*Stock*: Synthetic, ambidextrous pistol grip
*Barrel*: 20 in.
*Sights*: None
*Weight*: 8 lb.
*Caliber*: 5.56mm, .223 Rem.
*Magazine*: Detachable box, 5 rounds (accepts all M16/AR 15 type)
*Features*: Steel lined fluted barrel; two-stage competition trigger; vented tubular aluminum free-floater forend with bipod stud; shipped with safety block in lockable, foam-padded hard case
**MSRP** . . . . . . . . . . . . . . . . **$1414.80**

**BUSHMASTER O.R.C.**

**BUSHMASTER PREDATOR**

# Bushmaster Firearms Internat'l

## QUAD RAIL A3

**Action**: Semiautomatic
**Stock**: Synthetic
**Barrel**: 16 in.
**Sights**: None
**Weight**: 8 lb. 5 oz.
**Caliber**: 5.56mm, .223 Rem.
**Magazine**: Detachable box, 30 rounds
**Features**: Chrome-lined barrel; A2 birdcage-type suppressor; free-float quad rail forend; six-position telestock for light weight and quick handling; ships with lockable hard case and yellow safety block
**A3:** . . . . . . . . . . . . . . . . . . **$1391.48**

BUSHMASTER QUAD RAIL A3

BUSHMASTER TARGET MODEL RIFLE A2

## TARGET MODEL RIFLES

**Action**: Semiautomatic
**Stock**: Synthetic
**Barrel**: 20 in, 24 in.
**Sights**: None
**Weight**: 8 lb. 7 oz. (A2), 8 lb. 12 oz. (A3)
**Caliber**: 5.56mm, .223 Rem.
**Magazine**: Detachable box, 30 rounds (accepts all M16 / AR15 type)
**Features**: A3 upper receiver incorporates Pictatinny rail; A2 upper receiver 300-800 meter rear sight system; A3 receiver has 300-600 meter rear sight system; chromoly steel or polished stainless steel barrels; shipped in a lockable hard case with orange safety block
**A2:** . . . . . . . . . . . . . . . . . . . . . **$1105**
**A3:** . . . . . . . . . . . . . . . . . . . . . **$1187**
**SSA2:** . . . . . . . . . . . . . . . . . . . **$1112**
**SSA3:** . . . . . . . . . . . . . . . . . . . **$1187**

## VARMINTER

**Action**: Semiautomatic
**Stock**: Synthetic, ambidextrous pistol grip
**Barrel**: 24 in.
**Sights**: None
**Weight**: 8 lb. 6 oz.
**Caliber**: 5.56mm, .223 Rem.
**Magazine**: Detachable box, 5 rounds (accepts all M16/AR 15 type)
**Features**: Competition crowned muzzle; chromoly vanadium steel barrel with full-length fluting; two-stage competition trigger; twelve cooling vents in forend; bipod stud installed on forend; black stock with rubberized, non-slip surface; shipped in hard plastic, lockable storage case complete with orange safety block
**MSRP** . . . . . . . . . . . . . . . . **$1430.34**

BUSHMASTER VARMINTER

RIFLES

# Century International Arms

**CENTURY INTERNATIONAL ARMS M70**

**CENTURY INTERNATIONAL ARMS M85 MINI MAUSER**

## M70 STANDARD/MAGNUM
*Action*: Bolt
*Stock*: Walnut
*Barrel*: 23.6 in.
*Sights*: Adjustable
*Weight*: 7 lb. 11 oz.
*Caliber*: .30-06, .270 Win., .308 Win., .243 Win., 7mm Rem. Mag., .300 Win. Mag.
*Magazine*: 5 rounds
*Features*: New rifle from the famous Zastava factory in Serbia; oiled European walnut stock; adjustable sights; modernized thumb actuated safety; cold forged chrome-vanadium steel
**MSRP . . . . . . . . . . $530.95–$697.95**

## M85 MINI MAUSER
*Action*: Bolt
*Stock*: Walnut
*Barrel*: 20.07 in., 22.04 in.
*Sights*: Adjustable
*Weight*: 6 lb. 2 oz.–6 lb. 6 oz.
*Caliber*: .223 Rem., 7.62x39mm, .22 Hornet
*Magazine*: 5 rounds
*Features*: New rifle from the famous Zastava factory in Serbia; oiled European walnut stock; adjustable sights; modernized thumb actuated safety; cold forged chrome-vanadium steel
**MSRP . . . . . . . . . . $530.95–$697.95**

# Chipmunk Rifles

**CHIPMUNK RIFLES CHIPMUNK**

## CHIPMUNK
*Action*: Bolt
*Stock*: Walnut, laminated
*Barrel*: 16.125 in.
*Sights*: Target
*Weight*: 2 lb. 8 oz.
*Caliber*: .22LR
*Magazine*: None
*Features*: Designed with younger shooters in mind; single-shot; manual-cocking action; receiver-mounted rear sights; metal with blued finish or stainless steel; post sight on ramp front, fully adjustable peep rear; adjustable trigger; extendable buttplate and front rail; available in black, walnut, deluxe walnut, camo laminate, and brown laminate
**MSRP . . . . . . . . . . $163.99–$230.99**

# Cimarron Firearms Co.

**CIMARRON 1860 HENRY CIVILIAN**

## 1860 HENRY CIVILIAN
*Action*: Lever
*Stock*: Walnut
*Barrel*: 24 in.
*Sights*: Open
*Weight*: 9 lb. 1 oz.–9 lb. 2 oz.
*Caliber*: .45 LC, .44 WCF
*Magazine*: Under barrel tube, 12 rounds
*Features*: Reproduction of 1860 Civil War Henry rifle; includes military sling swivels; frame comes in charcoal blue or original finish
**Standard blue: . . . . . . . . . $1350.70**
**Charcoal blue: . . . . . . . . . $1420.70**
**Original finish: . . . . . . . . $1450.70**

**RIFLES**

# Cimarron Firearms Co.

### 1876 CENTENNIAL
**Action**: Lever
**Stock**: Walnut
**Barrel**: 28 in.
**Sights**: Open
**Weight**: 9 lb. 15 oz.–10 lb. 2 oz.
**Caliber**: .45-60, .45-75, .40-60, .50-95
**Magazine**: Under barrel tube, 12 rounds
**Features**: The favorite rifle of Teddy Roosevelt. Reproduction of 1876 Civil War Henry rifle; includes military sling swivels; frame comes in charcoal blue or original finish
**MSRP** . . . . . . . . . . . . . . . . **$1558.70**

### 1876 CROSSFIRE CARBINE
**Action**: Lever
**Stock**: Walnut
**Barrel**: 22 in.
**Sights**: None
**Weight**: 8 lb. 15 oz.
**Caliber**: .45-60, .45-75
**Magazine**: Under barrel tube, 8 rounds
**Features**: Gun was glorified in the movie *Crossfire Trail;* case-hardened stock with standard blued finish
**MSRP** . . . . . . . . . . . . . . . . . **$1706.90**

### 1876 N.W.M.P. (NORTH WEST MOUNTED POLICE) CARBINE
**Action**: Lever
**Stock**: Walnut
**Barrel**: 22 in.
**Sights**: None
**Weight**: 8 lb. 15 oz.
**Caliber**: .45-60, .45-75
**Magazine**: Under barrel tube, 8 rounds
**Features**: Available in walnut stock and all blued metal; reproduction of popular firearm used by mounted police in 1870s
**MSRP** . . . . . . . . . . . . . . . . . **$1748.50**

### 1885 HIGH WALL SPORTING RIFLE
**Action**: Dropping block
**Stock**: Walnut, pistol grip
**Barrel**: 30 in.
**Sights**: Open
**Weight**: 9 lb. 4 oz.–10 lb. 6 oz.
**Caliber**: .45-70, .40-65, .38-55, .45-90, .30-40 KRAG, .405 Win.
**Magazine**: None
**Features**: Reproduction of the Winchester single-shot hunting rifle popular in 1880s; standard blued

CIMARRON 1876 CENTENNIAL

CIMARRON 1876 CROSSFIRE CARBINE

CIMARRON 1876 N.W.M.P. CARBINE

CIMARRON 1885 HIGH WALL SPORTING RIFLE

CIMARRON 1886 RIFLE

CIMARRON ARMI SPORT "BILLY DIXON"

finish on octagonal barrel; single- or double- set triggers
**MSRP** . . . . . . . . **$1033.50–$1363.70**

### 1886 RIFLE
**Action**: Lever
**Stock**: Walnut
**Barrel**: 22 in., 26 in.
**Sights**: None
**Weight**: 8 lb.–9 lb.
**Caliber**: .45/70 Govt.
**Magazine**: 7+1, 8+1 rounds
**Features**: Made by Armi Sport in Italy; color case-hardened receiver and butt-plate; octagonal barrel; standard blued finish; carbine version available

**MSRP** . . . . . . . . . . . . . . . . . **$1558.70**
**Carbine** . . . . . . . . . . . . . . **$1258.60**

### ARMI SPORT "BILLY DIXON" SHARPS
**Action**: Dropping block
**Stock**: Walnut, straight grip
**Barrel**: 32 in.
**Sights**: Open
**Weight**: 10 lb. 4 oz.–10 lb. 10 oz.
**Caliber**: .45-70, .45-90, .45-110, .50-90, .38-55
**Magazine**: None
**Features**: Single-shot reproduction; patent markings as on original sharps
**MSRP** . . . . . . . . . . . . . . . . . **$1324.70**

**130** · Shooter's Bible 105th Edition

www.skyhorsepublishing.com

RIFLES

# Cimarron Firearms Co.

**CIMARRON "EVIL ROY" BRUSH POPPER**

## "EVIL ROY" BRUSH POPPER

**Action**: Lever
**Stock**: Walnut
**Barrel**: 18.5 in.
**Sights**: Open
**Weight**: 7 lb. 2 oz.–7 lb. 5 oz.

**Caliber**: .45 Colt, .44 WCF, .357/.38 Spl.
**Magazine**: Under barrel tube, 10 rounds
**Features**: Custom marble sights; Evil Roy signature barrel; leather butt sheath; short stroke kit; walnut straight stock with standard blued finish on metal; case-hardened frame; pistol grip optional
**MSRP** . . . . . . . . . . . . . . . . . $1277.70
**Pistol grip**: . . . . . . . . . . . . . $1350.70

# Citadel by Legacy Sports

## M-1 .22

**Action**: Bolt
**Stock**: Wood, synthetic
**Barrel**: 18 in.
**Sights**: Adjustable rear, fixed front
**Weight**: 4 lb. 13 oz.
**Caliber**: .22LR
**Magazine**: 10 rounds, 2 rounds
**Features**: Recreation of the M-1 carbine carried by the U.S. Military in

WWII and Korea; traditional wood stock and synthetic stock models; blow-back action

**Wood:** . . . . . . . . . . . . . . . . . . $399
**Synthetic:** . . . . . . . . . . . . . . $319

**CITADEL M-1 .22 CARBINE**

# Colt's Manufacturing Company

## ACCURIZED RIFLE

**Action**: Semiautomatic
**Stock**: Combat-style, synthetic
**Barrel**: 20 in., 24 in.
**Sights**: None
**Weight**: 9 lb.–9 lb. 4 oz.
**Caliber**: 5.56 NATO, .223
**Magazine**: Detachable box, 9 rounds
**Features**: Black stock with matte finish; heavy barrel; target crown muzzle; A2 rifle buttstock; free-floating tubular handguard; match trigger
**MSRP** . . . . . . . . . . . . . $1374–$1653

## LE901-16S

**Action**: Semiautomatic
**Stock**: Combat-style, synthetic
**Barrel**: 16.1 in.
**Sights**: Flip-up front, adjustable post, flip-up rear

**COLT ACCURIZED RIFLE**

**COLT LE901-16S**

**Weight**: 9 lb. 6 oz.
**Caliber**: .308 Win.
**Magazine**: Detachable box, 20 rounds
**Features**: Matte black, monolithic upper receiver; .308 Winchester upper receiver group can be swapped out for

Mil-Spec Colt upper in 5.56x45 NATO; ambidextrous controls on magazine release, bolt catch and safety selector; back up iron sights; full floated barrel; bayonet lug and flash hider
**MSRP** . . . . . . . . . . . . . . . . . . $2423

# Colt's Manufacturing Company

### LE6940, LE6920 CARBINES
*Action*: Semiautomatic
*Stock*: Combat-style, synthetic
*Barrel*: 16.1 in.
*Sights*: Flip-up front, adjustable post, flip-up rear
*Weight*: 6 lb. 13 oz.–7 lb.
*Caliber*: 5.56x45 NATO
*Magazine*: Detachable box 20, 30 rounds
*Features*: Chrome-lined barrel; direct gas or articulating link piston system with locking bolt; Magpul MOE handguards, MOE carbine stock, MOE pistol grip, MOE vertical grip, and a Magpul back-up sight; flip-up front sight with adjustable post for elevation; flip-up rear sight adjustable for both windage and elevation; matte black finish; additional models available: LE6920MP-FDE, LE6920MP-B, LE6920SOCOM, LE6940P, LE6920CA, LE6940CA, LE6920CMP-B
*MSRP* . . . . . . . . . . . . **$1155–$2105**

COLT LE6940

COLT MATCH TARGET RIFLE

### MATCH TARGET RIFLE
*Action*: Semiautomatic
*Stock*: Combat-style, synthetic
*Barrel*: 16.1 in., 20 in.
*Sights*: None
*Weight*: 7 lb. 5 oz.–9 lb. 4 oz.
*Caliber*: 5.56 NATO, .223
*Magazine*: Detachable box, 9 rounds

*Features*: Flat top with optional carry handle and scope mount; two-position safety; available with free-floating monolithic handguard; available with flip-up sights; available with match trigger; black stock with matte finish
*MSRP* . . . . . . . . . . . . **$1230–$1825**

# Connecticut Valley Arms (CVA)

CVA APEX

CVA SCOUT COMPACT

### APEX
*Action*: Break-action centerfire
*Stock*: Synthetic
*Barrel*: 25 in.
*Sights*: None
*Weight*: 7 lb. 8 oz.
*Caliber*: .45-70, 7mm-08, .308, .30-06, .300 Win. Mag., .35 Whelen, .270, .243, .223, .222, .22-250
*Magazine*: None
*Features*: Ambidextrous synthetic stock with rubber grip panels; comes in black or Realtree APG camo; stainless steel, fluted Bergara barrel; adjustable trigger; interchangeable barrels;

CrushZone recoil pad; DuraSight rail mount; QRBP (Quick Release Breech Plug); reversible hammer spur; Quake Claw Sling; also available in muzzleloading models
*MSRP* . . . . . . . . . . **$652.95–$737.95**

### SCOUT
*Action*: Centerfire, single shot
*Stock*: Synthetic
*Barrel*: 20 in. (compact), 22 in. (standard fluted barrels)

*Sights*: None
*Weight*: 5 lb. 13 oz.
*Caliber*: 7mm-08, .270, .30-06, .35 Whelen, .243 (compact only)
*Magazine*: None
*Features*: Stainless steel or blued barrel; ambidextrous black synthetic stock; DuraSight Dead-On integral scope rail; CrushZone recoil pad; reversible hammer spur; compact and alternate length stocks available
*MSRP* . . . . . . . . . . **$319.95–$369.95**

RIFLES

# Cooper Firearms

## MODEL 21

*Action*: Bolt
*Stock*: 1, 2, 3, 4, 10, 11, 13, 14, 15, 17 (see key on page 135)
*Barrel*: 22 in., 24 in.
*Sights*: None
*Weight*: 6 lb. 8 oz.–7 lb. 8 oz.
*Caliber*: .17 Rem., .19-.223, Tactical .20, .204 Ruger, .222 Rem., .222 Rem. Mag., .223 Rem., .223 Rem. Al., 6x45, 6x47, 6.8 SPC, .17 Fireball, .20 VarTarg, .221 Fireball
*Magazine*: None
*Features*: Three-front locking lug bolt action single shot; Sako style extraction machined from solid bar stock; plunger style ejector machined from solid bar; fully adjustable single-stage trigger
MSRP . . . . . . . . . . . . . . $1825–$4395

**COOPER FIREARMS MODEL 21 VARMINT EXTREME**

**COOPER FIREARMS MODEL 21 VARMINT LAMINATE**

## MODEL 22

*Action*: Bolt
*Stock*: 1, 2, 3, 4, 10, 11, 13, 14, 15
*Barrel*: 24 in., 26 in.
*Sights*: None
*Weight*: 7 lb. 8 oz.–8 lb. 4 oz.
*Caliber*: .22-250 Rem., .22-250 Rem. Al., .220 Swift, .25-06 Rem., .25-06 Rem. Al., .243 Win., .243 Rem. Al., .250 Savage, .250 Savage Al., .22BR, 6BR, .257 Roberts, .257 Roberts Al., .284 Win., 7mm-08, 6mm Rem., .260 Rem., 6x284, 6.5x284, 6.5x55 Swede, 6.5 Creedmoor, 7x57 Mauser, .308 Win.
*Magazine*: None
*Features*: Three-front locking lug bolt action single-shot; Sako style extraction machined from solid bar stock; plunger style ejector machined form solid bar; fully adjustable single-stage trigger
MSRP . . . . . . . . . . . . . $1825–$4495

**COOPER FIREARMS MODEL 38 JACKSON VARMINTER**

**COOPER FIREARMS MODEL 52 WESTERN CLASSIC**

## MODEL 38

*Action*: Bolt
*Stock*: 1, 2, 3, 4, 10, 11, 13, 14, 15, 17
*Barrel*: 22 in., 24 in.
*Sights*: None
*Weight*: 6 lb. 8 oz.–7 lb. 8 oz.
*Caliber*: .17 Squirrel, .17 Ackley Hornet, .17 He Bee, .19 Hornet, .22 Hornet, .22 K-Hornet, .22 Squirrel, .218 Bee, .218 Mashburn Bee
*Magazine*: None
*Features*: Three-front locking lug bolt action single-shot; Sako style extraction machined from solid bar stock; retractable tab ejector; fully adjustable single-stage trigger
MSRP . . . . . . . . . . . . . . $1825–$4395

## MODEL 52

*Action*: Bolt
*Stock*: 1, 2, 3, 4, 5, 6, 8, 9
*Barrel*: 22 in., 23 in., 24 in.
*Sights*: None
*Weight*: 7 lb. 8 oz.–8 lb.
*Caliber*: .30-06, .25-06, .25-06 Al., 6.5x284, 6.5-06, .270, .284, .280, .280 Al., .338-06, .35 Whelen
*Magazine*: 3 rounds
*Features*: Three-rear locking lug bolt action magazine fed repeater; center-fire action, also available in stainless steel; Sako style extraction machined from solid bar stock; retractable tab ejector machined from solid bar; fully adjustable single-stage trigger
MSRP . . . . . . . . . . . . . . $1975–$4995

RIFLES

# Cooper Firearms

**COOPER FIREARMS MODEL 57M CLASSIC**

**COOPER FIREARMS MODEL 57 LIGHT VARMINT TARGET - LVT**

## MODEL 54

*Action*: Bolt
*Stock*: 1, 2, 3, 4, 5, 6, 8, 9, 10, 11, 13, 14, 15
*Barrel*: 22 in., 23 in., 24 in.
*Sights*: None
*Weight*: 6 lb. 8 oz.–8 lb.
*Caliber*: .22-250 Rem., .22-250 Rem. AI., .220 Swift, .243 Win., .243 Rem. AI., 6mm Rem., .250 Savage, .250 Savage AI., .257 Roberts, .257 Roberts AI., 7mm-08, .260 Rem., 6.5 Creedmoor, 6.5x47 Lapua, .308 Win.
*Magazine*: 3 rounds
*Features*: Three-rear locking lug bolt action magazine fed repeater; center-fire action, also available in stainless steel; Sako style extraction machined from solid bar stock; plunger style ejector machined form solid bar; fully adjustable single-stage trigger
**MSRP . . . . . . . . . . . . . $1975–$4995**

## MODEL 56

*Action*: Bolt
*Stock*: 1, 2, 3, 4, 5, 6, 8, 9
*Barrel*: 22 in., 23 in., 24 in.
*Sights*: None
*Weight*: 8 lb. 4 oz.–8 lb. 8 oz.
*Caliber*: .257 Wby. Mag., .264 Win. Mag., .270 Wby. Mag., 7mm Rem. Mag., 7 mm Wby. Mag., 7mm STW, .300 H&H, .300 Win. Mag., .300 Wby. Mag., .308 Norma Mag., 8mm Rem. Mag., .338 Win. Mag., .340 Wby. Mag., .375 H&H
*Magazine*: 3 rounds
*Features*: Three-rear locking lug bolt action magazine fed repeater; center-fire action, also available in stainless steel; Sako style extraction machined from solid bar stock; retractable tab ejector machined from solid bar; fully adjustable single-stage trigger
**MSRP . . . . . . . . . . . . . $2795–$5995**

## MODEL 57M

*Action*: Bolt
*Stock*: 1, 2, 3, 4, 5, 7, 9, 12, 15, 16
*Barrel*: 22 in., 24 in.
*Sights*: None
*Weight*: 6 lb.–8 lb.
*Caliber*: .17 Mach 2, .22LR, .22 WMR, .17 HMR
*Magazine*: 4, 5 rounds
*Features*: Three-rear locking lug bolt action magazine fed repeater; twin extractor claw; fixed ejector; feed block; fully adjustable single-stage trigger
**MSRP . . . . . . . . . . . . . $1855–$4395**

# Cooper Stocks

**COOPER FIREARMS EXCALIBUR**

## 1. CLASSIC
AA Claro Walnut; steel grip; four-panel hand checkering; oil finish; matte metal finish; no options

## 2. CUSTOM CLASSIC
AAA Claro walnut; steel grip and stock metal; ebony tip; western-fleur wraparound hand checkering; oil finish; 4140 blued steel match barrel; gloss metal finish; all options

## 3. WESTERN CLASSIC
AAA Claro walnut; steel grip and stock metal; Doug Turnbull case color metal; octagon barrel; matte metal finish; wrap-around western-fleur hand checkering; oil finish; ebony tip; 4140 blued steel match barrel; all options

## 4. MANNLICHER
AAA Claro walnut; shadowline beaded cheek piece; African ebony tip; multipoint wrap around hand checkering; oil finish; Pachmayr pad; standard sling swivel studs; steel grip cap; chromoly premium match grade barrel; high gloss finish on metalwork; all options available

## 5. SCHNABEL
Available in models 52, 54, 56, and 57; AA+ Claro walnut; raised comb; slim taper forearm; multi-point two panel hand checkering; oil finish; standard grade sling swivel studs; Pachmayr pad; steel grip cap; chromoly premium match grade barrel; metal

work is matte finished; all options available

## 6. EXCALIBUR
Synthetic copy of the Classic; M52 only

## 7. JACKSON SQUIRREL
AA Select walnut; roll-over cheekpiece; fluted forearm; hand checkering; oil finish; steel grip cap

## 8. JACKSON GAME
Characteristics of Jackson Squirrel stock with a North American Hunting rifle (M52); some options

## 9. JACKSON HUNTER
Synthetic version of Jackson Squirrel in M57; in M52, this is a version of the Jackson Game

## 10. VARMINTER
AA Claro walnut; stainless match barrel; hand checkering; hand oil finish; matte metal finish; no options

## 11. MONTANA VARMINTER
AA Select Claro walnut; steel grip cap; cooling vents; stainless match barrel; hand checkering and hand oil finish; matte metal finish; all options

## 12. LIGHT VARMINT TARGET
AA Select Claro walnut; steel grip cap; cooling vents; stainless match barrel; hand checkering and hand oil finish; matte metal finish; all options

## 13. VARMINT EXTREME
AAA Claro walnut; steel grip and stock metal; stainless match barrel; hand checkering with cross-over grip pattern; hand oil finish; egg shell matte metal finish; all options

## 14. PHOENIX
Synthetic in flat black and brown spider-web finish; stainless match barrel; aluminum bedding block; cooling vents; matte metal finish; no options

## 15. VARMINT LAMINATE
Laminated hardwood stock; oil finish; Pachmayr pad; steel grip cap; ventilated forearm; stainless steel, straight taper, premium grade match barrel; sling swivel studs available upon request

## 16. TRP-3
Benchrest style; synthetic BR stock; straight stainless match barrel; matte metal finish; some options

## 17. JACKSON VARMINTER
AA Select walnut; roll-over cheekpiece; fluted forearm; hand checkering; oil finish; steel grip cap; stainless match barrel; matte metal finish; some options

# CZ-USA (Ceska Zbrojovka)

CZ 455 AMERICAN

CZ 455 FS

CZ 455 LUX

CZ 455 VARMINT PRECISION TRAINER

## 455 AMERICAN
*Action*: Bolt
*Stock*: Walnut
*Barrel*: 20.5 in.
*Sights*: None
*Weight*: 6 lb. 2 oz.
*Caliber*: .17 HMR, .22LR, .22 WMR, Combo .22LR with .17 HMR replacement barrel
*Magazine*: Detachable box, 5 rounds
*Features*: Cold hammer-forged barrel; blued receiver and barrel finish; integrated dovetail scope base; interchangeable barrel system; adjustable trigger
MSRP . . . . . . . . . . . . . . . $374–$541

## 455 FS
*Action*: Bolt
*Stock*: Walnut
*Barrel*: 20.6 in.
*Sights*: Adjustable iron sights

*Weight*: 6 lb. 6 oz.
*Caliber*: .22LR, .17 HMR
*Magazine*: Detachable box, 5 rounds
*Features*: Action machined from bar stock; adjustable trigger; detachable feed magazine; cold-hammer-forged barrels; standard 11mm optic-mounting dovetail; full length Mannlicher walnut stock; adjustable iron sights
MSRP . . . . . . . . . . . . . . . $499–$524

## 455 LUX
*Action*: Bolt
*Stock*: Walnut
*Barrel*: 20.6 in.
*Sights*: Open
*Weight*: 6 lb. 2 oz.
*Caliber*: .22LR, .22 WMR
*Magazine*: Detachable box, 5 rounds
*Features*: Interchangeable barrel system; adjustable trigger; hammer-forged barrel and billet machined receiver;

adjustable iron sights; lux pattern walnut stock
MSRP . . . . . . . . . . . . . . . $427–$456

## 455 VARMINT PRECISION TRAINER
*Action*: Bolt
*Stock*: Composite
*Barrel*: 20.5 in.
*Sights*: Optic mounting dovetail
*Weight*: 8 lb. 2 oz.
*Caliber*: .22LR
*Magazine*: Detachable box, 5 rounds
*Features*: Action machined from bar stock; adjustable trigger; detachable feed magazine; cold-hammer-forged barrels; standard 11mm optic-mounting dovetail; MCS-T4 Manners composite stock; heavy .886-inch diameter barrel; available in coyote tan; stocks can be ordered with custom weighting/filling
MSRP . . . . . . . . . . . . . . . . . $899

# CZ-USA (Ceska Zbrojovka)

**CZ 455 VARMINT**

**CZ 455 VARMINT EVOLUTION**

**CZ 512 RIMFIRE**

**CZ 527 VARMINT**

## 455 VARMINT

**Action**: Bolt
**Stock**: Walnut
**Barrel**: 20.5 in.
**Sights**: Optic mounting dovetail
**Weight**: 7 lb. 1 oz.
**Caliber**: .22LR, .22 WMR, .17 HMR
**Magazine**: Detachable box, 5 rounds
**Features**: Action machined from bar stock; adjustable trigger; detachable feed magazine; cold-hammer-forged barrels; standard 11mm optic-mounting dovetail; heavier and stiffer barrel for enhanced accuracy; accepts all accessory barrels for the 455 models
**MSRP** . . . . . . . . . . . . . . . . $456–$483

## 455 VARMINT WITH SS EVOLUTION STOCK

**Action**: Bolt
**Stock**: Laminate
**Barrel**: 20.5 in.
**Sights**: Optic mounting dovetail
**Weight**: 7 lb. 2 oz.
**Caliber**: .17 HMR, .22LR

**Magazine**: Detachable box, 5 rounds
**Features**: Action machined from bar stock; adjustable trigger; detachable feed magazine; cold-hammer-forged barrels; standard 11mm optic-mounting dovetail; sky blue/gray laminated stock; ambidextrous; free floated barrel; accepts all accessory barrels for the 455 models
**MSRP** . . . . . . . . . . . . . . . $522–$549

## 512 RIMFIRE RIFLE

**Action**: Semiautomatic
**Stock**: Lacquered beech wood
**Barrel**: 20.7 in.
**Sights**: Adjustable
**Weight**: 5 lb. 14 oz.
**Caliber**: .22LR, .22 WMR
**Magazine**: Detachable box, 5 rounds
**Features**: Aluminum alloy upper receiver and fiberglass reinforced polymer lower half; dual guide rods; hammer-forged CZ barrel; integral 11mm dovetail for mounting optics
**MSRP** . . . . . . . . . . . . . . . $465–$496

## 527

**Action**: Bolt
**Stock**: Walnut
**Barrel**: 18.5 in.-24 in.
**Sights**: Open
**Weight**: 5 lb. 14 oz.–7 lb. 13 oz.
**Caliber**: .222 Rem., .223 Rem., .22 Hornet; American: .17 Hornet .204 Ruger, .221 Fireball; Carbine: 7.62x39; Varmint Target: .204 Ruger
**Magazine**: Detachable box, 5 rounds
**Features**: Hammer-forged barrel; controlled round feed; single-set trigger; each model comes in a variety of calibers and a different stock; Turkish walnut stock in Bavarian pattern on Lux model; Varmint model comes in walnut, Kevlar, or laminated; left-hand version available in American model
**American**: . . . . . . . . . . . . $711–$764
**Carbine**: . . . . . . . . . . . . . . . . $711
**FS**: . . . . . . . . . . . . . . . . . . . $762
**Lux**: . . . . . . . . . . . . . . . $711–$755
**Varmint**: . . . . . . . . . . . . . . $704–$752
**Varmint Target** . . . . . . . . . . . . $885

Rifles • 137

# CZ-USA (Ceska Zbrojovka)

**CZ 550 MEDIUM, KEVLAR**

**CZ 550 CARBINE**

## 550

**Action**: Bolt
**Stock**: Walnut, Kevlar
**Barrel**: 20.5 in., 23.6 in.
**Sights**: Open
**Weight**: 7 lb.–7 lb. 10 oz.
**Caliber**: .22-250, .243 Win., .270 Win., .30-06, .308 Win.; 6.5x55, 9.3x62; (Medium Lux): 6.5x55 Swede
**Magazine**: Detachable box, 4, 5 rounds
**Features**: Adjustable single-set trigger; detachable magazine optional; full stocked model (FS) available; American model includes Pachmayr recoil pad; carbine has Kevlar stock
**American**: . . . . . . . . . . . **$815–$998**
**Carbine**: . . . . . . . . . **$1049–$1096**
**FS**: . . . . . . . . . . . . . . **$864–$911**

## 550 MEDIUM

**Action**: Bolt
**Stock**: Walnut, Kevlar
**Barrel**: 20.5 in., 23.6 in.

**Sights**: Open
**Weight**: 7 lb. 5 oz.–7 lb. 11 oz.
**Caliber**: .300 Win. Mag., 7mm Rem. Mag.
**Magazine**: Detachable box, 3 rounds
**Features**: Adjustable single-set trigger; detachable magazine optional; Battue model has hog-back cob and red fiber optic front sight; Kevlar model has adjustable back iron sights
**Kevlar**: . . . . . . . . . . . . . . . **$1096**
**Lux**: . . . . . . . . . . . . . . . . . **$919**

## 550 SAFARI MAGNUM

**Action**: Bolt
**Stock**: Walnut
**Barrel**: 25 in.
**Sights**: Express sights
**Weight**: 9 lb. 6 oz.
**Caliber**: .375 H&H Mag., .416 Rigby, .458 Win. Mag.
**Magazine**: Fixed, 3 (.416 Rigby), 5 rounds

**Features**: Known worldwide as the 602 BRNO; hammer-forged barrel; single-set trigger; controlled round feed and fixed ejector make the rifle reliable enough for heavy and dangerous game; express sights (1 standing, 2 folding); select Trukish walnut stock with classic safari shape
**MSRP**. . . . . . . . . . . . . **$1180–$1280**

## 550 ULTIMATE HUNTING RIFLE

**Action**: Bolt
**Stock**: Walnut, Kevlar
**Barrel**: 23.6 in.
**Sights**: Open
**Weight**: 7 lb. 11 oz.
**Caliber**: .300 Win. Mag.
**Magazine**: Fixed, 3 rounds
**Features**: Hammer-forged, blued barrel; single-stage trigger
**MSRP**. . . . . . . . . . . . . . . . **$1321**
**Kevlar**: . . . . . . . . . . . . . . . **$1453**

**CZ 550 SAFARI MAGNUM**

**CZ 550 ULTIMATE HUNTING RIFLE**

# CZ-USA (Ceska Zbrojovka)

CZ 550 VARMINT

CZ 550 URBAN COUNTER-SNIPER

CZ 750 SNIPER

## 550 URBAN COUNTER-SNIPER

**Action**: Bolt
**Stock**: Synthetic
**Barrel**: 16 in.
**Sights**: None
**Weight**: 8 lb. 5 oz.
**Caliber**: .308 Win.
**Magazine**: Detachable box, 10 rounds
**Features**: Floated bull barrel with target crown; Surefire muzzlebrake; Teflon coating; single-stage trigger; Bell & Carlson fiberglass stock; aluminum bedding block
**MSRP** . . . . . . . . . . . . . . . . . $2530

## 550 VARMINT

**Action**: Bolt
**Stock**: Walnut, laminate, Kevlar
**Barrel**: 25.6 in.
**Sights**: Open
**Weight**: 9 lb. 11 oz.
**Caliber**: .22-250, .308
**Magazine**: Detachable box, 4 rounds

**Features**: Heavy barreled, two position manual safety; firing-pin-block and bolt lock
**MSRP** . . . . . . . . . . . . . . . $840–$979

## 750 SNIPER

**Action**: Bolt
**Stock**: Synthetic thumbhole
**Barrel**: 26 in.
**Sights**: Open

**Weight**: 11 lb. 14 oz.
**Caliber**: .308 Win.
**Magazine**: Detachable box, 10 rounds
**Features**: Adjustable comb; underside of forend is fitted with a 220mm-long rail for bipod attachment; muzzlebrake; thread protector; mirage shield; blued barrel; single-stage trigger
**MSRP** . . . . . . . . . . . . . . . . . $1999

# Dakota Arms

## MODEL 10

**Action**: Falling block
**Stock**: Walnut
**Barrel**: 23 in.
**Sights**: None

**Weight**: 6 lb.–7 lb.
**Caliber**: .22LR to .300 Win., .338 to .375 H&H Mag.
**Magazine**: None
**Features**: Point wrap checkering; scope

ring bases installed; custom length of pull; barrel break in
**MSRP** . . . . . . . . . . . . . . from $5260
**Deluxe:** . . . . . . . . . . . . from $6690

DAKOTA MODEL 10

# Dakota Arms

DAKOTA MODEL 76 CLASSIC

DAKOTA MODEL 97 HUNTER

## MODEL 76 CLASSIC

**Action**: Bolt
**Stock**: Walnut
**Barrel**: 23 in.
**Sights**: None
**Weight**: 6 lb. 8 oz.–9 lb. 8 oz.
**Caliber**: Classic: .257 Roberts, .260 Rem., .270 Win., .280 Rem., .30-06 Spfd., .300 Dakota, .300 Win. Mag., .300 WSM, .308 Win., .330 Dakota, .416 Rem., 7mm Rem. Mag., 7mm-08 Rem.; Safari: .300 H&H, .375 Dakota, .416 Rem., 7mm Dakota; African: .338 Win. Mag., .375 H&H, .416 Rem., .404 Jeffery, .416 Rigby, .450 Dakota, .458 Lott
**Magazine**: Box, 4 rounds
**Features**: Barrel break in; custom length of pull; optional engraving; point panel checkering; Dakota swivel studs; 1-inch recoil pad; straddle floor plate; right- or left-hand configurations; Safari model has front island sight with flip-up night sight; African model has quarter rib sights with banded front sights and flip-up night sights
**Classic:** . . . . . . . . . . . . . **from $6030**
**Safari:** . . . . . . . . . . . . . **from $8010**
**African:** . . . . . . . . . . . . . **from $8890**

## MODEL 97 HUNTER

**Action**: Bolt
**Stock**: Fiberglass, composite, walnut
**Barrel**: 22 in. (short action), 25 in. (long action)
**Sights**: None
**Weight**: 7 lb.
**Caliber**: All-Weather: .30-06, .338 Win. Mag., .375 H&H, 7mm Rem. Mag., 7mm-08; Long Range: .280

Rem., .338 Win. Mag., 7mm Rem. Mag., 7mm-08
**Magazine**: Blind box
**Features**: Stainless Douglas barrel; black composite stock with two inletted Ken Howell swivel studs; stainless trigger bow
**All-weather:** . . . . . . . . . **from $4050**
**Deluxe:** . . . . . . . . . . . . **from $4820**
**Long Range:** . . . . . . . . **from $3720**

## SHARPS

**Action**: Falling block
**Stock**: Walnut
**Barrel**: 26 in.
**Sights**: Open
**Weight**: 8 lb.
**Caliber**: .17 HMR, .22 Hornet, .30-30, .30-40 Krag., .375 H&H
**Magazine**: None
**Features**: Octagon barrel; steel buttplate; single blade rear sight with front bead; matte blued metal finish

**Sharps:** . . . . . . . . . . . . . **from $4490**
**Miller:** . . . . . . . . . . . . . **from $5590**

## VARMINTER

**Action**: Bolt
**Stock**: Walnut
**Barrel**: 22 in.
**Sights**: None
**Weight**: 8 lb. 4 oz.
**Caliber**: .17 VarTag, .17 Rem., .17 Tactical, .20 PPC, .204 Ruger, .221 Rem. Fireball, .22 PPC, .223 Rem., 6mm PPC, 6.5 Grendel
**Magazine**: None
**Features**: Available in walnut sporter-style stock or XXX walnut varmint style stock with semi-beavertail forend; checkered grip; recessed target crown; vapor hone matte bead blast finish on stainless; stainless steel barrel
**MSRP** . . . . . . . . . . . . . . . **from $2840**
**All-weather:** . . . . . . . . . . **from $3390**
**Deluxe:** . . . . . . . . . . . . . **from $3390**
**Heavy:** . . . . . . . . . . . . . . **from $2840**

DAKOTA SHARPS

DAKOTA VARMINTER

# Dixie Gun Works

## 1873 TRAPDOOR OFFICER'S MODEL BY PEDERSOLI

**Action**: Breechloading
**Stock**: Walnut
**Barrel**: 26 in.
**Sights**: Adjustable
**Weight**: 8 lb.
**Caliber**: .45-70
**Magazine**: None
**Features**: Single-shot rifle; front sight is blued steel with brass bead; rear sight is adjustable tang sight; color case-hardened steel furniture, pewter nose cap; single set trigger; chambered for black powder cartridges or factory-loaded smokeless ammo
**MSRP** . . . . . . . . . . . . . . . . . . $1900

## 1874 SHILOH SHARPS MODEL

**Action**: Breechloading
**Stock**: Walnut, pistol grip
**Barrel**: 34 in. long range; 30 in. Sporting rifle No. 1; 26 in. Sporting Rifle
**Sights**: Adjustable
**Weight**: 10 lb.
**Caliber**: .45-70, .30-40 Krag. Sporting rifle
**Magazine**: None
**Features**: Sporting model has a spirit level dovetail; part round, part octagonal barrel; frame, lock plate, hammer, and lever have all the original color case-hardening; buttstock is mounted with checkered hard rubber plate; double-set triggers; chambered for black powder cartridges or factory-loaded smokeless ammo
**MSRP** . . . . . . . . . . . . . . . . . . $2850

## KODIAK DOUBLE RIFLE BY PEDERSOLI

**Action**: Lever
**Stock**: Walnut, pistol grip
**Barrel**: 24 in.
**Sights**: Flip up sights
**Weight**: 10 lb.–10 lb. 12 oz.
**Caliber**: .50, .54, .58 Kodiak, .45-70 Mark IV, .72 Express
**Magazine**: None
**Features**: Express has dovetail, steel ramp with brass bead as front sight; blued barrels; external hammers are rebounding style; double triggers; sling is included; English walnut buttstock and forearm are checkered; rubber recoil pad; chambered for black powder cartridges or factory-loaded smokeless ammo
**MSRP** . . . . . . . . . . . . . $1395–$1450

DIXIE GUN WORKS 1873 TRAPDOOR OFFICER'S MODEL

DIXIE GUN WORKS 1874 SHILOH SHARPS MODEL

DIXIE GUN WORKS KODIAK DOUBLE RIFLE

# DPMS Panther Arms

## 24 SPECIAL

**Action**: Semiautomatic
**Stock**: Synthetic; pistol grip
**Barrel**: 24 in.
**Sights**: None
**Weight**: 10 lb. 4 oz.
**Caliber**: .233 Rem
**Magazine**: Detachable box, 30 rounds
**Features**: Aircraft aluminum alloy, A3 style flattop receiver coated in black Teflon; aluminum trigger guard; black standard A2 Zytel Mil-Spec stock with Panther Tactical grip; aluminum ribbed free-float tube; nylon web sling included; adjustable buttplate
**MSRP**................... **$1229**

## A2 CLASSIC

**Action**: Semiautomatic
**Stock**: Synthetic
**Barrel**: 20 in.
**Sights**: Open
**Weight**: 9 lb.
**Caliber**: 5.56x45mm
**Magazine**: Detachable box, 30 rounds
**Features**: Chromoly steel barrel with A2 flash hider; forged aircraft aluminum alloy receiver with A2 fixed carry handle; black standardized A2 black style Mil-Spec stock; standard A2 round handguards; dual aperture adjustable rear sights, Mil-Spec front sight post
**MSRP**.................... **$869**

## AP4 CARBINE

**Action**: Semiautomatic
**Stock**: Synthetic
**Barrel**: 16 in.
**Sights**: Open
**Weight**: 7 lb. 2 oz.
**Caliber**: 5.56x45mm
**Magazine**: Detachable box, 30 rounds
**Features**: Chromoly steel barrel with A2 Flash hider; A3 aircraft aluminum alloy receiver with detachable carrying handle; adjustable rear sight and A2 front sight assembly; black AP4-6 position, telescoping fiber reinforced polymer stock; oval, carbine length GlacierGuards
**MSRP**.................... **$959**

## ARCTIC PANTHER

**Action**: Semiautomatic
**Stock**: Synthetic
**Barrel**: 20 in.
**Sights**: None
**Weight**: 9 lb.
**Caliber**: .223 Rem.
**Magazine**: Detachable box, 30 rounds
**Features**: Fluted and black Teflon coated barrel; aircraft aluminum alloy, A3 style flattop receiver coated in white; standard A2 black Zytel Mil-Spec stock; aluminum ribbed free-float handguard tube (coated white)
**MSRP**.................... **$1129**

DPMS 24 SPECIAL

DPMS A2 CLASSIC

DPMS AP4 CARBINE

DPMS ARCTIC PANTHER

# DPMS Panther Arms

DPMS CARBINE A2

DPMS DCM

DPMS COMPACT HUNTER

DPMS LO-PRO CLASSIC

DPMS LITE LR-308

## CARBINE A2

*Action*: Semiautomatic
*Stock*: Synthetic
*Barrel*: 16 in.
*Sights*: Open
*Weight*: 6 lb. 14 oz.
*Caliber*: 5.56x45mm
*Magazine*: Detachable box, 30 rounds
*Features*: Chromoly steel barrel with flash hider; A3 aircraft aluminum alloy receiver with detachable carrying handle; adjustable rear sight and A2 front sight assembly; DPMS Pardus black stock; oval, carbine length GlacierGuards
**MSRP** . . . . . . . . . . . . . . . . . . . $859

## COMPACT HUNTER

*Action*: Semiautomatic
*Stock*: Synthetic
*Barrel*: 16 in.
*Sights*: None
*Weight*: 7 lb. 12 oz.
*Caliber*: .308 Win.
*Magazine*: 4, 10, 20 rounds
*Features*: Designed for smaller statures and suitable for youth, female, and

hunters who prefer a compact firearm; Teflon-coated stainless steel barrel; carbon fiber free-float tube; Hogue pistol grip; B5 Systems-Special Operations Peculiar Modification (SOPMOD) stock
**MSRP** . . . . . . . . . . . . . . . . . . $1499

## DCM

*Action*: Semiautomatic
*Stock*: Synthetic
*Barrel*: 20 in.
*Sights*: Adjustable NM
*Weight*: 9 lb. 6 oz.
*Caliber*: .233 Rem.
*Magazine*: Detachable box, 30 rounds
*Features*: National Match dual aperture rear sight, NM front sight post; A2 fixed carry handle; forged aircraft aluminum alloy receiver; receiver coated in Teflon; aluminum trigger guard; standard black A2 style Mil-Spec stock with trap door assembly; DCM free-float handguard system
**MSRP** . . . . . . . . . . . . . . . . . . $1129

## LITE LR-308

*Action*: Semiautomatic
*Stock*: Synthetic
*Barrel*: 24 in.
*Sights*: None
*Weight*: 10 lb. 4 oz.
*Caliber*: .308 Win.
*Magazine*: 4, 10, 20 rounds
*Features*: 416 stainless steel lightweight fluted barrel; improved 2012 carbon fiber free-float tube; A3 receiver
**MSRP** . . . . . . . . . . . . . . . . . . $1499

## LO-PRO CLASSIC

*Action*: Semiautomatic
*Stock*: Synthetic
*Barrel*: 16 in.
*Sights*: None
*Weight*: 7 lb. 12 oz.
*Caliber*: 5.56x45mm
*Magazine*: Detachable box, 30 rounds
*Features*: Chromoly steel barrel; flattop Lo-Pro, extruded receiver made of aircraft aluminum alloy; semiauto trigger group; standard A2 black Zytel Mil stock with trap door assembly; GlacierGuards
**MSRP** . . . . . . . . . . . . . . . . . . $769

# DPMS Panther Arms

DPMS LR-204

DPMS LR-243H

DPMS LR-308

DPMS LR-260

**DPMS PRAIRIE PANTHER
KING'S DESERT SHADOW**

## LR-204

**Action**: Semiautomatic
**Stock**: Synthetic
**Barrel**: 24 in.
**Sights**: None
**Weight**: 10 lb. 4 oz.
**Caliber**: .204 Ruger
**Magazine**: Detachable box, 30 rounds
**Features**: Fluted barrel; standard A2 black stock; aluminum ribbed free-float tube; aircraft aluminum alloy, Teflon coated, forged A3 style receiver; nylon web sling included
**MSRP**. . . . . . . . . . . . . . . . . . . $1059

## LR-243H, LR-243L

**Action**: Semiautomatic
**Stock**: Synthetic
**Barrel**: 20 in. (LR-243), 18 in. (LR-243L)
**Sights**: None
**Weight**: 8 lb.–10 lb. 10 oz.
**Caliber**: .243 Win.
**Magazine**: Detachable box, 19 rounds
**Features**: Custom Miculek compensator, lightweight gas block (LR-243L); black Teflon-covered stainless steel barrel with 308 Panther Flash hider (LR-243H); A3 flattop lightweight receiver, extruded from T-5 Aluminum (LR-243L); A3 flattop thick walled aluminum receiver (LR-243H); two-stage trigger (LR-243L); standard AR-15 trig-

ger group (LR-243H); Carbon Fiber Free-Float tube with bipod stud (LR-243L); standard length ribbed free-float handguard tube (LR-243H)
**LR-243H:** . . . . . . . . . . . . . . . . $1239
**LR-243L:** . . . . . . . . . . . . . . . . $1499

## LR-260

**Action**: Semiautomatic
**Stock**: Synthetic
**Barrel**: 24 in.
**Sights**: None
**Weight**: 11 lb. 4 oz.
**Caliber**: .260 Rem.
**Magazine**: Detachable box, 19 rounds
**Features**: 416 Stainless steel bull barrel; A3 style flattop receiver made of thick walled aluminum; standard AR-15 trigger group; standard A2 black style Mil-Spec stock with trap door assembly; standard length ribbed free-float handguard tube
**MSRP**. . . . . . . . . . . . . . . . . . . $1239

## LR-308

**Action**: Semiautomatic
**Stock**: Synthetic
**Barrel**: 24 in.
**Sights**: None

**Weight**: 11 lb. 3 oz.
**Caliber**: .308 Win.
**Magazine**: Detachable box, 19 rounds
**Features**: 416 Stainless steel bull barrel; thick walled aluminum receiver coated with Teflon; internal trigger guard; raised Picatinny rail for easy scope mounting; standard A2 Black Zytel Mil-Spec stock
**MSRP**. . . . . . . . . . . . . . . . . . . $1199

## PRAIRIE PANTHER CAMO

**Action**: Semiautomatic
**Stock**: Synthetic
**Barrel**: 20 in.
**Sights**: None
**Weight**: 7 lb. 2 oz.
**Caliber**: .223 Rem.
**Magazine**: Detachable box, 20 rounds
**Features**: Target crowned, stainless steel heavy barrel; A3 flattop aircraft aluminum alloy receiver; Magpul winter trigger guard; King's Desert Shadow camo, King's Snow Shadow camo, or Mossy Oak Brush camo stock; receiver features durable ceramic over coat in either type of camo; nylon web sling included
**MSRP**. . . . . . . . . . . . . . . . . . . $1289

# DPMS Panther Arms

## RECON

*Action*: Semiautomatic
*Stock*: Synthetic
*Barrel*: 16 in.
*Sights*: Magpul BUIS
*Weight*: 9 lb.
*Caliber*: 5.56mm
*Magazine*: Detachable box, 30 rounds
*Features*: Bead-blasted stainless, mid length gas system; semi-auto trigger group; Magpul MOE stock in Teflon black
**MSRP** . . . . . . . . . . . . . . . . . . $1129

## REPR

*Action*: Semiautomatic
*Stock*: Synthetic
*Barrel*: 20 in.
*Sights*: None
*Weight*: 9 lb. 12 oz.
*Caliber*: 7.62 NATO
*Magazine*: Detachable box, 19 rounds
*Features*: Two-stage match grade trigger; dark earth Magpul PRS stock; Hogue rubber grip with finger grooves; A3 style flattop; ambi-selector installed; milled from solid billet of aluminum; AAC flash hider/suppressor adapter
**MSRP** . . . . . . . . . . . . . . . . . . $2589

## SWEET 16, BULL 20, BULL 24

*Action*: Semiautomatic
*Stock*: Synthetic
*Barrel*: 16 in., 20 in., 24 in.
*Sights*: None
*Weight*: 7 lb. 14 oz.–9 lb. 13 oz.
*Caliber*: .223 Rem.
*Magazine*: Detachable box, 30 rounds
*Features*: Aircraft aluminum alloy, A3 style flattop receiver coated in black Teflon; aluminum trigger guard; black standard A2 Zytel Mil-Spec stock; aluminum ribbed free-float tube; Nylon web sling included
**Bull Sweet 16:** . . . . . . . . . . . . $939
**Bull 20:** . . . . . . . . . . . . . . . . . $969
**Bull 24:** . . . . . . . . . . . . . . . . . $999

## TACTICAL 16

*Action*: Semiautomatic
*Stock*: Synthetic
*Barrel*: 16 in.
*Sights*: Open
*Weight*: 8 lb. 3 oz.
*Caliber*: 5.56x45mm
*Magazine*: Detachable box, 30 rounds

DPMS RECON

DPMS REPR

DPMS SWEET 16

DPMS TACTICAL 16

*Features*: Chromoly steel barrel with A3 Flash hider; A2 front and rear sight assembly; forged aircraft aluminum alloy receiver coated in Teflon; black standard A2 style mil stock; nylon web sling included
**MSRP** . . . . . . . . . . . . . . . . . . . $859

# E.M.F. Company

### 1866 "YELLOWBOY" SHORT RIFLE

*Action*: Lever
*Stock*: Walnut
*Barrel*: 20 in.
*Sights*: Open
*Weight*: 8 lb. 3 oz.
*Caliber*: .38 Spl., .45LC
*Magazine*: 10+1 rounds
*Features*: First true cowboy lever-action rifle; loading gate passes cartridges through side of the receiver; SASS badge engraved on both sides
**MSRP** . . . . . . . . . . . . . . . . . . **$1175**

### ROSSI 1892 TRAPPER CARBINE

*Action*: Lever
*Stock*: Hardwood

E.M.F. 1866 "YELLOWBOY" SHORT RIFLE

E.M.F. ROSSI 1892 TRAPPER CARBINE

*Barrel*: 16 in.
*Sights*: Fixed
*Weight*: 4 lb. 13 oz.
*Caliber*: .44 Mag.
*Magazine*: 8+1 rounds

*Features*: Stainless steel frame; round stainless steel barrel; hardwood forend and buttstock; fast western-style lever; crescent buttplates
**MSRP** . . . . . . . . . . . . . . . . . . **$585**

# E.R. Shaw

### E.R. SHAW MARK VII CUSTOM

*Action*: Bolt
*Stock*: Walnut, laminate wood, or synthetic
*Barrel*: 16.25 in.–26 in.
*Sights*: None
*Weight*: Depending on specifications
*Caliber*: 75 caliber choices from .17 Rem. to .458 Lott
*Magazine*: Internal magazine

*Features*: Right- or left-hand actions; stainless receivers; contour barrels; polished or matte blued finish; recoil pads and swivel studs; choice of two

barrel contours, stainless steel or blued chromoly steel
**Base price:** . . . . . . . . . . . . . . . . **$775**

E.R. SHAW MK VII CUSTOM RIFLE, WITH NUTMEG LAMINATE WOOD STOCK AND BLUED MATTE FINISH BARREL WITH SHAW'S PATENTED HELICAL FLUTING

# Excel Arms

EXCEL ARMS ACCELERATOR RIFLE

### ACCELERATOR RIFLE

*Action*: Semiautomatic
*Stock*: Polymer composite, pistol grip
*Barrel*: 18 in.

*Sights*: Standard includes Red/Green dot optic
*Weight*: 8 lb.
*Caliber*: .22 WMR, .17 HMR
*Magazine*: Detachable box, 9 rounds
*Features*: Weaver rail for scope, sights, and optics; pin-block safety; stainless steel barrel; polymer composite stock available in black or silver shroud
**MR-22:** . . . . . . . . . . . . . . . **$512–$549**
**MR-5.7:** . . . . . . . . . . . . . **$640–$795**

# Excel Arms

EXCEL ARMS X-5.7R

EXCEL ARMS X-22R

## X-5.7R

**Action**: Semiautomatic
**Stock**: Synthetic
**Barrel**: 18 in.
**Sights**: None
**Weight**: 6 lb. 4 oz.
**Caliber**: 5.7x28mm
**Magazine**: 25, 10 rounds
**Features**: CNC-machined aluminum; Picatinny rail; tactical AR styling; collapsible stock; tapped holes in the hand guard for mounting accessory rails

**MSRP** . . . . . . . . . . . . . . . . . . . . **$795**
**Iron sights:** . . . . . . . . . . . . . . . **$916**

## X-22R RIFLE

**Action**: Semiautomatic
**Stock**: Synthetic
**Barrel**: 18 in.
**Sights**: None
**Weight**: 4 lb. 12 oz.
**Caliber**: .22LR HV
**Magazine**: Detachable box, 25 rounds, (10 rounds optional)
**Features**: CNC-machined aluminum frame; optional 3-9x40 scope; tapped holes in hand guard for mounting accessory rails; integral weaver base to mount scopes, sights, and optics

**Basic:** . . . . . . . . . . . . . . . . . . . . **$461**
**Scoped:** . . . . . . . . . . . . . . . . . . **$548**
**10 RD:** . . . . . . . . . . . . . . . . . . **$461**

# FNH USA

FNH BALLISTA

## BALLISTA

**Action**: Semiautomatic
**Stock**: Synthetic
**Barrel**: 26 in.
**Sights**: None
**Weight**: 15 lb. 13 oz.
**Caliber**: .338 Lapua Mag., .300 Win. Mag., .308 Win.
**Magazine**: Detachable box, 6/9, 8/12, 9/13 rounds
**Features**: High strength vibration-isolated aluminum alloy receiver with a top mounted Mil-Spec 1913 rail; ambidextrous folding stock; integrated folding rear monopod; optional scopes and bipod

**MSRP** . . . . . . . . . . . . . . . . . . . . **$6999**

# FNH USA

FNH FNAR STANDARD HEAVY BARREL

FNH SCAR 17S CARBINE

## FNAR STANDARD
**Action**: Gas-operated autoloader
**Stock**: Synthetic
**Barrel**: 16 in., 20 in. standard fluted, 20 in. heavy fluted
**Sights**: Receiver mounted rail
**Weight**: 8 lb. 13 oz.–10 lb.
**Caliber**: .308 Win. (7.62x51mm NATO)
**Magazine**: 10, 20 rounds
**Features**: Extended bolt handle, hammer-forged barrel with crown; comes with one magazine, three interchange-able recoil pads, three comb inserts and shims for adjusting for cast-on, cast-off, and drop at comb; stock is matte black synthetic with pistol grip and adjustable comb
**MSRP** . . . . . . . . . . . . . . . . . . . **$1699**

## SCAR 17S CARBINE
**Action**: Gas-operated autoloader
**Stock**: Polymer
**Barrel**: 16.25 in.
**Sights**: Adjustable, folding, removable
**Weight**: 8 lb.
**Caliber**: .308 Win. (7.62x51mm NATO)
**Magazine**: 10, 20 rounds
**Features**: Fully adjustable stock; MIL-STD 1913 optical rail plus three accessory rails for attaching a variety of sights and lasers; free-floating, cold-hammer-forged barrel; available in black or Flat Dark Earth tactical, tele-scoping, side-folding polymer stock
**MSRP** . . . . . . . . . . . . . . . . . . . **$3349**

# Harrington & Richardson

## BUFFALO CLASSIC RIFLE
**Action**: Lever
**Stock**: Walnut
**Barrel**: 32 in.
**Sights**: Open
**Weight**: 8 lb.
**Caliber**: .45-70
**Magazine**: None
**Features**: Antique color case-hardened frame; cut-checkered American black walnut with case colored crescent steel buttplate
**MSRP** . . . . . . . . . . . . . . . . . . . **$479**

HARRINGTON & RICHARDSON BUFFALO CLASSIC RIFLE

RIFLES

# Harrington & Richardson

**HARRINGTON & RICHARDSON HANDI-GRIP HANDI RIFLE**

**HARRINGTON & RICHARDSON HANDI-RIFLE**

**HARRINGTON & RICHARDSON STAINLESS ULTRA HUNTER**

**HARRINGTON & RICHARDSON SUPERLIGHT HANDI-RIFLE COMPACT WITH SCOPE**

RIFLES

## HANDI-GRIP HANDI RIFLE
*Action*: Hinged breech
*Stock*: Ambidextrous thumbhole black polymer
*Barrel*: 22 in., 24 in., 26 in.
*Sights*: Scope mount rail and hammer extension
*Weight*: 7 lb.
*Caliber*: .204 Ruger, .223 Rem., .22-250 Rem., .308 Win., .45-70 Govt., .243 Win., .35-06 Rem.
*Magazine*: None
*Features*: Molded checkering at grip and forend for sure handling; transfer bar system
**MSRP . . . . . . . . . . . . . . . . . . . $341**

## HANDI-RIFLE
*Action*: Lever
*Stock*: Walnut finish hardwood stock
*Barrel*: 22 in.
*Sights*: None
*Weight*: 7 lb.
*Caliber*: .35 Whelen
*Magazine*: None
*Features*: Blued finish; scope mount included; hammer spur
**MSRP . . . . . . . . . . . . . . . . . . . $313**

## STAINLESS ULTRA HUNTER WITH THUMBHOLE STOCK
*Action*: Lever
*Stock*: Laminate
*Barrel*: 24 in.
*Sights*: None
*Weight*: 8 lb.
*Caliber*: .45-70
*Magazine*: None
*Features*: Cinnamon laminate stock with thumbhole pistol grip, swivel studs, and rubber rifle buttpad
**MSRP . . . . . . . . . . . . . . . . . . . $516**

## SUPERLIGHT HANDI-RIFLE COMPACT WITH SCOPE
*Action*: Lever
*Stock*: High-density polymer, matte black
*Barrel*: 20 in.
*Sights*: Open
*Weight*: 5 lb. 5 oz.
*Caliber*: .243 Win.
*Magazine*: None
*Features*: Sling swivel studs; recoil pad; ramp front sight, adjustable rear; drilled and tapped for scope rail; includes 3-9x32 scope, factory mounted and bore sighted
**MSRP . . . . . . . . . . . . . . . . . . . $359**

# Harrington & Richardson

### SURVIVOR

**Action**: Lever
**Stock**: Polymer
**Barrel**: 22 in., 24 in.
**Sights**: None
**Weight**: 6 lb. 8 oz.
**Caliber**: .223 Rem, .308 Win.
**Magazine**: None
**Features**: Bull barrel with blued finish; high-density polymer stock with black matte finish, thumbhole design; butt-stock storage compartment; sling swivel studs and sling
**MSRP** . . . . . . . . . . . . . . . . . . . . . $326

### ULTRA VARMINT RIFLE

**Action**: Lever
**Stock**: Cinnamon laminated American hardwood

**HARRINGTON & RICHARDSON SURVIVOR**

**Barrel**: 24 in. bull barrel
**Sights**: None
**Weight**: 7 lb.–8 lb.
**Caliber**: .223 Rem., .243 Win.
**Magazine**: None
**Features**: Monte Carlo pistol grip with checkering; sling swivel studs; ventilat-

ed recoil pad; scope mount and hammer extension, no iron sights; thumbhole optional
**MSRP** . . . . . . . . . . . . . . . . . . . . . $381

**HARRINGTON & RICHARDSON
ULTRA VARMINT THUMBHOLE**

# Heckler & Koch

### G28

**Action**: Semiautomatic gas operated
**Stock**: Synthetic
**Barrel**: 16.5 in.
**Sights**: Mounted 3-20x50 scope
**Weight**: 16 lb. 8 oz.
**Caliber**: 7.62mm
**Magazine**: 10, 20 rounds
**Features**: Steel upper receiver; STANAG 4694 NATO accessory rails; new two-stage gas regulator designed for suppressed and unsuppressed use; free-floating chrome-lined cold-hammer-forged steel barrel; retractable buttstocks; green/brown finish with special low IR observable color
**MSRP** . . . . . . . . . . . . . . . . . . . . .N/A
**(Special order only)**

**HECKLER & KOCH
G28 STANDARD**

**HECKLER & KOCH
MR556A1**

**HECKLER & KOCH MR762A1**

**HECKLER & KOCH USC**

## MR556A1

*Action*: Autoloading
*Stock*: Synthetic
*Barrel*: 16.50 in.
*Sights*: Open
*Weight*: 8 lb. 15 oz.
*Caliber*: 5.56x44mm
*Magazine*: Detachable box, 10 rounds
*Features*: Free-floating four-quadrant rail system; four Mil-Spec 1913 Picatinny rails; two-stage trigger; retractable buttstock
**MSRP**. . . . . . . . . . . . . . . . . . **$3295**

## MR762A1

*Action*: Semiautomatic gas operated
*Stock*: Synthetic
*Barrel*: 16.5 in.
*Sights*: None
*Weight*: 9 lb. 15 oz.
*Caliber*: 7.62mm
*Magazine*: 10, 20 rounds
*Features*: Match rifle features; direct descendant of HK416/417 series, but made for civilians; uses a piston and a solid operating "pusher" rod in place of the common gas tube normally used in AR-style rifles; cold-hammer-forged barrel; adjustable stock
**MSRP**. . . . . . . . . . . . . . . . . . **$3995**

## USC

*Action*: Autoloading
*Stock*: Synthetic
*Barrel*: 16.13 in.
*Sights*: None
*Weight*: 6 lb.
*Caliber*: .45 ACP
*Magazine*: Detachable box, 10 rounds
*Features*: Black reinforced polymer stock; steel barrel; skeletonized buttstock is topped with rubber cheek rest and recoil pad; Picatinny rails; ambidextrous safety
**MSRP**. . . . . . . . . . . . . . . . . . **$1788**

# Henry Repeating Arms

**HENRY .30-30**

## .30-30
**Action**: Lever
**Stock**: Walnut
**Barrel**: 20 in.
**Sights**: Open
**Weight**: 7 lb.
**Caliber**: .30-30
**Magazine**: 5 rounds
**Features**: Steel round barrel: deluxe checkered American walnut with rubber buttpad; XS Ghost Rings sights; blued steel receiver, drilled and tapped for easy scope mounting. Brass octagon barrel: straight-grip American walnut with buttplate; marble fully adjustable semi-buckhorn rear sight, with diamond insert, beaded front sight; brass receiver, drilled and tapped for easy scope mounting
**Steel**:...................**$749.95**
**Brass**:...................**$950**

**HENRY .45-70 LEVER ACTION**

## .45-70 LEVER ACTION
**Action**: Lever
**Stock**: Walnut
**Barrel**: 18.43 in.
**Sights**: Closed rear, blade front
**Weight**: 7 lb. 1 oz.
**Caliber**: .45-70
**Magazine**: 4 rounds
**Features**: Pistol-grip American walnut with buttplate; blued steel drilled and tapped for easy scope mounting; XS Ghost Rings rear sight with blade front
**MSRP**..................**$799.95**

**HENRY ACU-BOLT**

## ACU-BOLT
**Action**: Bolt
**Stock**: Synthetic
**Barrel**: 20 in.
**Sights**: Open
**Weight**: 4 lb. 4 oz.
**Caliber**: .22LR, .22 Mag., .17 HMR
**Magazine**: None
**Features**: Single-shot; one-piece fiberglass synthetic stock; Williams fire sights; stainless steel receiver and barrel
**MSRP**..................**$399.95**

**HENRY BIG BOY**

## BIG BOY
**Action**: Lever
**Stock**: Walnut
**Barrel**: 20 in.
**Sights**: Open
**Weight**: 8.68 lb.
**Caliber**: .44 Mag., .45 Colt, .357 Mag.
**Magazine**: Under-barrel tube, 10 rounds
**Features**: Adjustable marble semi-buckhorn rear with white diamond insert and brass beaded front sight; solid top brass receiver, brass buttplate and brass barrel band; straight-grip American walnut stock; octagonal barrel
**MSRP**..................**$899.95**

# Henry Repeating Arms

**HENRY GOLDEN BOY DELUXE**

**HENRY GOLDEN BOY "EAGLE SCOUT" TRIBUTE**

**HENRY GOLDEN BOY LAW ENFORCEMENT TRIBUTE EDITION**

## GOLDEN BOY DELUXE ENGRAVED II

**Action**: Lever
**Stock**: Walnut
**Barrel**: 20 in.
**Sights**: Open
**Weight**: 6 lb. 12 oz.
**Caliber**: .22
**Magazine**: Under-barrel tube, 16 rounds (LR), 21 rounds (S)
**Features**: American walnut stock; adjustable buckhorn rear sight, beaded front sight; brasslite receiver, brass buttplate, and blued barrel
**MSRP** . . . . . . . . . . . . . . . . . . . $1585

## GOLDEN BOY "EAGLE SCOUT" TRIBUTE

**Action**: Lever
**Stock**: American Walnut with Boy Scout Medallion on side
**Barrel**: 20 in.
**Sights**: Adjustable semi-buckhorn rear and brass bead front
**Weight**: 6 lb. 12 oz.
**Caliber**: .22LR, .22 Short
**Magazine**: 16 round (LR) and 21 round (short)
**Features**: Nickel-plated receiver with hand engraved eagle and Boy Scout motto in 24-karat gold; brass buttplate, barrel band, and receiver; blued barrel and lever
**MSRP** . . . . . . . . . . . . . . . . . $1049.95

## GOLDEN BOY LAW ENFORCEMENT TRIBUTE

**Action**: Lever
**Stock**: Walnut
**Barrel**: 20 in.
**Sights**: Open
**Weight**: 6 lb. 12 oz.
**Caliber**: .22 S/L/LR
**Magazine**: Under-barrel tube, 16 rounds (LR), 21 rounds (S)
**Features**: 24-kt. gold-plated engravings in American-style scrollwork; right side features law enforcement badge and banner, left side features Michael the Archangel with sword, scales, and banner; American walnut stock
**MSRP** . . . . . . . . . . . . . . . . . $899.95

# Henry Repeating Arms

HENRY LEVER ACTION .22

HENRY LEVER OCTAGON FRONTIER

HENRY MARE'S LEG

HENRY MINI BOLT YOUTH

RIFLES

## LEVER ACTION .22

**Action**: Lever
**Stock**: Walnut
**Barrel**: 16.13 in. (carbine, youth), 18.25 in.
**Sights**: Open
**Weight**: 4 lb. 8 oz. (carbine, youth), 5 lb. 4 oz., 5 lb. 8 oz. (Mag.)
**Caliber**: .22, .22L, .22LR
**Magazine**: Under-barrel tube, 11 rounds (.22 Mag.), 15 rounds (.22LR), 17 rounds (.22L), 18 rounds (.22S), 21 rounds (.22)
**Features**: Straight-grip American walnut stock; deluxe checkered American walnut stock (.22 Magnum); adjustable rear, hooded front sight; blued round barrel and lever
**Rifle, Youth, Carbine:** . . . $340–$355
**Magnum:** . . . . . . . . . . . . . . . . $475

## LEVER OCTAGON FRONTIER

**Action**: Lever
**Stock**: Walnut
**Barrel**: 20 in.

**Sights**: Open
**Weight**: 6 lb. 4 oz.
**Caliber**: .22LR, .22S, .17 HMR
**Magazine**: Under-barrel tube, 21 rounds (.22S), 16 rounds (.22LR); 12 rounds (.22 Mag.); 11 rounds (.17 HMR)
**Features**: American walnut; marble fully adjustable semi-buckhorn rear with reversible white diamond insert and brass beaded front sight; blued barrel and lever
**.22LR, .22S:** . . . . . . . . . . . . . . $430
**.22 Mag.:** . . . . . . . . . . . . . . . . $545
**.17 HMR:** . . . . . . . . . . . . . . . $540

## MARE'S LEG

**Action**: Lever
**Stock**: Walnut
**Barrel**: 12.9 in.
**Sights**: Open
**Weight**: 4 lb. 7 oz. (.22S/L/LR), 5 lb. 7 oz. (.45 Colt)
**Caliber**: .22S/L/LR, .45 Colt
**Magazine**: Under-barrel tube, 10 rounds (.22 S/L/LR); 5 rounds (.45 Colt)

**Features**: .45 Colt: American walnut; marble fully adjustable semi-buckhorn rear with reversible white diamond insert and brass beaded front sights; brasslite receiver, brass buttplate, and blued barrel. .22 S/L/LR: American walnut; fully adjustable rear, with hooded front sight; blued metal barrel and lever
**.22 S/L/LR:** . . . . . . . . . . . . . . $415
**.45 Colt, .44 Mag., .357 Mag.:** . . $975

## MINI BOLT YOUTH

**Action**: Bolt
**Stock**: Synthetic
**Barrel**: 16.25 in.
**Sights**: Open
**Weight**: 3 lb. 4 oz.
**Caliber**: .22LR, .22S
**Magazine**: None
**Features**: Single-shot; one-piece fiberglass synthetic stock in orange or black; Williams fire sights; stainless steel receiver and barrel
**MSRP** . . . . . . . . . . . . . . . . . . $260

## PUMP ACTION OCTAGON

**Action**: Pump
**Stock**: Walnut
**Barrel**: 19.75 in.
**Sights**: Open
**Weight**: 6 lb.
**Caliber**: .22LR, .22S, .22Mag

**Magazine**: Under-barrel tube, 15 rounds (.22LR, .22S), 12 rounds (.22 Mag.)
**Features**: American walnut stock; adjustable rear, beaded front sight; blued octagonal barrel
**MSRP** . . . . . . . . . . . . . . . . . . . . **$510**
**Magnum:** . . . . . . . . . . . . . . . . **$585**

HENRY PUMP ACTION OCTAGON

HENRY U.S. SURVIVAL AR-7

HENRY VARMINT EXPRESS

## U.S. SURVIVAL AR-7

**Action**: Semiautomatic
**Stock**: ABS Plastic
**Barrel**: 16 in.
**Sights**: Open
**Weight**: 2 lb. 4 oz.
**Caliber**: .22LR
**Magazine**: Detachable box, 8 rounds
**Features**: ABS plastic in black; adjustable rear sight, blade front sight; Teflon coated receiver and coated steel barrel
**Black:** . . . . . . . . . . . . . . . . . . . . **$280**
**Camo:** . . . . . . . . . . . . . . . . . . . **$345**

## VARMINT EXPRESS

**Action**: Lever
**Stock**: Walnut
**Barrel**: 20 in.
**Sights**: Open
**Weight**: 5 lb. 12 oz.
**Caliber**: .17 HMR
**Magazine**: Under-barrel tube, 11 rounds
**Features**: Checkered American walnut stock; Williams fire sights; blued round barrel and lever
**MSRP** . . . . . . . . . . . . . . . . . . . . **$540**

# High Standard

### AR-15 ENFORCER

*Action*: Semiautomatic
*Stock*: Synthetic
*Barrel*: 16 in.
*Sights*: Flip-up
*Weight*: 7 lb. 6 oz.
*Caliber*: 5.56mm NATO
*Magazine*: 20, 30 rounds
*Features*: SOCOM style six position synthetic stock; A2 flash hider; YHM quad rail with smooth side; YHM same plane flip-up sights; ergonomical grip; two-stage match trigger
**MSRP** . . . . . . . . . . . . . . . . . **$2275**

### AR-15 MIL-SPEC SERIES

*Action*: Gas-operated autoloader
*Stock*: 6-position
*Barrel*: 20 in. (16 in. carbine)
*Sights*: Adjustable
*Weight*: 8 lb. (7 lb. 5 oz. carbine)

HIGH STANDARD AR-15 MIL-SPEC SERIES

HIGH STANDARD AR-15 ENFORCER WITH EOTECH AND SIGHTS RS VIEW

*Caliber*: 5.56 NATO
*Magazine*: Detachable box, 30 rounds
*Features*: Matte black collapsible

stock, G.I. style; hard chrome bore; A2 flash holder
**MSRP** . . . . . . . . . . . . . . **$925–$1200**

# Hi-Point Firearms

HI-POINT FIREARMS MODEL 995TS

### MODEL 995TS

*Action*: Blow-back autoloader
*Stock*: Black, skeleton-style, all-weather molded polymer
*Barrel*: 16.5 in.
*Sights*: Adjustable
*Weight*: 7 lb.
*Caliber*: 9mm
*Magazine*: Detachable box, 10 rounds
*Features*: Sling, swivels, and base mount included; last round lock-open latch; multiple Picatinny rails; internal recoil buffer
**MSRP** . . . . . . . . . . . . . . . . . . . **$285**

# Howa by Legacy Sports

HOWA CLASSIC LAMINATE THUMBHOLE VARMINTER

### CLASSIC LAMINATE VARMINTER

*Action*: Bolt
*Stock*: Laminate
*Barrel*: 24 in.

*Sights*: None
*Weight*: 9 lb. 14 oz.
*Caliber*: .223, .204 Ruger, .22-250 Rem., .243 Win., .308 Win.
*Magazine*: Internal box, 5 rounds
*Features*: Nutmeg or Pepper stock color; optional thumbhole stock; heavy blued or stainless barrel; black recoil pad; sling swivel studs
**Blued barrel** . . . . . . . . . . . . . . **$813**
**Stainless barrel**. . . . . . . . . . . . **$918**

# Howa by Legacy Sports

**HOWA/HOGUE RANCHLAND COMPACT**

## HOWA/HOGUE RANCHLAND COMPACT

*Action*: Bolt
*Stock*: Synthetic
*Barrel*: 20 in.
*Sights*: None
*Weight*: 7 lb. 2 oz.–8 lb. 12 oz.
*Caliber*: .223, .204 Ruger, .22-250 Rem., .243 Win., .308 Win., 7mm-08
*Magazine*: Internal box
*Features*: Black, green, or sand overmolded stock; includes one-piece scope rail; color match combo option includes Nikko Stirling 3-10x42 Nighteater scope; rings and one-piece base; full camo packages include Desert Camo Stock
**MSRP . . . . . . . . . . . . . . . $585–$782**

## HOWA/HOGUE RIFLES

*Action*: Bolt
*Stock*: Synthetic
*Barrel*: 20 in., 22 in., 24 in.
*Sights*: None
*Weight*: 7 lb. 12 oz.
*Caliber*: Standard Blue, Stainless: .223, .204 Ruger, .22-250 Rem., .243 Win., .308 Win., 7mm-08, 6.5x 55SW, .25-06, .270 Win., .30-06; Magnum Blue, Stainless: .300 Win. Mag., .375 Ruger, .338 Win. Mag, 7mm Rem. Mag.
*Magazine*: Internal box
*Features*: Stainless or blued barrel; synthetic stock comes in black, sand, or green with matching Hogue Soft Grip; recoil pad; hinged floor plate; sling; swivel studs
**Standard: . . . . . . . . . . . . $570–$680**
**Magnum: . . . . . . . . . . . . $599–$704**
**Varmint: . . . . . . . . . . . . $631–$717**

## HOWA/HOGUE OR TALON SNOWKING

*Action*: Bolt
*Stock*: Synthetic
*Barrel*: 22 in.
*Sights*: Mounted 4-16x44 scope
*Weight*: 9 lb. 6 oz.
*Caliber*: .223, .243, .22-250, .308
*Magazine*: 4+1 rounds
*Features*: HACT 2-stage trigger system; 3 position safety; Blackhawk Talon or Hogue overmolded stock in Kings Snow Shadow Camo; Nikko Stirling Gameking 4-16x44 scope with LRK Range-finding Reticle; color matched scope, rings, and one-piece base; limited edition and limited availability only through Bill Hicks & Co.
**Hogue: . . . . . . . . . . . . . . $799**
**Talon: . . . . . . . . . . . . . . $1136**

**HOWA/HOGUE RIFLE**

**HOWA/TALON SNOWKING**

# Howa by Legacy Sports

## HOWA/HOGUE/ TARGETMASTER COMBO

**Action**: Bolt
**Stock**: Synthetic
**Barrel**: 20 in.
**Sights**: Mounted 4-16x44 scope
**Weight**: 9 lb. 6 oz.
**Caliber**: .223 Win., .22-250 Rem., .308 Win.
**Magazine**: 4+1 rounds
**Features**: Fluted barrels and heavy standard barrels available; black or OD green Hogue overmolded stocks; Nikko-Stirling Targetmaster 4-16x44 scopes; HACT two-stage trigger system; three-position safety; forged flat-bottomed receiver
**MSRP** . . . . . . . . . . . . . . . .$787–$837

HOWA/TARGETMASTER COMBO

HOWA HUNTER WITH SCOPE

## HOWA HUNTER

**Action**: Bolt
**Stock**: Walnut
**Barrel**: 20 in., 22 in., 24 in.
**Sights**: Optional mounted scope
**Weight**: 7 lb. 7 oz.
**Caliber**: .223 Rem., .204 Ruger, .22-250 Rem., .243 Win., 6.5x55SW, .25-06, .270 Win., .308 Win., .30-06, .300 Win. Mag., .338 Win. Mag., 7mm Rem. Mag., .375 Ruger
**Magazine**: 4+1 rounds

**Features**: Blued or stainless steel barrels; one-piece high grade walnut stock; checkering at forend and pistol grip; Monte Carlo cheekpiece; rubber recoil pad; sling swivel studs; scopes optional on blued models
**MSRP** . . . . . . . . . . . . . . .$709–$880

# H-S Precision

H-S PRECISION HTR

H-S PRECISION PHR

## HTR (HEAVY TACTICAL RIFLE)

**Action**: Bolt
**Stock**: Synthetic
**Barrel**: 20 in., 22 in., 24 in., 26 in., 28 in.
**Sights**: None
**Weight**: 10 lb. 12 oz.–11 lb. 4 oz.
**Caliber**: Any standard SAAMI, LR calibers
**Magazine**: Detachable box, 3, 10 rounds
**Features**: Pro-Series 2000; fully adjustable synthetic stock comes in a wide range of colors combinations including sand, black, olive, gray, and spruce green; heavy fluted barrel
**MSRP** . . . . . . . . . . . . . . . . . . $3600

## PHR (PROFESSIONAL HUNTER RIFLE)

**Action**: Bolt
**Stock**: Synthetic
**Barrel**: 20 in., 22 in., 24 in., 26 in., 28 in.
**Sights**: None
**Weight**: 7 lb. 12 oz.–8 lb. 4 oz.
**Caliber**: All popular magnum calibers up to .375 H&H and .338 Lapua
**Magazine**: Detachable box, 3, 4 rounds
**Features**: Pro-Series 2000; cheekpiece and built-in recoil reduction system; steel barrel; optional muzzlebrake; synthetic stock comes in a wide range of color combinations including sand, black, olive, gray, and spruce green; left-hand available for additional cost
**MSRP** . . . . . . . . . . . . . . . . . . $3555

RIFLES

# H-S Precision

**H-S PRECISION TTD**

### TTD (TACTICAL TAKE-DOWN RIFLE)
**Action**: Bolt
**Stock**: Composite
**Barrel**: 22 in., 24 in.
**Sights**: None
**Weight**: 11 lb. 4 oz.–11 lb. 12 oz.
**Caliber**: Available in all standard SA SAAMI and LR calibers

**Magazine**: Detachable box, 3, 4 rounds
**Features**: Stainless steel barrel and floor plate; synthetic stock with full length bedding block chassis system; metal parts are finished in matte black Teflon; wide variety of stock colors including sand, black, olive, gray, and spruce green
**MSRP** . . . . . . . . . . . . . . . . . . $5500

# Jarrett Rifles

**JARRETT BEANFIELD**

**JARRETT PROFESSIONAL HUNTER**

**JARRETT WIND WALKER**

**Sights**: None
**Weight**: Varies depending on options
**Caliber**: .375 H&H, .416 Rem., .416 Rigby, .450 Rigby
**Magazine**: Comes with 40 rounds
**Features**: Includes 40 rounds of soft pointed bullets and solids created custom for each gun; ballistics printout and last three targets the gun shot also provided; optional scopes; .416 Rem. comes with Jarrett Tri-Lock receiver
**MSRP** . . . . . . . . . . **starting at $10400**

### WIND WALKER
**Action**: Bolt
**Stock**: Synthetic
**Barrel**: Up to 24 in.
**Sights**: None
**Weight**: 7 lb. 8 oz.
**Caliber**: Any popular short-action
**Magazine**: Comes with 20 rounds
**Features**: Jarrett Tri-Lock action; muzzlebrake; Tally scope mounting system; phenolic resin metal finish with choice of stock colors; ballistic print out included
**MSRP** . . . . . . . . . . **starting at $7380**

### BEANFIELD
**Action**: Bolt
**Stock**: Synthetic
**Barrel**: Various lengths available
**Sights**: None
**Weight**: Varies depending on options
**Caliber**: Any popular standard or magnum chambering
**Magazine**: Comes with 20 rounds
**Features**: Can build rifle on any receiver provided; optional caliber, stock style, color, muzzlebrake, barrel size, and taper; includes load data and 20 rounds of custom ammo
**MSRP** . . . . . . . . . . **starting at $5380**

### PROFESSIONAL HUNTER
**Action**: Bolt
**Stock**: Synthetic or walnut
**Barrel**: Various lengths available

# J.P. Sauer & Sohn

J.P. SAUER S 303 CLASSIC XT

## S 202 CLASSIC BOLT ACTION RIFLE

*Action*: Bolt
*Stock*: Walnut
*Barrel*: 24 in.
*Sights*: None
*Weight*: 7 lb. 11 oz.
*Caliber*: .22, .22 Mag.
*Magazine*: Detachable box, 5 rounds
*Features*: Features stable, dark tan walnut heartwood; Monte Carlo stock with cheek-piece; luxury wood tip on the forend and pistol grip; polymer-coated steel surface; round bolt handle
*MSRP*. . . . . . . . . . . . . . . . . . . $3509
*Left-hand*: . . . . . . . . . . . . . . . $4192

## S 303 CLASSIC XT

*Action*: Semiautomatic
*Stock*: Synthetic with anti-slip elastomer inlays
*Barrel*: 20 in., 22 in.
*Sights*: Yellow triangle rear sight; red-dot front sight
*Weight*: 7 lb. 5 oz.
*Caliber*: .30-06, .300 Win. Mag.
*Magazine*: Detachable box, 2, 5 rounds

*Features*: Light-metal receiver; manual cocking safety; straight comb stock for either left- or right-handed shooters; rust protection with Nitrobond-X finish
*MSRP*. . . . . . . . . . . . . . . . . . . $3352

## S 303 ELEGANCE

*Action*: Semiautomatic
*Stock*: Walnut
*Barrel*: 20 in., 22 in.
*Sights*: High contrast
*Weight*: 7 lb. 3 oz.–7 lb. 6 oz.
*Caliber*: .30-06, .300 Win. Mag.
*Magazine*: Detachable box, 2, 5 rounds
*Features*: Manual cocking at the upper wrist; crisp single-stage trigger; four bolt lugs engage directly into the barrel; free-floating barrel
*MSRP*. . . . . . . . . . . . . . . . . . . $4752

# Kel-Tec

KEL-TEC SUB-2000

## SUB-2000

*Action*: Autoloader
*Stock*: Polymer
*Barrel*: 16.1 in.
*Sights*: Target
*Weight*: 4 lb.
*Caliber*: 9mm, .40 S&W
*Magazine*: 10+1 rounds
*Features*: Self-loading carbine for pistol cartridges; by rotating the barrel upwards and back, it can be reduced to a size of 16"x7" to facilitate secure storage
*MSRP*. . . . . . . . . . . . . . . . . . . $409

RIFLES

KIMBER CAPRIVI

KIMBER MODEL 84L CLASSIC SELECT GRADE

KIMBER MODEL 84M CLASSIC

KIMBER MODEL 84M LONGMASTER VT

## CAPRIVI

**Action**: Bolt
**Stock**: Walnut
**Barrel**: 24 in.
**Sights**: None
**Weight**: 8 lb. 8 oz.–8 lb. 10 oz.
**Caliber**: .375 H&H Mag., .416 Rem. Mag., .458 Lott
**Magazine**: Internal box, 4 rounds
**Features**: AA-grad walnut stock with wrap checkering; ebony forend tip; cheekpiece; double cross-bolts; sling swivel studs; front barrel band swivel stud; recoil pad; steel barrel with matte blued finish; front locking repeater; Mauser claw extractor; adjustable trigger
**MSRP** . . . . . . . . . . . . . . . . . . $3263

## MODEL 84L SERIES

**Action**: Bolt
**Stock**: Walnut, synthetic
**Barrel**: 24 in.
**Sights**: None
**Weight**: 5 lb. 5 oz.–6 lb. 3 oz.
**Caliber**: .270 Win., .30-06 Spfd.,
.25-06 Rem., .280 Ackley Improved
**Magazine**: Internal box, 5 rounds
**Features**: Full-length Mauser claw exactor; 1-in. Pachmayr recoil pad; full-length match-grade barrel with pillar and glass bedding; match-grade trigger and three-postion wing safety; Classic Select has French walnut stock with ebony forend tip; Montana has Kevlar/carbon fiber stocks
**Classic**: . . . . . . . . . . . . . . . . . $1223
**Classic Select Grade**: . . . . . . . $1427
**Classic SS Select Grade** . . . . . $1495
**Montana**: . . . . . . . . . . . . . . . . $1359

## MODEL 84M CLASSIC

**Action**: Bolt
**Stock**: Walnut
**Barrel**: 18 in., 22 in., 24 in.
**Sights**: None
**Weight**: 5 lb. 9 oz.–5 lb. 13 oz.
**Caliber**: .243 Win., .7mm-08 Rem., .308 Win.
**Magazine**: Internal box, 5, 6 rounds
**Features**: A-grade walnut stock with checkering panel, or AA walnut with ebony forend on Select Grade; recoil pad; sling swivel studs; steel matte blued or satin stainless steel finish; front locking repeater
**Classic**: . . . . . . . . . . . . . . . . . $1223
**Classic Select Grade**: . . . . . . . $1427
**Classic SS Select Grade**: . . . . $1495

## MODEL 84M LONGMASTER

**Action**: Bolt
**Stock**: Laminate
**Barrel**: 26 in.
**Sights**: None
**Weight**: 7 lb. 5 oz.–10 lb.
**Caliber**: Classic: .223 Rem., .308 Win.; VT: .22-250 Rem.
**Magazine**: Internal box, 5 rounds
**Features**: A-grade walnut with oil finish on Classic or gray laminated stock on VT model; sling swivel stud or front swivel stud for bipod; recoil pad; stainless steel barrel with satin finish; steel action with matte blued finish
**Classic**: . . . . . . . . . . . . . . . . . $1291
**VT**: . . . . . . . . . . . . . . . . . . . . $1427

RIFLES

# Kimber

## MODEL 84M SERIES

*Action*: Bolt
*Stock*: Walnut, laminate, Kevlar/carbon fiber
*Barrel*: 22 in.
*Sights*: None
*Weight*: 4 lb. 13 oz.–8 lb. 5 oz.
*Caliber*: 7mm-08 Rem., .308 Win., .204 Ruger, .22-250 Rem., .204 Ruger, .223 Rem., .243 Win., .257 Roberts, .338 Federal (among the various models)

*Magazine*: Internal box, 4, 5, 6 rounds
*Features*: A-grade walnut on Varmint; AAA-grade walnut stock with checkering panel on SuperAmerica; gray laminate on ProVarmint and SVT; Kevlar/carbon fiber on Montana; recoil pad; stainless steel barrel and action; front locking repeater; adjustable trigger

| | |
|---|---|
| **Montana:** | **$1359** |
| **ProVarmint:** | **$1427** |
| **SuperAmerica:** | **$2240** |
| **SVT:** | **$1427** |
| **Varmint:** | **$1291** |

**KIMBER MODEL 84M MONTANA**

**KIMBER MODEL 8400 POLICE TACTICAL**

**KIMBER MODEL 8400 WSM CLASSIC**

## MODEL 8400 POLICE TACTICAL

*Action*: Bolt
*Stock*: Laminate
*Barrel*: 24 in.
*Sights*: None
*Weight*: 8 lb. 12 oz.
*Caliber*: .308 Win., .300 Win. Mag.
*Magazine*: Internal box, 5 rounds
*Features*: Laminated wood stock with black epoxy finish; sling swivel studs; front swivel stud for bipod; recoil pad; steel barrel with matte blued finish;

fluted bolt front locking repeater; adjustable trigger
**MSRP** . . . . . . . . . . . . . . . . . . **$1495**

## MODEL 8400 WSM

*Action*: Bolt
*Stock*: Walnut, synthetic
*Barrel*: 24 in.
*Sights*: None
*Weight*: 6 lb. 3 oz.–6 lb. 10 oz.
*Caliber*: .270 WSM, .300 Swam, .325 Swam; SuperAmerica: .270 WSM, .300 WSM
*Magazine*: Internal box, 3 rounds

*Features*: Stock options: A-grade walnut with checkered panels, A-grade French walnut with checkered panels, gray synthetic Kevlar/carbon fiber stock; sling swivel studs; recoil pad; steel barrel with matte blued finish or stainless steel satin finish; front locking repeater; Mauser claw extractor

| | |
|---|---|
| **Classic:** | **$1223** |
| **Classic Select Grade:** | **$1427** |
| **Classic SS Select Grade:** | **$1495** |
| **SuperAmerica:** | **$2240** |
| **Montana:** | **$1359** |

RIFLES

KRIEGHOFF CLASSIC BIG FIVE

KRIEGHOFF CLASSIC STANDARD

KRIEGHOFF SEMPRIO

KRIEGHOFF SEMPRIO
THUMBHOLE

## CLASSIC BIG FIVE

**Action**: Hinged breech
**Stock**: Walnut
**Barrel**: 23.5 in.
**Sights**: Open
**Weight**: 9 lb. 8 oz.–10 lb. 8 oz.
**Caliber**: .375 H&H Mag., .375 Flanged Magnum N.E., .450/.400 NE, .500/.416 N.E., .470 N.E., .500 N.E.
**Magazine**: None
**Features**: Double triggers; V-shaped rear sight with a white, vertical middle line and a pearl front sight; optional Super-Express sight; Monte Carlo style cheekpiece; European walnut stock with small game scene engraving; steel trigger and floor plate; straight comb and large recoil pad
**MSRP** . . . . . . . . . . . . . . . . . **$13995**

## CLASSIC STANDARD

**Action**: Hinged breech
**Stock**: Walnut
**Barrel**: 23.5 in.
**Sights**: Open
**Weight**: 7 lb. 4 oz.–8 lb. 4 oz.
**Caliber**: 7x57R, 7x65R, .308 Win., .30-06, 8X57JRS, 8x75RS, 8.5x75RS, 9.3x74R
**Magazine**: None
**Features**: European walnut stock with conventional rounded cheekpiece and Kaiser Grip; adjustable, removable muzzle wedge integrated in the front sight ramp; Universal-Trigger-System; Combi-cocking device; ergonomically shaped "Kickspanner" manual cocking device
**MSRP** . . . . . . . . . . . . . . . . . **$10995**

## SEMPRIO

**Action**: Hinged breech
**Stock**: Walnut
**Barrel**: 21.5 in., 25 in.
**Sights**: Open
**Weight**: 7 lb. 8 oz.
**Caliber**: .223 Rem., .243 Win., 6.5x55SE, 6.5x57, .270 Win., 7x64, .308 Win., .30-06 Spfd., .338 Win. Mag., 8x57JS, 9.3x62; Magnum calibers: 7mm Rem. Mag., .300 Win. Mag., .375 Ruger
**Magazine**: Detachable box
**Features**: Barrels are plasma nitrated and blued to resist corrosion; open sights feature fluorescent front bead and rear sight, designed for target acquisition in low light conditions; accepts various types of scope-mounts; Turkish walnut stock available with or without the Semprio cheekpiece; rubber recoil pad; sling swivels; optional BreaKO recoil reducer; includes fitted case. New stock options include thumbhole stock and Next G-1 Vista Forest Green or Blaze Orange camouflage finishes
**Standard Caliber:** . . . . . . . . . **$4690**
**Magnum Caliber:** . . . . . . . . . **$4990**

# L.A.R. Grizzly Firearms

### GRIZZLY BIG BOAR
**Action**: Bolt
**Stock**: Steel
**Barrel**: 36 in.
**Sights**: None
**Weight**: 30 lb. 6 oz.
**Caliber**: .50 BMG
**Magazine**: None
**Features**: Bullpup single-shot; match grade steel barrel; steel receiver; very low recoil; thumb safety and bolt top safety; Harris bipod; Weaver scope mount; leather cheekpad; hard carry case
**Standard Blued:** . . . . . . . . . . $2350
**Parkerized:** . . . . . . . . . . . . . $2450
**Blued with Nickel Trigger**
**Housing Finish:** . . . . . . . . . . $2600
**Full Nickel Finish:** . . . . . . . . $2700
**Stainless Steel Barrel:** . . . . . . $2600

### GRIZZLY T-50
**Action**: Bolt
**Stock**: Steel
**Barrel**: 32 in.–36 in.
**Sights**: None
**Weight**: 30 lb. 6 oz.
**Caliber**: .50 BMG
**Magazine**: None

**Features**: Bullpup single-shot; steel stock; aircraft grade aluminum scope mount, bipod and monopod rails; steel receiver; very low recoil; thumb safety and bolt stop safety; 20 MOA scope mount Picatinny rail; integrated cheekpad; hard carry case
**MSRP** . . . . . . . . . . . . . . . . . . $3200

**L.A.R. GRIZZLY T-50**

# Lazzeroni Rifles

### L2012LLT LONG MAGNUM LITE
**Action**: Bolt
**Stock**: Graphite/composite
**Barrel**: 26 in.
**Sights**: None
**Weight**: 7 lb. 5 oz.
**Caliber**: 6.53 (.257) Scramjet, 7.82 (.308) Warbird, 7.21 (.284) Firebird, 8.59 (.338) Titan
**Magazine**: 4 rounds
**Features**: All new precision CNC-machined chromoly receiver; one-piece diamond-fluted bolt shaft; stainless steel match-grade button-barrel; custom molded hand-bedded graphite/composite stock designs; precision-machined aluminum alloy floor plate/trigger guard assembly; jewel competition trigger; Vais muzzlebrake; Limbsaver recoil pad
**MSRP** . . . . . . . . . . . . . . . . $5999.99

**LAZZERONI L2012LLT LONG MAGNUM LITE**

RIFLES

LAZZERONI
L2012LTH-XTLR
LONG MAGNUM
THUMBHOLE

LAZZERONI
L2012LSP-XTLR LONG
MAGNUM SPORTER

LAZZERONI
L2012TCT LONG
MAGNUM TACTICAL

### L2012LSP-XTLR LONG MAGNUM SPORTER

*Action*: Bolt
*Stock*: Graphite/composite
*Barrel*: 28 in.
*Sights*: None
*Weight*: 8 lb. 13 oz.
*Caliber*: 6.53 (.257) Scramjet, 7.82 (.308) Warbird, 7.21 (.284) Firebird, 8.59 (.338) Titan
*Magazine*: 6 rounds
*Features*: Heavy barrel contour; recoil reducing roll-over cheekpiece incorporated into stock design; 20 MOA Picatinny rail; 34mm or 30mm rings
**MSRP** . . . . . . . . . . . . . . . . $6999.99

### L2012LTH LONG MAGNUM THUMBHOLE

*Action*: Bolt
*Stock*: Graphite/composite
*Barrel*: 25 in.
*Sights*: None
*Weight*: 7 lb. 11 oz.
*Caliber*: 6.53 (.257) Scramjet, 7.82 (.284) Warbird, 7.21 (.284) Firebird, 8.59 (.338) Titan
*Magazine*: 4 rounds
*Features*: 20 MOA Picatinny style rail; 34mm or 30mm ring sets; right hand only
**MSRP** . . . . . . . . . . . . . . . . $6699.99

### L2012TCT LONG MAGNUM TACTICAL

*Action*: Bolt
*Stock*: Graphite/composite
*Barrel*: 26 in.
*Sights*: None
*Weight*: 10 lb. 14 oz.
*Caliber*: 7.82 (.308) Warbird, 8.59 (.338) Titan
*Magazine*: 6 rounds
*Features*: Tactical black rifle; right hand only
**MSRP** . . . . . . . . . . . . . . . . $7999.99

# Les Baer Custom

### .308 SEMI-AUTO MATCH RIFLE
**Action**: Bolt
**Stock**: Synthetic
**Barrel**: 18 in. or 20 in.
**Sights**: None
**Weight**: 11 lb. 3 oz.
**Caliber**: .308
**Magazine**: 20-round Magpul

**Features**: No forward assist; Picatinny style flat top rail; LBC carrier, chromed; chromed precision bolt; Geissele two-stage trigger group; steel gas block; LBC Custom grip; Harris bipod; DuPont S coating on barrel; enforcer muzzlebrake; Magpul stock
**MSRP** . . . . . . . . . . . . . . . . . . . **$3190**

LES BAER .308 SEMI-AUTO MATCH RIFLE

LES BAER AR .223 SUPER VARMINT

LES BAER MID-LENGTH MONOLITH .308 SEMI-AUTO SWAT MODEL

LES BAER MONOLITH .308 SEMI-AUTO SWAT

### AR .223 SUPER VARMINT
**Action**: Bolt
**Stock**: Synthetic
**Barrel**: 20 in. (optional 18 in., 22 in., 24 in.)
**Sights**: None
**Weight**: 9 lb.
**Caliber**: .223
**Magazine**: 20 rounds
**Features**: Includes targets; LBC forged and precision machined upper and lower receivers; Picatinny style flat top rail; LBC National Match chromed carrier; LBC chromed bolt; LBC extractor; Geissele two-stage trigger group; adjustable free-float handguard with locking ring; aluminum gas block; stainless steel barrel; Versa Pod installed
**MSRP** . . . . . . . . . . . . . . . . . . . **$2290**

### MID-LENGTH MONOLITH .308 SEMI-AUTO SWAT MODEL
**Action**: Semiautomatic
**Stock**: Synthetic
**Barrel**: 16 in.
**Sights**: Optional scope and rings
**Weight**: 11 lb. 5 oz.
**Caliber**: .308
**Magazine**: 20 rounds
**Features**: LBC carrier, chromed; LBC precision chromed bolt; Geissele two-stage trigger group; LBC steel gas block with Picatinny rail; LBC bench rest 416R stainless steel barrel with rifling; Magpul PRS stock; two twenty-round Magpul magazines
**MSRP** . . . . . . . . . . . . . . . . . . . **$3940**

### MONOLITH .308 SEMI-AUTO SWAT
**Action**: Bolt
**Stock**: Synthetic
**Barrel**: 20 in. (optional 18 in., 24 in.)
**Sights**: None
**Weight**: 9.04 lb.
**Caliber**: .308
**Magazine**: 20-round Magpul
**Features**: Geissele two-stage trigger group; LBC Steel gas block with Picatinny rail on top; LBC bench rest, stainless steel barrel; Magpul PRS stock in black; special Versa Pod and adapter; DuPont S coating in barrel
**MSRP** . . . . . . . . . . . . . . . . . . . **$3940**

RIFLES

# LWRC International

## M6A2

**Action**: Short-stroke gas piston
**Stock**: Vltor Emod
**Barrel**: 10.5 in., 12.7 in., 14.7 in.,
16.1 in.
**Sights**: LWRC Skirmish BUIS
**Weight**: 7 lb. 6 oz. (16.1 in. barrel)
**Caliber**: 5.56mm, 6.8mm
**Magazine**: 30 rounds
**Features**: Ideal for optical sights with
low-profile gas block and no A-frame
front sight to obscure field of view;
longer mid-length free-float rail system
with a removable return-to-zero top;
lightweight, self-regulating, self-scrap-
ing operating system; match grade
cold rotary hammer-forged barrel with
target crown; barrel treated with
NiCorr surface conversion technology;
available in black, OD green, patriot
brown, and Flat Dark Earth Cerakote
**5.56mm:** ................ $2216
**6.8mm:** ................ $2327

LWRCI M6A2

## M6A2 SPR

**Action**: Short-stroke gas piston
**Stock**: Magpul ACS
**Barrel**: 16.1 in.
**Sights**: LWRC Skirmish BUIS
**Weight**: 7 lb. 6 oz.
**Caliber**: 5.56mm
**Magazine**: 30 rounds
**Features**: Rifles uses a lightweight
sculpted rail derived from the LWRC
REPR platform; SPR-MOD rail is light-
er and longer than Mark-II-B rail; cold-
hammer-forged barrel; spiral fluting;
enhanced fire control group; Magpul
MIAD pistol grip; Magpul ACS stock;
available in black, Flat Dark Earth, OD
green, and patriot brown
**MSRP** ................. $2425

LWRCI M6A2 SPR

RIFLES

## M6 IC (INDIVIDUAL CARBINE)

**Action**: Short-stroke gas piston opera-
tion
**Stock**: Magpul MOE
**Barrel**: 14.7 in.
**Sights**: LWRCI folding BUIS
**Weight**: 6 lb. 14 oz.
**Caliber**: 5.56mm NATO, 6.8mm SPC
**Magazine**: 30 rounds
**Features**: New fully ambidextrous
lower receiver with dual controls for
bolt catch/release, magazine release,
and fire control; 2-position gas block;
user configurable rail system; features

LWRCI M6 IC

non-IR reflective Cerakote Stealth that
makes the rifle "disappear" to image
intensifying night vision (U.S. Military
applications only); initial production
run will be flat dark earth only
**MSRP** ................. N/A

## M6-SL (STRETCH LIGHTWEIGHT)

**Action**: Short-stroke gas piston opera-
tion
**Stock**: Magpul MOE
**Barrel**: 16.1 in.

LWRCI M6-SL

**Sights**: Fixed front, Daniel Defense
rear
**Weight**: 6 lb. 7 oz.
**Caliber**: 5.56mm
**Magazine**: 30 rounds
**Features**: Magpul MOE furniture; MOE
mid-length handguard; MOE stock;
MOE pistol grip; light contour barrel;
EXO (nickel-boron) plated advanced
combat bolt; one-piece EXO coated
carrier; EXO-coated enhanced fire
control group
**MSRP** ................. $1675

# LWRC International

## PSD (PERSONAL SECURITY DETAIL)

**Action**: Short-stroke gas piston operation

**Stock**: Magpul CTR

**Barrel**: 8 in.

**Sights**: LWRC Skirmish BUIS

**Weight**: 6 lb. 2 oz.

**Caliber**: 5.56mm, 6.8mm

**Magazine**: 30 rounds

**Features**: Patent-pending ARM-R rail system; removable top platform; return-to-zero reinstallation with no tools required; carbine-length rail over low profile gas block; available in black, OD green, patriot brown, and Flat Dark Earth Cerakote

**5.56mm**:. . . . . . . . . . . . . . . . . **$2216**
**6.8mm**: . . . . . . . . . . . . . . . . . **$2327**

LWRCI PSD

LWRCI R.E.P.R., 20 INCH

## R.E.P.R. (RAPID ENGAGEMENT PRECISION RIFLE)

**Action**: Short-stroke gas piston operation

**Stock**: Vltor Emod, Magpul UBR, Magpul PRS

**Barrel**: 12.7 in., 16 in., 18 in., 20 in.

**Sights**: LWRC Skirmish BUIS

**Weight**: 9 lb. 8 oz. (16 in. barrel)

**Caliber**: 7.62mm

**Magazine**: 20 rounds

**Features**: Patented self-regulating, short-stroke, gas-piston operating system; side-mounted charging handle, ARM-R top rail available in three models: Standard, Designated Marksman, Sniper; available in black, OD green, Flat Dark Earth, and patriot brown

**MSRP**. . . . . . . . . . . . . . **$3600–$3800**

## UCIW (ULTRA COMPACT INDIVIDUAL WEAPON)

**Action**: Short-stroke gas piston operation

**Stock**: 4-position collapsible stock

**Barrel**: 7 in.

**Sights**: LWRC Skirmish BUIS

**Weight**: 6 lb. 4 oz.

**Caliber**: 5.56mm

**Magazine**: 30 rounds

**Features**: Custom-made buffer tube; overall length of only 22 inches with stock collapsed; available in black, FDE, and OD green

**MSRP** . . . . . . . . . . . . . . . . . . **$2216**

LWRCI UCIW

# Magnum Research

MAGNUM RESEARCH
MAGNUMLITE BARRACUDA

MAGNUM RESEARCH MLR-22AT

## MAGNUMLITE BARRACUDA

**Action**: Semiautomatic
**Stock**: Composite or laminate
**Barrel**: 17 in.
**Sights**: None
**Weight**: 4 lb. 7 oz.–7 lb. 5 oz.
**Caliber**: .22LR, .22 Win. Mag.
**Magazine**: Box, 9, 10 rounds
**Features**: 17 in., 19 in. models have graphite barrels; 18 in. barrels come in stainless steel; .22 Win. Mag. version has patented gas-assisted blowback operation; CNC receivers machined from aircraft aluminum; include integral Weaver type rail for optics; heat treated steel with tight bolt face depth tolerances
**MSRP** . . . . . . . . . . . . . . . . . . . . . $819

## MLR-22AT

**Action**: Semiatuomatic rimfire
**Stock**: Synthetic
**Barrel**: 17 in.
**Sights**: None
**Weight**: 4 lb. 4 oz.
**Caliber**: .22LR
**Magazine**: 10+1
**Features**: Ambidextrous lightweight thumbhole stock made of polypropylene with fiber additives; semi palm swell on both sides of the pistol grip; molded-to-fit hard rubber buttplate attached with screws; graphite bull barrel with uni-directional graphite fibers parallel to the bore axis; full floating barrel; French gray anodized finish
**MSRP** . . . . . . . . . . . . . . . . . . . . . $599

## MOUNTAIN EAGLE MAGNUM LITE GRAPHITE

**Action**: Bolt
**Stock**: Composite
**Barrel**: 24 in., 26 in.
**Sights**: None
**Weight**: 7 lb. 4 oz.–9 lb. 2 oz.
**Caliber**: .30-06, .223, .308, .280, 7mm Rem. Mag., .300 Win. Mag., .22/250, .300 WSM, 7mm WSM
**Magazine**: Box, 4, 5 rounds
**Features**: Adjustable trigger; Kevlar-graphite stock in H-S Precision or Hogue Overmolded; open grip; free-floating match-grade barrel; hinged floor plate of solid steel; recoil pad; sling swivel studs; left-hand available for most calibers; action has been drilled and tapped for scope
**MSRP** . . . . . . . . . . . . . . $2173–$2475

MAGNUM RESEARCH MOUNTAIN
EAGLE MAGNUM LITE GRAPHITE

# Marlin

## 60

**Action**: Autoloading
**Stock**: Laminated hardwood
**Barrel**: 19 in.
**Sights**: Open
**Weight**: 5 lb. 8 oz.
**Caliber**: .22LR
**Magazine**: Tubular mag, 14 rounds with patented closure system
**Features**: Manual and automatic "last-shot" bolt hold-opens; receiver top has serrated, non-glare finish; cross-bolt safety; steel charging handle; Monte Carlo walnut-finished laminated hardwood; M60C comes with camouflage patterned Monte Carlo hardwood stock; full pistol grip; tough Mar-Shield finish; adjustable open rear sight, front ramp sight

**60**: . . . . . . . . . . . . . . . . . . . . .$196.83
**60C**: . . . . . . . . . . . . . . . . . .$232.06
**60SB**: . . . . . . . . . . . . . . . . . .$249.60

## 70PSS

**Action**: Autoloading
**Stock**: Synthetic
**Barrel**: 16.25 in.
**Sights**: Open
**Weight**: 3 lb. 4 oz.
**Caliber**: .22LR
**Magazine**: Clip, 7 rounds
**Features**: Automatic "last-shot" bolt hold-open; manual bolt hold-open; Monte Carlo black fiberglass-filled synthetic stock with abbreviated forend; nickel plated swivel studs; molded-in checkering; adjustable open rear sight; front ramp sight with high visibility orange post and cutaway wide-scan hood

**MSRP** . . . . . . . . . . . . . . . . . .$328.82

## 308 MARLIN EXPRESS

**Action**: Lever
**Stock**: Walnut or wood laminate with pistol grip
**Barrel**: 22 in., 24 in.
**Sights**: None
**Weight**: 7 lb.
**Caliber**: .308 Marlin Express, .338 Marlin Express
**Magazine**: Tubular mag, 5 rounds
**Features**: Hammer block safety; American black walnut stock or black/gray laminate with cut checkering; stainless steel receiver; rubber rifle buttpad; Mar-Shield finish; adjustable semi-buckhorn folding rear and ramp front sight with brass bead and wide-scan hood; solid top receiver tapped for scope mount; offset hammer spur for scope use

**Laminate**: . . . . . . . . . . . . . . .$904.57
**Walnut**: . . . . . . . . . . . . . . . .$685.52

MARLIN 60

MARLIN 70PSS

MARLIN 308 MARLIN EXPRESS

# Marlin

## 336C
**Action**: Lever
**Stock**: Walnut
**Barrel**: 20 in.
**Sights**: Open
**Weight**: 7 lb.
**Caliber**: .30-30 Win., .35 Rem.
**Magazine**: Tubular mag, 6 rounds
**Features**: Deeply blued surfaces; hammer block safety; American black walnut stock with pistol grip and checkering
**MSRP**..................$592.42

## 336SS
**Action**: Lever
**Stock**: Walnut
**Barrel**: 20 in.
**Sights**: Open
**Weight**: 7 lb.
**Caliber**: .30-30 Win., .35 Rem.
**Magazine**: Tubular mag, 6 rounds
**Features**: Stainless steel receiver, barrel, lever, and trigger guard; hammer block safety; American black walnut pistol grip stock with fluted comb and cut checkering; rubber rifle buttpad; adjustable semi-buckhorn folding rear, ramp front sight with brass bead and wide-scan hood; solid top receiver tapped for scope mount; offset hammer spur for scope use
**MSRP**..................$727.03

## 336XLR
**Action**: Lever
**Stock**: Laminated hardwood
**Barrel**: 24 in.
**Sights**: Open
**Weight**: 7 lb.
**Caliber**: .30-30
**Magazine**: Tubular mag, 5 rounds
**Features**: Stainless steel receiver, barrel, lever, and trigger guard plate; black/gray laminated hardwood stock with pistol grip and checkering; deluxe recoil pad; nickel plates swivel studs; adjustable semi-buckhorn folding rear sight and brass bead front sight with wide-scan hood; receiver tapped for scope mount
**MSRP**..................$904.57

MARLIN 336C

MARLIN 336SS

MARLIN 336XLR

# Marlin

**MARLIN 795SS**

**MARLIN 1894 COWBOY**

**MARLIN 795 SCOPED
AND SIGHTED COMBO**

## 795

*Action*: Autoloading
*Stock*: Synthetic
*Barrel*: 18 in.
*Sights*: Open
*Weight*: 4 lb. 8 oz.
*Caliber*: .22LR
*Magazine*: Clip, 10 rounds
*Features*: Automatic "last-shot" bolt
hold-open, manual bolt hold-open;
cross-bolt safety; Monte Carlo black
fiberglass-filled synthetic stock with
swivel studs and molded in checkering; adjustable open rear sight and
front ramp sight; receiver grooved for
scope mount
795: . . . . . . . . . . . . . . . . . . . $181.21
795SS: . . . . . . . . . . . . . . . . $259.13

## 795 SCOPED AND SIGHTED COMBO

*Action*: Autoloading
*Stock*: Synthetic
*Barrel*: 18 in.
*Sights*: Mounted 4x20 scope
*Weight*: 4 lb. 8 oz.
*Caliber*: .22LR
*Magazine*: 10 rounds
*Features*: Autoloading rimfire rifle; fac-
tory-mounted and bore-sighted 4x20
scope; side ejection; automatic "last-
shot" bolt hold-open; nickel-plated
clip magazine; Monte Carlo black
fiberglass-reinforced synthetic stock
with molded-in checkering; swivel
studs
MSRP . . . . . . . . . . . . . . . . $219.25

## 1894 COWBOY

*Action*: Lever
*Stock*: Walnut
*Barrel*: 20 in.
*Sights*: Open
*Weight*: 6 lb. 8 oz.
*Caliber*: .45 Colt, .357 Mag./.38 Spl.,
.44 Mag./.44 Spl.
*Magazine*: Tubular mag, 10 rounds
*Features*: Lever action with squared
finger lever; deeply blued metal surfaces; straight-grip American black
walnut stock; hard rubber buttplate;
tough Mar-Shield finish; blued steel
forend cap; tapered octagon barrel;
adjustable marble semi-buckhorn rear
sight and marble carbine front sight;
solid top receiver tapped for scope
mount
MSRP . . . . . . . . . . . . . . . . $1010.19

# Marlin

## 1895GBL

*Action*: Lever
*Stock*: Laminate
*Barrel*: 18.5 in.
*Sights*: Open
*Weight*: 7 lb.
*Caliber*: .45-70 Govt.
*Magazine*: Full length tubular magazine, 6 rounds
*Features*: Lever action with big loop finger lever; deeply blued metal surfaces; hammer block safety; American pistol grip two-tone brown laminate stock with cut checkering; ventilated recoil pad; tough Mar-Shield finish; swivel studs; adjustable semi-buckhorn folding rear sight and ramp front sight with brass bead; receiver tapped for scope mount; offset hammer spur for scope use
**MSRP . . . . . . . . . . . . . . . . . .$712.62**

## 1895SBL

*Action*: Lever
*Stock*: Laminated hardwood
*Barrel*: 18.5 in.
*Sights*: Open
*Weight*: 8 lb.
*Caliber*: .45-70 Govt.
*Magazine*: Full length tubular magazine, 6 rounds
*Features*: Lever action with big loop finger lever; deeply blued metal surfaces; stainless steel barrel and receiver; black/gray laminated hardwood with pistol-grip stock and cut checkering; fluted comb; deluxe recoil pad; compact version available
**MSRP . . . . . . . . . . . . . . . . .$1038.76**

## CLASSIC 1895

*Action*: Lever
*Stock*: Walnut
*Barrel*: 22 in.
*Sights*: Open
*Weight*: 7 lb. 8 oz.
*Caliber*: .45-70 Govt.
*Magazine*: Tubular mag, 4 rounds
*Features*: Deeply blued metal surfaces; hammer block safety; American black walnut pistol grip with fluted comb and cut checkering; rubber rifle buttpad; tough Mar-Shield finish; swivel studs; adjustable semi-buckhorn folding rear sight and front ramp sight with brass bead and wide-scan hood; model 1985 G has 18.5-in. barrel and straight grip; model 1985 Cowboy has a 26-in. octagonal barrel and straight grip
**Classic 1895: . . . . . . . . . . . . .$675.41**
**1895G: . . . . . . . . . . . . . . . .$680.17**
**1895GS: . . . . . . . . . . . . . . . .$812.59**

**MARLIN 1895GBL**

**MARLIN 1895SBL.**

**MARLIN CLASSIC 1895**

# Marlin

MARLIN GOLDEN 39A

MARLIN X7

MARLIN X7 SCOPED AND
SIGHTED COMBO

## GOLDEN 39A

**Action**: Lever
**Stock**: Walnut
**Barrel**: 24 in.
**Sights**: Open
**Weight**: 6 lb. 8 oz.
**Caliber**: .22S, L, LR
**Magazine**: Tubular mag, holds 26S, 21 LR or 19 LR rounds
**Features**: Rebounding hammer; hammer safety block; one-step takedown; deeply blued metal surfaces; gold plated steel trigger; genuine American black walnut with full pistol grip and forend; blued steel forend cap; swivel studs; rubber rifle buttpad; tough Mar-Shield finish; adjustable semi-buck-horn folding rear sight and front ramp sight with brass bead and wide-scan hood
**MSRP** . . . . . . . . . . . . . . . . . . **$702.22**

## X7

**Action**: Centerfire Bolt
**Stock**: Synthetic
**Barrel**: 22 in.
**Sights**: None
**Weight**: 6 lb. 8 oz.
**Caliber**: Long action: .25-06 Rem., .270 Win., .30-06 Spfd.; Short-action: .243 Win., 7mm-08 Rem., .308 Win.; Compact: .243 Win., 7mm-08 Rem., .308 Win., .223 Rem.
**Magazine**: 4+1 rounds
**Features**: Pro-Fire adjustable trigger; button-fired barrel with a target-style muzzle crown; soft-tech recoil pad; stainless steel barrel and receiver; pillar-bedded black synthetic stock with raised cheekpiece; Realtree APG HD stock for X7C long action version; two-position safety; red cocking indicator; fluted bolt design
**MSRP** . . . . . . . . . . . . . . . . . . **$391.03**

## X7 SCOPED AND SIGHTED COMBO

**Action**: Bolt
**Stock**: Synthetic
**Barrel**: 22 in.
**Sights**: Mounted 3-9x40mm riflescope
**Weight**: 7 lb. 4 oz.
**Caliber**: .243 Win., 7mm-08 Rem., .308 Win.
**Magazine**: 4+1 rounds
**Features**: Comes with pre-mounted and bore-sighted 3-9x40 riflescope; Pro-Fire adjustable trigger; Soft-Tech recoil pad; black synthetic stock; precision button rifled barrel; fluted bolt; compact version available in .243 Win., .270 Win., 30-06 Spfd.
**MSRP** . . . . . . . . . . . . . . . . . . **$443.27**

## X7 VARMINT HEAVY BARREL

**Action**: Bolt
**Stock**: Walnut
**Barrel**: 26 in.
**Sights**: None
**Weight**: 7 lb. 12 oz.
**Caliber**: .22-250 Rem., .308 Win.
**Magazine**: 4+1 rounds
**Features**: Pro-Fire adjustable trigger; fluted bolt; two-position safety; red cocking indicator; pillar-bedded satin-finished walnut with raised cheek piece; soft-tech recoil pad
**MSRP**. . . . . . . . . . . . . . . . . **$396.95**

## XT-22

**Action**: Bolt
**Stock**: Hardwood
**Barrel**: 22 in.
**Sights**: Open
**Weight**: 6 lb.
**Caliber**: .22LR
**Magazine**: Clip, 7 rounds
**Features**: Pro-Fire adjustable trigger; Micro-Groove rifling; blued bolt action; thumb safety; red cocking indicator; Monte Carlo walnut-finished hardwood with swivel studs; full pistol grip; tough Mar-Shield finish; adjustable rear sight and front ramp sights; receiver grooved for scope mount, drilled and tapped for scope bases
**MSRP**. . . . . . . . . . **$219.89–$265.31**

**MARLIN X7 VARMINT HEAVY BARREL**

**MARLIN XT-22**

# McMillan

## 50 LBR

**Action**: Bolt
**Stock**: Synthetic
**Barrel**: 32 in.
**Sights**: None
**Weight**: 28 lb.
**Caliber**: .50
**Magazine**: Internal box
**Features**: McMillan 50 light benchrest stock in orange and gray marbling; fluted match barrel with McMillan BR muzzlebrake and precision target crown; pillar-bedded action; adjustable Jewell trigger
**MSRP**. . . . . . . . . . . . . . . . . **$9450**

**MCMILLAN 50 LBR**

# McMillan

**MCMILLAN CS5**

## CS5

*Action*: Semiautomatic
*Stock*: Synthetic
*Barrel*: 12.5 in., 18.5 in.
*Sights*: None
*Weight*: 10 lb. 10 oz., 11 lb. 10 oz.
*Caliber*: .308 Win.
*Magazine*: 10/20 rounds
*Features*: Concealable Subsonic/
Supersonic Suppressed Sniper System;
available in "Stubby" suppressed con-
figuration for military and law enforce-
ment use; with buttstock and suppres-
sor detached, will fit in backpack;
adjustable buttstock; tactile safety but-
ton can be operated without moving
your trigger finger
MSRP. . . . . . . . . . . . . . . . . . . $6500
Standard:. . . . . . . . . . . . . . . $5500

## CUSTOM HUNTING RIFLES - LEGACY

*Action*: Bolt
*Stock*: Synthetic
*Barrel*: 22 in., 24 in.
*Sights*: None
*Weight*: 6 lb. 10 oz.–7 lb.
*Caliber*: .270 Win., .308 Win., .30-06,
.300 Win. Mag.
*Magazine*: Internal box
*Features*: McMillan classic sporter
fiberglass stock with shadow line
cheekpiece; McMillan G30 custom
action in long or short; match-grade
stainless steel barrel, with a matte finish and target crown; custom
machined one-piece aluminum hinged
floor plate; custom Jewell trigger;
includes scope base and travel case
with rollers
MSRP. . . . . . . . . . . . . . . . . . . $6235

## LONG RANGE HUNTING RIFLE

*Action*: Bolt
*Stock*: Synthetic
*Barrel*: 24 in., 26 in., 27 in.
*Sights*: None
*Weight*: 9 lb. 8 oz.–10 lb.
*Caliber*: .243 Win., 7mm Rem. Mag.,
7mm Rem. Ultra Mag., .308 Win.,
.300 Win. Mag., .338 Lapua Mag.
*Magazine*: Internal box
*Features*: McMillan A-3 Fiberglass
stock with fixed cheekpiece and recoil
pad; McMillan G30 Custom long or
short action; match grade, stainless
steel barrels with matte finish and tar-
get crown; hinged steel floor plate;
Remington-style trigger; optional box
magazine; comes with travel case with
rollers
LRH .243, .308:. . . . . . . . . . . $6575
LRH 7mm, .300:. . . . . . . . . . . $6575
LRH .338:. . . . . . . . . . . . . . . . $6575

**MCMILLAN CUSTOM HUNTING RIFLE - LEGACY**

**MCMILLAN LONG RANGE HUNTING RIFLE**

RIFLES

MCMILLAN TAC-50

MCMILLAN TAC-50 A1-R2

MCMILLAN TAC-338

## TAC-50

**Action**: Bolt
**Stock**: Composite
**Barrel**: 29 in.
**Sights**: None
**Weight**: 26 lb.
**Caliber**: .50 BMG
**Magazine**: Detachable box
**Features**: Bipod; match grade, stainless steel barrel; muzzlebrake; anti-glare Dura Coating; square-surfaced recoil lug; extra long bolt handle; tight benchrest tolerances; saddle cheekpiece; metal finish comes in black, olive, gray, tan, or dark earth to match composite stock
**MSRP**.................. $9990

## TAC-50 A1

**Action**: Semiautomatic
**Stock**: Synthetic
**Barrel**: 29 in.
**Sights**: Drilled and tapped for scopes
**Weight**: 26 lb.
**Caliber**: .50
**Magazine**: Detachable box, 5 rounds
**Features**: Take-down fiberglass stock with a longer forend that moves the balance point for the bipod forward; integral cheekpiece; monopod on the buttstock; smaller pistol grip; lighter, sturdier bipod; positive, self-locking magazine latch; magazine release lever repositioned ahead of trigger bow; match grade free floating barrel
**MSRP**.................. $9990

## TAC-50 A1-R2

**Action**: Semiautomatic
**Stock**: Synthetic
**Barrel**: 29 in.
**Sights**: Drilled and tapped for scopes
**Weight**: 26 lb.
**Caliber**: .50
**Magazine**: Detachable box, 5 rounds
**Features**: New hydraulic recoil mitigation system reducing peak recoil by 90 percent; take-down fiberglass stock with a longer forend that moves the balance point for the bipod forward; integral cheekpiece; monopod on the buttstock; smaller pistol grip; lighter, sturdier bipod; positive, self-locking magazine latch; magazine release lever repositioned ahead of trigger bow; match grade free floating barrel
**MSRP**.................. $11990

## TAC-338

**Action**: Bolt
**Stock**: Composite
**Barrel**: 26.5 in.

**Sights**: None
**Weight**: 11 lb.
**Caliber**: .338 Alpha Mag., .338 Norma Mag.
**Magazine**: Detachable box, 1 to 5 rounds
**Features**: G30 McMillan Long Action; hinged floor plate system; metal finish (to match stock)—black, olive, gray, tan, or dark earth; Vanguard Case; adjustable cheekpiece; tight benchrest tolerances; square-surfaced recoil lugs; threaded cap provided; match grade, stainless steel barrel with matte finish
**MSRP**.................. $6895

## TAC-416

**Action**: Single shot
**Stock**: Synthetic
**Barrel**: 29 in., 30 in.
**Sights**: Drilled and tapped for scopes
**Weight**: 26 lb.
**Caliber**: .416 Barrett
**Magazine**: None
**Features**: Stock with integral cheekpiece; action finished to match stock in variety of colors: black, olive, gray, tan, and dark earth; Lilja match grade barrel; configured as a single shot; Picatinny sight base
**MSRP**.................. $9990

# Merkel

## AFRICAN SAFARI SERIES DOUBLE RIFLE MODEL 140AE

**Action**: Boxlock
**Stock**: Walnut
**Barrel**: 23.6 in.
**Sights**: Bead front, four-leaf express rear
**Weight**: 10 lb. 8 oz.
**Caliber**: .375 H&H, .416 Rigby, .450/400 NE, .470 NE, .500 NE
**Magazine**: None
**Features**: Classic styling with cheekpiece, half luxus Turkish walnut; hand-engraved, English-style arabesque, gold relief Cape buffalo; tapered, octagonal barrel with rust blued finish
**MSRP** . . . . . . . . . . . . . . . . . **$12595**

## B3 OVER-AND-UNDER RIFLE

**Action**: Over/under
**Stock**: Checkered walnut
**Barrel**: 21.6 in.
**Sights**: Driven-hunt sight with integrated light elements
**Weight**: 6 lb. 6 oz.
**Caliber**: .30-06 and 9.3x74R
**Magazine**: None
**Features**: Short, light, and responsive; manual cocking mechanism; tilting breech block can be removed without tools; adjustable single trigger; pistol grip; cheekpiece and hogback comb; rubber buttpad
**Hunting**: . . . . . . . . . . . . . . . **$5495**

## RX HELIX HUNTING COMBINATION RIFLE/SHOTGUN

**Action**: Break-action
**Stock**: Walnut
**Barrel**: 23.6 in.
**Sights**: Open sights, 11mm prismatic scope mount rail
**Weight**: 6 lb. 6 oz.
**Caliber**: Rifle: .222 Rem., .243 Win., .308 Win., 7x65R, .30-06 Spfd., .30R Blaser, 8x57 IRS, 9.3x74R; Shotgun: 12 Ga./3-inch
**Magazine**: None
**Features**: Rotary bolt head with seven locking lugs; fully enclosed action with integral rail; interchangeable barrels and mags for tool-free caliber change in 60 seconds; tang-mounted safety, 8 models available; aluminum action; European walnut stock; manual cocking system; Elastomer recoil pad;

European style sling swivels; checkering on forend and pistol grip
**Standard:** . . . . . . . . . . . . . . . . **$3795**

## SIDE-BY-SIDE RIFLE 140

**Action**: Hinged breech
**Stock**: Wood
**Barrel**: 23.6 in.
**Sights**: None
**Weight**: 7 lb. 8 oz.
**Caliber**: 7x65R, .30-06, .30R Blaser, 8x57IRS, 9, 3x74R
**Magazine**: None
**Features**: Interchangeable barrel options; Anson & Deeley locks; steel action; Greener-style cross-bolt and double bottom bite; double trigger with front set trigger, optional single trigger; automatic trigger safety; optional with ejectors; hard soldered barrels with muzzle adjustment; engraving English arabesque or game scene "JAGD"; rubber buttplate; pistol grip; cheekpiece and hogback comb
**MSRP** . . . . . . . . . . . . . . . . . **$11995**

MERKEL AFRICAN SAFARI SERIES DOUBLE RIFLE MODEL 140AE

MERKEL B3 OVER-AND-UNDER RIFLE

MERKEL RX HELIX HUNTING COMBINATION RIFLE/SHOTGUN

MERKEL SIDE-BY-SIDE RIFLE 140

**MOSSBERG 4X4 BOLT-ACTION CENTERFIRE RIFLE**

## 4X4 BOLT-ACTION CENTERFIRE RIFLE

*Action*: Bolt
*Stock*: Synthetic, walnut, laminate
*Barrel*: 24 in.
*Sights*: None
*Weight*: 6 lb. 12 oz.–7 lb. 8 oz.
*Caliber*: .25-06 Rem., .270 Win., .30-06 Spfd., 7mm Rem., .300 Win. Mag., .338 Win. Mag., .22-250 Rem., .243 Win., 7mm-08 Rem., .308 Win.
*Magazine*: Detachable box, Standard: 5 rounds; Magnum: 4 rounds
*Features*: Classic style, gray laminate stock in Marinecote finish; free-floating, fluted, button rifled barrel with muzzlebrake; scoped combos available
**MSRP**. . . . . . . . . . . . . . . **$643–$742**

## 464 LEVER-ACTION RIFLE

*Action*: Lever
*Stock*: Walnut
*Barrel*: 18 in., 20 in.
*Sights*: Adjustable rifle sights
*Weight*: 5 lb. 8 oz.–6 lb. 12 oz.
*Caliber*: .330
*Magazine*: 18 in.: 14 rounds, 20 in.: 7 rounds
*Features*: Adjustable rifle sights; 18 in. model has dovetail receiver; drilled and tapped for scope; walnut stock with optional pistol grip
**18 in.:** . . . . . . . . . . . . . . . . . . . **$468**
**20 in.:** . . . . . . . . . . . . . . **$497–$535**

## 464 SPX

*Action*: Lever
*Stock*: Synthetic
*Barrel*: 16.25 in., 18 in.
*Sights*: Open
*Weight*: 6 lb.–6 lb. 8 oz.
*Caliber*: .22LR, .30-03 Win.
*Magazine*: 14, 6 rounds
*Features*: 6-position adjustable stocks; tri-rail forends with rail covers; adjustable fiber optic sights; optional flash suppressor and muzzlebrake; top-tang safety; dovetail receiver rifle sights or fiber optic 3-dot sights
**MSRP**. . . . . . . . . . . . . . . . **$497–$504**

**RIFLES**

**MOSSBERG 464 LEVER-ACTION RIFLE**

**MOSSBERG 464 SPX**

# Mossberg

MOSSBERG 702 BANTAM PLINKSTER

MOSSBERG 715T TACTICAL FLAT TOP

MOSSBERG 802 PLINKSTER BOLT-ACTION

MOSSBERG 817 BOLT-ACTION

## 702 BANTAM PLINKSTER

*Action*: Autoloading
*Stock*: Synthetic
*Barrel*: 18 in.
*Sights*: Rear sight
*Weight*: 4 lb. 2 oz.
*Caliber*: .22LR
*Magazine*: Detachable box, 10 rounds
*Features*: Fold down rear sight; synthetic stock comes in black or pink; blued finish on barrel and metal
**MSRP** . . . . . . . . . . . . . . . . . . . . **$176**

## 715T TACTICAL FLAT TOP

*Action*: Autoloading
*Stock*: Synthetic
*Barrel*: 16.25 in.
*Sights*: Adjustable
*Weight*: 5 lb. 4 oz.
*Caliber*: .22LR, .30-03 Win.
*Magazine*: 11, 26 rounds
*Features*: Fixed stock or six-position adjustable stock versions available; stock finish is black matte or Mossy Oak Brush camo; Red-Dot Combo package; optional 10 round or 25 round magazine; flat top receiver with full-length Picatinny top rail; free-floating barrels with matte blued finish; removable rear and front adjustable sights; pistol grip
**MSRP** . . . . . . . . . . . . . . . . **$364–$421**

## 802 PLINKSTER BOLT-ACTION

*Action*: Bolt
*Stock*: Synthetic or wood
*Barrel*: 18 in., 21 in.
*Sights*: Adjustable rifle sights
*Weight*: 4 lb. 2 oz.–4 lb. 10 oz.
*Caliber*: .22LR
*Magazine*: Detachable box, 11 rounds
*Features*: Stock comes in black, pink, or marble pink finish; receiver grooved to accept .375-inch scope mounts; cross-bolt safety and magazine release buttons; free-float barrel with blued or brushed chrome finish; includes free gun lock
**MSRP** . . . . . . . . . . . . . . . . **$162–$199**

## 817 BOLT-ACTION

*Action*: Bolt
*Stock*: Synthetic or wood
*Barrel*: 21 in.
*Sights*: None
*Weight*: 4 lb. 8 oz.–5 lb.
*Caliber*: .17 HMR
*Magazine*: Detachable box, 5 rounds
*Features*: Factory-mounted Weaver-style scope bases; cross-bolt safety and magazine release buttons; free gun lock included; stock available in black synthetic or wood; metal finishes include blued or brushed chrome; optional scope; optional muzzlebrake
**MSRP** . . . . . . . . . . . . . . . . **$205–$301**

RIFLES

## ATR SHORT ACTION

**Action**: Bolt
**Stock**: Synthetic, walnut
**Barrel**: 22 in.
**Sights**: None
**Weight**: 6 lb. 12 oz.–7 lb.
**Caliber**: .270 Win., .30-06, .243 Win., .308 Win.
**Magazine**: Top loading mag, 4+1 rounds
**Features**: Integral synthetic trigger guard; Weaver-style scope bases; integral swivel studs; free-floating, button-rifled barrels; recessed muzzle crown; barrel finishes include matte blued or Marinecote; rugged synthetic stocks include black, camo, and synthetic walnut finishes; rubber recoil pad; free gunlock; available in long-action and short-action
**MSRP** . . . . . . . . . . . . . . . . . . **$416**

## MMR HUNTER

**Action**: Semiautomatic
**Stock**: Synthetic
**Barrel**: 20 in.
**Sights**: None
**Weight**: 7 lb. 8 oz.
**Caliber**: 5.56mm NATO
**Magazine**: 5+1 rounds
**Features**: Carbon steel barrel with black phosphate finish; black synthetic, Mossy Oak Treestand, or Mossy Oak Brush stocks; single-stage trigger; oversized trigger guard for use with gloves; integral Picatinny rail
**Black:** . . . . . . . . . . . . . . . . . . **$978**
**Mossy Oak:** . . . . . . . . . . . . . **$1072**

## MVP SERIES PREDATOR

**Action**: Bolt
**Stock**: Laminate
**Barrel**: 18.5 in., 20 in.
**Sights**: Weaver-style bases
**Weight**: 7 lb. 8 oz.
**Caliber**: 5.56mm NATO
**Magazine**: 11 rounds
**Features**: Mossberg Varmint Predator series; gray laminate sporter-style stock; optional compact barrel lengths; scoped combo package available; Weaver-style bases for adding optics; carbon steel barrels; varmint style muzzle crown; helically-fluted bolt and barrel fluting; metalwork has dura-

**MOSSBERG ATR SHORT ACTION**

**MOSSBERG MMR HUNTER - MOSSY OAK TREESTAND**

**MOSSBERG MVP SERIES PREDATOR**

**MOSSBERG MVP SERIES VARMINT**

ble, non-reflective matte blued finish; front and rear sling swivel studs
**MSRP** . . . . . . . . . . . . . . . . . . . **$729**

## MVP SERIES VARMINT

**Action**: Bolt
**Stock**: Laminate

**Barrel**: 24 in.
**Sights**: Weaver-style bases
**Weight**: 7 lb. 8 oz.
**Caliber**: 5.56mm NATO
**Magazine**: 10+1 rounds
**Features**: Mossberg Varmint Predator series; Weaver-style bases for optics customization; button-rifled medium bull barrel; varmint style crown; fluting on the barrel; helically-fluted bolt; metalwork has matte blued finish; gray laminate benchrest stock with pistol grip
**MSRP** . . . . . . . . . . . . . . . . . . . **$861**

# New Ultra Light Arms

## MODEL 20 ULTIMATE MOUNTAIN RIFLE

**Action**: Bolt
**Stock**: Kevlar/graphite composite
**Barrel**: 22 in.
**Sights**: None
**Weight**: 5 lb.
**Caliber**: .308, .243 Win., 6mm Rem., .257 Roberts, 7mm-08, .284
**Magazine**: Detachable box
**Features**: Available in left-hand; choice of stock colors; 20-oz. action; two-position safety
**MSRP**. . . . . . . . . . . . . . . . . . . $3600
**Left-handed:**. . . . . . . . . . . . . $3700

## MODEL 20 RIMFIRE

**Action**: Bolt
**Stock**: Kevlar/graphite composite
**Barrel**: 22 in.
**Sights**: None
**Weight**: 5 lb. 4 oz.
**Caliber**: .22LR
**Magazine**: None or detachable box, 5 rounds
**Features**: Single-shot or repeater; drilled and tapped for scope; recoil pad; sling swivels; color stock options;

left-hand models available for no extra charge
**Single shot:** . . . . . . . . . . . . . $1900
**Repeater:** . . . . . . . . . . . . . . . $1958

## MODEL 209 MUZZLELOADER

**Action**: Bolt
**Stock**: Kevlar/graphite composite
**Barrel**: 24 in.
**Sights**: None
**Weight**: 4 lb. 14 oz.
**Caliber**: .45, .50
**Magazine**: None
**Features**: Adjustable Timney trigger; positive primer extraction; button-rifled barrel; Kevlar/graphite stock comes in various colors; recoil pad; sling swivels; ULA scope mounts; hard case; optional black powder
**MSRP** . . . . . . . . . . . . . . . . . . $1800

**NEW ULTRA LIGHT ARMS MODEL 20 ULTIMATE MOUNTAIN RIFLE**

**NEW ULTRA LIGHT ARMS MODEL 20 RIMFIRE**

**NEW ULTRA LIGHT ARMS MODEL 209**

# Nosler

NOSLER M48 CUSTOM SPORTER

## M48 CUSTOM SPORTER

**Action**: Bolt
**Stock**: Kevlar and carbon fiber
**Barrel**: 24 in.
**Sights**: None
**Weight**: 6 lb. 8 oz.–7 lb. 8 oz.
**Caliber**: .22-250 Rem., .257 Roberts +P, 6.5-284 Norma, .270 Win., .280 Ack. Imp., .30-06, .300 Win. Mag., .228 Win. Mag., .35 Whelen
**Magazine**: Internal box, 3, 4 rounds
**Features**: Onyx black stock with slate metal finish; rifle Basix trigger; glass pillar-bedded Kevlar and carbon fiber stock with Teflon overcoat; Cerakote and Micro Slick finishes prevent corrosion and weather damage; match-grade stainless Pac-Nor, fully free-floated hand lapped barrel
**MSRP** . . . . . . . . . . . . . . . . . . $3195

RIFLES

## M48 CUSTOM VARMINT

**Action**: Bolt
**Stock**: Composite
**Barrel**: 24 in.
**Sights**: None
**Weight**: 7 lb. 4 oz.
**Caliber**: .204 Ruger, .223 Rem., .22-250 Rem.
**Magazine**: Internal box, 4 rounds
**Features**: Coyote tan stock with graphite metal finish or onyx black with slate metal finish; rifle Basix trigger; glass pillar-bedded Kevlar and carbon fiber stock with Teflon overcoat; match-grade stainless Pac-Nor, full free-floated hand-lapped barrel
**MSRP** . . . . . . . . . . . . . . . . . . **$3195**

## M48 LEGACY

**Action**: Bolt
**Stock**: Walnut
**Barrel**: 24 in.
**Sights**: None
**Weight**: 7 lb. 8 oz.–8 lb.
**Caliber**: Short: .257 Roberts+P, .308 Win., .300 Win. Mag.; Long: .270 Win., .280 Ack. Imp., .30-06 Spfd., .388 Win. Mag., .35 Whelen
**Magazine**: Internal box, 3, 4 rounds
**Features**: Model 48 action; hand lapped PAC-NOR match-grade chromoly, fully free-floated barrel; hinged floor plate; custom rifle Basix trigger; hand oiled black walnut with 20 LPI checkering; classic American styled stock with shadow-line cheekpiece; glass-pillar bedded; sling swivel studs; Pachmayr decelerator recoil pad
**MSRP** . . . . . . . . . . . . . . . . . . **$2695**

## M48 TROPHY GRADE RIFLE

**Action**: Bolt
**Stock**: Composite
**Barrel**: 24 in., 24.75 in.
**Sights**: None
**Weight**: 6 lb. 8 oz.–7 lb. 8 oz.
**Caliber**: Short: .243 Win., .257 Roberts+P, .270 WSM, 7mm-08 Rem., .308 Win., .300 WSM, .325 WSM; Long: .270 Win., .280 Ack. Imp., 7mm Rem. Mag., .30-06 Spld., .300 Win. Mag., .338 Win. Mag., .35 Whelen
**Magazine**: Internal box, 3, 4 rounds
**Features**: Custom aluminum-bedded Bell and Carson composite stock in black with gray; Pachmayr Decelerator; recoil pad; sling swivel studs; Nosler Custom Action with standard scope mount; match-grade Pac-Nor chromoly barrel; two-position safety; Basix trigger; Cerakote and Micro Slick finishes
**MSRP** . . . . . . . . . . . . . . . . . . **$1995**

## NOSLER CUSTOM RIFLE

**Action**: Bolt
**Stock**: Walnut
**Barrel**: 24 in., 24.75 in.
**Sights**: Open
**Weight**: 8 lb. 4 oz.–8 lb. 12 oz.
**Caliber**: .300 WSM, .280 Ack. Imp., .338 Win. Mag.
**Magazine**: Internal box, 3, 4 rounds
**Features**: Leupold Custom Shop; match-grade stainless, fully free-floated hand lapped barrel; three-stage safety; glass pillar-bedded fancy walnut stock; custom case cruzer by Pelican; custom leather sling
**MSRP** . . . . . . . . . . . . . . . . . . **$4195**

NOSLER M48 CUSTOM VARMINT

NOSLER M48 LEGACY

NOSLER M48 TROPHY GRADE RIFLE

NOSLER CUSTOM RIFLE

# Olympic Arms

## GAMESTALKER

*Action*: Gas-operated autoloader
*Stock*: ACE Skeleton stock in camo
*Barrel*: 22 in. stainless fluted
*Sights*: None
*Weight*: 7 lb. 8 oz.
*Caliber*: .243 WSSM, .25 WSSM, .300 OSSM
*Magazine*: Detachable box, 5 rounds
*Features*: Flat-top upper receiver; free-floating aluminum handguard; ERGO grip; Picatinny rail
**MSRP . . . . . . . . . . . . . . . $1363.70**

## ULTIMATE MAGNUM AR (UMAR)

*Action*: Semiautomatic, gas-operated
*Stock*: Synthetic
*Barrel*: 24 in.
*Sights*: None
*Weight*: 9 lb. 6 oz.
*Caliber*: .22-250 Rem., .223 WSSM,

OLYMPIC ARMS GAMESTALKER

OLYMPIC ARMS UMAR

.243 WSSM, .25 WSSM, .300 OSSM
*Magazine*: 5 rounds
*Features*: Aluminum forged receiver machined by Olympic Arms; black matte anodized receiver, Parkerized steel parts; flat top with Picatinny rails; heavy match grade bull barrel; side-sling mount or bi-pod mount
**MSRP . . . . . . . . . . . . . . . . $1588.70**

# Pedersoli

## 1763 LEGER (1766) CHARLEVILLE

*Action*: Dropping block
*Stock*: Walnut
*Barrel*: 44.7 in.
*Sights*: Open
*Weight*: 10 lb. 2 oz.
*Caliber*: .69
*Magazine*: None
*Features*: Creedmoor sight; tunnel front sight; replica of French infantry musket
**MSRP . . . . . . . . . . . . . . . . . $1506**

## 1874 SHARPS OLD WEST MAPLE

*Action*: Dropping block
*Stock*: Maple
*Barrel*: 30 in.
*Sights*: None
*Weight*: 11 lb. 7 oz.
*Caliber*: .45-70
*Magazine*: None
*Features*: Optional Creedmoor and tunnel sights; brass plate on right side of butt stock can be personalized; forend has wedge plates; pistol grip cap is made of hardened steel
**MSRP . . . . . . . . . . . . . . . . . $2279**

PEDERSOLI 1763 LEGER (1766) CHARLEVILLE

PEDERSOLI 1874 SHARPS OLD WEST

RIFLES

**PEDERSOLI KODIAK MARK IV**

**PEDERSOLI MODEL 86/71 LEVER ACTION CLASSIC**

**PEDERSOLI MODEL 86/71 LEVER ACTION BOARBUSTER CAMO**

**PEDERSOLI MODEL 86/71 LEVER ACTION WILDBUSTER**

**PEDERSOLI ROLLING BLOCK TARGET**

## KODIAK MARK IV

**Action**: Breech loading
**Stock**: Walnut
**Barrel**: 22 in., 24 in.
**Sights**: Open
**Weight**: 9 lb. 11 oz.–10 lb. 5 oz.
**Caliber**: .45-70; 8x57JRS; 9.3x74R
**Magazine**: None
**Features**: Double-leave rear sight in a dovetail; tapered round barrels made of blued steel; select walnut stock with checkering and oil finish
**MSRP** . . . . . . . . . . . . . . . . . . **$6009**

## MODEL 86/71 LEVER ACTION BOARBUSTER

**Action**: Lever
**Stock**: Walnut
**Barrel**: 19 in.
**Sights**: Drilled and tapped for scopes
**Weight**: 7 lb. 4 oz.
**Caliber**: .444 Marlin, .45-70
**Magazine**: 5 rounds
**Features**: Barrel equipped with European Picatinny style base with integral rear sight; half cock safety on hammer; safety slide catch at the rear of the frame; checkered pistol grip stock and forend are made from walnut; also available in soft touch orange

camo color; metal parts are blued; drilled and tapped for sights
**MSRP** . . . . . . . . . . . . . . . . . . **$1771**

## MODEL 86/71 LEVER ACTION CLASSIC

**Action**: Lever
**Stock**: Walnut
**Barrel**: 24 in.
**Sights**: Drilled and tapped for scopes
**Weight**: 8 lb. 3 oz.
**Caliber**: .45-70
**Magazine**: 5 rounds
**Features**: Last "big frame" rifle for Winchester; drilled and tapped for scopes; broach rifled barrel and magazine are blued finished; checkered walnut pistol grip; frame is forged and CNC-machined, with a blued finish on the standard version and case-hardened frame and buttcap on the Premium model with select walnut stock and forend
**MSRP** . . . . . . . . . . . . . . . . . . **$1771**

## MODEL 86/71 LEVER ACTION WILDBUSTER

**Action**: Lever
**Stock**: Walnut
**Barrel**: 24 in.

**Sights**: Drilled and tapped for scopes
**Weight**: 8 lb. 3 oz.
**Caliber**: .45-70
**Magazine**: 5 rounds
**Features**: Ramp rear sight; walnut forend and pistol grip stock with checkered buttplate; blued finish on metal parts; drilled and tapped for scopes
**MSRP** . . . . . . . . . . . . . . . . . . **$1709**

## ROLLING BLOCK TARGET

**Action**: Dropping block
**Stock**: Walnut
**Barrel**: 30 in.
**Sights**: Open
**Weight**: 10 lb. 9 oz.
**Caliber**: .357 Mag., .45-70
**Magazine**: None
**Features**: Octagonal, conical blued barrel; case-hardened color frame is equipped with ramp rear sight adjustable in elevation; steel buttplate and trigger guard; straight stock and forend made of walnut with oil finish
**MSRP** . . . . . . . . . . . . . . . . . . **$1151**

# Puma By Legacy Sports

PUMA M-86, OCTAGONAL BARREL

PUMA M-92, ROUND BARREL

## PUMA M-86

*Action*: Lever
*Stock*: Walnut
*Barrel*: 22 in., 26 in.
*Sights*: Open
*Weight*: 9 lb.
*Caliber*: .45-70
*Magazine*: Tubular mag, 7, 8 rounds
*Features*: Octagonal steel barrel; graduated rear and blade front sights; double locking lugs; high grade Italian walnut stock; standard loop lever
**MSRP . . . . . . . . . . . . . . . . . . . $1390**

## PUMA M-92

*Action*: Lever
*Stock*: Walnut
*Barrel*: 16 in., 20 in., 24 in.
*Sights*: Open
*Weight*: 6 lb. 10 oz.
*Caliber*: .45 Colt, .357 Mag., .44/40, .44 Mag.
*Magazine*: Tubular mag, 16-in. holds 9 rounds, 20-in. holds 10 rounds, octagonal barrels hold 10 rounds
*Features*: Octagonal or round steel barrel available; walnut stock with straight grip; crescent buttplate; blued barrel; color case receiver; factory magazine tube plug is included limiting it to 5 rounds until removed; high grade Italian walnut stock
**MSRP . . . . . . . . . . . . . . . . . . . $1053**

# Purdey

PURDEY BOLT ACTION RIFLE

PURDEY DOUBLE RIFLE

## DOUBLE RIFLES

*Action*: Self-Opening
*Stock*: Walnut
*Barrel*: 23 in.–26 in.
*Sights*: Open
*Weight*: 12 lb. 4 oz.
*Caliber*: .375, .416, .470, .475, .500, .577, .600
*Magazine*: None
*Features*: Hinged front trigger; bolted non-automatic safety catch; sling swivels optional; full pistol grip; cheekpiece and leather covered recoil pad; chopper lump barrel construction; express rear sights with bead foresight with flip-up moon sight; optional beavertail forend and telescopic sights

.375 or smaller: . . . . . . . . . . $166091
.416, .470, .475, .500: . . . . . $175493
.557, .600: . . . . . . . . . . . . . $175493
**(All prices excluding UK taxes)**

## BOLT ACTION RIFLES

*Action*: Bolt
*Stock*: Walnut
*Barrel*: 25 in.
*Sights*: Open
*Weight*: 10 lb. 8 oz.
*Caliber*: .375 H&H, 7mm Mag.
*Magazine*: None
*Features*: Original Mauser '98 or modern Mauser type magnum square bridge; model 70 type safety catch for use with telescopic sights; quick detachable claw or Purdey rail mounts depending on the type of action and telescopic sight chosen; Purdey's rail mount system with integral recoil bar; Turkish walnut stock with pistol grip; cheekpiece and rubber recoil pad; single trigger
**Original Mauser Action: . . . $43873**
**Magnum Square Bridge Action
(.375 caliber & above): . . . . . $43873**
**(All prices excluding UK taxes)**

RIFLES

## MODEL 552 BDL SPEEDMASTER

*Action*: Semiautomatic
*Stock*: Walnut
*Barrel*: 22 in.
*Sights*: Open
*Weight*: 5 lb. 12 oz.
*Caliber*: .22S, L, LR
*Magazine*: Tubular mag
*Features*: Adjustable iron sights for open sight plinking; grooved receiver for scope mounts; high-gloss American walnut stock and forend checkering; richly blued carbon-steel barrel; positive cross-bolt safety
MSRP . . . . . . . . . . . . . . . . . . . . $650

## MODEL 572 BDL FIELDMASTER

*Action*: Pump
*Stock*: Walnut
*Barrel*: 21 in.
*Sights*: Open
*Weight*: 5 lb. 12 oz.
*Caliber*: .22S, L, LR
*Magazine*: Tubular mag
*Features*: Smooth classic side action; high-gloss American walnut stock and forend with cut checkering; richly blued carbon-steel barrel; adjustable iron sights for open slight plinking; receiver grooved for scope mounts; positive cross-bolt safety
MSRP . . . . . . . . . . . . . . . . . . . . $665

## MODEL 597

*Action*: Semiautomatic
*Stock*: Synthetic
*Barrel*: 22 in.
*Sights*: Open
*Weight*: 5 lb. 8 oz.
*Caliber*: .22LR, .22 WMR
*Magazine*: Detachable box, 10 rounds
*Features*: Bolt-guidance system features twin, tool-steel guide rails; sear and hammer are Teflon/nickel-plated; non-glare matte finish; adjustable big game iron sights; last-shot "hold open" bolt for added safety
MSRP . . . . . . . . . . . . . . . . . . . . $204

## MODEL 597 HEAVY BARREL

*Action*: Semiautomatic
*Stock*: Synthetic
*Barrel*: 22 in.
*Sights*: None
*Weight*: 5 lb. 12 oz.
*Caliber*: .22 LR
*Magazine*: Detachable box, 10 rounds
*Features*: Heavy barrel with rugged green synthetic stock; bolt-guidance system features twin tool-steel guide rails; Teflon nickel plated sear and hammer; patented drop-out staggered stack, detachable metal magazine; last-shot "hold open" bolt; scope rail
MSRP . . . . . . . . . . . . . . . . . . . . $249

RIFLES

REMINGTON MODEL 552 BDL SPEEDMASTER

REMINGTON MODEL 572 BDL FIELDMASTER

REMINGTON MODEL 597 WITH SCOPE

REMINGTON MODEL 597 HB

# Remington Arms

REMINGTON MODEL 597
HEAVY BARREL A-TACS CAMO

REMINGTON MODEL 700 BDL

REMINGTON MODEL 700 BDL
50TH ANNIVERSARY EDITION

## MODEL 597 HEAVY BARREL A-TACS CAMO

*Action*: Semiautomatic
*Stock*: Synthetic
*Barrel*: 22 in.
*Sights*: None
*Weight*: 5 lb. 12 oz.
*Caliber*: .22 LR
*Magazine*: Detachable box, 10 rounds
*Features*: Heavy barrel with A-TACS camo synthetic stock; bolt-guidance system features twin tool-steel guide rails; Teflon nickel plated sear and hammer; patented drop-out staggered stack, detachable metal magazine; last-shot "hold open" bolt; scope rail
**MSRP.................... $349**

## MODEL 700 BDL

*Action*: Bolt
*Stock*: Walnut
*Barrel*: 22 in., 24 in., 26 in.
*Sights*: Open
*Weight*: 7 lb. 4 oz.–7 lb. 10 oz.
*Caliber*: .243 Win., .270 Win., .30-06 Spfd., 7mm Rem. Mag., .300 Rem. Ultra Mag.
*Magazine*: Internal box
*Features*: Adjustable X-Mark Pro Trigger system; walnut stock with black forend cap; Monte Carlo comb with raised cheekpiece and skipline cut checkering; hinged magazine floor plate; sling swivel studs; hooded ramp front sight and adjustable rear sight; cylindrical receiver machined from solid-steel bar
**MSRP.................... $985**

## MODEL 700 BDL 50TH ANNIVERSARY EDITION

*Action*: Bolt
*Stock*: Walnut
*Barrel*: 24 in.
*Sights*: Open
*Weight*: 7 lb. 10 oz.
*Caliber*: 7mm Rem. Mag.
*Magazine*: Internal box
*Features*: 50th anniversary edition in the first chambering released in 1962, 7mm Remington Magnum; laser-engraved commemorative floorplate; B grade walnut stock with fleur-de-lis checkering and white line spacers at the recoil pad, grip cap, and forend; sling swivel studs; black vented recoil pad; satin bluing on the receiver; X-Mark Pro externally adjustable trigger
**MSRP.................... $1399**

# Remington Arms

REMINGTON MODEL 700 CDL

REMINGTON MODEL 700 CDL 375 H&H 100TH ANNIVERSARY EDITION

REMINGTON MODEL 700 CDL DM

REMINGTON MODEL 700 CDL SF LIMITED EDITION

## MODEL 700 CDL

**Action**: Bolt
**Stock**: Walnut
**Barrel**: 24 in., 26 in.
**Sights**: None
**Weight**: 7 lb. 5 oz.–7 lb. 10 oz.
**Caliber**: .243 Win., .270 Win., 7mm-08 Rem., .300 Win. Mag., .300 Rem. Ultra Mag.
**Magazine**: Internal box
**Features**: Adjustable X-Mark Pro Trigger system; cylindrical receiver machined from solid-steel bar stock; walnut stock with oil finish
**MSRP** . . . . . . . . . . . . . . . . . **$1019**

## MODEL 700 CDL 375 H&H 100TH ANNIVERSARY EDITION

**Action**: Bolt
**Stock**: Walnut
**Barrel**: 22 in.

**Sights**: Front and rear
**Weight**: 7 lb. 10 oz.
**Caliber**: .375 H&H
**Magazine**: Internal box
**Features**: Walnut stock with satin finish; matte-finished rifle sighted barrel; externally adjusted X-Mark Pro trigger system; rear sling swivel stud; front barrel band; New England custom gun rear adjustable sight and hooded front sight; steel hinged floorplate
**MSRP** . . . . . . . . . . . . . . . . . . **$1450**

## MODEL 700 CDL DM

**Action**: Bolt
**Stock**: Walnut, synthetic
**Barrel**: 24 in., 26 in.
**Sights**: None
**Weight**: 7 lb. 5 oz.–7 lb. 10 oz.
**Caliber**: .243 Win., 7mm-08 Rem., .270 Win., .30-06 Spfd., 7mm Rem. Mag., .300 Win. Mag.

**Magazine**: Detachable box
**Features**: Receiver machined from solid-steel bar stock; X-Mark Pro externally adjustable trigger system; walnut stock with satin finish
**MSRP** . . . . . . . . . . . . . . . . . **$1041**

## MODEL 700 CDL SF LIMITED EDITION

**Action**: Bolt
**Stock**: Walnut
**Barrel**: 24 in.
**Sights**: None
**Weight**: 7 lb. 6 oz.
**Caliber**: 7mm Rem. Mag.
**Magazine**: Internal box
**Features**: 50th anniversary edition; satin-finished American walnut stock; sling swivel studs; satin finished stainless steel drilled and tapped barrel; X-Mark Pro trigger
**MSRP** . . . . . . . . . . . . . . . . . **$1250**

# Remington Arms

**REMINGTON MODEL 700 SENDERO SF II**

**REMINGTON MODEL 700 MOUNTAIN SS**

## MODEL 700 MOUNTAIN SS

**Action**: Bolt
**Stock**: Synthetic
**Barrel**: 22 in.
**Sights**: Drilled and tapped for scopes
**Weight**: 6 lb. 8 oz.
**Caliber**: .25-06 Rem., .270 Win., .280 Rem., .30-06 Spfd., 7mm-08 Rem., .308 Win.
**Magazine**: Internal box
**Features**: Bell & Carson aramid fiber reinforced stock; X-Mark Pro trigger system; cylindrical receiver design; sling swivel studs; stainless steel barrel and action; hinged magazine floor plate
**MSRP** . . . . . . . . . . . . . . . . . . . **$1123**

## MODEL 700 SENDERO SF II

**Action**: Bolt
**Stock**: Composite
**Barrel**: 26 in.
**Sights**: None
**Weight**: 8 lb. 8 oz.
**Caliber**: 7mm Rem. Mag., .300 Win. Mag., .300 Rem. Ultra Mag.
**Magazine**: Internal box
**Features**: Composite stock in black with gray webbing, reinforced with aramid fibers; features contoured beavertail forend with ambidextrous finger grooves and palm swells; heavy contour barrels are fluted for rapid cooling; full-length aluminum bedding stocks; twin front swivel studs for sling and bipod; concave target-style barrel crown
**MSRP** . . . . . . . . . . . . . . . . . . . **$1451**

## MODEL 700 SPS

**Action**: Bolt
**Stock**: Synthetic
**Barrel**: 24 in., 26 in.
**Sights**: None
**Weight**: 7 lb.–7 lb. 10 oz.
**Caliber**: .270 WSM, .300 WSM, .223 Rem., .243 Win., 7mm-08 Rem., .308 Win., .270 Win., .20-06 Spfd., .300 Win. Mag., .300 Rem. Ultra Mag., 7mm Rem. Mag.
**Magazine**: Internal box
**Features**: Black ergonomic synthetic stock; carbon steel sight drilled and tapped for scope mounts; exterior metal-work features matte blued finish; hinged floor plate; swivel studs
**MSRP** . . . . . . . . . . . . . . . . . . . **$702**

## MODEL 700 SPS CAMO

**Action**: Bolt
**Stock**: Synthetic
**Barrel**: 20 in., 22 in., 24 in.
**Sights**: None
**Weight**: 7 lb.–7 lb. 6 oz.
**Caliber**: .270 Win., .30-06 Spfd., 7mm Rem. Mag., .300 Win. Mag., .243 Win., 7mm-08 Rem.
**Magazine**: None
**Features**: Hammer-forged barrel; X-Mark Pro externally adjustable trigger system; SuperCell recoil pad; synthetic stock in Mossy Oak Break-Up Infinity pattern; Hogue over-molded grips; receivers tapped and drilled
**MSRP** . . . . . . . . . . . . . . . . . . . **$777**

**REMINGTON MODEL 700 SPS LEFT-HAND**

**REMINGTON MODEL 700 SPS CAMO**

## MODEL 700 SPS TACTICAL

**Action**: Bolt
**Stock**: Synthetic
**Barrel**: 20 in.
**Sights**: None
**Weight**: 7 lb. 4 oz.–7 lb. 11 oz.
**Caliber**: .223 Rem., .308 Win.
**Magazine**: Detachable box
**Features**: Ergonomic tactical stock in black; sling swivel studs; carbon steel barrel is drilled and tapped for sights; metal features blued finish; X-Mark Pro adjustable trigger; SuperCell recoil pad; semi-beavertail forend; hinged floor plate
**MSRP** . . . . . . . . . . . . . . . . . . . . **$757**

## MODEL 700 SPS TACTICAL AAC-SD

**Action**: Bolt
**Stock**: Synthetic
**Barrel**: 20 in.
**Sights**: None
**Weight**: 7 lb. 5 oz.
**Caliber**: .308 Win.
**Magazine**: Internal box
**Features**: Heavy barrel with threaded muzzle; accepts AAC and other threaded flash hiders, muzzlebrakes and suppressors; Hogue overmolded hillier green pillar bedded stock; X-Mark Pro adjustable trigger; optional Leupold Mark IV scope
**MSRP** . . . . . . . . . . . . . . . . . . . . **$833**

## MODEL 700 SPS VARMINT

**Action**: Bolt
**Stock**: Synthetic
**Barrel**: 26 in.
**Sights**: None
**Weight**: 8 lb. 8 oz.
**Caliber**: .204 Ruger, .223 Rem., .22-250 Rem., .243 Win., .308 Win.
**Magazine**: Internal box
**Features**: Ergonomic black synthetic stock has a vented beavertail forend; non-reflective matte blued finish on barrel and receiver; hinged floor plate; sling swivel studs; drilled and tapped for scope mounts
**MSRP** . . . . . . . . . . . . . . . . . . . . **$732**

## MODEL 700 TARGET TACTICAL

**Action**: Bolt
**Stock**: Synthetic
**Barrel**: 26 in.
**Sights**: Target
**Weight**: 11 lb. 12 oz.
**Caliber**: .308 Win.
**Magazine**: Internal box
**Features**: Triangular VTR barrel configuration; Bell & Carson Medalist varmint/tactical stock in black; 5-R hammer-forged tactical target rifling; adjustable length of comb and pull; tactical style bolt knob; X-Mark Pro adjustable trigger
**MSRP** . . . . . . . . . . . . . . . . . . . . **$2117**

## MODEL 700 VLS

**Action**: Bolt
**Stock**: Laminate
**Barrel**: 26 in.
**Sights**: Target
**Weight**: 9 lb. 6 oz.
**Caliber**: .204 Ruger, .22-250 Rem., .223 Rem., .243 Win., .308 Win.
**Magazine**: Internal box
**Features**: Varmint laminated stock; Monte Carlo cheekpiece; beavertail shape forend; blued, satin finish metal; concave target-style barrel crown
**MSRP** . . . . . . . . . . . . . . . . . . . . **$1045**

REMINGTON MODEL 700 SPS TACTICAL

REMINGTON MODEL 700 SPS TACTICAL AAC-SD

REMINGTON MODEL 700 SPS VARMINT

REMINGTON MODEL 700 TARGET TACTICAL WITH SCOPE

REMINGTON MODEL 700 VLS

RIFLES

# Remington Arms

## MODEL 700 VTR

**Action**: Bolt
**Stock**: Synthetic
**Barrel**: 22 in.
**Sights**: None
**Weight**: 7 lb. 8 oz.
**Caliber**: .223 Rem., .308 Win., .243 Win., .204 Ruger, .223 Rem., .22-250 Rem.
**Magazine**: Internal box
**Features**: Triangular barrel contour; integral muzzlebrake; green stock with black overmolded grips
**MSRP** . . . . . . . . . . . . . . . . . . . . **$825**

## MODEL 700 VTR A-TACS

**Action**: Bolt
**Stock**: Synthetic, laminate
**Barrel**: 22 in.
**Sights**: None
**Weight**: 7 lb. 1 oz.
**Caliber**: .308 Win.
**Magazine**: 4 rounds
**Features**: Triangular barrel design; A-TACS camo pattern on synthetic or laminate stock; integral muzzlebrake; vents in forend for quick cooling; X-Mark Pro adjustable trigger; dual front swivel studs; concave target-style barrel crown; SuperCell recoil pad
**MSRP** . . . . . . . . . . . . . . . . . . . . **$930**

## MODEL 700 XCR II

**Action**: Bolt
**Stock**: Synthetic
**Barrel**: 24 in., 26 in.
**Sights**: Iron sights on .375 chamberings
**Weight**: 7 lb. 6 oz.–7 lb. 10 oz.
**Caliber**: .270 Win., .30-06 Spfd., 7mm Rem. Mag., .300 WSM, .300 Win. Mag., .338 Win. Mag., .300 Rem. Ultra Mag., .338 Rem. Ultra Mag., .375 H&H
**Magazine**: Internal box
**Features**: Engraved floor plate; synthetic stock in; drilled and tapped for scope mounting; rubber overmolding on grip and forestock; SuperCell recoil pad; TriNyte corrosion-control system; X-Mark Pro trigger system
**MSRP** . . . . . . . . . . . . . . . . . . . . **$1005**

## MODEL 750 WOODSMASTER

**Action**: Semiautomatic, gas action
**Stock**: Walnut, synthetic
**Barrel**: 22 in.
**Sights**: Open
**Weight**: 7 lb. 8 oz.
**Caliber**: .270 Win., .30-06 Spfd., .308 Win., .243 Win.
**Magazine**: None
**Features**: American walnut or black synthetic stock and forend; iron sights; receiver drilled and tapped for model 7400 scope mounts; rotary-bolt lock-up; sling swivel studs
**MSRP** . . . . . . . . . . . . . . . . . . . . **$1004**

REMINGTON MODEL 700 VTR

REMINGTON MODEL 700 VTR A-TACS

REMINGTON MODEL 700 XCR II

REMINGTON MODEL 750 WOODSMASTER

# Remington Arms

## MODEL 770
**Action**: Bolt
**Stock**: Synthetic
**Barrel**: 22 in.
**Sights**: Boresighted 3-9x40mm scope
**Weight**: 8 lb. 8 oz.–8 lb. 10 oz.
**Caliber**: .243 Win., 7mm-08 Rem., .270 Win., .30-06 Spfd., 7mm Rem. Mag., .300 Win. Mag., .308 Win.
**Magazine**: Detachable box, standard 4 rounds, magnum 3 rounds
**Features**: Button rifling; ergonomically contoured stock with a raised cheekpiece; textured grips; black synthetic stock; blued or stainless barrel with nickel-plated action and bolt; easy-camming 60 degree bolt; stainless steel barrel
**MSRP** . . . . . . . . . . . . . . . . . . . . $373

## MODEL 770 STAINLESS CAMO
**Action**: Bolt
**Stock**: Synthetic
**Barrel**: 22 in., 24 in.
**Sights**: Boresighted 3-9x40mm scope
**Weight**: 8 lb. 8 oz.
**Caliber**: .270 Win., .30-06 Spfd., 7mm Rem. Mag., .300 Win. Mag.
**Magazine**: Detachable box, standard 4 rounds, magnum 3 rounds
**Features**: Realtree AP HD camo synthetic stock design; molded swing swivel studs; stainless barrel with nickel-plated action and bolt; easy-camming 60 degree bolt
**MSRP** . . . . . . . . . . . . . . . . . . . . $455

## MODEL 7600
**Action**: Pump
**Stock**: Wood
**Barrel**: 22 in.
**Sights**: Open
**Weight**: 7 lb. 8 oz.
**Caliber**: .243 Win., .270 Win., .30-06 Spfd., .308 Win.
**Magazine**: Detachable box, 4 rounds
**Features**: Free-floated barrel; Monte Carlo walnut stock with satin finish as standard; metal work has black non-reflective finish; iron sights and drilled and tapped receiver for scope mounts; rotary-bolt lock-up
**MSRP** . . . . . . . . . . . . . . . . . . . . $900

RIFLES

**REMINGTON MODEL 770**

**REMINGTON MODEL 770 STAINLESS CAMO**

**REMINGTON MODEL 7600**

# Remington Arms

## MODEL 7600 SYNTHETIC

*Action*: Pump
*Stock*: Synthetic
*Barrel*: 22 in.
*Sights*: Open
*Weight*: 7 lb. 8 oz.
*Caliber*: .243 Win., .270 Win., .30-06 Spfd., .308 Win.
*Magazine*: Detachable box, 4 rounds
*Features*: Fiberglass-reinforced synthetic stock and forend; free-floated barrel; metal work has black non-reflective finish; iron sights and drilled and tapped receiver for scope mounts; rotary-bolt lock-up
**MSRP** . . . . . . . . . . . . . . . . . . **$756**

REMINGTON MODEL 7600 SYNTHETIC

REMINGTON MODEL R-15 450 BUSHMASTER WITH SCOPE

## MODEL R-15 450 BUSHMASTER

*Action*: Semiautomatic, gas action
*Stock*: Synthetic
*Barrel*: 18 in., 22 in.
*Sights*: None
*Weight*: 7 lb. 8 oz.–7 lb. 12 oz.
*Caliber*: .450 Bushmaster, .30 Rem. AR
*Magazine*: Detachable box, 4 rounds
*Features*: Free-floated, fluted barrel; clean-breaking single-state trigger; receiver-length Picatinny rail; aluminum receiver; synthetic full Mossy Oak camo stock with ergonomic pistol grip; lockable hard case included
**MSRP** . . . . . . . . . . . . . . . . . . **$1276**

REMINGTON MODEL R-25

## MODEL R-25

*Action*: Semiautomatic, gas action
*Stock*: Synthetic
*Barrel*: 20 in.
*Sights*: None
*Weight*: 8 lb. 12 oz.
*Caliber*: .243 Win, 7mm-08 Rem., .308 Win.
*Magazine*: Detachable box, 4 rounds
*Features*: Free-floated, fluted barrel; clean-breaking single state trigger; receiver length Picatinny rail; aluminum receiver; synthetic full Mossy Oak camo stock with ergonomic pistol grip; lockable hard case included
**MSRP** . . . . . . . . . . . . . . . . . . **$1631**

REMINGTON MODEL SEVEN CDL

## MODEL SEVEN CDL

*Action*: Bolt
*Stock*: Walnut
*Barrel*: 20 in.
*Sights*: Open
*Weight*: 6 lb. 8 oz.
*Caliber*: .243 Win., .260 Rem., 7mm-08 Rem., .308 Win.

*Magazine*: Internal box
*Features*: SuperCell recoil pad; American walnut CDL stock with satin-finished barrel; compact design for fast handling; cylindrical receiver; available in Rem. short-action magnum and Winchester short magnum
**MSRP** . . . . . . . . . . . . . . . . . . **$1029**

# Remington Arms

**REMINGTON MODEL SEVEN PREDATOR**

**REMINGTON MODEL SEVEN SYNTHETIC**

## MODEL SEVEN PREDATOR

**Action**: Bolt
**Stock**: Synthetic
**Barrel**: 22 in.
**Sights**: None
**Weight**: 7 lb.
**Caliber**: .223 Rem., .22-250 Rem., .243 Win.
**Magazine**: Internal box
**Features**: Mossy Oak Brush camo stock; fluted magnum-contour barrel; X-Mark Pro trigger system
**MSRP** . . . . . . . . . . . . . . . . . . . **$886**

## MODEL SEVEN SYNTHETIC

**Action**: Bolt
**Stock**: Synthetic
**Barrel**: 18 in., 20 in.
**Sights**: None
**Weight**: 6 lb. 2 oz.–6 lb. 8 oz.

**Caliber**: .223 Rem., .243 Win., .260 Rem., 7mm-08 Rem., .308 Win.
**Magazine**: Internal box
**Features**: Synthetic black stock; compact design for fast handling; cylindrical receiver design
**MSRP** . . . . . . . . . . . . . . . . . . . **$702**

# Rifles Inc.

**RIFLES INC. CANYON**

**RIFLES INC. CLASSIC**

## CANYON

**Action**: Bolt
**Stock**: McMillan HTG
**Barrel**: 24 in.
**Sights**: None
**Weight**: 10 lb.
**Caliber**: Most popular calibers
**Magazine**: Internal box
**Features**: Blind or hinged floor plate; customer-supplied Rem. 700 action; match grade stainless steel Lilja number 6 barrel; optional muzzle-brake; matte stainless metal finish, optional black Teflon; adjustable cheekpiece; custom buttpad
**MSRP** . . . . . . . . . . . . . . . . . . . **$3500**

## CLASSIC

**Action**: Bolt
**Stock**: Laminated fiberglass
**Barrel**: 24 in.-26 in.
**Sights**: None
**Weight**: 6 lb. 8 oz.

**Caliber**: All popular chamberings up to .375 H&H
**Magazine**: Internal box
**Features**: Customer-supplied Rem. 700 action; match grade stainless steel Lilja barrel; blind or hinged floor plate; matte stainless metal finish, optional Black Teflon finish; black laminated fiberglass, pillar glass bedded stock
**MSRP** . . . . . . . . . . . . . . . . . . . **$2600**

# Rifles Inc.

RIFLES INC. LIGHTWEIGHT STRATA

RIFLES INC. MASTER'S SERIES

RIFLES INC. SAFARI

## LIGHTWEIGHT STRATA

*Action*: Bolt
*Stock*: Laminate
*Barrel*: 22 in.-26 in.
*Sights*: None
*Weight*: 4 lb. 8 oz.–5 lb. 12 oz.
*Caliber*: All popular chamberings up to .375 H&H
*Magazine*: Internal box
*Features*: Customer-supplied Rem. 700 action; match grade stainless steel Lilja barrel; fluted bolt and hollowed-handle; blind or hinged floor plate; matte stainless metal finish, optional black Teflon finish; hand-laminated blend of Kevlar/graphite and boron, pillar glass bedded stock; Titanium Strata has hand-laminated graphite stock with pillar glass bedded; custom buttpad; Quiet Slimbrake II muzzlebrake
**Lightweight Strata:** ........ **$2900**
**Lightweight 70:** ........... **$2800**
**Titanium Strata:** .......... **$3500**

## MASTER'S SERIES

*Action*: Bolt
*Stock*: Laminated fiberglass
*Barrel*: 24 in.-27 in.
*Sights*: None
*Weight*: 7 lb. 12 oz.
*Caliber*: All popular chamberings up to .375 H&H
*Magazine*: Internal box
*Features*: Customer-supplied Rem. 700 action; match grade stainless steel Lilja number 5 barrel; hinged floor plate; matte stainless metal finish, optional black Teflon finish; black laminated fiberglass, pillar glass bedded stock; optional muzzlebrake
**MSRP** .................. **$2900**

## SAFARI

*Action*: Bolt
*Stock*: Laminated fiberglass
*Barrel*: 23 in.-25 in.
*Sights*: Optional Express Sights
*Weight*: 8 lb. 8 oz.
*Caliber*: .375 H&H, .416 Rem. Mag., and other large game cartridges
*Magazine*: Drop box, 4 rounds
*Features*: Customer-supplied Winchester Model 70 Classic action; lapped and face trued bolt; match grade stainless steel Lilja barrel; Quiet Slimbrake II muzzlebrake; hinged floor plate or optional drop box; matte stainless finish, optional black Teflon; double laminated fiberglass, pillar glass bedded stock; Pachmayr decelerator; optional barrel band
**MSRP** .................. **$3200**

# Rock River Arms

**ROCK RIVER ARMS LAR-6.8 COYOTE CARBINE**

**ROCK RIVER ARMS LAR-8 PREDATOR HP**

**ROCK RIVER ARMS LAR-15 HUNTER SERIES**

## LAR-6.8 COYOTE CARBINE

**Action**: Semiautomatic
**Stock**: Synthetic
**Barrel**: 16 in.
**Sights**: None
**Weight**: 7 lb.
**Caliber**: 6.8mm SPC II
**Magazine**: 1 round
**Features**: Smith Vortex flash hider; chromoly barrel; RRA two-stage match trigger
**MSRP** . . . . . . . . . . . . . . . . . . . . $1270

## LAR-8 PREDATOR HP

**Action**: Semiautomatic
**Stock**: Synthetic
**Barrel**: 20 in.
**Sights**: None
**Weight**: 8 lb. 10 oz.
**Caliber**: .308 Win., 7mm-08 Rem., .243 Win.
**Magazine**: Detachable box
**Features**: Forged A4 receiver with forward assist and port door; stainless steel barrel; gas block sight Base; two-stage trigger; Hogue rubber grip; RRA aluminum free-float tube; A2 buttstock or operator stock
**MSRP** . . . . . . . . . . . . . . $1605–$1655

## LAR-15 HUNTER SERIES

**Action**: Semiautomatic
**Stock**: Synthetic
**Barrel**: 16 in.
**Sights**: None
**Weight**: 7 lb. 10 oz.
**Caliber**: 5.56mm NATO, .223
**Magazine**: 20 rounds
**Features**: Finish in choice of WYL-Ehide or PRK-Ehide, digitalized imagery of real coyote or wild hog; finish is in the hardcoat anodizing, not a film dip or applique; camo anodized to the lower receiver, upper receiver, charging handle, trigger guard, and RRA half quad rail handguard; Hogue rubber pistol grip; low profile gas block; RRA operator CAR stock
**MSRP** . . . . . . . . . . . . . . . . . . . $1550

# Rock River Arms

### LAR-15LH LEFT-HANDED SERIES

*Action*: Semiautomatic
*Stock*: Synthetic
*Barrel*: 16 in.
*Sights*: None
*Weight*: 8 lb.
*Caliber*: 5.56mm NATO, .223
*Magazine*: 30 rounds
*Features*: Re-engineered and outfitted specifically for the left-handed shooter; left side ejection port; right side safety selector and bolt catch; ambidextrous mag release and charging handle; mid-length gas system; RRA tactical muzzle break; RRA two-stage triggerr; RRA operator CAR stock
*MSRP* . . . . . . . . . . . . . $1360–$1415

### LAR-40 MID-LENGTH A4

*Action*: Semiautomatic
*Stock*: Synthetic
*Barrel*: 16 in.
*Sights*: None
*Weight*: 7 lb. 2 oz.
*Caliber*: .40 S&W
*Magazine*: 1 round
*Features*: Flash hider; single-stage trigger; RRA tactical CAR stock with Hogue grip
*A4*: . . . . . . . . . . . . . . . . . . . $1260

### LAR-47 CAR A4

*Action*: Semiautomatic
*Stock*: Synthetic
*Barrel*: 16 in.
*Sights*: None
*Weight*: 6 lb. 6 oz.
*Caliber*: 7.62x39mm
*Magazine*: 30 rounds, standard AK-47 mag
*Features*: RRA 6-postion tactical CAR stock; A2 pistol grip; CAR handguards; RRA two-stage trigger; A2 flash hider; ambidextrous mag release
*MSRP* . . . . . . . . . . . . . . . . . . . $1270

**ROCK RIVER ARMS LAR-15LH**

**ROCK RIVER ARMS LAR-40 MID-LENGTH A4**

**ROCK RIVER ARMS LAR-47 CAR A4**

# Rock River Arms

**ROCK RIVER ARMS LAR-47 DELTA CARBINE**

**ROCK RIVER ARMS LAR-458 CAR A4**

**ROCK RIVER ARMS LAR-PDS CARBINE**

## LAR-47 DELTA CARBINE

*Action*: Semiautomatic
*Stock*: Synthetic
*Barrel*: 16 in.
*Sights*: None
*Weight*: 7 lb. 12 oz.
*Caliber*: 7.62x39mm
*Magazine*: 30 rounds, standard AK-47 mag
*Features*: RRA 6-position delta CAR stock; RRA delta pistol grip; RRA 2-piece quad rail; RRA delta muzzle-brake; RRA two-stage trigger; ambidextrous mag release
**MSRP** . . . . . . . . . . . . . . . . . . **$1545**

## LAR-458 CAR A4

*Action*: Semiautomatic
*Stock*: Synthetic
*Barrel*: 16 in.
*Sights*: None
*Weight*: 7 lb. 10 oz.
*Caliber*: .458 SOCOM
*Magazine*: Detachable box
*Features*: Forged A4 receiver; A2 flash hider; chromoly bull barrel; varmint gas block with sight rail; RRA two-stage trigger; RRA aluminum free-float tube; A2 pistol grip; A2 buttstock
**MSRP** . . . . . . . . . . . . . . . . . . **$1220**

## LAR-PDS CARBINE

*Action*: Semiautomatic
*Stock*: Synthetic
*Barrel*: 16 in.
*Sights*: None
*Weight*: 7 lb. 6 oz.
*Caliber*: .223 Rem.
*Magazine*: Detachable box
*Features*: Ambidextrous non-reciprocating charging handle; A2 flash hider; RRA two-stage trigger; Hogue rubber grip; tri-rail handguard available
**MSRP** . . . . . . . . . . . . . . **$1595–$1750**

# Rossi

ROSSI CIRCUIT JUDGE

ROSSI CIRCUIT JUDGE TACTICAL SYNTHETIC

ROSSI FULL SIZE CENTERFIRE MATCHED PAIR

RIFLES

## CIRCUIT JUDGE

*Action*: DA Revolver
*Stock*: Hardwood
*Barrel*: 18.5 in.
*Sights*: Fiber optic front sight
*Weight*: 5 lb. 5 oz.
*Caliber*: .410 Ga./.45LC
*Magazine*: 5 rounds
*Features*: Shotgun/rifle crossover allows you to fire .410 3-inch magnum shotshells, .410 2.5-inch shotshells, and .45 Colt ammunition in any order without switching barrels; available in smooth-bore shotgun or rifled barrel shotgun; yoke detent; transfer bar; Taurus Security System
**MSRP . . . . . . . . . . . . . . . . . . . $732**

## CIRCUIT JUDGE TACTICAL SYNTHETIC

*Action*: Revolver
*Stock*: Synthetic
*Barrel*: 18.5 in.
*Sights*: Red fiber optic front sight
*Weight*: 4 lb. 11 oz.
*Caliber*: .45 LC, .410 Ga.
*Magazine*: 5 rounds
*Features*: This gun utilizes the revolver and extends its range for hunting and shooting. One can fire .410 Ga 3-inch magnum shotshells, .410 Ga. 2.5-inch shotshells, and .45 Colt ammunition in any order, without switching barrels. It includes modern features like yoke detent, transfer bar, and the Taurus Security System.
**MSRP . . . . . . . . . . . . . . . . . . . $684**

## FULL SIZE CENTERFIRE MATCHED PAIR

*Action*: Break Open, single-shot
*Stock*: Synthetic
*Barrel*: 23 in., 28 in.
*Sights*: Adjustable sights
*Weight*: 5 lb. 4 oz.–6 lb. 4 oz.
*Caliber*: 20 Ga./.243 Win., 12 Ga., .243 Win., 20 Ga./.223 Rem., 12 Ga./.223 Rem.
*Magazine*: None
*Features*: Quick-interchangeable rifle and shotgun barrels; single shot; recoil pad; sling swivels; black synthetic stock; steel barrel with matte blued finish; button rifled barrel
**MSRP . . . . . . . . . . . . . . . . . . . $352**

### R92 .44-40
**Action**: Lever
**Stock**: Wood
**Barrel**: 20 in., 24 in.
**Sights**: None
**Weight**: 7 lb.
**Caliber**: Most popular calibers:
.38/.357 Mag., .44 Mag., .45 Colt, .44-40 Win.
**Magazine**: 12+1 rounds
**Features**: Octagonal barrel with a variety of metal finishes: blued, blued/case-hardened, blued/brass, and stainless; curved buttplate
**MSRP** . . . . . . . . . . . . . . . . . . . . $577

### R92 CARBINE .45 COLT STAINLESS
**Action**: Lever
**Stock**: Wood
**Barrel**: 20 in.
**Sights**: Open
**Weight**: 5 lb.
**Caliber**: .45 Colt
**Magazine**: Tubular mag, 10+1 rounds
**Features**: Stainless steel or blued round barrel; crescent buttplates and extended front sight; for brush hunting and wilderness packing; recoil absorbing buttpad
**MSRP** . . . . . . . . . . . . . . . . . . . . $599

### RIO GRANDE
**Action**: Lever
**Stock**: Hardwood
**Barrel**: 20 in.
**Sights**: Open
**Weight**: 5 lb. 13 oz.–7 lb.
**Caliber**: .30-30 Win., .45-70, .410,
**Magazine**: 6+1 rounds
**Features**: Blued or stainless steel barrel; authentic buckhorn sights; Taurus Safety System
**MSRP** . . . . . . . . . . . . . . . $541–$644

**ROSSI R92 .44-40**

**ROSSI R92 CARBINE .45 STAINLESS COLT**

**ROSSI RIO GRANDE**

# Rossi

ROSSI SINGLE SHOT RIFLE

ROSSI WIZARD

ROSSI YOUTH CENTERFIRE MATCHED PAIR

### SINGLE SHOT RIFLE

**Action**: Break-open, single-shot
**Stock**: Synthetic
**Barrel**: 23 in.
**Sights**: Adjustable fiber optic front
**Weight**: 6 lb. 4 oz.–7 lb.
**Caliber**: .243 Win., .44 Mag.
**Magazine**: None
**Features**: Steel barrel in matte blued finish; equipped with scope rail and hammer extension that accommodates all popular optics; black synthetic stock with removable cheekpiece; soft recoil pad; white line spacer; button rifled barrels; sling swivels
**MSRP** . . . . . . . . . . . . . . . $314–$320

### WIZARD

**Action**: Single-shot
**Stock**: Wood or Hi-Def Green camo
**Barrel**: 23 in.
**Sights**: Fiber optic front sight
**Weight**: 7 lb.
**Caliber**: .243 Win., .308 Win., .22-250 Win., .223 Win., .30-06 Win., .270 Win.
**Magazine**: None
**Features**: Interchangeable rifle and barrel system allows barrels to be changed quickly without tools; blued finish, cushioned recoil pad; Monte Carlo stock
**MSRP** . . . . . . . . . . . . . . . . . . $378

### YOUTH SIZE CENTERFIRE MATCHED PAIR

**Action**: Break-open, single-shot
**Stock**: Synthetic
**Barrel**: 22 in.
**Sights**: Adjustable fiber optic front (rifle barrels), brass bead front (shotgun)
**Weight**: 5 lb., 6 lb. 4 oz.
**Caliber**: 20 Ga./.44 Mag., 20 Ga./.243 Win., 20 Ga./.223 Rem.
**Magazine**: None
**Features**: Quick-interchangeable rifle and shotgun barrels in youth size; matte blued finish
**MSRP** . . . . . . . . . . . . . . . . . . $352

**RUGER 10/22 CARBINE**

**RUGER 10/22 TACTICAL**

**RUGER 10/22 TARGET**

## 10/22 CARBINE

*Action*: Autoloading
*Stock*: Synthetic or hardwood
*Barrel*: 18.5 in.
*Sights*: Gold bead front sight, adjustable rear
*Weight*: 5 lb.
*Caliber*: .22LR
*Magazine*: Rotary, 10 rounds
*Features*: Stock comes in black synthetic and hardwood; extended magazine release; push-button manual safety; combination scope base adapter; hammer-forged barrel; polymer trigger housing; aluminum receiver; contoured buttpad; barrel band; available LaserMax laser
**MSRP** . . . . . . . . . . . . . . . **$279–$399**

## 10/22 TACTICAL

*Action*: Autoloading
*Stock*: Synthetic
*Barrel*: 16.1 in.
*Sights*: None
*Weight*: 4 lb. 5 oz.
*Caliber*: .22LR
*Magazine*: Rotary box, 10 rounds
*Features*: Precision-rifled cold-hammer-forged alloy-steel barrel in black matte finish; black synthetic stock or black Hogue overmolded
**Synthetic:** . . . . . . . . . . . . . . . **$329**
**Hogue:** . . . . . . . . . . . . . . . . . **$579**

## 10/22 TARGET

*Action*: Autoloading
*Stock*: Laminate
*Barrel*: 20 in.
*Sights*: None
*Weight*: 7 lb. 8 oz.

*Caliber*: .22LR
*Magazine*: Rotary, 10 rounds
*Features*: Stock comes in black or brown laminate; extended magazine release; push-button manual safety; combination scope base adapter; hammer-forged barrel; polymer trigger housing; aluminum receiver; target trigger; flat buttplate
**MSRP** . . . . . . . . . . . . . . . **$529–$569**

## 77/17

*Action*: Bolt
*Stock*: Walnut or laminate
*Barrel*: 22 in., 24 in.
*Sights*: None
*Weight*: 6 lb. 8 oz.–7 lb. 8 oz.
*Caliber*: .17 HMR
*Magazine*: Detachable rotary, 9 rounds
*Features*: Stock options include American walnut with blued finish or black laminate with target gray finish;

alloy steel or stainless steel barrel; integral scope mounts; three-position safety; sling swivel stud mounts
**Walnut:** . . . . . . . . . . . . . . . . . . **$899**
**Laminate:** . . . . . . . . . . . . . . . . **$969**

## 77/22

*Action*: Bolt
*Stock*: Laminate, walnut, synthetic
*Barrel*: 20 in., 24 in.
*Sights*: None
*Weight*: 6 lb.–7 lb. 8 oz.
*Caliber*: .22LR, .22 Mag., .22 Hornet
*Magazine*: Detachable rotary, 6, 9, 10 rounds
*Features*: Stock options include black synthetic, American walnut, or brown laminate; alloy steel or stainless steel barrel in target gray, blued, or brushed stainless finish; integral scope mounts; three-position safety; sling swivel studs
**Walnut, Synthetic:** . . . . . . . . . **$899**
**Laminate:** . . . . . . . . . . . . . . . . **$969**

## 77/44

*Action*: Bolt
*Stock*: Vista Camo, synthetic
*Barrel*: 18.5 in.
*Sights*: Front bead sight, adjustable rear
*Weight*: 5 lb. 4 oz.
*Caliber*: .44 Mag.
*Magazine*: Detachable rotary, 4 rounds
*Features*: Stock options include Next G1 Vista Camo or black synthetic; stainless steel barrel with brushed steel finish; integral scope mounts; three-position safety; sling swivel studs
**Vista Camo:** . . . . . . . . . . . . . . **$999**
**Synthetic:** . . . . . . . . . . . . . . . **$969**

**RUGER 77/17**

**RUGER 77/22**

**RUGER 77/44**

# Ruger

RUGER AMERICAN RIFLE

RUGER GUNSITE SCOUT RIFLE

RUGER M77 HAWKEYE

RUGER M77 HAWKEYE AFRICAN

## AMERICAN RIFLE
**Action**: Bolt
**Stock**: Synthetic
**Barrel**: 22 in.
**Sights**: Drilled and tapped for scopes
**Weight**: 6 lb. 2 oz.–6 lb. 4 oz.
**Caliber**: .22-250 Rem., 7mm-08 Rem., .243 Win., .270 Win., .30-06 Spfd., .308 Win.
**Magazine**: Rotary, 4 rounds
**Features**: Ruger Marksman adjustable trigger; ergonomic, lightweight stock; soft rubber recoil pad; three-lug 70 degree bolt; Power Bedding positively locates the receiver and free-floats the barrel; hammer-forged barrel; tang safety; round rotary magazine
**MSRP** . . . . . . . . . . . . . . . . . . . . . $449

## GUNSITE SCOUT RIFLE
**Action**: Bolt
**Stock**: Laminate
**Barrel**: 16.50 in.
**Sights**: Post front sight, adjustable rear
**Weight**: 7 lb.
**Caliber**: .308 Win.
**Magazine**: Detachable box, 10 rounds
**Features**: Flash suppressor, Picatinny rail; recoil pad; accurate sighting system; integral scope mounts; Mauser-type extractor; developed with Gunsite and features their logo
**MSRP** . . . . . . . . . . . . . . . . . . $1039

## M77 HAWKEYE
**Action**: Bolt
**Stock**: Walnut
**Barrel**: 22 in., 24 in.
**Sights**: None
**Weight**: 7 lb.–8 lb. 4 oz.
**Caliber**: .204 Ruger, .22-250 Rem., .223 Rem., .243 Win., 6.5 Creedmoor, .257 Roberts, .270 Win., 7mm Rem. Mag., 7mm-08 Rem., .300 RCM, .30-06 Spfd., .300 Win. Mag., .308 Win., .338 RCM, .338 Win. Mag.
**Magazine**: 5 rounds
**Features**: American walnut stock; alloy steel, satin blued barrel; LCG Trigger; positive floor plate latch; integral scope mounts; three-position safety
**MSRP** . . . . . . . . . . . . . . . . . . . . . $899

## M77 HAWKEYE AFRICAN
**Action**: Bolt
**Stock**: Walnut
**Barrel**: 23 in.
**Sights**: Bead front sight, adjustable rear V notch sight
**Weight**: 7 lb. 12 oz.
**Caliber**: .223 Rem., .300 Win. Mag., .338 Win. Mag., 9.3x 62, .375 Ruger
**Magazine**: 3, 4, 5 rounds
**Features**: Walnut stock with pistol grip; LC6 Trigger; non-rotating, Mauser-type controlled round feed extractor; steel floor plate; three-position safety; integral scope mounts; muzzle brake
**MSRP** . . . . . . . . . . . . . . . . . . $1199

## M77 HAWKEYE PREDATOR
**Action**: Bolt
**Stock**: Green Mountain Laminate
**Barrel**: 22 in., 24 in.
**Sights**: None
**Weight**: 7 lb. 12 oz.–8 lb.
**Caliber**: .204 Ruger, .22-250 Rem., .223 Rem., 6.5 Creedmoore, .308 Win.

**Magazine**: 4, 5 rounds
**Features**: Hawkeye matte stainless steel finish on barrel; two-stage adjustable target trigger; non-rotating, Mauser-type controlled round feed extractor; hinged solid-steel floor plate; three-position safety; integral scope mounts; sling swivel studs
**MSRP** . . . . . . . . . . . . . . . . . . $1029

## M77 MARK II TARGET
**Action**: Bolt
**Stock**: Laminate
**Barrel**: 26 in., 28 in.
**Sights**: None
**Weight**: 9 lb. 4 oz.–9 lb. 12 oz.
**Caliber**: .204 Ruger, .22-250 Rem., .223 Rem., .243 Win., .25-06 Rem., 6.5 Creedmoor, .308 Win.
**Magazine**: 4, 5 rounds
**Features**: Black laminate stock; stainless steel barrel; two-stage target trigger; non-rotating, Mauser-type controlled round feed extractor, hinged solid-steel floor plate, three-position safety; integral scope mounts; sling swivel studs
**MSRP** . . . . . . . . . . . . . . . . . . $1029

RUGER M77 HAWKEYE PREDATOR

RUGER M77 MARK II TARGET

RUGER MINI-14 RANCH RIFLE

RUGER MINI-14 TACTICAL

RUGER MINI-14 TARGET RIFLE

RUGER MINI THIRTY RIFLE

## MINI-14 RANCH RIFLE
**Action**: Autoloading
**Stock**: Hardwood, synthetic
**Barrel**: 18.5 in.
**Sights**: Blade front sight, adjustable rear
**Weight**: 6 lb. 12 oz.–7 lb.
**Caliber**: .56mm NATO/ .223 Rem., 6.8 SPC
**Magazine**: 5 rounds, or detachable box, 20 rounds
**Features**: Stock comes in hardwood or black synthetic; Garand style action; hammer-forged barrel; sighting system; integral scope mounts; flat buttpad; integral sling swivels on hardwood or black synthetic stocks
**MSRP** . . . . . . . . . . . . . . . $909–$1039

## MINI-14 TACTICAL
**Action**: Autoloading
**Stock**: Synthetic
**Barrel**: 16.1 in.

**Sights**: Adjustable
**Weight**: 6 lb. 12 oz.–7 lb. 4 oz.
**Caliber**: 7.62x39mm
**Magazine**: 5, 20 rounds
**Features**: Black synthetic stock; blued barrel with a flash suppressor; adjustable ghost ring rear sight, non-glare protected-post front sight
**MSRP** . . . . . . . . . . . . . . $989–$1069

## MINI-14 TARGET RIFLE
**Action**: Autoloading
**Stock**: Laminate or Hogue overmolded
**Barrel**: 22 in.
**Sights**: None
**Weight**: 8 lb. 8 oz.–9 lb. 8 oz.
**Caliber**: .223 Rem.
**Magazine**: 5 rounds
**Features**: Black laminate with thumb hole stock or Black Hogue overmolded stock; matte stainless finish on stainless steel barrel; Garand style action;

hammer-forged barrel; integral scope mounts; harmonic dampener; sling swivel studs
**MSRP** . . . . . . . . . . . . . . . . . . $1149

## MINI THIRTY RIFLE
**Action**: Autoloading
**Stock**: Synthetic
**Barrel**: 16.12 in., 18.5 in.
**Sights**: Blade front sight, adjustable rear
**Weight**: 6 lb. 12 oz.
**Caliber**: 7.62x39mm
**Magazine**: 5 rounds, or detachable box, 20 rounds
**Features**: Garand style action, hammer-forged barrel; sighting system; integral scope mounts; black synthetic stock; sling swivels; stainless steel or alloy steel barrel in matte or blued finish
**MSRP** . . . . . . . . . . . . . . . $979–$1039

# Ruger

## NO. 1 LIGHT SPORTER

**Action**: Falling block, single-shot
**Stock**: Walnut
**Barrel**: 22 in.
**Sights**: Front bead sight, adjustable rear
**Weight**: 7 lb. 4 oz.
**Caliber**: .222 Rem.
**Magazine**: None
**Features**: Falling block breech mechanism, sliding tang safety; sculptured receiver; Ruger scope mounting system; Alexander Henry-style forend; sporting style buttpad; grip cap and sling swivel studs; American walnut stock
**MSRP** . . . . . . . . . . . . . . . . . . **$1349**

## NO. 1 VARMINTER

**Action**: Falling block, single-shot
**Stock**: Walnut
**Barrel**: 26 in.
**Sights**: None
**Weight**: 8 lb. 8 oz.
**Caliber**: 6.5 Creedmoor, .22-250 Rem., .223 Rem., .25-06 Rem.
**Magazine**: None
**Features**: Falling block breech mechanism, sliding tang safety; sculptured receiver; Ruger scope mounting system; Alexander Henry-style forend; sporting style buttpad; grip cap and sling swivel studs; American walnut stock
**MSRP** . . . . . . . . . . . . . . . . . . **$1349**

## SR-22

**Action**: Autoloading
**Stock**: Synthetic
**Barrel**: 16.12 in.
**Sights**: None
**Weight**: 6 lb. 8 oz.–6 lb. 14 oz.
**Caliber**: .22LR
**Magazine**: Detachable rotary, 10 rounds
**Features**: Black laminate stock in standard or collapsible; AR-style ergonomic Hogue Monogrip and six-position telescoping buttstock; hammer-forged barrel; round handguard; barrel support block
**MSRP** . . . . . . . . . . . . . . . . . . **$649**

## SR-556

**Action**: Autoloading
**Stock**: Synthetic
**Barrel**: 16.12 in.

**Sights**: Folding BattleSights
**Weight**: 7 lb. 15 oz.
**Caliber**: 5.56mm NATO/.223 Rem., 6.8 SPC
**Magazine**: Detachable box, 10, 30 rounds
**Features**: Stock options include black synthetic standard or collapsible; two-stage piston with adjustable regulator; chrome-lined gas block; quad rail handguard; Troy Industries Sights; telescoping buttstock; hammer-forged barrel; pistol grip stock; rail covers and soft case
**MSRP** . . . . . . . . . . . . . . . . . . **$1995**

## SR-556E

**Action**: Autoloading
**Stock**: Synthetic
**Barrel**: 16.12 in.
**Sights**: Folding battle sights
**Weight**: 7 lb. 6 oz.
**Caliber**: 5.56mm NATO/.223 Rem.
**Magazine**: 10, 30 rounds
**Features**: Stock is black synthetic standard; two-stage piston with adjustable regulator; chrome-lined gas block; quad rail handguard; Troy Industries sights; telescoping buttstock; hammer-forged barrel; pistol grip stock; rail covers and soft case
**MSRP** . . . . . . . . . . . . . . . . . . **$1375**

RIFLES

RUGER NO. 1 LIGHT SPORTER

RUGER NO. 1 VARMINTER

RUGER SR-22

RUGER SR-556

RUGER SR-556E

# Sako

SAKO 85 BAVARIAN

SAKO 85 BLACK BEAR

SAKO 85 BROWN BEAR

## 85 BAVARIAN

**Action**: Bolt
**Stock**: Walnut
**Barrel**: 22 in., 24 in.
**Sights**: None
**Weight**: 7 lb.–7 lb. 8 oz.
**Caliber**: .308 Win., .270 Win., .30-06 Spfd., .300 Win. Mag., .270 WSM, .300 WSM, 6.5x55 Swede, 7mm-08 Rem., 7mm Rem. Mag.
**Magazine**: 4, 5 rounds
**Features**: High grade walnut stock in traditional European style; single-set trigger
**MSRP** . . . . . . . . . . . . . $2200–$2250

## 85 BLACK BEAR

**Action**: Bolt
**Stock**: Black composite
**Barrel**: 21.25 in.
**Sights**: Adjustable Express "V" rear, white bead front and integral dovetail for scope mounts
**Weight**: 6 lb. 13 oz.–7 lb.
**Caliber**: .308 Win., .338 Fed., .30-06 Spfd., 8x57IS, 9.3x62, 9.3x66 Sako
**Magazine**: Detachable box, 5 rounds
**Features**: Purpose built weapon for bear and wild boar hunters; adjustable single-stage trigger; adjustable shallow "V" Express style rear sight with white bead front sight for fast target acquisition and a barrel band for front swivel; patented Total Control Magazine Latch (TCL) prevents accidental release of the stainless steel magazine under the heaviest recoil or harshest hunting conditions
**MSRP** . . . . . . . . . . . . . . . . . . $1850

## 85 BROWN BEAR

**Action**: Bolt
**Stock**: Brown laminate
**Barrel**: 21.25 in.
**Sights**: Adjustable open rear, blade style front and integral dovetail for

scope mounts
**Weight**: 7 lb. 15 oz.
**Caliber**: .338 Win. Mag., .375 H&H Mag.
**Magazine**: Detachable box, 4 rounds
**Features**: Open adjustable rear sight and blade style front sight; short free-floated bull barrel has a band type front swivel; forged one-piece bolt with three locking lugs offers fast, smooth cycling with controlled round feed and mechanical case ejection; patented Total Control Magazine Latch (TCL) prevents accidental release of the stainless steel magazine
**MSRP** . . . . . . . . . . . . . . . . . $2500

## 85 CLASSIC

**Action**: Bolt
**Stock**: Walnut
**Barrel**: 22.4 in., 24.4 in.
**Sights**: Open
**Weight**: 7 lb.–7 lb. 12 oz.
**Caliber**: (Short): .243 Win., .260 Rem., 7mm-08 Rem., .308 Win., .338 Federal; (SM) .270 Win. S Mag., .300 Win. S Mag.; (Medium) .25-06 Rem., 6.5x55 SE, .270 Win., .30-06 Spfd., 9.3x66 Sako; (Long): 7mm Rem. Mag.,

SAKO 85 CLASSIC

SAKO 85 FINNLIGHT ST

.300 Win. Mag., .338 Win. Mag., .375 H&H Mag.
**Magazine**: Detachable box, S/M 6 rounds, SM/L 5 rounds
**Features**: Comes in short actions Extra Short (XS), Short (S) and Short Magnum (SM), medium action (M), and long action (L); straight, classic walnut stock with rosewood forend tip and pistol grip cap; integral rails for scope mounts; free-floating barrel is cold-hammer-forged; adjustable single-stage trigger
**MSRP** . . . . . . . . . . . . . $2200–$2250

## 85 FINNLIGHT ST

**Action**: Bolt
**Stock**: Synthetic
**Barrel**: 20.25 in., 22.4 in.
**Sights**: None
**Weight**: 6 lb. 3 oz.–6 lb. 13 oz.
**Caliber**: (Short): .22-250 Rem., .243 Win., .260 Rem., .7mm-08 Rem., .308 Win.; (SM) .270 Win. Short Mag., .300 Win. Short Mag.; (Medium): .25-06 Rem., 6.5x55 SE, .270 Win., .30-06 Spfd.; (Long) 7mm Rem. Mag., .300 Win. Mag.
**Magazine**: Detachable box, S/M 6 rounds, SM/L 5 rounds
**Features**: Comes in short actions Short (S) and Short magnum (SM), Medium action (M), and Long action (L); single-stage trigger; two-way Sako safety locks both trigger and bolt handle; black synthetic stock with soft gray grip areas; pistol grip stock; integral rails for scope mounts; free-floating barrel is cold-hammer-forged of stainless steel
**MSRP** . . . . . . . . . . . . . $1650–$1700

RIFLES

# Sako

**SAKO 85 GREY WOLF**

**SAKO 85 KODIAK**

**SAKO 85 SAFARI**

## 85 GREY WOLF

**Action**: Bolt
**Stock**: Gray laminate
**Barrel**: 22 in., 24 in.
**Sights**: None
**Weight**: 7 lb. 4 oz.
**Caliber**: .270 Win., .30-06 Spfd., .300 Win. Mag., .270 WSM, .300 WSM, 7mm Rem. Mag.
**Magazine**: 4 or 5 rounds
**Features**: Stainless steel barrel and action; Warp-free stock makes the rifle suitable for hunting in extreme conditions
**MSRP**. . . . . . . . . . . . . . **$1600–$1650**

## 85 KODIAK

**Action**: Bolt
**Stock**: Laminated hardwood
**Barrel**: 12.25 in.
**Sights**: Open
**Weight**: 7 lb. 15 oz.
**Caliber**: .338 Win. Mag., .375 H&H Mag.
**Magazine**: Detachable box, 5 rounds
**Features**: Adjustable single-stage trigger; barrel band for front swivel; integral dovetail rails for secure scope mounting; straight stock made of gray matte-lacquered laminated hardwood and reinforced with two cross-bolts; free-floating "bull" barrel
**MSRP**. . . . . . . . . . . . . . . . . . **$1925**

## 85 SAFARI

**Action**: Bolt
**Stock**: Walnut
**Barrel**: 24.2 in.
**Sights**: Front bead, adjustable iron sights rear
**Weight**: 9 lb.
**Caliber**: .375 H&H Mag.

**Magazine**: Detachable box, 6 rounds
**Features**: Free-floating barrel; ergonomic walnut stock with checkering; staggered, two-row magazine with total control latch; single-set adjustable trigger; steel trigger guard; two-way Sako safety locks both trigger and bolt handle; Pachmayr recoil pad; limited models imported to U.S.
**MSRP**. . . . . . . . . . . **$10000–$10500**

## 85 VARMINT LAMINATED STAINLESS

**Action**: Bolt
**Stock**: Laminated hardwood
**Barrel**: 20 in., 23.6 in.
**Sights**: None
**Weight**: 8 lb. 10 oz.–9 lb.
**Caliber**: (XS) .204 Ruger, .222 Rem., .223 Rem.; (Short) .22-250 Rem., .243 Win., .260 Rem., 7mm-08 Rem., .308 Win., .338 Federal
**Magazine**: Detachable box, XS 7 rounds, S 6 rounds
**Features**: Comes in short actions Extra Short (XS) and Short (S); single-set trigger; two-way Sako safety locks both

trigger and bolt handle; straight stock with wide forend is made of brown matte laquered laminated hardwood; integral rail for scope mounts
**MSRP**. . . . . . . . . . . . . . . . . . **$2000**

## A7 TECOMATE ST

**Action**: Bolt
**Stock**: Synthetic
**Barrel**: 22 in., 24 in.
**Sights**: None
**Weight**: 6 lb. 8 oz.–7 lb.
**Caliber**: .22-250 Rem., .243 Win., .308 Win., .25-06 Rem., .270 Win., .30-06 Spfd., .300 Win. Mag., .270 WSM, .300 WSM, 7mm-08 Rem., 7mm Rem. Mag.
**Magazine**: 4 rounds
**Features**: Stainless or blued finish
**MSRP**. . . . . . . . . . . . . . . . . . **$1375**

## TRG 22

**Action**: Bolt
**Stock**: Synthetic
**Barrel**: 20 in., 26 in., 27.1 in.
**Sights**: None
**Weight**: 10 lb. 4 oz.–10 lb. 12 oz.
**Caliber**: .308 Win, .300 Win. Mag., .338 Lapua Mag.
**Magazine**: Detachable box, 5, 7, 10 rounds
**Features**: Double-stage trigger; two-way Sako safety locks both trigger and bolt handle; base of stock is made of polyurethane with aluminum skeleton; adjustable cheekpiece and buttplate; Ambidextrous stock in green or desert tan color; includes integral dovetail on receiver and is drilled and tapped for Picatinny rail mounting
**Green:**. . . . . . . . . . . . . . . . . **$3450**
**Tan:**. . . . . . . . . . . . . . **$5825–$6800**

**SAKO 85 VARMINT LAMINATED ST**

**SAKO A7 TECOMATE ST**

**SAKO TRG 22**

## 10 XP PREDATOR HUNTER PACKAGE BRUSH

**Action**: Bolt
**Stock**: Synthetic
**Barrel**: 22 in.
**Sights**: 4-12x40mm Scope
**Weight**: 8 lb. 8 oz.
**Caliber**: .223 Rem., .204 Ruger, .22-250 Rem., .243 Win.
**Magazine**: 4 rounds
**Features**: Mounted and bore-sighted scope; AccuTrigger; carbon steel barrel; synthetic camo stock
**MSRP** . . . . . . . . . . . . . . . . . . . . . **$945**

## 12 VARMINT SERIES BTCSS

**Action**: Bolt
**Stock**: Laminate
**Barrel**: 26 in.
**Sights**: None
**Weight**: 10 lb.
**Caliber**: .204 Ruger, .223 Rem., .22-250 Rem.
**Magazine**: Detachable box, 4 rounds
**Features**: Drilled and tapped for scope mounts; stainless steel barrel with high luster finish; AccuTrigger; wood laminate with thumbhole and satin finish
**MSRP** . . . . . . . . . . . . . . . . . . . **$1175**

## 14/114 AMERICAN CLASSIC

**Action**: Bolt
**Stock**: Wood
**Barrel**: 22 in., 24 in.
**Sights**: None
**Weight**: 7 lb. 4 oz.–7 lb. 12 oz.
**Caliber**: .243 Win., .250 Sav., .270 Win., .300 WSM, .30-06 Spfd., .300 Win. Mag., .308 Win., 7mm Rem. Mag., 7mm-08 Rem.
**Magazine**: Hinged floor plate, 2, 4 rounds
**Features**: Drilled and tapped for scope mounts; carbon steel barrel with matte blued finish; short action; AccuTrigger; satin finish wood stock
**MSRP** . . . . . . . . . . . . . . . . . . . . . **$885**

SAVAGE ARMS 10 XP PREDATOR HUNTER PACKAGE BRUSH

SAVAGE ARMS 12 VARMINT SERIES BTCSS

SAVAGE ARMS 14/114 AMERICAN CLASSIC

RIFLES

# Savage Arms

RIFLES

SAVAGE ARMS 25 LIGHTWEIGHT VARMINTER

SAVAGE ARMS 25 WALKING VARMINTER

SAVAGE ARMS AXIS

## 25 LIGHTWEIGHT VARMINTER

**Action**: Bolt
**Stock**: Wood laminate
**Barrel**: 24 in.
**Sights**: None
**Weight**: 8 lb. 4 oz.
**Caliber**: .17 Hornet, .204 Ruger, .22 Hornet, .223 Rem.
**Magazine**: Detachable box, 4 rounds
**Features**: Drilled and tapped for scope mounts; carbon steel barrel with blued satin finish; wood laminate stock with satin finish
**MSRP** . . . . . . . . . . . . . . . . . . . $730

## 25 WALKING VARMINTER

**Action**: Bolt
**Stock**: Synthetic
**Barrel**: 22 in.
**Sights**: None
**Weight**: 6 lb. 14 oz.
**Caliber**: .17 Hornet, .204 Ruger, .22 Hornet, .222 Rem., .223 Rem.
**Magazine**: Detachable box, 4 rounds
**Features**: Matte black synthetic stock; matte black carbon steel barrel; AccuTrigger
**MSRP** . . . . . . . . . . . . . . . . . . . $585

## AXIS

**Action**: Bolt
**Stock**: Synthetic
**Barrel**: 22 in.
**Sights**: None
**Weight**: 6 lb. 8 oz.
**Caliber**: .22-250 Rem., .223 Rem., .243 Win., .25-06 Rem., .270 Win., .30-06 Spfd., .308 Win., 7mm-08 Rem.
**Magazine**: Detachable box, 4 rounds
**Features**: New modern design, smooth bolt operation; drilled and tapped for scope mounts; carbon steel barrel with black matte finish; synthetic stock with matte black finish
**MSRP** . . . . . . . . . . . . . . . . . . . $375

# Savage Arms

SAVAGE ARMS HUNTER
SERIES 11/111 BTH

## HUNTER SERIES 11/111 BTH
*Action*: Bolt
*Stock*: Wood laminate
*Barrel*: 22 in.
*Sights*: None
*Weight*: 6 lb. 12 oz.–7 lb.
*Caliber*: .22-250 Rem., .243 Win.,
.223 Rem., .25-06 Rem., .270 Win.,
.30-06 Spfd., .308 Win.
*Magazine*: Hinged floor plate, 4
rounds
*Features*: Drilled and tapped for scope
mounts; carbon steel barrel with blued
satin finish; AccuTrigger; wood lami-
nate stock with thumbhole in satin fin-
ish
**MSRP**. . . . . . . . . . . . . . . . . . . . **$890**

## MAGNUM SERIES 93 BRJ
*Action*: Bolt
*Stock*: Wood laminate
*Barrel*: 21 in.
*Sights*: None
*Weight*: 7 lb.
*Caliber*: .22 WMR
*Magazine*: 5 rounds
*Features*: Carbon steel barrel in blued
satin finish; wood laminate stock;
AccuTrigger
**MSRP**. . . . . . . . . . . . . . . . . . . . **$510**

## MARK II SERIES BTV
*Action*: Bolt
*Stock*: Wood laminate
*Barrel*: 21 in.
*Sights*: None
*Weight*: 6 lb. 8 oz.
*Caliber*: .22LR
*Magazine*: Detachable box, 5 rounds
*Features*: Carbon steel barrel with
blued satin finish; wood laminate
stock with thumbhole; AccuTrigger
**MSRP**. . . . . . . . . . . . . . . . . . . . **$445**

SAVAGE ARMS MAGNUM
SERIES 93 BRJ

SAVAGE ARMS MARK II
SERIES BTV

# Savage Arms

## PACKAGE SERIES 16-116 INTERNATIONAL TROPHY HUNTER XP

**Action**: Bolt
**Stock**: Synthetic
**Barrel**: 22 in., 24 in.
**Sights**: Mounted Weaver 3-9x40 scope
**Weight**: 7 lb. 4 oz.–7 lb. 8 oz.
**Caliber**: .204 Ruger, .243 Win., .260 Rem., .270 WSM, .300 WSM, .308 Win., .375 Ruger, 6.5 Creedmoor, 7mm-08 Rem.
**Magazine**: Detachable box, 2, 4 rounds
**Features**: Matte black synthetic stock; stainless steel barrel with satin finish
**MSRP** . . . . . . . . . . . . . . . $795–$825

## RASCAL SINGLE SHOT

**Action**: Bolt
**Stock**: Synthetic, hardwood
**Barrel**: 16.125 in.
**Sights**: Adjustable
**Weight**: 2 lb. 10 oz.–2 lb. 15 oz.
**Caliber**: .22LR
**Magazine**: None
**Features**: Matte synthetic stock available in seven colors; adjustable peep sights; drilled and tapped for scope mounts; AccuTrigger; carbon steel barrel with satin blued finish
**Synthetic:** . . . . . . . . . . . . . . . $180
**Hardwood:** . . . . . . . . . . . . . . $225

## SEMI-AUTOMATIC SERIES 64 F

**Action**: Semiautomatic
**Stock**: Synthetic
**Barrel**: 20.5 in.
**Sights**: Open
**Weight**: 5 lb.
**Caliber**: .22LR
**Magazine**: Detachable box, 10 rounds
**Features**: Drilled and tapped for scope mounts; carbon steel barrel with satin blued finish; synthetic matte black stock
**MSRP** . . . . . . . . . . . . . . . . . . $175

## SPECIALTY SERIES 11-111 HOG HUNTER

**Action**: Bolt
**Stock**: Synthetic
**Barrel**: 20 in.
**Sights**: Adjustable
**Weight**: 7 lb. 4 oz.–8 lb.
**Caliber**: .223 Rem., .308 Win., .338 Win.
**Magazine**: Internal box, 4 rounds
**Features**: Green composite synthetic stock; matte black carbon steel barrel; LPA adjustable sights; threaded barrel; AccuTrigger
**MSRP** . . . . . . . . . . . . . . . . . . $535

SAVAGE ARMS PACKAGE SERIES 16-116 INTERNATIONAL TROPHY HUNTER XP

SAVAGE ARMS RASCAL SINGLE SHOT

SAVAGE ARMS SEMI-AUTOMATIC SERIES 64 F

SAVAGE ARMS SPECIALTY SERIES 11-111 HOG HUNTER

RIFLES

SAVAGE ARMS SPECIALTY SERIES 11-111 LADY HUNTER

SAVAGE ARMS SPECIALTY SERIES 11/111 LONG RANGE HUNTER

SAVAGE ARMS SPECIALTY SERIES 16/116 BEAR HUNTER

SAVAGE ARMS SPECIALTY SERIES 220

## SPECIALTY SERIES 11-111 LADY HUNTER

**Action**: Bolt
**Stock**: Wood
**Barrel**: 20 in.
**Sights**: None
**Weight**: 6 lb.–6 lb. 8 oz.
**Caliber**: .22-250 Rem., .223 Rem., .243 Win., .270 Win., .30-06 Spfd., .308 Win., 6.5 Creedmoor, 7mm-08 Rem.
**Magazine**: Detachable box, 4 rounds
**Features**: Oil-finish American walnut stock with ladies-specific geometry; carbon steel barrel in matter black
**MSRP** . . . . . . . . . . . . . . . . . . . **$840**

## SPECIALTY SERIES 11/111 LONG RANGE HUNTER

**Action**: Bolt
**Stock**: Synthetic
**Barrel**: 26 in.
**Sights**: None
**Weight**: 8 lb. 6 oz.
**Caliber**: .25-06 Rem., .260 Rem., .300 Win. Mag., .300 WSM, .308 Win., .338 Lapua Mag., 6.5 Creedmoor, 6.5x284 Norma, 7mm Rem. Mag.
**Magazine**: Hinged floor plate, 2, 4 rounds
**Features**: Drilled and tapped for scope mounts; carbon steel barrel with black matte finish; synthetic stock with black matte finish; AccuTrigger
**MSRP** . . . . . . . . . . . . . **$1020–$1290**

## SPECIALTY SERIES 16/116 BEAR HUNTER

**Action**: Bolt
**Stock**: Synthetic
**Barrel**: 23 in.
**Sights**: None
**Weight**: 7 lb. 8 oz.
**Caliber**: .300 Win. Mag., .300 WSM, .325 WSM, .338 Win. Mag., .375 Ruger
**Magazine**: Hinged floor plate, 2 rounds
**Features**: Drilled and tapped for scope mounts; adjustable muzzlebrake; stainless steel barrel; synthetic stock with matte camo finish; AccuTrigger; AccuStock
**MSRP** . . . . . . . . . . . . . . **$995–$1030**

## SPECIALTY SERIES 220 STANDARD, YOUTH, CAMO

**Action**: Bolt
**Stock**: Synthetic
**Barrel**: 22 in.
**Sights**: None
**Weight**: 7 lb. 8 oz.
**Caliber**: 20 Ga.
**Magazine**: 2 rounds
**Features**: Drilled and tapped for scope mounts; carbon steel barrel with matte blued finish; AccuTrigger; synthetic stock in matte black finish or camo
**Standard:** . . . . . . . . . . . . . . . . **$565**
**Camo:** . . . . . . . . . . . . . . . . . **$630**
**Youth:** . . . . . . . . . . . . . . . . . **$565**

# Savage Arms

SAVAGE ARMS STEVENS 200

SAVAGE ARMS TARGET
SERIES 12 BENCH REST

## STEVENS 200

*Action*: Bolt
*Stock*: Synthetic
*Barrel*: 22 in., 24 in.
*Sights*: None
*Weight*: 6 lb. 12 oz.
*Caliber*: .22-250 Rem., .223 Rem., .243 Win., .270 Win., .30-06 Spfd., .300 Win. Mag., .308 Win., 7mm Rem. Mag.
*Magazine*: Internal box, 3, 4 rounds
*Features*: Drilled and tapped for scope mounts; carbon steel barrel with satin blued barrel; synthetic stock with matte gray finish stock
MSRP . . . . . . . . . . . . . . . . . . . $420

## TARGET SERIES 12 BENCH REST

*Action*: Bolt, single shot
*Stock*: Wood laminate

*Barrel*: 29 in.
*Sights*: None
*Weight*: 12 lb. 12 oz.
*Caliber*: .308 Win., 6.5 x284 Norma, 6 Norma BR
*Magazine*: None
*Features*: Drilled and tapped for scope mounts; stainless steel barrel with high luster finish; wood laminate stock with satin finish; AccuTrigger
MSRP . . . . . . . . . . . . . . . . . $1550

## WEATHER WARRIOR SERIES 16/116 FCSS

*Action*: Bolt
*Stock*: Synthetic
*Barrel*: 22 in., 24 in.
*Sights*: None
*Weight*: 6 lb. 14 oz.–7.15 lb.
*Caliber*: .204 Ruger, .22-250 Rem., .223 Rem., .243 Win., .25-06 Rem., .260 Rem., .270 WSM, .270 Win., .30-06 Spfd., .300 WSM, .300 Win. Mag., .308 Win., .308 Win. Mag., .375 Ruger, 6.5 Creedmoor, 6.5x284 Norma, 7mm Rem. Mag., .7mm-08 Rem.
*Magazine*: Detachable box, 2, 4 rounds
*Features*: Drilled and tapped for scope mounts; stainless steel barrel with high luster finish; synthetic stock with black matte finish; AccuTrigger
MSRP . . . . . . . . . . . . . . . . $850–$885

SAVAGE ARMS WEATHER WARRIOR
SERIES 16/116 FCSS

# Sig Sauer

**SIG SAUER SIG516 PATROL**

**SIG SAUER 522 COMMANDO**

**SIG SAUER 551-A1**

## SIG522 COMMANDO
*Action*: Semiautomatic
*Stock*: Tactical synthetic
*Barrel*: 16 in.
*Sights*: Mini red-dot
*Weight*: 6 lb. 2 oz.
*Caliber*: .22LR
*Magazine*: Detachable box, 10, 25 rounds
*Features*: Removable inert training suppressor; anodized alloy upper receiver and M1913 mounted rail; folding telescopic stock
**MSRP** . . . . . . . . . . . . . . . . . . . **$600**

## 551-A1
*Action*: Semiautomatic
*Stock*: Swiss type
*Barrel*: 16 in.
*Sights*: Rotary diopter rear and hooded front
*Weight*: 7 lb.
*Caliber*: 5.56x45 NATO
*Magazine*: 20, 30 rounds
*Features*: Ambidextrous controls; 2-position gas piston operating system; 1:7 chrome-lined barrel; gray finish in honor of the Swiss 550 series barrel; SWAT variant features 1913 quad rail
**MSRP** . . . . . . . . . . . . . . . . . . **$1599**

## SIG516 PATROL
*Action*: Semiautomatic
*Stock*: Tactical synthetic
*Barrel*: 16 in.
*Sights*: None
*Weight*: 7 lb. 5 oz.
*Caliber*: 5.56mm NATO
*Magazine*: Detachable box, 30 rounds

*Features*: Gas piston operating system; three-position gas regulator; free-floating military grade chrome-lined barrel; M1913 Picatinny flat top upper; aircraft grade aluminum upper and lower receiver with hard coat anodize finish
**MSRP** . . . . . . . . . . . . . . . . . . **$1666**

# Sig Sauer

### SIG556 CLASSIC SWAT

**Action**: Semiautomatic
**Stock**: Tactical synthetic
**Barrel**: 16 in.
**Sights**: Rear rotary diopter sight
**Weight**: 8 lb. 3 oz.
**Caliber**: 5.56 x.45mm NATO
**Magazine**: Detachable box, 30 rounds
**Features**: Features full length gas piston operating system; quad rail and rotary diopter sight; black Swiss-type folding stock that adjusts to length; cold-hammer-forged barrel; alloy trigger housing; AR style magazine and flash suppressor
**MSRP**.................... $1399

### SIG556 PATROL RIFLE

**Action**: Semiautomatic
**Stock**: Tactical synthetic
**Barrel**: 14.4 in.
**Sights**: Rear rotary diopter sight
**Weight**: 7 lb. 8 oz.
**Caliber**: 5.56x45mm NATO, .223
**Magazine**: Detachable box, 30 rounds
**Features**: A2 Type flash suppressor; reduced length gas piston with two-position gas valve; improved design trigger casing; Swiss-type folding stock, adjustable for length; Swiss-type reduced lengthy polymer handguards; alloy quad rail reduced length tactical forend; RDSS rotary diopter sight system
**MSRP**.................... $1266

### SIG716

**Action**: Semiautomatic
**Stock**: Synthetic
**Barrel**: 12 in., 14.5 in., 16 in.
**Sights**: SIG flip-up front & rear
**Weight**: 9 lb.–9 lb. 11 oz.
**Caliber**: 7.62x51 NATO
**Magazine**: 20 rounds
**Features**: 4-position gas piston system; 1:10 16" chrome-lined chamber and bore; Magpul ACS stock & MIAD grip; M1913 quad rail; ambi selector; ambi mag release; integral QD sling points; machined into lower receiver & quad; offered in black, OD, and FDE; also offered in a 14.5" SBR variant
**MSRP**.............. $2066–$2172

### SIG716 PATROL RIFLE

**Action**: Semiautomatic
**Stock**: Tactical synthetic
**Barrel**: 16 in.

SIG SAUER SIG556 CLASSIC SWAT

SIG SAUER SIG556 PATROL RIFLE

SIG SAUER SIG716

SIG SAUER SIG716 PATROL RIFLE

**Sights**: None
**Weight**: 9 lb. 5 oz.
**Caliber**: 7.62x51mm NATO
**Magazine**: Detachable box, 20 rounds
**Features**: Short stroke pushrod operating system; M1913 MIL-STD rail; free-floating barrel; aluminum quad rail forend; telescoping stock
**MSRP**.................... $2132

# Sig Sauer

## SIG M400

**Action**: Semiautomatic
**Stock**: Synthetic
**Barrel**: 16 in.
**Sights**: Adjustable front post, dual aperture
**Weight**: 5.59 lb.
**Caliber**: 5.56x45mm NATO
**Magazine**: Detachable box, 30 rounds
**Features**: Military grade, chrome-lined barrel, flat top upper with M1913 accessory rail
**MSRP**. . . . . . . . . . . . . . . . . . $1200

## SIG M400 ENHANCED

**Action**: Semiautomatic
**Stock**: Magpul MOE
**Barrel**: 16 in.
**Sights**: None
**Weight**: 6 lb. 11 oz.
**Caliber**: 5.56x45 NATO
**Magazine**: 30 rounds
**Features**: SIG's first direct gas impingement system; taking the enhancements of the 516 platform into a traditional Stoner design; 1:7 chrome lined barrel; ambi selector & mag release; integral QD sling swivel mounts machined into lower; upper/lower tension adjustment device; offered in traditional configuration with removable carry handle with poly or 1913 quad rail; offered as 'enhanced' variants with Magpul MOE furniture in black, FDE, and OD; new variants also include a Sight Ready Platform (SRP), a lightweight with contoured barrel
**MSRP**. . . . . . . . . . . . . . . . . . $1234

SIG SAUER SIG M400

SIG SAUER M400
ENHANCED CARBINE

RIFLES

# Smith & Wesson

SMITH & WESSON M&P15-22 RIFLE

## M&P15-22 RIFLE

**Action**: Semiautomatic
**Stock**: Synthetic
**Barrel**: 18 in.
**Sights**: Adjustable A2 front post, adjustable dual aperture
**Weight**: 5 lb. 6 oz.
**Caliber**: .22LR
**Magazine**: Detachable box, 25 rounds
**Features**: Six-position collapsible stock; functioning charging handle; two-position receiver mounted safety selector; cartridge case deflector; bolt catch; recessed magazine release button; match grade precision, threaded barrel
**MSRP**. . . . . . . . . . . . . . . . . . $499

# Smith & Wesson

SMITH & WESSON
M&P15 300 WHISPER

SMITH & WESSON
M&P15 MOE MID

SMITH & WESSON M&P15

SMITH & WESSON M&P15 PC

## M&P15 300 WHISPER

*Action*: Semiautomatic
*Stock*: Synthetic
*Barrel*: 16 in.
*Sights*: None
*Weight*: 6 lb. 6 oz.
*Caliber*: .300 Whisper, .300 AAC Blackout
*Magazine*: Detachable box, 10 rounds
*Features*: Sub-sonic and super-sonic capabilities; 4140 chromoly steel barrel; forged 7075 aluminum receivers coated with Realtree APG finish; gas-operated rifle; single-stage trigger; integral one-piece trigger guard; six-position collapsible CAR stock; optics ready
**MSRP** . . . . . . . . . . . . . . . . . . . **$1119**

## M&P15

*Action*: Semiautomatic
*Stock*: Synthetic
*Barrel*: 16 in.
*Sights*: Troy adjustable front post, folding rear battle sight
*Weight*: 6 lb. 12 oz.
*Caliber*: 5.56 mm NATO, .223
*Magazine*: Detachable box, 30 rounds
*Features*: Six-position telescopic black stock; chrome-lined gas key and bolt carrier; flash suppressor compensator; two-position safety lever
**MSRP** . . . . . . . . . . . . . . . . . . . **$1249**

## M&P15 MOE MID

*Action*: Semiautomatic
*Stock*: Synthetic
*Barrel*: 16 in.
*Sights*: M4-A2 post front, folding Magpul rear
*Weight*: 6 lb. 8 oz.
*Caliber*: 5.56mm NATO
*Magazine*: Detachable box, 30 rounds
*Features*: Mid-length operating system, patent-pending flash hider; available in black and dark earth finish; Magpul designed forged lower receiver with flared magazine; one-piece integrated trigger guard; Melonite finish on barrel; MOE six-position collapsible buttstock
**MSRP** . . . . . . . . . . . . . . . . . . . **$1259**

## M&P15 PC

*Action*: Semiautomatic
*Stock*: Synthetic
*Barrel*: 20 in.
*Sights*: None
*Weight*: 8 lb. 2 oz.
*Caliber*: 5.56mm NATO, .223
*Magazine*: Detachable box, 10 rounds
*Features*: Hogue Green pistol grip; A2 buttstock; two-stage trigger; Realtree Advantage Max-1 Camo finish stock; chromed gas key and bolt carrier
**Black:** . . . . . . . . . . . . . . . . . . **$1509**
**Camo:** . . . . . . . . . . . . . . . . . **$1539**

### M&P15 SPORT

*Action*: Semiautomatic
*Stock*: Synthetic
*Barrel*: 16 in.
*Sights*: Adjustable A2 front post, adjustable dual aperture
*Weight*: 6 lb. 8 oz.
*Caliber*: 5.56mm NATO
*Magazine*: Detachable box, 10, 30 rounds
*Features*: Six-position telescopic black stock or fixed stock; chrome-lined gas key and bolt carrier; flash suppressor compensator; two-position safety lever
**MSRP** . . . . . . . . . . . . . . . . . . . . **$839**

### M&P15T

*Action*: Semiautomatic
*Stock*: Synthetic
*Barrel*: 16 in.
*Sights*: Folding Magpul
*Weight*: 6.85 lb.
*Caliber*: 5.56mm NATO
*Magazine*: Detachable box, 30 rounds
*Features*: 10-in. patent-pending, anti-twist, free-floating quad rail; melonite barrel; chromed bolt carrier and gas key; gas operated; single-stage trigger
**MSRP** . . . . . . . . . . . . . . . . . . . **$1159**

### M&P15 VTAC II

*Action*: Semiautomatic
*Stock*: Synthetic
*Barrel*: 16 in.
*Sights*: None
*Weight*: 6 lb. 4 oz.
*Caliber*: 5.56mm NATO
*Magazine*: Detachable box, 30 rounds
*Features*: Mid-length operating system, patent-pending flash hider; 4150 CMV steel barrel with Melonite finish; VTAC/Troy Extreme TRX handguard that reduces heat transfer; packaged with 2-inch adjustable Picatinny-style rails; Geissele Super V trigger
**MSRP** . . . . . . . . . . . . . . . . . . . **$1949**

**RIFLES**

SMITH & WESSON M&P15 SPORT

SMITH & WESSON M&P15T

SMITH & WESSON
M&P15 VTAC II

# Springfield Armory

**SPRINGFIELD ARMORY M1A SOCOM 16**

**SPRINGFIELD ARMORY NATIONAL MATCH M1A**

**SPRINGFIELD ARMORY SCOUT SQUAD**

**SPRINGFIELD ARMORY STANDARD M1A**

## M1A SOCOM 16
*Action*: Autoloading
*Stock*: Composite
*Barrel*: 16.25 in.
*Sights*: Tritium front sight
*Weight*: 8 lb. 13 oz.
*Caliber*: 7.62x51mm NATO, .308 Win
*Magazine*: Detachable box, 10 rounds
*Features*: Muzzlebrake; forward mounted scope base; two-stage military trigger; composite black or green stock
**MSRP** . . . . . . . . . . . . . . . . . . **$1893**

## NATIONAL MATCH M1A
*Action*: Autoloading
*Stock*: Walnut
*Barrel*: 22 in.
*Sights*: National Match front military post sight; rear National Match hooded aperture

*Weight*: 9 lb. 13 oz.
*Caliber*: 7.62x51mm NATO, .308 Win.
*Magazine*: Detachable box, 10 rounds
*Features*: Glass bedded; NM gas cylinder; NM recoil spring guide; NM flash suppressor; walnut stock; stainless steel or carbon barrel; two-stage military trigger
**MSRP** . . . . . . . . . . . . . . **$2318–$2373**

## SCOUT SQUAD
*Action*: Autoloading
*Stock*: Walnut, composite
*Barrel*: 18 in.
*Sights*: National Match front military post sight; rear military aperture
*Weight*: 9 lb. 5 oz.
*Caliber*: 7.62x51mm NATO, .308 Win.
*Magazine*: Detachable box, 10 rounds
*Features*: Mounted optical sight base; muzzle stabilizers; black or green

fiberglass composite, American walnut stock or Mossy Oak camo stock; two-stage military trigger
**MSRP** . . . . . . . . . . . . . **$1761–$1893**

## STANDARD M1A
*Action*: Autoloading
*Stock*: Composite or walnut
*Barrel*: 22 in.
*Sights*: National Match military front post, adjustable rear aperture sight
*Weight*: 9 lb. 5 oz.
*Caliber*: 7.62x51mm NATO, .308 Win.
*Magazine*: Detachable box, 10 rounds
*Features*: Black fiberglass with rubber buttplate, Mossy Oak stock with metal buttplate or American walnut with original military buttplate; two-stage military trigger
**MSRP** . . . . . . . . . . . . . **$1640–$1739**

**RIFLES**

## MODEL 3G

**Action**: Semiautomatic
**Stock**: Synthetic
**Barrel**: 18 in.
**Sights**: Optional iron sights
**Weight**: 7 lb. 13 oz.
**Caliber**: 5.56 NATO
**Magazine**: 30 rounds
**Features**: Stainless steel fluted heavy barrel with rifle length gas system; Stag Arms 3G compensator; Samson Evolution handguard; Geissele Super 3-Gun trigger; Magpul collapsible ACS buttstock and MOE pistol grip; optional Dueck Defense Rapid Transition sights
**MSRP** . . . . . . . . . . . . . . . . . . **$1459**
**Left-hand**: . . . . . . . . . . . . . . . **$1479**

## MODEL 8

**Action**: Gas-operated piston autoloader
**Stock**: Synthetic
**Barrel**: 20 in.
**Sights**: Midwest Industries front and rear flip-up
**Weight**: 6 lb. 14 oz.

**Caliber**: 5.56 NATO
**Magazine**: Detachable box, 30 rounds
**Features**: Right-and left-hand available; six-position collapsible stock; chrome-lined barrel
**MSRP** . . . . . . . . . . . . . . . . . . **$1145**

STAG ARMS 3G

STAG ARMS MODEL 8

## AUG/A3 SA USA

**Action**: Semiautomatic
**Stock**: Synthetic
**Barrel**: 16 in.
**Sights**: None
**Weight**: 8 lb. 2 oz.
**Caliber**: .223 Rem.
**Magazine**: Detachable transparent box, 30 rounds
**Features**: Synthetic black stock; lateral push-through type, locks trigger; 1913 Picatinny rail; changeable barrel; includes factory AUG sling and cleaning kit that fits inside butt stock
**MSRP** . . . . . . . . . . . . . . . . . . **$2099**

## DUETT HUNTING COMBINATION RIFLE/ SHOTGUN

**Action**: Break-action
**Stock**: Walnut
**Barrel**: 23.6 in.
**Sights**: Open sights, 11mm prismatic scope mount rail

STEYR ARMS AUG/A3 SA USA

**Weight**: 6 lb. 6 oz.
**Caliber**: Rifle: .222 Rem., .243 Win., .308 Win., 7x65R, .30-06 Spfd., .30R Blaser, 8x57 IRS, 9.3x74R; Shotgun: 12 Ga./3-inch
**Magazine**: None
**Features**: Break-action over-under combination rifle/shotgun; dual gold-plated single-stage triggers; free-floated cold-hammer-forged barrels, Mannox finish; tang-mounted manual cocking lever; 5 models available; manual cocking system; European walnut stock; checkered forend and pistol grip
**Standard**: . . . . . . . . . . . . . . . . **$2850**

## CLASSIC

**Action**: Bolt
**Stock**: European Walnut
**Barrel**: 20 in., 23.6 in., 25.6 in.
**Sights**: Open
**Weight**: 7 lb. 5 oz.
**Caliber**: .222 Rem., .223 Rem., .243 Win., 6.5x55 SE, .270 Win., 7x64, .25-06 Rem., .308 Win., .30-06 Spfd., 8x57 JS, 9.3x62, 6.5x57
**Magazine**: Detachable box, 3, 4 rounds
**Features**: Set or direct trigger; sights included for full stock only; Bavarian-styled cheekpiece; safe bolt system; case hardening surface finish on European walnut stock
**Half stock**: . . . . . . . . . . . . . . . **$2795**
**Full stock**: . . . . . . . . . . . . . . . **$2995**

STEYR ARMS DUETT COMBO

STEYR ARMS MANNLICHER CLASSIC

# Steyr Arms

**STEYR ARMS MANNLICHER PRO HUNTER**

**STEYR ARMS MANNLICHER SCOUT**

**STEYR ARMS SSG 08**

## PRO HUNTER
*Action*: Bolt
*Stock*: Synthetic
*Barrel*: 20 in., 23.6 in., 25.6 in.
*Sights*: None
*Weight*: 7 lb. 5 oz.–8 lb. 3 oz.
*Caliber*: .222 Rem., .223 Rem., .243 Win., 6.5x55SE, .25-06 Rem., .270 Win., 7x64, 7mm-08 Rem., .308 Win., .30-06 Spfd., 9.3x62, .338 Fed. Mag. Magnum Caliber: .300 Win. Mag., 9.3x62, 7mm Swam, .270 WSM, .300 WSM
*Magazine*: Detachable box
*Features*: Direct trigger, optionally set trigger; durable synthetic stock adjusted by spacers; Mannotm metal surface finish protects against corrosion; three-position safety

**MSRP** . . . . . . . . . . . . . . . . . . **$1150**
**Stainless:** . . . . . . . . . . . . . . . **$1250**

## SCOUT
*Action*: Bolt
*Stock*: Synthetic
*Barrel*: 19 in.
*Sights*: None
*Weight*: 6 lb. 10 oz.
*Caliber*: .243 Rem., 7mm-08 Rem., .308 Win.
*Magazine*: Box, 5 rounds (optional 10 round magazine)

*Features*: Weaver scope mounting rail; set trigger or direct trigger; synthetic stock in black or gray wood imitation; optional bipod integrated into forearm; matte black or stainless steel finish on barrel

**MSRP** . . . . . . . . . . . . . . . . . . **$2099**

## SSG 08
*Action*: Bolt
*Stock*: Synthetic
*Barrel*: 20 in., 23.6 in.
*Sights*: None

*Weight*: 5 lb. 8 oz.–5 lb. 11 oz.
*Caliber*: .308 Win.
*Magazine*: Box, 10 rounds
*Features*: Direct trigger; Mannox TM system; high grade aluminum folding stock; adjustable cheekpiece and buttplate with height marking; ergonomic exchangeable pistol grip; UIT rail and Picatinny rail; muzzlebrake; Versa-Pod

**MSRP** . . . . . . . . . . . . . . **$5895–$6795**

# Szecsei & Fuchs

**SZECSEI & FUCHS DOUBLE BOLT REPEATER**

## DOUBLE BOLT REPEATER
*Action*: Bolt
*Stock*: Turkish walnut
*Weight*: 11 lb. 6 oz. round barrel, 13 lb.–15 lb. 3 oz. octagonal barrel
*Caliber*: Available in many popular calibers. The larger caliber rifles are available in .17 to .700. Their most affordable options are the .17 and .22 rifles.
*Magazine*: Detachable box, 4+2 rounds

*Features*: Hungarian inventor Joseph Szecsei developed his innovative design after being charged simultaneously by three elephants in 1989. Built with great care and much handiwork from the finest materials, it follows a design remarkable for its cleverness. While the rifle is not light-weight, it can be aimed quickly and offers more large-caliber firepower than any competitor. The six-shot magazine feeds two rounds simultaneously, both of

which can then be fired by two quick pulls of the trigger. Optical sight is secured with titanium mounting; triggers have integrated, noiseless double-firing safety catch; titanium and steel barrels in octagon or round; one-piece bolt reloads two rounds. *As these rifles are custom order only and with the fluctuation of the U.S. dollar, it is best to contact the sales representative listed in back to obtain a firm quotation. Average product delivery currently 14 months.

**Small caliber (.17 and .22) rifle base price:** . . . . . . . . . . **$30000**
**Larger caliber rifle base price:** . . . . . . . . . . . . . . **$75000**

# Tactical Rifles

## CLASSIC SPORTER

**Action**: Chimera bolt
**Stock**: Walnut
**Barrel**: 22 in.
**Sights**: None
**Weight**: 8 lb. 14 oz.
**Caliber**: .308 Win., .260 Rem., 6.5 Creedmoor and Lapua, .243 Win., 7mm-08 Rem. (short action); .30-06 Spfd., .270 Win., .300 Win. Mag., 7mm Rem. Mag. (long action)
**Magazine**: 4+1 rounds
**Features**: Chimera action is constructed from stainless steel with a hand-fitted spiral-groove bolt and "Magnum" extractor; Picatinny rail; XXX grade English walnut stock with 22 lpi checkering at grip and forearm; extreme environment matte black finish
**MSRP** . . . . . . . . . . . . . . . . . . . $5895

## SPECIAL PURPOSE GRENDEL (SPG)

**Action**: Semiautomatic
**Stock**: Magpul PRS
**Barrel**: 20 in.
**Sights**: None
**Weight**: 10 lb. 8 oz.
**Caliber**: 6.5 Grendel, .264 Les Baer Custom
**Magazine**: 17+1 rounds
**Features**: Stainless steel match grade barrel; SureFire muzzlebrake; enhanced upper and lower receivers; Magpul MOE pistol grip; Picatinny rail
**MSRP** . . . . . . . . . . . . . . . . . . $3595

## TACTICAL L.R.

**Action**: Bolt, 700 Rem.
**Stock**: Synthetic
**Barrel**: 18 in.-26 in.
**Sights**: None
**Weight**: 12 lb.–13 lb. 6 oz.
**Caliber**: 7.62 NATO, .308 Win.
**Magazine**: Detachable box, 5, 10 rounds
**Features**: Ergonomic thumbhole stock comes in black or green; raised cheekpiece; free-floating chromoly match grade barrel; ambidextrous sling swivel studs; soft rubber recoil pad; 1913 MIL-STD Picatinny rail; aluminum block chassis stock system; optional bipod
**MSRP** . . . . . . . . . . . . . . . . . . $2950

**RIFLES**

TACTICAL RIFLES CLASSIC SPORTER

TACTICAL RIFLES SPG

TACTICAL RIFLES TACTICAL L.R.

# Taylor's & Co. Firearms

### 1860 HENRY LEVER ACTION RIFLE

**Action**: Lever
**Stock**: Walnut
**Barrel**: 24.25 in.
**Sights**: Open
**Weight**: 9 lb. 3 oz.
**Caliber**: .44-40
**Magazine**: Under-barrel tube, 9-13 rounds
**Features**: Brass frame; octagonal barrel with blued finish; includes sling swivels
**MSRP** . . . . . . . . . . . . . **$1533–$1663**

### 1860 HENRY RIFLE WITH STANDARD ENGRAVING

**Action**: Lever
**Stock**: Walnut
**Barrel**: 24.25 in.
**Sights**: Open
**Weight**: 9 lb. 3 oz.
**Caliber**: .45LC
**Magazine**: Under-barrel tube, 9-13 rounds
**Features**: Standard engraved brass; octagonal barrel with blued finish
**MSRP** . . . . . . . . . . . . . . . . . **$1782**

TAYLOR'S & CO. 1873 RIFLE - CHECKERED STRAIGHT STOCK

TAYLOR'S & CO. ALASKAN TAKE-DOWN MODEL

TAYLOR'S & CO. 1860 HENRY LEVER ACTION RIFLE

TAYLOR'S & CO. 1860 HENRY RIFLE WITH STANDARD ENGRAVING

TAYLOR'S & CO. LIGHTNING SLIDE ACTION RIFLE

### 1873 RIFLE - CHECKERED STRAIGHT STOCK

**Action**: Lever
**Stock**: Walnut
**Barrel**: 20 in.
**Sights**: Open
**Weight**: 8 lb. 8 oz.
**Caliber**: .357 Mag., .45 LC
**Magazine**: 10+1 rounds
**Features**: Case-hardened frame; straight stock with checkering; available with full octagon barrel
**MSRP** . . . . . . . . . . . . . . . . . **$1341**

### 1892 ALASKAN TAKE-DOWN MODEL

**Action**: Lever
**Stock**: Synthetic
**Barrel**: 16 in., 20 in.
**Sights**: Skinner rear
**Weight**: 6 lb. 10 oz.
**Caliber**: .44RM, .45 LC
**Magazine**: 10 rounds
**Features**: Matte chrome finish; soft touch stock
**MSRP** . . . . . . . . . . . . . . . . . **$1324**

### LIGHTNING SLIDE ACTION RIFLE

**Action**: Slide
**Stock**: Walnut
**Barrel**: 24.25 in., 26 in.
**Sights**: Open
**Weight**: 6 lb. 3 oz.–6 lb. 8 oz.
**Caliber**: .45LC, .44-40, .357 Mag.
**Magazine**: Under-barrel tube
**Features**: Case-hardened frame; walnut stock with checkered forend; octagonal barrel
**MSRP** . . . . . . . . . . . . . **$1236–$1264**

# Thompson/Center

THOMPSON/CENTER ENCORE PRO
HUNTER CENTERFIRE

THOMPSON/CENTER G2 CONTENDER

THOMPSON/
CENTER
DIMENSION

## DIMENSION

*Action*: Bolt
*Stock*: Composite
*Barrel*: 22 in., 24 in.
*Sights*: None
*Weight*: 7 lb.
*Caliber*: .204 Ruger, .223 Rem., .22-250 Rem., .243 Win., 7mm-08 Rem., .308 Win., .270 Win., .30-06 Spfd., 7mm Rem. Mag., .300 Win. Mag.
*Magazine*: 3 rounds
*Features*: A bolt action platform you can build on season after season; switch out barrels, bolts, magazines, and and other components such as scopes and mounts
**MSRP** . . . . . . . . . . . . . . . . . . **$689**

## ENCORE PRO HUNTER CENTERFIRE

*Action*: Single-shot, break-open
*Stock*: Composite, hardwood
*Barrel*: 20 in., 28 in.
*Sights*: Optional fiber optic sights and peep sights
*Weight*: 6 lb. 4 oz.–7 lb. 12 oz.
*Caliber*: .204 Ruger, .223 Ruger, .22-250 Rem., .243 Win., .25-06 Rem., .270 Win., .280 Rem., .7mm Rem. Mag., 7mm-08 Rem., .300 Win. Mag., .308 Win., .30-06 Spfd., .45-70 Govt., .460 S&W, .500 S&W
*Magazine*: None
*Features*: Swing hammer; Flextech stock in black or Realtree Hardwoods camo; fluted barrel; thumbhole stock optional; SIMS recoil pad; engraved stainless steel frame; readily interchangeable barrels
**MSRP** . . . . . . . . . . . . . . . . . . **$1015**

## G2 CONTENDER

*Action*: Single-shot, break-open
*Stock*: Walnut, composite
*Barrel*: 18 in., 23 in.
*Sights*: None
*Weight*: 5 lb. 6 oz.
*Caliber*: .17 HMR, .22LR Match, 5mm Rem. Mag., .204 Ruger, .223 Rem., 6.8 Rem., 7-30 Waters, .30-30 Win., .45-70 Govt.
*Magazine*: None
*Features*: Blued or stainless steel barrel; automatic hammer block with bolt interlock; drilled and tapped for scope mounts; button rifled
**MSRP** . . . . . . . . . . . . . . . . . . **$906**

# Thompson/Center

RIFLES

**THOMPSON/
CENTER PROHUNTER
PREDATOR**

**THOMPSON/
CENTER VENTURE
COMPACT**

**THOMPSON/
CENTER VENTURE
PREDATOR SNOW**

## PROHUNTER PREDATOR
***Action***: Single-shot, break-open
***Stock***: Composite
***Barrel***: 28 in.
***Sights***: None
***Weight***: 7 lb. 12 oz.
***Caliber***: .204 Ruger, .223 Rem., .22-250 Rem., .308 Win.
***Magazine***: None
***Features***: Realtree MAX-1 camo composite stock and barrel; FlexTech; mounted and drilled for scopes
**MSRP** . . . . . . . . . . . . . . . . . . . **$882**

## VENTURE COMPACT
***Action***: Bolt
***Stock***: Composite
***Barrel***: 20 in.
***Sights***: None
***Weight***: 6 lb. 12 oz.
***Caliber***: .22-250 Rem., .243 Win., .308 Win., 7mm-08
***Magazine***: Detachable box, 3+1 rounds
***Features***: Adjustable trigger; included spacer and buttpad; Hogue traction inlays; Melanite coated bolt; two position safety
**MSRP** . . . . . . . . . . . . . . . . . . . **$537**

## VENTURE PREDATOR SNOW
***Action***: Bolt
***Stock***: Composite
***Barrel***: 22 in., 24 in.
***Sights***: Bases for mounting scopes
***Weight***: 6 lb. 12 oz.
***Caliber***: 7mm-08, .243 Rem., .22-250 Rem., .308 Win.
***Magazine***: 3+1 rounds
***Features***: Adjustable trigger; Hogue rubber inlays; sling swivel studs; Weather Shield bolt handle
**MSRP** . . . . . . . . . . . . . . . . . . . **$638**

TIKKA T3 HUNTER

## T3 HUNTER

**Action**: Bolt
**Stock**: Walnut
**Barrel**: 20 in., 22.4 in., 24.4 in.
**Sights**: None
**Weight**: 6 lb. 10 oz.–7 lb.
**Caliber**: .204 Ruger, .222 Rem, .223 Rem., .22-250 Rem., .243 Win., .260 Rem., 7mm-08 Rem., .308 Win., .338 Federal, .25-06 Rem., 6.5x55 SE, .270 Win., 7x64, .30-06 Spfd., 8x57IS, 9.3x62, 7mm Rem. Mag., .300 Win. Mag., .338 Win. Mag., .270 Win. Short Mag., .300 Win. Short Mag.
**Magazine**: Detachable box, 4, 5 rounds
**Features**: Sling swivels; free-floating cold-hammer-forged barrel; two locking Lug T3 action; two-stage safety; single-set trigger; walnut stock in oil finish and optional matte lacquered stock; integral scope mounts
**MSRP** . . . . . . . . . . . . . . . . . . . . . **$745**

## T3 LITE

**Action**: Bolt
**Stock**: Synthetic
**Barrel**: 20 in., 22.4 in., 24.4 in.
**Sights**: None
**Weight**: 6 lb.–6 lb. 6 oz.
**Caliber**: .204 Ruger, .222 Rem., .223 Rem., .22-250 Rem., .243 Win., .260 Rem., 7mm-08 Rem., .308 Win., .338 Federal, .25-06 Rem., 6.5x55 SE, .270 Win., 7x64, .30-06 Spfd., 8x57IS, 9.3x62, 7mm Rem. Mag., .300 Win. Mag., .338 Win. Mag., .270 Win. Short Mag., .300 Win. Short Mag.
**Magazine**: Detachable box, 4, 5 rounds
**Features**: Stainless steel bolt; two-stage safety; single-set trigger; fiberglass synthetic stock in black; Weaver scope mount bases; free-floating, cold-hammer-forged barrel
**MSRP** . . . . . . . . . . . . . . . **$625–$660**
**Stainless:** . . . . . . . . . . . . . **$750–$800**
**Stainless, LH:** . . . . . . . . . . **$825–$850**

## T3 SPORTER

**Action**: Bolt
**Stock**: Laminated wood, oiled
**Barrel**: 20 in., 24 in.
**Sights**: Scope rail and threads for Weaver-type scope rail
**Weight**: 9 lb.–9 lb. 11 oz.
**Caliber**: .222 Rem., .223 Rem., 6.5x55 SE, .260 Rem., .308 Win.
**Magazine**: 5, 6 rounds
**Features**: Adjustable cheekpiece; adjustable recoil pad in length and height; various rail placements that allow rifle to be carried in biathlon style; metal parts are matte blued; limited number of left-handed models imported to U.S.
**MSRP** . . . . . . . . . . . . . . . . . . **$1850**
**Left-handed:** . . . . . . . . . . . . . **$1925**

**RIFLES**

TIKKA T3 LITE

TIKKA T3 SPORTER LEFT-HANDED

# Uberti

## 1860 HENRY RIFLE
*Action*: Lever
*Stock*: Walnut
*Barrel*: 18.5 in., 24.5 in.
*Sights*: Adjustable
*Weight*: 9 lb.
*Caliber*: .45 Colt, .44-40
*Magazine*: Under-barrel tube, 8+1, 13+1 rounds
*Features*: Blued or standard buttplate; case-hardened lever and frame; A-grade walnut stock; octagonal barrel
**MSRP** . . . . . . . . . . . . . . **$1399–$1429**

UBERTI 1860 HENRY RIFLE

## 1866 YELLOWBOY
*Action*: Lever
*Stock*: Walnut
*Barrel*: 19 in., 20 in., 24.25 in.
*Sights*: Adjustable
*Weight*: 8 lb. 3 oz.
*Caliber*: .45 Colt, .44-40, .38 Spl.
*Magazine*: Under barrel tube, 10+1, 13+1 rounds
*Features*: Brass forend nose cap; solid brass crescent buttplate; case-hardened lever; brass frame and buttplate
**MSRP** . . . . . . . . . . . . . . **$1099–$1149**

UBERTI 1866 YELLOWBOY

## 1871 ROLLING BLOCK HUNTER CARBINE
*Action*: Rolling block
*Stock*: Walnut
*Barrel*: 22 in.
*Sights*: Fixed
*Weight*: 4 lb. 8 oz.
*Caliber*: .38-55, .30-30, .45-70
*Magazine*: None
*Features*: Rubber buttpad; case-colored receiver
**MSRP** . . . . . . . . . . . . . . . . . . . **$799**

UBERTI 1871 ROLLING BLOCK HUNTER CARBINE

## 1871 ROLLING BLOCK HUNTER RIMFIRE
*Action*: Rolling block
*Stock*: Walnut
*Barrel*: 22 in.
*Sights*: Adjustable
*Weight*: 4 lb. 8 oz.
*Caliber*: .22LR, .22 Mag., .17 HMR
*Magazine*: None
*Features*: Round blued barrel; brass trigger guard; case-hardened frame; A-grade walnut stock with rubber buttpad
**MSRP** . . . . . . . . . . . . . . . . . . . **$709**

UBERTI 1871 ROLLING BLOCK HUNTER RIMFIRE

# Uberti

UBERTI 1873 CARBINE

UBERTI 1874 CAVALRY CARBINE SHARPS

UBERTI 1874 SHARPS RIFLE

UBERTI 1876 CENTENNIAL

UBERTI 1883 BURGESS RIFLE

## 1873 RIFLE & CARBINE

**Action**: Lever
**Stock**: Walnut
**Barrel**: 16.1 in., 18 in., 19 in., 20 in., 24.5 in.
**Sights**: Adjustable
**Weight**: 7 lb. 3 oz.–8 lb. 3 oz.
**Caliber**: .45 Colt, .357 Mag., .44-44
**Magazine**: Under-barrel tube, 9+1, 10+1, 13+1 rounds
**Features**: Octagonal barrel on rifle; round barrel on carbine and trapper; A-grade walnut with checkered pistol grip and forend
**Trapper:**................. $1259
**Rifle:**.............. $1259–$1309
**Carbine:**.......... $1219–$1309
**Sporting:**.......... $1259–$1399

## 1874 CAVALRY CARBINE SHARPS

**Action**: Falling block
**Stock**: Walnut
**Barrel**: 22 in.
**Sights**: Creedmoor Sight
**Weight**: 8 lb.
**Caliber**: .45-70
**Magazine**: None
**Features**: Round blued barrel; case-hardened levers and blued buttplate
**MSRP**.................. $1739

## 1874 SHARPS RIFLE

**Action**: Falling block
**Stock**: Walnut
**Barrel**: 32 in., 34 in.
**Sights**: Creedmoor Sight
**Weight**: 10 lb. 4 oz.–11 lb.
**Caliber**: .45-70
**Magazine**: None
**Features**: Blued octagonal barrel; checkered walnut stock; case-hardened, except Extra Deluxe model; double-set trigger; pewter forend cap
**Special:**.................. $1949
**Deluxe:**................. $3059
**Down Under:**........... $2509
**Buffalo Hunter:**........... $2469
**Extra Deluxe:**............. $4869

## 1876 CENTENNIAL

**Action**: Lever
**Stock**: Walnut
**Barrel**: 28 in.
**Sights**: Adjustable
**Weight**: 10 lb.
**Caliber**: .45-60, .45-75, .50-95
**Magazine**: 11+1 rounds
**Features**: Case-hardened frame and lever; blued buttplate; octagonal barrel; straight stock
**MSRP**.................... $1609

## 1883 BURGESS RIFLE & CARBINE

**Action**: Lever
**Stock**: Walnut
**Barrel**: 20 in. (carbine), 25.5 in. (rifle)
**Sights**: Fixed
**Weight**: 7 lb. 10 oz.–8 lb. 2 oz.
**Caliber**: .45 Colt
**Magazine**: Under-barrel tube, 10, 13 rounds
**Features**: Case-hardened, round barrel; straight grip
**MSRP**.................. $1499

RIFLES

# Uberti

### 1885 HIGH-WALL SINGLE-SHOT

**Action**: Falling block
**Stock**: Walnut
**Barrel**: 28 in., 30 in., 32 in.
**Sights**: Adjustable
**Weight**: 9 lb. 5 oz. (carbine), 10 lb.
**Caliber**: .45-70, .45-90, .45-120
**Magazine**: None
**Features**: Case-hardened frame and lever; blued buttplate; octagonal barrel; carbine model has round barrel; carbine and sporting rifle have straight stock
**Carbine**: . . . . . . . . . . . . . . . . . $1009
**Sporting Rifle**: . . . . . . . $1079–$1139
**Special Sporting Rifle**: . $1199–$1279

### LIGHTNING

**Action**: Pump
**Stock**: Walnut
**Barrel**: 20 in., 24.25 in.
**Sights**: Adjustable
**Weight**: 6 lb. 3 oz.–6 lb. 8 oz.
**Caliber**: .45 Colt, .357 Mag.
**Magazine**: Under-barrel tube, 10+1 round (short rifle), 13+1 rounds (standard)
**Features**: Case-hardened frame and trigger guard; octagonal barrel
**MSRP**. . . . . . . . . . . . . . . . . . $1279

### SILVERBOY LEVER ACTION

**Action**: Lever
**Stock**: Walnut
**Barrel**: 19 in.
**Sights**: Fixed
**Weight**: 5 lb. 13 oz.
**Caliber**: .22LR, .22 Mag.
**Magazine**: 15+1 rounds
**Features**: Chrome-plated alloy reciever; walnut straight stock; cartridge-control mechanism allows controlled-round-feed; blued barrel
**MSRP**. . . . . . . . . . . . . . .$589–$599

### SPRINGFIELD TRAPDOOR CARBINE

**Action**: Hinged breech
**Stock**: Walnut
**Barrel**: 22 in.
**Sights**: Adjustable
**Weight**: 7 lb. 5 oz.
**Caliber**: .45-70
**Magazine**: None
**Features**: Blued steel, case-hardened breechblock and buttplate; fitted with sliding ring and bar for cavalryman to

UBERTI 1885 HIGH-WALL SINGLE-SHOT SPECIAL SPORTING MODEL

UBERTI LIGHTNING

UBERTI SILVERBOY LEVER ACTION

UBERTI SPRINGFIELD TRAPDOOR CARBINE

UBERTI SPRINGFIELD TRAPDOOR RIFLE

carry it clipped to carbine sling
**MSRP**. . . . . . . . . . . . . . . . . . $1599

### SPRINGFIELD TRAPDOOR RIFLE

**Action**: Hinged breech
**Stock**: Walnut
**Barrel**: 32.5 in.

**Sights**: Adjustable
**Weight**: 8 lb. 13 oz.
**Caliber**: .45-70
**Magazine**: None
**Features**: Blued steel, case-hardened breechblock and buttplate
**MSRP**. . . . . . . . . . . . . . . . . . $1879

# Volquartsen Custom

## TF-17 & TF-22

**Action**: Autoloader
**Stock**: Ambidextrous birch
**Barrel**: 18.5 in.
**Sights**: Picatinny Mil-Spec rail
**Weight**: 8 lb. 8 oz.
**Caliber**: .17 HMR, .22 WMR
**Magazine**: Rotary mag, 9 rounds
**Features**: Blowback design, TG2000 trigger unit with 2.25-lb. pull; black stainless barrel
**MSRP**. . . . . . . . . . . . . . . . . . . $1086

**VOLQUARTSEN CUSTOM TF-17**

# Walther

RIFLES

**WALTHER G22 CARBINE**

## G22 CARBINE

**Action**: Autoloading
**Stock**: Synthetic
**Barrel**: 20 in.

**Sights**: Adjustable on handle and front strut
**Weight**: 6 lb.
**Caliber**: .22LR
**Magazine**: Detachable box, 10 rounds
**Features**: Single-action trigger; employs an innovative "Bullpup" design; Weaver-style universal rails for sight mounts, bipods, and other accessories; includes Walther safety package with cocking indicator, slide safety and integral lock; available in left-hand models; synthetic stock comes in black or green
**MSRP**. . . . . . . . . . . . . . . $420–$530

# Weatherby

## MARK V ACCUMARK

**Action**: Bolt
**Stock**: Composite
**Barrel**: 24 in., 26 in., 28 in.
**Sights**: None
**Weight**: 7 lb. 4 oz.–9 lb.
**Caliber**: .270 Win., .208 Win., .257 Wby. Mag., .270 Wby. Mag., 7mm Rem. Mag., 7mm Wby. Mag., .300 Win. Mag., .300 Wby. Mag., .30-378 Wby. Mag., .340 Wby. Mag., .247 Wby. Mag., .300 Wby. Mag., .30-378

Wby. Mag.
**Magazine**: Box, 2+1, 3+1, 5+1 rounds
**Features**: Adjustable trigger; hand-laminated raised comb; Monte Carlo composite stock with matte gel coat finish and spider web accents; Pachmayr

decelerator pad; button rifled; CNC-machined 6061 T-6 aluminum bedding plate; cocking indicator; fluted bolt body
**MSRP**. . . . . . . . . . . . . . . . . . $2100

**WEATHERBY MARK V ACCUMARK**

# Weatherby

**WEATHERBY MARK V ACCUMARK .338 LAPUA**

**WEATHERBY MARK V DELUXE**

**WEATHERBY MARK V FIBERMARK**

**WEATHERBY MARK V LAZERMARK**

## MARK V ACCUMARK .338 LAPUA

*Action*: Bolt
*Stock*: Composite
*Barrel*: 26 in.
*Sights*: None
*Weight*: 9 lb.
*Caliber*: .338 Lapua Mag.
*Magazine*: 2+1 rounds
*Features*: Button-rifled; chromoly free-floated barrel with recessed target crown; features fluted barrel with matching Accubrake; matte bead blasted blued finish
*MSRP* . . . . . . . . . . . . . . . . . . . $2300

## MARK V DELUXE

*Action*: Bolt
*Stock*: Walnut
*Barrel*: 24 in., 26 in., 28 in.
*Sights*: None
*Weight*: 6 lb. 12 oz.–10 lb.
*Caliber*: .270 Win., .308 Win., .30-06 Spfd., .257 Wby. Mag., .270 Wby. Mag., 7mm Wby. Mag., .300 Wby. Mag., .340 Wby. Mag., .378 Wby. Mag., .416 Wby. Mag., .460 Wby. Mag.
*Magazine*: Box, 2+1, 3+1, 5+1 rounds
*Features*: Adjustable trigger; walnut Monte Carlo stock with rosewood forend and pistol grip cap and maplewood spacers; blued metalwork in high luster finish; Pachmayr decelerator pad
*MSRP* . . . . . . . . . . . . . . . . . . . $2400

## MARK V FIBERMARK

*Action*: Bolt
*Stock*: Composite
*Barrel*: 24 in., 26 in., 28 in.
*Sights*: None
*Weight*: 6 lb.–8 lb. 8 oz.
*Caliber*: .240 Wby. Mag., .270 Win., .30-06 Spfd., .257 Wby. Mag., .270 Wby. Mag., 7mm Rem. Mag., 7mm Wby. Mag., .300 Win. Mag., .300 Wby. Mag., .30-378 Wby. Mag., .340 Wby. Mag., .375 H&H Mag.
*Magazine*: Box, 2+1, 3+1 rounds
*Features*: Adjustable trigger; pillar-bedded, hand-laminated raised comb Monte Carlo composite stock with strategically placed bedding points assures consistent, repeatable accuracy
*MSRP* . . . . . . . . . . . . . . . . . . . $1500

## MARK V LAZERMARK

*Action*: Bolt
*Stock*: Walnut
*Barrel*: 26 in.
*Sights*: None
*Weight*: 8 lb. 8 oz.
*Caliber*: .257 Wby. Mag., .270 Wby. Mag., 7mm Rem. Mag., 7mm Wby. Mag., .300 Win. Mag., .300 Wby. Mag.
*Magazine*: Box, 3+1 rounds
*Features*: Adjustable trigger; hand-selected, raised comb Monte Carlo stock with laser-carved oak leaf pattern; blued metalwork in high luster finish; Pachmayr decelerator pad
*MSRP* . . . . . . . . . . . . . . . . . . . $2600

# Weatherby

**WEATHERBY MARK V SPORTER**

**WEATHERBY MARK V ULTRA LIGHTWEIGHT**

**WEATHERBY MARK V ULTRAMARK**

## MARK V SPORTER

*Action*: Bolt
*Stock*: Walnut
*Barrel*: 24 in., 26 in.
*Sights*: None
*Weight*: 8 lb.
*Caliber*: .257 Wby. Mag., .270 Wby. Mag., 7mm Rem. Mag., 7mm Wby. Mag., .300 Win. Mag., .300 Wby. Mag., .340 Wby. Mag.
*Magazine*: Box, 3+1 rounds
*Features*: Adjustable trigger; raised comb Monte Carlo walnut stock with satin finish; features fine line diamond point checkering and rosewood forend and grip cap; bead blasted, blued metalwork with low luster finish; Pachmayr decelerator pad
**MSRP**. . . . . . . . . . . . . . . . . **$1600**

## MARK V ULTRA LIGHTWEIGHT

*Action*: Bolt
*Stock*: Composite
*Barrel*: 24 in., 26 in.
*Sights*: None
*Weight*: 5.75 lb.–6.75 lb.
*Caliber*: .243 Win., .240 Wby. Mag., .25-06 Rem., .270 Win., 7mm-08 Rem., .308 Win., .30-06 Spfd., .257 Wby. Mag., 7mm Rem. Mag., 7mm Wby. Mag., .300 Win. Mag., .257 Wby. Mag., .300 Wby. Mag.
*Magazine*: Box, 3+1, 5+1 rounds
*Features*: Adjustable trigger; contoured fluted stainless steel barrel, blackened to reduce glare; Bell & Carlson composite stock with spider web accents; CNC-machined 6061 T-6 aluminum bedding plate; one-piece forged bolt; Pachmayr decelerator pad
**MSRP**. . . . . . . . . . . . . . . . . **$2100**

## MARK V ULTRAMARK

*Action*: Bolt
*Stock*: Walnut
*Barrel*: 26 in.
*Sights*: None
*Weight*: 8 lb. 8 oz.
*Caliber*: .257 Wby. Mag., .300 Wby. Mag.
*Magazine*: Box, 3+1 rounds
*Features*: Adjustable trigger; hand-selected, AAA fancy exhibition grade walnut stock; features 20 lpi checkering, maplewood/ebony spacers and rosewood forend and grip caps; blued metalwork in high luster finish; Pachmayr decelerator pad
**MSRP**. . . . . . . . . . . . . . . . . **$3200**

# Weatherby

## VANGUARD 2 SPORTER

**Action**: Bolt
**Stock**: Walnut
**Barrel**: 24 in.
**Sights**: None
**Weight**: 7 lb. 4 oz.–7 lb. 8 oz.
**Caliber**: .223 Rem., .22-250 Rem., .243 Win., .25-06 Rem., .270 Win., 7mm-08 Rem., .308 Win., .30-06 Spfd., .257 Wby. Mag., .270 WSM, 7mm Rem. Mag., .300 Win. Mag., .300 WSM, .300 Wby. Mag., .338 Win. Mag.
**Magazine**: Box 3+1, 5+1 rounds
**Features**: Two-stage trigger; raised comb, Monte Carlo stock with satin urethane finish; hand-selected A fancy grade Turkish walnut; rosewood forend; low luster, matte blued metalwork; fine line diamond point checkering; low density recoil pad
**MSRP** . . . . . . . . . . . . . . . . . . . . $849

## VANGUARD 2 SPORTER DBM

**Action**: Bolt
**Stock**: Walnut Monte Carlo
**Barrel**: 24 in.
**Sights**: None
**Weight**: 7 lb. 4 oz.
**Caliber**: .25-06 Rem., .270 Win., .30-06 Spfd.
**Magazine**: Detachable box, 3 rounds
**Features**: Rosewood forend; raised comb; satin urethane finish; matte blued metalwork; adjustable trigger
**MSRP** . . . . . . . . . . . . . . . . . . . . $899

## VANGUARD 2 SYNTHETIC

**Action**: Bolt
**Stock**: Synthetic
**Barrel**: 24 in.
**Sights**: None
**Weight**: 7 lb. 4 oz.–7 lb. 8 oz.
**Caliber**: .223 Rem., .22-250 Rem., .243 Win., .25-06 Rem., .270 Win., 7mm-08 Rem., .308 Win., .30-06 Spfd., .257 Wby. Mag., .270 WSM, 7mm Rem. Mag., .300 Win. Mag., .300 WSM, .300 Wby. Mag., .338 Win. Mag.
**Magazine**: Box 3+1, 5+1 rounds
**Features**: Two-stage trigger; injection-molded, Monte Carlo Griptonite composite stock; matte bead blasted blued metalwork; hammer-forged barrel
**MSRP** . . . . . . . . . . . . . . . . . . . . $649

WEATHERBY VANGUARD 2 SPORTER

WEATHERBY VANGUARD 2 SPORTER DBM

WEATHERBY VANGUARD 2 SYNTHETIC

# Weatherby

WEATHERBY VANGUARD 2 SYNTHETIC DBM

WEATHERBY VANGUARD 2 SYNTHETIC YOUTH

## VANGUARD 2 SYNTHETIC DBM

*Action*: Bolt
*Stock*: Injection-molded Monte Carlo
*Barrel*: 24 in.
*Sights*: None
*Weight*: 7 lb. 4 oz.
*Caliber*: .25-06 Rem., .270 Win., .30-06 Spfd.
*Magazine*: Detachable box, 3 rounds
*Features*: Matte bead blasted blued metalwork; low density recoil pad; two-stage trigger
**MSRP**. . . . . . . . . . . . . . . . . . . . **$749**

## VANGUARD 2 SYNTHETIC YOUTH

*Action*: Bolt
*Stock*: Injection-molded Monte Carlo
*Barrel*: 20 in.
*Sights*: None
*Weight*: 6 lb. 8 oz.

*Caliber*: .223 Rem., .22-250 Rem., .243 Win., 7mm-08 Rem., .308 Win.
*Magazine*: Internal box, 5 rounds
*Features*: Removable spacer to allow stock to be lengthened as shooter grows; low-density recoil pad; two-stage trigger
**MSRP**. . . . . . . . . . . . . . . . . . . . **$599**

## VANGUARD 2 TRR RC (RANGE CERTIFIED)

*Action*: Bolt
*Stock*: Composite
*Barrel*: 22 in.
*Sights*: None
*Weight*: 8 lb. 12 oz.
*Caliber*: .223 Rem., .308 Win.
*Magazine*: 5+1 rounds
*Features*: Match quality, two-stage trigger; includes factory-shot target certified and signed by Ed Weatherby and special RC engraved floorplate; hand-

laminated Monte Carlo composite stock with aluminum bedding plate, beavertail forearm, and Pachmayr decelerator pad
**MSRP**. . . . . . . . . . . . . . . . . . . . **$1199**

## VANGUARD 2 VARMINT SPECIAL

*Action*: Bolt
*Stock*: Composite
*Barrel*: 22 in.
*Sights*: None
*Weight*: 8 lb. 12 oz.
*Caliber*: .223 Rem., .22-250 Rem., .308 Win.
*Magazine*: Box, 5+1 rounds
*Features*: Adjustable trigger; Monte Carlo composite stock in Griptonite; matte bead blasted blued metalwork; features recessed target crown to enhance accuracy and protect rifling
**MSRP**. . . . . . . . . . . . . . . . . . . . **$849**

WEATHERBY VANGUARD 2 TRR RC

WEATHERBY VANGUARD 2 VARMINT SPECIAL

# Wild West Guns

**WILD WEST GUNS ALASKAN CO-PILOT**

## ALASKAN CO-PILOT
**Action**: Lever
**Stock**: Walnut
**Barrel**: 16 in., 18.5 in., 20 in.
**Sights**: Fiber optic front bead, ghost ring sight

**Weight**: 6 lb. 8 oz.
**Caliber**: .457 Mag., .45-70, .50 Alaskan, .30-30, .35 Rem., .44 Mag., .357, .45 Colt
**Magazine**: Under-barrel tube

**Features**: 1859 Marlin Action; features the trigger happy kit; Pachmayr decelerator pad; includes soft carry case; WWG recoil control porting system; WWG bear proof ejector installed; Mil-Spec Parkerized, stainless, or matte blue finish
**Base price**:. . . . . . . . . . . . . . **$2400**

# Wilson Combat

## RECON TACTICAL
**Action**: Semiautomatic
**Stock**: Synthetic tactical
**Barrel**: 16 in.
**Sights**: Optional rail
**Weight**: 7 lb.
**Caliber**: 5.56mm, 6.8 SPC, .300 Blackout, 7.62x40WT, .458 SOCOM
**Magazine**: Detachable box, 30 rounds
**Features**: Match grade medium weight stainnless steel barrel; forged 7075 upper (flat top) and lower receiver; mid-length gas system with low-profile gas block; Wilson Combat T.R.I.M. rail; ergo pistol grip
**MSRP**. . . . . . . . . . . . . **$2250–$2600**

**WILSON COMBAT RECON TACTICAL**

# Winchester Repeating Arms

**WINCHESTER MODEL 70 ALASKAN**

## MODEL 70 ALASKAN
**Action**: Bolt
**Stock**: Walnut
**Barrel**: 25 in.
**Sights**: Open
**Weight**: 8 lb. 8 oz.

**Caliber**: .30-06 Spfd., .300 Win. Mag. .338 Win. Mag.
**Magazine**: None
**Features**: Satin finish Monte Carlo walnut stock with cut checkering; folding adjustable rear sight with hooded gold bead front sight; recessed target crown
**MSRP**. . . . . . . . . . . . . . . . **$1269.99**

# Winchester Repeating Arms

WINCHESTER MODEL 70 COYOTE LIGHT

## MODEL 70 COYOTE LIGHT

**Action**: Bolt
**Stock**: Composite
**Barrel**: 24 in.
**Sights**: None
**Weight**: 7 lb. 8 oz.
**Caliber**: .22-250 Rem., .243 Win., .308 Win., .300 WSM, .270 WSM, 7mm WSM, .325 WSM
**Magazine**: 3 rounds
**Features**: Bipod mounting studs; matte-blued receiver and medium-heavy fluted stainless barrel mount; Pachmayr Decelerator
**MSRP** . . . . . . . . $1099.99–$1149.99

## MODEL 70 FEATHERWEIGHT COMPACT

**Action**: Bolt
**Stock**: Walnut
**Barrel**: 20 in.
**Sights**: None
**Weight**: 6 lb. 8 oz.
**Caliber**: .22-250 Rem., .243 Win., 7mm-08 Rem., .308 Win.
**Magazine**: 5 rounds
**Features**: Pachmayr decelerator recoil pad; action is drilled and tapped for optics
**MSRP** . . . . . . . . . . . . . . . . . $879.99

## MODEL 70 SAFARI EXPRESS

**Action**: Bolt
**Stock**: Satin-finished checkered walnut with deluxe cheekpiece
**Barrel**: 24 in.
**Sights**: Hooded-blade front and express-style rear
**Weight**: 9 lb.
**Caliber**: .375 H&H Mag., .416 Rem. Mag., .458 Win. Mag.
**Magazine**: 3 rounds
**Features**: Pre-'64 type claw extractor; Pachmayr decelerator recoil pad; barrel band front swivel base; dual recoil lugs and three-position safety; MOA trigger system; matte blued finish; two steel cross-bolts and one-piece steel trigger guard and hinged floor plate
**MSRP** . . . . . . . . . . . . . . . . $1419.99

WINCHESTER MODEL 70 FEATHERWEIGHT COMPACT

WINCHESTER MODEL 70 SAFARI EXPRESS

WINCHESTER MODEL 70 ULTIMATE SHADOW

## MODEL 70 ULTIMATE SHADOW

**Action**: Bolt
**Stock**: Composite
**Barrel**: 22 in., 24 in., 26 in.
**Sights**: None
**Weight**: 6 lb. 12 oz.–7 lb. 4 oz.
**Caliber**: .300 WSM, .270 WSM, .243 Win., 7mm-08 Rem., .308 Win., .25-06 Rem., .270 Win., .30-06 Spfd., .264 Win. Mag., 7mm Rem. Mag., .300 Win. Mag., .338 Win. Mag., .325 WSM
**Magazine**: 3 rounds
**Features**: Features integrated, rubberized oval-dot gripping surfaces; pistol grip; controlled round feed action
**MSRP** . . . . . . . . . . . $759.99–$799.99

# Winchester Repeating Arms

RIFLES

## MODEL 94 SHORT RIFLE

**Action**: Lever
**Stock**: Walnut
**Barrel**: 20 in.
**Sights**: Front, adjustable rear
**Weight**: 6 lb. 12 oz.
**Caliber**: .30-30 Win., .38-50 Win.
**Magazine**: Under-barrel tube, 7 rounds
**Features**: Straight grip; rifle-style forearm and black grip cap; semi-buckhorn rear sights, Marble Arms gold-bead front sight; drilled and tapped for optics
**MSRP** . . . . . . . . . . . . . . . . $1229.99

WINCHESTER MODEL 94 SHORT RIFLE

## MODEL 94 SPORTER

**Action**: Lever
**Stock**: Walnut
**Barrel**: 24 in.
**Sights**: Marble Arms front, adjustable rear
**Weight**: 7 lb. 8 oz.
**Caliber**: .30-30 Win., .38-55 Win.
**Magazine**: 8 rounds
**Features**: Half-round, half-octagon blued barrel; straight grip stock with a crescent butt and finely checkered blued-steel buttplate with double-line bordering; drilled and tapped for optics
**MSRP** . . . . . . . . . . . . . . . . $1399.99

WINCHESTER MODEL 94 SPORTER

## MODEL 94 TRAILS END TAKEDOWN

**Action**: Lever
**Stock**: Walnut
**Barrel**: 20 in.
**Sights**: Adjustable
**Weight**: 6 lb. 12 oz.

WINCHESTER MODEL 94 TRAILS END TAKEDOWN

**Caliber**: .30-30 Win., .450 Marlin
**Magazine**: 2 rounds
**Features**: Walnut stock and forearm with satin finish and straight-grip styling; blued steel receiver and barrel; Marble Arms front sight with semi-buckhorn rear sight; Pachmayr Decelerator recoil pad (450 model)
**MSRP** . . . . . . . . . . . . . . . . $1459.99

## MODEL 1886 SHORT RIFLE

**Action**: Lever
**Stock**: Walnut
**Barrel**: 20 in., 24 in.
**Sights**: Front with brass bead, adjustable rear
**Weight**: 8 lb. 6 oz.
**Caliber**: .45-70 Govt.
**Magazine**: Tubular mag., 6 rounds
**Features**: Deeply blued receiver and lever; end cap and steel crescent buttplate; straight grip
**MSRP** . . . . . . . . . . . . . . . . $1339.99

## MODEL 1892 CARBINE

**Action**: Lever
**Stock**: Walnut
**Barrel**: 20 in.
**Sights**: Front, adjustable rear
**Weight**: 6 lb.
**Caliber**: .45 Long Colt, .44-40 Win., .44 Mag., .357 Mag.
**Magazine**: 10 rounds
**Features**: Round, deeply blued finish on receiver and lever; straight grip and satin walnut finish
**MSRP** . . . . . . . . . . . . . . . . $1159.99

WINCHESTER MODEL 1886 SHORT RIFLE

WINCHESTER MODEL 1892 CARBINE

# AirForce Airguns

AIRFORCE AIRGUNS CONDOR

AIRFORCE AIRGUNS EDGE

AIRFORCE AIRGUNS TALON

## CONDOR

**Power**: Pre-charged pneumatic, user adjustable
**Stock**: Composite
**Overall Length**: 38.7 in.
**Sights**: None
**Weight**: 6 lb. 8 oz.
**Caliber**: .25, .22, .20, .177
**Features**: Black, red, or blue composite stock; integral extended scope rail; detachable air tank; Lothar Walther barrel; pressure relief device; adjustable power; scopes optional
**Quick-Detach**: . . . . . . . . . . . $689.50
**Spin-Loc**: . . . . . . . . . . . . . $709.50

## EDGE

**Power**: Pre-charged pneumatic
**Stock**: Composite
**Overall Length**: 35–40 in.
**Sights**: TS1 peep sight system
**Weight**: 6 lb. 2 oz.
**Caliber**: .177
**Features**: Ambidextrous cocking knob; regulated air system; adjustable length of pull; adjustable forend; hooded front sight only or front and rear sight available; two-stage adjustable trigger; composite stock in red or blue finish; scopes optional
**Front sight**: . . . . . . . . . . . . $545.95
**Rear & front sights**: . . . . . . $679.95

## TALON

**Power**: Compressed air
**Stock**: Composite
**Overall Length**: 32.6 in.
**Sights**: None
**Weight**: 5 lb. 8 oz.
**Caliber**: .25, .22, .20, .177
**Features**: Lothar Walther barrel; pressure relief device; adjustable power; detachable air tank; black composite stock; scopes optional
**Quick-Detach**: . . . . . . . . . . . . $562
**Spin-Loc**: . . . . . . . . . . . . . . $582

## TALON P

**Power**: Compressed air
**Stock**: Composite
**Overall Length**: 24 in.
**Sights**: None
**Weight**: 3 lb. 8 oz.
**Caliber**: .25
**Features**: Designed to deliver over 50 ft.-lbs. of energy with a .25-caliber hunting pellet; integral extended scope rail; Lothar Walther barrels; scopes optional
**Quick-Detach**: . . . . . . . . . . $433.50
**Spin-Loc**: . . . . . . . . . . . . . . $453.50

## TALON SS

**Power**: Compressed air
**Stock**: Composite
**Overall Length**: 32.7 in.
**Sights**: None
**Weight**: 5 lb. 4 oz.
**Caliber**: .25, .22, .20, .177
**Features**: Improved sound reduction; Lothar Walther barrel; pressure relief device; adjustable power; detachable air tank; black, red, or blue composite stock; multiple mounting rails; two-stage trigger; innovative muzzle cap that strips away air turbulence and reduces discharge sound levels; scopes optional
**Quick-Detach**: . . . . . . . . . . . . $585
**Spin-Loc**: . . . . . . . . . . . . . . $605

AIRFORCE AIRGUNS
TALON P

AIRFORCE AIRGUNS TALON SS

AIR RIFLES

ANSCHÜTZ 8001 CLUB

ANSCHÜTZ 8001 JUNIOR

ANSCHÜTZ 8002 S2 ALU

ANSCHÜTZ 8002 S2 BLACK AIR

## 8001 CLUB
**Power**: Compressed air
**Stock**: Walnut
**Overall Length**: 42.1 in.
**Sights**: Open, includes sight set 6834
**Weight**: 8 lb. 6 oz.
**Caliber**: .177
**Features**: Walnut stock with stippled checkering and non-stained aluminum or rubber buttplate; adjustable trigger; match grade barrel
**MSRP** . . . . . . . . . . . . . . . . . . $1730

## 8001 JUNIOR
**Power**: Compressed air
**Stock**: Laminate
**Overall Length**: 37.4 in.
**Sights**: Open, includes sight set 6834
**Weight**: 8 lb. 2 oz.
**Caliber**: .177
**Features**: Laminated wood in blue and orange with aluminum buttplate stock; cylindrical match grade barrel; comes with accessory box
**MSRP** . . . . . . . . . . . . . . . . . . $1859

## 8002 S2 ALU
**Power**: Compressed air
**Stock**: Aluminum and synthetic pistol grip or laminated wood pistol grip
**Overall Length**: 42.1 in.
**Sights**: Open, includes sight set 6834
**Weight**: 10 lb. 2 oz.
**Caliber**: .177
**Features**: Aluminum stock in silver and blue with laminated wood or synthetic pistol grip; blue air cylinder; ProGrip cheekpiece and forend; includes accessory box; aluminum accessory rail
**Aluminum**: . . . . . . . . . . . . . . $2564
**Wood**: . . . . . . . . . . . . . . . . . $2244

## 8002 S2 BLACK AIR
**Power**: Compressed air
**Stock**: Plastic
**Length**: 43.3 in.
**Sights**: Rear, turnable front
**Weight**: 9 lb. 8 oz.
**Caliber**: .177
**Features**: IWA special edition equipped with new Anschütz SOFT-Grip stock, combining the vibration damping and recoil absorbing characteristics of a naturally grown wooden stock with the characteristics of an easy-care and weather-proof plastic stock; match barrel; aluminum buttplate; cheekpiece; two-stage trigger
**MSRP** . . . . . . . . . . . . . . . . . . $2308

**AIR RIFLES**

# J. G. Anschütz

### 9003 PREMIUM S2 PRECISE
*Power*: Compressed air
*Stock*: Aluminum
*Overall Length*: 43.7 in.
*Sights*: Open, includes sight set 6834
*Weight*: 9 lb. 15 oz.
*Caliber*: .177
*Features*: Silver/black aluminum stock pistol grip; Soft Link shock absorber pads; adjustable forend stock, cheek-piece, and buttplate; includes plastic rifle case; steel match barrel; aluminum accessory rail on stock
*MSRP* . . . . . . . . . . . . . . . . . . **$4040**

### 9003 PREMIUM S2 BENCHREST PRECISE
*Power*: Compressed air
*Stock*: Aluminum
*Length*: 39.96 in.
*Sights*: Open, includes sight set 6834
*Weight*: 11 lb. 11 oz.
*Caliber*: .177
*Features*: Aluminum stock with wedge-shaped design; pistol grip; Soft Link shock absorber pads; adjustable forend stock, cheekpiece and buttplate;

ANSCHÜTZ 9003 PREMIUM S2 ALU

ANSCHÜTZ 9003 PREMIUM S2 BENCHREST PRECISE

includes plastic rifle case; valve and valve body coated with gold; steel match barrel; aluminum accessory rail on stock
*MSRP* . . . . . . . . . . . . . . . . . . **$4040**

# Beeman Precision Airguns

### HW 97K
*Power*: Spring piston
*Stock*: Beech, laminated
*Overall Length*: 44.1 in.
*Sights*: Adjustable
*Weight*: 9 lb. 6 oz.
*Caliber*: .177, .20, .22
*Features*: Underlever cocking method; blued steel action, barrel, and cocking lever; stippling on the pistol grip and forearm; soft rubber recoil pad; grooved receiver for optical sights; adjustable two-stage trigger; automatic safety
**Blue:** . . . . . . . . . . . . . . . . . .**$839.95**
**Elite:** . . . . . . . . . . . . . . . .**$889.95**
**Thumbhole:** . . . . . . . . . . . . . . **$890**

### MODEL R1 SUPERMAGNUM, R1 SUPERMAGNUM CARBINE
*Power*: Spring piston
*Stock*: Hardwood
*Overall Length*: 45.2 in., 42 in.
*Sights*: Adjustable
*Weight*: 8 lb. 5 oz.–8 lb. 13 oz.
*Caliber*: .22, .20, .177; Carbine: .177, .20

BEEMAN HW 97K ELITE

BEEMAN R1 ELITE

BEEMAN R9 ELITE

*Features*: Beech-stained hardwood stock; adjustable two-stage trigger; automatic safety
**Carbine:** . . . . . . . . . . . . . . **$734.95**
**MSRP** . . . . . . . . . . . . . . . . . . **$749.95**

### MODEL R9, R9 ELITE
*Power*: Spring piston
*Stock*: Hardwood
*Overall Length*: 43 in.
*Sights*: Adjustable
*Weight*: 7 lb. 5 oz.–7 lb. 8 oz.

*Caliber*: .20, .177
*Features*: Beech-stained hardwood stock with Monte Carlo cheekpiece; ambidextrous rifle; soft rubber butt-plate; adjustable two-stage trigger; automatic safety; R9 Elite has hand checkered panels, pistol cap, carved Monte Carlo cheekpiece, and inter-changeable globe front sight
**MSRP** . . . . . . . . . . . . . . . . . . **$549.95**
**Elite:** . . . . . . . . . . . . . . . . . **$669.95**

AIR RIFLES

CROSMAN
BENJAMIN
DISCOVERY

CROSMAN BENJAMIN
MAV 77 UNDERLEVER
AIR RIFLE

CROSMAN
BENJAMIN
ROGUE .357

CROSMAN
BENJAMIN
TITAN NP

CROSMAN
CHALLENGER PCP

## BENJAMIN DISCOVERY
*Power*: Dual fuel compressed air
*Stock*: Walnut
*Overall Length*: 39 in.
*Sights*: Fiber optic front, adjustable rear
*Weight*: 5 lb. 2 oz.–5 lb. 3 oz.
*Caliber*: .22, .177
*Features*: Rifled steel barrel; velocity up to 900 fps; cross-bolt safety; built-in pressure gauge; high pressure pump included
**MSRP** . . . . . . . . . . . . . . . . . . . **$409**

## BENJAMIN MAV 77 UNDERLEVER AIR RIFLE
*Power*: Spring piston
*Stock*: Hardwood
*Length*: 42 in.
*Sights*: 3-9x32mm scope included
*Weight*: 8 lb. 14 oz.
*Caliber*: .177
*Features*: Fixed barrel design; rifled barrel; two-stage trigger; ambidextrous hardwood stock; includes 3-9x32mm CenterPoint precision scope with a

Mil-Dot reticle; delivers velocities up to 1100 fps with alloy pellets
**MSRP** . . . . . . . . . . . . . . . . . . . **$530**

## BENJAMIN ROGUE .357
*Power*: Electro pre-charged pneumatic
*Stock*: Synthetic
*Overall Length*: 48 in.
*Sights*: None
*Weight*: 9 lb. 8 oz.
*Caliber*: .357
*Features*: Uses electronic valve technology to provide precise regulation of pressure and provide more shots per fill through the control of pressure; rifled steel barrel; velocity up to 700–1000 fps; built in LCD screen to control eValve and trigger; sling studs; fill adaptor; degassing tool; magazine holds six shots
**MSRP** . . . . . . . . . . . . . . . . . . . **$1349**

## BENJAMIN TITAN NP
*Power*: Nitro piston
*Stock*: Hardwood
*Length*: 43 in., 44.5 in.

*Sights*: 4x32mm scope included
*Weight*: 6 lb. 10 oz.–6 lb. 14 oz.
*Caliber*: .177, .22
*Features*: Powered by Nitro Piston technology; delivers velocities up to 1200 fps (.177) with alloy pellets; included 4x32mm scope; ambidextrous hardwood stock with thumbhole; two-stage adjustable trigger; ventilated rubber recoil pad
**MSRP** . . . . . . . . . . . . . . . . . . **$159.99**

## CHALLENGER PCP
*Power*: Pneumatic pump and CO2
*Stock*: Synthetic
*Overall Length*: 41.5 in.
*Sights*: Open
*Weight*: 7 lb. 2 oz.
*Caliber*: .177
*Features*: Two-stage match grade adjustable trigger; Lothar Walther barrel; adjustable cheekpiece and butt-piece; black synthetic stock; 11mm scope mount rails; ambidextrous
**MSRP** . . . . . . . . . . . . . . . . . . **$529.99**

# Crosman

**CROSMAN CLASSIC 2100**

**CROSMAN M4-177**

**CROSMAN MARAUDER**

**CROSMAN OPTIMUS**

**CROSMAN PHANTOM 1000**

### CLASSIC 2100
**Power**: Pneumatic pump
**Stock**: Synthetic
**Overall Length**: 39.75 in.
**Sights**: Visible impact front, adjustable rear
**Weight**: 4 lb. 13 oz.
**Caliber**: .177
**Features**: Cross-bolt safety; BB up to 755 fps, pellet up to 725 fps
**MSRP** . . . . . . . . . . . . . . . . . .$69.99

### M4-177 RIFLE
**Power**: Multi-pump pneumatic
**Stock**: Synthetic
**Length**: 34 in.
**Sights**: Adjustable front and rear
**Weight**: 3 lb. 9 oz.
**Caliber**: .177
**Features**: Rifled steel barrel; shoots both pellets and BBs; variable pump action easy to use for right- or left-handed shooters; Picatinny rails; front and rear sights and stock are removable for upgrades; adjustable stock; velocities up to 660 fps with BBs

and 625 fps with 7.9gr, .177 caliber pellets
**MSRP** . . . . . . . . . . . . . . . . . . . .$75

### MARAUDER
**Power**: Pre-charged pneumatic
**Stock**: Hardwood
**Overall Length**: 42.5 in.
**Sights**: None
**Weight**: 7 lb. 2 oz.
**Caliber**: .177, .22, .25
**Features**: Crosman custom choked barrel and internal shroud for unsurpassed accuracy and ultra quiet operation; two-stage adjustable match grade trigger; rifle can be filled with Benjamin hand pump or a high pressure tank; velocity up to 1100 fps; ambidextrous hardwood stock
**MSRP** . . . . . . . . . . $509.99–$529.99

### OPTIMUS
**Power**: Break action
**Stock**: Hardwood
**Overall Length**: 43 in.
**Sights**: 4x32mm CenterPoint scope

**Weight**: 6 lb. 8 oz.
**Caliber**: .177, .22
**Features**: Ambidextrous hardwood stock; relatively light cocking force and a two-stage adjustable trigger; velocities of up to 1200 fps with alloy pellets; barrel incorporates a micro-adjustable rear sight and fiber optic front sight
**MSRP** . . . . . . . . . . . . . . . . . .$139

### PHANTOM 1000
**Power**: Spring piston
**Stock**: Synthetic
**Overall Length**: 44.5 in.
**Sights**: Fiber optic front, adjustable rear
**Weight**: 6 lb.
**Caliber**: .177
**Features**: All-weather, synthetic black stock and forearm; checkered grip and forearm; velocity up to 1000 fps; rifled steel barrel; two-stage adjustable trigger
**MSRP** . . . . . . . . . . . . . . . . . .$99.99

# Crosman

CROSMAN PUMPMASTER 760

CROSMAN RECRUIT

CROSMAN REPEATAIR 1077

CROSMAN TR77

CROSMAN VANTAGE NP

## PUMPMASTER 760

**Power**: Pneumatic pump
**Stock**: Synthetic
**Overall Length**: 33.5 in.
**Sights**: Fiber optic front, adjustable rear
**Weight**: 2 lb. 12 oz.
**Caliber**: .177
**Features**: Cross-bolt safety; BB up to 625 fps; pellet up to 600 fps
**MSRP** . . . . . . . . . . . . . . . . . .$43.99

## RECRUIT

**Power**: Pneumatic pump
**Stock**: Synthetic
**Overall Length**: 38.25 in.
**Sights**: Fiber optic front, adjustable rear
**Weight**: 2 lb. 15 oz.

**Caliber**: .177
**Features**: Adjustable buttstock; adjustable synthetic stock; 11mm dovetail scope rail; cross-bolt safety
**MSRP** . . . . . . . . . . . . . . . . . .$69.99

## REPEATAIR 1077

**Power**: $CO_2$
**Stock**: All-weather, synthetic
**Overall Length**: 36.88 in.
**Sight**: Fiber optic front, adjustable rear
**Weight**: 3 lb. 11 oz.
**Caliber**: .177
**Features**: Exclusive 12-shot rotary pellet clip lets you shoot longer; maximum velocity 625 fps; cross-bolt safety
**MSRP** . . . . . . . . . . . . . . . . . .$89.99

## TR77

**Power**: Nitro piston
**Stock**: Synthetic
**Length**: 41.5 in.

**Sights**: Fiber optic front, adjustable rear
**Weight**: 6 lb.
**Caliber**: .177
**Features**: Tactical break air rifle with military styling and all-weather tactical, synthetic stock; two-stage adjustable trigger; pistol grip; includes CenterPoint 4x32mm scope; velocities up to 1000 fps
**MSRP** . . . . . . . . . . . . . . . . . .$149.95

## VANTAGE NP

**Power**: Break action
**Stock**: Hardwood
**Length**: 45 in.
**Sights**: Fiber optic front, adjustable rear 4x32mm scope included
**Weight**: 7 lb. 2 oz.
**Caliber**: .177
**Features**: Crosman's own version of the Bantage NP; hardwood stock; fiber optic front sight and fully adjustable rear sight
**MSRP** . . . . . . . . . . . . . . . . . . $160

AIR RIFLES

# Daisy

**DAISY AVANTI MODEL 853 LEGEND**

**DAISY AVANTI MODEL 887 GOLD MEDALIST**

## AVANTI MODEL 853 LEGEND

**Power**: Single-pump pneumatic
**Stock**: Hardwood
**Overall Length**: 38.5 in.
**Sights**: Hooded front with interchangeable aperture inserts, micrometer adjustable rear
**Weight**: 5 lb. 8 oz.
**Caliber**: .177

**Features**: Diecast receiver with dovetail scope mount; Lothar Walther rifled high-grade steel barrel; full-length, sporter-style hardwood with adjustable length
**MSRP** . . . . . . . . . . . . . . . . . $399.99

## AVANTI MODEL 887 GOLD MEDALIST

**Power**: CO2 single shot bolt
**Stock**: Laminated hardwood

**Overall Length**: 39.5 in.
**Sights**: Front globe with changeable aperture inserts, rear diopter with micrometer
**Weight**: 7 lb. 5 oz.
**Caliber**: .177
**Features**: Laminated hardwood stock; Lothar Walther rifled high-grade steel barrel; manual, cross-bolt trigger block; includes scope rail adapter
**MSRP** . . . . . . . . . . . . . . . . . $499.99

**DAISY POWERLINE MODEL 880**

## POWERLINE MODEL 880

**Power**: Multi-pump pneumatic
**Stock**: Molded wood grain
**Overall Length**: 37.6 in.
**Sights**: TruGlo fiber optic front, adjustable rear
**Weight**: 3 lb. 11 oz.

**Caliber**: .177
**Features**: Wood-grained, Monte Carlo stock and forearm; rifled steel barrel; cross-bolt trigger block; velocity up to 750 fps; engineering resin with dovetail mount for scope
**MSRP** . . . . . . . . . . . . . . . . . $49.99

# Daisy

DAISY POWERLINE MODEL 901

DAISY POWERLINE TARGETPRO 953

DAISY WINCHESTER M-14

DAISY WINCHESTER MODEL 77XS

## POWERLINE MODEL 901
**Power**: Multi-pump pneumatic
**Stock**: Composite
**Overall Length**: 37.5 in.
**Sights**: Fiber optic front, adjustable rear
**Weight**: 3 lb. 11 oz.
**Caliber**: .177
**Features**: Rifled steel barrel; black advanced composite stock; dovetail mounts for optics
**MSRP**...................$69.99

## POWERLINE TARGETPRO 953
**Power**: Pneumatic single-pump cocking lever
**Stock**: Composite
**Overall Length**: 37.75 in.
**Sights**: Front and rear fiber optic
**Weight**: 6 lb. 6 oz.
**Caliber**: .177
**Features**: Full-length, match-style black composite stock; rifled high-grade steel barrel; diecast metal receiver; manual cross-bolt trigger block with red indicator
**MSRP**...................$119.99

## WINCHESTER M-14
**Power**: CO2 semiautomatic
**Stock**: Composite
**Length**: 44.5 in.
**Sights**: Blade front, adjustable rear
**Weight**: 4 lb. 6 oz.
**Caliber**: .177
**Features**: Dual ammo BB or pellet rifle; rifled steel barrel; adjustable rear

sight, fixed front sight; brown composite stock; 700 fps maximum velocity
**MSRP**...................$219.99

## WINCHESTER MODEL 77XS
**Power**: Multi-pump pneumatic
**Stock**: Composite
**Length**: 37.6 in.
**Sights**: TruGlo fiber optic front, adjustable rear
**Weight**: 3 lb. 2 oz.
**Caliber**: .177
**Features**: Rifled steel barrel; TruGlo fiber optic front, adjustable rear sight; 4x32mm air rifle scope included; black composite stock; 800 fps maximum velocity
**MSRP**...................$129.99

# Gamo USA

## BIG CAT 1250

**Power**: Break action/spring piston
**Stock**: Synthetic
**Overall Length**: 43.3 in.
**Sights**: 4x32mm scope
**Weight**: 6 lb. 2 oz.
**Caliber**: .177
**Features**: Tough all-weather molded synthetic stock; ventilated rubber pad for recoil; twin cheekpads; non-slip texture design on grip and forearm; manual trigger system; fluted barrel; two-stage adjustable trigger
**MSRP** . . . . . . . . . . . . . . . . . **$199.95**

GAMO BIG CAT 1250

GAMO RECON WHISPER

## RECON WHISPER

**Power**: Break action/spring piston
**Stock**: Synthetic
**Overall Length**: 37.2 in.
**Sights**: 4x20mm scope
**Weight**: 4 lb. 10 oz.
**Caliber**: .177
**Features**: All-weather black molded synthetic stock; ventilated rubber butt-pad; twin cheekpads; automatic cocking safety system; 525 fps maximum velocity
**MSRP** . . . . . . . . . . . . . . . . . **$119.95**

GAMO VARMINT HUNTER HP 177

## VARMINT HUNTER HP 177

**Power**: Break action/spring piston
**Stock**: Synthetic
**Length**: 43.78 in.
**Sights**: Mounted 4x32mm scope
**Weight**: 6 lb. 10 oz.
**Caliber**: .177
**Features**: Lightweight synthetic stock; match grade fluted barrel; 1400 fps maximum velocity; 4x32mm air rifle scope with laser sight and flashlight; break barrel single cocking system
**MSRP** . . . . . . . . . . . . . . . . . **$299.95**

GAMO WHISPER

GAMO WHISPER CFR

## WHISPER

**Power**: Break action/spring piston
**Stock**: Synthetic
**Overall Length**: 37.2 in.
**Sights**: Mounted scope with rings
**Weight**: 4 lb. 10 oz.
**Caliber**: .177
**Features**: Raised rail scope mount with 39x40mm scope; two-stage adjustable trigger; manual safety; non-removable noise dampener; black synthetic all-weather stock; ventilated rubber butt-plate; non-slip checkering on grip and forearm
**MSRP** . . . . . . . . . . . . . . . . . **$269.95**

## WHISPER CFR

**Power**: Single shot/spring piston
**Stock**: Synthetic
**Length**: 46.85 in.
**Sights**: Fiber optic sights, mounted 4x32 standard reticle scope
**Weight**: 8 lb.
**Caliber**: .177
**Features**: First Whisper Air Rifle with a fixed barrel; integrated ND52 noise dampener system; fixed rifled steel barrel; capable of 1100 fps; newly designed recoil pad with 74 percent more recoil absorbing pressure; all-weather synthetic molded stock with thumbhole
**MSRP** . . . . . . . . . . . . . . . . . **$329.95**

AIR RIFLES

**RWS MODEL 34**

**RWS MODEL 48 WITH SCOPE**

## MODEL 34

**Power**: Break action/spring piston
**Stock**: Hardwood, synthetic
**Overall Length**: 45 in.
**Sights**: 4x32mm scope
**Weight**: 7 lb. 8 oz.–8 lb.
**Caliber**: .177, .22
**Features**: Polished with blued metal-work; full-sized hardwood stock; two-stage adjustable trigger; automatic safety; finely rifled barrel; 34 Pro large muzzlebrake
**MSRP** . . . . . . . . . . . . . . . . . .$362.90
**With scope:** . . . . . . . . . . . . .$419.35

## MODEL 48

**Power**: Side lever/spring piston
**Stock**: Hardwood
**Overall Length**: 42.5 in.
**Sights**: Adjustable rear
**Weight**: 8 lb. 8 oz.
**Caliber**: .177
**Features**: Extended breech stock to reduce recoil; fixed barrel system; adjustable trigger; automatic safety; optional RWS 4x32mm scope and mounts
**MSRP** . . . . . . . . . . . . . . . . . .$564.52
**With scope:** . . . . . . . . . . . . .$625.81

**RWS MODEL 54 AIR KING**

**RWS MODEL 350 MAGNUM**

## MODEL 54 AIR KING

**Power**: Side lever/spring piston
**Stock**: Hardwood
**Overall Length**: 43.75 in.
**Sights**: Adjustable rear
**Weight**: 9 lb.
**Caliber**: .177, .22, .25
**Features**: Adjustable trigger; scope rail; Monte Carlo hardwood stock with cheekpiece and checkering; automatic safety; 1100 fps maximum velocity
**MSRP** . . . . . . . . . . . . . . . . . .$846.53
**With scope:** . . . . . . . . . . . . .$896.77

## MODEL 350 MAGNUM

**Power**: Break action/spring piston
**Stock**: Hardwood
**Overall Length**: 48.3 in.
**Sights**: 4x32mm scope
**Weight**: 8 lb. 3 oz.
**Caliber**: .177, .22
**Features**: Two-stage trigger; mounted scope rail
**MSRP** . . . . . . . . . . . . . . . . . .$564.52
**With scope:** . . . . . . . . . . . . .$625.81

## SCHÜTZE

**Power**: Break action/spring piston
**Stock**: Hardwood
**Overall Length**: 41 in.
**Sights**: TruGlo fiber optic
**Weight**: 5 lb. 11 oz.
**Caliber**: .177
**Features**: Classic straight hardwood stock; ambidextrous safety
**MSRP** . . . . . . . . . . . . . . . . . .$222.56

**AIR RIFLES**

**RWS SCHÜTZE**

# Stoeger Airguns

**STOEGER X-5 SYNTHETIC**

**STOEGER X-20 SUPPRESSOR**

**STOEGER X-50 AIR RIFLE COMBO**

## X-5

**Power**: Break action/spring piston
**Stock**: Hardwood, black synthetic
**Overall Length**: 41 in.
**Sights**: Hooded front with red, fiber optic insert; rear fiber optic
**Weight**: 5 lb. 11 oz.
**Caliber**: .177
**Features**: Automatic, ambidextrous safety mounted on back of receiver; Monte Carlo-style stock; integral dovetail scope rail on receiver
**MSRP** . . . . . . . . . . . . . . . . . . . . **$149**

## X-20 SUPPRESSOR

**Power**: Break action/spring piston
**Stock**: Black synthetic
**Overall Length**: 43 in.
**Sights**: 4x32mm illuminated red green scope
**Weight**: 7 lb.
**Caliber**: .177
**Features**: Air Flow Control system; adjustable two-stage trigger; integral dovetail scope rail on receiver; non-slip, deluxe rubber recoil pad; Monte Carlo-style, black synthetic stock with checkering; rifled, blued steel barrel
**MSRP** . . . . . . . . . . . . . . . . . . . . **$249**

## X-50

**Power**: Break action/spring piston
**Stock**: Black synthetic
**Overall Length**: 50 in.
**Sights**: 3-9x40mm parallax adjustable scope with rings
**Weight**: 9 lb. 14 oz.
**Caliber**: .177
**Features**: Ergonomic cocking grip; rifled blued steel barrel; synthetic Monte Carlo-style stock; ambidextrous automatic safety
**MSRP** . . . . . . . . . . . . . . . . . . . . **$359**

# AYA (Aguirre y Aranzabal)

AYA ARRATE

AYA IMPERIAL

AYA MODEL NO. 4/53

AYA MODEL NO. 37

## ARRATE
*Action*: Over/under
*Stock*: Walnut
*Barrel*: 28 in.–32 in.
*Chokes*: Fixed or multichokes
*Weight*: 6 lb. 10 oz.
*Bore/Gauge*: 12
*Magazine*: None
*Features*: F125 steel receiver; chrome steel barrels; detachable trigger mechanism; walnut stock AYA grade 2
*From* . . . . . . . . . . . . . . . . . . $6500

## IMPERIAL
*Action*: Side-by-side hammerless sidelock
*Stock*: Walnut
*Barrel*: 28 in., with other lengths to order
*Chokes*: Screw-in tubes
*Weight*: 6 lb. 12 oz.
*Bore/Gauge*: 12, 16, 20, 28, .410
*Magazine*: None
*Features*: Forged steel action with double locking mechanism and gas vents; gold washed internal lock parts; gold lined cocking indicators; optional selective or non-selective single trigger; concave rib; straight hand, finely checkered walnut stock; gold initial oval
*From* . . . . . . . . . . . . . . . . . $20995

## MODEL NO. 4/53
*Action*: Side-by-side hammerless boxlock ejector
*Stock*: Walnut
*Barrel*: 28 in., with other lengths to order
*Chokes*: Screw-in tubes
*Weight*: 6 lb. 10 oz.
*Bore/Gauge*: 12, 16, 20, 28, .410
*Magazine*: None
*Features*: Double locking mechanism with replaceable hinge pin; disk set firing pins; double trigger; chopper lump barrels with concave rib; light scroll engraving; metal finish available in hardened, old silver, or white finish; automatic safety
*From* . . . . . . . . . . . . . . . . . . $3895

## MODEL NO. 37
*Action*: Over/under sidelock
*Stock*: Walnut
*Barrel*: 28 in.
*Chokes*: Screw-in tubes
*Weight*: 7 lb. 8 oz.
*Bore/Gauge*: 12
*Magazine*: None
*Features*: Double underlocking lugs and double crossbolt; chopper lump chrome nickel steel barrels; hardened steel intercepting safety sears; gold line cocking indicators; gold washed internal lock parts; double trigger with hinged front trigger; fine rose and scroll, game scene, or bold relief engraving on action plates; full pistol grip walnut stock
*From* . . . . . . . . . . . . . . . . . $14999

## CORDOBA COMFORTECH

**Action**: Inertia operated semiautomatic
**Stock**: Synthetic
**Barrel**: 28 in., 30 in.
**Chokes**: Extended Crio Chokes
**Weight**: 7 lb.
**Bore/Gauge**: 12, 20
**Magazine**: 4+1 rounds
**Features**: Black synthetic stock with GripTight; Crio ported barrels; ComforTech gel recoil pad and comb insert; heavy duty magazine cap
**MSRP** . . . . . . . . . . . . . . **$2069–$2099**

BENELLI CORDOBA COMFORTECH

BENELLI LEGACY

## LEGACY

**Action**: Inertia operated semiautomatic
**Stock**: Walnut
**Barrel**: 24 in., 26 in., 28 in.
**Chokes**: Crio Choke (C, IC, M, IM, F); 28 gauge: (C & M)
**Weight**: 4 lb. 14 oz.–7 lb. 6 oz.
**Bore/Gauge**: 12, 20, 28
**Magazine**: 4+1, 28 Ga.: 2+1 rounds
**Features**: Satin walnut with Weathercoat or AA-grade stock; classic game scene etchings on receiver; red front sight and metal bead mid sight
**MSRP** . . . . . . . . . . . . . . **$1799–$2039**

## LEGACY SPORT

**Action**: Inertia operated semiautomatic
**Stock**: Walnut
**Barrel**: 28 in., 30 in.
**Chokes**: Extended Crio Chokes (C, CI, M, IM, F)
**Weight**: 7 lb. 6 oz.–7 lb. 8 oz.
**Bore/Gauge**: 12
**Magazine**: 4+1 rounds
**Features**: Acid-etched game scenes on receiver plates; AA-grade walnut stock; red front sight and metal bead mid sight
**MSRP** . . . . . . . . . . . . . . . . . . **$2439**

BENELLI LEGACY SPORT

## M2 FIELD –12 GA.

**Action**: Inertia operated semiautomatic
**Stock**: Synthetic, Realtree APG
**Barrel**: 21 in., 24 in., 26 in., 28 in.
**Chokes**: Crio Chokes (IC, M, F)
**Weight**: 6 lb. 14 oz.–7 lb. 3 oz.
**Bore/Gauge**: 12
**Magazine**: 3+1 rounds
**Features**: ComforTech gel recoil pad and comb insert; ComforTech shim kit; red bar front sight; stock comes in black synthetic, Realtree APG, and Realtree MAX-4 Camo
**Synthetic:** . . . . . . . . . . . . . . . **$1359**
**Realtree APG:** . . . . . . . . . . . . **$1469**

BENELLI M2 FIELD –12 GA.

SHOTGUNS

# Benelli USA

**BENELLI M2 FIELD 20 GA.**

**BENELLI NOVA PUMP H2O**

## M2 FIELD 20 GA.

*Action*: Inertia operated semiautomatic
*Stock*: Synthetic
*Barrel*: 24 in., 26 in.
*Chokes*: Crio Chokes (IC, M, F)
*Weight*: 7 lb. 2 oz.–7 lb. 3 oz.
*Bore/Gauge*: 20
*Magazine*: 3+1 rounds
*Features*: ComforTech gel recoil pad and comb insert; ComforTech shim kit; red bar front sight; synthetic stock in Realtree Max-4 Camo or matte black finish
**Synthetic** . . . . . . . . . . . . . . . **$1409**
**Realtree APG** . . . . . . . . . . . . **$1519**

## NOVA PUMP H2O

*Action*: Pump
*Stock*: Synthetic
*Barrel*: 18.5 in.
*Chokes*: Fixed cylinder choke
*Weight*: 7 lb. 3 oz.
*Bore/Gauge*: 12
*Magazine*: 4+1 round
*Features*: Available with ghost-ring or open rifle sights; push-button shell stop; grooved grip surface black synthetic stock
**MSRP** . . . . . . . . . . . . . . . . . . . **$669**

## NOVA PUMP TACTICAL

*Action*: Pump
*Stock*: Synthetic
*Barrel*: 18.5 in.
*Chokes*: Fixed cylinder choke
*Weight*: 7 lb. 3 oz.
*Bore/Gauge*: 12
*Magazine*: 4+1 rounds
*Features*: Available with ghost-ring or open rifle sights; push-button shell stop; grooved grip surface stocks in black synthetic stock
**MSRP** . . . . . . . . . . . . . . **$419–$459**

## PERFORMANCE SHOP M2 3-GUN COMFORTECH

*Action*: Inertia operated semiautomatic
*Stock*: Synthetic
*Barrel*: 21 in.
*Chokes*: Crio chokes (C, IC, M, IM, F)

*Weight*: 7 lb. 5 oz.
*Bore/Gauge*: 12
*Magazine*: 8+1 rounds
*Features*: ComforTech gel recoil pad and comb insert; ComforTech shim kit; extended magazine; ergonomic bolt release
**MSRP** . . . . . . . . . . . . . . . . . . **$2699**

## PERFORMANCE SHOP SUPER BLACK EAGLE II TURKEY EDITION

*Action*: Inertia operated semiautomatic
*Stock*: Synthetic
*Barrel*: 24 in.
*Chokes*: Custom XTF extended choke
*Weight*: 7 lb. 2 oz.
*Bore/Gauge*: 12
*Magazine*: 3+1 rounds
*Features*: Burris FastFire sight; ComforTech gel recoil pad and comb insert; larger trigger guard for use with gloves; EDM ported Crio barrel; ComforTech synthetic stock with Realtree APG finish
**MSRP** . . . . . . . . . . . . . . . . . . **$2949**

**BENELLI NOVA PUMP TACTICAL**

**BENELLI PERFORMANCE SHOP M2 3-GUN COMFORTECH**

**BENELLI PERFORMANCE SHOP SUPER BLACK EAGLE II TURKEY EDITION**

SHOTGUNS

BENELLI SPORT II

BENELLI SUPER BLACK EAGLE II

BENELLI SUPERNOVA FIELD

BENELLI SUPERSPORT

## SPORT II

**Action**: Inertia operated semiautomatic
**Stock**: Walnut
**Barrel**: 28 in., 30 in.
**Chokes**: Extended Crio Chokes (C, CI, M, IM, F)
**Weight**: 6 lb. 5 oz.–7 lb. 5 oz.
**Bore/Gauge**: 12, 20
**Magazine**: 4+1 rounds
**Features**: Red bar front sight and metal bead mid sight; Crio ported barrels; ComforTech gel recoil pad and comb insert; heavy duty magazine cap
**MSRP** . . . . . . . . . . . . . . . . . . $1899

## SUPER BLACK EAGLE II

**Action**: Inertia operated semiautomatic
**Stock**: Walnut, synthetic, Realtree APG, Mossy Oak
**Barrel**: 24 in., 26 in., 28 in.
**Chokes**: Crio Choke (C, IC, M, IM, F)
**Weight**: 7 lb. 2 oz.–7 lb. 5 oz.
**Bore/Gauge**: 12
**Magazine**: 3+1 rounds

**Features**: Red bar front sight and metal bead mid sight; ComforTech gel recoil pad and comb insert; larger trigger guard for use with gloves; stock in black synthetic, Realtree Max-4 camo, Realtree APG camo, or walnut
**MSRP** . . . . . . . . . . . . . $1569–$1999

## SUPERNOVA FIELD

**Action**: Pump
**Stock**: Synthetic
**Barrel**: 24 in., 26 in., 28 in.
**Chokes**: Standard choke (IC, M, F)
**Weight**: 7 lb. 13 oz.–8 lb.
**Bore/Gauge**: 12
**Magazine**: 4+1 rounds
**Features**: Stock comes in black synthetic, Realtree APG camo, or Realtree Max-4 camo; receiver drilled and tapped for scope mounting; standard chokes; vented recoil pad
**ComforTech Stock**: . . . . . $549–$669
**SteadyGrip Stock**: . . . . . . . . . $669

## SUPERSPORT

**Action**: Inertia operated semiautomatic
**Stock**: Synthetic
**Barrel**: 28 in., 30 in.
**Chokes**: Extended Crio Chokes( C, IC, M, IM, F)
**Weight**: 6 lb. 5 oz.–7 lb. 5 oz.
**Bore/Gauge**: 12, 20
**Magazine**: 4+1 rounds
**Features**: Stock comes in black SuperSport carbon fiber finish; red bar front sight and metal bead mid sight; Crio ported barrels; ComforTech gel recoil pad and comb insert
**MSRP** . . . . . . . . . . . . . . . . . . $2199

**SHOTGUNS**

# Benelli USA

## SUPER VINCI
**Action**: Inertia operated semiautomatic
**Stock**: Synthetic, Realtree APG
**Barrel**: 26 in., 28 in.
**Chokes**: Crio Chokes (C, IC, M, IM, F)
**Weight**: 6 lb. 14 oz.–7 lb.
**Bore/Gauge**: 12
**Magazine**: 3+1 rounds
**Features**: In-line inertia driven system; enlarged trigger and trigger guard for use with gloves; ComforTech Plus recoil pad; QuadraFit shim kit; drilled and tapped for scopes; synthetic stock in black, Realtree APG camo, or Realtree MAX-4 camo
**MSRP** . . . . . . . . . . . . . . **$1799–$1899**

## ULTRA LIGHT
**Action**: Inertia operated semiautomatic
**Stock**: Walnut
**Barrel**: 24 in., 26 in.
**Chokes**: Crio Chokes (IC, M, F)
**Weight**: 5 lb. 3 oz.–6 lb. 2 oz.
**Bore/Gauge**: 12, 20, 28
**Magazine**: 2+1
**Features**: Weather coated walnut stock; red bar front sight and metal bead mid sight; gel recoil pad; option of checkered Montefeltro forend or ultra light forend
**MSRP** . . . . . . . . . . . . . . **$1669–$1799**

## VINCI
**Action**: Inertia operated semiautomatic
**Stock**: Synthetic
**Barrel**: 24 in., 26 in., 28 in.
**Chokes**: Crio Chokes (C, IC, M, IM, F)
**Weight**: 6 lb. 13 oz.–6 lb. 14 oz.
**Bore/Gauge**: 12
**Magazine**: 3+1 rounds
**Features**: Stock in black, Realtree APG, Realtree APG HD SteadyGrip, or Realtree MAX-4 camo; red bar front sight and metal bead mid sight; drilled and tapped for scope mounting; ComforTech Plus recoil pads
**MSRP** . . . . . . . . . . . . . . **$1359–$1629**

## VINCI CORDOBA
**Action**: Inertia operated semiautomatic
**Stock**: Synthetic with GripTight coating
**Barrel**: 28 in., 30 in.
**Chokes**: Extended Crio Chokes
**Weight**: 7 lb.–7 lb. 2 oz.
**Bore/Gauge**: 12
**Magazine**: 4+1 rounds
**Features**: Crio ported barrels; ComforTech gel recoil pad and comb insert; heavy duty magazine cap; black synthetic stock; red bar front sight and metal bead mid sight
**MSRP** . . . . . . . . . . . . . . . . . . **$2069**

BENELLI SUPER VINCI

BENELLI ULTRA LIGHT

BENELLI VINCI

BENELLI VINCI CORDOBA

SHOTGUNS

# Beretta USA

## 686 SILVER PIGEON I

**Action**: Over/under
**Stock**: Walnut
**Barrel**: 26 in., 28 in., 30 in.
**Chokes**: MC
**Weight**: 6 lb. 13 oz.
**Bore/Gauge**: 12, 20, 28, .410
**Magazine**: None
**Features**: Extensive but refined floral and scroll decoration on the frame; dual-conical locking mechanism; automatic safety; oil finish on checkered walnut stock and forend; metal bead sight
**MSRP** . . . . . . . . . . . . . . . . . . . $2240

## 687 SILVER PIGEON V

**Action**: Over/under
**Stock**: Walnut
**Barrel**: 28 in.
**Chokes**: Screw-in tubes
**Weight**: 6 lb. 13 oz.
**Bore/Gauge**: 12, 20, 28, .410
**Magazine**: None
**Features**: Oil-finished walnut stock detailed with gold game bird inlays and a gold Beretta medallion underneath; color-case finish; single selective trigger; 3-inch chambers; available with English stock or standard stock with pistol grip
**MSRP** . . . . . . . . . . . . . . . . . . . $4075

## A300 OUTLANDER

**Action**: Semiautomatic gas operated
**Stock**: Synthetic, camo, walnut
**Barrel**: 28 in.
**Chokes**: MC3
**Weight**: 7 lb. 10 oz.
**Bore/Gauge**: 12
**Magazine**: 3+1 rounds
**Features**: Gas operation with compensating exhaust valve and self-cleaning piston; adjustable shim system on stock; aluminum alloy receiver; cross-bolt safety with ergonomics; front metal bead sight; black synthetic, camo, or oiled wood stock finish
**Synthetic**: . . . . . . . . . . . . . . . . $725
**Wood**: . . . . . . . . . . . . . . . . . . . $825
**Camo**: . . . . . . . . . . . . . . . . . . . $825

## A400 XCEL PARALLEL TARGET

**Action**: Semiautomatic gas operated
**Stock**: Walnut
**Barrel**: 28 in., 30 in., 32 in.

BERETTA 686 SILVER PIGEON I

BERETTA 687 SILVER PIGEON V

BERETTA A300 OUTLANDER

BERETTA A400 XCEL PARALLEL TARGET

BERETTA A400 XPLOR ACTION

**Chokes**: Optima Bore HP Extended
**Weight**: 7 lb. 11 oz.
**Bore/Gauge**: 12
**Magazine**: 3+1, 2+1 rounds
**Features**: Gun Pod digital display provides digital readout of the ambient air temperature, cartridge pressure, and overall number of rounds fired; interchangeable balance caps; select walnut checkered stock/forend; blued toned aluminum-alloyed receiver; Blink operating system; recoil-dissipating Kick-Off, Micro-core pad; cold-hammer-forged barrel; white front, steel mid-bead
**MSRP** . . . . . . . . . . . . . . . . . . . $1900

## A400 XPLOR ACTION

**Action**: Semiautomatic
**Stock**: Walnut
**Barrel**: 26 in., 28 in., 30 in.
**Chokes**: Optima-Choke HP
**Weight**: 6 lb. 13 oz.
**Bore/Gauge**: 12
**Magazine**: 3+1, 2+1 rounds
**Features**: Blink gas operating system for fast cycling; bronze anodized receiver resistant to corrosion; Kick-Off recoil system; Micro-Core recoil pad; electronic Gun Pod that counts shells, measures temperature, and other functions comes standard
**MSRP** . . . . . . . . . . . . . . $1620–$1825

**SHOTGUNS**

# Beretta USA

### A400 XPLOR LIGHT 12 GA.
**Action**: Semiautomatic
**Stock**: Walnut and polymer
**Barrel**: 26 in., 28 in.
**Chokes**: OptimaChoke screw-in tube
**Weight**: 6 lb. 3 oz.–6 lb. 10 oz.
**Bore/Gauge**: 12
**Magazine**: 3+1, 2+1 rounds
**Features**: Steelium barrel design, walnut stock with polymer forend insert, trigger guard and kick-off interface; 3-in. chamber; blink operating system; Micro-Core recoil pad; available with kick-off damper system
**MSRP** . . . . . . . . . . . . . $1515–$1620

### A400 XPLOR UNICO
**Action**: Semiautomatic
**Stock**: Walnut and polymer
**Barrel**: 26 in., 28 in.
**Chokes**: OptimaChoke screw-in tube
**Weight**: 6 lb. 10 oz.–7 lb.
**Bore/Gauge**: 12
**Magazine**: 3+1, 2+1 rounds
**Features**: Single-selective trigger; green receiver; walnut stock with polymer forend insert, trigger guard and kick-off interface; 3.5-in. chamber; metal bead front sight; camo or green anodized available
**MSRP** . . . . . . . . . . . . . $1730–$1865

### A400 XTREME
**Action**: Semiautomatic
**Stock**: Synthetic, camo
**Barrel**: 26 in., 28 in.
**Chokes**: Optima Bore HP (C, Mod, Full)
**Weight**: 7 lb. 10 oz.
**Bore/Gauge**: 12
**Magazine**: 4+1, 3+1 rounds
**Features**: Advanced Kick-Off Mega recoil system; Micro-Core recoil pad; overmolded grip panels; Aqua Technology's corrosion proof barrier; synthetic black or MAX4 camo.
**Synthetic:** . . . . . . . . . . . . . . . $1730
**MAX4:** . . . . . . . . . . . . . . . . . $1840

**BERETTA A400 XTREME**

**BERETTA A400
XPLOR UNICO**

**BERETTA A400
XPLOR LIGHT**

BERETTA SV10 PERENNIA I

## SV10 PERENNIA I

**Action**: Over/under
**Stock**: Walnut, synthetic
**Barrel**: 26 in., 28 in., 30 in.
**Chokes**: Optima-Choke HP
**Weight**: 7 lb.
**Bore/Gauge**: 12, 20
**Magazine**: None
**Features**: Nano-Ceramic forend iron reduces wear and corrosion; choice between automatic ejection and mechanical extraction; floral engraving; Kick-Off recoil system available; Micro-Core recoil pad.
**Standard:** . . . . . . . . . . . . . . . . $2890
**KO:** . . . . . . . . . . . . . . . . . . . $3295

## SV10 PERENNIA III 20 GA

**Action**: Over/under
**Stock**: Walnut
**Barrel**: 26 in., 28 in.
**Chokes**: OptimaChoke HP Extended
**Weight**: 7 lb. 5 oz.
**Bore/Gauge**: 12
**Magazine**: None
**Features**: Optional Kick-Off hydraulic dampening reduction system; sling swivels; plastic pad; Optima-bore high-performance cold, hammer-forged barrels; automatic safety; chrome-lined bore and chamber
**MSRP** . . . . . . . . . . . . . . $3620–$3945

## SV10 PREVAIL I

**Action**: Over/under
**Stock**: Walnut
**Barrel**: 30 in., 32 in.
**Chokes**: Optima Bore HP Extended
**Weight**: 7 lb. 13 oz.
**Bore/Gauge**: 12
**Magazine**: None
**Features**: Kick-Off, extraction/ejection selection system; easy-removable trigger group; Xtra-Grain walnut checkered stock with oil finish; manual safety; white front bead with steel mid-bead sights; available in sporting and trap versions
**MSRP** . . . . . . . . . . . . . $2900–$3450

BERETTA SV10 PERENNIA III 20 GA.

BERETTA SV10 PREVAIL I, SPORTING

SHOTGUNS

# Bernardelli

**BERNARDELLI CIGNO**

**BERNARDELLI HEMINGWAY DELUXE**

**BERNARDELLI PA 12**

**BERNARDELLI RISERVA**

**BERNARDELLI SIRBONE**

## CIGNO
**Action**: Semiautomatic
**Stock**: Walnut
**Barrel**: 24 in., 26 in., 28 in., 30 in.
**Chokes**: Steel chokes (M, F, IM, IC, CYL, F)
**Weight**: 6 lb. 13 oz.
**Bore/Gauge**: 12
**Magazine**: 2+1, 4+1 rounds
**Features**: Select walnut stock with pistol grip; rubber recoil pad; includes carrying case; receiver is black anodized and finely sand blasted
**MSRP** . . . . . . . . . . . . . . . . . . . **$1269**

## HEMINGWAY DELUXE
**Action**: Side-by-side
**Stock**: Walnut
**Barrel**: 24 in., 26 in., 27 in., 28 in., 29 in.
**Chokes**: Fixed cylinder chokes
**Weight**: 6 lb. 2 oz.–6 lb. 3 oz.
**Bore/Gauge**: 12, 20
**Magazine**: None
**Features**: Simple or automatic extrac-
tors; double trigger or single trigger with selector; beavertail buttstock; forged steel frame; English walnut stock with pistol grip
**MSRP** . . . . . . . . . . . . . . . . . . **$5887**

## PA 12
**Action**: Pump
**Stock**: Synthetic
**Barrel**: 20 in.
**Chokes**: Steel cylinder chokes
**Weight**: 6 lb.
**Bore/Gauge**: 12
**Magazine**: 6+1 rounds
**Features**: Synthetic black matte stock; shipped in carton box; steel barrel
**MSRP** . . . . . . . . . . . . . . . . . . . **$596**

## RISERVA
**Action**: Side-by-side
**Stock**: Walnut
**Barrel**: 24 in., 26 in., 27 in., 28 in., 29 in.
**Chokes**: Fixed cylinder chokes
**Weight**: 6 lb. 13 oz.

**Bore/Gauge**: 12
**Magazine**: None
**Features**: Forged steel frame; double trigger or single trigger with selector; simple or automatic extractor; English walnut stock with pistol grip; beavertail buttstock
**Standard**: . . . . . . . . . . . . . . . **$5069**
**De Luxe**: . . . . . . . . . . . . . . . . **$5646**

## SIRBONE
**Action**: Semiautomatic
**Stock**: Walnut
**Barrel**: 24 in., 26 in., 28 in., 30 in.
**Chokes**: Steel chokes (M, F, IM, IC, CYL, F)
**Weight**: 6 lb. 13 oz.
**Bore/Gauge**: 12
**Magazine**: 2+1, 4+1 rounds
**Features**: Optical fiber front sight with rear sight dovetail optical fiber; select walnut stock with pistol grip; rubber recoil pad
**MSRP** . . . . . . . . . . . . . . . . . . . **$1744**

SHOTGUNS

# Blaser USA, Inc.

**BLASER F3 SPORTING**

## F3 SPORTING

*Action*: Over/under
*Stock*: Walnut
*Barrel*: 28 in., 30 in., 32 in., 34 in.
*Chokes*: Briley Spectrum chokes (SK, IC, M., IM, F)
*Weight*: 7 lb. 5 oz.
*Bore/Gauge*: 12, 20, 28, .410
*Magazine*: None
*Features*: Sporting stock, forearm with Schnabel; internal block system; ergonomically optimized, adjustable trigger

blade; Triplex Bore design; ejection-ball-system; balancer
Standard:................ $7613
Luxus: .................. $9340
Grand Luxus:............ $12233

Super Luxus: ........... $13913
Baronesse:............. $15010
Exclusive:........Price on request
Super Exclusive:...Price on request
Imperial: .......Price on request

# Browning

**BROWNING A5 HUNTER**

**BROWNING A5 STALKER**

**BROWNING A-BOLT SHOTGUN HUNTER**

**BROWNING A-BOLT SHOTGUN STALKER**

## A5 HUNTER

*Action*: Autoloader
*Stock*: Walnut
*Barrel*: 26 in., 28 in., 30 in.
*Chokes*: Invector-DS
*Weight*: 6 lb. 15 oz.
*Bore/Gauge*: 12
*Magazine*: None
*Features*: Strong, lightweight aluminum alloy; black anodized bi-tone finish; flat, ventilated rib; recoil operated Kinematic Drive is ultra-reliable and cycles a wide range of loads; gloss finish walnut with close radius pistol grip; 22 lines-per-inch checkering; shim adjustable for length of pull, cast and drop; Vector Pro lengthened forcing cone; three invector-DS™ choke tubes; Inflex II technology recoil pad; brass

front bead sight; ivory mid-bead sight; included ABS case
MSRP . . . . . . . . .$1559.99–$1699.99

## A5 STALKER

*Action*: Autoloader
*Stock*: Composite
*Barrel*: 26 in., 28 in., 30 in.
*Chokes*: Invector-DS
*Weight*: 7 lb. 3 oz.–7 lb. 7 oz.
*Bore/Gauge*: 12
*Magazine*: None
*Features*: Strong, lightweight aluminum alloy; flat, ventilated rib; recoil operated Kinematic Drive is ultra-reliable and cycles a wide range of loads; composite with close radius pistol grip; textured gripping surfaces; shim adjustable for cast and drop; matte black finish;

Dura-Touch armor coating; Vector Pro lengthened forcing cone; Inflex II technology recoil pad; fiber-optic front sight; included ABS case
MSRP . . . . . . . . .$1399.99–$1559.99

## A-BOLT SHOTGUN HUNTER

*Action*: Bolt
*Stock*: Walnut
*Barrel*: 22 in.
*Chokes*: None
*Weight*: 7 lb. 2 oz.
*Bore/Gauge*: 12
*Magazine*: Detachable, 2+1 rounds
*Features*: Sling swivel studs; satin finish walnut stock with checkered forearm; low-luster blued finish, steel receiver; drilled and tapped for scope mounts
MSRP . . . . . . . . . . . . . . . . $1279.99

## A-BOLT SHOTGUN STALKER & INFINITY CAMO

*Action*: Bolt
*Stock*: Composite
*Barrel*: 22 in.
*Chokes*: None
*Weight*: 7 lb.
*Bore/Gauge*: 12
*Magazine*: Detachable, 2+1 rounds
*Features*: Black composite (Stalker model); Mossy Oak Break-Up Infinity composite (Infinity Camo Model); textured gripping surfaces; Dura-touch armor coating; sling swivel studs installed; recoil pad; Truglo/Marble's fiber optic front sight, adjustable rear sight
Stalker: . . . . . . . . . . . . . . $1149.99
Infinity Camo: . . . . . . . . . . $1299.99

# Browning

## BPS HUNTER

*Action*: Bottom ejection pump
*Stock*: Walnut
*Barrel*: 26 in., 28 in.
*Chokes*: Three Invector-Plus choke tubes with 12 and 20 gauges; Standard Invectors with 16, 28, and .410
*Weight*: 6 lb. 15 oz.–7 lb. 11 oz.
*Bore/Gauge*: 12, 16, 20, 28, .410
*Magazine*: None
*Features*: Satin finish walnut stock; forged and machined steel receiver; ventilated rib barrel; top-tang safety
**MSRP . . . . . . . . . . $649.99–$699.99**

## BPS RIFLED DEER HUNTER

*Action*: Bottom ejection pump
*Stock*: Walnut
*Barrel*: 22 in.
*Chokes*: Screw-in tubes
*Weight*: 7 lb. 4 oz.–7 lb. 10 oz.
*Bore/Gauge*: 12, 20
*Magazine*: None
*Features*: Satin finish walnut stock; forged and machined steel receiver; thick-walled barrel for slug ammunition only; dual steel action bars
**MSRP . . . . . . . . . . $779.99–$799.99**

## BPS TRAP

*Action*: Bottom ejection pump
*Stock*: Walnut
*Barrel*: 30 in.
*Chokes*: Three Invector-Plus choke tubes
*Weight*: 8 lb. 2 oz.
*Bore/Gauge*: 12
*Magazine*: None
*Features*: Satin finish walnut stock with raised comb; forged and machined steel receiver with engraving; dual steel action bars; top-tang safety; magazine cut-off; HiViz ProComp fiber optic sight with mid-bead
**MSRP . . . . . . . . . . . . . . . . . . . $799.99**

## BT-99

*Action*: Bottom ejection pump
*Stock*: Walnut
*Barrel*: 32 in., 34 in.
*Chokes*: Screw-in tubes
*Weight*: 8 lb. 3 oz.–8 lb. 5 oz.
*Bore/Gauge*: 12
*Magazine*: None
*Features*: Satin finish walnut stock with beavertail forearm; steel receiver with blued finish; high-post ventilated rib
**MSRP . . . . . . . . . . . . . . . . . . $1429.99**

BROWNING BPS HUNTER

BROWNING BPS RIFLED DEER HUNTER

BROWNING BPS TRAP

BROWNING BT-99

BROWNING CITORI 625 SPORTING SMALL GA.

BROWNING CITORI 725 FIELD

## CITORI 625 SPORTING SMALL GA.

*Action*: Over/under
*Stock*: Walnut
*Barrel*: 28 in., 30 in., 32 in.
*Chokes*: Five Diamond Grade Extended Invector-Plus choke tubes on 12 and 2 Standard Invector on 28 and .410
*Weight*: 6 lb. 15 oz.–7 lb. 7 oz.
*Bore/Gauge*: 20, 28, .410
*Magazine*: None
*Features*: Steel receiver with high-relief engraving with gold embellishment; single selective trigger; hammer ejectors; top-tang barrel selector/safety; sporting recoil pad; triple trigger system; HiViz Pro-Comp fiber optic sight
**MSRP . . . . . . . . . $3549.99–$3579.99**

## CITORI 725 FIELD

*Action*: Over/under
*Stock*: Walnut
*Barrel*: 26 in., 28 in.
*Chokes*: Invector-DS
*Weight*: 7 lb. 4 oz.–7 lb. 6 oz.
*Bore/Gauge*: 12
*Magazine*: None
*Features*: Steel receiver with silver nitride finish; accented, high-relief engraving; ventilated top rib action; mechanical trigger system; hammer ejectors; top-tang barrel selector/safety; gloss oil finish Grade II/III walnut with close radius pistol grip; Vector Pro lengthened forcing cones; ivory front and mid-bead sights
**MSRP . . . . . . . . . . . . . . . . . $2469.99**

SHOTGUNS

**BROWNING CITORI 725 SPORTING**

**BROWNING CITORI FEATHER LIGHTNING**

## CITORI 725 SPORTING

**Action**: Over/under
**Stock**: Walnut
**Barrel**: 28 in., 30 in., 32 in.
**Chokes**: Invector-DS
**Weight**: 7 lb. 6 oz.–7 lb. 10 oz.
**Bore/Gauge**: 12
**Magazine**: None
**Features**: Steel receiver with silver nitride finish; gold accented engraving; ventilated top and side rib action; mechanical trigger system; hammer ejectors; top-tang barrel selector/safety; gloss oil finish Grade III/IV walnut with close radius pistol grip; Vector Pro lengthened forcing cones; five Invector-DS choke tubes; HiViz Pro-Comp sight and ivory mid-bead
**MSRP** . . . . . . . . . . . . . . . . . $3139.99

## CITORI FEATHER LIGHTNING

**Action**: Over/under
**Stock**: Walnut
**Barrel**: 26 in., 28 in.

**Chokes**: Invector-Plus (F, M, IC)
**Weight**: 5 lb. 14 oz.–6 lb. 9 oz.
**Bore/Gauge**: 12, 20
**Magazine**: None
**Features**: With a lightweight alloy receiver and lightning style stock and forearm, the popular Browning Citori is now available in the new Citori Feather Lightning model. This lightweight Citori makes it easy to carry for long days on the range or out hunting.
**MSRP** . . . . . . . . . . . . . . . . . $2179.99

## CITORI GRADE IV LIGHTNING

**Action**: Over/under
**Stock**: Walnut
**Barrel**: 26 in.
**Chokes**: Three Invector-Plus choke tubes
**Weight**: 6 lb. 8 oz.–8 lb. 1 oz.
**Bore/Gauge**: 12, .410
**Magazine**: None
**Features**: Steel grayed finish receiver with full coverage engraving; ventilated rib barrel; single selective trigger; hammer ejectors; lightning style walnut stock and forearm
**MSRP** . . . . . . . . . $3499.99–$3589.99

## CITORI LIGHTNING

**Action**: Over/under
**Stock**: Walnut
**Barrel**: 26 in., 28 in.
**Chokes**: Three Invector-Plus choke tubes on 12 and 20, three standard Invector tubes on 28 and .410
**Weight**: 6 lb. 7 oz.–8 lb. 2 oz.
**Bore/Gauge**: 12, 20, 28, .410
**Magazine**: None
**Features**: Walnut stock with pistol grip; ventilated rib; single selective trigger; hammer ejectors; top-tang barrel selector/safety; ivory front bead sight
**MSRP** . . . . . . . . $1989.99–$2069.99

**BROWNING CITORI LIGHTNING**

12 Gauge

20 & 28 Ga., .410

**BROWNING CITORI GRADE IV LIGHTNING AND VII LIGHTNING**

# Browning

BROWNING CITORI MAPLE LIGHTNING

BROWNING CITORI SUPERLIGHT FEATHER

BROWNING CITORI XT TRAP

BROWNING CYNERGY CLASSIC FIELD

BROWNING CYNERGY CLASSIC FIELD GRADE III

BROWNING CYNERGY CLASSIC FIELD GRADE VI

## CITORI MAPLE LIGHTNING

**Action**: Over/under
**Stock**: Maple
**Barrel**: 26 in., 28 in., 30 in.
**Chokes**: Invector-Plus (F, M, IC)
**Weight**: 6 lb. 9 oz.–8 lb.
**Bore/Gauge**: 12, 20
**Magazine**: None
**Features**: Steel receiver with blued finish; high-relief standard Lightning engraving; high gloss blued finish; ventilated rib; single selector trigger; hammer ejectors; top-tang barrel; selector/safety; gloss finish maple; recoil pad on 12 gauge model; ivory front bead sight
**MSRP** . . . . . . . . . . . . . . . . $2069.99

## CITORI SUPERLIGHT FEATHER

**Action**: Over/under
**Stock**: Walnut
**Barrel**: 26 in.
**Chokes**: Invector-Plus

**Weight**: 5 lb. 11 oz.–6 lb. 4 oz.
**Bore/Gauge**: 12, 20, 28, .410
**Magazine**: None
**Features**: Lightweight alloy receiver with steel breech face and hinge pin; high-relief engraving; single selective trigger; hammer ejectors; top-tang barrel selector/safety; gloss finish walnut, English-style straight grip stock, Schnabel forearm; three Invector-Plus choke tubes
**MSRP** . . . . . . . . . . . . . . . . $2389.99

## CITORI XT TRAP

**Action**: Over/under
**Stock**: Walnut
**Barrel**: 30 in., 32 in.
**Chokes**: Three Invector-plus choke tubes
**Weight**: 8 lb. 6 oz.–8 lb. 8 oz.
**Bore/Gauge**: 12
**Magazine**: None
**Features**: Triple-trigger system; HiViz Pro-Comp sight; steel receiver with gold accented engravings; ventilated

barrel; walnut stock with close radius pistol grip and right-hand palm swell; semi-beavertail forearm with finger grooves
**MSRP** . . . . . . . . . . . . . . . . $2949.99

## CYNERGY CLASSIC FIELD

**Action**: Over/under
**Stock**: Walnut
**Barrel**: 26 in., 28 in.
**Chokes**: Three Invector-Plus choke tubes on 12 and 20; three standard Invector chokes on 28 and .410
**Weight**: 6 lb. 4 oz.–7 lb. 13 oz.
**Bore/Gauge**: 12, 20, 28, .410
**Magazine**: None
**Features**: Reverse striker ignition system; impact ejectors; top-tang barrel selector/safety; gloss oil finish on grade III/IV walnut; steel receiver; ivory front and mid-bead sights
**MSRP** . . . . . . . . $2529.99–$2589.99

## CYNERGY CLASSIC FIELD GRADE III

**Action**: Over/under
**Stock**: Walnut
**Barrel**: 26 in., 28 in.
**Chokes**: Three Invector-Plus choke tubes
**Weight**: 6 lb. 8 oz.–8 lb. 1 oz.
**Bore/Gauge**: 12, 20
**Magazine**: None
**Features**: Steel receiver with MonoLock hinge; full coverage high-relief engraving; ventilated top and side ribs; reverse striker ignition system; gloss finish grade III/IV walnut; recoil pad on 12-gauge model
**MSRP** . . . . . . . . $3999.99–$4049.99

## CYNERGY CLASSIC FIELD GRADE VI

**Action**: Over/under
**Stock**: Walnut
**Barrel**: 26 in., 28 in.
**Chokes**: Three Invector-Plus
**Weight**: 6 lb. 8 oz.–8 lb. 1 oz.
**Bore/Gauge**: 12, 20
**Magazine**: None
**Features**: Steel receiver with MonoLock hinge; full coverage high-relief engraving; ventilated top and side ribs; reverse striker ignition system; gloss finish grade III/IV walnut; recoil pad on 12-gauge model
**MSRP** . . . . . . . . $6099.99–$6129.99

SHOTGUNS

# Browning

BROWNING CYNERGY CLASSIC SPORTING

BROWNING CYNERGY CLASSIC SPORTING MAPLE

BROWNING CYNERGY CLASSIC TRAP

BROWNING CYNERGY CLASSIC TRAP UNSINGLE COMBO WITH ADJUSTABLE COMB

## CYNERGY CLASSIC SPORTING

**Action**: Over/under
**Stock**: Walnut
**Barrel**: 28 in., 30 in., 32 in.
**Chokes**: Three Invector-Plus Midas Grade choke tubes on 12 and 20; three Standard Invector chokes on 28 and .410
**Weight**: 6 lb. 4 oz.–7 lb. 15 oz.
**Bore/Gauge**: 12, 20, 28, .410
**Magazine**: None
**Features**: Steel receiver; ventilated top and side ribs; reverse striker ignition system; impact ejectors; top-tang barrel selector/safety; gloss oil finish grade III/IV walnut; HiViz Pro-Comp fiber optic sight
**MSRP** . . . . . . . . **$3599.99–$3629.99**

## CYNERGY CLASSIC SPORTING MAPLE

**Action**: Over/under
**Stock**: Maple
**Barrel**: 28 in., 30 in., 32 in.
**Chokes**: Midas Grade Invector Plus
**Weight**: 7 lb. 11 oz.–7 lb. 15 oz.
**Bore/Gauge**: 12

**Magazine**: None
**Features**: Steel receiver with silver nitride finish; jeweled monobloc; MonoLock hinge; high-relief engraving; high gloss blued; ventilated top and side ribs; reverse striker ignition system; impact ejectors; top-tang barrel selector/safety
**Stock**: Grade III/IV maple, gloss finish
**Features**: Vector Pro lengthened forcing cones; Three Midas Grade Invector Plus choke tubes (M,IC,SK); Triple Trigger System; HiViz Pro-Comp fiber-optic sight
**MSRP** . . . . . . . . . . . . . . . . **$3599.99**

## CYNERGY CLASSIC TRAP

**Action**: Over/under
**Stock**: Walnut
**Barrel**: 30 in., 32 in.
**Chokes**: Three Invector-Plus Midas Grade choke tubes
**Weight**: 8 lb.10 oz.–8 lb. 12 oz.
**Bore/Gauge**: 12
**Magazine**: None
**Features**: Reverse striker ignition system; impact ejectors; top-tang barrel selector/safety; Monte Carlo walnut

stock with right-hand palm swell; HiViz Pro-Comp fiber-optic sight
**MSRP** . . . . . . . . . . . . . . . . **$3879.99**

## CYNERGY CLASSIC TRAP UNSINGLE COMBO WITH ADJUSTABLE COMB

**Action**: Single shot and over/under
**Stock**: Walnut
**Barrel**: 30 in., 32 in.
**Chokes**: Four Invector-Plus Midas Grade choke tubes
**Weight**: 8 lb. 13 oz.–8 lb. 15 oz.
**Bore/Gauge**: 12
**Magazine**: None
**Features**: Steel receiver with MonoLock hinge; double- and single-barrel sets included; reverse striker ignition system; impact ejectors; top-tang barrel selector/safety; gloss finish Monte Carlo grade III/IV walnut stock with right-hand palm swell
**MSRP** . . . . . . . . . . . . . . . . **$5999.99**

SHOTGUNS

# Browning

BROWNING CYNERGY FEATHER

BROWNING CYNERGY FIELD

## CYNERGY FEATHER

**Action**: Over/under
**Stock**: Walnut
**Barrel**: 26 in., 28 in.
**Chokes**: Three Invector-Plus choke tubes on 12 and 20, Standard Invector on 28 and .410
**Weight**: 5 lb. 8 oz.–6 lb. 13 oz.
**Bore/Gauge**: 12, 20, 28, .410
**Magazine**: None
**Features**: Lightweight alloy receiver; gold enhanced grayed finish; MonoLock hinge; reverse striker ignition system; top-tang barrel selector/safety; Inflex technology recoil pad system; ivory front and mid-bead sights
**MSRP** . . . . . . . . **$2899.99–$2929.99**

## CYNERGY FIELD

**Action**: Over/under
**Stock**: Walnut
**Barrel**: 26 in., 28 in.
**Chokes**: Three Invector-Plus choke tubes on 12 and 20; Standard Invector on 28 and .410
**Weight**: 6 lb. 1 oz.–7 lb. 11 oz.
**Bore/Gauge**: 12, 20, 28, .410
**Magazine**: None
**Features**: Steel receiver with MonoLock hinge; reverse striker ignition system; impact ejectors; oil finish walnut stock; ivory front and mid-bead sights
**MSRP** . . . . . . . . **$2799.99–$2849.99**

## CYNERGY SPORTING

**Action**: Over/under
**Stock**: Walnut
**Barrel**: 28 in., 30 in., 32 in.
**Chokes**: Three Invector-Plus choke tubes
**Weight**: 6 lb. 4 oz.–8 lb. 1 oz.
**Bore/Gauge**: 12, 20
**Magazine**: None
**Features**: Reverse striker ignition system; impact ejectors; top-tang barrel selector/safety; gloss oil finish on grade III/IV walnut; steel receiver; Inflex technology recoil pad system; HiViz Pro-Comp fiber optic sight
**MSRP** . . . . . . . . **$3999.99–$4029.99**

BROWNING CYNERGY SPORTING

**BROWNING GOLD LIGHT 10 GA., MOSSY OAK DUCK BLIND**

**BROWNING MAXUS HUNTER**

**BROWNING MAXUS SPORTING**

**BROWNING MAXUS STALKER**

## GOLD LIGHT 10 GA.

*Action*: Autoloader, gas-operated
*Stock*: Composite
*Barrel*: 26 in., 28 in.
*Chokes*: Three Standard Invector choke tubes
*Weight*: 9 lb. 9 oz.–9 lb. 10 oz.
*Bore/Gauge*: 10
*Magazine*: 4+1 rounds
*Features*: Aluminum alloy receiver; ventilated rib barrel; composite stock and forearm in MO Break-Up Infinity or MO Shadow Grass Blades; DuraTouch armor coating
**MSRP** . . . . . . . . . . . . . . . . **$1739.99**

## MAXUS HUNTER

*Action*: Autoloader, gas-operated
*Stock*: Composite
*Barrel*: 26 in., 28 in., 30 in.
*Chokes*: Three Invector-Plus
*Weight*: 6 lb. 15 oz.–7 lb. 1 oz.
*Bore/Gauge*: 12
*Magazine*: None
*Features*: Aluminum alloy receiver with durable satin nickel finish; laser engraving of pheasant and mallard on receiver; Inflex technology recoil pad; ivory front bead sight
**MSRP** . . . . . . . . **$1499.99–$1639.99**

## MAXUS SPORTING

*Action*: Autoloader, gas-operated
*Stock*: Walnut
*Barrel*: 28 in., 30 in.
*Chokes*: Five Invector-Plus choke tubes
*Weight*: 7 lb. 3 oz.–7 lb. 4 oz.
*Bore/Gauge*: 12
*Magazine*: None
*Features*: Aluminum alloy receiver with durable satin nickel finish; laser engraving of game birds transforming into clay birds; speed lock forearm; ivory mid bead sight, HiVix Tri-Comp fiber optic front sight
**MSRP** . . . . . . . . . . . . . . . **$1699.99**

## MAXUS STALKER

*Action*: Autoloader, gas-operated
*Stock*: Composite
*Barrel*: 26 in., 28 in.
*Chokes*: Three Invector Plus choke tubes
*Weight*: 7 lb.–7 lb. 2 oz.
*Bore/Gauge*: 12
*Magazine*: None
*Features*: Magazine cut-off, matte black composite stock with pistol grip; speed lock forearm; textured gripping surfaces; Dura Touch armor coating; Inflex technology recoil pads; lightning trigger system; ventilated rib
**MSRP** . . . . . . . . **$1339.99–$1499.99**

**SHOTGUNS**

# Browning

**BROWNING MAXUS ULTIMATE**

**BROWNING SILVER HUNTER**

## MAXUS ULTIMATE
*Action*: Autoloader, gas operated
*Stock*: Walnut
*Barrel*: 26 in., 28 in., 30 in.
*Chokes*: Invector Plus (F, M, IC)
*Weight*: 7 lb. 1 oz.–7 lb. 4 oz.
*Bore/Gauge*: 12
*Magazine*: None
*Features*: Strong, lightweight aluminum alloy receiver; durable satin nickel finish; laser engraved (pintails on the left-hand side and pheasants on the right); gloss blued finish; ventilated rib; gloss oil finished grade III walnut with close radius pistol grip; speed lock forearm; shim adjustable for length of pull, cast, and drop; Inflex technology recoil pad; brass bead front sight; ABS case included
**MSRP . . . . . . . . . . . . . . . . $1869.99**

## SILVER HUNTER
*Action*: Autoloader, gas operated
*Stock*: Walnut
*Barrel*: 26 in., 28 in., 30 in.
*Chokes*: Three Invector-Plus choke tubes
*Weight*: 6 lb. 5 oz.–7 lb. 9 oz.
*Bore/Gauge*: 12, 20
*Magazine*: None
*Features*: Aluminum alloy receiver; ventilated rib barrel; satin finish walnut stock
**MSRP . . . . . . . . $1179.99–$1339.99**

## SILVER HUNTER MICRO MIDAS
*Action*: Autoloader, gas-operated
*Stock*: Walnut
*Barrel*: 24 in., 26 in.
*Chokes*: Three Invector-Plus choke tubes
*Weight*: 6 lb.–7 lb. 5 oz.
*Bore/Gauge*: 12, 20
*Magazine*: None
*Features*: Semi-humpback receiver design with silver finish; ivory front bead sight
**MSRP . . . . . . . . . . . . . . . . $1179.99**

**BROWNING SILVER HUNTER MICRO MIDAS**

# Caesar Guerini

**CAESAR GUERINI ELLIPSE EVO**

**CAESAR GUERINI MAXUM IMPACT**

## ELLIPSE EVO

**Action**: Over/under
**Stock**: Walnut
**Barrel**: 28 in.
**Chokes**: 5 choke tube options
**Weight**: 6 lb.–7 lb. 4 oz.
**Bore/Gauge**: 12, 20, 28
**Magazine**: None
**Features**: Single trigger; rounded forend; chrome-lined barrel; non-ventilated center rib; hand-polished coin finish receiver with Invisalloy protective finish
**MSRP** . . . . . . . . . . . . . . $5950–$7875

## MAXUM IMPACT

**Action**: Over/under
**Stock**: Checkered walnut with adjustable cheekpiece

**Barrel**: 30 in.–34 in.
**Chokes**: Maxis choke system
**Weight**: 7 lb. 11 oz.–8 lb. 7 oz.
**Bore/Gauge**: 12, 20
**Magazine**: None
**Features**: Engraved receiver; 17mm-tall D.T.S. rib for more upright shooting; 5 in. dual conical forcing cones; selective and non-selective triggers available; left-hand available
**MSRP** . . . . . . . . . . . $8195–$10495

## TEMPIO FIELD GUN

**Action**: Over/under
**Stock**: Turkish walnut
**Barrel**: 26 in., 28 in., 30 in.
**Chokes**: 5 nickel plated, flush fitting chokes
**Weight**: 6 lb.–7 lb.

**Bore/Gauge**: 12, 20, 28, .410
**Magazine**: None
**Features**: Designed to be a sleek and fast pointing shotgun in the field; perfect companion for upland game hunters; low-profile receiver matched with a trim stock, classic Prince-of-Wales grip and schnabel forend make the gun a perfect match for fast game birds; contemporary style of "ornato" style scroll with tasteful gold accents; Invisalloy protective coating
**MSRP** . . . . . . . . . . . . . . $3595–$7070

## WOODLANDER

**Action**: Over/under
**Stock**: English walnut
**Barrel**: 26 in., 28 in., 30 in.
**Chokes**: Five precision patterned flush chokes (CYL, IC, M, IM, F)
**Weight**: 6 lb.–7 lb.
**Bore/Gauge**: 12, 20, 28, .410
**Magazine**: None
**Features**: This gun reflects passion for fall coverts, autumn foliage, wet gun dogs, and the smell of wood smoke. With the understated elegance of color case hardening and nicely figured, oil-finished English walnut that speaks of quality from a bygone era, this is a superior-handling upland game gun that's perfect for tight cover and fast-flushing birds.
**MSRP** . . . . . . . . . . . . . . $3250–$6725

**CAESAR GUERINI TEMPIO FIELD GUN**

**CAESAR GUERINI WOODLANDER**

# Cimarron Firearms Co.

**CIMARRON 1881 HAMMERLESS SHOTGUN**

### 1881 HAMMERLESS SHOTGUN
**Action**: Side-by-side
**Stock**: Walnut
**Barrel**: 20 in., 22 in., 26 in., 28 in., 30 in.

**Chokes**: Double Barrel STD
**Weight**: N/A
**Bore/Gauge**: 12
**Magazine**: None
**Features**: Authentic frontier styling; manual ejectors; threaded for inter-

changeable choke tubes; stock and forend is American walnut; deluxe stock available
**MSRP** . . . . . . . . . . $721.50–$760.50

# Connecticut Shotgun Mfg. Co.

### A-10 AMERICAN
**Action**: Sidelock over/under
**Stock**: Checkered American black walnut
**Barrel**: 26 in.–32 in.
**Chokes**: 5 TruLock tubes
**Weight**: 6 lb. 8 oz.–7 lb. 8 oz.

**Bore/Gauge**: 12, 20, 28
**Magazine**: None
**Features**: Finely engraved, cut checkering; ventilated rib; pistol grip or straight grip; auto ejectors, single selective trigger; Galazan pad

**Standard:** . . . . . . . . . . . . . . . $7995
**Deluxe:** . . . . . . . . . . . . . . . . $8995
**Rose & Scroll:** . . . . . . . . . . . $10000
**Platinum:** . . . . . . . . . . . . . . $15000

**CONNECTICUT SHOTGUN MFG. CO.
A-10 AMERICAN PLATINUM**

# CZ-USA (Ceska Zbrojovka)

## 712 ADJUSTABLE LENGTH STOCK

**Action**: Gas-operated semiautomatic
**Stock**: Polymer
**Barrel**: 28 in.
**Chokes**: Interchangeable chokes (F, M, IC)
**Weight**: 7 lb. 13 oz.
**Bore/Gauge**: 12
**Magazine**: 4+1 rounds
**Features**: Polymer ATI adjsutable stock; fiber optic front sight; adjustable length of pull from 12 to 14 inches
**MSRP** . . . . . . . . . . . . . . . . . . . . $562

## 712 SEMIAUTO

**Action**: Semiautomatic
**Stock**: Walnut
**Barrel**: 26 in., 28 in.
**Chokes**: Screw-in chokes (IC, M, F, C, IM)
**Weight**: 7 lb. 5 oz.
**Bore/Gauge**: 12
**Magazine**: 4+1 rounds
**Features**: 3-in. chamber; cross bolt safety; matte black chrome barrel finish; matte anodized receiver finish; gas-operated system; chrome-lined barrel
**MSRP** . . . . . . . . . . . . . . . . . . . . $488

## 712 TARGET

**Action**: Gas-operated semiautomatic
**Stock**: Walnut
**Barrel**: 30 in.
**Chokes**: Interchangeable chokes (F, M, IC)
**Weight**: 7 lb. 10 oz.
**Bore/Gauge**: 12
**Magazine**: 4+1 rounds
**Features**: Gas operated aluminum alloy action with target-grade enhancements; chrome-lined barrel; fiber optic front sight on a 10mm stepped rib; Schnabel forend; smooth rounded heel; Monte Carlo buttstock
**MSRP** . . . . . . . . . . . . . . . . . . . . $660

## 712 UTILITY

**Action**: Semiautomatic
**Stock**: Synthetic
**Barrel**: 20 in.
**Chokes**: Screw-in chokes (F, IM, M, IC, C)
**Weight**: 6 lb. 10 oz.
**Bore/Gauge**: 12
**Magazine**: 4+1 rounds
**Features**: 3 in.-chamber cross-bolt safety; black synthetic stock; matte chrome black barrel
**MSRP** . . . . . . . . . . . . . . . . . . . . $488

CZ 712 ALS
CZ 712 SEMIAUTO
CZ 712 TARGET
CZ 712 UTILITY
CZ 912 SEMIAUTO

## 912 SEMIAUTO

**Action**: Recoil-operated semiautomatic
**Stock**: Walnut
**Barrel**: 28 in.
**Chokes**: 5 interchangeable choke tubes
**Weight**: 7 lb. 5 oz.
**Bore/Gauge**: 12
**Magazine**: 4+1 rounds
**Features**: Fiber optic front bead; features a gloss black finish on metalwork; cross-bolt safety; chrome-lined barrel; aluminum frame
**MSRP** . . . . . . . . . . . . . . . . . . . . $528

# CZ-USA (Ceska Zbrojovka)

## REDHEAD TARGET

**Action**: Over/under
**Stock**: Walnut
**Barrel**: 30 in.
**Chokes**: Interchangeable chokes (C, F, M, IC, IM)
**Weight**: 8 lb. 4 oz.
**Bore/Gauge**: 12
**Magazine**: None
**Features**: Boxlock frame system; single selective mechanical trigger; coil spring operated hammers; auto ejectors; chrome-lined barrels; Turkish walnut stock; 10mm stepped rib
**MSRP** . . . . . . . . . . . . . . . . . . . $1348

## RINGNECK STRAIGHT GRIP

**Action**: Over/under
**Stock**: Walnut
**Barrel**: 26 in.
**Chokes**: Interchangeable chokes (C, F, M, IC, IM)
**Weight**: 6 lb. 5 oz.
**Bore/Gauge**: 20
**Magazine**: None
**Features**: Turkish walnut stock with a straight English pistol grip; case hardened receiver; polished blued barrels; single selective mechanical trigger; extractors; Greener Top Cross Bolt system and bottom-locking action
**MSRP** . . . . . . . . . . . . . . . . . . . $993

## RINGNECK TARGET

**Action**: Over/under
**Stock**: Walnut
**Barrel**: 30 in.
**Chokes**: Interchangeable chokes (C, F, M, IC, IM)
**Weight**: 7 lb. 5 oz.
**Bore/Gauge**: 12
**Magazine**: None
**Features**: Turkish walnut stock with a full size target grip; case-hardened receiver; polished blued barrels; single selective mechanical trigger; extractors; Greener Top Cross Bolt system and bottom-locking action
**MSRP** . . . . . . . . . . . . . . . . . . . $1260

## UPLAND ULTRALIGHT

**Action**: Over/under
**Stock**: Turkish Walnut
**Barrel**: 26 in., 28 in.
**Chokes**: Multi-choke
**Weight**: 6 lb.
**Bore/Gauge**: 12
**Magazine**: None
**Features**: Lightweight, black alloy receiver; vent rib
**MSRP** . . . . . . . . . . . . . . . . . . . $739

## WINGSHOOTER DELUXE

**Action**: Over/under
**Stock**: Turkish Walnut
**Barrel**: 28 in.
**Chokes**: 5 Interchangeable choke tubes
**Weight**: 6 lb.–7 lb. 6 oz.
**Bore/Gauge**: 12, 20
**Magazine**: None
**Features**: Single trigger; black chrome barrel finish; box-lock frame; Schnabel forend; manual tang safety
**MSRP** . . . . . . . . . . . . . . . . . . . $999

CZ REDHEAD TARGET

CZ RINGNECK STRAIGHT GRIP

CZ RINGNECK TARGET

CZ UPLAND ULTRALIGHT

CZ WINGSHOOTER DELUXE

SHOTGUNS

# Escort by Legacy Sports

## AIMGUARD, MARINEGUARD HOME DEFENSE

**Action**: Pump
**Stock**: Synthetic
**Barrel**: 18 in.
**Chokes**: Cylinder bore
**Weight**: 6 lb. 4 oz.
**Bore/Gauge**: 12
**Magazine**: Tubular, 5 rounds
**Features**: Rifle-style front sight; black synthetic stock; AimGuard has black metal finish, MarineGuard has water resistant nickel finish; sling swivel studs; dovetail receiver for mounting accessory sights
**AimGuard**:................ $299
**MarineGuard**: ............. $369

## EXTREME MAGNUM SEMI-AUTO

**Action**: Semiautomatic
**Stock**: Synthetic
**Barrel**: 24 in., 26 in., 28 in.
**Chokes**: 5+1 chokes
**Weight**: 7 lb.–7 lb. 10.4 oz.
**Bore/Gauge**: 12, 20
**Magazine**: Tubular, 5+1 rounds
**Features**: Non-slip grip pads on the forend and pistol grip; SMART Valve gas pistons; HiVis MagniSight fiber optic, magnetic sight; available in Realtree MAX-4, Realtree AP Camo, Realtree AP Camo Turkey, and black synthetic
**Black**:................ $549–$649
**Realtree**: ............. $729–$799
**Realtree Turkey**:........... $659

## SILVER STANDARD

**Action**: Over/under
**Stock**: Walnut, synthetic
**Barrel**: 28 in.
**Chokes**: Choke tubes (M, IC, F, IM, Skeet)
**Weight**: 7 lb. 10 oz.–8 lb. 3 oz.
**Bore/Gauge**: 12
**Magazine**: None
**Features**: 3-in. chamber; Turkish walnut stock; trio recoil pad; blued tang lever; barrel selector switch and trigger guard; auto safety; nickel plated receiver; blued barrel
**MSRP**.................... $639

## SILVER SYNTHETIC SHORTY

**Action**: Over/under
**Stock**: Synthetic
**Barrel**: 18 in.
**Chokes**: Choke tubes (M, IC, F, IM, Skeet)
**Weight**: 7 lb.
**Bore/Gauge**: 12
**Magazine**: None
**Features**: Nickel plated receiver; adjustable comb; auto safety; blued tang lever, barrel selector switch, and trigger guard; soft rubber grey synthetic stock with cobblestone grip inserts
**MSRP**.................... $659

ESCORT MARINEGUARD HOME DEFENSE

ESCORT EXTEME MAGNUM SEMI-AUTO, REALTREE AP CAMO

ESCORT SILVER STANDARD

ESCORT SILVER SYNTHETIC SHORTY

SHOTGUNS

# Fausti USA

FAUSTI USA CALEDON

FAUSTI USA CLASS

FAUSTI USA DEA ROUND BODY

## CALEDON

*Action*: Over/under
*Stock*: Walnut
*Barrel*: 26 in., 28 in., 30 in.
*Chokes*: Fixed or interchangeable choke tubes
*Weight*: 5 lb. 12 oz.–7 lb. 4 oz.
*Bore/Gauge*: 12, 16, 20, 28, .410
*Magazine*: None
*Features*: Single selectable trigger; A+ Turkish walnut stock with oil finish; laser-engraved lower receiver; automatic ejectors; metallic bead sight
**MSRP** . . . . . . . . . . . . . **$1999–$2569**

## CLASS

*Action*: Over/under
*Stock*: Walnut
*Barrel*: 26 in., 28 in., 30 in.
*Chokes*: Fixed or interchangeable choke tubes
*Weight*: 5 lb. 12 oz.–7 lb. 5 oz.
*Bore/Gauge*: 12, 16, 20, 28, .410

*Magazine*: None
*Features*: Features automatic ejectors; metallic bead; single-selectable trigger; 14-3/8-in. length of pull; timeless AA walnut oil-polished stock; Prince of Wales style stock; receiver laser-engraved with flushing quail
**MSRP** . . . . . . . . . . . . . **$2449–$2999**

## DEA ROUND BODY

*Action*: Side-by-side
*Stock*: Oil-finished select walnut
*Barrel*: 28 in.
*Chokes*: Fixed or interchangeable choke tubes
*Weight*: 6 lb.
*Bore/Gauge*: 16, 20
*Magazine*: None
*Features*: Scottish-style round-body action and stock; low-profile coin or case-colored receiver; selective ejectors and extractors
**MSRP** . . . . . . . . . . . . . **$5899–$6489**

## MAGNIFICENT

*Action*: Over/under
*Stock*: Walnut
*Barrel*: 26 in., 28 in., 30 in.
*Chokes*: Fixed or interchangeable choke tubes
*Weight*: 5 lb. 12 oz.–7 lb. 6 oz.
*Bore/Gauge*: 12, 16, 20, 28, .410
*Magazine*: None
*Features*: AAA+ walnut stock with oil finish; precision scroll engraving accompanies Aphrodite, the Greek goddess of love and beauty, on the receiver; the Crest of the city of Brescia, Italy, where all Fausti shotguns are produced, is on the underside of the receiver; single selectable trigger; automatic ejectors; metallic bead sight
**MSRP** . . . . . . . . . . . . . **$4999–$5559**

FAUSTI USA MAGNIFICENT

FAUSTI USA MAGNIFICENT

## FLODMAN SHOTGUN

**Action**: Over/under
**Stock**: Walnut
**Barrel**: 28 in.–34 in.
**Chokes**: Multichoke

**Weight**: 6 lb. 3 oz.–8 lb. 6 oz.
**Bore/Gauge**: 12, 20
**Magazine**: None
**Features**: Boxlock offered in any standard gauge or rifle/shotgun combination; walnut stock with pistol grip available; auto or manual safety; Combi stainless steel barrel
**From**: . . . . . . . . . . . . . . . . . . **$23000**
**Extra double rifle barrels**: . . . . **$18500**

FLODMAN SHOTGUN

# Franchi

## 48 AL

**Action**: Autoloader
**Stock**: Walnut
**Barrel**: 24 in., 26 in., 28 in.
**Chokes**: Screw-in tubes Standard (IC, M, F, wrench), optional (C, IC, M, IM, F)
**Weight**: 5 lb. 6 oz.–5 lb. 10 oz.
**Bore/Gauge**: 20, 28
**Magazine**: 4+1 rounds
**Features**: Matte blue steel barrel; polished steel barrel on deluxe model; satin walnut stock on Field model; A-grade satin walnut on Deluxe model; optional custom-fitted hard case
**Field**: . . . . . . . . . . . . . . . . . . **$899**
**Deluxe**: . . . . . . . . . . . . **$999–1249**

## FRANCHI AFFINITY

**Action**: Semiautomatic, inertia driven
**Stock**: Black synthetic, Realtree Max-4, Realtree APG
**Barrel**: 24 in., 26 in., 28 in., 30 in.
**Chokes**: Interchangeable (IC, M, F)
**Weight**: 5 lb. 8 oz.–6 lb. 12 oz.
**Bore/Gauge**: 12, 20
**Magazine**: 4+1 rounds
**Features**: Red fiber optic bar; durable synthetic stock impervious to all-weather elements as well as gun solvents and lubricants; newly designed recoil pad; aluminum alloy receiver strengthened with steel inserts
**Black**: . . . . . . . . . . . . . . . . . . **$849**
**Realtree**: . . . . . . . . . . . . . . . . **$949**
**Compact**: . . . . . . . . . . . **$899–999**
**Black, brushed nickel**: . . . . . . **$1159**

## FRANCHI INSTINCT L

**Action**: Over/under
**Stock**: Walnut

FRANCHI 48 AL FIELD

FRANCHI AFFINITY 20 GA. - REALTREE APG

FRANCHI INSTINCT L 12 GA.

FRANCHI INSTINCT SL 20 GA.

**Barrel**: 26 in., 28 in.
**Chokes**: Interchangeable (IC, M, F)
**Weight**: 6 lb. 2 oz.–6 lb. 6 oz.
**Bore/Gauge**: 12, 20
**Magazine**: None
**Features**: Ventilated raised rib; red fiber optic front sight; blued and color-case-hardened finish on the receiver, with gold inlay; A-grade walnut stock in Prince-of-Wales style with cut checkering on the forend and pistol grip; satin oil finish; single gold-plated trigger; chrome-lined barrels proofed for steel shot; hard-shell custom-fitted gun case included
**MSRP**. . . . . . . . . . . . . . . . . . **$1149**

## FRANCHI INSTINCT SL

**Action**: Over/under
**Stock**: Walnut
**Barrel**: 26 in., 28 in.
**Chokes**: Interchangeable (IC, M, F)
**Weight**: 5 lb. 6 oz.–5 lb. 11 oz.
**Bore/Gauge**: 12, 20
**Magazine**: None
**Features**: Vent rib; red fiber optic front bead; aluminum alloy receiver; blued barrels; AA-grade satin walnut stock in Prince-of-Wales style with cut checkering and oil finish; tang-mounted automatic safety; custom-fitted, hard-shell gun case included
**MSRP**. . . . . . . . . . . . . . . . . . **$1349**

SHOTGUNS

# Harrington & Richardson

**HARRINGTON & RICHARDSON PARDNER PUMP**

## PARDNER PUMP
*Action*: Pump
*Stock*: Walnut, synthetic
*Barrel*: 26 in., 28 in.
*Chokes*: Screw-in modified choke
*Weight*: 7 lb. 8 oz.
*Bore/Gauge*: 12, 20
*Magazine*: 5 rounds
*Features*: American walnut stock with grooved and ventilated recoil pad or synthetic with camo; bead front sight; drilled and tapped for scope base; chrome-plated bolt; vent-rib barrel
**MSRP** . . . . . . . . . . . . . . . . . . . **$253**

## PARDNER SINGLE-SHOT
*Action*: Break-open single shot
*Stock*: Hardwood
*Barrel*: 22 in., 26 in., 28 in., 32 in.
*Chokes*: Modified or Full (12 Ga., 20 Ga.), Modified (28 Ga.), Full (12 Ga., .410 bore)
*Weight*: 5 lb.–6 lb.
*Bore/Gauge*: 12, 20, 28, .410

*Magazine*: None
*Features*: American hardwood, walnut finish with pistol grip; bead front sight; side lever release; automatic ejection; transfer bar safety system
**Compact:** . . . . . . . . . . . . . . . . . **$206**
**Standard:** . . . . . . . . . . . . . . . . . **$225**

## PARDNER TURKEY
*Action*: Break-open single shot
*Stock*: Synthetic, hardwood
*Barrel*: 24 in.
*Chokes*: Extra-Full Screw-in Chokes, Full in camo 12 Ga.
*Weight*: 6 lb.–9 lb.
*Bore/Gauge*: 10, 12
*Magazine*: None
*Features*: American hardwood stock in black matte finish or with camo pattern; pistol grip; ventilated rubber recoil pad; sling swivel studs; sling; bead sights; drilled and tapped for scope mount
**MSRP** . . . . . . . . . . . . . . . . . . . **$276**

HARRINGTON & RICHARDSON PARDNER SINGLE-SHOT

HARRINGTON & RICHARDSON PARDNER TURKEY

# Harrington & Richardson

HARRINGTON & RICHARDSON TAMER 20 GA.

## TAMER 20 GA.
**Action**: Hinged single-shot
**Stock**: High density polymer
**Barrel**: 20 in.
**Chokes**: Modified choke
**Weight**: 6 lb.
**Bore/Gauge**: 20
**Magazine**: None
**Features**: High density polymer stock with matte black finish, pistol grip and thumbhole design with storage compartment
**MSRP**. . . . . . . . . . . . . . . . . . . $223

## TRACKER II
**Action**: Single-shot
**Stock**: Hardwood
**Barrel**: 24 in.
**Chokes**: Rifled bore choke
**Weight**: 5 lb. 4 oz.
**Bore/Gauge**: 12, 20
**Magazine**: None
**Features**: Adjustable rifle sights; American hardwood with walnut finish; full pistol grip; recoil pad; sling swivel studs
**MSRP**. . . . . . . . . . . . . . . . . . . $290

## ULTRA LIGHT SLUG HUNTER
**Action**: Break-open single-shot
**Stock**: Hardwood
**Barrel**: 24 in.
**Chokes**: None
**Weight**: 5 lb. 4 oz.
**Bore/Gauge**: 12, 20
**Magazine**: None
**Features**: American hardwood with walnut finish, full pistol grip, recoil pad and sling swivel studs; Ultragon rifling; scope base included
**MSRP**. . . . . . . . . . . . . . . . $290–$293

## ULTRA SLUG HUNTER
**Action**: Hinged single-shot
**Stock**: Hardwood
**Barrel**: 24 in.
**Chokes**: None
**Weight**: 8 lb.–9 lb.
**Bore/Gauge**: 12, 20
**Magazine**: None
**Features**: Walnut-stained American hardwood Monte Carlo pistol grip stock; sling swivels; nylon sling; ventilated recoil pad; drilled and tapped for scope mount rail; optional 3-9x32 scope; thumbhole optional
**MSRP**. . . . . . . . . . . . . . . $290–$336

**HARRINGTON & RICHARDSON TRACKER II**

**HARRINGTON & RICHARDSON ULTRA SLUG HUNTER**

**HARRINGTON & RICHARDSON ULTRA LIGHT SLUG HUNTER**

**SHOTGUNS**

# Ithaca Gun Company

ITHACA
DEERSLAYER II

ITHACA
LARABEE

ITHACA
DEERSLAYER III

ITHACA MODEL 37
DEFENSE SYNTHETIC

## DEERSLAYER II

**Action**: Pump
**Stock**: Walnut
**Barrel**: 24 in.
**Chokes**: None
**Weight**: 6.8 lb.–8 lb. 6 oz.
**Bore/Gauge**: 12, 20
**Magazine**: 4+1 rounds
**Features**: Solderless barrel system; thumbhole or standard black walnut Monte Carlo stock; fat deluxe checkered forend; sling swivel studs; Pachmayr 750 Decelerator recoil pad; matte blued finish on barrel; gold-plated trigger; Marble Arms rifle sights; drilled and tapped for Weaver #62 scope rail
**MSRP** . . . . . . . . . . . . . . . . . . . $899

## DEERSLAYER III

**Action**: Pump
**Stock**: Walnut

**Barrel**: 20 in., 26 in., 28 in.
**Chokes**: None
**Weight**: 8.1 lb.–9 lb. 8 oz.
**Bore/Gauge**: 12, 20
**Magazine**: 4+1 rounds
**Features**: Heavy-walled, fluted, fixed barrel in blue matted finish; walnut Monte Carlo stock with optional thumbhole; Pachmayr 750 Decelerator recoil pad; sling swivel studs; gold-plated trigger; Weaver #62 rail pre-installed on receiver
**MSRP** . . . . . . . . . . . . . . . . . . . $1189

## LARABEE

**Action**: Single-barrel break-top
**Stock**: Semi-pistol style
**Barrel**: 30 in., 32 in., 34 in.
**Chokes**: 3 interchangeable tubes
**Weight**: 8 lb. 8 oz.
**Bore/Gauge**: 12
**Magazine**: None

**Features**: Receiver and mono block machined from solid 4140 steel; unique solder-less barrel-attachment system; three possible grades of engraving
**MSRP** . . . . . . . . . . . . . . . . . . . $1799

## MODEL 37 DEFENSE

**Action**: Pump
**Stock**: Synthetic, walnut
**Barrel**: 18.5 in., 20 in.
**Chokes**: None
**Weight**: 6.5 lb.–7 lb. 2 oz.
**Bore/Gauge**: 12, 20
**Magazine**: 4+1, 7+1 rounds
**Features**: Choice of walnut or black synthetic stock; 3 in. chamber; matte blued finish barrel; Pachmayr decelerator recoil pad
**Walnut**: . . . . . . . . . . . . . . . . . $769
**Synthetic**: . . . . . . . . . . . . . . . $685

SHOTGUNS

# Ithaca Gun Company

ITHACA MODEL 37 FEATHERLIGHT

ITHACA MODEL 37 TRAP

ITHACA PHOENIX

## MODEL 37 FEATHERLIGHT

*Action*: Pump
*Stock*: Walnut
*Barrel*: 26 in., 28 in., 20 in.
*Chokes*: 3 Briley Choke tubes (F, M, IC, and wrench)
*Weight*: 6.1 lb.–7 lb. 10 oz.
*Bore/Gauge*: 12, 16, 20, 28
*Magazine*: 4+1 rounds
*Features*: Solderless barrel system; classic game scene engraving; black walnut stock with semi-pistol butt stock; TruGlo red front sight; Pachmayr 752 Decelerator recoil pad
**MSRP** . . . . . . . . . . . . . . **from $859**

## MODEL 37 TRAP

*Action*: Pump
*Stock*: Walnut
*Barrel*: 30 in.
*Chokes*: Briley Choke tubes
*Weight*: 7 lb. 13 oz.
*Bore/Gauge*: 12
*Magazine*: 4+1
*Features*: Bottom ejection; 3 in. chamber; gold plated tubes; walnut Monte Carlo stock; vent rib barrel; classic game scene engraving
**MSRP** . . . . . . . . . . . . . . . . . . . **$899**

## PHOENIX

*Action*: Over/under
*Stock*: Semi-pistol style
*Barrel*: 28 in., 30 in., 32 in., 34 in.
*Chokes*: 5 interchangeable tubes
*Weight*: 9 lb.
*Bore/Gauge*: 12
*Magazine*: None
*Features*: Machined from solid steel; barrels attach via front dovetail for a free-floating unit; different engraving grades available
**MSRP** . . . . . . . . . . . . . . . . . . . **$2499**

**SHOTGUNS**

# Krieghoff

## MODEL K-20

**Action**: Over/under
**Stock**: Walnut
**Barrel**: 30 in., 32 in.
**Chokes**: 5 choke tubes (C, S, IC, LM, M, LIM, IM, F)
**Weight**: 7 lb. 8 oz.
**Bore/Gauge**: 20, 28, .410
**Magazine**: None
**Features**: Top-tang push safety button; classic scroll engraving; white pearl front bead and metal center bead; single-selective mechanical trigger; hand-checkered select European walnut stock with satin epoxy finish

| | |
|---|---|
| 20 Ga.: | $11395 |
| 28 Ga.: | $11495 |
| .410: | $11495 |
| 20/28 Ga. Set: | $15890 |
| Set of 3: | $20405 |

## K-20 PRO-SPORTER

**Action**: Over/under
**Stock**: Walnut
**Barrel**: 30 in., 32 in.
**Chokes**: Titanium choke tubes
**Weight**: 8 lb.
**Bore/Gauge**: 20, 28, .410
**Magazine**: None
**Features**: Higher rib and stock allows shooter to keep their head more erect, increasing sight range, allowing for quicker target acquisition, reduced neck fatigue, and perceived recoil; high rib easily adjustable

| | |
|---|---|
| MSRP | $11695–$11795 |
| 20/28 Ga. Set: | $16390 |
| 3 Ga. Set: | $21105 |

## MODEL K-80

**Action**: Over/under
**Stock**: Walnut
**Barrel**: 30 in., 32 in., 34 in.
**Chokes**: Steel or Titanium choke tubes (C, S, IC, LM, M, LIM, IM, F, SF)
**Weight**: 8 lb. 4 oz.
**Bore/Gauge**: 12
**Magazine**: None
**Features**: White pearl front sight and metal center bead; nickel plated steel receiver with satin grey finish; single select trigger; top-tang push button safety; fine-checkered Turkish walnut

| | |
|---|---|
| **Standard Models:** | $10595–$13000 |

**KRIEGHOFF K-20**

**KRIEGHOFF K-20 PRO-SPORTER**

**KRIEGHOFF K-80 ACS**

## MODEL K-80 ACS

**Action**: Over/under
**Stock**: Walnut
**Barrel**: 30 in., 32 in., 34 in.
**Chokes**: 8 factory steel choke tubes
**Weight**: 8 lb. 12 oz.
**Bore/Gauge**: 12
**Magazine**: None
**Features**: White pearl front bead and metal center bead sight; case-hardened action, nickel-plated steel receiver with nitride silver finish; single selective trigger

| | |
|---|---|
| **From:** | $17370 |

**KRIEGHOFF K-80**

## ADJUSTABLE RIB MONO GUN

**Action**: Single barrel
**Stock**: Walnut
**Barrel**: 34 in.
**Chokes**: Fixed or Ljutic SIC
**Weight**: 10 lb.
**Bore/Gauge**: .740, 12
**Magazine**: None
**Features**: "One Touch" adjustable rib

allows you to change your point-of-impact; adjustable comb stock
**Adjustable Rib**: . . . . . . . . . . . **$7550**
**Stainless Adjustable**: . . . . . . . **$8495**

## MONO GUN

**Action**: Single barrel
**Stock**: Walnut
**Barrel**: 32 in.–34 in.
**Chokes**: Optional screw in chokes (Fixed, Ljutic SIC, Briley SIC)
**Weight**: 10 lb.
**Bore/Gauge**: .740, 12
**Magazine**: None
**Features**: Comes with American walnut wood; optional roll over combs

and cheek pieces; various upgrades available
**Mono**: . . . . . . . . . . . . . . . . . **$7495**
**Stainless**: . . . . . . . . . . . . . . . **$8495**

## PRO 3

**Action**: Single barrel
**Stock**: Walnut
**Barrel**: 34 in.
**Chokes**: 4 Briley Series 12 chokes
**Weight**: 9 lb.
**Bore/Gauge**: .740, 12
**Magazine**: None
**Features**: Aluminum baseplate; interchangeable two-pad system; adjustable comb; English or American walnut stock; screw in hinge pin; stainless or blued barrel
**Blued barrel**: . . . . . . . . . . . . . **$8495**
**Stainless**: . . . . . . . . . . . . . . . **$8995**

LJUTIC ADJUSTABLE RIB MONO GUN

LJUTIC MONO GUN

LJUTIC PRO 3

SHOTGUNS

# Marocchi

### MODEL 100
**Action**: Over/under
**Stock**: Walnut
**Barrel**: 28 in.–32 in.
**Chokes**: Trap: (IM/F); Sporter (MC), Skeet( SK/SK); Electrocibles (MC); Double Trap (MC/Full)
**Weight**: 7 lb. 3 oz.–8 lb. 2 oz.
**Bore/Gauge**: 12
**Magazine**: None
**Features**: Steel action; single adjustable trigger; mechanically assisted ejector system; steel barrels; boss type locking system; walnut stock available in various grades
**Sporting**: . . . . . . . . . . . . . . . $3450
**Trap**: . . . . . . . . . . . . . . . . . $3400

MAROCCHI MODEL 100

# Merkel

### MODEL 47E, 147E, 147EL
**Action**: Side-by-side
**Stock**: Wood
**Barrel**: 27 in., 28 in.
**Chokes**: Steel-shot proofed chokes
**Weight**: 6 lb. 3 oz.
**Bore/Gauge**: 12, 20
**Magazine**: None
**Features**: English stock finished with fine hand-cut checkering at buttplate; silver monogram plate; steel action is gray nitrated; Anson & Deeley locks; Greener-style cross bolt and double bottom bite; double trigger; automatic safety
**47E**: . . . . . . . . . . . . . . . . . $4595
**147E**: . . . . . . . . . . . . . . . . $5795
**147EL**: . . . . . . . . . . . . . . . $7195

### MODEL 303EL
**Action**: Over/under
**Stock**: Wood
**Barrel**: 27 in., 28 in.
**Chokes**: Steel-shot proofed chokes
**Weight**: 6 lb. 13 oz.
**Bore/Gauge**: 12/76, 20/76
**Magazine**: None
**Features**: Sidelocks with V-springs; Kersten cross-bolt with double conventional bottom bite; double trigger; front trigger articulated; optional selective single trigger; engraving English arabesque; luxury grade walnut stock with pistol grip; optional English-styled stock
**MSRP**. . . . . . . . . . . . . . . . . $24995

### MODEL 2000CL
**Action**: Over/under
**Stock**: Wood
**Barrel**: 27 in., 28 in.
**Chokes**: 2 interchangeable chokes steel-shot proofed
**Weight**: 6 lb. 13 oz.
**Bore/Gauge**: 12/76, 20/76
**Magazine**: None
**Features**: Disconnectable ejectors; arabesque engraving; Anson & Deeley locks in steel receiver; Kersten crossbolt; selective single trigger, adjustable in length; manual safety; wood stock with pistol grip and cheekpiece
**MSRP**. . . . . . . . . . . . . . . . . $8495

MERKEL MODEL 47E

MERKEL MODEL 303EL

MERKEL MODEL 2000CL

SHOTGUNS

**MOSSBERG 500 CLASSIC ALL-PURPOSE FIELD**

**MOSSBERG 500 FLEX ALL-PURPOSE SERIES**

## 500 CLASSIC ALL-PURPOSE FIELD

*Action*: Pump
*Stock*: Walnut, synthetic
*Barrel*: 28 in.
*Chokes*: Interchangeable Accu-Choke tubes
*Weight*: 7 lb. 8 oz.

*Bore/Gauge*: 12
*Magazine*: 6 rounds
*Features*: High-gloss walnut stock and forend; fine checkering on the pistol grip and wrapping around the underside of the forend; classic red recoil pad with white Pachmayr line spacer; distinctive jeweled bolt, gold trigger, and high polished blued metal finish; non-binding twin action bars; anodized aluminum receiver; vent rib Accu-Choke barrel; ambidextrous top-mounted safety; available in MO Break-up Infinity
**MSRP**....................... **$401**

## 500 FLEX ALL-PURPOSE SERIES

*Action*: Pump
*Stock*: Synthetic
*Barrel*: 26 in., 28 in.
*Chokes*: Accu-Set
*Weight*: 7 lb. 8 oz.
*Bore/Gauge*: 12
*Magazine*: 6 rounds
*Features*: Matte metal finishes or Marinecote finish; stock with medium recoil pad; stock and forend constructed of synthetic with black matte finish; twin bead sights
**MSRP**..................... **$661**

**MOSSBERG 500 FLEX HUNTING SERIES**

**MOSSBERG 500 JIC MARINER**

**MOSSBERG 500 PERSUADER**

## 500 FLEX HUNTING SERIES

*Action*: Pump
*Stock*: Synthetic
*Barrel*: 24 in.
*Chokes*: Accu-Set
*Weight*: 7 lb. 8 oz.
*Bore/Gauge*: 12
*Magazine*: 6 rounds
*Features*: OD green, coyote tan, Mossy Oak Break-Up Infinity, or Realtree Max-4 cam receiver finishes; standard stocks and forends feature Infinity or Realtree Max-4 camo finishes
**MSRP**..................... **$747**

## 500 JIC MARINER

*Action*: Pump
*Stock*: Synthetic
*Barrel*: 18.5 in.
*Chokes*: Cylinder bore chokes
*Weight*: 5 lb. 8 oz.
*Bore/Gauge*: 12
*Magazine*: 6 rounds
*Features*: Bead sight; Marinecote metal finish; comes with multi-tool, survival knife and cordura carrying case; gun lock; swivel studs; black synthetic stock; only pump-action shotguns to pass all U.S. Military Mil-Spec 3443 standards
**MSRP**..................... **$621**

## 500 PERSUADER, CRUISER

*Action*: Pump
*Stock*: Synthetic
*Barrel*: 20 in.
*Chokes*: Cylinder bore
*Weight*: 7 lb.
*Bore/Gauge*: 12
*Magazine*: 8 rounds
*Features*: Ghost ring sights; six-position adjustable stock; matte blued finish; pistol grip standard on some models
**MSRP**..................... **$447**

**SHOTGUNS**

# Mossberg

### 500 SLUGSTER

*Action*: Pump
*Stock*: Synthetic
*Barrel*: 24 in.
*Chokes*: None
*Weight*: 6 lb. 12 oz.–7 lb. 4 oz.
*Bore/Gauge*: 12
*Magazine*: 6 rounds
*Features*: Fully-rifled bore; integral scope base; ported barrel; ambidextrous thumb-operated safety; available in MO Break-up Infinity
*MSRP* . . . . . . . . . . . . . . . . . . . . $434

### 500 SUPER BANTAM SLUGSTER

*Action*: Pump
*Stock*: Synthetic
*Barrel*: 24 in.
*Chokes*: None
*Weight*: 5 lb. 4 oz.
*Bore/Gauge*: 20
*Magazine*: 6 rounds
*Features*: Fully-rifled bore; adjustable synthetic stock; Blued or Realtree AP finish; drilled and tapped for scopes; ported barrels; adjustable rifle sights
*MSRP* . . . . . . . . . . . . . . . . . . . . $401

### 500 SUPER BANTAM TURKEY

*Action*: Pump
*Stock*: Synthetic
*Barrel*: 22 in.
*Chokes*: Interchangeable Accu-Choke (X-full and wrench)
*Weight*: 5 lb. 4 oz.
*Bore/Gauge*: 20
*Magazine*: 6 rounds
*Features*: Adjustable synthetic stock in Mossy Oak Break-Up Infinity camo or Hardwoods HD Green camo; adjustable fiber optic sights; drilled and tapped for scopes; gun lock
*MSRP* . . . . . . . . . . . . . . . . . . . . $466

### 500 TRI-RAIL TACTICAL

*Action*: Pump
*Stock*: Synthetic
*Barrel*: 18.5 in., 20 in.
*Chokes*: Cylinder-choked barrel
*Weight*: 6 lb. 12 oz.
*Bore/Gauge*: 12
*Magazine*: 6, 8, 9 rounds
*Features*: Bead front sight; matte black synthetic, adjustable stock; tri-rail forend
*MSRP* . . . . . . . . . . . . . . . . . . . . $593

MOSSBERG 500 SLUGSTER

MOSSBERG 500 SUPER BANTAM SLUGSTER

MOSSBERG 500 SUPER BANTAM TURKEY

MOSSBERG 500 TRI-RAIL TACTICAL

SHOTGUNS

**MOSSBERG 500 TURKEY**

**MOSSBERG 510 MINI ALL PURPOSE**

## 500 TURKEY

**Action**: Pump
**Stock**: Synthetic
**Barrel**: 24 in.
**Chokes**: Accu-Choke tubes (XX-Full)
**Weight**: 7 lb. 4 oz.–8 lb. 4 oz.
**Bore/Gauge**: 12
**Magazine**: 6, 7 rounds
**Features**: Adjustable front sight; synthetic finish in Mossy Oak Break-Up Infinity camo; ported barrel; ambidextrous thumb-operated safety; includes gun lock; LPA (Lightning Pump Action) trigger system providing creepfree rifle-like trigger available
**MSPR** . . . . . . . . . . . . . . . . **$438–$506**

## 510 MINI ALL PURPOSE

**Action**: Pump
**Stock**: Synthetic
**Barrel**: 18.5 in.
**Chokes**: Accu-set in 20 Ga., Fixed-Mod. in .410 bore
**Weight**: 5 lb.
**Bore/Gauge**: 20, .410
**Magazine**: 3 (.410) and 4 (20 Ga.) rounds
**Features**: Good choice for petite or younger shooter; adjustable synthetic stock in black; blued barrel finish; dual bead sights
**MSRP** . . . . . . . . . . . . . . . . . . . **$401**

## 510 MINI CAMO

**Action**: Pump
**Stock**: Synthetic
**Barrel**: 18.5 in.
**Chokes**: Interchangeable Accu-Choke tubes
**Weight**: 5 lb.
**Bore/Gauge**: 20, .410
**Magazine**: 3, 4 rounds
**Features**: Dual bead sights; synthetic stock comes in Mossy Oak Infinity camo
**MSRP** . . . . . . . . . . . . . . . . . . . **$451**

## 535 ATS THUMBHOLE TURKEY

**Action**: Pump
**Stock**: Synthetic
**Barrel**: 20 in., 22 in.
**Chokes**: Interchangeable, X-factor patented choke tube
**Weight**: 6 lb. 8 oz.
**Bore/Gauge**: 12
**Magazine**: 6 rounds
**Features**: Adjustable front sights; synthetic thumbhole stock comes in black with matte blue metal finish, Mossy Oak break-up infinity or Hardwoods HD green camo; ventilated rib barrel; includes gun lock
**MSRP** . . . . . . . . . . . . . . . . . . . **$497**

**MOSSBERG 510 MINI CAMO**

**MOSSBERG 535 ATS THUMBHOLE TURKEY**

**SHOTGUNS**

# Mossberg

MOSSBERG 535 ATS TURKEY THUG

MOSSBERG 590A1 ADJUSTABLE TACTICAL TRI-RAIL 9 SHOT

MOSSBERG 835 ULTI-MAG

### 535 ATS TURKEY THUG

**Action**: Pump
**Stock**: Synthetic
**Barrel**: 20 in.
**Chokes**: X-factor ported choke tube
**Weight**: 6 lb. 12 oz.
**Bore/Gauge**: 12
**Magazine**: 6 rounds
**Features**: Adjustable fiber optic sights; user-adjustable trigger; camouflage Picatinny rail; adjustable stock with Mossy Oak Infinity camo finish; TruGlo red-dot sight
**MSRP**. . . . . . . . . . . . . . . . . . . . . **$656**

### 590A1 ADJUSTABLE TACTICAL TRI-RAIL 9 SHOT

**Action**: Pump
**Stock**: Synthetic
**Barrel**: 18.5 in., 20 in.
**Chokes**: Cylinder bore
**Weight**: 7 lb. 8 oz.
**Bore/Gauge**: 12
**Magazine**: 9 rounds
**Features**: Six-position adjustable stock with a tri-rail forend; ghost ring sights; Parkerized finish; speedfeed, black stock; heavy barrel wall; Blackwater logo
**MSRP**. . . . . . . . . . . . . . . . . . . . . **$839**

### 835 ULTI-MAG

**Action**: Pump
**Stock**: Synthetic
**Barrel**: 20 in., 24 in.
**Chokes**: Ulti-full tube chokes
**Weight**: 7 lb. 4 oz.
**Bore/Gauge**: 12
**Magazine**: 6 rounds
**Features**: Overbored, ported barrel; synthetic stock comes in woodlands, Mossy Oak Break-Up Infinity, Hardwoods HD Green Camo, or blued; ambidextrous, thumb-operated safety; drilled and tapped for scope mounts
**MSRP**. . . . . . . . . . . . . . . . . . . . . **$559**

### 935 MAGNUM TURKEY

*Action*: Autoloader
*Stock*: Synthetic
*Barrel*: 24 in.
*Chokes*: Ulti-full tube chokes
*Weight*: 7 lb. 8 oz.
*Bore/Gauge*: 12
*Magazine*: 5 rounds
*Features*: Overbored barrel; synthetic stock in Mossy Oak Break-Up Infinity or Hardwoods HD Green camo; quick-empty magazine button; adjustable fiber optic sights; wide ventilated rib
MSRP . . . . . . . . . . . . . . . . . . . $815

### RHYTHM 930 - PATRICK FLANIGAN SIGNATURE SERIES

*Action*: Autoloader
*Stock*: Synthetic
*Barrel*: 28 in.
*Chokes*: Accu-Set
*Weight*: 8 lb. 4 oz.
*Bore/Gauge*: 12
*Magazine*: 13 rounds
*Features*: Dual vent gas-operating autoloading system; Uni-Line stock and receiver alignment; stock drop spacer system; drilled and tapped receiver; versatile Accu-Choke system; synthetic stock and forend with marbled blue and yellow finish; blued metal finishes on metalwork; non-ported vent rib barrel; red fiber optic front bead sight
MSRP . . . . . . . . . . . . . . . . . . . $890

### SA-20 TACTICAL

*Action*: Autoloader
*Stock*: Synthetic
*Barrel*: 20 in.
*Chokes*: Cylinder bore
*Weight*: 6 lb.
*Bore/Gauge*: 20
*Magazine*: 5 rounds
*Features*: Quick-load shell elevator; ghost ring sights; Picatinny rail on top of receiver, plus three-sided rail mount below the barrel; standard full-length stock or full-length stock with a pistol grip
MSRP . . . . . . . . . . . . . . . . . . . $518

**MOSSBERG 935
MAGNUM TURKEY**

**MOSSBERG RHYTHM
930 - PATRICK FLANIGAN
SIGNATURE SERIES**

**MOSSBERG
SA-20 TACTICAL**

SHOTGUNS

# Perazzi

**PERAZZI MODEL MX8**

## MX8 SPORTING CLAYS

**Action**: Over/under
**Stock**: Walnut
**Barrel**: 29 in., 30 in., 31 in.
**Chokes**: Interchangeable chokes
**Weight**: 7 lb. 5 oz.
**Bore/Gauge**: 12, 20
**Magazine**: None
**Features**: Custom walnut stock with beavertail forend; half-ventilated side ribs on barrel; removable trigger with flat or coil springs; blue or nickel plating; Sporting, Skeet and Trap models; 28 Ga. and .410 models also available
**MSRP** . . . . . . . . . . . . . . . . . . . **$9861**

**PERAZZI TM-9X**

## TM-9X

**Action**: Autoloader
**Stock**: Monte Carlo
**Barrel**: 34 in.
**Chokes**: Full
**Weight**: 7 lb.
**Bore/Gauge**: 12
**Magazine**: None
**Features**: Adjustable stock; adjustable rib single barrel
**MSRP** . . . . . . . . . . . . . . . . . . . **$9755**

# Purdey

**PURDEY OVER AND UNDER GUN**

**PURDEY SIDE-BY-SIDE GAME GUN**

## OVER AND UNDER GUN

**Action**: Over/under
**Stock**: Walnut
**Barrel**: 26 in. –30 in.
**Chokes**: Interchangeable choke tubes
**Weight**: 4 lb. 14 oz.–7 lb. 8 oz.
**Bore/Gauge**: 12, 16, 20, 28, .410
**Magazine**: None
**Features**: Available in round, square, or ultra-round action shapes; available with double or non-selective single triggers and automatic safety catch; demi-bloc construction; solid game rib with hand matted finish; Turkish walnut with straight, semi, or full pistol grip; gold oval or inlaid gold letters; sporter scroll engraving

| | |
|---|---|
| Game 12, 16, 20 Ga,: | . . . . . . $126144 |
| 28 Ga.: | . . . . . . . . . . . . . . . . . $134605 |
| .410: | . . . . . . . . . . . . . . . . . . . $134605 |
| Sporter: | . . . . . . . . . . . . . . . . $50144 |

**(All prices excluding UK taxes)**

## SIDE-BY-SIDE GAME GUN

**Action**: Side-by-side
**Stock**: Walnut
**Barrel**: 26 in. to 30 in.
**Chokes**: Interchangeable choke tubes
**Weight**: 4 lb. 10 oz.–6 lb. 12 oz.
**Bore/Gauge**: 10, 12, 16, 20, 28, .410
**Magazine**: None
**Features**: Built on self-opening system; available with double or non-selective single triggers and automatic safety catch; Turkish walnut in straight, semi or full pistol grip; gold oval or inlaid gold letters; sporter scroll engraving; traditional splinter or beavertail forend available

| | |
|---|---|
| 12, 16, 20-bore: | . . . . . . . . . $113608 |
| 28-bore, .410: | . . . . . . . . . . . $121913 |
| 10-bore: | . . . . . . . . . . . . . . . . $115958 |

**(All prices excluding UK taxes)**

**SHOTGUNS**

# Remington

REMINGTON MODEL 11-87 SPORTSMAN FIELD

REMINGTON MODEL 870 EXPRESS

REMINGTON MODEL 870 EXPRESS SUPER MAGNUM TURKEY WATERFOWL

## MODEL 11-87 SPORTSMAN FIELD

*Action*: Autoloading
*Stock*: Walnut
*Barrel*: 26 in., 28 in.
*Chokes*: Rem. modified choke
*Weight*: 7 lb. 4 oz.–8 lb. 4 oz.
*Bore/Gauge*: 12, 20
*Magazine*: None
*Features*: Solid walnut stock and forend with satin finish and fleur-de-lis checkering; nickel-plated bolt and gold-plated trigger; vent rib with dual bead sights
**MSRP** . . . . . . . . . . . . . . . . . . . . **$845**

## MODEL 870 EXPRESS

*Action*: Pump
*Stock*: Hardwood, synthetic, laminate, or camo
*Barrel*: 18 in.–28 in.
*Chokes*: Modified Remington choke, extra full Rem.
*Weight*: 6 lb.–7 lb. 4 oz.
*Bore/Gauge*: 12, 20
*Magazine*: 2–7 rounds depending on model
*Features*: Single bead sight; standard express finish on barrel and receiver; rubber recoil pad; twin action bars ensure smooth, reliable non-binding action; solid steel receiver; optional thumbhole stock in some models
**Express:** . . . . . . . . . . . . . . . . . . . **$411**
**Syn. 7-round:** . . . . . . . . . . . . . . **$428**
**Syn. Deer:** . . . . . . . . . . . . . . . . **$457**
**Turkey Camo:** . . . . . . . . . . . . . **$485**

## MODEL 870 EXPRESS SUPER MAGNUM

*Action*: Pump
*Stock*: Hardwood, synthetic, or camo
*Barrel*: 26 in.
*Chokes*: Wingmaster HD Waterfowl and Turkey Extra Full Rem chokes
*Weight*: 7 lb. 4 oz.
*Bore/Gauge*: 12
*Magazine*: None
*Features*: Synthetic stock in full Mossy Oak Bottomland camo; HiVix fiber-optics; SuperCell recoil pad; drilled and tapped receiver
**Express Super Mag:** . . . . . . . . . **$462**
**Synthetic:** . . . . . . . . . . . . . . . . . **$462**
**Turkey/Waterfowl:** . . . . . . . . . . **$620**
**Waterfowl Camo:** . . . . . . . . . . . **$620**

# Remington

**REMINGTON MODEL 870 EXPRESS TACTICAL A-TACS CAMO**

## MODEL 870 EXPRESS TACTICAL

**Action**: Pump
**Stock**: Synthetic
**Barrel**: 18.5 in.
**Chokes**: Screw-in tube
**Weight**: 7 lb. 8 oz.

**Bore/Gauge**: 12
**Magazine**: None
**Features**: Synthetic stock available in A-tacs digitized camo; Tactical Rem. choke SpeedFeed IV; pistol grip stock; SuperCell recoil pad; adjustable XS Ghost Ring sight rail with removable with bead front sight; Picatinny-style rail
**Express Tactical:**. . . . . . . . . . . **$572**
**A-Tacs Camo:**. . . . . . . . . . . . . **$685**

**REMINGTON MODEL 870 EXPRESS TACTICAL WITH BLACKHAWK! SPECIAL OPS II**

## MODEL 870 EXPRESS TACTICAL WITH BLACKHAWK! SPECIAL OPS II

**Action**: Pump
**Stock**: Synthetic
**Barrel**: 18 in.
**Chokes**: Screw-in tube
**Weight**: 7 lb.
**Bore/Gauge**: 12

**Magazine**: 6+1 rounds
**Features**: Plain barrel with front bead; 7 position LOP adjustment; recoil reduction system; enhanced pistol grip; sling mount; drilled and tapped receiver; SuperCell recoil pad; Blackhawk Ops II buttstock features built-in recoil reduction system and is adjustable over several increments of length of pull
**MSRP**. . . . . . . . . . . . . . . . . . . **$638**

**REMINGTON MODEL 870 SHURSHOT SYNTHETIC SUPER SLUG**

## MODEL 870 SHURSHOT SYNTHETIC

**Action**: Pump
**Stock**: Synthetic
**Barrel**: 25 in.
**Chokes**: Screw-in tubes
**Weight**: 7 lb. 13 oz.
**Bore/Gauge**: 12

**Magazine**: None
**Features**: Ambidextrous Shurshot pistol-grip synthetic stock; rubberized overmolding; SuperCell recoil pad; receiver is drilled and tapped; Weaver rail; sling swivels
**Turkey:**. . . . . . . . . . . . . . . . . . **$528**
**Cantilever:**. . . . . . . . . . . . . . . . **$571**

**REMINGTON MODEL 870 SP MARINE MAGNUM**

## MODEL 870 SP MARINE MAGNUM

**Action**: Pump
**Stock**: Synthetic
**Barrel**: 18 in.
**Chokes**: Cylinder chokes

**Weight**: 7 lb. 8 oz.
**Bore/Gauge**: 12
**Magazine**: 6 rounds
**Features**: Single-bead front sight; padded Cordura; sling swivels; electroless nickel plating covers all metal; twin action bars ensure smooth, reliable non-binding action
**MSRP**. . . . . . . . . . . . . . . . . . . **$829**

**REMINGTON MODEL 870 SPS SHURSHOT SYNTHETIC TURKEY**

## MODEL 870 SPS SHURSHOT SYNTHETIC

**Action**: Pump
**Stock**: Synthetic
**Barrel**: 23 in.
**Chokes**: Wingmaster HD extended Rem Choke
**Weight**: 7 lb. 8 oz.

**Bore/Gauge**: 12
**Magazine**: None
**Features**: Synthetic stock covered in Realtree APG HD camo; features ShurShot synthetic pistol grip stock; adjustable TruGlo fiber-optic sights; receiver drilled and tapped for scope mounts
**Turkey:**. . . . . . . . . . . . . . . . . . **$671**
**Super Slug:** . . . . . . . . . . . . . . . **$829**

SHOTGUNS

## MODEL 870 WINGMASTER

*Action*: Pump
*Stock*: Walnut
*Barrel*: 25 in.
*Chokes*: Screw-in tubes
*Weight*: 6 lb.–6 lb. 4 oz.
*Bore/Gauge*: 12, 20, 28, .410
*Magazine*: None
*Features*: Twin action bars for non-binding action; receiver machined from solid billet of steel; highly polished and richly blued receiver; wide array of barrel and choke options
**MSRP** . . . . . . . . . . . . . . . . . . . $818

## MODEL 870 WINGMASTER CLASSIC TRAP

*Action*: Pump
*Stock*: Walnut
*Barrel*: 30 in.
*Chokes*: Screw-in tube, Rem. Choke
*Weight*: 8 lb. 4 oz.
*Bore/Gauge*: 12
*Magazine*: None
*Features*: American walnut, Monte Carlo stock; forend with deep cut checkering and a high-gloss finish; twin bead sights; three specialized trap Rem. choke tubes; twin action bars ensure smooth, reliable non-binding action; choke vent rib barrel
**MSRP** . . . . . . . . . . . . . . . . . . . $1081

## MODEL 887 NITRO MAG CAMO COMBO

*Action*: Autoloading
*Stock*: Synthetic
*Barrel*: 22 in., 28 in.
*Chokes*: Screw-in tubes
*Weight*: 7 lb.–7 lb. 4 oz.
*Bore/Gauge*: 12
*Magazine*: None
*Features*: Synthetic camo stock with ArmorLkt coating; SuperCell recoil pad; HiViz front sight; contoured grip panels; sling swivel
**MSRP** . . . . . . . . . . . . . . . . . . . $728

## MODEL 1100 CLASSIC TRAP

*Action*: Autoloading
*Stock*: Walnut
*Barrel*: 30 in.
*Chokes*: Screw-in tubes
*Weight*: 8 lb. 4 oz.
*Bore/Gauge*: 12
*Magazine*: None
*Features*: American walnut stock with cut-checkering; bead blasted top and bottom radius; blued finish on receiver and barrel; gold triggers and gold embellishments on receiver
**MSRP** . . . . . . . . . . . . . . . . . . . $1270

REMINGTON MODEL 870 WINGMASTER

REMINGTON MODEL 870 WINGMASTER CLASSIC TRAP

REMINGTON MODEL 887 NITRO MAG CAMO COMBO

REMINGTON MODEL 1100 CLASSIC TRAP

SHOTGUNS

# Remington

**REMINGTON MODEL 1100 COMPETITION SYNTHETIC**

## MODEL 1100 COMPETITION SYNTHETIC
*Action*: Autoloading
*Stock*: Synthetic
*Barrel*: 30 in.
*Chokes*: 5 extended Briley (Target) choke tubes (Skeet, IC, LM, M, Full)
*Weight*: 8 lb. 2 oz.
*Bore/Gauge*: 12

*Magazine*: None
*Features*: Nickel-Teflon finish on receiver and all internal parts; barrel has 10mm target-style rib; adjustable comb and cast adjustment options; high-gloss blued barrel; fully adjustable target-style stock with recoil reduction; synthetic polymer stock and forend finished with carbon graphite appearance; twin target-style bead sights
**MSRP . . . . . . . . . . . . . . . . . . . $1242**

**REMINGTON VERSA MAX MO DUCK BLIND**

## VERSA MAX
*Action*: Autoloading
*Stock*: Synthetic
*Barrel*: 26 in., 28 in.
*Chokes*: 5 Flush Mount Pro Bore chokes (F, M, IM, LB, IC)
*Weight*: 7 lb. 8 oz.–7 lb. 11 oz.
*Bore/Gauge*: 12
*Magazine*: 3+1, 2+1 rounds

*Features*: Remington patented gas-piston system; synthetic stock and forend with gray overmolded grips, comes in black or a Mossy Oak Duck blind camo; drilled and tapped receiver; enlarged trigger guard opening and larger safety for easier use with gloves; TriNyte Barrel and nickel Teflon plated internal components
**Black: . . . . . . . . . . . . . . . . . . $1399**
**Camo: . . . . . . . . . . . . . . . . . $1599**

**REMINGTON VERSAMAX TACTICAL**

## VERSAMAX TACTICAL
*Action*: Autoloading
*Stock*: Synthetic
*Barrel*: 22 in.
*Chokes*: IC and Tactical ProBore tube
*Weight*: 7 lb. 12 oz.
*Bore/Gauge*: 12

*Magazine*: 8+1 rounds
*Features*: Ventilated rib; fiberoptic HiViz front sight; receiver is drilled and tapped for optics; Picatinny rail; recoil pad; size bolt-release button; oversized trigger guard for easy operation when wearing gloves
**MSRP . . . . . . . . . . . . . . . . . . . $1399**

**SHOTGUNS**

## FIELD GRADE SHOTGUN

*Action*: Single-shot, break-open
*Stock*: Synthetic
*Barrel*: 28 in.
*Chokes*: Modified screw-in chokes
*Weight*: 3 lb. 12 oz.–5 lb. 4 oz.
*Bore/Gauge*: 12, 20, .410
*Magazine*: None
*Features*: Steel receiver; black synthetic stock with grips; blue finish metal; transfer bar safety action
**Full size:** . . . . . . . . . . . . . . . . . **$175**
**Youth 22-in. barrel:** . . . . . . . . **$175**

**ROSSI FIELD GRADE SHOTGUN**

## "TUFFY" .410 SINGLE SHOT

*Action*: Single-shot, hinged breech
*Stock*: Synthetic
*Barrel*: 18.5 in.
*Chokes*: Screw-in chokes
*Weight*: 3 lb.
*Bore/Gauge*: .410
*Magazine*: None
*Features*: Black synthetic stock with thumbhole grip; Taurus Security System; matte blued metal finish or matte nickel; steel receiver
**MSRP** . . . . . . . . . . . . . . . **$203–$211**

**ROSSI TUFFY .410 SINGLE SHOT**

## YOUTH RIFLED BARREL SLUG GUN

*Action*: Single shot, break open
*Stock*: Synthetic
*Barrel*: 23 in.
*Chokes*: Screw-in tubes
*Weight*: 6 lb. 4 oz.
*Bore/Gauge*: 12
*Magazine*: None
*Features*: Steel receiver; black synthetic stock with grips; blued matte finish on metal; removable cheekpiece; Trifecta three-barrel youth gun includes either .243 Win. or 44 Mag. barrel with fiber optic sights or .22 LR barrel with adjustable fiber optics and 20 Ga. shotgun barrel with brass bead front sight
**MSRP** . . . . . . . . . . . . . . . . . . . **$330**

**ROSSI YOUTH RIFLED BARREL SLUG GUN**

# Savage Arms

## STEVENS 320 PUMP

**Action**: Pump
**Stock**: Synthetic
**Barrel**: 18.5 in.
**Chokes**: None

**Weight**: 7 lb.
**Bore/Gauge**: 12
**Magazine**: 5 rounds
**Features**: Proven rotary bolt design; dual side bars; carbon steel barrel with

matte black finish; optional pistol grip, front bead, rifle sights, or ghost ring sights on some models
**MSRP** . . . . . . . . . . . . . . . **$245–$295**

**SAVAGE ARMS STEVENS 320 PUMP**

**SAVAGE ARMS STEVENS 350 PUMP FIELD**

**SAVAGE ARMS STEVENS 350 PUMP SECURITY**

**SAVAGE ARMS STEVENS 512 GOLD WING**

## STEVENS 350 PUMP FIELD

**Action**: Pump
**Stock**: Synthetic
**Barrel**: 28 in.
**Chokes**: None
**Weight**: 8 lb. 3 oz.
**Bore/Gauge**: 12
**Magazine**: Internal box, 5 rounds
**Features**: Vent rib, bead sights; carbon steel barrel; blued metal finish; matte black synthetic stock
**MSRP** . . . . . . . . . . . . . . . . . . . . **$294**

## STEVENS 350 PUMP SECURITY

**Action**: Pump
**Stock**: Synthetic
**Barrel**: 18.25 in.
**Chokes**: None
**Weight**: 7 lb. 10 oz.
**Bore/Gauge**: 12
**Magazine**: Internal box, 5 rounds
**Features**: Bead sights; carbon steel barrel with matte blued finish; synthetic stock in matte black finish
**MSRP** . . . . . . . . . . . . . . . . . . . . **$285**

## STEVENS 512 GOLD WING

**Action**: Over/under
**Stock**: Walnut
**Barrel**: 26 in.
**Chokes**: None
**Weight**: 6 lb.–8 lb.
**Bore/Gauge**: 12, 20, 28, .410
**Magazine**: None
**Features**: Vent rib with front sight bead; carbon steel barrel; blued metal finish
**Standard:** . . . . . . . . . . . . . . . . . **$690**
**Youth:** . . . . . . . . . . . . . . . . . . . **$690**

**SHOTGUNS**

# Smith & Wesson

**SMITH & WESSON ELITE
GOLD GRADE I - PRINCE OF WALES**

## ELITE GOLD GRADE I
**Action**: Side-by-side
**Stock**: Walnut
**Barrel**: 28 in.
**Chokes**: Improved cylinder/mod bore
**Weight**: 6 lb. 11 oz.

**Bore/Gauge**: 20
**Magazine**: None
**Features**: Ivory sight with mid-bead; English or Prince of Wales walnut stock; features the S&W trigger plate; true bone-charcoal case hardening; hand-engraved receiver, English scroll
**MSRP** . . . . . . . . . . . . . . . . . . . **$2380**

**SMITH & WESSON ELITE
SILVER GRADE I**

## ELITE SILVER GRADE I
**Action**: Over/under
**Stock**: Walnut
**Barrel**: 30 in.
**Chokes**: 5 Thin-wall, English Teague Style Choke Tubes (C, K, M, IM, F)

**Weight**: 7 lb. 13 oz.
**Bore/Gauge**: 12
**Magazine**: None
**Features**: Ivory sight with mid-bead; English or Prince of Wales walnut stock; features the S&W trigger plate; true bone-charcoal case hardening; hand-engraved receiver, English scroll
**MSRP** . . . . . . . . . . . . . . . . . . . **$2380**

# Stoeger

## COACH GUN
**Action**: Side-by-side
**Stock**: Walnut, hardwood
**Barrel**: 20 in.
**Chokes**: Fixed chokes (IC, M)
**Weight**: 6 lb. 5 oz.–6 lb. 8 oz.
**Bore/Gauge**: 12, 20, .410
**Magazine**: None

**Features**: A-grade satin or black finished hardwood stock; brass bead sights; nickel or blued metal finish
**MSRP** . . . . . . . . . . . . . . **$449–$499**

## CONDOR
**Action**: Over/under
**Stock**: Walnut
**Barrel**: 22 in., 24 in., 26 in., 28 in.
**Chokes**: Screw-in and fixed chokes on 12 Ga., 20 Ga., 28 Ga. (IC, M), 16 Ga. (M, F), .410 (F&F )
**Weight**: 5 lb. 8 oz.–7 lb. 6 oz.
**Bore/Gauge**: 12, 16, 20, 28, .410
**Magazine**: None
**Features**: Walnut stock; brass bead sight; single trigger; auto-ejectors

**Condor**: . . . . . . . . . . . . . . . . . **$449**
**Condor Supreme**: . . . . . . . . . **$599**
**Condor Youth**: . . . . . . . . . . . . **$449**
**Condor Longfowler**: . . . . . . . . **$449**

## CONDOR COMPETITION
**Action**: Over/under
**Stock**: Walnut
**Barrel**: 30 in.
**Chokes**: Screw-in (IC, M, F)
**Weight**: 7 lb. 5 oz.–7 lb. 13 oz.
**Bore/Gauge**: 12, 20
**Magazine**: None
**Features**: Walnut stock; brass bead with silver mid-bead sight; single selective trigger; automatic ejector; ported barrel
**MSRP** . . . . . . . . . . . . . . . . . . . **$669**

**STOEGER COACH GUN**

**STOEGER CONDOR**

**STOEGER CONDOR COMPETITION**

# Stoeger

**STOEGER CONDOR OUTBACK**

### CONDOR OUTBACK
*Action*: Over/under
*Stock*: Walnut, hardwood
*Barrel*: 20 in.
*Chokes*: Screw-in (IC, M)
*Weight*: 6 lb. 8 oz.–7 lb.

*Bore/Gauge*: 12, 20
*Magazine*: None
*Features*: Notched rear sight and fixed blade front sight; shell extractor; single trigger; A-grade satin walnut or black finished hardwood
**MSRP** . . . . . . . . . . . . . . **$449–$499**

**STOEGER DOUBLE DEFENSE OVER/UNDER**

### DOUBLE DEFENSE OVER/UNDER
*Action*: Over/under
*Stock*: Hardwood
*Barrel*: 20 in.
*Chokes*: Screw-in chokes (IC/IC fixed)
*Weight*: 6 lb. 3 oz.–6 lb. 8 oz.

*Bore/Gauge*: 12, 20
*Magazine*: None
*Features*: Black hardwood stock; green fiber optic front sight; ported barrels; two Picatinny rails; single trigger design; tang-mounted automatic safety
**MSRP** . . . . . . . . . . . . . . . . . . . **$479**

**STOEGER DOUBLE DEFENSE**

### DOUBLE DEFENSE SIDE-BY-SIDE
*Action*: Side-by-side
*Stock*: Hardwood
*Barrel*: 20 in.
*Chokes*: Screw-in chokes (IC/IC fixed)
*Weight*: 6 lb. 8 oz.

*Bore/Gauge*: 12, 20
*Magazine*: None
*Features*: Black hardwood stock; fiber optic front sight; ported barrels; two Picatinny rails; single trigger design; tang-mounted automatic safety
**MSRP** . . . . . . . . . . . . . . . . . . . **$499**

SHOTGUNS

# Stoeger

**STOEGER MODEL 3500**

**STOEGER P350 PUMP**

**STOEGER UPLANDER**

## MODEL 3500
**Action**: Semiautomatic
**Stock**: Synthetic
**Barrel**: 24 in., 26 in., 28 in.
**Chokes**: Screw-in choke tubes (C, IC, M, F, XFT) and wrench
**Weight**: 7 lb. 7 oz.–7 lb. 10 oz.
**Bore/Gauge**: 12
**Magazine**: 4+1 rounds
**Features**: Synthetic stock comes in black or camo finish in Advantage Max-4, Realtree APG, inertia drive sys-tem; recoil reducer; red-bar front sight; Weaver scope base; includes shim kit
**Black synthetic**: . . . . . . . . . . . . $629
**Realtree**: . . . . . . . . . . . . . . . . $719

## P350 PUMP
**Action**: Pump
**Stock**: Walnut
**Barrel**: 18.5 in., 24 in., 26 in., 28 in.
**Chokes**: Screw-in (C, IC, M, F, XFT)
**Weight**: 6 lb. 6 oz.–6 lb. 14 oz.
**Bore/Gauge**: 12
**Magazine**: 4+1 rounds
**Features**: Red bar front sight and metal bead mid-sight; shipped with limiter plug installed; synthetic stock comes in black, Realtree APG, or Realtree Max-4 HD; ergonomic forend
**Synthetic**: . . . . . . . . . . . . . . . . . $349
**Realtree**: . . . . . . . . . . . . . . . . . $449
**Realtree APG Steady Grip**: . . . . $479
**Synthetic Pistol Grip**: . . . . . . . . $379

## UPLANDER
**Action**: Side-by-side
**Stock**: Walnut
**Barrel**: 22 in. (youth), 26 in., 28 in., 28 in.
**Chokes**: Screw-in and fixed tubes
**Weight**: 6 lb. 8 oz.–7 lb. 8 oz.
**Bore/Gauge**: 12, 16, 20, 28, .410
**Magazine**: None
**Features**: Brass bead sights; A-grade satin walnut stock; tang-mounted safe-ty; single or double triggers; extractors included
**Uplander**: . . . . . . . . . . . . . . . . . $449
**Uplander Supreme**: . . . . . . . . . $539
**Uplander Youth**: . . . . . . . . . . . . $449
**Uplander Longfowler**: . . . . . . . $449

# Taylor's & Co.

**TAYLOR'S & CO. 1887 T-SERIES PISTOL**

## 1887 T-SERIES PISTOL
**Action**: Lever
**Stock**: Synthetic
**Barrel**: 18.5 in.
**Chokes**: None
**Weight**: 7 lb.
**Bore/Gauge**: 12
**Magazine**: 5+1 rounds
**Features**: Black soft touch stock, matte blued finish; available in Zombie Blaster Edition and Bootleg Model
**MSRP** . . . . . . . . . . . . . . . . . . . $995

# Thompson/Center

**THOMPSON/CENTER PRO HUNTER TURKEY**

## PRO HUNTER TURKEY
**Action**: Hinged-breech single-shot
**Stock**: AP camo with Flextech
**Barrel**: 24 in. or 26 in.
**Chokes**: T/C extra full
**Weight**: 6 lb. 4 oz.–6 lb. 12 oz.
**Bore/Gauge**: 12, 20
**Magazine**: None
**Features**: Fiber optic sights; 14 in. length pull
**MSRP** . . . . . . . . . . . . . . . . . . . $879

# Tristar Sporting Arms

## COBRA FIELD PUMP

*Action*: Pump
*Stock*: Synthetic
*Barrel*: 24 in., 26 in., 28 in.
*Chokes*: 1 Beretta-style choke (M)
*Weight*: 6 lb. 8 oz.–6 lb. 14 oz.
*Bore/Gauge*: 12
*Magazine*: None
*Features*: Fiber optic front sight; extended forearm to keep out dirt; sling swivel studs
**MSRP** . . . . . . . . . . . . . . . . $329–$379
**Camo:** . . . . . . . . . . . . . . . $409–$469

## COBRA TACTICAL PUMP

*Action*: Pump
*Stock*: Synthetic
*Barrel*: 20 in.
*Chokes*: Screw-in tubes
*Weight*: 6 lb. 5 oz.
*Bore/Gauge*: 12
*Magazine*: 5+1 rounds
*Features*: Faux extended magazine tube; spring-loaded forearm; synthetic stock in matte black; 3-in. chamber
**MSRP** . . . . . . . . . . . . . . . . . . . . . $304

## HUNTER MAG BLACK 3 1/2 IN.

*Action*: Over/under
*Stock*: Black synthetic
*Barrel*: 26 in., 28 in.
*Chokes*: Interchangeable tubes (SK, IC, M, IM, F)
*Weight*: 7 lb. 6 oz.–7 lb. 10 oz.
*Bore/Gauge*: 12

**TRISTAR SPORTING ARMS COBRA FIELD PUMP**

**TRISTAR SPORTING ARMS COBRA TACTICAL PUMP**

**TRISTAR SPORTING ARMS HUNTER MAG BLACK**

*Magazine*: 2 rounds
*Features*: Fiber optic front sight; synthetic stock and forearm; single selective trigger
**MSRP** . . . . . . . . . . . . . . . . . . . $619
**Camo:** . . . . . . . . . . . . . . . . . . $719

## SETTER S/T

*Action*: Over/under
*Stock*: Walnut
*Barrel*: 26 in., 28 in.
*Chokes*: 3-Beretta style tubes (IC, M, F)
*Weight*: 6 lb. 5 oz.–7 lb. 3 oz.
*Bore/Gauge*: 12, 20
*Magazine*: None

*Features*: Fiber optic front sight; high-gloss wood; single selective trigger; extractors; ventilated rib
**MSRP** . . . . . . . . . . . . . . . . . . . $549

## TSA 3 1/2" BLACK

*Action*: Semiautomatic
*Stock*: Black synthetic
*Barrel*: 24 in., 26 in., 28 in.
*Chokes*: Interchangeable tubes (IC, M, F)
*Weight*: 7 lb. 3 oz.–7 lb. 6 oz.
*Bore/Gauge*: 12
*Magazine*: 5+1 rounds
*Features*: Now in black synthetic stock; also available in camo; two piston system; magnum recoil pad; fiber optic front sight
**MSRP** . . . . . . . . . . . . . . . . . . . $639
**Camo:** . . . . . . . . . . . . . . . . . . $699

## VIPER G2 YOUTH CAMO

*Action*: Semiautomatic
*Stock*: Camo synthetic
*Barrel*: 24 in.
*Chokes*: Beretta/Benelli style chokes (IC, M, F)
*Weight*: 5 lb. 11 oz.
*Bore/Gauge*: 20
*Magazine*: 5+1 rounds
*Features*: Now in Realtree Advantage Timber stock; manual E-Z load magazine cut-off; vent rib with matted sight plane; fiber optic front sight; chrome-lined chamber and barrel; soft touch stock
**MSRP** . . . . . . . . . . . . . . . . . . . $589

**TRISTAR SPORTING ARMS SETTER ST**

**TRISTAR SPORTING ARMS TSA MAG BLACK**

**TRISTAR SPORTING ARMS VIPER G2 YOUTH CAMO**

SHOTGUNS

WEATHERBY PA-08 SYNTHETIC SLUG GUN COMBO

WEATHERBY PA-08 TR

WEATHERBY PA-08 TURKEY

WEATHERBY PA-08 UPLAND

WEATHERBY PA-08 UPLAND SLUG GUN COMBO

## PA-08 SYNTHETIC SLUG GUN COMBO

**Action**: Pump
**Stock**: Synthetic
**Barrel**: 24 in., 28 in.
**Chokes**: Interchangeable tubes (IC, M, F)
**Weight**: 7 lb. 4 oz.
**Bore/Gauge**: 12
**Magazine**: 4+1, 5+1 rounds
**Features**: Lightweight and durable injection-molded synthetic stock; comes with 28 in. field barrel and 24 in. rifled barrel with cantilever scope mount base; swivel studs; aircraft-grade aluminum alloy action; chrome-plated bolt in operating action
**MSRP** . . . . . . . . . . . . . . . . . . . **$549**

## PA-08 TR

**Action**: Pump
**Stock**: Synthetic
**Barrel**: 18.5 in.
**Chokes**: Cylinder
**Weight**: 6 lb.–6 lb. 8 oz.
**Bore/Gauge**: 12, 20
**Magazine**: None
**Features**: Dual-action-bar pump; black, injection-molded synthetic composite stock; black metal finish; white blade front sight
**MSRP** . . . . . . . . . . . . . . . . . . . **$399**

## PA-08 TURKEY

**Action**: Pump
**Stock**: Synthetic with Mothwing Spring Mimicry camo
**Barrel**: 22 in.
**Chokes**: Removeable choke tube (F)
**Weight**: 6 lb. 12 oz.
**Bore/Gauge**: 12
**Magazine**: 4+1, 5+1 rounds
**Features**: Dependable dual action bar system; features Mothwing Spring Mimicry camouflage pattern; special "dipping" process adheres camo directly to all stock components; swivel studs included; chrome-lined barrels
**MSRP** . . . . . . . . . . . . . . . . . . . **$399**

## PA-08 UPLAND

**Action**: Pump
**Stock**: Walnut
**Barrel**: 26 in., 28 in.
**Chokes**: Screw in tubes (IC, M, F)
**Weight**: 6 lb. 8 oz.–7 lb. 4 oz.
**Bore/Gauge**: 12, 20
**Magazine**: None
**Features**: Walnut stock with gloss finish; gloss black finish on metalwork; vented top dissipates heat and aids in target acquisition; chrome-lined barrels
**MSRP** . . . . . . . . . . . . . . . . . . . **$449**

## PA-08 UPLAND SLUG GUN COMBO

**Action**: Pump
**Stock**: Walnut
**Barrel**: 24 in., 28 in.
**Chokes**: Interchangeable tubes (IC, M, F)
**Weight**: 7 lb. 4 oz.
**Bore/Gauge**: 12
**Magazine**: 4+1, 5+1 rounds
**Features**: Walnut stock with gloss finish; receiver with 28 in. field barrel is gloss black for a distinctive look; 24 in. rifled barrel with cantilever scope mount base in matte black; swivel studs; aircraft-grade aluminum alloy action; chrome-plated bolt in operating action
**MSRP** . . . . . . . . . . . . . . . . . . . **$649**

**SHOTGUNS**

# Weatherby

WEATHERBY SA-08 DELUXE

WEATHERBY SA-08 UPLAND

WEATHERBY SA-459 TR

WEATHERBY SA-459 TURKEY

## SA-08 DELUXE

*Action*: Semiautomatic
*Stock*: Walnut
*Barrel*: 26 in., 28 in.
*Chokes*: Screw in tubes (IC, M, F)
*Weight*: 6 lb.–6 lb. 12 oz.
*Bore/Gauge*: 12, 20
*Magazine*: None
*Features*: Walnut stock with high–gloss finish and metalwork; vented top rib dissipates heat and aids in target acquisition; dual valve system
*MSRP* . . . . . . . . . . . . . . . . . . . $799

## SA-08 UPLAND

*Action*: Semiautomatic
*Stock*: Walnut
*Barrel*: 26 in., 28 in.

*Chokes*: Screw-in tubes (IC, M, F)
*Weight*: 6 lb.–6 lb. 12 oz.
*Bore/Gauge*: 12, 20
*Magazine*: None
*Features*: Walnut stock with satin finish; matte black finish on metalwork; vented top rib dissipates heat and aids in target acquisition; dual valve system
*MSRP* . . . . . . . . . . . . . . . . . . . $799

## SA-459 TR

*Action*: Semiautomatic
*Stock*: Synthetic
*Barrel*: 18.5 in.
*Chokes*: Ported cylinder choke tube
*Weight*: 6 lb.–6 lb. 8 oz.
*Bore/Gauge*: 12, 20
*Magazine*: 5+1 rounds
*Features*: Pistol grip stock with a rubber textured area; chrome-lined barrel; Picatinny rail for mounting scopes and optics; ghost ring style rear sight, front

bead sight; black synthetic injection-molded stock is matched by black matte metal finishing
*MSRP* . . . . . . . . . . . . . . . . . . . $699

## SA-459 TURKEY

*Action*: Semiautomatic, gas-operated
*Stock*: Synthetic with Mothwing Spring Mimicry camo
*Barrel*: 21.25 in.
*Chokes*: Interchangeable tubes (X-F)
*Weight*: 6 lb. 4 oz.–6 lb. 12 oz.
*Bore/Gauge*: 12, 20
*Magazine*: 4+1, 5+1 rounds
*Features*: Trimmer forend for easier handling; swivel studs; Mil-Spec Picatinny rail for mounting optics; LPA-style ghost ring rear sight that is adjustable for windage and elevation; front blade sight with fiber optic insert; over-size hourglass-shaped bolt handle for quick and positive chambering; pistol grip stock
*MSRP* . . . . . . . . . . . . . . . . . . . $699

SHOTGUNS

# Winchester Repeating Arms

## MODEL 101

**Action**: Over/under
**Stock**: Walnut
**Barrel**: 26 in., 28 in., 30 in., 32 in.
**Chokes**: Invector-Plus choke system, 3 tubes
**Weight**: 6 lb. 12oz.–7 lb. 6 oz.
**Bore/Gauge**: 12
**Magazine**: None
**Features**: Solid brass bead front sight on Field; Truglo front sight on Sporting; deep relief receiver engraving; high-gloss grade II/III walnut stock; vented Pachmayr Decelerator pad with classic white line spacer
**Field**: . . . . . . . . . . . . . . . . $1869.99
**Sporting**: . . . . . . . . . . . . . . . $2320

## SUPER X PUMP BLACK SHADOW

**Action**: Pump
**Stock**: Synthetic
**Barrel**: 26 in., 28 in.
**Chokes**: Invector Plus
**Weight**: 6 lb. 12 oz.–7 lb.
**Bore/Gauge**: 12
**Magazine**: 4 rounds
**Features**: Hard chrome chamber and bores; drop-out trigger group for easy cleaning; synthetic stock with non-glare black matte finish on barrel and receiver
**MSRP** . . . . . . . . . . $379.99–$429.99

## SUPER X PUMP DEFENDER

**Action**: Pump
**Stock**: Composite
**Barrel**: 18 in.
**Chokes**: Fixed cylinder choked barrel
**Weight**: 6 lb. 4 oz.
**Bore/Gauge**: 12
**Magazine**: 5+1 rounds
**Features**: Uses Foster-type slugs; non-glare metal surfaces with a tough black composite stock; deeply grooved fore-arm for control and stability
**MSRP** . . . . . . . . . . . . . . . . . . . $400

## SUPER X PUMP TURKEY HUNTER

**Action**: Pump
**Stock**: Synthetic
**Barrel**: 24 in.
**Chokes**: Invector Plus
**Weight**: 6 lb. 10 oz.
**Bore/Gauge**: 12
**Magazine**: 4 rounds
**Features**: Hard chrome chamber and bores; drop-out trigger group for easy cleaning; Invector Plus Extra-Full Turkey Choke Tube; crossbolt safety; Inflex technology recoil pad; synthetic stock with textured gripping surfaces in Mossy Oak Break-Up Infinity
**MSRP** . . . . . . . . . . . . . . . . . . $519.99

## SUPER X PUMP WATERFOWL HUNTER

**Action**: Pump
**Stock**: Synthetic
**Barrel**: 26 in.
**Chokes**: Invector Plus
**Weight**: 6 lb. 14 oz.
**Bore/Gauge**: 12
**Magazine**: 4 rounds
**Features**: Hard chrome chamber and bores; drop-out trigger group for easy cleaning; synthetic stock with textured gripping surfaces in Mossy Oak Shadow Grass Blades
**MSRP** . . . . . . . . . . . . . . . . . . $499.99

WINCHESTER MODEL 101 FIELD

WINCHESTER SUPER X PUMP BLACK SHADOW

WINCHESTER SUPER X PUMP DEFENDER.

WINCHESTER SUPER X PUMP TURKEY HUNTER

WINCHESTER SUPER X PUMP WATERFOWL HUNTER

# Winchester Repeating Arms

## SUPER X3 BLACK FIELD

**Action**: Semiautomatic
**Stock**: Walnut
**Barrel**: 26 in., 28 in.
**Chokes**: Invector Plus
**Weight**: 6 lb. 8 oz.–6 lb. 14 oz.
**Bore/Gauge**: 12, 20
**Magazine**: 4 rounds
**Features**: Satin oil finish walnut stock with classic cut checkering; matte black receivers in lightweight aluminum alloy; Invector Plus choke system
**MSRP** . . . . . . . . . . . . . . . . . $1069.99

WINCHESTER SX3 BLACK FIELD

## SUPER X3 FIELD COMPACT

**Action**: Semiautomatic
**Stock**: Walnut
**Barrel**: 26 in., 28 in.
**Chokes**: Invector Plus
**Weight**: 6 lb. 6 oz.–6 lb. 14 oz.
**Bore/Gauge**: 12, 20
**Magazine**: 4 rounds
**Features**: Stock dimensions trimmed for smaller-frame shooters and hunters with a 13-inch length of pull; satin oil finish walnut stock with classic cut checkering; matte black receivers in lightweight aluminum alloy
**MSRP** . . . . . . . . . . . . . . . . . $1069.99

WINCHESTER SX3 BLACK FIELD COMPACT

## SUPER X3 SPORTING ADJUSTABLE

**Action**: Autoloader
**Stock**: Walnut
**Barrel**: 28 in., 30 in., 32 in.
**Chokes**: Five extended signature choke tubes
**Weight**: 7 lb. 6 oz.–7 lb. 10 oz.
**Bore/Gauge**: 12
**Magazine**: holds up to 4 rounds depending on shell size
**Features**: Aluminum-alloy receiver, and barrel; ventilated rib; buttstock features an adjustable comb; chrome-plated chamber and bore; Pachmayr decelerator recoil pad; molded red case included
**MSRP** . . . . . . . . . . . . . . . . $1699.99

WINCHESTER SX3 SPORTING ADJUSTABLE

# Accu-Tek

**ACCU-TEK AT-380 II**

## AT-380 II
*Action*: Semi-automatic
*Grips*: Composite
*Barrel*: 2.8 in.
*Sights*: Target
*Weight*: 23.5 oz.
*Caliber*: .380 ACP
*Capacity*: 6+1 rounds
*Features*: Stainless steel construction; adjustable rear sight; one hand manual safety blocks; stainless steel magazine
**MSRP** . . . . . . . . . . . . . . . . . . . . $275

## HC-380
*Action*: Semi-automatic
*Grips*: Composite
*Barrel*: 2.8 in.
*Sights*: Target
*Weight*: 26 oz.
*Caliber*: .380 ACP
*Capacity*: 13 rounds
*Features*: Adjustable rear sight; black checkered grip; one hand manual safety block; includes two magazines and cable lock
**MSRP** . . . . . . . . . . . . . . . . . . . . $314

**ACCU-TEK HC-380**

# American Derringer

**AMERICAN DERRINGER
LADY DERRINGER**

**AMERICAN DERRINGER MODEL 1**

## LADY DERRINGER
*Action*: Hinged breech
*Grips*: Camo, Pink, Scrimshaw
*Barrel*: 3 in.
*Sights*: Open, fixed
*Weight*: 15.5 oz.
*Caliber*: .38 Special, .32 Mag.
*Capacity*: 2 rounds

*Features*: Lady Derringer Survivor Series in memory of breast cancer survivors; highly-polished brass or stainless steel frame; each pistol is handmade, custom serial numbers are available
**Camo/Pink:** . . . . . . . . . . . . . . $835
**Engraved Scrimshaw:** . . . . . . . $2300

## MODEL 1
*Action*: Hinged breech
*Grips*: Rosewood or stag
*Barrel*: 3 in.
*Sights*: Fixed, open
*Weight*: 15 oz.
*Caliber*: .45, .410
*Capacity*: 2 rounds
*Features*: Single-action; automatic barrel selection; manually operated hammer-block safety
**MSRP** . . . . . . . . . . . . . . . . . . . . $710

**HANDGUNS**

# American Derringer

**AMERICAN DERRINGER MODEL 4**

**AMERICAN DERRINGER MODEL 6**

## MODEL 4

**Action**: Hinged breech
**Grips**: Rosewood
**Barrel**: 4.1 in
**Sights**: Fixed open
**Weight**: 16.5 oz.
**Caliber**: .375 Mag., 357 Max., 45-70, .45 Colt/.410, .44 Mag.
**Capacity**: 2 rounds
**Features**: Satin or high polish stainless steel finish; single-action; automatic barrel selection; manually operated hammer-block type safety
**MSRP** . . . . . . . . . . . . . . . $760–$870

## MODEL 6

**Action**: Hinged breech
**Grips**: Rosewood, walnut, black
**Barrel**: 6 in.
**Sights**: Fixed open
**Weight**: 21 oz.
**Caliber**: .357 Mag., .45 Auto, .45 Colt/.410
**Capacity**: 2 rounds
**Features**: Satin or high polish stainless steel finish; single-action; automatic barrel selection; manually operated hammer-block type safety
**MSRP** . . . . . . . . . . . . . . . . . . $895

## MODEL 7 LIGHTWEIGHT & ULTRA LIGHTWEIGHT

**Action**: Hinged breech
**Grips**: Blackwood
**Barrel**: 3 in.
**Sights**: Fixed open
**Weight**: 7.5 oz.
**Caliber**: .44 Special, .380 Auto, .38 Special, .32 Mag./.32 S&W Long, .22LR, .22 Mag.
**Capacity**: N/A
**Features**: Grey matte finish; single-action; automatic barrel selection; manually operated hammer-block type safety
**MSRP** . . . . . . . . . . . . . . . . . . $700

**AMERICAN DERRINGER MODEL 7**

## MODEL 8

**Action**: Hinged breech
**Grips**: Rosewood, walnut, black
**Barrel**: 6 in.
**Sights**: Optional Adco red dot scope
**Weight**: 24 oz.
**Caliber**: .357 Mag., .45 Auto, .45 Colt/.410
**Capacity**: 2 rounds
**Features**: Satin or high polish stainless steel finish; single-action; automatic barrel selection; manually operated hammer-block type safety
**MSRP** . . . . . . . . . . . . . . . . . . $935

**AMERICAN DERRINGER MODEL 8**

# American Tactical Imports

AMERICAN TACTICAL IMPORTS
FX 45 1911 GI

AMERICAN TACTICAL
IMPORTS FX 45 1911
MILITARY

AMERICAN TACTICAL
IMPORTS FX 1911
THUNDERBOLT

AMERICAN TACTICAL
IMPORTS FX 1911
TITAN BLUE

AMERICAN TACTICAL
IMPORTS FX
THUNDERBOLT
STAINLESS

## FX 1911 GI
**Action**: Semi-automatic
**Grips**: Mahogany
**Barrel**: 4.25 in.
**Sights**: Fixed
**Weight**: 32 oz.
**Caliber**: .45 ACP
**Capacity**: 8+1 rounds
**Features**: Steel parts; black matte military-style fixed front and rear sights; military-style slide stop and thumb safety, solid mahogany grip panels
**MSRP** . . . . . . . . . . . . . . . . .**$499.95**

## FX 1911 MILITARY
**Action**: Semi-automatic
**Grips**: Mahogany
**Barrel**: 5 in.
**Sights**: Fixed
**Weight**: 37 oz.
**Caliber**: .45 ACP
**Capacity**: 8+1 rounds
**Features**: Steel parts; black matte military-style fixed front and rear sights; military-style slide stop and thumb safety, solid mahogany grip panels
**MSRP** . . . . . . . . . . . . . . . . .**$499.95**

## FX 1911 THUNDERBOLT
**Action**: Semi-automatic
**Grips**: Mahogany
**Barrel**: 5 in.
**Sights**: Fixed
**Weight**: 39 oz.
**Caliber**: .45 ACP
**Capacity**: 8+1 rounds
**Features**: Picatinny rail; steel parts; Solid mahogany grips
**MSRP** . . . . . . . . . . . . . . . .**$857.95**

## FX 1911 TITAN BLUE & STAINLESS
**Action**: Semi-automatic
**Grips**: Mahogany
**Barrel**: 3.13 in.
**Sights**: Fixed
**Weight**: 28 oz.
**Caliber**: .45 ACP
**Capacity**: 7+1 rounds
**Features**: Carbon-steel construction or stainless-steel construction; two-stage recoil spring system; low-profile rear sights with a dovetailed front sight; military-style slide stop and thumb safety; bull barrel
**Titan Blue:** . . . . . . . . . . . . .**$584.95**
**Titan Stainless:** . . . . . . . . .**$669.95**

## FX THUNDERBOLT ENHANCED
**Action**: Semiautomatic
**Grips**: Mahogany
**Barrel**: 5 in.
**Sights**: Adjustable 3-dot combat sights
**Weight**: N/A
**Caliber**: .45 ACP
**Capacity**: 8 rounds
**Features**: Picatinny rail; ambidextrous safety; grip checkering; enhanced model has barrel porting for less felt recoil
**MSRP** . . . . . . . . . . . . . . . . .**$869.95**
**Blued:** . . . . . . . . . . . . . . . .**$899.00**

# American Tactical Imports

## GSG 922

**Action**: Semiautomatic
**Grips**: Plastic
**Barrel**: 3.2 in.
**Sights**: Click-adjustable target
**Weight**: 31 oz.
**Caliber**: .22 LR
**Capacity**: 10 rounds
**Features**: Frame is constructed of Zamak-5 zinc alloy; loaded chamber indicator, grip safety, magazine safety, firing-pin-block, external hammer; optional AD OP's faux suppressor
**MSRP**. . . . . . . . . . . . . . . . . . **$374.95**
**With suppressor:**. . . . . . . . **$399.95**

AMERICAN TACTICAL
IMPORTS GSG 922

AMERICAN TACTICAL
IMPORTS GSG 1911
PISTOL

## GSG 1911 PISTOL

**Action**: Semi-automatic
**Grips**: Classic wood (standard), or black polymer grips
**Barrel**: 3.2 in., 5 in.

**Sights**: Fixed
**Weight**: 39.5 oz.
**Caliber**: .22LR
**Capacity**: 10 rounds
**Features**: Picatinny rail; faux suppressor optional

**MSRP**. . . . . . . . . . . . . . . . . . **$374.95**
**Black:**. . . . . . . . . . . . . . . . . **$367.00**
**Suppressor:**. . . . . . . . . . . . **$391.00**

# Arsenal Firearms

## AF-1 STRIKE ONE

**Action**: Semiautomatic
**Grips**: 3D polymer
**Barrel**: 5 in.
**Sights**: Fixed or adjustable
**Weight**: 26.4 oz. (poly), 31.4 oz. (ergal)
**Caliber**: 9x19 Para, 9x21 IMI, .357 SIG, .40 S&W
**Capacity**: 17 rounds
**Features**: Geometric lock, semiautomatic hammerless pistol; short recoil, in line barrel, patented locking block system; automatic

safety; single-action only trigger; ambidextrous magazine release button; reinforced polymer or ergal light alloy frame in ordnance black, desert tan, and olive drab with 360 degree integral mini-skirt; underbarrel integral Picatinny rail; interchangeable back plate/sight, fixed or adjustable, or Micro-Dot ready; available with a Long Range Conversion
**MSRP** . . . . . . . **Price on request**

ARSENAL FIREARMS
AF-1 STRIKE ONE

## AF2011-A1 DOUBLE BARREL PISTOL

**Action**: Semiautomatic double barrel
**Grips**: Steel
**Barrel**: 4.9 in.
**Sights**: Fixed or adjustable
**Weight**: 65.3 oz.
**Caliber**: .45 ACP, .38 Super Auto
**Capacity**: 18 rounds
**Features**: First industrial double barrel semiautomatic pistol; single slide, single frame, single spur double hammer; single grip safety; single body double

mainspring housing and single double cavity magazine floorplate (two single magazines); long and double magazine latch; most internal parts are interchangeable with standard 1911 replacement parts; can be ordered with two independent triggers and one sear group or with two triggers permanently joined and one or two sear groups; deep blued mirror finish or 3400 Vickers surface hardness white ash nitrite coating
**MSRP** . . . . . . . **$4400–$4950**

ARSENAL FIREARMS AF2011-A1 DOUBLE BARREL PISTOL

# Auto-Ordnance

## 1911PKZSE

*Action*: Semi-automatic
*Grips*: Brown checkered plastic, checkered wood grips
*Barrel*: 5 in.
*Sights*: Blade front, rear drift adjustable sight
*Weight*: 39 oz.
*Caliber*: .45 ACP
*Capacity*: 7+1 rounds
*Features*: Single-action 1911 Colt design; WWII parkerized; stainless steel or blued metal finish
**MSRP . . . . . . . . . . . . . . . . . . . . . $668**

**AUTO-ORDNANCE 1911PKZSE**

# Beretta USA

**BERETTA 21 BOBCAT**

**BERETTA 87 TARGET**

## 21 BOBCAT

*Action*: Autoloader
*Grips*: Plastic
*Barrel*: 2.4 in.
*Sights*: Fixed, open
*Weight*: 11.5 oz.
*Caliber*: .22LR, .25 ACP
*Capacity*: 7 or 8 rounds
*Features*: Double-action; tip-up barrel; stainless steel slide and barrel; alloy gray frame; other metal parts come in black or Inox finish
**Black Finish: . . . . . . . . . . . . . . $310**
**Inox Finish: . . . . . . . . . . . . . . $350**

## 87 TARGET

*Action*: Autoloader
*Grips*: Plastic
*Barrel*: 5.9 in.
*Sights*: Fixed open
*Weight*: 2.1 oz.
*Caliber*: .22LR
*Capacity*: 10+1 rounds
*Features*: Optional wood grips; ambidextrous safety; steel barrel with

**BERETTA 90-TWO TYPE F**

hard chromed bore; open slide design; firing pin block; reversible magazine release; anodized alloy frame with matte black finish or nickel; combat-style trigger guard; double-action trigger
**MSRP . . . . . . . . . . . . . . . . . . . . . $880**

## 90-TWO TYPE F

*Action*: Autoloader
*Grips*: Technopolymer single-piece wraparound, standard or slim size
*Barrel*: 4.9 in.
*Sights*: Super-Lumi Nova
*Weight*: 32.5 oz.
*Caliber*: 9mm, .40 S&W
*Capacity*: 12 or 17 rounds, restricted capacity 10 rounds
*Features*: Slide serrations; Guigiaro Design grips; removable front sight; internal recoil buffer; Picatinny MIL-STD-1913 rail
**MSRP . . . . . . . . . . . . . . . . . . . . . $700**

# Beretta USA

## 92A1

**Action**: Autoloader
**Grips**: Plastic
**Barrel**: 4.9 in.
**Sights**: 3-Dot System
**Weight**: 34.4 oz.
**Caliber**: 9mm, .40 S&W
**Capacity**: 12 or 17 rounds, restricted capacity 10 rounds
**Features**: Removable front sight; MIL-STD-1913, internal recoil buffer; captive recoil spring assembly
**MSRP** . . . . . . . . . . . . . . . . . . . $725

## 92FS TYPE M9A1

**Action**: Autoloader
**Grips**: Plastic
**Barrel**: 4.9 in.
**Sights**: 3-Dot System
**Weight**: 33.9 oz.
**Caliber**: 9mm
**Capacity**: 15+1 rounds, restricted capacity 10+1 rounds
**Features**: Picatinny MIL STD-1913 rail; magazine well bevel; sand-resistant magazine
**MSRP** . . . . . . . . . . . . . . . . . . . $725

## 3032 TOMCAT

**Action**: Autoloader
**Grips**: Plastic
**Barrel**: 2.5 in.
**Sights**: Fixed, open
**Weight**: 14.5 oz.
**Caliber**: .32 ACP, .380
**Capacity**: 7+1 round
**Features**: Double-action; tip-up barrel latch; Inox has stainless steel slide and barrel; titanium alloy frame in black or gray; double- or single-trigger
**Standard**: . . . . . . . . . . . . . . . . $390
**Inox**: . . . . . . . . . . . . . . . . . . . $430

## BU-9 NANO

**Action**: Autoloader
**Grips**: Technopolymer
**Barrel**: 3.07 in.
**Sights**: 3-dot low profile
**Weight**: 17.67 oz.
**Caliber**: 9mm
**Capacity**: 6+1 rounds
**Features**: Interchangeable sights; ambidextrous magazine release button; serialized sub-chassis; patent-pending striker deactivator; technopolymer grip frame
**MSRP** . . . . . . . . . . . . . . . . . . . $475

BERETTA 92A1

BERETTA BU-9 NANO

BERETTA 92FS TYPE M9A1

BERETTA 3032 TOMCAT

# Beretta USA

HANDGUNS

**BERETTA M9
COMMERCIAL**

## M9 COMMERCIAL

*Action*: Autoloader
*Grips*: Plastic
*Barrel*: 4.9 in.
*Sights*: Dot-and-Post system
*Weight*: 33.3 oz.
*Caliber*: 9mm
*Capacity*: 15 rounds, restricted capacity 10+1 rounds
*Features*: Has distinctive military style markings; chrome-lined bore; double-action; automatic firing pin block; ambidextrous manual safety; lightweight forged aluminum alloy frame w/ combat-style trigger guard
**MSRP** . . . . . . . . . . . . . . . . . . . . . **$700**

**BERETTA PX4 STORM COMPACT**

**BERETTA PX4 STORM FULL SIZE**

## PX4 STORM COMPACT

*Action*: Autoloader
*Grips*: Plastic
*Barrel*: 3.2 in.
*Sights*: 3-Dot System
*Weight*: 27.3 oz.
*Caliber*: 9mm, .40 S&W
*Capacity*: 12 or 15 rounds; full size magazines 9mm: 17 or 20 rounds, .40: 14 or 17 rounds; restricted capacity 10 rounds
*Features*: Ambidextrous side stop lever; integral Picatinny MIL-STD-1913 rail; bruiton non-reflective black coating; visible automatic firing pin block
**MSRP** . . . . . . . . . . . . . . . . . . . . . **$575**

## PX4 STORM FULL SIZE

*Action*: Autoloader
*Grips*: Plastic
*Barrel*: 4 in.
*Sights*: 3-Dot System
*Weight*: 27.7 oz.
*Caliber*: 9mm, .40 S&W, .45 ACP
*Capacity*: 14 or 17 rounds, restricted Capacity: 10 rounds
*Features*: Picatinny MIL STD-1913 rail; innovative locked-breech with a rotating barrel system; visible automatic firing pin block; ambidextrous safety; reversible magazine release; available in Inox finish
**MSRP** . . . . . . . . . . . . . . . . . **$575–$650**

## U22 NEOS

*Action*: Autoloader
*Grips*: Plastic
*Barrel*: 4.5 in., 6 in.
*Sights*: Target
*Weight*: 31.7–36.2 oz.
*Caliber*: .22LR
*Capacity*: 10+1 rounds
*Features*: Single-action; removable colored grip inserts; deluxe model features adjustable trigger, replaceable sights; optional 7.5 in. barrel
**Standard:** . . . . . . . . . . . . . . . . . **$280**
**Inox:** . . . . . . . . . . . . . . . . . . . **$375**

**BERETTA U22 NEOS**

# Bersa

## BP CC 9

*Action*: Short reset DAO
*Grips*: Integral to frame
*Barrel*: 3.3 in.
*Sights*: Interchangeable front and rear
*Weight*: 21.5 oz.
*Caliber*: 9mm, .40 SW
*Capacity*: 6+1, 8+1 rounds
*Features*: Bersa polymer concealed carry; high impact polymer frame; Picatinny rail, polygonal rifling, and loaded chamber indicator; ambidextrous magazine release; striker fired; micro-polished bore with sharp, deep rifling; 3-dot sight system; integral locking system; automatic firing pin safety; matte black or duotone finish
**MSRP** . . . . . . . . . . . . . . . **$427–$440**

**BERSA BP CC 9**

**BERSA THUNDER 40 ULTRA COMPACT PRO**

**BERSA THUNDER 9 ULTRA COMPACT PRO**

**BERSA THUNDER 45 ULTRA COMPACT PRO**

## THUNDER 9 ULTRA COMPACT

*Action*: Autoloader
*Grips*: Black polymer
*Barrel*: 3.25 in.
*Sights*: 3-Dot system
*Weight*: 23 oz.
*Caliber*: 9mm
*Capacity*: 10+1, 13+1 rounds
*Features*: Picatinny rail; precision machined lightweight alloy; ambidextrous safety; lifetime service contract; integral locking system; anatomically designed polymer grips; double-action; available in matte or duotone finish
**Matte:** . . . . . . . . . . . . . . . . . **$500**
**Duotone:** . . . . . . . . . . . . . . . . **$510**

## THUNDER 40 ULTRA COMPACT

*Action*: Autoloader
*Grips*: Black polymer
*Barrel*: 3.25 in.
*Sights*: 3-Dot system
*Weight*: 23 oz.
*Caliber*: .40 S&W
*Capacity*: 10+1 rounds
*Features*: Picatinny rail; precision machined lightweight alloy; ambidextrous safety; lifetime service contract; integral locking system;

anatomically designed polymer grips; double-action; available in matte or duotone finish
**Matte:** . . . . . . . . . . . . . . . . . **$500**
**Duotone:** . . . . . . . . . . . . . . . . **$510**

## THUNDER 45 ULTRA COMPACT

*Action*: Autoloader
*Grips*: Black polymer
*Barrel*: 3.6 in.
*Sights*: 3-Dot system
*Weight*: 27 oz.
*Caliber*: .45 ACP
*Capacity*: 7+1 rounds
*Features*: Double-action; Picatinny rail; precision machined lightweight alloy; ambidextrous safety; lifetime service contract; integral locking system; anatomically designed polymer grips; available in matte or duotone finish
**Matte:** . . . . . . . . . . . . . . . . . **$500**
**Duotone:** . . . . . . . . . . . . . . . . **$510**

**BERSA THUNDER 380**

## THUNDER 380

*Action*: Autoloader
*Grips*: Black polymer
*Barrel*: 3.5 in.
*Sights*: 3-Dot system
*Weight*: 20 oz.
*Caliber*: .380 ACP
*Capacity*: 7+1 rounds
*Features*: Combat style trigger guard; extended slide release; micro-polished bore with sharp, deep rifling; integral locking system; available in matte, satin, nickel, or duotone finish
**Matte:** . . . . . . . . . . . . . . . . . **$335**
**Duotone:** . . . . . . . . . . . . . . . . **$335**
**Nickel:** . . . . . . . . . . . . . . . . . . **$353**
**Combat:** . . . . . . . . . . . . . . . . **$353**

# Bersa

## THUNDER 380 CONCEALED CARRY

**Action**: Autoloader
**Grips**: Black polymer
**Barrel**: 3.2 in.
**Sights**: Blade front and notched-bar dovetailed rear
**Weight**: 16.4 oz.
**Caliber**: .380 ACP
**Capacity**: 8+1 rounds
**Features**: Extra low profile sights; combat style trigger guard; slim slide release; integral locking system
**Matte**: . . . . . . . . . . . . . . . . . . $350
**Duotone**: . . . . . . . . . . . . . . . . $360

BERSA THUNDER 380
CONCEALED CARRY

# Bond Arms

## BOND MINI

**Action**: SA
**Grips**: Rosewood or pink
**Barrel**: 2.5 in.
**Sights**: Blade front, fixed rear
**Weight**: 18 oz.–19 oz.
**Caliber**: .357 Mag./.38 Spl., .45 ACP, .45 Colt, .45 Glock Auto, .44 Spl., .44-40 Win., .40 S&W, 10mm, 9mm, .32 H&R Mag., .22 LR, .22 Mag. (3 in. barrel .410/.45 LC with 2.5 in. chambers-rifled)
**Capacity**: 2 rounds
**Features**: The Bond Mini was developed as a special edition gun that is even easier to conceal and carry, but still packs the same power Bond Arms guns are known for. This gun comes in two models the Mini .45 and the Girl Mini (.357/.38). The Girl Mini has slightly smaller barrel included and pink grips.
**MSRP** . . . . . . . . . . . . . . . . . . . . $395

BOND ARMS BOND MINI

## BOND RANGER

**Action**: SA
**Grips**: Black ash star
**Barrel**: 4.25 in.
**Sights**: Blade front and fixed rear
**Weight**: 23.5 oz.
**Caliber**: .357 Mag./.38 Spl., .45 ACP, .45 Colt, .45 Glock Auto, .44 Spl., .44-40 Win., .40 S&W, 10mm, 9mm, .32 H&R Mag., .22 LR, .22 Mag.; .410/.45 LC with 3 in. chambers-rifled
**Capacity**: 2 rounds
**Features**: Interchangeable barrels; automatic extractor; retracting firing pins; crossbolt safety; spring-loaded cammed locking lever; stainless steel with satin polish finish
**MSRP** . . . . . . . . . . . . . . . . . . . . $634

BOND ARMS
BOND RANGER

BOND ARMS
BOND GIRL MINI

# Bond Arms

**BOND ARMS
CENTURY 2000**

**BOND ARMS SNAKE SLAYER**

**BOND TEXAS RANGER -
SPECIAL EDITION**

**BOND ARMS
SNAKE SLAYER IV**

**BOND ARMS TEXAS
DEFENDER**

## CENTURY 2000
*Action*: SA
*Grips*: Custom laminated black ash or rosewood
*Barrel*: 3.5 in.
*Sights*: Blade front and fixed rear
*Weight*: 21 oz.
*Caliber*: .357 Mag./.38 Spl., .45 ACP, .45 Colt, .45 Glock Auto, .44 Spl., .44-40 Win., .40 S&W, 10mm, 9mm, .32 H&R Mag., .22 LR, .22 Mag.; .410/.45 LC
*Capacity*: 2 rounds
*Features*: Interchangeable barrels; automatic extractor; rebounding hammer; retracting firing pins; crossbolt safety; spring-loaded cammed locking lever; trigger guard; stainless steel with satin polish finish
**MSRP** . . . . . . . . . . . . . . . . . . . . $420

## SNAKE SLAYER
*Action*: SA
*Grips*: Extended custom rosewood
*Barrel*: 4.25 in.
*Sights*: Blade front and fixed rear
*Weight*: 22 oz.
*Caliber*: .357 Mag./.38 Spl., .45 ACP, .45 Colt, .45 Glock Auto, .44 Spl., .44-40 Win., .40 S&W, 10mm, 9mm, .32 H&R Mag., .22 LR, .22 Mag.; .410/.45 LC with 3 in. chambers-rifled
*Capacity*: 2 rounds

*Features*: Interchangeable barrels; automatic extractor; rebounding hammer; retracting firing pins; crossbolt safety; spring-loaded cammed locking lever; trigger guard; stainless steel with satin polish finish
**MSRP** . . . . . . . . . . . . . . . . . . . . $489

## SNAKE SLAYER IV
*Action*: SA
*Grips*: Extended custom rosewood
*Barrel*: 4.25 in.
*Sights*: Blade front and fixed rear
*Weight*: 23.5 oz.
*Caliber*: .357 Mag./.38 Spl., .45 ACP, .45 Colt, .45 Glock Auto, .44 Spl., .44-40 Win., .40 S&W, 10mm, 9mm, .32 H&R Mag., .22 LR, .22 Mag.; .410/.45 LC with 3 in. chambers-rifled
*Capacity*: 2 rounds
*Features*: Automatic extractor; interchangeable barrels; rebounding hammer; retracting firing pins; crossbolt safety; spring-loaded cammed locking lever; trigger guard; stainless steel with satin polish finish
**MSRP** . . . . . . . . . . . . . . . . . . . . $519

## TEXAS DEFENDER
*Action*: SA
*Grips*: Custom laminated black ash or rosewood

*Barrel*: 3 in.
*Sights*: Blade front and fixed rear
*Weight*: 20 oz.
*Caliber*: 45 Colt/.410 Shot Shell(rifled), .357 Mag./.38 Spl., .357 Max, .45 ACP, .45 Colt, .45 Glock Auto, .44-40 Win., .40 S&W, 10mm, .32 H&R Mag., .22LR
*Capacity*: 2 rounds
*Features*: Interchangeable barrels; automatic extractor; rebounding hammer; retracting firing pins; crossbolt safety; spring-loaded cammed locking lever; trigger guard; stainless steel with satin polish finish
**MSRP** . . . . . . . . . . . . . . . . . . . . $415

## TEXAS RANGER - SPECIAL EDITION
*Action*: SA
*Grips*: Texas mesquite
*Barrel*: 4.25 in.
*Sights*: Blade front, fixed rear
*Weight*: 23.5 oz.
*Caliber*: .410/.45LC, .357 Mag., .45 ACP, .45 Colt., .45 Glock Auto, .44 Spl., .44-40 Win., .40 S&W, 10mm, 9mm, .32 H&R Mag., .22 LR, .22 Mag.
*Capacity*: 2 rounds
*Features*: Bond Arms has been chosen to represent the prestigious Texas Rangers in their historic 200th Anniversary. The gun and knife grips are made from real Texas mesquite wood, the Texas Ranger Stars are handmade by Texas inmates in the Texas Department of Corrections, and it is gold engraved on the barrel. Custom glass top display case included.
**MSRP** . . . . . . . . . . . . . . . . . . . . $1297

# Browning

HANDGUNS

**BROWNING 1911-22 A1**

**BROWNING BUCK MARK CAMPER**

**BROWNING BUCK MARK LITE GREEN 5.5**

**BROWNING BUCK MARK PLUS UDX**

**BROWNING BUCK MARK PRACTICAL URX**

## 1911-22 A1

*Action*: Autoloader
*Grips*: Brown composite
*Barrel*: 4.25 in.
*Sights*: Fixed
*Weight*: 16 oz.
*Caliber*: 22 L.R.
*Capacity*: 10+1 rounds
*Features*: Alloy frame in matte blued finish; stainless steel barrel block with matte blued finish; blowback action; single-action trigger; detachable magazine; manual thumb safety; grip safety
**MSRP** . . . . . . . . . . . . . . . . . **$599.99**

## BUCK MARK LITE GREEN 5.5

*Action*: Autoloader
*Grips*: Ultragrip RX ambidextrous
*Barrel*: 5.5 in.
*Sights*: Pro-Target adjustable rear sight; Truglo/Marble's fiber-optic front
*Weight*: 28 oz.
*Caliber*: 22 L.R.
*Capacity*: 10+1 rounds
*Features*: Matte green finish; fluted barrel; alloy sleeved barrel; matte black grips and receiver; single action trigger
**MSRP** . . . . . . . . . . . . . . . . . **$559.99**

## BUCK MARK PLUS UDX

*Action*: Autoloader
*Grips*: Rosewood, black laminated, or walnut Ultragrip DX ambidextrous
*Barrel*: 5.5–7.25 in.
*Sights*: Adjustable pro-target rear sight, Truglo/Marble fiber-optic front
*Weight*: 34 oz.
*Caliber*: 22 L.R.
*Capacity*: 10+1 rounds
*Features*: Matte blued, polished barrel flats; blowback action; single-action trigger
**Walnut:** . . . . . . . . . . . . . . . **$519.99**
**Rosewood:** . . . . . . . . . . . . **$519.99**
**Black laminated:** . . . . . . . . **$559.99**

## BUCK MARK PRACTICAL URX

*Action*: Autoloader
*Grips*: Ultragrip RX ambidextrous
*Barrel*: 5.5 in.
*Sights*: Pro-target adjustable rear; Truglo/Marble's fiber-optic front
*Weight*: 34 oz.
*Caliber*: .22LR
*Capacity*: 10+1 rounds
*Features*: Tapered bull barrel with matte blued finish; matte gray finish receiver
**MSRP** . . . . . . . . . . . . . . . . . **$429.99**

## BUCK MARK SERIES

*Action*: Autoloader
*Grips*: Composite, black
*Barrel*: 5.5–7.25 in.
*Sights*: Adjustable
*Weight*: 34–39 oz.
*Caliber*: .22LR
*Capacity*: 10+1 rounds
*Features*: Alloy, matte blued finish receiver; tapered barrel; blowback action; single-action trigger; URX ambidextrous grip in contour models; cocobolo, ambidextrous grip on hunter model; lite gray model has matte gray barrel finish and truglo/marble fiber-optic front sight
**Camper UFX:** . . . . . . . . . . . . **$429.99**
**Stainless UFX:** . . . . . . . . . . . **$429.99**
**Contour 5.5 URX:** . . . . . . . . **$539.99**
**Contour 7.25 URX:** . . . . . . . **$549.99**
**Hunter:** . . . . . . . . . . . . . . . **$479.99**
**Lite Gray 5.5:** . . . . . . . . . . . **$559.99**

**BROWNING HI-POWER STANDARD**

## HI-POWER STANDARD
*Action*: Autoloader
*Grips*: Select walnut, cut checkering
*Barrel*: 4.6 in.
*Sights*: Low profile fixed or adjustable with ramped front post
*Weight*: 32 oz.
*Caliber*: 9mm
*Capacity*: 10+1 rounds
*Features*: Locked breech action; single-action trigger; ambidextrous thumb safety; extra magazine; steel, polished blued finish barrel
**MSRP . . . . . . . . . .$1069.99–$1149.99**

# Charter Arms

**CHARTER ARMS .22 PATHFINDER**

**CHARTER ARMS .32 H&R UNDERCOVERETTE - PINK LADY**

**CHARTER ARMS .38 CHIC LADY DAO**

## .22 PATHFINDER
*Action*: DA revolver
*Grips*: Rubber; Crimson Trace lasergrips
*Barrel*: 2 in., 4 in., 5 in.
*Sights*: Fixed, adjustable rear on Target model
*Weight*: 19 oz.–20 oz.
*Caliber*: .22LR, .22 Mag.
*Capacity*: 6 rounds
*Features*: Stainless steel frame
**Standard:. . . . . . . . . . . . $369–$410**
**Target: . . . . . . . . . . . . . . $412–$472**
**Target Combo:. . . . . . . . . . . . $548**

## .32 H&R UNDERCOVERETTE
*Action*: DA revolver
*Grips*: Rubber; Crimson Trace lasergrips
*Barrel*: 2 in.
*Sights*: Fixed
*Weight*: 12 oz.–16 oz.
*Caliber*: .32 H&R
*Capacity*: 5 rounds
*Features*: Gun with less kick for women; standard or Crimson Trace grip; two-tone pink, stainless, gold & black, or lavender finish; high-grade cast aluminum revolver features
**Pink Lady: . . . . . . . . . . . . . . . $428**
**Gold & Black: . . . . . . . . . . . . $477**
**Lavender Lady: . . . . . . . . . . . $428**
**SS Standard: . . . . . . . . . . . . . $378**

## .38 CHIC LADY
*Action*: DA/SA, DAO revolver
*Grips*: Rubber
*Barrel*: 2 in.
*Sights*: Fixed
*Weight*: 12 oz.
*Caliber*: .38 Special
*Capacity*: 5 rounds
*Features*: High-polish stainless-steel pink anodized aluminum frame; comes in a faux alligator pink attaché case with high-polish stainless-steel trim; serrated front sight; quick-release cylinder
**DA/SA:. . . . . . . . . . . . . . . . . . $481**
**DAO: . . . . . . . . . . . . . . . . . . . $492**

# Charter Arms

**CHARTER ARMS .38 OFF DUTY HIGH POLISH**

**CHARTER ARMS .38 UNDERCOVER**

**CHARTER ARMS .38 UNDERCOVER LITE**

## .38 OFF DUTY HIGH POLISH

*Action*: DA revolver
*Grips*: Crimson Trace lasergrip
*Barrel*: 2 in.
*Sights*: Serrated front, rear notch
*Weight*: 12 oz.
*Caliber*: .38 Special +P
*Capacity*: 5 rounds
*Features*: High-polish stainless-steel finish; matte black frame; off duty model has internal DA hammer; Undercover Lite has external standard hammer
**Off Duty:**................. **$445**
**Crimson:**................. **$669**

## .38 UNDERCOVER

*Action*: DA revolver
*Grips*: Checkered compact rubber or Crimson Trace lasergrips
*Barrel*: 2 in.
*Sights*: Fixed
*Weight*: 16 oz.
*Caliber*: .38 Special +P
*Capacity*: 5 rounds
*Features*: Stainless steel frame; blued, stainless, tiger & black, OD green & black, grey/SS finishes; DAO available; Crimson Trace grips available; compact and lightweight, this revolver

is ideal for concealed carry situations; 3-point cylinder lock-up
**Blue/Black:**........... **$319–$429**
**SS:**................. **$331–$337**
**Crimson Trace:**........... **$576**

## .38 UNDERCOVER LITE

*Action*: DA revolver
*Grips*: Rubber, compact
*Barrel*: 2 in.
*Sights*: Fixed
*Weight*: 12 oz.
*Caliber*: .38 Special +P
*Capacity*: 5 rounds
*Features*: Frame is constructed from aircraft-grade aluminum and steel; traditional spurred hammer; optional DAO (double action trigger); many finishes and special editions available
**Black DAO:**............. **$428**
**Alum. Standard:**........... **$404**
**Red or Black & SS:**.......... **$422**
**Red or Bronze & Black:**...... **$422**

## .38 UNDERCOVER ON DUTY

*Action*: DA revolver
*Grips*: Rubber; Crimson Trace lasergrips
*Barrel*: 2 in.
*Sights*: Fixed
*Weight*: 12 oz.
*Caliber*: .38 Special +P
*Capacity*: 5 rounds
*Features*: Unique hammer block design; constructed of heat-treated aluminum; allows single-action and double-action operations while minimizing the risk of snagging the hammer on clothing; standard or Crimson Trace grip
**Standard:**................. **$410**
**Crimson Trace:**........... **$664**

## .44 BULLDOG HELLER COMMEMORATIVE

*Action*: DA revolver
*Grips*: Walnut
*Barrel*: 2.5 in.
*Sights*: Fixed
*Weight*: 12 oz.
*Caliber*: .44 Special
*Capacity*: 5 rounds
*Features*: This fully engraved .44 Bulldog commemorates the historic win of the U.S. Supreme Court case "Heller vs. D.C." In this case the Supreme Court struck down Washington D.C.'s handgun ban and affirmed the Second Amendment as an individual right. Only 250 models will be made. Each firearm will be packaged with an engraved knife, hardcase with etched glass top, and certificate of authenticity.
**MSRP**.................. **$1595**

**CHARTER ARMS .38 UNDERCOVER ON DUTY**

**CHARTER ARMS .44 BULLDOG HELLER COMMEMORATIVE**

## .44 SPECIAL BULLDOG

**Action**: DA revolver
**Grips**: Rubber; Crimson Trace lasergrips
**Barrel**: 2.5 in., 4 in. or 5 in. in target model
**Sights**: Fixed, adjustable rear on Target model
**Weight**: 21 oz.
**Caliber**: .44 Special
**Capacity**: 5 rounds
**Features**: Stainless steel frame; optional DAO trigger; standard hammer; stainless or blued finish
**Blued STD:** . . . . . . . . . . . . . . . **$414**
**SS STD:** . . . . . . . . . . . . . . . . . **$426**
**DAO:** . . . . . . . . . . . . . . . **$431–$465**
**Target Bulldog:** . . . . . . . . **$479–$485**
**Crimson:** . . . . . . . . . . . . . . . . . **$696**

## .357 MAG. PUG

**Action**: DA revolver
**Grips**: Rubber; Crimson Trace lasergrips
**Barrel**: 2.2 in., 4 in., 5 in.
**Sights**: Fixed, adjustable rear on Target model
**Weight**: 23 oz.
**Caliber**: .357 Mag.
**Capacity**: 5 rounds
**Features**: Traditional spurred hammer and full-size grips; optional Crimson Trace grip; stainless steel frame; blued and stainless finish
**Standard:** . . . . . . . . . . . . . . . . **$396**
**Crimson:** . . . . . . . . . . . . . . . . . **$665**
**Stainless:** . . . . . . . . . . . . . . . . **$400**
**SS DAO:** . . . . . . . . . . . . . . . . . **$404**
**Target:** . . . . . . . . . . . . . . **$479–$496**

## RIMLESS REVOLVER PITBULL

**Action**: DA/SA revolver
**Grips**: Rubber, neoprene
**Barrel**: 2.2 in., 2.3 in.
**Sights**: Fixed
**Weight**: 20 oz.–22 oz.
**Caliber**: 9mm, .40
**Capacity**: 5, 6 rounds
**Features**: Dual coil spring assembly; stainless steel frame; 9mm has spurred hammer, .40 has standard hammer
**9mm:** . . . . . . . . . . . . . . . . . . . **$465**
**.40:** . . . . . . . . . . . . . . . . . . . . **$465**

**CHARTER ARMS .44 SPECIAL BULLDOG**

**CHARTER ARMS .357 MAG. PUG**

**CHARTER ARMS RIMLESS REVOLVER PITBULL**

# Cimarron Firearms Co.

CIMARRON 1872 OPEN TOP NAVY

## 1872 OPEN TOP NAVY

**Action**: SA revolver
**Grips**: Walnut
**Barrel**: 4.75 in., 5.5 in., 7.5 in.
**Sights**: Fixed, open
**Weight**: 40 oz.
**Caliber**: .44 Special; .44 Colt & Russian, .45 Schofield, .45 Colt, .38 Colt & Special
**Capacity**: 6 rounds
**Features**: Forged, color case-hardened frame; Army or Navy grip; charcoal blued, standard blued, or original barrel finish
**MSRP**. . . . . . . . . . **$492.70–$627.91**

## 1911 .45 ACP

**Action**: Semi-automatic
**Grips**: Walnut
**Barrel**: 5 in.
**Sights**: Open, fixed
**Weight**: 39.52 oz.
**Caliber**: .45 ACP
**Capacity**: 8+1 rounds
**Features**: Next generation of firearm widely used in the First World War. Correct historical markings; diamond checkered walnt grips; nickel, polished high luster blued, and standard parkerized finish; optional World War I-style lanyard magazine
**MSRP**. . . . . . . . . . **$540.80–$633.10**

CIMARRON BISLEY MODEL

CIMARRON GEORGE ARMSTRONG CUSTER 7TH U.S. CAVALRY MODEL

## BISLEY MODEL

**Action**: SA revolver
**Grips**: Walnut
**Barrel**: 4.75 in., 5.5 in., 7.5 in.
**Sights**: Fixed, open
**Weight**: 4.3–44 oz.
**Caliber**: .45 LC, .44 Special, .44 WCF, .357 Mag.
**Capacity**: 6 rounds
**Features**: Reproduction of the original Colt Bisley; forged, color case-hardened frame; blued, charcoal blued, or nickel finish
**MSRP**. . . . . . . . . . . . . . . . . **$596.70**

## GEORGE ARMSTRONG CUSTER 7TH U.S. CAVALRY MODEL

**Action**: SA revolver
**Grips**: Walnut
**Barrel**: 7.5 in.
**Sights**: Fixed, open
**Weight**: 4.4 oz.
**Caliber**: .45 LC
**Capacity**: 6 rounds
**Features**: Old model case-hardened with 7th Cavalry markings; made with 1 piece of walnut with OWA (Ainsworth) Cartouche; blued, charcoal blued or nickel barrel finish
**MSRP**. . . . . . . . . . **$583.70–$770.90**

# Cimarron Firearms Co.

**CIMARRON HOLY SMOKER**

**CIMARRON LIGHTNING**

**CIMARRON MAN WITH NO NAME**

**CIMARRON MODEL P**

## HOLY SMOKER
*Action*: SA revolver
*Grips*: Walnut
*Barrel*: 4.75 in.
*Sights*: Open, fixed
*Weight*: 36 oz.
*Caliber*: .45 Colt
*Capacity*: 6 rounds
*Features*: Revolver made famous in *3:10 to Yuma* film; standard blued finish; case-hardened pre-war frame; gold-plated sterling silver cross inlayed on both sides of one-piece walnut grip
**MSRP . . . . . . . . . . . . . . . . .$760.50**

## LIGHTNING
*Action*: SA revolver
*Grips*: Walnut
*Barrel*: 3.5 in., 4.75 in., 5.5 in., 6.5 in.
*Sights*: Fixed, open
*Weight*: 28.5–30.75 oz.
*Caliber*: .38 Special, .22LR, .41 Colt, 32-20/.32 H&R Dual Cylinder
*Capacity*: 6 rounds
*Features*: Forged, pre-war color case-hardened frame; charcoal blued, standard blued, or original barrel finish; walnut stock smooth or checkered
**MSRP . . . . . . . . . . $487.50–$609.70**

## MAN WITH NO NAME
*Action*: SA revolver
*Grips*: Walnut
*Barrel*: 4.75 in., 5.5 in.
*Sights*: Open, fixed
*Weight*: 42.56 oz.–44.16 oz.
*Caliber*: .45 Colt
*Capacity*: 6 rounds
*Features*: Model P in .45 Colt; sterling silver snake on both sides of walnut grip; conversion version available in .38 Special/.38 Colt
**MSRP . . . . . . . . . . $773.50–$817.70**

## MODEL P
*Action*: SA revolver
*Grips*: Walnut
*Barrel*: 4.75 in., 5.5 in., 7.5 in.
*Sights*: None
*Weight*: 44 oz.
*Caliber*: 32 WCF, 38 WCF, .357 Mag., .44 WCF, .44 Special, .45 LC; .45LC/.45 ACP Dual Cylinder
*Capacity*: 6 rounds
*Features*: Fashioned after the 1873 Colt SAA; standard blued, charcoal blued, or original finish; available in old model or pre-war (new) model
**MSRP . . . . . . . . . . $519.87–$630.50**

# Cimarron Firearms Co.

CIMARRON MODEL P JR

CIMARRON NEW SHERIFF MODEL

CIMARRON ROOSTER SHOOTER

CIMARRON THUNDERER

## MODEL P JR.

*Action*: SA revolver
*Grips*: Walnut
*Barrel*: 3.5 in., 4.75 in., 5.5 in.
*Sights*: Fixed, open
*Weight*: 35.2 oz.
*Caliber*: .41 Colt, .38 Special, .22LR, .41 Colt, .32-20/.32 H&R Dual Cylinder
*Capacity*: 6 rounds
*Features*: Fashioned after the 1873 Colt SAA but on a smaller scale; color case-hardened frame; blue, charcoal blue, or nickel finish
**MSRP** . . . . . . . . . . **$438.10–$583.70**

## NEW SHERIFF MODEL

*Action*: SA revolver
*Grips*: Walnut, black hard rubber
*Barrel*: 3.5 in.
*Sights*: Fixed, open
*Weight*: 33.5 oz.
*Caliber*: .45 LC, .44 WCF, .357 Mag.
*Capacity*: 6 rounds
*Features*: Forged, color case-hardened frame; standard blued barrel finish
**MSRP** . . . . . . . . . . . . . . . . . **$519.87**

## ROOSTER SHOOTER

*Action*: SA revolver
*Grips*: Orange finger
*Barrel*: 4.75 in.
*Sights*: Open, fixed
*Weight*: 36.68 oz.–40.48 oz.
*Caliber*: .357/.38 Spl., .45 Colt, .44 W.C.F.
*Capacity*: 6 rounds
*Features*: Replica of John Wayne's Colt Single Action
**MSRP** . . . . . . . . . . . . . . . . . **$882.70**

## THUNDERER

*Action*: SA revolver
*Grips*: Walnut, ivory, mother of pearl or black hard rubber
*Barrel*: 3.5 in. w/ ejector, 4.75 in., 5.5 in., 7.5 in.
*Sights*: Fixed, open
*Weight*: 38–43.60 oz.
*Caliber*: .45 LC, .44 Special, 44WCF, .357 Mag., .45LC/45 ACP Dual Cylinder
*Capacity*: 6 rounds
*Features*: Designed in 1990 by Cimarron founder & president "Texas Jack" Harvey; forged, color case-hardened frame; blued, charcoal blued or nickel finish
**MSRP** . . . . . . . . . . **$544.70–$698.60**

# Cimarron Firearms Co.

**CIMARRON THUNDERSTORM**

**CIMARRON TITAN DERRINGER,
POLISHED STAINLESS STEEL**

**CIMARRON U.S.V. ARTILLERY MODEL**

**CIMARRON WYATT EARP BUNTLINE**

## THUNDERSTORM

*Action*: SA revolver
*Grips*: Walnut
*Barrel*: 3.5 in., 4.75 in.
*Sights*: Front, rear
*Weight*: 35.7 oz.–39.68 oz.
*Caliber*: .45 Colt, .357/.38 Sp.
*Capacity*: 6 rounds
*Features*: Checkered grips; stainless steel or standard blued finishes; wide front sights and deep rear notch; smooth action and hand-knurled hammer; available in Model P or Thunderer versions
**MSRP . . . . . . . . . . $713.70–$986.70**

## TITAN DERRINGER

*Action*: SA revolver
*Grips*: Rosewood
*Barrel*: 3.5 in., 4.75 in.
*Sights*: Open, fixed
*Weight*: 16.4 oz.
*Caliber*: .45 LC/.410, 9mm
*Capacity*: 2 rounds
*Features*: Largest of Cimarron's pocket pistols; available in polished, brushed, or black stainless steel
**MSRP . . . . . . . . . . . . . . . . $427.70**

## U.S.V. ARTILLERY MODEL

*Action*: SA revolver
*Grips*: Walnut
*Barrel*: 5.5 in.
*Sights*: Fixed, open
*Weight*: 40 oz.
*Caliber*: .45 LC
*Capacity*: 6 rounds
*Features*: Old model case-hardened with U.S. Artillery markings; stock is a solid piece of walnut with RAC Cartouche; blued, charcoal blued, or original finish
**MSRP . . . . . . . . . . . . . . . . $583.70**

## WYATT EARP BUNTLINE

*Action*: SA revolver
*Grips*: Walnut
*Barrel*: 10 in.
*Sights*: Open, fixed
*Weight*: 43.04 oz.
*Caliber*: .45 LC
*Capacity*: 6 rounds
*Features*: Revolver made famous in the film *Tombstone*; old model case-hardened; walnut grip hand cast in solid sterling silver and hand inlaid into stock; standard blued or original finish
**MSRP . . . . . . . . . . $856.70–$881.40**

# Citadel by Legacy Sports

## M-1911

**Action**: Semi-automatic
**Grips**: Full size or compact, wood, or Hogue synthetic grips
**Barrel**: 3.5 in., 5 in.
**Sights**: Fixed
**Weight**: 33.6–37.6 oz.
**Caliber**: 9mm, .45 ACP, .38 Super
**Capacity**: 7 or 8 rounds, 2 magazines
**Features**: Available in compact and full sized models; matte black, brush nickel, or polished nickel finish; optional Hogue wrap around grip in black, green, or sand; comes with lockable, hard plastic case; Wounded Warrior Project model includes laser cut wood grips with WWP insignia and inscription "Never Forget" and engraved commemorative slide
**MSRP** . . . . . . . . . . . . . . . . **$589–$699**
**Wounded Warrior:** . . . . . . . . **$840**

CITADEL M-1911 PISTOLS

## M-1911 .22 G.I.

**Action**: SA autoloader
**Grips**: Wood
**Barrel**: 5 in.
**Sights**: G.I. standard
**Weight**: 33.6 oz.
**Caliber**: .22 LR
**Capacity**: 10 rounds
**Features**: Alloy and steel parts; standard G.I. sights; two-piece wooden grip panels
**MSRP** . . . . . . . . . . . . . . . . . . . **$310**

CITADEL M-1911 .22 G.I.

CITADEL M-1911 .22 TACTICAL

## M-1911 .22 TAC

**Action**: SA autoloader
**Grips**: Rubber
**Barrel**: 5 in.
**Sights**: Fiber optic
**Weight**: 33.6 oz.
**Caliber**: .22 LR
**Capacity**: 10 rounds
**Features**: Fixed barrel and blowback action; alloy and steel parts; one-piece wrap around rubber grip from Hogue; fiber optic front and rear sights; two magazines
**MSRP** . . . . . . . . . . . . . . . . . . . **$349**

# Colt's Manufacturing Company

## .380 MUSTANG POCKETLITE

*Action*: SA
*Grips*: Composite
*Barrel*: 2.75 in.
*Sights*: High-profile
*Weight*: 12.5 oz.
*Caliber*: .380 ACP
*Capacity*: 6+1 rounds
*Features*: Aluminum alloy frame
with a CNC-machined stainless steel slide and barrel;
thumb safety and firing-pin-block safety; solid
aluminum trigger; lowered ejection port; electroless
nickeled aluminum receiver
MSRP . . . . . . . . . . . . . . . . . . . $649

COLT .380 MUSTANG POCKETLITE

## 1991 SERIES

*Action*: Autoloader
*Grips*: Rosewood or composite
*Barrel*: 5 in.
*Sights*: Fixed
*Weight*: 39 oz.
*Caliber*: .45 ACP
*Capacity*: 7+1 rounds
*Features*: Beveled magazine well; single- and double-
action; carbon steel, aluminum alloy, or stainless steel
frame; standard or beavertail grip safety; blued, black
anodized, brushed stainless steel, bright stainless steel
frame finish
MSRP . . . . . . . . . . . . . . $928–$1311

COLT 1991 SERIES

## DEFENDER

*Action*: Autoloader
*Grips*: Rubber finger-grooved
*Barrel*: 5 in.
*Sights*: White dot carry front and rear
*Weight*: 30 oz.
*Caliber*: .45 ACP
*Capacity*: 7+1 rounds
*Features*: Beveled magazine well; black skeletonized
aluminum trigger; series 80 firing system; beavertail grip
and standard thumb safety; stainless steel slide, Teflon
coated receiver; aluminum alloy frame
MSRP . . . . . . . . . . . . . . . . . . . $1066

COLT DEFENDER

# Colt's Manufacturing Company

**COLT GOLD CUP TROPHY**

**COLT NEW AGENT DAO**

**COLT NEW FRONTIER**

## GOLD CUP SERIES

**Action**: Autoloader
**Grips**: Black composite
**Barrel**: 5 in.
**Sights**: Dovetail front, adjustable rear
**Weight**: 39 oz.
**Caliber**: .45ACP
**Capacity**: 8+1 rounds
**Features**: Beveled magazine well; beavertail grip safety; black wrap around grips; wide aluminum 3-Hole trigger adjustable for over travel; stainless steel frame finish and material; enhanced hammer
**MSRP** . . . . . . . . . . . . . **$1158–$1180**

## NEW AGENT

**Action**: SA or DAO autoloader
**Grips**: Rosewood, Crimson Trace
**Barrel**: 3 in.
**Sights**: Trench style
**Weight**: 39 oz.
**Caliber**: .45 ACP, 9mm
**Capacity**: 7+1, 8+1 rounds
**Features**: Single-action or .45 ACP double action only; black anodized frame with beveled magazine well; front strap serrations
**MSRP** . . . . . . . . . . . . . **$1041–$1326**

## NEW FRONTIER

**Action**: SA revolver
**Grips**: Walnut stock with gold medallions
**Barrel**: 4.75 in., 5.5 in., 7.5 in.
**Sights**: Ramp style front; adjustable rear
**Weight**: 46 oz.
**Caliber**: .357 Mag., .44 special, .45 Colt
**Capacity**: 6 rounds
**Features**: Royal blued barrel and cylinder; flat top case colored frame
**MSRP** . . . . . . . . . . . . . . . . . **$1455**

# Colt's Manufacturing Company

## SERIES 70

**Action**: Autoloader
**Grips**: Double diamond rosewood grips
**Barrel**: 5 in.
**Sights**: Fixed
**Weight**: 39 oz.
**Caliber**: .45 ACP
**Capacity**: 7+1 rounds
**Features**: Spur hammer; single-action; blued or brushed steel finish; carbon steel or stainless steel frame; short steel trigger; original series 70 firing system with titanium firing pin
**Blued**: . . . . . . . . . . . . . . . . . $1043
**Brushed Steel**: . . . . . . . . . . . $1078

## SINGLE ACTION ARMY

**Action**: SA revolver
**Grips**: Black composite eagle grips
**Barrel**: 4.75 in., 5.5 in., 7.5 in.
**Sights**: Fixed
**Weight**: 46 oz.
**Caliber**: .32/20, .38 Special, .38/40, .357 Mag., .44/40, .45 Colt
**Capacity**: 6 rounds
**Features**: Case-colored frame; transfer bar; 2nd generation style cylinder bushing; features 175th anniversary rollmark; blued or nickel finish
**MSRP** . . . . . . . . . . . . . . . $1349–$1551

## XSE SERIES

**Action**: Autoloader
**Grips**: Checkered, double diamond rosewood
**Barrel**: 5 in.
**Sights**: Fixed
**Weight**: 39 oz.
**Caliber**: .45 ACP
**Capacity**: 8+1 rounds
**Features**: Front and rear slide serrations; extended ambidextrous thumb safeties; enhanced hammer; new roll marking and enhanced tolerances; single-action; white-dot carry sights; beavertail safety grip; blued, brushed stainless steel, Teflon coated, or black anodized finish; carbon steel, stainless steel or aluminum alloy frame
**MSRP** . . . . . . . . . . . . . . $1072–$1223

## RAIL GUN

**Action**: Autoloader
**Grips**: Double diamond rosewood or blackened rosewood grips
**Barrel**: 5 in.
**Sights**: White dot, Novak rear
**Weight**: 39 oz.
**Caliber**: .45 ACP
**Capacity**: 8+1 rounds
**Features**: Stainless steel, blackened receiver and brushed slide, blackened receiver and slide frame finish options; stainless steel frame material; Colt upswept beavertail with palm swell; enhanced hammer; M1913 Picatinny rail; National Match barrel; single-slide tactical thumb safety
**MSRP** . . . . . . . . . . . . . . $1141–$1223

**COLT RAIL GUN**

**COLT SERIES 70**

**COLT SINGLE ACTION ARMY**

**COLT XSE SERIES**

# CZ-USA (Ceska Zbrojovka)

**CZ 75 B**

**CZ 75 COMPACT**

**CZ 75 SHADOW**

**CZ 75 SHADOW CTS LS-P**

**CZ 75 SHADOW T**

## 75 B
**Action**: Autoloader
**Grips**: Plastic
**Barrel**: 4.6 in.
**Sights**: Fixed, 3-dot system
**Weight**: 35.2 oz.
**Caliber**: .40 S&W, 9mm
**Capacity**: .40 S&W: 10 rounds, 9mm: 16 rounds
**Features**: Steel frame; high capacity double column magazines; hammer forged barrels; ergonomic grip and controls; double-action or single-action; firing pin block safety; black polycoat finish
**.40 S&W:** . . . . . . . . . . . . . . . . . **$569**
**9mm:** . . . . . . . . . . . . . . . . . . **$499**

## 75 COMPACT
**Action**: Autoloader
**Grips**: Plastic
**Barrel**: 3.8 in.
**Sights**: Fixed, 3-dot system
**Weight**: 32.48 oz.
**Caliber**: 9mm Luger
**Capacity**: 14 rounds

**Features**: Black polycoat, dual tone, satin nickel frame finishes; manual safety; steel frame; high capacity double column magazines; hammer forged barrels
**Black polycoat:** . . . . . . . . . . . **$528**

## 75 SHADOW
**Action**: DA/SA
**Grips**: Rubber
**Barrel**: 4.61 in.
**Sights**: Fixed
**Weight**: 39 oz.
**Caliber**: 9mm
**Capacity**: 18+1 rounds
**Features**: Full package of Custom Shop competition features; Shadow fixed rear sight; fiber optic front sight; black polycoat finish; two magazines included
**MSRP** . . . . . . . . . . . . . . . . . . . **$1053**

## 75 SHADOW CTS LS-P
**Action**: DA/SA
**Grips**: Textured
**Barrel**: 5.4 in.

**Sights**: Adjustable rear
**Weight**: N/A
**Caliber**: 9mm
**Capacity**: 18+1 rounds
**Features**: Long-slide version of the 75 Shadow; fully adjustable Champion rear sight; black frame and blued slide; two magazines included
**MSRP** . . . . . . . . . . . . . . . . . . **$1450**

## 75 SHADOW T
**Action**: DA/SA
**Grips**: Rubber
**Barrel**: 4.61 in.
**Sights**: Adjustable rear, fiber optic front
**Weight**: 39 oz.
**Caliber**: 9mm
**Capacity**: 18+1 rounds
**Features**: Black rubber grips; adjustable Champion rear sight; fiber optic front sight; black polycoat finish
**MSRP** . . . . . . . . . . . . . . . . . . **$1180**

# CZ-USA (Ceska Zbrojovka)

CZ 75 SP-01

CZ 75 TS CZECHMATE

CZ 75 SP-01
SHADOW TARGET

CZ 97 B

## 75 SP-01

*Action*: Autoloader
*Grips*: Rubber
*Barrel*: 4.6 in.
*Sights*: 3-Dot tritium night
*Weight*: 38.4 oz.
*Caliber*: 9mm Luger
*Capacity*: 18 rounds
*Features*: Based upon the Shadow Target; decocking lever; safety stop on hammer; firing pin safety; steel frame
**MSRP** . . . . . . . . . . . . . . . . . . **$660**

## 75 SP-01 SHADOW TARGET

*Action*: Autoloader
*Grips*: Cocobolo wood
*Barrel*: 4.6 in.
*Sights*: Competition style, fiber optic
*Weight*: 38.4 oz.

*Caliber*: 9mm
*Capacity*: 18 rounds
*Features*: Single- or double-action; manual safety; steel frame; TRT rear sight; competition springs; CZ custom stainless guide rod
**MSRP** . . . . . . . . . . . . . . . . . . **$1321**

## 75 TS CZECHMATE

*Action*: Autoloader
*Grips*: Aluminum
*Barrel*: 5.4 in.
*Sights*: Fixed, C-more red dot
*Weight*: 48 oz.
*Caliber*: 9mm
*Capacity*: 20 or 26 rounds
*Features*: Built upon a modified version of the CZ 75 TS frame; interchangeable parts allow the user to quickly configure the gun for both

roles; features a single-action trigger mechanism; red-dot sight; includes spare barrel; includes three 20-round magazines and one 26-round magazine; all-steel pistol is finished in black matte
**MSRP** . . . . . . . . . . . . . . . . . . **$3220**

## 97 B

*Action*: Autoloader
*Grips*: Plastic
*Barrel*: 4.8 in.
*Sights*: Fixed
*Weight*: 40 oz.
*Caliber*: .45 ACP
*Capacity*: 10 rounds
*Features*: Manual safety; cold hammer-forged barrel; single- or double-action
**Black polycoat**: . . . . . . . . . . . . **$686**
**Glossy blued**: . . . . . . . . . . . . . **$713**

# CZ-USA (Ceska Zbrojovka)

**CZ 2075 RAMI**

## 2075 RAMI

**Action**: Autoloader
**Grips**: Rubber
**Barrel**: 3 in.
**Sights**: Fixed
**Weight**: 25.6 oz.
**Caliber**: .40 S&W, 9mm Luger
**Capacity**: .40 S&W: 7 or 9 rounds, 9mm: 14 rounds
**Features**: Operates in selective DA and SA mode depending on shooter's preferences; firing pin block; manual safety; double-stack magazine; black polycoat alloy frame; cold hammer forged
**.40 S&W:** . . . . . . . . . . . . . . . . **$615**
**9mm Luger:** . . . . . . . . . . . . . . **$595**

## P-01

**Action**: Autoloader
**Grips**: Rubber
**Barrel**: 3.8 in.
**Sights**: Fixed
**Weight**: 28.8 oz.
**Caliber**: 9mm Luger
**Capacity**: 14 rounds
**Features**: Decocking lever; safety stop on hammer; firing pin safety; black polycoat frame finish; black or pink grips; single- or double-action
**MSRP** . . . . . . . . . . . . . . . . . . . **$608**

**CZ P-01**

## P-07 DUTY

**Action**: DA/SA autoloader
**Grips**: Polymer
**Barrel**: 3.8 in.
**Sights**: Fixed
**Weight**: 27.2 oz.
**Caliber**: .40 S&W, 9mm Luger
**Capacity**: .40 S&W: 12 rounds, 9mm: 16 rounds
**Features**: Omega double- or single-action trigger; cold-hammer-forged barrel; accessory rail and two magazines included; 9mm available in black or green poly frame; threaded barrel to accept sound suppressor available; elevated sights to clear sound suppressor
**.40 S&W:** . . . . . . . . . . . . . . . . **$496**
**9mm:** . . . . . . . . . . . . . . . . **$483–$528**
**9mm (OD Green):** . . . . . . . . . **$489**

**CZ P-07 DUTY**

# Dan Wesson Firearms

## ECO

**Action**: SA semiautomatic
**Grips**: Composite
**Barrel**: 3.5 in.
**Sights**: Fixed tritium
**Weight**: 25 oz.
**Caliber**: 9mm, .45 ACP
**Capacity**: 7+1 rounds
**Features**: Single-stack Officer's size 1991; aluminum alloy frame; undercut trigger guards; 25 lpi checkering; mainspring housing is aluminum with 25 lpi checkering; Ed Brown high rise grip safety; forged steel slide; tritium night sights with tactical ledge rear sight; flush cut ramped bull barrel with target crown
**9mm:** . . . . . . . . . . . . . . . . . . $1623
**.45 ACP:** . . . . . . . . . . . . . . . . $1662

## GUARDIAN

**Action**: SA autoloader
**Grips**: Stippled shadow
**Barrel**: 4.25 in.
**Sights**: Novak low mount style, night
**Weight**: 28.8 oz.
**Caliber**: .45 ACP, 9mm
**Capacity**: 8 rounds
**Features**: Bobtail alloy frame; aluminum alloy frame; commander length barrel; finished in matte black with tritium sights
**.45:** . . . . . . . . . . . . . . . . . $1619
**9mm:** . . . . . . . . . . . . . . . . . $1558

## RAZORBACK R2-10

**Action**: SA semiautomatic
**Grips**: Diamond-checkered cocobolo
**Barrel**: 5 in.
**Sights**: Fixed
**Weight**: 38.4 oz.
**Caliber**: 10mm
**Capacity**: 9 rounds
**Features**: Razorback is back in 2012 in limited quantities; serrated Clark-style target rib; 1911 model; stainless steel frame; manual thumb safety, grip safety
**MSRP** . . . . . . . . . . . . . . . . . $1350

## SPECIALIST

**Action**: SA semiautomatic
**Grips**: G10 VZ Operator II grips
**Barrel**: 5 in.
**Sights**: Fixed tritium
**Weight**: 37 oz.
**Caliber**: .45 ACP
**Capacity**: 8+1 rounds

DAN WESSON ECO

DAN WESSON GUARDIAN

DAN WESSON RAZORBACK

DAN WESSON SPECIALIST

DAN WESSON VALOR

**Features**: Full size single-stack pistol; matte stainless steel or black Duty finishes; forged slide and frame; Clark-style serrated rib with tritium dual-colored night sights stacked in a straight eight-type pattern; tactical ledge rear sight with single rear amber dot and green front with white target ring; 1913 Picatinny rail; undercut trigger guard with 25 lpi front strap checkering; ambidextrous thumb safety; two magazines with bumper pads included
**SS:** . . . . . . . . . . . . . . . . . . . $1558
**Black:** . . . . . . . . . . . . . . . . . . $1870

## VALOR

**Action**: SA autoloader
**Grips**: Slim line G10
**Barrel**: 5 in.
**Sights**: Heinie Ledge straight eight night
**Weight**: 35.2 oz.
**Caliber**: .45 ACP
**Capacity**: 8 rounds
**Features**: Matte black duty receiver finish; manual thumb safety; forged stainless steel frame
**SS:** . . . . . . . . . . . . . . . . . . . $1701
**Black:** . . . . . . . . . . . . . . . . . . $2012

# Ed Brown

ED BROWN EXECUTIVE CARRY

ED BROWN CLASSIC CUSTOM

ED BROWN KOBRA

ED BROWN EXECUTIVE ELITE

## CLASSIC CUSTOM

**Action**: Autoloader
**Grips**: Cocobolo wood
**Barrel**: 5 in.
**Sights**: Adjustable rear, cross dovetail front
**Weight**: 40 oz.
**Caliber**: .45 ACP
**Capacity**: 7+1 rounds
**Features**: Single-action; single-stack government model frame; special mirror finished side; two-piece guide rod for smoother cycling and easier disassembly; stainless or blued finish
**MSRP** . . . . . . . . . . . . . . . . . . $3495

## EXECUTIVE CARRY

**Action**: Autoloader
**Grips**: Checkered cocobolo wood
**Barrel**: 4.25 in.
**Sights**: Fixed, night
**Weight**: 35 oz.
**Caliber**: .45 ACP
**Capacity**: 7+1 rounds
**Features**: Frame modified with an innovative Ed Brown Bobtail; stainless or blued frame finish with stainless, black or blued slide finish; fixed dovetail 3-dot night sights with high visibility white outlines
**MSRP** . . . . . . . . . . . . . . . . . . $2945

## EXECUTIVE ELITE

**Action**: Autoloader
**Grips**: Checkered cocobolo wood
**Barrel**: 5 in.
**Sights**: Fixed, night
**Weight**: 38 oz.

**Caliber**: .45 ACP
**Capacity**: 7+1 rounds
**Features**: Single-stack government model frame; matte finished slide for low glare, with traditional square cut serrations on rear of slide only; blued or stainless finish
**MSRP** . . . . . . . . . . . . . . . . . . $2695

## KOBRA

**Action**: Autoloader
**Grips**: Cocobolo wood
**Barrel**: 5 in.

**Sights**: Fixed, night
**Weight**: 38 oz.
**Caliber**: .45 ACP
**Capacity**: 7+1 rounds
**Features**: Single-stack government model frame; John Browning traditional design; exclusive snakeskin treatment on forestrap and mainspring housing; matte finished slide for low glare; 3-dot night sights with high visibility white outlines; blued or stainless finish
**MSRP** . . . . . . . . . . . . . . . . . . $2495

# Ed Brown

## KOBRA CARRY LIGHTWEIGHT

*Action*: Autoloader
*Grips*: Cocobolo wood
*Barrel*: 4.25 in.
*Sights*: Fixed dovetail front night with high visibility white outlines
*Weight*: 27 oz.
*Caliber*: .45 ACP
*Capacity*: 7+1 rounds
*Features*: Lightweight aluminum frame and Bobtail housing; all other components are steel; exclusive snakeskin treatment on forestrap and housing; matte finished Gen III coated slide for low glare
**MSRP** . . . . . . . . . . . . . . . . . . . **$3120**

ED BROWN KOBRA CARRY LIGHTWEIGHT

ED BROWN SIGNATURE EDITION

## SIGNATURE EDITION

*Action*: Autoloader
*Grips*: Cocobolo wood
*Barrel*: 5 in.
*Sights*: Adjustable rear, cross dovetail front
*Weight*: 40 oz.

*Caliber*: .45 ACP
*Capacity*: 7+1 rounds
*Features*: The Ed Brown Signature Edition is based on our timeless Classic Custom pistol, with hand relief engraving by our master engraver; single stack government model frame; special mirror finished slide; 50 lpi serrations on back of slide to match serrated adjustable sight; hand relief engraved package; adjustable rear sight buried deep into slide; cross dovetail front sight; blued metal parts
**MSRP** . . . . . . . . . . . . . . . . . . . **$7195**

# E.M.F. Company

E.M.F. GREAT WESTERN II
ALCHIMISTA II

## GREAT WESTERN II ALCHIMISTA II

*Action*: SA revolver
*Grips*: Walnut
*Barrel*: 4.75 in., 5.5 in.
*Sights*: Fixed
*Weight*: 33.6 oz.
*Caliber*: .357, .45 LC
*Capacity*: 6 rounds
*Features*: Standard case-hardening; stainless steel; checkered walnut grips; express grips available
**MSRP** . . . . . . . . . . . . . . . . . . . **$650**

# E.M.F. Company

**E.M.F. GREAT WESTERN II CALIFORNIAN**

**E.M.F. GREAT WESTERN II PONY EXPRESS**

## GREAT WESTERN II CALIFORNIAN

*Action*: SA revolver
*Grips*: Walnut
*Barrel*: 4.75 in., 5.5 in., 7.5 in.
*Sights*: Fixed
*Weight*: 48 oz.
*Caliber*: .22LR, .357, .44 Mag., .44/40, .45 LC
*Capacity*: 6 rounds
*Features*: Standard case-hardening; steel frame
**MSRP** . . . . . . . . . . . . . . . . . . . **$530**

## GREAT WESTERN II PONY EXPRESS

*Action*: SA revolver
*Grips*: Walnut express grips
*Barrel*: 3.5 in.
*Sights*: Fixed
*Weight*: 32 oz.
*Caliber*: .357, .45 LC
*Capacity*: 6 rounds
*Features*: Case-hardened steel; checkered walnut express grips; turned down hammer
**MSRP** . . . . . . . . . . . . . . . **$625–$820**

# Entréprise Arms

## ELITE

*Action*: Autoloader
*Grips*: Composite
*Barrel*: 3.25 in., 4.25 in., or 5 in.
*Sights*: Fixed
*Weight*: 36–40 oz.
*Caliber*: .45 ACP
*Capacity*: 10 or 14 rounds
*Features*: Three Hi-visible dot sight; black oxide finish; extended thumb lock; match grade disconnector with polished contact points; hardened steel magazine release; adjustable anti-lash match trigger
**MSRP** . . . . . . . . . . . . . . . . . . **$749**

**ENTRÉPRISE ARMS ELITE**

**ENTRÉPRISE ARMS MEDALIST**

## MEDALIST

*Action*: Autoloader
*Grips*: Composite
*Barrel*: 5 in.
*Sights*: Fixed
*Weight*: 40 oz.
*Caliber*: .40 Cal., .45 ACP
*Capacity*: 10 or 14 rounds
*Features*: Wide body frame; adjustable

Anti-lash match trigger; High Ride beavertail grip safety; 4140 Chromoly steel firing pin; match extractor
**MSRP** . . . . . . . . . . . . . . . . . . **$999**

**EUROPEAN AMERICAN ARMORY BOUNTY HUNTER**

**EUROPEAN AMERICAN ARMORY WITNESS - POLYMER**

**EUROPEAN AMERICAN ARMORY WITNESS COMPACT - STEEL**

**EUROPEAN AMERICAN ARMORY WITNESS HUNTER**

## BOUNTY HUNTER

*Action*: SA revolver
*Grips*: Walnut
*Barrel*: 4.5 in., 6.75 in., 7.5 in.
*Sights*: Fixed, open
*Weight*: 39–41 oz.
*Caliber*: .44 Mag., .22LR/.22WMR, 45LC
*Capacity*: 6 or 8 rounds
*Features*: Transfer bar safety; steel or alloy frame; blued, silver, case color, or blued/ivory finish
**Nickel:** . . . . . . . . . . . . . . . **$354–$480**
**Blued:** . . . . . . . . . . . . . . . **$320–$452**
**Case Color:** . . . . . . . . . . **$446–$448**

## WITNESS

*Action*: Autoloader
*Grips*: Rubber
*Barrel*: 4.5 in.
*Sights*: 3-Dot
*Weight*: 33 oz.

*Caliber*: 9mm, .38 Super, .40 S&W, 10mm, .45ACP, 45/22, 9/22
*Capacity*: 10+1, 15+1, or 17+1 rounds
*Features*: Wonder finish, windage adjustable sight; double- or single-action; polymer or steel frame; integral accessory rail
**Polymer:** . . . . . . . . . . . . . . . . **$525**
**Steel:** . . . . . . . . . . . . . . . . . . **$557**
**Combo:** . . . . . . . . . . . . . . . . . **$691**

## WITNESS COMPACT

*Action*: Autoloader
*Grips*: Rubber
*Barrel*: 3.6 in.
*Sights*: Adjustable
*Weight*: 30 oz.
*Caliber*: 9mm, .38 Super, .40 S&W, 10mm, .45ACP
*Capacity*: 8+1, 12+1, or 14+1 rounds
*Features*: Wonder finish, windage adjustable sight; double- or single-

action; polymer or steel frame; integral accessory rail; blued finish
**Polymer:** . . . . . . . . . . . . . . . . **$525**
**Steel:** . . . . . . . . . . . . . . . . . . **$557**

## WITNESS HUNTER

*Action*: Autoloader
*Grips*: Rubber
*Barrel*: 6 in.
*Sights*: Dovetail front
*Weight*: 41 oz.
*Caliber*: 10mm, .45 ACP
*Capacity*: 10+1 or 15+1 rounds
*Features*: Single-action with over travel stop; extended manual safety; super sight; cone barrel, slide lockup; checkered non-slip frame; drilled and tapped for scope mount; auto-firing pin block
**MSRP** . . . . . . . . . . . . . . . . . . **$1187**

# FNH USA

**FNH FN FIVE-SEVEN SERIES**

**FNH FNS-9**

**FNH FNX-9**

**FNH FNX-45 TACTICAL**

## FN FIVE-SEVEN SERIES

*Action*: SA autoloader
*Grips*: Plastic
*Barrel*: 4.8 in.
*Sights*: Adjustable 3-dot
*Weight*: 20.8 oz.
*Caliber*: 5.7x28mm
*Capacity*: 10 or 20 round magazines
*Features*: Integrated accessory rail for mounting tactical lights or lasers; reversible magazine button; ambidextrous manual safety levers; hammer-forged, chrome lined barrel; choice of adjustable three-dot target sights or fixed C-More Systems; available with matte black, olive drab green, or flat dark earth
**MSRP. . . . . . . . . . . . . . . . . . . $1329**

## FNS-9/FNS-40

*Action*: DA autoloader
*Grips*: Polymer
*Barrel*: 4 in.
*Sights*: Night sights
*Weight*: 25.2 oz.
*Caliber*: 9mm, .40 S&W
*Capacity*: 17 (FNS-9), 14 (FNS-40) rounds
*Features*: Striker-fired autoloader; manual safety levers; stainless steel slide in matte black or silver finish; external extractor with loaded chamber indicator; three-dot night sights; hammer-forged stainless steel barrel; black polymer frame; fully ambidextrous
**MSRP. . . . . . . . . . . . . . . . . . . $699**
**Night Sights: . . . . . . . . . . . . . . $749**

## FNX-9/FNX-40

*Action*: Autoloader
*Grips*: Interchangeable backstraps with lanyard eyelets
*Barrel*: 4 in.
*Sights*: 3-Dot system
*Weight*: 21.9 oz. (9mm), 24.4 oz. (.40)
*Caliber*: 9mm and .40 S&W
*Capacity*: 17 (9mm), 14 (.40)
*Features*: Ergonomic polymer black frame with low bore axis; checkered and ribbed grip panels; stainless steel slide and hammer-forged stainless barrel; DA/SA ambidextrous operating controls
**MSRP. . . . . . . . . . . . . . . . . . . $699**

## FNX-45 TACTICAL

*Action*: DA/SA
*Grips*: Textured polymer
*Barrel*: 5.3 in.
*Sights*: High-profile night sights
*Weight*: 33.6 oz.
*Caliber*: .45 ACP
*Capacity*: 15 rounds
*Features*: Stainless steel slide; external extractor with loaded chamber indicator; high-profile combat night sights; red-dot sight optional; hammer-forged stainless steel barrel; flat dark earth or black polymer frame; Mil-Spec 1913 accessory mounting rail; fully ambidextrous
**MSRP. . . . . . . . . . . . . . . . . . . $1399**

**FREEDOM ARMS MODEL 83 PREMIER GRADE**

## MODEL 83 PREMIER GRADE

*Action*: SA revolver
*Grips*: Hardwood
*Barrel*: 4.75 in., 6 in., 7.5 in., 10 in.
*Sights*: Fixed or adjustable
*Weight*: 52.5 oz.
*Caliber*: .500 Wyoming Express, .475 Linebaugh, .454
Casull, .44 Remington Mag., .41 Remington Mag., .357 Mag.
*Capacity*: 5 rounds
*Features*: Adjustable sight models are drilled and tapped for
scope mounts; stainless steel, brush finish and impregnated
hardwood grips
**MSRP** . . . . . . . . . . . . . **$2365–$2460**

## MODEL 83 RIMFIRE

*Action*: SA revolver
*Grips*: Hardwood
*Barrel*: 10 in.
*Sights*: Adjustable
*Weight*: 55.5 oz.
*Caliber*: .22LR match grade chambers
*Capacity*: 5 rounds
*Features*: Drilled and tapped for scope mounts; stainless steel
frame; matte finish
**MSRP** . . . . . . . . . . . . . . . . **$2270**

**FREEDOM ARMS MODEL
83 RIMFIRE**

## MODEL 97 PREMIER GRADE

*Action*: SA revolver
*Grips*: Laminated hardwood
*Barrel*: 4.5 in., 5.5 in., 7.5 in., or 10 in.
*Sights*: Adjustable or fixed
*Weight*: 39 oz.
*Caliber*: .45 colt, .44 Special, .41 Rem. Mag., .357 Mag,
.327 Fed, 224-32 FA, .22LR, .17 HMR,
*Capacity*: 5 or 6 rounds
*Features*: Impregnated hardwood grips; stainless steel frame;
brush stainless finish
**MSRP** . . . . . . . . . . . . . **$1855–$2020**

**FREEDOM ARMS MODEL
97 PREMIER GRADE**

## MODEL 2008 SINGLE SHOT

*Action*: Hinged breech with top slide latch
*Grips*: Impregnated hardwood
*Barrel*: 10–16 in.
*Sights*: None; drilled and tapped for scope mounts
*Weight*: 63 oz.
*Caliber*: .223 Rem. To .375 Win.
*Capacity*: 1 round
*Features*: Hammer block safety; stainless matte finish
**MSRP** . . . . . . . . . . . . . . . . **$1495**

**FREEDOM ARMS MODEL 2008 SINGLE
SHOT**

# Glock

## COMPACT PISTOLS G19, G23, G25, G32, G38

*Action*: Autoloader
*Grips*: Composite
*Barrel*: 4.02 in.
*Sights*: Fixed
*Weight*: 20.11–24.16 oz.
*Caliber*: 9mm, .40, .45 G.A.P., .380 Auto, .357
*Capacity*: 8, 10, 13, 15 rounds
*Features*: Trigger safety; double-action
**MSRP** . . . . . . . . . . . . . . . . **$599–$696**

**GLOCK COMPACT G19**

## COMPETITION G34, G35

*Action*: Autoloader
*Grips*: Synthetic
*Barrel*: 5.32 in.
*Sights*: Adjustable
*Weight*: 22.92–24.5 oz.
*Caliber*: 9mm, .40
*Capacity*: 15, 17 rounds
*Features*: Safe action system; hexagonal barrel; right handed; extended barrel
**MSRP** . . . . . . . . . . . . . . . . **$679–$729**

**GLOCK COMPETITION G34**

## G21 GEN4

*Action*: DAO autoloader
*Grips*: Synthetic
*Barrel*: 4.61 in.
*Sights*: Fixed
*Weight*: 26.28 oz.
*Caliber*: .45 Auto
*Capacity*: 13+1 rounds
*Features*: The GLOCK Pistol that validates the .45 cartridge and its 100 year history by providing all the necessities for superb accuracy and functionality. The dual recoil spring assembly and adjustable backstraps offer increased shooting comfort and control. Sleek, powerful, and affordable are the hallmarks of this remarkable handgun.
**MSRP** . . . . . . . . . . . . . . . . . . . . **$687**

**GLOCK G21 GEN4**

## G32 GEN4

*Action*: DAO autoloader
*Grips*: Synthetic
*Barrel*: 4.02 in.
*Sights*: Fixed
*Weight*: 21.52 oz.
*Caliber*: .357
*Capacity*: 13+1 rounds
*Features*: The G32 is the size of the old .38 compacts with the magnum performance of the .357 Auto round without the felt recoil and 10/13/14 shots ready to fire when fully loaded. Meet the accurate, powerful, flat-shooting G32, in essence a magnumized GLOCK 19.
**MSRP** . . . . . . . . . . . . . . . . . . . . **$649**

**GLOCK G32 GEN4**

# Glock

**GLOCK G34 GEN4**

**GLOCK STANDARD G17**

**GLOCK SUBCOMPACT G26**

**GLOCK GEN4 G26**

**GLOCK SUBCOMPACT SLIMLINE G36**

## G34 GEN4

*Action*: DAO autoloader
*Grips*: Synthetic
*Barrel*: 5.31 in.
*Sights*: Fixed
*Weight*: 22.9 oz.
*Caliber*: 9mm
*Capacity*: 10, 17, 19 rounds
*Features*: This "Tactical/Practical" GLOCK 9x19 is the G17 extended to the overall length of the Government Model 1911 pistols.
**MSRP**.....................**$729**

## GEN4 G26, G27

*Action*: Autoloader
*Grips*: Synthetic
*Barrel*: 3.46 in.
*Sights*: Fixed or adjustable
*Weight*: 19.75 oz.
*Caliber*: 9x19, .40
*Capacity*: 15 rounds
*Features*: Rough textured frame; interchangeable backstrap system; two magazine-release catches for ambidextrous operation; dual-recoil

spring system replaces the original single spring model
**Fixed Sights:** .............. **$649**
**Adjustable:** ............... **$667**
**Steel:**.................... **$671**

## STANDARD PISTOL G17, G20, G21, G22, G31, G37

*Action*: Autoloader
*Grips*: Composite
*Barrel*: 4.49 in.
*Sights*: Fixed
*Weight*: 22.04–27.68 oz.
*Caliber*: 9mm, .40, 10mm Auto, .45 G.A.P., .45 Auto, .380 Auto, .357
*Capacity*: 10, 13, 15, 17 rounds
*Features*: Double action; safe action trigger system; G20 model has recoil-damping Glock hi-tech polymer
**MSRP**................**$599–$734**

## SUBCOMPACT PISTOLS G26, G27, G29, G28, G30, G33, G39

*Action*: Autoloader
*Grips*: Composite
*Barrel*: 3.46–3.78 in.

*Sights*: Fixed
*Weight*: 18.66–24.69 oz.
*Caliber*: 9mm, .40, 10mm Auto, .45 G.A.P., .45 Auto, .380 Auto, .357
*Capacity*: 6, 9, 10 rounds
*Features*: Trigger safety; double-action
**MSRP**................**$599–$734**

## SUBCOMPACT SLIMLINE PISTOL G36

*Action*: Autoloader
*Grips*: Synthetic
*Barrel*: 3.78 in.
*Sights*: Fixed
*Weight*: 20.11 oz.
*Caliber*: .45 Auto
*Capacity*: 6 rounds
*Features*: Safe action system; single stack magazine for slim grip
**MSRP**................**$637–$684**

# Hämmerli

**HÄMMERLI MODEL SP20 TARGET PISTOL**

**HÄMMERLI MODEL X-ESSE LONG**

## MODEL SP20 TARGET PISTOL

*Action*: Autoloader
*Grips*: Synthetic
*Barrel*: 4.86 in.
*Sights*: Target
*Weight*: 41 oz.
*Caliber*: .22LR, .32 S&W
*Capacity*: 5 rounds
*Features*: Front end magazine; counterweight with new recoil reduction system; various grip sizes
MSRP . . . . . . . . . . . . . . . . . . $1805

## MODEL X-ESSE

*Action*: Autoloader
*Grips*: Composite
*Barrel*: 4.5 in., 5.9 in.
*Sights*: Adjustable
*Weight*: 27.9–31 oz.
*Caliber*: .22LR
*Capacity*: 10 rounds
*Features*: Single-action, two-stage trigger; universal hi-grip
MSRP . . . . . . . . . . . . . . $902–$1018

# Heckler & Koch

## HK45

*Action*: Autoloader
*Grips*: Polymer
*Barrel*: 4.53 in.
*Sights*: Fixed
*Weight*: 31 oz.
*Caliber*: .45 ACP
*Capacity*: 10 rounds
*Features*: DA/SA with control lever; integral Picatinny rail; ambidextrous controls with dual slide releases; modified Browning linkless recoil operating system; polygonal rifling; open square notch rear sight with contrast points; low profile drift adjustable three-dot sights
MSRP . . . . . . . . . . . . . . . . . . $1187

## HK45 COMPACT TACTICAL

*Action*: DA/SA
*Grips*: Textured polymer
*Barrel*: 4.57 in.
*Sights*: 3-dot
*Weight*: 29.12 oz.
*Caliber*: .45 ACP
*Capacity*: 10 rounds
*Features*: Proprietary internal mechanical recoil reduction system; O-ring barrel; cold-hammer-forged barrel
MSRP . . . . . . . . . . . . . . . . . . $1392

**HECKLER & KOCH HK45**

**HECKLER & KOCH MARK 23**

## MARK 23

*Action*: Autoloader
*Grips*: Polymer
*Barrel*: 5.9 in.
*Sights*: 3-Dot
*Weight*: 39.4 oz.
*Caliber*: .45 ACP
*Capacity*: 12+1 rounds
*Features*: Threaded O-ring barrel with polygonal bore profile; match grade trigger; one piece machined steel slide; frame mounted decocking lever and separate ambidextrous safety lever; HK recoil reduction system; ambidextrous magazine release lever
MSRP . . . . . . . . . . . . . . . . . . $2310

**HECKLER & KOCH HK45 COMPACT TACTICAL**

# Heckler & Koch

## P30

**Action**: Autoloader
**Grips**: Polymer
**Barrel**: 3.86 in.
**Sights**: Fixed
**Weight**: 26.08 oz.
**Caliber**: 9mm, .40 S&W
**Capacity**: 15 rounds
**Features**: Corrosion proof fiber-reinforced polymer frame; multiple trigger firing modes; HK recoil reduction system; blued finish; Picatinny rail; ambidextrous magazine release levers and side release
**MSRP** . . . . . . . . . . . . . . . . . . **$1054**

## P30 L

**Action**: Autoloader
**Grips**: Polymer
**Barrel**: 4.4 in.
**Sights**: Fixed
**Weight**: 27.5 oz.
**Caliber**: 9mm, .40 S&W
**Capacity**: 10, 13, or 15 rounds
**Features**: Interchangeable backstraps and side panel grips in small, medium, and large sizes; ambidextrous slide and magazine releases levers; integral Picatinny rail; modular design allows DA trigger or DA/SA system, with a decocking button
**MSRP** . . . . . . . . . . . . . . . . . . **$1108**

## P2000 & P2000 SK

**Action**: Autoloader
**Grips**: Polymer
**Barrel**: 3.26–3.66 in.
**Sights**: 3-Dot
**Weight**: 23.8–25.9 oz.
**Caliber**: 9mm, .40 S&W, .357 SIG
**Capacity**: 9-13 rounds
**Features**: LEM trigger system; double-action; pre-cock hammer; ambidextrous magazine release and interchangeable grip straps; mounting rail
**P2000**: . . . . . . . . . . . . . . . . . . . **$941**
**P2000 SK**: . . . . . . . . . . . . . . . **$1037**

## USP

**Action**: Autoloader
**Grips**: Polymer
**Barrel**: 4.25–4.41 in.
**Sights**: 3-Dot
**Weight**: 27.2–31.36 oz.
**Caliber**: 9mm, .40 S&W, .45 Auto
**Capacity**: 12, 13, 15 rounds
**Features**: Browning-type action with a

**HECKLER & KOCH P30**

**HECKLER & KOCH P30 L**

**HECKLER & KOCH USP COMPACT**

**HECKLER & KOCH P2000**

patented recoil reduction system; double and single action modes; available in nine trigger/firing mode configurations; fiber-reinforced polymer frame; blued finish; ambidextrous magazine release trigger
**MSRP** . . . . . . . . . . . . . . **$952–$1056**

## USP COMPACT

**Action**: Autoloader
**Grips**: Polymer
**Barrel**: 3.58–3.80 in.
**Sights**: Fixed
**Weight**: 25.6–28.2 oz.
**Caliber**: 9mm, .40 S&W, .45 Auto
**Capacity**: 8, 12, 13 rounds
**Features**: Corrosion proof fiber-reinforced polymer frame;

**HECKLER & KOCH USP**

ambidextrous magazine release lever; grooved target triggers; can be converted to any of nine trigger firing modes
**MSRP** . . . . . . . . . . . . . . . **$992–$1108**

# Heritage Manufacturing

**HERITAGE ROUGH RIDER BIG BORE**

**HERITAGE ROUGH RIDER EXOTIC GRIP**

**HERITAGE ROUGH RIDER SMALL BORE**

## ROUGH RIDER BIG BORE

**Action**: SA revolver
**Grips**: Cocobolo wood
**Barrel**: 4.5 in., 5.5 in., 7.5 in.
**Sights**: Fixed, open
**Weight**: 38 oz.
**Caliber**: .357, .45
**Capacity**: 6 rounds
**Features**: Patterned after 1873 Colt; blued, nickel, stainless and blued/ color-case-hardened finishes are available; frame mounted inertia firing pin and transfer bar
**MSRP** . . . . . . . . . . **$479.99–$549.99**

## ROUGH RIDER EXOTIC GRIP

**Action**: SA revolver
**Grips**: Cocobolo wood
**Barrel**: 4.75 in.
**Sights**: Fixed
**Weight**: 31 oz.
**Caliber**: .22-9 Shot combo
**Capacity**: 9 rounds
**Features**: Machined barrel is micro-threaded; frame finish comes in

smooth silver satin, deep matte black, low gloss black satin or case-hardened finish
**MSRP** . . . . . . . . . . .**$279.99–$349.99**

## ROUGH RIDER SMALL BORE

**Action**: SA revolver
**Grips**: Cocobolo wood
**Barrel**: 3.5 in., 4.75 in., 6.5 in., 9 in.
**Sights**: Fixed
**Weight**: 31 oz.
**Caliber**: .22LR & .22 Mag.
**Capacity**: 6 rounds
**Features**: Machined barrel is micro-

threaded; optional cocobolo grips include white mother of pearl, black mother of pearl, or green camo laminate grips; frame finish comes in smooth silver satin, deep matte black, low gloss black satin or case-hardened finish
**MSRP** . . . . . . . . . . **$199.99–$359.99**

# High Standard

**HIGH STANDARD OLYMPIC**

**HIGH STANDARD SUPERMATIC CITATION**

## OLYMPIC

**Action**: Autoloader
**Grips**: Cocobolo wood
**Barrel**: 5.5 in.
**Sights**: Adjustable
**Weight**: 44 oz.
**Caliber**: .22 Short
**Capacity**: 10+1 rounds
**Features**: Lightweight aluminum alloy slide; precision carbon steel frame; drilled and tapped for scopes; single-action
**MSRP** . . . . . . . . . . . . . . . . . . . **$965**

## SUPERMATIC CITATION

**Action**: Autoloader
**Grips**: Walnut
**Barrel**: 5.5 in.
**Sights**: Adjustable
**Weight**: 44 oz.
**Caliber**: .22LR
**Capacity**: 10+1 rounds

**Features**: Durable parkerized finish and black epoxy-finished wood; ambidextrous grips; drilled and tapped for scopes
**MSRP** . . . . . . . . . . . . . **$1095–$1295**

**HIGH STANDARD US MODEL 1911 CUSTOM**

**HIGH STANDARD SUPERMATIC TROPHY**

**HIGH STANDARD VICTOR**

## SUPERMATIC TROPHY

*Action*: Autoloader
*Grips*: Walnut
*Barrel*: 5.5 in., 7.25 in.
*Sights*: Adjustable
*Weight*: 44 oz.–46 oz.
*Caliber*: .22LR
*Capacity*: 10+1 rounds
*Features*: Features gold plated components: trigger, safety, slide stop and magazine catch; adjustable trigger; checkered deluxe grips; blued finish
**MSRP . . . . . . . . . . . . . . . $785–$895**

## US MODEL 1911 CUSTOM

*Action*: Autoloader
*Grips*: Walnut

*Barrel*: 5 in.
*Sights*: Novak style adjustable
*Weight*: 40 oz.
*Caliber*: .45 ACP
*Capacity*: 7+1 rounds
*Features*: Beveled magazine well; match trigger with overtravel stop; available in stainless steel, blued or parkerized finish
**MSRP . . . . . . . . . . . . . . . . . . . $995**

## VICTOR

*Action*: Autoloader
*Grips*: Walnut
*Barrel*: 4.5 in., 5.5 in.

*Sights*: Adjustable
*Weight*: 45 oz.
*Caliber*: .22LR
*Capacity*: 10+1 rounds
*Features*: Removable aluminum rib; drilled and tapped for scopes; optional slide conversion kit for .22 short; various customization options
**MSRP . . . . . . . . . . . . . . . . $785–$845**

# Hi-Point Firearms

**HI-POINT FIREARMS MODEL CF-380**

**HI-POINT FIREARMS MODEL C-9 9MM**

## MODEL C-9 9MM

*Action*: Autoloader
*Grips*: Polymer
*Barrel*: 3.5 in.
*Sights*: 3-Dots adjustable
*Weight*: 29 oz.
*Caliber*: 9mm
*Capacity*: 8 or 10 rounds
*Features*: Polymer frame; last round lock open; quick on-off thumb safety; free trigger lock; free extra peep sight; black finish
**MSRP . . . . . . . . . . . . . . . . . . . $179**

## MODEL CF-380

*Action*: Autoloader
*Grips*: Polymer
*Barrel*: 3.5 in.
*Sights*: 3-Dots adjustable
*Weight*: 29 oz.
*Caliber*: .380 ACP
*Capacity*: 8 or 10 rounds
*Features*: High-impact polymer frame; black powder coat with chrome rail; durable, easy-grip finish; quick on-off

**HI-POINT FIREARMS MODEL JHP45 ACP**

thumb safety; free extra rear peep sight
**MSRP . . . . . . . . . . . . . . . . . . . $149**

## MODEL JHP45 ACP & JCP 40 S&W

*Action*: Autoloader
*Grips*: Polymer
*Barrel*: 4.5 in.
*Sights*: 3-Dots adjustable
*Weight*: 35 oz.
*Caliber*: .40 S&W, .45 ACP
*Capacity*: 10 rounds
*Features*: Polymer frame; quick on-off thumb safety; operations safety sheet; +P rated; free extra rear peep sight; free trigger lock; black finish; available with laserlyte laser and green slide
**MSRP . . . . . . . . . . . . . . . . . . . $199**

**HANDGUNS**

# Kahr Arms

**KAHR ARMS CM9**

**KAHR ARMS CM40**

**KAHR ARMS CW45**

**KAHR ARMS P9 SERIES**

**KAHR ARMS P40 SERIES**

## CM9

**Action**: Autoloader
**Grips**: Textured polymer
**Barrel**: 3 in.
**Sights**: Adjustable
**Weight**: 15.9 oz.
**Caliber**: 9mm
**Capacity**: 6+1 rounds
**Features**: Trigger cocking double-action; lock breech; Browning-type recoil lug; passive striker block; no magazine disconnect; drift adjustable, white bar-dot combat sights; black finish; matte stainless steel slide
MSRP . . . . . . . . . . . . . . . . . . . . $517

## CM40

**Action**: Autoloader
**Grips**: Textured polymer
**Barrel**: 3 in.
**Sights**: Adjustable
**Weight**: 17.7 oz.
**Caliber**: .40 S&W
**Capacity**: 5+1 rounds
**Features**: Trigger cocking DAO; lock breech; "Browning-type" recoil lug; passive striker block; no magazine disconnect; black polymer frame, matte stainless steel slide
MSRP . . . . . . . . . . . . . . . . . . . . $517

## CW45

**Action**: Autoloader
**Grips**: Textured polymer
**Barrel**: 3.64 in.
**Sights**: Adjustable
**Weight**: 21.7 oz.
**Caliber**: .45 ACP
**Capacity**: 6+1 rounds
**Features**: Trigger cocking double-action; lock breech; Browning-type recoil lug; passive striker block; no magazine disconnect; drift adjustable, white bar-dot combat rear sight, pinned in polymer front sight; black finish; matte stainless steel slide
MSRP . . . . . . . . . . . . . . . . . . . . $485

## P9 SERIES

**Action**: Autoloader
**Grips**: Textured polymer
**Barrel**: 3.6 in.
**Sights**: Adjustable
**Weight**: 16.9 oz.
**Caliber**: 9mm
**Capacity**: 7+1 rounds
**Features**: Trigger cocking DAO; lock breech; Browning-type recoil lug; passive striker block; no magazine disconnect; black polymer frame;

model available with external safety and LCI
MSRP . . . . . . . . . . . . . . . $739–$996

## P40 SERIES

**Action**: Autoloader
**Grips**: Textured polymer
**Barrel**: 3.6 in.
**Sights**: Adjustable
**Weight**: 18.7 oz.
**Caliber**: .40 S&W
**Capacity**: 6+1 rounds
**Features**: Trigger cocking DAO; lock breech; Browning-type recoil lug; passive striker block; no magazine disconnect; black polymer frame
**P40**: . . . . . . . . . . . . . . . . . . . . . $739
**P40 w/ Night Sights**: . . . . . . . . . $857
**P40 Black**: . . . . . . . . . . . . . . . $786
**P40 Ext Safety & LCI**: . . . . . . . . $876
**P40 Ext Safety & LCI w/ Night Sights**: . . . . . . . . . . . . . . $996

# Kahr Arms

## P45 SERIES

**Action**: Autoloader
**Grips**: Textured polymer
**Barrel**: 3.54 in.
**Sights**: Adjustable
**Weight**: 18.5 oz.
**Caliber**: .45 ACP
**Capacity**: 5+1, 6+1 rounds
**Features**: Trigger cocking DAO; lock breech; Browning-type recoil lug; passive striker block; no magazine disconnect; black polymer frame
**P45:** . . . . . . . . . . . . . . . . . . . . . **$805**
**P45 w/ Night Sights:** . . . . . . . . **$921**
**P45 Black:** . . . . . . . . . . . . . . . **$855**
**P45 Black w/ Night sights:** . . . . **$973**

## P380 SERIES

**Action**: Autoloader
**Grips**: Textured polymer
**Barrel**: 2.5 in.
**Sights**: Adjustable
**Weight**: 11.27 oz.
**Caliber**: .380 ACP
**Capacity**: 6+1 rounds
**Features**: Trigger cocking DAO; Lock breech; Browning-type recoil lug; passive striker block; no magazine disconnect; black polymer frame,

matte stainless steel slide; premium Lothar Walther match grade barrel; available in Black Rose and with night sights or LCI
**MSRP** . . . . . . . . . . . . . . . **$649–$949**

## PM9 SERIES

**Action**: Autoloader
**Grips**: Textured polymer
**Barrel**: 3 in.
**Sights**: Adjustable
**Weight**: 15.9 oz.
**Caliber**: 9mm
**Capacity**: 6+1 or 7+1 rounds
**Features**: Trigger cocking DAO; lock breech; Browning-type recoil lug; passive striker block; no magazine disconnect; black polymer frame; available in Black Rose, with night sights, LCI, and an external safety
**MSRP** . . . . . . . . . . . . . . . **$786–$1049**

## PM40 - EXTERNAL SAFETY & LCI

**Action**: Autoloader
**Grips**: Textured polymer
**Barrel**: 3 in.
**Sights**: Adjustable
**Weight**: 17.7 oz.

**Caliber**: .40 S&W
**Capacity**: 5+1, 6+1 rounds
**Features**: Trigger cocking DAO; lock breech; "Browning-type" recoil lug; passive striker block; no magazine disconnect; black polymer frame, matte stainless steel slide; drift adjustable, white bar-dot combat sights (tritium night sights, Crimson Trace laser sight optional)
**MSRP** . . . . . . . . . . . . . . . . . . **$828**

## PM45 SERIES

**Action**: Autoloader
**Grips**: Textured polymer
**Barrel**: 3.24 in.
**Sights**: Adjustable
**Weight**: 19.3 oz.
**Caliber**: .45 ACP
**Capacity**: 6+1 rounds
**Features**: Trigger cocking double action; lock breech; Browning-type recoil lug; passive striker block; no magazine disconnect; drift adjustable, white bar-dot combat sights; black polymer frame, matte blackened stainless steel slide; available with night sights or CT laser sight
**MSRP** . . . . . . . . . . . . . . . **$855–$1022**

KAHR ARMS P380

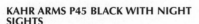

KAHR ARMS P45 BLACK WITH NIGHT SIGHTS

KAHR ARMS PM40 WITH EXTERNAL SAFETY & LCI

KAHR ARMS PM9 SERIES

KAHR ARMS PM45

# Kel-Tec

**KEL-TEC P-3AT**

**KEL-TEC P-11**

**KEL-TEC P-32**

**KEL-TEC PF-9**

**KEL-TEC PMR-30**

## P-3AT

*Action*: Autoloader
*Grips*: Polymer
*Barrel*: 2.7 in.
*Sights*: Fixed
*Weight*: 8.3 oz.
*Caliber*: .380 Auto
*Capacity*: 6+1 rounds
*Features*: Double-action only; steel barrel and slide; aluminum frame; transfer bar
**Blued Finish**: . . . . . . . . . . . . . $318
**Parkerized Finish**: . . . . . . . . . $361
**Hard Chrome Finish**: . . . . . . . $377

## P-11

*Action*: Autoloader
*Grips*: Polymer
*Barrel*: 3.1 in.
*Sights*: Fixed
*Weight*: 14 oz.
*Caliber*: 9mm
*Capacity*: 10+1 rounds, optional 12 rounds
*Features*: Double-action only; steel barrel and slide; aluminum frame; locked breech; high-impact polymer DuPont grips
**Blued Finish**: . . . . . . . . . . . . . $333
**Parkerized Finish**: . . . . . . . . . $377
**Hard Chrome Finish**: . . . . . . . $390

## P-32

*Action*: Autoloader
*Grips*: Polymer
*Barrel*: 2.7 in.
*Sights*: Fixed
*Weight*: 6.6 oz.
*Caliber*: 32 Auto
*Capacity*: 7+1 rounds
*Features*: Steel barrel and slide; locked breech mechanism
**Blued Finish**: . . . . . . . . . . . . . $318
**Parkerized Finish**: . . . . . . . . . $361
**Hard Chrome Finish**: . . . . . . . $377

## PF-9

*Action*: Autoloader
*Grips*: Polymer
*Barrel*: 3.1 in.
*Sights*: Adjustable

*Weight*: 12.7 oz.
*Caliber*: 9mm
*Capacity*: 7+1 rounds
*Features*: Firing mechanism is double-action only with an automatic hammer block safety; grips available in black, grey, and olive drab; rear sight is a new design and is adjustable for windage
**Blued Finish**: . . . . . . . . . . . . . $333
**Parkerized Finish**: . . . . . . . . . $377
**Hard Chrome Finish**: . . . . . . . $390

## PMR-30

*Action*: SA autoloader
*Grips*: Nylon
*Barrel*: 4.3 in.
*Sights*: Picatinny accessory rail under barrel
*Weight*: 13.6 oz.
*Caliber*: .22 WMR
*Capacity*: 30 rounds
*Features*: Blowback/locked breech system; lightweight but full sized; urethane recoil buffer; disassembles for cleaning with removal of one pin
**MSRP**. . . . . . . . . . . . . . . . . . . $415

**HANDGUNS**

# Kimber

**KIMBER CLASSIC CARRY PRO**

## CLASSIC CARRY PRO
*Action*: SA autoloader
*Grips*: Bone
*Barrel*: 4 in.
*Sights*: Fixed low-profile, 3-dot
*Weight*: 35 oz.
*Caliber*: .45 ACP
*Capacity*: 8 rounds
*Features*: Deep charcoal blued finish; steel frame and slide; match grade bull barrel; serrated flat top slide; night sights; front strap checkering
**MSRP** . . . . . . . . . . . . . . . . . **$2056**

**KIMBER COMPACT STAINLESS II**

## COMPACT STAINLESS II
*Action*: Autoloader
*Grips*: Black synthetic double diamond
*Barrel*: 4 in.
*Sights*: Fixed, low profile
*Weight*: 27 oz.
*Caliber*: .45 ACP
*Capacity*: 7 rounds
*Features*: Full-length guide rod; aluminum frame in satin silver finish; steel Match Grade barrel; aluminum match grade trigger
**MSRP** . . . . . . . . . . . . . . . . . **$1052**

**KIMBER CUSTOM II**

## CUSTOM II
*Action*: Autoloader
*Grips*: Black synthetic double diamond
*Barrel*: 5 in.
*Sights*: Fixed, low profile
*Weight*: 38 oz.
*Caliber*: .45 ACP
*Capacity*: 7 rounds
*Features*: Full-length guide rod; aluminum frame in matte black finish; steel Match Grade barrel; aluminum match grade trigger
**MSRP** . . . . . . . . . . . . . . . . . **$871**

**KIMBER ECLIPSE ULTRA II**

## ECLIPSE ULTRA II
*Action*: Autoloader
*Grips*: Laminated double diamond
*Barrel*: 3 in.
*Sights*: Meprolight Tritium 3-dot night, fixed
*Weight*: 38 oz.
*Caliber*: .45 ACP
*Capacity*: 7 rounds
*Features*: Full-length guide rod; stainless steel frame with brush polished finish; stainless steel slide; Match Grade steel barrel; aluminum Match Grade trigger
**MSRP** . . . . . . . . . . . . . . . . . **$1289**

# Kimber

KIMBER GOLD MATCH II

KIMBER SAPPHIRE ULTRA II

## GOLD MATCH II

*Action*: Autoloader
*Grips*: Rosewood double diamond
*Barrel*: 5 in.
*Sights*: Kimber adjustable
*Weight*: 38 oz.
*Caliber*: .45 ACP
*Capacity*: 8 rounds
*Features*: Premium aluminum, Match Grade trigger; full length guide rod; steel frame with highly polished blued finish; stainless steel, Match Grade barrel
**MSRP** . . . . . . . . . . . . . . . . . . **$1393**

## SAPPHIRE ULTRA II

*Action*: SA autoloader
*Grips*: G-10 thin grips
*Barrel*: 3 in.
*Sights*: Tactical Wedge night sights
*Weight*: 25 oz.
*Caliber*: 9mm
*Capacity*: 8 rounds
*Features*: Highly-polished stainless steel slide and small parts are finished with bright blue PVD finish accented with fine engraving; blue/black ball-milled G-10 thin grips and short trigger; ambidextrous thumb safety; Tactical Wedge night sights
**MSRP** . . . . . . . . . . . . . . . . . . **$1652**

KIMBER SOLO CARRY

KIMBER SOLO CDP (LG)

## SOLO CARRY

*Action*: SA autoloader
*Grips*: Black synthetic checkered/ smooth
*Barrel*: 2.7 in.
*Sights*: Fixed low profile
*Weight*: 17 oz.
*Caliber*: 9mm
*Capacity*: 6 rounds
*Features*: Aluminum finish frame; stainless steel barrel; single-action striker trigger
**MSRP** . . . . . . . . . . . . . . . . . . **$815**

## SOLO CDP (LG)

*Action*: SA striker-fired
*Grips*: Synthetic, rosewood finish
*Barrel*: 2.7 in.
*Sights*: Fixed 3-dot night sights
*Weight*: 17 oz.
*Caliber*: 9mm
*Capacity*: 6, 8 rounds
*Features*: Single-action striker-fired trigger system; Crimson Trace Lasergrips; Carry Melt treatment to round endges; black KimPro II frame finish; checkering on front and back straps
**MSRP** . . . . . . . . . . . . . . . . . . **$1223**

## STAINLESS PRO RAPTOR II

**Action**: SA autoloading, recoil operated
**Grips**: Zebra wood, scale pattern
**Barrel**: 4 in.
**Sights**: Tactical wedge 3-dot
**Weight**: 35 oz.
**Caliber**: .45 ACP
**Capacity**: 8 rounds
**Features**: Stainless steel slide and frame with satin silver finish; Match Grade barrel; ambidextrous thumb safety; full-length guide rod
**MSRP** . . . . . . . . . . . . . . . . . . **$1415**

KIMBER STAINLESS
PRO RAPTOR II

## STAINLESS PRO TLE II (LG)

**Action**: Autoloader
**Grips**: Tactical gray double diamond, Crimson Trace lasergrips
**Barrel**: 4 in.
**Sights**: Meprolight tritium 3-dot night, fixed
**Weight**: 35 oz.
**Caliber**: .45 ACP
**Capacity**: 7 rounds
**Features**: Full-length guide rod; stainless steel frame with satin silver; Match Grade steel barrel; aluminum Match Grade trigger
**MSRP** . . . . . . . . . . . . . . . . . . **$1518**

KIMBER STAINLESS
PRO TLE II (LG)

## STAINLESS ULTRA TLE II

**Action**: SA autoloader
**Grips**: Tactical gray double diamond
**Barrel**: 3 in.
**Sights**: Meprolight tritium 3-dot night, fixed
**Weight**: 25 oz.
**Caliber**: .45 ACP
**Capacity**: 7 rounds
**Features**: Full-length guide rod; front strap checkering; aluminum frame with satin silver finish; steel match grade barrel; aluminum match grade trigger
**MSRP** . . . . . . . . . . . . . . . . . . **$1253**

KIMBER STAINLESS
ULTRA TLE II

## SUPER CARRY PRO

**Action**: SA autoloader
**Grips**: Micarta/ laminated rosewood
**Barrel**: 4 in.
**Sights**: Night, tritium
**Weight**: 28 oz.
**Caliber**: .45 ACP
**Capacity**: 8 rounds
**Features**: Ambidextrous thumb safety; carry melt; full-length guide rod; aluminum frame in satin silver; super carry serrations; high cut under trigger guard; steel Match Grade barrel; aluminum Match Grade trigger
**MSRP** . . . . . . . . . . . . . . . . . . **$1596**

KIMBER SUPER
CARRY PRO

# Kimber

KIMBER TACTICAL
ENTRY II

KIMBER ULTRA
CARRY II

## TACTICAL ENTRY II

**Action**: SA autoloading, recoil operated
**Grips**: Laminated double diamond, Kimber logo
**Barrel**: 5 in.
**Sights**: Meprolight tritium 3-dot night, fixed
**Weight**: 40 oz.
**Caliber**: .45 ACP
**Capacity**: 7 rounds
**Features**: Ambidextrous thumb safety; full-length guide rod; stainless steel frame and slide; matte gray Kim Pro II frame finish
**MSRP** . . . . . . . . . . . . . . . . . . . $1490

## ULTRA CARRY II

**Action**: SA autoloading, recoil operated
**Grips**: Black synthetic double diamond
**Barrel**: 3 in.
**Sights**: Fixed, low profile
**Weight**: 25 oz.
**Caliber**: .45 ACP
**Capacity**: 7 rounds
**Features**: Black matte finish; aluminum frame; steel slide; full-length guide rod
**MSRP** . . . . . . . . . . . . . . . . . . . $919

KIMBER ULTRA
CDP II

KIMBER ULTRA
CRIMSON CARRY II

## ULTRA CDP II

**Action**: Autoloader
**Grips**: Rosewood double diamond
**Barrel**: 3 in.
**Sights**: Meprolight tritium 3-dot night, fixed
**Weight**: 25 oz.
**Caliber**: .45 ACP
**Capacity**: 7 rounds
**Features**: Ambidextrous thumb safety; full-length guide rod; matte black Kim Pro frame finish; aluminum frame; stainless steel slide and barrel; Match Grade trigger
**MSRP** . . . . . . . . . . . . . . . . . . . $1331

## ULTRA CRIMSON CARRY II

**Action**: SA autoloading, recoil operated
**Grips**: Rosewood double diamond, Crimson Trace lasergrips
**Barrel**: 3 in.
**Sights**: Fixed low profile
**Weight**: 25 oz.
**Caliber**: .45 ACP
**Capacity**: 7 rounds
**Features**: Full-length guide rod; aluminum frame in satin silver finish; steel Match Grade barrel; aluminum Match Grade trigger
**MSRP** . . . . . . . . . . . . . . . . . . . $1206

## SPHINX SDP COMPACT

*Action*: DA/SA autoloader
*Grips*: Composite
*Barrel*: 3.7 in.
*Sights*: Fiber optic/tritium front, tritium rear
*Weight*: 27.5 oz.
*Caliber*: 9mm
*Capacity*: 15+1 rounds
*Features*: Upper frame machined from aeronautic-grade hard-anodized aluminum; integral recoil buffer; Mil-Spec 1913 rail; polymer lower frame; interchangeable grip sizes available; Defiance sights feature fiber optic/tritium day-night green front sight with tritium two-dot red rear sight; internal firing pin safety, drop safety, hammer safety, and integrated slide-position safety
**MSRP** . . . . . . . . . . . . . . . . . . **$1295**

**KRISS USA SPHINX SDP COMPACT**

# Magnum Research

## BABY DESERT EAGLE

*Action*: Autoloader
*Grips*: Plastic composite
*Barrel*: 3.64 in., 3.93 in., 4.52 in.
*Sights*: 3-Dot combat
*Weight*: 26.8–38.6 oz.
*Caliber*: 9mm, .40 S&W, .45 ACP
*Capacity*: 10, 12, 13, 15 rounds
*Features*: Black steel or polymer frame; slide safety; decocker; double and single action; polygonal rifling; Picatinny rail; available in full-size, compact, and semi-compact
**Polymer:** . . . . . . . . . . . . . . . . . **$616**
**Steel:** . . . . . . . . . . . . . . . . . . . **$630**

**MAGNUM RESEARCH
BABY DESERT EAGLE**

## BFR (BIG FRAME REVOLVER)

*Action*: SA revolver
*Grips*: Rubber, optional wood
*Barrel*: 5 in., 6.5 in., 7.5 in., 10 in.
*Sights*: Adjustable rear, fixed front
*Weight*: 57.6–85 oz.
*Caliber*: Long Cylinder: .30/30 Win., .444 Marlin, .45 Long Colt/.410, .45/70 Gov't., .450 Marlin, .44 Mag., .460 S&W Mag., .500 S&W Mag.; Short Cylinder: .22 Hornet, .454 Casull, .480 Ruger/ .475 Linebaugh, .50AE

**MAGNUM RESEARCH BFR**

*Capacity*: 5 rounds
*Features*: Both long and short-cylinder models are made of stainless steel; barrels are stress-relieved and cut rifled; current production revolvers are shipped with rubber grips and Weaver style scope mount
**MSRP** . . . . . . . . . . . . . . . . . . **$1050**

# Magnum Research

**MAGNUM RESEARCH DESERT EAGLE 1911**

**MAGNUM RESEARCH MARK XIX DESERT EAGLE**

**MAGNUM RESEARCH MICRO DESERT EAGLE**

**MAGNUM RESEARCH MR EAGLE**

## DESERT EAGLE 1911
*Action*: SA autoloader
*Grips*: Checkered wood
*Barrel*: 5 in., 4.3 in.
*Sights*: Fixed
*Weight*: 36 oz. (5 in. barrel), 32 oz. (4.3 in. barrel)
*Caliber*: .45 ACP
*Capacity*: 8 rounds
*Features*: Grip safety; extended thumb safety; blued finish
**MSRP . . . . . . . . . . . . . . . . . . . . $874**

## MARK XIX DESERT EAGLE
*Action*: Autoloader
*Grips*: Plastic composite
*Barrel*: 6 in., 10 in.
*Sights*: Fixed combat
*Weight*: 62.4–71.4 oz.
*Caliber*: .357 Mag., .44 Mag., .50 A.E.
*Capacity*: 7, 8, 9 rounds
*Features*: Gas operated; polygonal rifling; integral scope bases; many finishes available, including: black oxide, brushed/matte/polished chrome, bright/satin nickel, 24K gold, titanium gold, and titanium gold with tiger stripes
**MSRP . . . . . . . . . . . . . $1563–$2264**

## MICRO DESERT EAGLE
*Action*: Autoloader
*Grips*: Black polymer
*Barrel*: 2.22 in.
*Sights*: Fixed, non-adjustable
*Weight*: 14 oz.
*Caliber*: .380 Auto (9mm Browning)
*Capacity*: 6 rounds
*Features*: Gas-assisted blowback system; alloy frame; steel slide; oversized trigger guard; nickel finish
**Nickel/Nickel-Blued: . . . . . . . . $479**
**Blued: . . . . . . . . . . . . . . . . . . . $467**

## MR EAGLE "FAST ACTION"
*Action*: Autoloader
*Grips*: Black polymer
*Barrel*: 4 in. (9mm), 4.15 in. (.40)
*Sights*: Adjustable rear, fixed front
*Weight*: 24.8 oz. (9mm), 26.4 oz. (.40 S&W)
*Caliber*: 9mm or .40 S&W
*Capacity*: 10, 15 rounds (9mm), 10, 11 rounds (.40 SUW)
*Features*: 6-groove filing; hammer forged barrel; full Picatinny rail; ergonomic polymer grip frame; four separate safety devices
**MSRP . . . . . . . . . . . . . . . . . . . . $559**

# MOA

## MAXIMUM

**Action**: Hinged breech
**Grips**: Walnut
**Barrel**: 8.5 in., 10.5 in., 14 in.
**Sights**: Adjustable, open
**Weight**: 56–67 oz.
**Caliber**: most rifle chamberings from .22 Hornet to .375 H&H
**Capacity**: single-shot
**Features**: Falling block action; free

MOA MAXIMUM

floating barrel; multiple length barrels; receiver tapped for scope mounts
**MSRP**.....................**$966**

# Nighthawk Custom

NIGHTHAWK CUSTOM
GLOBAL RESPONSE PISTOL

NIGHTHAWK
CUSTOM HEINIE
SIGNATURE RECON

NIGHTHAWK CUSTOM BOB
MARVEL CUSTOM

## BOB MARVEL CUSTOM

**Action**: Autoloader
**Grips**: Custom Mil Tac
**Barrel**: 4.25 in.
**Sights**: Novak tritium night sight front, tritium adjustable rear
**Weight**: 38 oz.
**Caliber**: .45
**Capacity**: 8+1 rounds
**Features**: Late in 2011 Bob Marvel decided that he would train one of our Master Gunsmiths to build one of his most popular custom models. This model incorporates new Nighthawk/Marvel Everlast Recoil System, which allows a shooter to go at least 10,000 rounds before a spring change is necessary. Felt recoil and muzzle flip are also dramatically reduced. The proprietary barrel system is unique to any we have ever produced. The groups at 50 yards are beyond the capabilities of the average shooter.
**MSRP**................... **$3995**

## GLOBAL RESPONSE PISTOL (GRP)

**Action**: SA autoloader
**Grips**: Micarta gator grips
**Barrel**: 5 in.
**Sights**: Night
**Weight**: 39 oz.

**Caliber**: .45 ACP, 10mm, 9mm
**Capacity**: 8 rounds
**Features**: 1911 design; Lanyard loop integrated into the mainspring housing; forged slide stop axle is cut flush with the frame; Heinie Slant-Pro Night Sights, Novak Low Mount Night Sights, or Novak Extreme Duty Adjustable Night Sights are standard; Perma Kote finish in black, sniper gray, green, coyote tan, titanium blued, and hard chrome
**MSRP**................... **$2895.95**

## HEINIE SIGNATURE COMPACT, RECON

**Action**: Autoloader
**Grips**: Thin Proprietary G10
**Barrel**: 4.25 in., 5 in.

**Sights**: Tritium front night sight, Heinie Slant-Pro Rear
**Weight**: 38 oz.–40 oz.
**Caliber**: 9mm, .45
**Capacity**: 7+1, 8+1 rounds
**Features**: Features a proprietary thinned frame and mainspring housing that are scalloped to provide a positive grip without the abrasion some people feel from checkering. The grips are a new pattern of G10 that are thinned to make concealed carry even easier, and feature a relieved area on the side to allow easy access to the magazine release.
**Compact:**................ **$3450**
**PDP:** ................... **$3395**
**Recon:** .................. **$3550**

# Nighthawk Custom

## T3 - THE ULTIMATE CONCEALED CARRY 1911

**Action**: SA autoloader
**Grips**: G10 grips
**Barrel**: 4.25 in.
**Sights**: Heinie Straight Eight Slant-Pro, night
**Weight**: 40 oz.
**Caliber**: .45 ACP, 9mm
**Capacity**: 7 rounds
**Features**: Frame based on Officer model; extended magazine well; Heinie Slant-Pro Straight Eights Night Sights are standard; mainspring housing and rear of slide are horizontally serrated to match; top of slide serrated to reduce glare; Nighthawk Custom lightweight aluminum trigger that has been blacked-out using Perma Kote; available in black, gun metal grey, green coyote tan, titanium blued, and hard chrome Perma Kote or stainless steel model
**Standard**: . . . . . . . . . . . . . . . **$3250**
**Stainless**: . . . . . . . . . . . . . . . **$3400**
**Thin (35.5 oz.)**: . . . . . . . . . . . **$3400**

NIGHTHAWK CUSTOM T3

# North American Arms

NORTH AMERICAN ARMS .32 ACP GUARDIAN

NORTH AMERICAN ARMS .380 ACP GUARDIAN

## .32 ACP GUARDIAN

**Action**: DAO
**Grips**: Polymer
**Barrel**: 2.5 in.
**Sights**: Fixed, open
**Weight**: 13.5 oz.
**Caliber**: .32 ACP
**Capacity**: 6+1 rounds
**Features**: Stainless steel; double action only; integral locking system safety; also available in .25 caliber
**MSRP** . . . . . . . . . . . . . . . . . . . **$402**

## .380 ACP GUARDIAN

**Action**: DAO
**Grips**: Composite
**Barrel**: 2.49 in.
**Sights**: Fixed, open
**Weight**: 18.72 oz.
**Caliber**: .380 ACP
**Capacity**: 6+1 rounds
**Features**: Stainless steel; double action only; integral locking system safety
**MSRP** . . . . . . . . . . . . . . . . . . . **$449**

## 1860 EARL 4" BARREL

**Action**: SA revolver
**Grips**: Rosewood
**Barrel**: 4 in. heavy octagonal
**Sights**: Bead front
**Weight**: 9.1 oz.
**Caliber**: .22 Mag.
**Capacity**: 5 rounds
**Features**: 1860s style mini revolver resembles 150-yr-old percussion revolver; also available with 3 in. barrel
**MSRP** . . . . . . . . . . . . . . . . . . . **$284**

NORTH AMERICAN ARMS 1860 EARL

# North American Arms

**NORTH AMERICAN ARMS MINI MASTER SERIES REVOLVER**

**NORTH AMERICAN ARMS MINI-REVOLVER**

**NORTH AMERICAN ARMS PUG MINI-REVOLVER**

**NORTH AMERICAN ARMS THE WASP**

## MINI MASTER SERIES REVOLVER

*Action*: SA revolver
*Grips*: Rubber
*Barrel*: 4 in.
*Sights*: Fixed or adjustable
*Weight*: 10.7 oz.
*Caliber*: .22LR, .22 Mag.
*Capacity*: 5 rounds
*Features*: Conversion cylinder or adjustable sights available
**.22LR, .22 Mag.:** . . . . . . . . **$284–$314**
**Conversion:** . . . . . . . . . . . **$319–$349**

## MINI-REVOLVER

*Action*: SA revolver
*Grips*: Laminated rosewood
*Barrel*: 1.2 in., 1.625 in.
*Sights*: Fixed, open
*Weight*: 4 oz.–6.2 oz.
*Caliber*: .22 Short, .22LR, .22 Mag.
*Capacity*: 5 rounds
*Features*: Features NAA's safety cylinder so mini-revolver can be carried fully loaded
**.22:** . . . . . . . . . . . . . . . . . . . . **$209**
**.22LR:** . . . . . . . . . . . . . . . . . . **$209**
**.22 Mag:** . . . . . . . . . . . . . . . . . **$219**

## PUG MINI-REVOLVER

*Action*: Revolver
*Grips*: Rubber
*Barrel*: 1 in.
*Sights*: Tritium and white dot
*Weight*: 6.4 oz.
*Caliber*: .22 Mag.
*Capacity*: 5 rounds
*Features*: Oversized pebble-textured rubber grips enable the handler to keep a firm grip
**White dot sight:** . . . . . . . . . . . . **$314**
**Tritium sight:** . . . . . . . . . . . . . . **$334**

## THE WASP

*Action*: SA revolver
*Grips*: Rubber pebble finish
*Barrel*: 1.125 in., 1.625 in.
*Sights*: Stainless post
*Weight*: 5.9 oz.–7.2 oz.
*Caliber*: .22 Mag.
*Capacity*: 5 rounds
*Features*: Stainless steel frame; vent rib barrel; skeleton hammer; .22LR conversion cylinders available; brushed sides, matte contours, black inlay
**MSRP** . . . . . . . . . . . . . . . . **$249–$284**

# Olympic Arms

OLYMPIC ARMS COHORT

OLYMPIC ARMS ENFORCER

## COHORT

**Action**: Autoloader
**Grips**: Walnut, fully checkered
**Barrel**: 4 in. bull
**Sights**: Target
**Weight**: 36 oz.
**Caliber**: .45 ACP
**Capacity**: 7+1 rounds
**Features**: Single-action on 1911 Colt design; short slide on a full size frame; grooved frame front strap; satin bead blast finish
**MSRP** . . . . . . . . . . . . . . . . . . **$973.70**

## ENFORCER

**Action**: Autoloader
**Grips**: Smooth, laser etched widow icon, walnut
**Barrel**: 4 in. bull
**Sights**: Low-profile
**Weight**: 35 oz.
**Caliber**: .45 ACP
**Capacity**: 6+1 rounds
**Features**: Single-action on 1911 Colt design; satin bead blast finish; hooked frame trigger guard; Triplex Counterwound self-contained spring recoil system
**MSRP** . . . . . . . . . . . . . . . . **$1033.50**

OLYMPIC ARMS MATCHMASTER

OLYMPIC ARMS WESTERNER

## MATCHMASTER

**Action**: Autoloader
**Grips**: Smooth, laser etched scorpion icon, walnut
**Barrel**: 5 in.
**Sights**: Adjustable rear
**Weight**: 40 oz.–44 oz.
**Caliber**: .45 ACP
**Capacity**: 7+1 rounds
**Features**: Single-action on 1911 Colt design; satin bead blast or parkerized finish; grooved frame front strap
**5 in.:** . . . . . . . . . . . . . . . . **$1033.50**
**6 in.:** . . . . . . . . . . . . . . . . . **$973.70**

## WESTERNER

**Action**: Autoloader
**Grips**: Smooth, laser etched westerner icon, ivory color
**Barrel**: 5 in.
**Sights**: Target
**Weight**: 39 oz.
**Caliber**: .45ACP
**Capacity**: 7+1 rounds
**Features**: Single-action; color case-hardened frame and slide; stainless steel barrel; round frame trigger guard; straight front frame strap
**MSRP** . . . . . . . . . . . . . . . . **$1163.50**

# Puma by Legacy Sports

**PUMA M-1873 REVOLVER**

## M-1873 REVOLVER
*Action*: SA revolver
*Grips*: Walnut, synthetic
*Barrel*: 4.625 in., 5.5 in., 7.5 in.
*Sights*: Fixed front, rear notch
*Weight*: 35.2 oz.–38.4 oz.

*Caliber*: .22LR, .22 Mag
*Capacity*: 6 rounds
*Features*: Same frame size and weight of a Single Action Army revolver; antique or matte black finish; checkered grips; key operated, hammer block safety; side loading gate
*MSRP*. . . . . . . . . . . . . . . .$189–$285

## MODEL 1911 R1
*Action*: Autoloading
*Grips*: Double diamond walnut
*Barrel*: 5 in.
*Sights*: Fixed
*Weight*: 38.5 oz.
*Caliber*: .45 Auto
*Capacity*: 7 rounds
*Features*: Short trigger; double diamond walnut grips; modern enhancements include a lowered and flared ejection port; beveled magazine well; loaded chamber indicator; high-profile fixed sights in a three-white-dot pattern; match grade stainless-steel barrel; available in stainless steel
*MSRP*. . . . . . . . . . . . . . . . . . . .$729
*SS*:. . . . . . . . . . . . . . . . . . . . .$789

# Remington Arms

**REMINGTON MODEL
1911 R1**

# Rock River Arms

**ROCK RIVER ARMS
1911 POLY PISTOL**

**ROCK RIVER ARMS LAR-PDS PISTOL**

## 1911 POLY PISTOL
*Action*: SA
*Grips*: Polymer
*Barrel*: 5 in.
*Sights*: Dovetail front and rear
*Weight*: 32.6 oz.
*Caliber*: .45
*Capacity*: 7 rounds
*Features*: Chromoly barrel; polymer frame and mainspring housing; steel frame insert; steel slide; parkerized finish on metal; RRA overmolded grips; aluminum speed trigger; beavertail grip safety; RRA dovetail front and rear sights
*MSRP*. . . . . . . . . . . . . . . . . . . .$800

## LAR-PDS PISTOL
*Action*: Gas-operated autoloader with PPS (Performance Piston System)-AR style
*Grips*: Hogue rubber
*Barrel*: 8 in. chromoly

*Sights*: MS 1913 rail
*Weight*: 80 oz.
*Caliber*: 5.56mm Nato chamber for 5.56mm & .223
*Capacity*: 30 rounds
*Features*: A2 Flash Hider; aluminum tri-rail handguard; ambidextrous non-reciprocating charging handle
*MSRP*. . . . . . . . . . . . . .$1245–$1395

# Rossi

**ROSSI MODEL R352**

**ROSSI MODEL R461**

**ROSSI MODEL R851**

**ROSSI MODEL R972**

**ROSSI RANCH HAND**

## MODEL R351 AND R352

**Action**: DA revolver
**Grips**: Rubber
**Barrel**: 2 in.
**Sights**: Fixed, open
**Weight**: 24 oz.
**Caliber**: .38 Spl., .38 Spl. +P
**Capacity**: 5 rounds
**Features**: Blued or stainless steel finish; checkered grips; forged steel frame
R35102: . . . . . . . . . . . . . $401–$414
R35202: . . . . . . . . . . . . . $465–$479

## MODEL R462 AND R461

**Action**: DA revolver
**Grips**: Rubber
**Barrel**: 2 in.
**Sights**: Fixed, open
**Weight**: 26 oz.
**Caliber**: .357 Mag.
**Capacity**: 6 rounds
**Features**: Blued or stainless steel finish; checkered grips; forged steel frame
R46102: . . . . . . . . . . . . . $401–$414
R46202: . . . . . . . . . . . . . $465–$479

## MODEL R851

**Action**: DA revolver
**Grips**: Rubber
**Barrel**: 4 in.
**Sights**: Adjustable
**Weight**: 32 oz.
**Caliber**: .38 Spl., .38 Spl. +P
**Capacity**: 6 rounds
**Features**: Adjustable rear sight; blued finish; forged steel frame
MSRP . . . . . . . . . . . . . . $401–$414

## MODEL R971 AND R972

**Action**: DA revolver
**Grips**: Rubber
**Barrel**: 4 in., 6 in.
**Sights**: Target
**Weight**: 35 oz.
**Caliber**: .357 Mag., .38 Special

**Capacity**: 6 rounds
**Features**: Stainless steel or blued finish; deep contoured finger grooves in the grip for solid grasp and comfort; frame forged from steel
Blued: . . . . . . . . . . . . . . $465–$479
SS: . . . . . . . . . . . . . . . $523–$537

## RANCH HAND

**Action**: Lever-action repeating pistol
**Grips**: Walnut
**Barrel**: 12 in.
**Sights**: Gold-bead front w/adjustable buckhorn rear
**Weight**: 64 oz.
**Caliber**: .38 Special/.357 Mag., .45 Long Colt, .44 Mag., .45 LC
**Capacity**: 6 rounds
**Features**: Matte blued finish or blued case-hardened; Brazilian hardwood stock; oversize loop lever; investment-cast receiver
Blued: . . . . . . . . . . . . . . $595
Blued case-hardened: . . . . . . . $676

# Ruger

**RUGER 22/45 TARGET RIMFIRE PISTOL**

## 22/45 TARGET RIMFIRE PISTOL
*Action*: SA autoloader
*Grips*: Checkered cocobolo wood
*Barrel*: 4 in., 5.5 in.
*Sights*: Adjustable rear
*Weight*: 31–33 oz.
*Caliber*: .22LR
*Capacity*: 10 rounds
*Features*: Replaceable panels; Zytel polymer frame; blued finish; classic 1911 style pistol
**MSRP** . . . . . . . . . . . . . . . . **$359–$399**

**RUGER BISLEY**

**RUGER GP100**

## BISLEY
*Action*: SA revolver
*Grips*: Hardwood
*Barrel*: 7.5 in.
*Sights*: Ramp front, adjustable rear
*Weight*: 48 oz.–50 oz.
*Caliber*: .44 Mag, .45 Colt
*Capacity*: 6 rounds
*Features*: Blued alloy steel frame; patented Ruger transfer bar mechanism and loading gate interlock; traditional western style hand-filling grip featuring rosewood grip panels; ramp front and precision adjustable rear sights
**MSRP** . . . . . . . . . . . . . . . . . . . **$799**

## GP100
*Action*: DA revolver
*Grips*: Black hogue monogrip
*Barrel*: 3 in., 4.2 in., 6 in.
*Sights*: Ramp front, fixed or adjustable rear
*Weight*: 36 oz.–45 oz.
*Caliber*: .327 Fed Mag., .357 Mag.
*Capacity*: 6, 7 rounds
*Features*: Satin stainless or blued finish; stainless steel or alloy steel frame; cushioned rubber grip; transfer bar; triple-locking cylinder
**MSRP** . . . . . . . . . . . . . . . . $699–$759

# Ruger

**RUGER LC9 9MM**

**RUGER LCP .380 ACP**

**RUGER LCP CENTERFIRE PISTOL**

**RUGER LCR**

### LC9 9MM

**Action**: Autoloader
**Grips**: Glass-filled nylon
**Barrel**: 3.12 in.
**Sights**: Adjustable 3-dot
**Weight**: 17.6 oz.
**Caliber**: 9mm Luger
**Capacity**: 7+1 rounds
**Features**: Alloy steel barrel and slide; blued finish; adjustable 3-dot/LaserMax CenterFire sights; black, high performance, glass-filled nylon grips
**MSRP**. . . . . . . . . . . . . . . . . . . **$529**

### LCP .380 ACP

**Action**: Autoloader
**Grips**: Glass-filled nylon
**Barrel**: 2.75 in.
**Sights**: Crimson Trace/LaserMax
**Weight**: 9.9 oz.
**Caliber**: .380 Auto

**Capacity**: 6+1 rounds
**Features**: Alloy steel barrel and slide; blued finish; fixed/LaserMax CenterFire sights; black, high performance, glass-filled nylon grips
**MSRP**. . . . . . . . . . . . . . . . . . . **$449**

### LCP CENTERFIRE PISTOL

**Action**: DA autoloader
**Grips**: Black, glass-filled nylon
**Barrel**: 2.75 in.
**Sights**: Fixed, optional Crimson Trace laserguard or LaserMax CenterFire
**Weight**: 9.4–10 oz.
**Caliber**: .380 Auto
**Capacity**: 6+1 rounds
**Features**: Blued, alloy slide and barrel; fixed front and rear sights are integral to the slide; hammer is recessed within the slide; factory-fitted trigger-guard-mounted laser available from

LaserMaz and Crimson Trace
**MSRP**. . . . . . . . . . . . . . . . **$379–$449**
**Crimson Trace:** . . . . . . . . . . . . **$559**

### LCR (LIGHTWEIGHT COMPACT REVOLVER)

**Action**: DA revolver
**Grips**: Hogue Tamer and Crimson Trace lasergrips
**Barrel**: 1.8 in.
**Sights**: U-Notch Integral rear
**Weight**: 13 oz.–17.1 oz.
**Caliber**: .22 Mag., .22LR, .38 Spl. +P, .357 Mag.
**Capacity**: 5, 6, 8 rounds
**Features**: Advanced target gray cylinder finish; option of replaceable, pinned ramp or XS standard dot tritium front sight
**MSRP**. . . . . . . . . . . . . . . . **$529–$879**

RUGER MARK III HUNTER

RUGER MARK III STANDARD

RUGER NEW BEARCAT

RUGER NEW MODEL SINGLE-SIX .17 HMR

RUGER NEW MODEL SUPER BLACKHAWK

## MARK III HUNTER

**Action**: SA autoloading, recoil operated
**Grips**: Brown or Target laminate
**Barrel**: 6.88 in.
**Sights**: Fiber optic front, adjustable rear
**Weight**: 41 oz.–43.7 oz.
**Caliber**: .22LR
**Capacity**: 10 rounds
**Features**: Stainless steel frame with satin finish; fluted bull barrel; visible loaded chamber indicator
**MSRP** . . . . . . . . . . . . . . . .**$679–$729**

## MARK III STANDARD

**Action**: Autoloader
**Grips**: Checkered plastic
**Barrel**: 4.75 in., 6 in.
**Sights**: Open, adjustable
**Weight**: 35–37 oz.
**Caliber**: .22LR
**Capacity**: 10 rounds
**Features**: Steel frame with blued finish;
loaded chamber indicator; manual safety; internal cylindrical bolt
**MSRP** . . . . . . . . . . . . . . . . . . . **$389**

## NEW BEARCAT

**Action**: SA revolver
**Grips**: Hardwood
**Barrel**: 4.2 in.
**Sights**: Blade front, integral notch
**Weight**: 24 oz.
**Caliber**: .22LR
**Capacity**: 6 rounds
**Features**: Alloy steel with blued finish or stainless steel frame with satin stainless finish; decorative cylinder; transfer bar mechanism; features one piece frame reminiscent of old Remington Civil War-era revolvers
**Alloy Steel:** . . . . . . . . . . . . . . **$569**
**SS:** . . . . . . . . . . . . . . . . . . . . . **$619**

## NEW MODEL SINGLE-SIX .17 HMR

**Action**: SA revolver
**Grips**: Black checkered hard rubber
**Barrel**: 6.5 in.
**Sights**: Ramp front, adjustable rear
**Weight**: 35 oz.
**Caliber**: .17 HMR
**Capacity**: 6 rounds
**Features**: Alloy steel frame with blued finish; transfer bar mechanism
**MSRP** . . . . . . . . . . . . . . . . . . . **$569**

## NEW MODEL SUPER BLACKHAWK

**Action**: SA revolver
**Grips**: Hardwood
**Barrel**: 4.62 in., 5.5 in., 7.5 in., 10.5 in.
**Sights**: Ramp front, adjustable rear
**Weight**: 45–55 oz.
**Caliber**: .44 Mag
**Capacity**: 6 rounds
**Features**: Alloy steel or stainless steel frame; blued or satin stainless finish; transfer bar mechanism; western-style grip
**MSRP** . . . . . . . . . . . . . . . .**$739–$769**

# Ruger

**RUGER P-SERIES**

**RUGER SP101**

**RUGER SP101 .22LR**

**RUGER REDHAWK**

**RUGER SR9C**

## P-SERIES

**Action**: Autoloader
**Grips**: Black polymer
**Barrel**: 3.9 in.
**Sights**: Fixed 3-dot
**Weight**: 27 oz.
**Caliber**: .45 Auto, 9mm Luger
**Capacity**: 10+1, 15+1 rounds
**Features**: Stainless or blued barrel;
ambidextrous manual safety; slide;
grip frame; contoured grip
**MSRP** . . . . . . . . . . . . . . . $399–$439

## REDHAWK

**Action**: DA revolver
**Grips**: Hardwood or black Hogue
monogrip
**Barrel**: 4.2 in., 5.5 in., 7.5 in.
**Sights**: Ramp front, adjustable rear
**Weight**: 46–54 oz.
**Caliber**: .44 Mag., .45 Colt
**Capacity**: 6 rounds
**Features**: Satin stainless finish; triple-
locking cylinder; single spring
mechanism; easy sighting; stainless
steel construction; dual chambering;
transfer bar
**MSRP** . . . . . . . . . . . . . $989–$1049

## SP101

**Action**: DA revolver
**Grips**: Black rubber
**Barrel**: 2.25 in., 3.06 in., 4.2 in.
**Sights**: Fixed, windage adjustable
**Weight**: 25 oz.–30 oz.
**Caliber**: .357 Mag., .22LR, .38 Spl.
**Capacity**: 5 or 6 rounds
**Features**: Stainless steel frame with
satin finish; cushioned rubber grip;
grip frame; transfer bar; triple-locking
cylinder
**MSRP** . . . . . . . . . . . . . . . $659–$699

## SP101 .22LR

**Action**: DA Revolver
**Grips**: Rubber, wood
**Barrel**: 4.20 in.
**Sights**: Fiber optic
**Weight**: 29.5 oz.
**Caliber**: .22LR
**Capacity**: 8 rounds

**Features**: Stainless steel frame with
satin finish; cushioned rubber grip with
engraved wood; grip frame; transfer
bar; triple-locking cylinder
**MSRP** . . . . . . . . . . . . . . . . . . $699

## SR9C

**Action**: DA autoloader
**Grips**: Black, glass-filled, nylon
**Barrel**: 3.4 in.
**Sights**: Adjustable 3-dot
**Weight**: 23.4 oz.
**Caliber**: 9mm Luger
**Capacity**: 10 or 17 rounds
**Features**: Compact version of SR9;
black alloy or brushed stainless
6-groove rifling; high visibility sights;
accessory mounting rail
**MSRP** . . . . . . . . . . . . . . . . . . $529

RUGER SR22 RIMFIRE PISTOL

RUGER SR40

RUGER SUPER REDHAWK

RUGER VAQUERO BISLEY

RUGER VAQUERO BLUED

## SR22 RIMFIRE PISTOL
**Action**: DA autoloader
**Grips**: Polymer
**Barrel**: 3.5 in.
**Sights**: Adjustable 3-dot
**Weight**: 17.5 oz.
**Caliber**: .22LR
**Capacity**: 10 rounds
**Features**: 3-dot sight system has fixed front sight and adjustable rear sight; polymer frame and two interchangeable rubberized grips; underside Picatinny rail; aluminum slide; ambidextrous manual thumb safety/decocking lever; ambidextrous magazine release
**MSRP** . . . . . . . . . . . . . . . . . . $399
**Silver:** . . . . . . . . . . . . . . . . . $419
**Threaded Barrel:** . . . . . . . . . . $439

## SR40
**Action**: Autoloader
**Grips**: Black, high performance, glass-filled nylon
**Barrel**: 4.1 in.
**Sights**: Adjustable 3-dot
**Weight**: 27.25 oz.
**Caliber**: .40 S&W
**Capacity**: 10 or 15 rounds

**Features**: Glass-filled nylon frame; ambidextrous operating controls; trigger system and reversible; fully adjustable three-dot sights; integral accessory rail; backstraps are identical to SR9; Nitridox pro black or brushed stainless finish
**MSRP** . . . . . . . . . . . . . . . . . . $529

## SUPER REDHAWK
**Action**: DA revolver
**Grips**: Black Hogue Tamer monogrip
**Barrel**: 7.5 in., 9.5 in.
**Sights**: Ramp front, adjustable rear
**Weight**: 53 oz.–58 oz.
**Caliber**: .44 Mag., .454 Casull, .480 Ruger
**Capacity**: 6 rounds
**Features**: Satin stainless finish; triple-locking cylinder; integral scope system; corrosion-resistant; extended frame; dual chambering; transfer bar
**MSRP** . . . . . . . . . . . . . $1049–$1079

## VAQUERO BISLEY
**Action**: SA revolver
**Grips**: Simulated ivory
**Barrel**: 5.5 in.
**Sights**: Fixed
**Weight**: 41 oz.–45 oz.
**Caliber**: .45 Colt, .357 Mag
**Capacity**: 6 rounds
**Features**: Stainless steel frame with high-gloss stainless finish
**MSRP** . . . . . . . . . . . . . . . . . . $809

## VAQUERO BLUED
**Action**: SA revolver
**Grips**: Black checkered
**Barrel**: 4.62 in., 5.5 in.
**Sights**: Fixed
**Weight**: 40 oz.–43 oz.
**Caliber**: .45 Colt, .357 Mag.
**Capacity**: 6 rounds
**Features**: Blued finish alloy steel; reverse Indexing Pawl; ejector rod head; transfer bar mechanism; internal lock
**MSRP** . . . . . . . . . . . . . . . . . . $739

# Sig Sauer

HANDGUNS

**SIG SAUER 1911 TRADITIONAL**

**SIG SAUER 1911 ULTRA TWO-TONE**

**SIG SAUER MOSQUITO**

**SIG SAUER P210**

## 1911 TRADITIONAL
*Action*: SA autoloader
*Grips*: Custom shop wood, aluminum, or polymer grips
*Barrel*: 4.2 in.
*Sights*: Novak Night, platinum elite model has adjustable combat night sights
*Weight*: 35.5 oz.
*Caliber*: .45 ACP
*Capacity*: 8 rounds
*Features*: Accessory rail; beavertail frame; checkered grip; match grade barrel, hammer/sear set and trigger; stainless finish on stainless model; duo-tone finish on two-tone model; nitron finish on TACOPS model
**Compact stainless:** . . . . . . . . **$1142**
**Match Elite stainless:** . . . . . . . **$1128**
**Two-Tone Match Elite:** . . . . . . **$1128**
**TACOPS:** . . . . . . . . . . . . . . . **$1213**

## 1911 ULTRA
*Action*: SA
*Grips*: Black diamondwood, rosewood
*Barrel*: 3.3 in.
*Sights*: Low-pro night sights

*Weight*: 28 oz.
*Caliber*: .45 ACP
*Capacity*: 6+1 rounds
*Features*: Smallest SIG 1911 yet; stainless slide over alloy frame; unique recoil system; 26 lpi front strap checkering; combine to make a very controllable and comfortable small .45; skeletonized trigger; two variants: Nitron (all black with black diamondwood grips) and Two-Tone (natural stainless slide over black hardcoat anodized aluminum frame; rosewood grips)
**Nitron:** . . . . . . . . . . **$1142**
**Two-Tone:** . . . . . . . **$1156**

## MOSQUITO
*Action*: Autoloader
*Grips*: Black polymer
*Barrel*: 3.9 in.
*Sights*: Adjustable rear
*Weight*: 24.6 oz.
*Caliber*: .22LR
*Capacity*: 10 rounds
*Features*: Integrated accessory rail; rugged blowback system; fixed barrel;

superior ergonomic grip; internal locking device; slide mounted ambidextrous safety; blued slide finish; black polymer frame finish; other models available with various color schemes and features
**MSRP** . . . . . . . . . . . . . . . . . . . **$390**

## P210
*Action*: SA autoloader
*Grips*: Custom wood
*Barrel*: 4.7 in.
*Sights*: Post & notch
*Weight*: 37.4 oz.
*Caliber*: 9mm
*Capacity*: 8 rounds
*Features*: Durable nitron frame and slide finish; chrome-moly barrel; carbon steel slide; frame machined from solid billet steel; slide magazine release
**MSRP** . . . . . . . . . . . . . . . . . . . **$2199**

**SIG SAUER P220**

**SIG SAUER P224 EQUINOX**

**SIG SAUER P226**

**SIG SAUER P226 MK25**

## P220

**Action**: Autoloader
**Grips**: Polymer, laminated or custom shop wood
**Barrel**: 4.4 in.
**Sights**: Siglite night
**Weight**: 30.4 oz.–31.2 oz.
**Caliber**: .45 ACP
**Capacity**: 8 rounds
**Features**: Nitron finish, light-weight alloy frame; accessory rail
**Standard:**.................. $993
**Night Sights:** ............. $1068
**Two-Tone Dak:**............ $1079

## P224

**Action**: SA/DA or DAO
**Grips**: Hogue, ergonomic
**Barrel**: 3.5 in.
**Sights**: Tritium, fiber optic, or night sights
**Weight**: 25.4 oz.
**Caliber**: 9mm, .40, .357
**Capacity**: 10+1, 11+1 rounds
**Features**: Classic SIG in a true sub-compact; 4 variants: SIG Anti-Snag (de-horned slide, ergonomic grips, night sights), Equinox (2-tone Nitron SS slide, Tru-Glo Tritium fiber optic front, SIGLITE rear, black diamondwood grips), Nickel (nickel slide and controls, Hogue grips, night sights), Extreme (Hogue black and gray Piranha grips, night sights)
**Equinox:** ................. $1218
**Extreme:** ................. $1146
**Nickel:**................... $1125
**SAS:**..................... $1125

## P226

**Action**: DA/SA autoloader
**Grips**: One-piece ergo grip, extreme model features Hogue custom G10 grips, custom wood w/ SIG Medallion
**Barrel**: 4.4 in.
**Sights**: Contrast, Siglite night optional
**Weight**: 34 oz.–34.4 oz.
**Caliber**: 9mm, .357 Sig, .40 S&W
**Capacity**: 9mm: 10 or 15 rounds; .357 Sig: 10 or 12 rounds, .40 S&W: 10 or 12 rounds
**Features**: Black hard anodized frame finish; nitron slide finish; accessory rail; extreme model features SRT trigger and front cocking serrations

**Standard:**................. $993
**Night Sights:** ............. $1068
**Extreme:** ................. $1213
**Elite SAO:** ................ $1218
**Engraved:**................. $1289
**Engraved Stainless:** ........ $1402

## P226 MK25

**Action**: SA/DA
**Grips**: Polymer
**Barrel**: 4.4 in.
**Sights**: SIGLITE night sights
**Weight**: 34.4 oz.
**Caliber**: 9mm
**Capacity**: 10, 15 rounds
**Features**: New designation of the Navy's P226 9mm variant issued to NSWG; still with phosphated internals; (three) 15 round magazines; classic two-piece polymer grips; anchor engraved on slide; now with M1913 Picatinny rail; actual UID scanable serial number label; packaged with FDE grip band and a certificate of authenticity
**MSRP**................... $1142

# Sig Sauer

**SIG SAUER P229**

**SIG SAUER P232**

**SIG SAUER P238**

**SIG SAUER P239**

## P229

*Action*: Autoloader
*Grips*: Black polymer factor grips
*Barrel*: 3.9 in.
*Sights*: Contrast, Siglite night optional
*Weight*: 32 oz.
*Caliber*: 9mm, .40 S&W, .357 Sig
*Capacity*: 9mm: 10, 13 rounds; .357 Sig: 10, 12 rounds, .40 S&W: 10, 12 rounds
*Features*: Black hard anodized frame finish; nitron slide finish; accessory rail
**MSRP** . . . . . . . . . . . . . . . . . . . **$993**
**Night Sights:** . . . . . . . . . . . . . **$1068**

## P232

*Action*: Autoloader
*Grips*: Polymer
*Barrel*: 3.6 in.
*Sights*: Siglite night
*Weight*: 18.5 oz.
*Caliber*: .380 ACP
*Capacity*: 7 rounds
*Features*: Black polymer factor grips; blued finish
**MSRP** . . . . . . . . . . . . . . . . . . . **$649**
**Night Sights:** . . . . . . . . . . . . . **$720**

## P238

*Action*: SA autoloader
*Grips*: Fluted polymer, Rosewood Tribal, Pearl, Tribal Engraved Aluminum, Hogue pink rubber
*Barrel*: 2.7 in.
*Sights*: Siglite night
*Weight*: 15.2 oz.
*Caliber*: .380 ACP (9mm Short)
*Capacity*: 6 rounds
*Features*: Nitron slide finish; beavertail style frame
**MSRP** . . . . . . . . . . . . . . . **$679–$779**

## P239

*Action*: DA autoloader
*Grips*: Polymer, tactical model features black polymer factory grips
*Barrel*: 3.6 in., 4 in.
*Sights*: Contrast, Siglite night optional
*Weight*: 29.5 oz.
*Caliber*: 9mm, .40 S&W, .357 Sig
*Capacity*: 8 rounds (9mm), 7 rounds (.40 S&W, .357 Sig)
*Features*: Black polymer factor grips; black hard anodized frame finish; nitron frame finish
**Contrast Sights:** . . . . . . . . . . . . **$993**
**Night Sights:** . . . . . . . . . . . . . **$1085**
**Tactical:** . . . . . . . . . . . . . . . . **$1176**
**Hogue G-10 Piranha:** . . . . . . . **$1219**

# Sig Sauer

## P250 COMPACT

**Action**: Locked breech DAO semiauto
**Grips**: Interchangeable polymer
**Barrel**: 3.9 in.
**Sights**: Siglite Night
**Weight**: 25.1 oz.
**Caliber**: 9mm, .40 S&W, .45 ACP
**Capacity**: 9, 13, 15 rounds
**Features**: Interchangeable polymer grip shell with stainless insert; nitron slide finish; interchangeable grip sizes and calibers
**Contrast:** . . . . . . . . . . . . . . . . . **$570**
**Night Sights:** . . . . . . . . . . . . . **$642**

SIG SAUER P250 COMPACT

SIG SAUER P250 2SUM

SIG SAUER P250 2SUM

## P250 2SUM

**Action**: DA autoloader
**Grips**: Black polymer
**Barrel**: 4.7 in.
**Sights**: Siglite Night
**Weight**: 29.4 oz.
**Caliber**: 9mm, .40 S&W
**Capacity**: 17 (full-size 9mm), 14 (full-size .40 S&W) rounds
**Features**: Full size P250 with all the components to rapidly convert it to the P250 subcompact with 3.6 in. barrel (24.9 oz.)
**MSRP** . . . . . . . . . . . . . . . . . . . . **$813**
**Night Sights:** . . . . . . . . . . . . . **$885**

SIG SAUER P290

SIG SAUER SP2022

## P290

**Action**: Autoloader
**Grips**: Black polymer
**Barrel**: 2.9 in.
**Sights**: Siglite or Contrast
**Weight**: 20.5 oz.
**Caliber**: 9mm
**Capacity**: 6+1 rounds
**Features**: Polymer frame; slide is machined from solid stainless-steel billet; interchangeable grips; features drift-adjustable Siglite sights or high-contrast black sight; available with Rainbow Titanium-Coated slide finish
**MSRP** . . . . . . . . . . . . . . . . . . . . **$570**

SIG SAUER P938
BLACKWOOD

## P938

**Action**: SA
**Grips**: Synthetic or wood
**Barrel**: 3 in.
**Sights**: SIGLITE night sights, TFO front on Equinox
**Weight**: 16 oz.
**Caliber**: 9mm, .40, .357
**Capacity**: 6+1, 7+1 rounds
**Features**: Ambi safety; SIG's most compact 9mm; initial offerings in 5 variants: Rosewood (nitron coated stainless slide over hard anodized alloy frame; rosewood grips), Blackwood (natural stainless slide over hard anodized black alloy frame; black diamondwood grips), Extreme (nitron coated stainless slide over hard anodized alloy frame; Hogue G-10 piranha grips in black/gray), SAS (SIG anti-snag dehorned slide and frame; natural stainless slide over hard anodized black alloy frame; walnut stippled grips), Equinox (polished Nitron two-tone slide over hardcoat anodized frame; TFO front with SIGLITE rear; black diamondwood grips)
**Black Aluminum:** . . . . . . . . . . . **$823**
**Blackwood:** . . . . . . . . . . . . . . . **$809**
**Equinox:** . . . . . . . . . . . . . . . . . **$823**
**Extreme:** . . . . . . . . . . . . . . . . . **$823**
**Rosewood:** . . . . . . . . . . . . . . . . **$795**
**SAS:** . . . . . . . . . . . . . . . . . . . . . **$838**

## SP2022

**Action**: Autoloader
**Grips**: Polymer
**Barrel**: 3.9 in., 4.4 in.
**Sights**: Contrast, Siglite Night optional
**Weight**: 29 oz.
**Caliber**: 9mm, .40 S&W
**Capacity**: 10 or 15 rounds (9mm), 10 or 12 rounds (.40 S&W)
**Features**: Accessory rail; wear-resistant polymer frame; black polymer frame finish; nitron slide finish
**MSRP** . . . . . . . . . . . . . . . . . . . . **$570**
**Night sights:** . . . . . . . . . . . . . . **$642**
**Nitron threaded barrel:** . . . . . . **$713**

# Smith & Wesson

### BODYGUARD 38
**Action**: DA revolver
**Grips**: Matte black synthetic
**Barrel**: 1.9 in.
**Sights**: Integrated Insight laser system
**Weight**: 4.3 oz.
**Caliber**: .38 S&W Special +P
**Capacity**: 5 rounds
**Features**: Stainless steel cylinder with PVD coating
**MSRP** . . . . . . . . . . . . . . . . . . . **$509**

### BODYGUARD 380
**Action**: DA autoloader
**Grips**: Polymer
**Barrel**: 2.75 in.
**Sights**: Stainless steel drift-adjustable front and rear
**Weight**: 11.85 oz.
**Caliber**: .380 Auto
**Capacity**: 6+1 rounds
**Features**: Manual thumb safety external takedown lever; external slide stop; barrel and slide stainless with Melonite finish; integrated Insight laser sighting system
**MSRP** . . . . . . . . . . . . . . . . . . . **$419**

### CLASSIC M57
**Action**: DA N-frame revolver
**Grips**: Checkered square-butt walnut
**Barrel**: 6 in.
**Sights**: Pinned red ramp front, Micro adjustable white outline rear;
**Weight**: 4.8 oz.
**Caliber**: .41 Magnum
**Capacity**: 6 rounds
**Features**: Bright blued or nickel finish; carbon steel frame; classic style thumbpiece; color case wide spur hammer; color case wide serrated target trigger
**M57:** . . . . . . . . . . . . . . . . . . . **$979**

### CLASSIC M586 REVOLVER
**Action**: SA/DA revolver
**Grips**: Wood
**Barrel**: 4 in., 6 in.
**Sights**: Adjustable
**Weight**: 40.9 oz.–46.3 oz.
**Caliber**: .357 Mag., .38 S&W Special +P
**Capacity**: 6 rounds
**Features**: Carbon steel frame and cylinder with blued finish; adjustable white outline rear sight and red ramp

**SMITH & WESSON BODYGUARD 38**

**SMITH & WESSON BODYGUARD 380**

**SMITH & WESSON CLASSIC M57**

**SMITH & WESSON CLASSIC M586 REVOLVER**

**SMITH & WESSON GOVERNOR**

**SMITH & WESSON M10**

front sight; square-butt design; checkered wood grips
**MSRP** . . . . . . . . . . . . . . . . . . . **$809**

### GOVERNOR
**Action**: SA/DA revolver
**Grips**: Synthetic, Crimson Trace
**Barrel**: 2.75 in.
**Sights**: Fixed
**Weight**: 29.6 oz.
**Caliber**: .45 Colt, .45 ACP, .410 Ga. 2.5 in. shotshells
**Capacity**: 6 rounds
**Features**: Patented heat-treated scandium frame; PVD coated cylinder; dovetailed Tritium front night sight; fixed rear sight; matte black finish;

optional factory-installed Crimson Trace Lasergrips
**Standard:** . . . . . . . . . . . . . . . . . **$796**
**Crimson Trace:** . . . . . . . . . . **$1019**

### M10
**Action**: SA/DA revolver
**Grips**: Wood
**Barrel**: 4 in.
**Sights**: Black blade, fixed
**Weight**: 36 oz.
**Caliber**: .38 S&W Special +P
**Capacity**: 6 rounds
**Features**: Carbon steel frame; carbon steel cylinder; blued finish; medium size frame; exposed hammer
**MSRP** . . . . . . . . . . . . . . . . . . . **$719**

**SMITH & WESSON M27 CLASSIC**

**SMITH & WESSON M29**

**SMITH & WESSON M36**

**SMITH & WESSON M60**

**SMITH & WESSON M317**

**SMITH & WESSON M325 THUNDER RANCH**

## M27 CLASSIC
**Action**: SA/DA revolver
**Grips**: Checkered square butt walnut
**Barrel**: 4 in.
**Sights**: Pinned serrated ramp front; Micro adjustable with cross serrations
**Weight**: 48.5 oz.
**Caliber**: .357 Mag., .38 S&W Special +P
**Capacity**: 6 rounds
**Features**: Carbon steel frame; bright blued or blued finish
**MSRP** . . . . . . . . . . . . . . . . . . . **$989**

## M29
**Action**: Revolver
**Grips**: Checkered square butt walnut; 6 in. model features Altamont Service walnut grips
**Barrel**: 4 in., 6.5 in.
**Sights**: Red ramp, micro adjustable rear
**Weight**: 48.5 oz.
**Caliber**: .44 Mag., .44 S&W Special
**Capacity**: 6 rounds
**Features**: Carbon steel frame with nickel finish, available blued
**4 in.:** . . . . . . . . . . . . . . . **$969–$1019**
**6.5 in.:** . . . . . . . . . . . . . **$1129–$1219**

## M36
**Action**: Revolver
**Grips**: Wood
**Barrel**: 1.8 in.
**Sights**: Integral front, fixed rear
**Weight**: 19.5 oz.
**Caliber**: .38 S&W Special +P
**Capacity**: 5 rounds
**Features**: Small sized frame; exposed hammer; carbon steel frame and cylinder; blued or nickel finish; single or double action
**MSRP** . . . . . . . . . . . . . . . . . . . **$729**

## M60
**Action**: Revolver
**Grips**: Synthetic, wood
**Barrel**: 2.125 in., 3 in.
**Sights**: Black blade front, adjustable rear
**Weight**: 22.6 oz.–23.2 oz.
**Caliber**: .357 Mag., .38 S&W Special +P
**Capacity**: 5 rounds
**Features**: Satin stainless finish; single- or double-action; stainless steel fame and cylinder
**MSRP** . . . . . . . . . . . . . . . . **$729–$779**

## M317
**Action**: SA/DA revolver
**Grips**: Synthetic
**Barrel**: 1.875 in.
**Sights**: Integral front, fixed rear
**Weight**: 10.8 oz.
**Caliber**: .22LR
**Capacity**: 8 rounds
**Features**: Aluminum alloy frame and cylinder; clear coat finish; small frame with exposed hammer; double- or single-action
**MSRP** . . . . . . . . . . . . . . . . . . . **$699**

## M325 THUNDER RANCH
**Action**: SA/DA revolver
**Grips**: Synthetic
**Barrel**: 4 in.
**Sights**: Interchangeable gold bead front; adjustable rear
**Weight**: 31 oz.
**Caliber**: .45 ACP
**Capacity**: 6 rounds
**Features**: Scandium alloy frame; stainless steel cylinder; matte black
**MSRP** . . . . . . . . . . . . . . . . . . . **$1289**

# Smith & Wesson

SMITH & WESSON
M327

SMITH & WESSON
M327 TRR8

SMITH & WESSON
M386 XL HUNTER

SMITH & WESSON M442

SMITH & WESSON M442
MACHINE ENGRAVED

## M327

**Action**: Revolver
**Grips**: Wood
**Barrel**: 2 in.
**Sights**: Red ramp front, fixed rear
**Weight**: 21.4 oz.
**Caliber**: .357 Mag., .38 S&W Special +P
**Capacity**: 8 rounds
**Features**: Color case with overtravel stop; color case tear drop with pinned sear; large frame size; exposed hammer; matte black finish; scandium alloy frame and titanium alloy cylinder; Polish button rifling; smooth double action with Wolff Mainspring
**MSRP** . . . . . . . . . . . . . . . . . . $1269

## M327 TRR8

**Action**: SA/DA revolver
**Grips**: Synthetic
**Barrel**: 5 in.
**Sights**: Interchangeable front; adjustable V-notch rear
**Weight**: 35.3 oz.
**Caliber**: .357 Mag., .38 S&W Special +P
**Capacity**: 8 rounds
**Features**: Scandium alloy frame; stainless steel cylinder; matte black; large size frame; exposed hammer; equipment rails
**MSRP** . . . . . . . . . . . . . . . . . . $1289

## M386 XL HUNTER

**Action**: SA/DA revolver
**Grips**: Synthetic
**Barrel**: 6 in.
**Sights**: Hi-Viz fiber optic red front, adjustable rear
**Weight**: 30 oz.
**Caliber**: .357 Mag., .38 S&W Special +P
**Capacity**: 7 rounds
**Features**: Scandium alloy frame; stainless steel cylinder; matte black; medium size frame; exposed hammer
**MSRP** . . . . . . . . . . . . . . . . . . $899

## M442

**Action**: DA revolver
**Grips**: Synthetic
**Barrel**: 1.87 in.
**Sights**: Integral front, fixed rear
**Weight**: 15 oz.
**Caliber**: .38 S&W Special +P

**Capacity**: 5 rounds
**Features**: Aluminum alloy frame; stainless steel cylinder; matte black finish; small size frame; internal hammer; cylinder cut for moon clips
**MSRP** . . . . . . . . . . . . . . . . . . $459

## M442 MACHINE ENGRAVED

**Action**: DA revolver
**Grips**: Engraved wood
**Barrel**: 1.875 in.
**Sights**: Integral front, fixed rear
**Weight**: 15 oz.
**Caliber**: .38 S&W Special +P
**Capacity**: 5 rounds
**Features**: Aluminum alloy frame; stainless steel barrel/cylinder; matte black
**MSRP** . . . . . . . . . . . . . . . . . . $729

## M460 XVR

**Action**: SA/DA revolver
**Grips**: Synthetic
**Barrel**: 10.5 in.
**Sights**: Interchangeable front, adjustable rear
**Weight**: 82.5 oz.
**Caliber**: .460 S&W Mag.
**Capacity**: 5 rounds
**Features**: Satin stainless finish; stainless steel frame and cylinder; X-Large size frame; exposed tear drop chrome hammer; .312 chrome trigger; multi-caliber capability: .454 Casull, .45 Colt; integral weaver base for optic mounting
**MSRP** . . . . . . . . . . . . . . . . . . $1519

SMITH & WESSON M460 XVR

# Smith & Wesson

SMITH & WESSON M500

SMITH & WESSON M617

## M500

**Action**: SA/DA revolver
**Grips**: Synthetic
**Barrel**: 6.5 in.
**Sights**: Red ramp front, adjustable white outline rear
**Weight**: 60.7 oz.
**Caliber**: .500 S&W mag.
**Capacity**: 5 rounds
**Features**: Stainless steel frame and cylinder; satin stainless finish; integral compensator; internal lock; recoil tamed with effective muzzle compensator
**MSRP** . . . . . . . . . . . . . . . . . . . **$1249**

## M617

**Action**: SA/DA revolver
**Grips**: Synthetic
**Barrel**: 4 in.
**Sights**: Partridge front, adjustable rear
**Weight**: 38.9 oz.
**Caliber**: .22LR
**Capacity**: 10 rounds
**Features**: Stainless steel frame and cylinder with satin stainless finish; medium size frame with exposed hammer
**MSRP** . . . . . . . . . . . . . . . . . . . **$829**

## M625

**Action**: SA/DA revolver
**Grips**: Hogue combat laminate, red, white & blue
**Barrel**: 4 in.
**Sights**: Gold bead S&W interchangeable front; Black adjustable rear
**Weight**: 42 oz.
**Caliber**: .45 ACP
**Capacity**: 6 rounds
**Features**: Stainless steel frame and cylinder with satin stainless finish; deep cut broached rifling; chambered charge holes; PC trigger with stop
**MSRP** . . . . . . . . . . . . . . . . . . . **$1049**

## M625 JM

**Action**: SA/DA revolver
**Grips**: Jerry Miculek wood
**Barrel**: 4 in.
**Sights**: Gold bead partridge front, adjustable rear
**Weight**: 40.3 oz.
**Caliber**: .45 ACP
**Capacity**: 6 rounds
**Features**: Stainless steel frame and cylinder; matte stainless; large size frame; exposed hammer; Miculek style .265 wide grooved speed trigger; low reflection bead blast finish
**MSRP** . . . . . . . . . . . . . . . . . . . **$979**

## M627

**Action**: SA/DA revolver
**Grips**: Synthetic
**Barrel**: 5 in.
**Sights**: Interchangeable front; adjustable rear

SMITH & WESSON M625

SMITH & WESSON M627

**Weight**: 44 oz.
**Caliber**: .357 Mag., .38 S&W Special +P
**Capacity**: 8 rounds
**Features**: Stainless steel frame and cylinder; matte stainless; large size frame; exposed hammer
**MSRP** . . . . . . . . . . . . . . . . . . . **$1249**

## M629

**Action**: SA/DA revolver
**Grips**: Synthetic
**Barrel**: 5 in.
**Sights**: Red ramp, adjustable white outline
**Weight**: 44.3 oz.
**Caliber**: .44 Mag, .44 S&W Special
**Capacity**: 6 rounds
**Features**: Stainless steel frame and cylinder with satin stainless finish; exposed hammer
**MSRP** . . . . . . . . . . . . . . . . . . . **$949**

SMITH & WESSON M625 JM

SMITH & WESSON M629

# Smith & Wesson

SMITH & WESSON
M629 V-COMP

SMITH & WESSON M640

SMITH & WESSON M686

SMITH & WESSON
M686 SSR

SMITH & WESSON
M&P 9MM

SMITH & WESSON
M&P40 COMPACT

SMITH & WESSON
M&P45

## M629 V-COMP
*Action*: SA/DA revolver
*Grips*: Synthetic
*Barrel*: 4 in.
*Sights*: Adjustable orange dovetail front, adjustable black rear
*Weight*: 40.3 oz.
*Caliber*: .44 Mag., .44 S&W Special
*Capacity*: 6 rounds
*Features*: Stainless steel frame and cylinder with matte finish; removable compensator and cap muzzle protector; chambered charge holes; ball detent lock-up; chromed hammer and trigger with overtravel stop
**MSRP** . . . . . . . . . . . . . . . . . **$1509**

## M640
*Action*: DA revolver
*Grips*: Synthetic
*Barrel*: 2.1 in.
*Sights*: Black blade front, fixed rear
*Weight*: 23 oz.
*Caliber*: .357 Mag., .38 S&W Special +P
*Capacity*: 5 rounds
*Features*: Stainless steel frame and cylinder; satin stainless finish; Pro Series
**MSRP** . . . . . . . . . . . . . . . . . . **$809**

## M686
*Action*: Revolver
*Grips*: Synthetic
*Barrel*: 2.5 in.
*Sights*: Red ramp front, adjustable white outline rear
*Weight*: 34.7 oz.
*Caliber*: .357 Mag., .38 S&W Special +P

*Capacity*: 6 rounds
*Features*: Stainless steel frame and cylinder; satin stainless finish; exposed hammer; single- and double-action; built on L frame
**MSRP** . . . . . . . . . . . . . . . . . . **$829**

## M686 SSR
*Action*: Revolver
*Grips*: Wood
*Barrel*: 4 in.
*Sights*: Interchangeable front, adjustable rear
*Weight*: 38.3 oz.
*Caliber*: .357 Mag., .38 S&W Special +P
*Capacity*: 6 rounds
*Features*: Stainless steel frame and barrel with satin finish; exposed hammer; chambered charge holes; bossed mainspring; ergonomic grip to force high-hand hold; custom barrel with recessed precision crown
**MSRP** . . . . . . . . . . . . . . . . . . **$969**

## M&P 9MM
*Action*: Autoloader
*Grips*: Polymer
*Barrel*: 4.25 in.
*Sights*: Steel ramp dovetail mount front, steel Novak Lo-Mount Carry
*Weight*: 24 oz.
*Caliber*: 9mm
*Capacity*: 17+1 rounds
*Features*: Zytel polymer frame, stainless steel barrel/slide and structural components; optional tritium sights; black melonite finish
**MSRP** . . . . . . . . . . . . . . . . . . **$569**

## M&P40 COMPACT
*Action*: Autoloader
*Grips*: Polymer
*Barrel*: 3.5 in.
*Sights*: White dot dovetail front; steel low profile carry rear
*Weight*: 21.9 oz.
*Caliber*: .40 S&W
*Capacity*: 10 rounds
*Features*: 3 interchangeable palm swell grip sizes; black melonite; thumb safety
**MSRP** . . . . . . . . . . . . . . . . . . **$569**

## M&P45
*Action*: Autoloader
*Grips*: Polymer
*Barrel*: 4.5 in.
*Sights*: White dot dovetail front; steel low profile carry rear
*Weight*: 29.6 oz.
*Caliber*: .45 ACP
*Capacity*: 10+1 rounds
*Features*: Zytel polymer frame, stainless steel barrel/slide and structural components; black melonite finish; CA compliant; 3 interchangeable palm swell grip sizes
**MSRP** . . . . . . . . . . . . . . . . . . **$599**

**SMITH & WESSON M&P357**

**SMITH & WESSON M&P R8**

**SMITH & WESSON SW1911 COMPACT ES**

### M&P357
*Action*: Autoloader
*Grips*: Polymer
*Barrel*: 4.25 in.
*Sights*: White-dot dovetail front; steel low profile carry rear
*Weight*: 25.5 oz.
*Caliber*: .357 Auto
*Capacity*: 15 rounds
*Features*: 3 interchangeable palm swell grip sizes; black melonite; thumb safety; polymer frame/stainless steel barrel and slide
MSRP . . . . . . . . . . . . . . . . . . . $727

### M&P R8
*Action*: SA/DA revolver
*Grips*: Polymer
*Barrel*: 5 in.
*Sights*: Interchangeable front, adjustable v-notch
*Weight*: 36.3 oz.
*Caliber*: .357 Mag., .38 S&W Special +P
*Capacity*: 8 rounds
*Features*: Single- or double-action; scandium alloy frame; stainless steel cylinder; integral accessory Picatinny style rail; precision barrel forcing cone
MSRP . . . . . . . . . . . . . . . . . . . $1289

### SW1911 COMPACT ES
*Action*: Autoloader
*Grips*: Wood
*Barrel*: 4.25 in.
*Sights*: White-dot dovetail front; steel low profile carry rear
*Weight*: 29.6 oz.
*Caliber*: .45 ACP
*Capacity*: 7+1 rounds
*Features*: Single-action; scandium alloy frame; stainless steel slide; two-tone finish; compact extended slide
MSRP . . . . . . . . . . . . . . . . . . . $1139

# Springfield Armory

**SPRINGFIELD ARMORY EMP**

**SPRINGFIELD ARMORY LIGHTWEIGHT CHAMPION OPERATOR**

**SPRINGFIELD ARMORY LOADED FULL SIZE TROPHY MATCH STAINLESS STEEL**

### EMP (ENHANCED MICRO PISTOL)
*Action*: Autoloader
*Grips*: Thin line cocobolo wood, G10
*Barrel*: 3 in.
*Sights*: Fixed low profile combat rear, dovetail
*Weight*: 26 oz.–33 oz.
*Caliber*: 9mm, .40 S&W
*Capacity*: 3–9 rounds (9mm), 3–8 rounds (.40 S&W)
*Features*: Forged stainless steel, satin finish; dual spring recoil system with full length guide rod
MSRP . . . . . . . . . . . . . $1345–$1424

### LIGHTWEIGHT CHAMPION OPERATOR
*Action*: Autoloader
*Grips*: Cocobolo wood
*Barrel*: 4 in.
*Sights*: Fixed low profile combat rear, dovetail
*Weight*: 31 oz.
*Caliber*: .45 ACP
*Capacity*: 2–7 rounds
*Features*: Stainless steel match grade, fully supported ramped bull barrel; long aluminum Match Grade trigger; forged aluminum alloy with integral accessory rail; black hard coat anodized; dual spring with full length guide rod
MSRP . . . . . . . . . . . . . . . . . . . $1076

### LOADED FULL SIZE TROPHY MATCH STAINLESS STEEL
*Action*: Autoloader
*Grips*: Cocobolo wood
*Barrel*: 5 in.
*Sights*: Low profile adjustable rear, Dovetail front target
*Weight*: 40 oz.
*Caliber*: .45 ACP
*Capacity*: 2–7 rounds
*Features*: Wide-mouth magazine well; tuned trigger; checkered front strap; forged stainless steel frame; two-piece full length guide rod
MSRP . . . . . . . . . . . . . . . . . . . $1605

# Springfield Armory

## MIL-SPEC FULL SIZE STAINLESS

**Action**: Autoloader
**Grips**: Cocobolo wood and black plastic
**Barrel**: 5 in.
**Sights**: Fixed combat, 3-dot
**Weight**: 39 oz.
**Caliber**: .45 ACP
**Capacity**: 2–7 rounds
**Features**: Forged stainless steel, matte rounds with polished flats; GI style recoil system; available Parkerized finish
**MSRP** . . . . . . . . . . . . . . . . . . . **$851**

## RANGE OFFICER

**Action**: Autoloader
**Grips**: Cocobolo wood
**Barrel**: 5 in.
**Sights**: Low profile adjustable target
**Weight**: 40 oz.
**Caliber**: .45 ACP
**Capacity**: 2–7 rounds
**Features**: Standard guide rod; forged steel frame with blued finish; stainless Match Grade barrel
**MSRP** . . . . . . . . . . . . . . . . . . . **$977**

## TRP (TACTICAL RESPONSE PISTOL)

**Action**: Autoloader
**Grips**: G10 composite
**Barrel**: 5 in.
**Sights**: Front tritium 3-dot, fixed low profile combat rear, dovetail
**Weight**: 42 oz.
**Caliber**: .45 ACP
**Capacity**: 2–7 rounds
**Features**: Forged steel frame with black armory kote; two piece full length guide rod; wide-mouth magazine well; tuned trigger; available in Armory Kote, Light Rail Armory Kote, and stainless
**MSRP** . . . . . . . . . . . . . . . . . . . **$1777**

## XD (M)

**Action**: DA autoloader
**Grips**: Polymer
**Barrel**: 3.8 in., 4.5 in. Match Grade
**Sights**: 3-dot
**Weight**: 27.5 oz.–32 oz.
**Caliber**: 9mm, .40 S&W, .45 ACP
**Capacity**: 19 (9mm), 16 (.40 S&W), 13 (.45 ACP) rounds
**Features**: "M" features include carrying case, two magazines, paddle holster, magi loader, double magi pouch and three interchangeable backstraps and two magazines; "all-terrain" texture and deep slide serrations are standard
**9mm:** . . . . . . . . . . . . . . . . **$697–$815**
**.40 S&W:** . . . . . . . . . . . . . **$697–$876**
**.45 ACP:** . . . . . . . . . . . . . . **$709–$896**

## XD(M) COMPACT

**Action**: Autoloader
**Grips**: Synthetic
**Barrel**: 3.8 in., 5.25 in.
**Sights**: Fiber optic front, adjustable rear
**Weight**: 27 oz.–32 oz.
**Caliber**: 9mm, .45 ACP, .40 S&W
**Capacity**: 13, 19 rounds
**Features**: A handgun with improved accuracy, lessened recoil, faster shot recovery and greater sight radius of its newly enhanced performance. The lightening cut in the slide reduces reciprocating mass which allows for faster cycling and allows a larger variety of loads to be used.
**MSRP** . . . . . . . . . . . . . . . . **$705–$797**

SPRINGFIELD ARMORY MIL-SPEC FULL SIZE STAINLESS

SPRINGFIELD ARMORY RANGE OFFICER

SPRINGFIELD ARMORY TRP

SPRINGFIELD ARMORY XD (M)

SPRINGFIELD ARMORY XD(M) COMPACT

# Steyr Arms

**STEYR ARMS C9-A1**

**STEYR ARMS M40-A1**

**STEYR ARMS S9-A1**

## C9-A1
*Action*: Autoloader, striker-fired
*Grips*: Textured polymer
*Barrel*: 3.6 in.
*Sights*: Fixed triangular/trapezoid
*Weight*: 25.6 oz.
*Caliber*: 9mm
*Capacity*: 17+1 rounds
*Features*: Polymer frame; trigger, internal striker, internal gun-lock safeties; polygonal rifling; black matte Mannox finish; Picatinny rail
**MSRP . . . . . . . . . . . . . . . . . . . . $560**

## M40-A1
*Action*: Autoloader
*Grips*: Synthetic
*Barrel*: 4 in.
*Sights*: Fixed triangular/trapezoid
*Weight*: 27 oz.
*Caliber*: 9mm, .40 S&W
*Capacity*: 12 or 15 rounds
*Features*: Triangular or trapezoid shaped sights; synthetic black grips; Picatinny rail; ergonomic handle
**MSRP . . . . . . . . . . . . . . . . . . . . $560**

## S9-A1
*Action*: Autoloader
*Grips*: Synthetic
*Barrel*: 3.62 in.
*Sights*: Fixed triangular/trapezoid
*Weight*: 23.4–23.9 oz.
*Caliber*: 9mm, .40 S&W
*Capacity*: 10 rounds
*Features*: Ergonomical improved grip with Picatinny rail; low profile; optional sling mount on grip; drop firing safety
**MSRP . . . . . . . . . . . . . . . . . . . . $560**

# STI International

**STI APEIRO**

**STI EAGLE 5.0**

**STI EDGE**

## APEIRO
*Action*: Autoloader
*Grips*: STI patented modular polymer
*Barrel*: 5 in.
*Sights*: Dawson fiber optic front mounted on barrel, STI adjustable rear
*Weight*: 39 oz.
*Caliber*: 9mm, .40 S&W, .45 ACP
*Capacity*: 11+1, 14+1, 17+1 rounds
*Features*: Full length stainless steel bar stock slide features STI's unique sabertooth rear cocking serrations; Schuemann barrel; STI recoil master; STI long curved trigger; blued finish with two toned blued/stainless steel slide
**MSRP . . . . . . . . . . . . . . . . . . . . $2805**

## EAGLE 5.0
*Action*: Autoloader
*Grips*: STI patented modular polymer
*Barrel*: 5 in.
*Sights*: STI front, STI adjustable rear
*Weight*: 35.2 oz.

*Caliber*: 9mm, .357 Sig, .38 Super, .40 S&W, .45 ACP
*Capacity*: 11+1, 14+1, 17+1 rounds
*Features*: Stainless STI grip, ambi thumb, ramped bull barrel; STI patented modular steel frame; STI rear serrations; blued finish
**MSRP . . . . . . . . . . . . . . . . . . . . $1985**

## EDGE
*Action*: Autoloader
*Grips*: STI patented modular polymer with aluminum mag well
*Barrel*: 5 in.
*Sights*: STI front, STI adjustable rear
*Weight*: 37.6 oz.
*Caliber*: 9mm, .38 Super, .40 S&W, .45 ACP
*Capacity*: 11+1, 14+1, 17+1 rounds
*Features*: STI fully supported, ramped bull barrel; stainless STI grip and ambi slided thumb; STI recoil master guide rod; blued finish
**MSRP . . . . . . . . . . . . . . . . . . . . $2040**

# STI International

**STI EXECUTIVE**

**STI LAWMAN 4**

**STI RANGEMASTER**

**STI RANGER II**

**STI TACTICAL**

**STI TARGETMASTER**

## EXECUTIVE

*Action*: Autoloader
*Grips*: STI patented modular polymer with stainless mag well
*Barrel*: 5 in.
*Sights*: Dawson fiber optic front, STI adjustable rear
*Weight*: 39.2 oz.
*Caliber*: .40 S&W
*Capacity*: 14+1 rounds
*Features*: Stainless STI grip, ambi thumb, ramped bull barrel; STI patented modular steel, long wide frame; STI rear serrations; blued finish
**MSRP** . . . . . . . . . . . . . . . . . . **$2520**

## LAWMAN FAMILY

*Action*: Autoloader
*Grips*: G10 Mycarta grip panels
*Barrel*: 3.24 in., 4.26 in., 5.11 in.
*Sights*: STI ramped front, tactical adjustable rear
*Weight*: 23.8 oz.–38.9 oz.
*Caliber*: 9×19, .45 ACP
*Capacity*: 6+1 rounds
*Features*: Forged aluminum frame; carbon steel slide; blue high rise beavertail grip safety and single sided thumb safety; available in traditional polished blue, two tone polymer light brown/coyote tan, and two tone black/olive drab
**MSRP** . . . . . . . . . . . . . . . . . . **$1455**

## RANGEMASTER

*Action*: Autoloader
*Grips*: STI logo, checkered, cocobolo wood, standard thickness
*Barrel*: 5 in.
*Sights*: STI front, STI adjustable rear
*Weight*: 41.4 oz.
*Caliber*: 9mm, .45 ACP
*Capacity*: 8, 9 rounds
*Features*: STI long curved trigger; ramped bull barrel; STI polished stainless grip and ambi thumb; STI recoil master guide rod; matte blued finish
**MSRP** . . . . . . . . . . . . . . . . . . **$1555**

## RANGER II

*Action*: Autoloader
*Grips*: STI logo, checkered, cocobolo wood, thin
*Barrel*: 4.26 in.
*Sights*: STI front, STI fixed low mount snag free rear
*Weight*: 33.7 oz.
*Caliber*: 9mm, .40 S&W, .45 ACP
*Capacity*: 7+1 rounds
*Features*: STI long curved trigger with stainless bow; STI hi-rise blue grip and single sided thumb safeties; blued finish
**MSRP** . . . . . . . . . . . . . . . . . . **$1135**

## TACTICAL FAMILY

*Action*: Autoloader
*Grips*: Polymer
*Barrel*: 3.75 in., 4.26 in., 5.01 in.
*Sights*: STI ramped front, Novak style fixed rear
*Weight*: 30.1 oz.–34.2 oz.
*Caliber*: 9×19, .40 S&W, .45 ACP
*Capacity*: 11+1, 14+1, 17+1 rounds
*Features*: STI International's patented 2011 technology gives the STI Tactical more fire power advantage than 1911 tactical pistols without greatly increasing the size of the grip; less recoil felt; aluminum frame; light tactical rail milled into the dust cover of the frame; STI patented glass filled polymer modular grips; blued slide
**MSRP** . . . . . . . . . . . . . . . . . . **$2045**

## TARGETMASTER

*Action*: Autoloader
*Grips*: STI logo, checkered, cocobolo wood, standard thickness
*Barrel*: 6 in.
*Sights*: Aristocrat adjustable
*Weight*: 45.5 oz.
*Caliber*: 9mm, .45 ACP
*Capacity*: 8, 9 rounds
*Features*: STI long curved trigger; STI stainless grip and ambi sided thumb; STI two piece rail guide rod; matte blued finish
**MSRP** . . . . . . . . . . . . . . . . . . **$1745**

**STI TOTAL ECLIPSE**

**STI VIP**

**STI TROJAN 5.0**

## TOTAL ECLIPSE

**Action**: SA autoloader
**Grips**: Black polymer
**Barrel**: 3 in. ramped, bull contour
**Sights**: 2-dot tritium night
**Weight**: 23.1 oz.
**Caliber**: .45 ACP, .40 S&W, 9mm
**Capacity**: 9+1, 10+1, 12+1 rounds
**Features**: 2011 double stack pistol; double-column magazine; steel frame; single-sided blued thumb safety and beavertail grip safety
**MSRP**.................... $1870

## TROJAN 5.0

**Action**: Autoloader
**Grips**: STI logo, checkered, cocobolo

wood, thin
**Barrel**: 5 in., 6 in.
**Sights**: STI front, STI adjustable rear
**Weight**: 36 oz.
**Caliber**: 9mm, .38 Super, .40 S&W, .45 ACP
**Capacity**: 8, 9 rounds
**Features**: STI standard blue grip and single-slided thumb safeties; STI one-piece steel guide rod; flat blued finish
**5-inch**: ................. $1135
**6-inch**: ................. $1455

## VIP

**Action**: Autoloader
**Grips**: STI patented modular polymer
**Barrel**: 3.9 in.
**Sights**: STI front, STI adjustable rear
**Weight**: 30 oz.
**Caliber**: 9mm, .40 S&W, .45 ACP
**Capacity**: 15+1, 12+1, 10+1 rounds
**Features**: STI rear slide serrations; STI long curved trigger; STI stainless grip and single-sided thumb; matte blued slide with blued steel frame
**MSRP**.................... $1690

# Stoeger

**STOEGER COUGAR**

**STOEGER COUGAR COMPACT**

## COUGAR

**Action**: DA/SA
**Grips**: Black plastic
**Barrel**: 3.6 in.
**Sights**: White 3-dot
**Weight**: 32 oz.–32.6 oz.
**Caliber**: .45 ACP, .40 S&W, 9mm
**Capacity**: 8+1, 11+1, 15+1 rounds
**Features**: Ambidextrous safety; rotary-locking principal; available in a non-glare Bruniton silver steel slide with an

anodized alloy matte-silver frame or two-tone style, featuring a matte Bruniton black steel slide combined with an anodized alloy matte-silver frame
**MSRP**............... $469–$509

## COUGAR COMPACT

**Action**: DA/SA
**Grips**: Black plastic
**Barrel**: 3.6 in.

**Sights**: Quick read 3-dot
**Weight**: 32 oz.
**Caliber**: 9mm
**Capacity**: 13+1 rounds
**Features**: Ambidextrous safety; rotary-locking principal; Bruniton matte black finish
**MSRP**.................... $469

# Taurus

### 22BR
**Action**: Autoloader
**Grips**: Rosewood
**Barrel**: 2.75 in.
**Sights**: Fixed
**Weight**: 12.3 oz.
**Caliber**: .22LR
**Capacity**: 8+1 rounds
**Features**: Steel/alloy frame with blued finish; manual safety; tip-up barrel; Taurus security system
**MSRP** . . . . . . . . . . . . . . . . . . . . **$282**

### 22/25 PLY
**Action**: DA autoloading, recoil operated
**Grips**: Polymer
**Barrel**: 2.3 in.
**Sights**: Fixed
**Weight**: 11.3 oz.
**Caliber**: .22LR, .25 ACP
**Capacity**: 8+1, 9+1 rounds
**Features**: Polymer/blued steel construction; blued steel finish; tip-up barrel
**MSRP** . . . . . . . . . . . . . . . . . . . . **$282**

### 24/7 G2
**Action**: DA/SA autoloader
**Grips**: Checkered polymer with metallic inserts
**Barrel**: 4.2 in.
**Sights**: Low-profile, adjustable rear
**Weight**: 28 oz.
**Caliber**: 9mm, .40, .45 ACP
**Capacity**: 17+1 rounds (9mm), 15+1 rounds (.40), 12+1 rounds (.45 ACP)
**Features**: Blued or stainless steel; DA/SA trigger system; SA or DA only; contoured thumb rests; Picatinny accessory rail; compact model available at same price
**Blued:** . . . . . . . . . . . . . . . . . . . **$539**
**Stainless:** . . . . . . . . . . . . . . . . . **$555**

### 44
**Action**: Autoloader
**Grips**: Soft rubber
**Barrel**: 4 in., 6.5 in., 8.4 in.
**Sights**: Fixed
**Weight**: 45–57 oz.
**Caliber**: .44 Mag.
**Capacity**: 6 rounds
**Features**: Transfer bar; ported barrel; matte stainless steel finish; double and single-action
**4 in.:** . . . . . . . . . . . . . . . . . . . **$742**
**6.5 in.:** . . . . . . . . . . . . . . . . . . **$758**
**8.4 in.:** . . . . . . . . . . . . . . . . . . **$758**

TAURUS 22BR

TAURUS 22/25 PLY

TAURUS 24/7 G2

TAURUS 44

TAURUS 82

TAURUS 92

### 82
**Action**: Autoloader
**Grips**: Rubber
**Barrel**: 4 in.
**Sights**: Fixed
**Weight**: 36.5 oz.
**Caliber**: .38 SPL +P
**Capacity**: 6 rounds
**Features**: Transfer bar; steel construction with blued finish; single/double-action trigger
**Blued:** . . . . . . . . . . . . . . . . . . . **$481**

### 92
**Action**: Autoloader
**Grips**: Checkered rubber
**Barrel**: 5 in.
**Sights**: Fixed-1 dot front, fixed-2 dots rear
**Weight**: 34 oz.
**Caliber**: 9mm
**Capacity**: 10+1 and 17+1 rounds
**Features**: Blued, stainless steel finish; steel/alloy construction; firing pin block, hammer decocker, manual safety
**Blued:** . . . . . . . . . . . . . . . . . . . **$660**
**Stainless:** . . . . . . . . . . . . . . . . . **$668**

## 94/941

**Action**: Revolver
**Grips**: Rubber
**Barrel**: 2 in., 4 in.
**Sights**: Fixed front, adjustable rear
**Weight**: 18.5 oz.–27 oz.
**Caliber**: .22LR, .22 Mag.
**Capacity**: 8, 9 rounds
**Features**: Steel construction; blued or matte stainless steel finish; single- and double-action; transfer bar; 2-inch Ultra-Lite models also available
**Blued:** . . . . . . . . . . . . . . . . . **$465**
**Stainless:** . . . . . . . . . . . . . . . **$513**
**Ultra-Lite:** . . . . . . . . . . . . **$499–$531**

## .380 MINI REVOLVER

**Action**: Revolver
**Grips**: Rubber
**Barrel**: 1.75 in.
**Sights**: Adjustable rear
**Weight**: 15.5 oz.
**Caliber**: .380 ACP
**Capacity**: 5 rounds
**Features**: Double-action trigger; fully enclosed hammer; blued or matte stainless finish; bobbed hammer
**Blued:** . . . . . . . . . . . . . . . . . **$443**
**Stainless:** . . . . . . . . . . . . . . . **$475**

## 605

**Action**: Revolver
**Grips**: Rubber
**Barrel**: 2 in.
**Sights**: Fixed
**Weight**: 24 oz.
**Caliber**: .357 Mag
**Capacity**: 5 rounds
**Features**: Transfer bar safety; steel construction with blued or stainless finish; single-double action trigger
**Blued:** . . . . . . . . . . . . . . . . . **$459**
**Stainless:** . . . . . . . . . . . . . . . **$507**

## 608

**Action**: Revolver
**Grips**: Rubber
**Barrel**: 4 in., 6.5 in.
**Sights**: Fixed front, adjustable rear
**Weight**: 44 oz.–51 oz.
**Caliber**: .357 Mag
**Capacity**: 8 rounds
**Features**: Matte stainless steel finish; transfer bar; large frame; steel frame; Taurus security system; porting
**4 in.:** . . . . . . . . . . . . . . . . . **$702**
**6.5 in.** . . . . . . . . . . . . . . . . . **$724**

TAURUS 94/941

TAURUS .380 MINI REVOLVER

TAURUS 605

TAURUS 608

TAURUS 709 "SLIM"

TAURUS 738 TCP

## 709 "SLIM"

**Action**: Autoloader
**Grips**: Checkered polymer
**Barrel**: 3 in.
**Sights**: Fixed
**Weight**: 19 oz.
**Caliber**: 9mm
**Capacity**: 7+1 rounds
**Features**: Steel construction; blued or stainless finish; single- and double-action
**Blued:** . . . . . . . . . . . . . . . . . **$349**
**Stainless:** . . . . . . . . . . . . . . . **$513**

## 738 TCP

**Action**: DA autoloader
**Grips**: Checkered polymer
**Barrel**: 2.84 in.
**Sights**: Fixed
**Weight**: 10.2 oz.
**Caliber**: .380 ACP
**Capacity**: 6+1 rounds
**Features**: Titanium construction; compact frame; smooth trigger
**MSRP** . . . . . . . . . . . . . . . . . . **$362**

# Taurus

**TAURUS 809**

**TAURUS 905**

**TAURUS 1911 AL**

**TAURUS DT HYBRID**

**TAURUS JUDGE .45/.410**

**TAURUS PUBLIC DEFENDER POLYMER**

## 809

**Action**: Autoloader
**Grips**: Checkered polymer
**Barrel**: 3.5 in., 4 in.
**Sights**: Fixed
**Weight**: 30.2 oz.
**Caliber**: 9mm
**Capacity**: 17+1 rounds
**Features**: Black Tennifer finish; smooth trigger type;
strike-two capability.
**MSRP** . . . . . . . . . . . . . . . . . . . . **$497**

## 905

**Action**: DA/SA revolver
**Grips**: Rubber
**Barrel**: 2 in.
**Sights**: Fixed
**Weight**: 22.2 oz.
**Caliber**: 9mm
**Capacity**: 5 rounds
**Features**: Blued finish; transfer bar; steel frame; porting; Taurus security system
**Blued**: . . . . . . . . . . . . . . . . . . . **$491**
**Stainless**: . . . . . . . . . . . . . . . . **$539**

## 1911 AL

**Action**: Autoloader
**Grips**: Checkered black
**Barrel**: 5 in.
**Sights**: Heinie
**Weight**: 38 oz.
**Caliber**: .45 ACP

**Capacity**: 8+1 rounds
**Features**: Steel/alloy construction with blued/gray finish; single-action; forged slide and frame; ventilated trigger type
**Blued** . . . . . . . . . . . . . . . . . . . . **$853**
**Duotone**. . . . . . . . . . . . . . . . . **$906**
**Stainless**. . . . . . . . . . . . . . . . . **$927**
**Walnut Grip** . . . . . . . . . . . . . . . **$975**

## DT HYBRID

**Action**: SA/DA autoloader
**Grips**: Polymer
**Barrel**: 3.2 in.
**Sights**: Adjustable rear
**Weight**: 24 oz.
**Caliber**: 9mm, .40
**Capacity**: 13+1 and 11+1 rounds
**Features**: Matte stainless steel or blued finish; stainless steel construction; polymer over steel frame
**Blued**: . . . . . . . . . . . . . . . . . . . **$589**
**Stainless**: . . . . . . . . . . . . . . . . **$605**

## JUDGE .45/.410

**Action**: DA/SA revolver
**Grips**: Taurus rubber grips

**Barrel**: 3 in.
**Sights**: Red fiber optic, fixed
**Weight**: 29–36.8 oz.
**Caliber**: .45/.410
**Capacity**: 5 rounds
**Features**: Firing pin block, transfer bar safety; compact frame; matte stainless steel finish; steel construction
**MSRP** . . . . . . . . . . . . . . . . **$620–$668**

## PUBLIC DEFENDER POLYMER

**Action**: DA/SA revolver
**Grips**: Rubber
**Barrel**: 2 in., 2.5 in.
**Sights**: Red fiber optic, fixed front
**Weight**: 27 oz.–28.2 oz.
**Caliber**: .45/.410
**Capacity**: 5 rounds
**Features**: Polymer frame, stainless or blued finish; target hammer and trigger; fires both .410 shotshells and .45 Colt ammunition
**Blued**: . . . . . . . . . . . . . . . **$459–$620**
**Stainless**: . . . . . . . . . . . . . . . . **$668**

**TAURUS RAGING BULL 444**

**TAURUS RAGING JUDGE MAGNUM**

**TAURUS SLIM 740**

**TAURUS TRACKER 992**

**TAURUS TRACKER SERIES**

## RAGING BULL 444

**Action**: Revolver
**Grips**: Rubber w/cushioned insert
**Barrel**: 6.5 in., 8.38 in.
**Sights**: Partridge front, adjustable rear
**Weight**: 53 oz.–63 oz.
**Caliber**: .44 Mag
**Capacity**: 6 rounds
**Features**: Steel construction with blued or stainless steel finish; transfer bar; dual lockup cylinder; porting; Taurus security system
**Blued:** . . . . . . . . . . . . . . . . . . $769
**Stainless:** . . . . . . . . . . . . . . . . $818

## RAGING JUDGE MAGNUM

**Action**: DA/SA revolver
**Grips**: Rubber with soft cushion insert
**Barrel**: 3 in., 6.5 in.
**Sights**: Fiber optic front, fixed rear
**Weight**: 60.6 oz.–73 oz.
**Caliber**: .410/.45 LC, .454 Casull
**Capacity**: 6 rounds
**Features**: Stainless steel or blued finish; "Raging Bull" backstrap for added cushioning
**Blued:** . . . . . . . . . . . . . . . . . . $1012
**Stainless:** . . . . . . . . . . . . . . . . $1061

## SLIM 740

**Action**: DA/SA autoloader
**Grips**: Polymer metallic inserts
**Barrel**: 3.2 in.
**Sights**: Adjustable rear
**Weight**: 19 oz.

**Caliber**: .40
**Capacity**: 6+1 rounds
**Features**: Sub-compact pistol in blued, black Tenifer, or stainless steel; loaded chamber indicator; low-profile sights; short, crisp DA/SA trigger pull
**Blued:** . . . . . . . . . . . . . . . . . . $349
**Stainless:** . . . . . . . . . . . . . . . . $513

## TRACKER 992

**Action**: SA/DA revolver
**Grips**: Taurus Ribber
**Barrel**: 4 in., 6.5 in.
**Sights**: Adjustable
**Weight**: 55 oz.
**Caliber**: .22 LR
**Capacity**: 9 rounds
**Features**: The versatile Tracker 992 easily transforms from .22LR to .22

Magnum in seconds with its breakthrough removable cylinder; perfect for plinking, target practice, or varmint hunting
**Blued:** . . . . . . . . . . . . . . . . . . $589
**Stainless:** . . . . . . . . . . . . . . . . $637

## TRACKER SERIES

**Action**: Revolver
**Grips**: Rubber with ribs
**Barrel**: 4 in., 4.5 in., 6.5 in.
**Sights**: Fixed front, adjustable rear
**Weight**: 28.8 oz.–46 oz.
**Caliber**: .17HMR, .22LR, .22 Mag., .357 Mag., .44 Mag.
**Capacity**: 5, 7, 9 rounds
**Features**: Matte stainless steel or blued finish; transfer bar; steel frame; porting
**MSRP** . . . . . . . . . . . . . . . . $472–$684

# Taylor's & Co.

TAYLOR'S & CO. 1873 CATTLEMAN PHOTO ENGRAVED

TAYLOR'S & CO. 1873 GUNFIGHTER CATTLEMAN

TAYLOR'S & CO. 1873 TAYLOR GAMBLER

TAYLOR'S & CO. 1873 TAYLOR MARSHALL

TAYLOR'S & CO. RUNNIN' IRON

## 1873 CATTLEMAN PHOTO ENGRAVED

*Action*: SA revolver
*Grips*: Walnut
*Barrel*: 4.75 in., 5.5 in., 7.5 in.
*Sights*: Fixed
*Weight*: 2 lb. 4 oz.–3 lb. 6 oz.
*Caliber*: .357 Mag., .45 LC
*Capacity*: 6 rounds
*Features*: White, heat-treated steel finish with charcoal blued screws; laser-engraved and hand chased; forged frame
*MSRP* . . . . . . . . . . . . . . . . . . . **$876**

## 1873 GUNFIGHTER CATTLEMAN

*Action*: SA revolver
*Grips*: Walnut
*Barrel*: 5.5 in.
*Sights*: Fixed
*Weight*: 2 lb. 5 oz.

*Caliber*: .357 Mag., .45 LC
*Capacity*: 6 rounds
*Features*: Special Army-sized grip; steel trigger guard and backstrap; blued finish with case-hardened frame; forged frame
*MSRP* . . . . . . . . . . . . . . . . . . . **$547**

## 1873 TAYLOR GAMBLER CATTLEMAN

*Action*: SA revolver
*Grips*: Walnut
*Barrel*: 5.5 in.
*Sights*: Fixed
*Weight*: 2 lb. 5 oz.
*Caliber*: .357 Mag., .45 LC
*Capacity*: 6 rounds
*Features*: Fancy checkered walnut grip; blued color case-hardened forged frame
*MSRP* . . . . . . . . . . . . . . . . . . . **$570**

## 1873 TAYLOR MARSHALL CATTLEMAN

*Action*: SA revolver
*Grips*: White PVC
*Barrel*: 5.5 in.

*Sights*: Fixed
*Weight*: 2 lb. 5 oz.
*Caliber*: .45 LC
*Capacity*: 6 rounds
*Features*: Checkered white PVC grip; blued color case-hardened forged frame
*MSRP* . . . . . . . . . . . . . . . . . . . **$658**

## RUNNIN' IRON

*Action*: SA revolver
*Grips*: Checkered walnut
*Barrel*: 3.5 oz.–5.5 in.
*Sights*: Wider fixed, open
*Weight*: 39 oz.
*Caliber*: .45 LC or .357 Mag.
*Capacity*: 6 rounds
*Features*: Designed for the sport of mounted shooting; offered in stainless or blued finish with low, wide hammer spur; checkered, one-piece gunfighter style grips in walnut or black polymer; wide trigger and extra clearance at front and rear of cylinder
**Stainless:** . . . . . . . . . . . . . **$705–$852**
**Blued:** . . . . . . . . . . . . . . . **$551–$699**

# Taylor's & Co.

**TAYLOR'S & CO. THE SMOKE WAGON**

## THE SMOKE WAGON
*Action*: SA revolver
*Grips*: Checkered wood
*Barrel*: 4.75 in., 5.5 in.
*Sights*: Open rear sight groove, wide angle front sight blade

*Weight*: 40 oz.
*Caliber*: .38 Sp., .357 Mag., .45 LC, .44-40
*Capacity*: 6 rounds
*Features*: Low profile hammer; deluxe edition model includes custom tuning, custom hammer and base pin springs; jig-cut positive angles on trigger and sears; wire bolt and trigger springs
**Standard:**. . . . . . . . . . . . . . . . **$540**
**Deluxe:** . . . . . . . . . . . . . . . . . **$650**

# Thompson/Center

## ENCORE
*Action*: Single-shot, break open design
*Grips*: Walnut or rubber
*Barrel*: 12 in., 15 in.
*Sights*: Adjustable rear; ramp front blade
*Weight*: 68–72 oz.
*Caliber*: .204 Ruger, .223 Rem, .22-250 Rem., .243 Win., .25-06 Rem., .270 Win., 7mm-08 Rem., .308 Win., .30-06 Spfd., .45-70 Gov't., .44 Rem. Mag., .45 Colt/.410, .17HMR, .22LR, .460 S&W, .500 S&W
*Capacity*: 1 round
*Features*: Interchangeable barrels; button rifled; drilled and tapped for T/C scope mounts; adjustable trigger for overtravel; ambidextrous pistol grip with finger grooves and butt cap; matching forend; blued or stainless steel finish; patented automatic hammer block with bolt interlock
**MSRP**. . . . . . . . . . . . . . . **$679–$969**
**Pro Hunter:** . . . . . . . . . . . . . **$1199**

**THOMPSON/CENTER ENCORE**

**THOMPSON/CENTER G2 CONTENDER**

## G2 CONTENDER
*Action*: Single shot, break open design
*Grips*: Walnut or rubber
*Barrel*: 12 in., 14 in.
*Sights*: Adjustable rear; ramp front blade
*Weight*: 56–60 oz.

*Caliber*: .22LR Match, .357 Mag., .44 Rem. Mag., .45/410 Vent Rib, .223 Rem., .17 HMR, .204 Ruger, .22 Hornet, 6.8 mm Rem., 7-30 Waters, .45–70 Gov't., .30-30 Win
*Capacity*: 1 round

*Features*: .45/410 models include removable choke tube and wrench; stainless steel or walnut frame; manual firing pin selector; button rifled; drilled and tapped for T/C scope mounts
**MSRP**. . . . . . . . . . . . . . . . . . . **$729**

# Uberti

### 1851 NAVY CONVERSION

**Action**: SA revolver
**Grips**: Walnut
**Barrel**: 4.75 in., 5.5 in., 7.5 in.
**Sights**: Fixed, open
**Weight**: 42 oz.
**Caliber**: .38 Spl.
**Capacity**: 6 rounds
**Features**: Case-hardened frame octagonal barrel; brass backstrap and trigger guard; conversion revolver frames are retro-fitted with loading gates to accommodate metallic cartridges like the originals
**MSRP** . . . . . . . . . . . . . . . . . . . . **$549**

### 1860 ARMY CONVERSION

**Action**: SA revolver
**Grips**: Walnut
**Barrel**: 4.75 in., 5.5 in., 8 in.
**Sights**: Fixed, open
**Weight**: 42 oz.
**Caliber**: .38 Spl., .45 Colt
**Capacity**: 6 rounds
**Features**: Case-hardened frame; round barrel; steel backstrap and trigger guard; conversion revolver frames are retro-fitted with loading gates to accommodate metallic cartridges like the originals
**MSRP** . . . . . . . . . . . . . . . . . . . . **$579**

### 1871–1872 OPEN-TOP CONVERSION

**Action**: SA revolver
**Grips**: Walnut
**Barrel**: 4.75 in., 5.5 in., 7.5 in.
**Sights**: Fixed, open
**Weight**: 42 oz.
**Caliber**: .38 Spl., .45 Colt
**Capacity**: 6 rounds
**Features**: 1872 model has steel backstrap and trigger guard; 1871 model has brass backstrap and trigger guard; case-hardened frame; round barrel; blued finish conversion revolver frames are retro-fitted with loading gates to accommodate metallic cartridges like the originals
**1871**: . . . . . . . . . . . . . . . . . . . . **$529**
**1872**: . . . . . . . . . . . . . . . . . . . . **$549**

### 1873 CATTLEMAN BIRD'S HEAD

**Action**: SA revolver
**Grips**: Walnut
**Barrel**: 3.5 in., 4.75 in., 5.5 in.
**Sights**: Fixed, open
**Weight**: 35 oz.

UBERTI 1851 NAVY CONVERSION

UBERTI 1860 ARMY CONVERSION

UBERTI 1871–1872 OPEN-TOP CONVERSION

UBERTI 1873 CATTLEMAN BIRD'S HEAD

UBERTI 1873 CATTLEMAN BISLEY

**Caliber**: .45 Colt, .357 Mag.
**Capacity**: 6 rounds
**Features**: Case-hardened frame; steel backstrap and trigger guard; blued finish; bird head shape grip
**MSRP** . . . . . . . . . . . . . . . . . . . . **$569**

### 1873 CATTLEMAN BISLEY

**Action**: SA revolver
**Grips**: Bisley target style walnut

**Barrel**: 4.75 in., 5.5 in., 7.5 in.
**Sights**: Fixed, open
**Weight**: 40 oz.
**Caliber**: .45 Colt, .357 Mag.
**Capacity**: 6 rounds
**Features**: Case-hardened frame; steel backstrap and trigger guard; blued finish; fluted barrel
**MSRP** . . . . . . . . . . . . . . . . . . . . **$599**

UBERTI 1873 CATTLEMAN CALLAHAN

UBERTI 1873 CATTLEMAN CHISHOLM

UBERTI 1873 CATTLEMAN DESPERADO

UBERTI 1873 CATTLEMAN MATCHING SET

### 1873 CATTLEMAN CALLAHAN

**Action**: SA revolver
**Grips**: Walnut, black or mother-of-pearl synthetic
**Barrel**: 4.75 in., 6 in., 7.5 in.
**Sights**: Fixed
**Weight**: 42 oz.
**Caliber**: .44 Mag.
**Capacity**: 6 rounds
**Features**: Blued, stainless, case-hardened or Old West finish; target model has angled front target sight and adjustable notched rear blade sight
**MSRP** . . . . . . . . . . . . . . . **$619–$649**

### 1873 CATTLEMAN CHISHOLM

**Action**: SA revolver
**Grips**: Checkered walnut
**Barrel**: 4.75 in., 5.5 in.
**Sights**: Fixed, open
**Weight**: 37 oz.
**Caliber**: .45 Colt
**Capacity**: 6 rounds
**Features**: Complete matte finished steel; fluted barrel
**MSRP** . . . . . . . . . . . . . . . . . . . **$549**

### 1873 CATTLEMAN DESPERADO

**Action**: SA revolver
**Grips**: Bison horn style
**Barrel**: 4.75 in., 5.5 in.
**Sights**: Fixed, open
**Weight**: 37 oz.
**Caliber**: .45 Colt
**Capacity**: 6 rounds
**Features**: Full nickel-plated steel; fluted barrel
**MSRP** . . . . . . . . . . . . . . . . . . . **$819**

### 1873 CATTLEMAN MATCHING SETS

**Action**: SA revolver
**Grips**: Walnut
**Barrel**: 5.5 in.
**Sights**: Fixed, open
**Weight**: 37 oz.
**Caliber**: .45 Colt and .357 Mag
**Capacity**: 6 rounds
**Features**: Fluted barrel; blued case-hardened frame; steel backstrap; trigger guard; the set shares matching serial numbers; also available in nickel and ivory-style grip
**Walnut:** . . . . . . . . . . . **$1079 per set**
**Ivory-style:** . . . . . . . . . **$1659 per set**

# Uberti

**UBERTI 1873 EL PATRÓN COWBOY MOUNTED SHOOTER (CMS)**

## 1873 EL PATRÓN COWBOY MOUNTED SHOOTER (CMS)

*Action*: SA revolver
*Grips*: Checkered walnut
*Barrel*: 3.5 in., 4 in.
*Sights*: EasyView
*Weight*: 37 oz.
*Caliber*: .45 Colt, .357 Mag.
*Capacity*: 6 rounds
*Features*: Blued or stainless steel finish; optional case-hardened frame; fluted barrel; fitted with U.S.-made Wolff springs; numbered cylinders
**Blued: . . . . . . . . . . . . . . . . . . . $639**
**Stainless steel:. . . . . . . . . . . . $779**

## 1873 SINGLE-ACTION CATTLEMAN

*Action*: SA revolver
*Grips*: Walnut
*Barrel*: 4.75 in., 5.5 in., 7.5 in.
*Sights*: Fixed, open
*Weight*: 37 oz.
*Caliber*: .45 Colt, .44/40, .357 Mag.
*Capacity*: 6 rounds
*Features*: Case-hardened frame; brass or steel backstrap and trigger guard; blued, nickel or stainless steel finish; fluted barrel
**MSRP. . . . . . . . . . . . . . . . $509–$689**

**UBERTI 1873 SA CATTLEMAN**

## 1873 STALLION/STALLION TARGET

*Action*: SA revolver
*Grips*: Walnut
*Barrel*: 4.75 in., 5.5 in.
*Sights*: Fixed, open
*Weight*: 32 oz.
*Caliber*: .22LR, .22LR/Mag
*Capacity*: 6 and 10 round models
*Features*: Case-hardened frame; brass or steel backstrap and trigger guard; blued finish; fluted barrel
**MSRP. . . . . . . . . . . . . . . . $439–$579**

**UBERTI 1873 STALLION TARGET**

## 1875 OUTLAW & FRONTIER

*Action*: SA revolver
*Grips*: Walnut
*Barrel*: 5.5 in. (Frontier), 7.5 in.
*Sights*: Fixed, open
*Weight*: 40–45 oz.
*Caliber*: .45 Colt
*Capacity*: 6 rounds
*Features*: Case-hardened or full nickel plated steel frame; steel backstrap and

**UBERTI 1875 FRONTIER**

trigger guard; fluted barrel
**Outlaw: . . . . . . . . . . . . . . . . . . $559**
**Outlaw Nickel: . . . . . . . . . . . . $659**
**Frontier: . . . . . . . . . . . . . . . . . $559**

**UBERTI 1890 SA POLICE REVOLVER**

**UBERTI TOP BREAK REVOLVER**

## 1890 SINGLE ACTION POLICE REVOLVER

*Action*: SA revolver
*Grips*: Walnut with lanyard ring
*Barrel*: 5.5 in.
*Sights*: Fixed, open
*Weight*: 42 oz.
*Caliber*: .45, .357 Mag.
*Capacity*: 6 rounds
*Features*: Blued steel frame, backstrap and trigger guard; fluted barrel
**MSRP . . . . . . . . . . . . . . . . . . . . $579**

## TOP BREAK REVOLVERS

*Action*: SA revolver
*Grips*: Walnut or pearl-style
*Barrel*: 3.5 in., 5 in., 7 in.
*Sights*: Fixed, open
*Weight*: 40 oz.
*Caliber*: .45 Colt, .38 Spl., .44/40
*Capacity*: 6 rounds
*Features*: Full nickel plated steel or blued steel frame and blackstrap; case-hardened trigger guard; fluted barrel
**Pearl-style grip: . . . . . . . . . . . $1419**
**Walnut grip:. . . . . . . . . . . . . . $1069**

# U.S. Fire Arms

## OLD ARMORY ORIGINAL SERIES 1ST GENERATION

*Action*: SA revolver
*Grips*: U.S. hard rubber or walnut
*Barrel*: 4.75 in., 5.5 in., 7.5 in.
*Sights*: Blade front
*Weight*: N/A
*Caliber*: .45 Colt
*Capacity*: 6 rounds
*Features*: Historically correct OEM 1st Generation; frame window is smaller; small cylinder profile correct for early Colt production; early flutes and beveled cylinder; choice of B.P. frame, V notch or cross pin frame V notch
**MSRP . . . . . . . . . . . . . . . . . . $2095**

## SHOOTING MASTER .357 MAGNUM

*Action*: SA revolver
*Grips*: U.S. hard rubber
*Barrel*: 7.5 in.
*Sights*: Front blade, rear golden
*Weight*: N/A
*Caliber*: .357 S&W Mag.
*Capacity*: 6 rounds
*Features*: Heavy Magnum frame; full dome blued finish
**MSRP . . . . . . . . . . . . . . . . . . $1495**

## SPARROWHAWK .327 MAGNUM

*Action*: SA revolver
*Grips*: U.S. hard rubber
*Barrel*: 7.5 in.
*Sights*: Fully adjustable rear
*Weight*: N/A
*Caliber*: .327 Fed. Mag.

**U.S. FIRE ARMS OLD ARMORY ORIGINAL SERIES 1ST GENERATION**

**U.S. FIRE ARMS SHOOTING MASTER .357 MAGNUM**

**U.S. FIRE ARMS SPARROWHAWK .327 MAGNUM**

**U.S. FIRE ARMS THE ORIGINAL RODEO**

*Capacity*: 8 rounds
*Features*: Full dome blued; new scaled .32 caliber frame; includes removable firing pin
**MSRP . . . . . . . . . . . . . . . . . . $1495**

## THE ORIGINAL RODEO

*Action*: SA revolver
*Grips*: U.S. hard rubber
*Barrel*: 4.75 in., 5.5 in.

*Sights*: Square notch rear, square front blade
*Weight*: 37 oz.
*Caliber*: .45 Colt, .38 Special
*Capacity*: 6 rounds
*Features*: Handcrafted with cowboy action in matte blued, glare-reducing finish; standard white sided hammer; cross-pin frame style
**MSRP . . . . . . . . . . . . . . . . . . $760**

# Walther

## P22

*Action*: DA/SA autoloader
*Grips*: Polymer
*Barrel*: 3.42 in., 5 in.
*Sights*: 3-dot adjustable low-profile
*Weight*: 17.6 oz. (3.42 in. barrel), 21.3 oz. (5 in. barrel)
*Caliber*: .22LR
*Capacity*: 10 rounds
*Features*: Threaded barrel, interchangeable with target barrel; loaded chamber indicator; external slide stop; 3 safeties; two magazine styles; ergonomic grip; ambidextrous magazine release lever; available with integrated laser-set; available in black, nickel, and military finish
*MSRP* . . . . . . . . . . . . . . . $379–$539

## P99AS

*Action*: DA autoloader
*Grips*: Black polymer frame and grips
*Barrel*: 4 in. stainless steel with Tenifer finish
*Sights*: Front and rear tritium night
*Weight*: 24 oz.–25.6 oz.
*Caliber*: 9mm or .40 S&W
*Capacity*: 15 (9mm), 12 (.40 S&W) rounds
*Features*: The first pistol with a firing pin block combines advantages of a traditional DA pull with SA trigger and a decocking button safety integrated into slide, allowing users the ability to decock the striker, preventing inadvertent firing in both DA and SA mode
*From*: . . . . . . . . . . . . . . . . . $599

## P99AS COMPACT

*Action*: Striker fire action autoloader
*Grips*: Polymer
*Barrel*: 3.5 in.
*Sights*: 3-dot adjustable low-profile
*Weight*: 20.8 oz.–22.4 oz.
*Caliber*: 9mm, .40 S&W
*Capacity*: 10 rounds (9mm), 8 rounds (.40 S&W)
*Features*: Flat-bottom magazine buttplate, finger rest magazine buttplate; molded with a Weaver-style rail; interchangeable backstraps; hammerless striker system and integral safety devices come standard
*From*: . . . . . . . . . . . . . . . . . $599

## PPK AND PPK/S

*Action*: DA/SA autoloader
*Grips*: Polymer

WALTHER P22

WALTHER P99AS

WALTHER P99AS COMPACT

WALTHER PKK/S

WALTHER PPS

*Barrel*: 3.3 in.
*Sights*: Fixed, open
*Weight*: 22.4 oz. (PPK), 24 oz. (PPK/S)
*Caliber*: .380 ACP
*Capacity*: 6 rounds (PPK), 7 rounds (PPK/S)
*Features*: Firing pin safety; manual safety with decocking function; double- and single-action trigger; extended beaver tail; nickel plated or blued finish
*MSRP* . . . . . . . . . . . . . . . . . $629

## PPS (POLICE PISTOL SLIM)

*Action*: Striker fire action autoloader
*Grips*: Black polymer
*Barrel*: 3.2 in.

*Sights*: 3-dot low profile contoured
*Weight*: 20.8 oz.
*Caliber*: 9mm, 40 S&W
*Capacity*: 6 and 8 rounds (9mm), 5 and 7 rounds (.40 S&W)
*Features*: Ambidextrous magazine release; loaded chamber and cocking indicators; small and large backstrap; trigger safety; Walther QuickSafe safety
*MSRP* . . . . . . . . . . . . . . . . . $599

# Connecticut Valley Arms (CVA)

CVA ACCURA MR

CVA ACCURA V2

CVA APEX

CVA BUCKHORN

CVA ELKHORN

## ACCURA MR

**Lock**: Break-action in-line
**Stock**: Synthetic
**Barrel**: 25 in.
**Sights**: Scope mount
**Weight**: 6 lb. 6 oz.
**Bore/Caliber**: .50
**Features**: Aluminum frame; quick release breech plug; trigger guard actuated breeching action; Bergara barrel; neutral center of gravity trigger; premium SoftTouch stock with rubber grip panels; WeatherGuard barrel finish on the stainless steel barrel; Realtree Max-1 or black stock finishes; Quake Claw sling included; DuraSight Dead-On scope mount
**MSRP . . . .$537.95–$612.95**

## ACCURA V2

**Lock**: Break-action muzzle-loading
**Stock**: Composite stock in standard or thumbhole
**Barrel**: 27 in.
**Sights**: DuraSight fiber optic
**Weight**: 7 lb. 5 oz.
**Bore/Caliber**: .45 or .50
**Features**: 416 stainless Bergara barrel; quick-release breech plug; CrushZone recoil pad; drilled and tapped for scope mount; SoftTouch coating and rubber grip panels; Quake Claw sling
**MSRP . . . .$493.95–$595.95**

## APEX

**Lock**: Hinged breech muzzleloading
**Stock**: Synthetic
**Barrel**: 27 in.
**Sights**: DuraSight rail mount
**Weight**: 8 lb.
**Bore/Caliber**: .45 or .50
**Features**: Multibarrel interchangeable rifle system; ambidextrous buttstock; 416 stainless steel Bergara barrels; quick-release breech plug; Quake Claw sling; CrushZone recoil pad; available in black or Realtree APG camo; also available in centerfire models
**MSRP . . . .$652.99–$737.95**

## BUCKHORN

**Lock**: In-line
**Stock**: Solid composite
**Barrel**: 24 in.
**Sights**: DuraSight fiber optic
**Weight**: 6 lb. 5 oz.
**Bore/Caliber**: .50
**Features**: 209 ignition; bullet guiding muzzle; DuraSight all-metal fiber optic sights; solid composite stock in black, with molded-in grip panels and sling swivel studs; CrushZone recoil pad; thumb-actuated safety; drilled and tapped for scope mounts
**MSRP . . . . . . . . . $176.95**

## ELKHORN

**Lock**: Bolt-action muzzle-loading
**Stock**: Synthetic
**Barrel**: 26 in.
**Sights**: DuraSight fiber optic
**Weight**: 7 lb.
**Bore/Caliber**: .50
**Features**: Fluted barrel with bullet-guiding muzzle; 3-way ignition with primer ejecting bolt face; DuraBright all metal fiber optic sights; composite stock in Realtree or black; Quake Claw sling; CrushZone recoil pad
**MSRP . . . .$289.95–$349.95**

# Connecticut Valley Arms (CVA)

CVA WOLF

## WOLF

**Lock**: Break-action in-line
**Stock**: Synthetic
**Barrel**: 24 in.
**Sights**: DuraSight fiber optic; includes 3-9x40mm duplex scope
**Weight**: 6 lb. 4 oz.
**Bore/Caliber**: .50

**Features**: Bullet-guiding muzzle; new tool-free QR breech plug system; ambidextrous compact or standard stock in black or camo; CrushZone recoil pad; reversible hammer spur; blued barrel
**MSRP** . . . . . . . . . . **$238.95–$328.95**

# Dixie Gun Works

DIXIE GUN WORKS 1853 ENFIELD THREE-BAND

DIXIE GUN WORKS DIXIE SHARPS NEW MODEL 1859 MILITARY CARBINE

## 1853 ENFIELD THREE-BAND RIFLE MUSKET

**Lock**: Traditional caplock
**Stock**: Walnut
**Barrel**: 39 in.
**Sights**: Fixed
**Weight**: 10 lb. 4 oz.
**Bore/Caliber**: .58
**Features**: Color case-hardened lock; single trigger; single swivels; steel ramrod
**MSRP** . . . . . . . . . . . . . . . **$725–$1695**

## DIXIE SHARPS NEW MODEL 1859 MILITARY CARBINE

**Lock**: Dropping block
**Stock**: Walnut
**Barrel**: 22 in.
**Sights**: Adjustable open
**Weight**: 8 lb.
**Bore/Caliber**: .54
**Features**: Steel furniture; color case-hardened; single trigger; single barrel band; saddle bar with ring
**MSRP** . . . . . . . . . . . . . . . . . . **$1350**

BLACK POWDER

# Dixie Gun Works

## FR4055 SPANISH MUSKET

*Lock*: Flintlock muzzleloading
*Stock*: Full, European walnut 56 in.
*Barrel*: 44.75 in.
*Sights*: Steel stud front
*Weight*: 10 lb.
*Bore/Caliber*: .68 round ball
*Features*: Brass buttplate, trigger guard, and barrel bands; bright steel side-plates; steel ramrod
**MSRP** . . . . . . . . . . . . . . . . . **$1400**

DIXIE GUN WORKS FR4055 SPANISH MUSKET

## PEDERSOLI SCREW BARREL PISTOL

*Lock*: Traditional caplock
*Stock*: European walnut
*Barrel*: 3 in.
*Sights*: None
*Weight*: 12 oz.
*Bore/Caliber*: .44
*Features*: Color case-hardened lock; single folding trigger; combination nipple/barrel wrench included
**MSRP** . . . . . . . . . . . . . . . . . . . **$185**

DIXIE GUN WORKS PEDERSOLI SCREW BARREL PISTOL

DIXIE GUN WORKS U.S. MODEL 1816 SPRINGFIELD MUSKET

## U.S. MODEL 1816 SPRINGFIELD MUSKET

*Lock*: Traditional flintlock
*Stock*: Walnut
*Barrel*: 42 in.
*Sights*: Fixed

*Weight*: 9 lb. 13 oz.
*Bore/Caliber*: .69
*Features*: Most common military flintlock from U.S. armories, complete with bayonet lug and swivels
**MSRP** . . . . . . . . . . . . . . . . . . **$1450**

E.M.F. 1851 NAVY

## 1851 NAVY

*Lock*: Caplock revolver
*Stock*: Walnut
*Barrel*: 7.5 in.
*Sights*: Fixed
*Weight*: 40 oz.
*Bore/Caliber*: .36, .44
*Features*: Brass, case-hardened stainless steel frame; blued barrel optional
**Brass**:..................... **$215**
**Case-hardened**:............ **$240**

## 1851 NAVY SHERIFF

*Lock*: Caplock revolver
*Stock*: Walnut
*Barrel*: 5.5 in.
*Sights*: None
*Weight*: 32 oz.
*Bore/Caliber*: .44
*Features*: Brass, case-hardened stainless steel frame; blued barrel optional
**Brass**:.................... **$220**
**Case-hardened**:........... **$250**

E.M.F. 1851 NAVY SHERIFF

## 1858 REMINGTON ARMY REVOLVER

*Lock*: Caplock revolver
*Stock*: Walnut
*Barrel*: 8 in.
*Sights*: Fixed
*Weight*: 40 oz.
*Bore/Caliber*: .44
*Features*: Brass or stainless steel frame; blued barrel optional
**Brass**:.................... **$240**
**Blued**: ................... **$290**
**Stainless**:................ **$490**

E.M.F. 1858 REMINGTON ARMY REVOLVER

# E.M.F. Company

E.M.F. 1860 ARMY REVOLVER

## 1860 ARMY REVOLVER

*Lock*: Caplock revolver
*Stock*: Walnut
*Barrel*: 8 in.
*Sights*: Fixed
*Weight*: 41.6 oz.
*Bore/Caliber*: .44
*Features*: Case-hardened frame; blued barrel
**Brass**: . . . . . . . . . . . . . . . . . . . . **$270**
**Steel**: . . . . . . . . . . . . . . . . . . . **$290**

E.M.F. MISSOURI RIVER HAWKEN

E.M.F. 1863 POCKET REMINGTON

## 1863 POCKET REMINGTON

*Lock*: Caplock revolver
*Stock*: Walnut
*Barrel*: 3.5 in.
*Sights*: Fixed
*Weight*: 21 oz.
*Bore/Caliber*: .36
*Features*: Steel frame, blued barrel
**MSRP** . . . . . . . . . . . . . . . . . . . . **$295**

E.M.F. KENTUCKY FLINTLOCK PISTOL

E.M.F. PENNSYLVANIA PERCUSSION RIFLE

## KENTUCKY FLINTLOCK PISTOL

*Lock*: Flintlock
*Stock*: Walnut
*Barrel*: 10.375 in.
*Sights*: Fixed
*Weight*: 37 oz.
*Bore/Caliber*: .45, .50
*Features*: Classic American pistol during the American Revolution and a favorite of pioneers; case-hardened frame; octagonal rifled blued barrel, polished brass fittings
**.45**: . . . . . . . . . . . . . . . . . . . . . . **$525**
**.50**: . . . . . . . . . . . . . . . . . . . . . . **$555**

## MISSOURI RIVER HAWKEN BY PEDERSOLI

*Lock*: Caplock muzzleloading
*Stock*: Maple or walnut
*Barrel*: 30 in.
*Sights*: Open
*Weight*: 9 lb. 4 oz.
*Bore/Caliber*: .45, .50
*Features*: Replica percussion rifle; available in maple or walnut stock in rust brown color finish; barrel features an octagonal cross-section; case-hardened color lock; equipped with a double-set trigger
**Maple**: . . . . . . . . . . . . . . . . . . **$1360**
**Walnut**: . . . . . . . . . . . . . . . . . **$1355**

## PENNSYLVANIA PERCUSSION RIFLE

*Lock*: Caplock
*Stock*: Walnut
*Barrel*: 41.625 in.
*Sights*: Adjustable
*Weight*: 7 lb. 11 oz.
*Bore/Caliber*: .45
*Features*: Reproduction of the American rifles used by Pennsylvania hunters; evolved from the German Jaeger hunting rifle; adjustable rear and front sights; case-hardened frame; double set trigger; rust brown octagonal barrel; polished brass fitting
**MSRP** . . . . . . . . . . . . . . . . . . **$1035**

BLACK POWDER

LYMAN DEERSTALKER FLINTLOCK

LYMAN GREAT PLAINS FLINTLOCK

LYMAN MUSTANG BREAKAWAY 209 MAGNUM

LYMAN PLAINS PISTOL

## DEERSTALKER RIFLE

**Lock**: Traditional cap or flint
**Stock**: Walnut
**Barrel**: 24 in.
**Sights**: Fiber optic front and rear
**Weight**: 10 lb. 6 oz.
**Bore/Caliber**: .50 or .54
**Features**: Quiet single trigger; metal blackened to avoid glare; black rubber recoil pad; left-hand available
**Flintlock:** . . . . . . . . $559.95–$614.95
**Percussion:** . . . . . . $524.95–$624.95

## GREAT PLAINS RIFLE

**Lock**: Traditional cap or flint
**Stock**: Walnut
**Barrel**: 32 in.
**Sights**: Adjustable open
**Weight**: 11 lb. 10 oz.
**Bore/Caliber**: .50 or .54
**Features**: Double-set triggers; Hawken style percussion "snail" with clean-out screw; separate ramrod entry thimble and nose cap; reliable coil-spring lock with correct lock plate; left-hand available
**Flintlock:** . . . . . . . . $769.95–$784.95
**Percussion:** . . . . . . $719.95–$749.95

## MUSTANG BREAKAWAY 209 MAGNUM

**Lock**: In-line
**Stock**: Hardwood
**Barrel**: 26 in.
**Sights**: Fiber optic front and rear
**Weight**: 11 lb.
**Bore/Caliber**: .50
**Features**: Pachmayr "Decelerator" recoil pad; comes drilled and tapped for Weaver style bases; hammerless; removable, stainless breech plug and easy take-down; "magnetized" primer retention system
**MSRP** . . . . . . . . . . . . . . . . . . $525

## PLAINS PISTOL

**Lock**: Traditional caplock
**Stock**: Walnut
**Barrel**: 6 in.
**Sights**: Fixed
**Weight**: 3 lb. 2 oz.
**Bore/Caliber**: .50 or .54
**Features**: Blackened iron furniture; polished brass trigger guard and ramrod tips; hooked patent breech takes down quickly for easy cleaning; thimble is recessed into the rib; detachable belt hook; spring-loaded trigger
**Plains Pistol:** . . . . . . . . . . . . $374.95
**Kit:** . . . . . . . . . . . . . . . . . . . $319.95

## TRADE RIFLE

**Lock**: Traditional cap or flint
**Stock**: Walnut
**Barrel**: 28 in.
**Sights**: Adjustable open
**Weight**: 10 lb. 13 oz.
**Bore/Caliber**: .50 or .54
**Features**: Brass furniture; originally developed for the early Indian fur trade
**Flintlock:** . . . . . . . . . . . . . . $569.95
**Percussion:** . . . . . . . . . . . . $524.95

LYMAN TRADE RIFLE

# Pedersoli

## BAKER STYLE COACH GUN

**Lock**: Caplock
**Stock**: Walnut
**Barrel**: 11.25 in.
**Sights**: None
**Weight**: 5 lb. 12 oz.
**Bore/Caliber**: 12 Ga.
**Features**: Single trigger back action, side-by-side shotgun; reproduces a gun made by London gunsmith Ezekiel Baker in 1850; case-hardened locks
**MSRP** . . . . . . . . . . . . . . . . . . . . **$945**

## CAVALRY SHOTGUN WITH SINGLE TRIGGER

**Lock**: Caplock
**Stock**: Walnut
**Barrel**: 20 in.
**Sights**: None
**Weight**: 6 lb. 10 oz.
**Bore/Caliber**: 12 Ga.
**Features**: Single trigger back action; side-by-side hunting shotgun; shortened barrel for riding a horse; case-hardened locks
**MSRP** . . . . . . . . . . . . . . . . . . . . **$913**

## COOK & BROTHER ARTILLERY CARBINE

**Lock**: Caplock
**Stock**: Walnut
**Barrel**: 24 in.
**Sights**: None
**Weight**: 6 lb. 10 oz.
**Bore/Caliber**: .58
**Features**: Inspired by English model guns; originally produced by Cook & Brother beginning in 1861; brass garnitures; blued barrel; case-hardened lock
**MSRP** . . . . . . . . . . . . . . . . . . . **$1055**

## DERRINGER PHILADELPHIA

**Lock**: Flintlock
**Stock**: Walnut
**Barrel**: 3.06 in.
**Sights**: None
**Weight**: 8.6 oz.
**Bore/Caliber**: .45
**Features**: Reproduction of the popular pocket pistols originally manufactured by John Henry Derringer. Brass furniture; case-hardened lock; original markings on the lock: Derringer/ Philadelphia
**MSRP** . . . . . . . . . . . . . . . . . . . . **$505**

## ENFIELD 3 BAND P1853 RIFLE MUSKET

**Lock**: Caplock
**Stock**: Walnut
**Barrel**: 39 in.
**Sights**: Adjustable rear
**Weight**: 8 lb. 13 oz.
**Bore/Caliber**: .577

**Features**: Ladder rear sight with a slider assembled on a base with steps; steel barrel bands; brass furniture; ramrod tip is shaped with characteristic jag slot; barrel is blued and lock case-hardened
**MSRP** . . . . . . . . . . . . . . . . . . **$1210**

PEDERSOLI BAKER STYLE COACH GUN

PEDERSOLI CAVALRY SHOTGUN WITH SINGLE TRIGGER

PEDERSOLI COOK & BROTHER ARTILLERY CARBINE

PEDERSOLI DERRINGER PHILADELPHIA

PEDERSOLI ENFIELD 3 BAND P1853 RIFLE MUSKET

PEDERSOLI GIBBS SHOTGUN

PEDERSOLI HOWDAH HUNTER PISTOL

PEDERSOLI LA BOHEMIENNE SIDE-BY-SIDE SHOTGUN

PEDERSOLI LE PAGE TARGET FLINTLOCK PISTOL

PEDERSOLI MANG IN GRAZ MATCH

PEDERSOLI MISSISSIPPI U.S. MODEL 1841

## LA BOHEMIENNE SIDE-BY-SIDE SHOTGUN
*Lock*: Hinged breech muzzleloading
*Stock*: Checkered walnut
*Barrel*: 28 in.
*Chokes*: cyl/mod choke tubes
*Weight*: 7 lb.
*Bore/Caliber*: 12 Ga.
*Features*: Rust brown finish barrel; interchangeable chokes; color case-hardened frame; hand-engraved locks
MSRP . . . . . . . . . . . . . . . . . . $2050

## LE PAGE TARGET FLINTLOCK PISTOL
*Lock*: Traditional flintlock
*Stock*: Walnut
*Barrel*: 10.5 in.
*Sights*: Adjustable
*Weight*: 2 lb. 10 oz.
*Bore/Caliber*: .44 or .45
*Features*: Smoothbore .45 available; adjustable single-set trigger; brightly polished lock with a roller frizzen spring
MSRP . . . . . . . . . . . . . . . . . . $1230

## MANG IN GRAZ MATCH
*Lock*: Traditional caplock
*Stock*: Walnut
*Barrel*: 11.4 in.
*Sights*: Fixed
*Weight*: 2 lb. 10 oz.
*Bore/Caliber*: .38 or .44
*Features*: Fluted grip; octagonal, rifled barrel in brown rust finish; adjustable single set trigger; breech plug shows a typical mask of the period; barrel and tang enriched with gold inlays
MSRP . . . . . . . . . . . . . . . . . . $1750

## MISSISSIPPI U.S. MODEL 1841
*Lock*: Caplock
*Stock*: Walnut
*Barrel*: 33 in.
*Sights*: Open rear
*Weight*: 9 lb. 8 oz.
*Bore/Caliber*: .54, .58
*Features*: Considered the best-looking ordnance rifle of its period; brass furniture; browned barrel; notched rear sight; case-hardened lock; ramrod with brass tip
MSRP . . . . . . . . . . . . . . . . . . $1261

## GIBBS SHOTGUN
*Lock*: Caplock
*Stock*: Walnut
*Barrel*: 32.3 in.
*Sights*: None
*Weight*: 8 lb. 9 oz.
*Bore/Caliber*: 12 Ga.
*Features*: Octagonal to round barrel; case-hardened color-finished lock; grip and forend caps with ebony inserts; pistol grip stock
MSRP . . . . . . . . . . . . . . . . . . $1514

## HOWDAH HUNTER PISTOL
*Lock*: Caplock
*Stock*: Walnut
*Barrel*: 11.25 in.
*Sights*: None
*Weight*: 5 lb. 1 oz.
*Bore/Caliber*: 20 Ga., .50, .58
*Features*: Engraved locks with wild animal scenes; case-hardened color finish; checkered walnut pistol grip with steel butt cap
MSRP . . . . . . . . . . . . . . . . . . $821

# Pedersoli

## MORTIMER TARGET RIFLE

*Lock*: Flintlock
*Stock*: English-style European walnut
*Barrel*: 36.4 in.
*Sights*: Target
*Weight*: 10 lb. 2 oz.
*Bore/Caliber*: .54
*Features*: Case-colored lock; stock has cheekpiece and hand checkering; 7-groove barrel
**MSRP** . . . . . . . . . . . . . . . . . . . **$1758**

## PLAINS SHOTGUN "THE FAST BACK ACTION"

*Lock*: Caplock
*Stock*: Walnut
*Barrel*: 27.5 in., 28.5 in.
*Sights*: None
*Weight*: 7 lb. 5 oz.–7 lb. 8 oz.
*Bore/Caliber*: 12, 20 Ga.
*Features*: Single trigger; side-by-side shotgun; fast second shot, thanks to back action lock reducing minor residues of black powder in lock parts
**MSRP** . . . . . . . . . . . . . . . . . . . **$1191**

## RICHMOND 1861, TYPE III

*Lock*: Caplock
*Stock*: Walnut
*Barrel*: 39.75 in.
*Sights*: None
*Weight*: 9 lb. 14 oz.
*Bore/Caliber*: .58
*Features*: Manufactured based on the U.S. 1855 Model with the Maynard tape ignition system; except for the lock's profile, the brass buttplate, and the stock nose cap, the gun's appearance resembles the U.S. Model 1861
**MSRP** . . . . . . . . . . . . . . . . . . . **$1261**

## SPRINGFIELD MODEL 1861 U.S.

*Lock*: Caplock
*Stock*: Walnut
*Barrel*: 40 in.
*Sights*: None
*Weight*: 9 lb. 14 oz.
*Bore/Caliber*: .58
*Features*: More efficient than earlier smooth bored muskets used by both sides in the American Civil War; satin finish barrel; stock with three bands; coin-colored finish on the steel furniture
**MSRP** . . . . . . . . . . . . . . . . . . . **$1253**

## SWISS MATCH STANDARD FLINTLOCK

*Lock*: Traditional flintlock
*Stock*: Walnut
*Barrel*: 30.8 in.
*Sights*: Adjustable
*Weight*: 16 lb. 5 oz.
*Bore/Caliber*: .40
*Features*: Octagonal conical profile barrel with rust brown finish; lock is case-hardened; steel ramrod; double-set trigger; steel hook buttplate
**MSRP** . . . . . . . . . . . . . . . . . . . **$3191**

## TYRON TARGET STANDARD RIFLE

*Lock*: Traditional caplock
*Stock*: Walnut
*Barrel*: 36.4 in.
*Sights*: Adjustable open
*Weight*: 9 lb. 11 oz.
*Bore/Caliber*: .45, .50, .54
*Features*: Creedmoor version with aperture sight available
**MSRP** . . . . . . . . . . . . . . . . . . . **$1098**

PEDERSOLI MORTIMER TARGET RIFLE

PEDERSOLI PLAINS SHOTGUN

PEDERSOLI RICHMOND 1861, TYPE III

PEDERSOLI SPRINGFIELD MODEL 1861 U.S.

PEDERSOLI SWISS MATCH STANDARD FLINTLOCK

PEDERSOLI TYRON TARGET STANDARD RIFLE

# Savage Arms

SAVAGE ARMS 10ML-II MUZZLELOADER

## 10ML-II MUZZLELOADER
**Lock**: In-line
**Stock**: Synthetic, camo
**Barrel**: 24 in.
**Sights**: Adjustable fiber optics
**Weight**: 7 lb. 12 oz.
**Bore/Caliber**: .50

**Features**: Bolt-action mechanism; drilled and tapped for scope mounts; AccuTrigger; free-floating barreled action; sling swivel studs; stock comes in black synthetic, Realtree Hardwoods HD camouflage synthetic, or brown laminate; blued or stainless steel barrel
**Synthetic:** . . . . . . . . . . . . . . . $638
**Camo:** . . . . . . . . . . . . . . . . . . $753

# Shiloh Rifle

SHILOH RIFLE 1874 SHARPS BUFFALO–"QUIGLEY"

SHILOH RIFLE 1874 TARGET CREEDMOOR RIFLE

## 1863 RIFLES
**Lock**: Traditional caplock
**Stock**: Walnut
**Barrel**: 30 in.
**Sights**: Adjustable open
**Weight**: 9 lb. 8 oz.
**Bore/Caliber**: .50 or .54
**Features**: Sporting model has half-stock; double set trigger on military model with 3-band full stock; military steel buttstock on all models
**Sporting:** . . . . . . . . . . . . . . . $1854
**Carbine:** . . . . . . . . . . . . . . . $1854
**Military:** . . . . . . . . . . . . . . . $2154

## 1874 SHARPS BUFFALO– "QUIGLEY"
**Lock**: Falling block
**Stock**: Walnut
**Barrel**: 34 in.
**Sights**: Semi buckhorn rear, midrange vernier tang, #111 globe aperture front
**Weight**: 12 lb. 8 oz.
**Bore/Caliber**: .45-70 or .45-110
**Features**: Military buttstock; patchbox; heavy octagonal barrel; pewter tip; Hartford collars; double set triggers; antique or standard color finish; gold inlay initials in gold oval
**MSRP** . . . . . . . . . . . . . . . . . $3396

## 1874 TARGET CREEDMOOR RIFLE
**Lock**: Blackpowder cartridge
**Stock**: Walnut
**Barrel**: 32 in.
**Sights**: V aiming rear; blade front
**Weight**: 9 lb.
**Bore/Caliber**: All popular black powder cartridges from .38-55 to .50-90
**Features**: Pistol grip; single trigger; AA finish on American black walnut; polished barrel; octagon barrel; pewter tip
**MSRP** . . . . . . . . . . . . . . . . . $2825

# Taylor's & Co.

TAYLOR'S & CO. 1848 DRAGOONS

TAYLOR'S & CO. LE MAT CAVALRY

TAYLOR'S & CO. 1847 WALKER

TAYLOR'S & CO. 1842 SMOOTHBORE MUSKET

## 1842 SMOOTHBORE MUSKET

*Lock*: Caplock
*Stock*: Walnut
*Barrel*: 42 in.
*Sights*: Military style
*Weight*: 9 lb. 12 oz.
*Bore/Caliber*: .69
*Features*: The Springfield replica has all the features of the original, including a one-piece, oil-finished walnut stock; original-style barrel bands; and completely interchangeable parts. The percussion lock has a V-style mainspring. This model features the lock with stamping noting 1842 and Springfield. NSSA approved, with certificate of authenticity and a brass medallion featuring the model and serial number.
**MSRP** . . . . . . . . . . . . . . . . . . . . **$750**

## 1847 WALKER

*Lock*: Caplock revolver
*Stock*: Walnut
*Barrel*: 9 in.
*Sights*: Fixed
*Weight*: 4 lb. 12 oz.
*Bore/Caliber*: .44
*Features*: Blued finish; round barrel
**MSRP** . . . . . . . . . . . . . . . . . . . **$407**

## 1848 DRAGOONS

*Lock*: Caplock revolver
*Stock*: Walnut
*Barrel*: 7.5 in.
*Sights*: Fixed
*Weight*: 4 lb.–4 lb. 14 oz.
*Bore/Caliber*: .44
*Features*: These Dragoon revolvers were first used by the U.S. Army's Mounted Rifles 1st Cavalry in 1833. Soon they went on to see considerable use during the 1850 and during the Civil War. Blued finish; six-round capacity
**1st Model:** . . . . . . . . . . . . . . . . **$381**
**2nd Model:** . . . . . . . . . . . . . . . **$391**
**3rd Model:** . . . . . . . . . . . . . . . . **$402**

## LE MAT CAVALRY

*Lock*: Caplock revolver
*Stock*: Walnut
*Barrel*: 8 in.
*Sights*: Fixed
*Weight*: 5 lb.
*Bore/Caliber*: .44 or 20 Ga.
*Features*: Blued steel finish; nine-shot .44 caliber revolver with a 20 Ga. single-shot barrel was a favorite among Confederate cavalry troops; case-hardened hammer and trigger; lanyard ring; trigger guard with spur
**MSRP** . . . . . . . . . . . . . . . . . . . . **$1169**

# Thompson/Center

THOMPSON/CENTER ENCORE ENDEAVOR PRO HUNTER XT

THOMPSON/CENTER FIRE STORM

THOMPSON/CENTER IMPACT

THOMPSON/CENTER NORTHWEST EXPLORER

THOMPSON/CENTER TRIUMPH BONE COLLECTOR

## ENCORE ENDEAVOR PRO HUNTER XT
**Lock**: Hinged breech muzzleloading
**Stock**: Camo or black FlexTech with SIMS recoil pad
**Barrel**: 28 in.
**Sights**: Fiber optic
**Weight**: 8 lb. 4 oz.
**Bore/Caliber**: .50
**Features**: 209 ignition primer, swing hammer, power rod, QLA muzzle system; speed breech XT; stainless, fluted barrel
**MSRP** . . . . . . . . . . . . . . . $779–$849

## FIRE STORM
**Lock**: Traditional cap or flint
**Stock**: Composite
**Barrel**: 26 in.
**Sights**: Steel fiber optic

**Weight**: 7 lb.
**Bore/Caliber**: .50
**Features**: Aluminum ramrod; single trigger with large trigger guard bow; Fire Storm positive ignition; magnum capabilities
**MSRP** . . . . . . . . . . . . . . . . . . . $599

## IMPACT
**Lock**: Hinged breech muzzleloading
**Stock**: Black or LongLeaf camo
**Barrel**: 28 in.
**Sights**: Fiber optic
**Weight**: 6 lb. 8 oz.
**Bore/Caliber**: .50
**Features**: Triple lead thread breech plug; 1-inch adjustable buttstock
**MSRP** . . . . . . . . . . . . . . . $259–$309

## NORTHWEST EXPLORER
**Lock**: Dropping block
**Stock**: Black composite or Realtree Hardwoods camo
**Barrel**: 28 in.

**Sights**: Adjustable
**Weight**: 7 lb.
**Bore/Caliber**: .50
**Features**: Design meets legal regulations of western states; exposed breech system; #11 cap ignition and metal sights; QLA (Quick Load Accurizor); weather shield coating available; blued barrel
**MSRP** . . . . . . . . . . . . . . . $359–$439

## TRIUMPH BONE COLLECTOR
**Lock**: In-line
**Stock**: Composite, black or Realtree AP HD camo
**Barrel**: 28 in.
**Sights**: Adjustable fiber optic
**Weight**: 6 lb. 8 oz.
**Bore/Caliber**: .50
**Features**: Blued, stainless, and weather shield finish; speed breech XT
**MSRP** . . . . . . . . . . . . . . . . . . . $669

# Traditions Firearms

TRADITIONS FIREARMS
1851 NAVY REVOLVER

TRADITIONS FIREARMS 1858
ARMY REVOLVER

TRADITIONS FIREARMS 1860
ARMY REVOLVER

TRADITIONS FIREARMS BUCKSTALKER

## 1851 NAVY REVOLVER

*Lock*: Caplock revolver
*Stock*: Walnut
*Barrel*: 7.5 in.
*Sights*: Fixed
*Weight*: 2 lb. 8 oz.
*Bore/Caliber*: .44
*Features*: Octagonal barrel and lever-style loader; brass, antiqued, or old silver frame and guard
**Brass:**. . . . . . . . . . . . . .**$229**
**Steel:** . . . . . . . . . . . . . .**$259**

## 1858 ARMY REVOLVER

*Lock*: Caplock
*Stock*: Walnut
*Barrel*: 8 in.
*Sights*: Fixed
*Weight*: 2 lb. 12 oz.
*Bore/Caliber*: .44
*Features*: Octagonal barrel and lever style loader; steel, brass, or stainless steel frame and guard; top strap and post sights
**Steel:** . . . . . . . . . . . . . . . . . . . . **$335**
**Brass:**. . . . . . . . . . . . . . . . . . . . **$269**
**SS:** . . . . . . . . . . . . . . . . . . . . . **$550**

## 1860 ARMY REVOLVER

*Lock*: Caplock
*Stock*: Simulated ivory, walnut
*Barrel*: 8 in.
*Sights*: Fixed
*Weight*: 2 lb. 12 oz.
*Bore/Caliber*: .44
*Features*: Blued barrel; steel frame; brass guard; hammer/blade sights
**Walnut/Steel:**. . . . . . . . . . . . . . **$305**
**Walnut/Brass:**. . . . . . . . . . . . . . **$250**
**Ivory/Nickel:** . . . . . . . . . . . . . . **$350**

## BUCKSTALKER

*Lock*: Break-action muzzleloading
*Stock*: Synthetic
*Barrel*: 24 in.
*Sights*: Tru-Glo fiber optics
*Weight*: 7 lb. 8 oz.
*Bore/Caliber*: .50
*Features*: Dual safety system; nickel guard coating; synthetic black or G1 Vista camo stock; nickel or blued finish barrel; Monte Carlo stock; drilled and tapped for a scope; sling swivel studs
**MSRP**. . . . . . . . . . . . . . . .**$215–$289**

# Traditions Firearms

TRADITIONS FIREARMS CROCKETT PISTOL

TRADITIONS FIREARMS DEERHUNTER RIFLE

TRADITIONS FIREARMS HAWKEN
WOODSMAN RIFLE

## CROCKETT PISTOL
*Lock*: Traditional caplock
*Stock*: Hardwood
*Barrel*: 15 in.
*Sights*: Fixed
*Weight*: 2 lb.
*Bore/Caliber*: .32
*Features*: Blued, octagonal barrel
**MSRP** . . . . . . . . . . . . . . . . . . . **$248**

## DEERHUNTER RIFLE
*Lock*: Traditional cap or flint
*Stock*: Synthetic or hardwood
*Barrel*: 24 in.
*Sights*: Lite Optic adjustable
*Weight*: 6 lb.
*Bore/Caliber*: .32, .50, .54
*Features*: Octagonal performance barrels; blued or nickel barrel finish; percussion models are drilled and tapped to accept scope mounts; non-slip recoil pad; stock comes in black synthetic, Mossy Oak Tree Stand camo, or hardwood
**MSRP** . . . . . . . . . . . . . . **$249–$389**

TRADITIONS FIREARMS
KENTUCKY PISTOL

## HAWKEN WOODSMAN RIFLE
*Lock*: Traditional cap or flint
*Stock*: Hardwood
*Barrel*: 28 in.
*Sights*: Adjustable rear hunting
*Weight*: 7 lb. 13 oz.
*Bore/Caliber*: .50
*Features*: Hooked breech for easy barrel removal; double-set triggers in an oversized glove-fitting trigger guard; inletted solid brass patch box; left-hand model available; octagonal blued barrel

**Flint:** . . . . . . . . . . . . . . . . . . . **$495**
**Percussion:** . . . . . . . . . . . . . . **$454**

## KENTUCKY PISTOL
*Lock*: Traditional caplock
*Stock*: Hardwood
*Barrel*: 10 in.
*Sights*: Fixed
*Weight*: 2 lb. 8 oz.
*Bore/Caliber*: .50
*Features*: Brass furniture; case-colored sidelock and brass ramrod thimble
**MSRP** . . . . . . . . . . . . . . . . . . . **$235**

# Traditions Firearms

TRADITIONS FIREARMS PENNSYLVANIA RIFLE

TRADITIONS FIREARMS PURSUIT ULTRALIGHT

TRADITIONS FIREARMS PURSUIT ULTRALIGHT XLT

TRADITIONS FIREARMS TRACKER 209

### PENNSYLVANIA RIFLE
*Lock*: Traditional cap or flint
*Stock*: Walnut
*Barrel*: 20 in.
*Sights*: Adjustable primitive style rear
*Weight*: 8 lb. 8 oz.
*Bore/Caliber*: .50
*Features*: Brass stock inlay ornamentation and toe plate; cheekpiece; solid brass patch box
**Percussion:** . . . . . . . . . . . . . . . **$754**
**Flint:** . . . . . . . . . . . . . . . . . . . **$799**

### PURSUIT ULTRALIGHT
*Lock*: Hinged breech muzzleloading
*Stock*: Black synthetic, Reaper Buck camo, or MO Infinity camo
*Barrel*: 28 in.
*Sights*: Metal fiber optic
*Weight*: 5 lb. 2 oz.

*Bore/Caliber*: .50
*Features*: Accelerator breech plug; drilled and tapped for scopes; 209 shotgun primer ignition; black synthetic with blued or CeraKote finish; speed load system; fluted barrel; 3-9x40 scope available
**MSRP** . . . . . . . . . . . . . . . **$309–$439**

### PURSUIT ULTRALIGHT XLT
*Lock*: Hinged breech muzzleloading
*Stock*: MO Infinity camo, Monte Carlo style cob
*Barrel*: 28 in.
*Sights*: Metal fiber optic
*Weight*: 5 lb. 14 oz.
*Bore/Caliber*: .50
*Features*: Alloy, lightweight frame, aluminum ramrod; QuickRelief recoil pad; SoftTouch rubberized coating on

stock; 209 ignition primer; drilled and tapped for scope mounts; sling swivel; fluted, Premium CeraKote barrel; thumbhole stock available
**MSRP** . . . . . . . . . . . . . . . **$339–$429**

### TRACKER 209
*Lock*: In-line
*Stock*: Synthetic, camo
*Barrel*: 22 in.
*Sights*: Light optic adjustable
*Weight*: 6 lb. 8 oz.
*Bore/Caliber*: .50
*Features*: Removable 209 primer ignition; projectile alignment system; in-line bolt with a quiet thumb safety; removable breech plug system; rugged synthetic ramrod
**MSRP** . . . . . . . . . . . . . . . . . . . **$184**

# Traditions Firearms

## TRAPPER PISTOL

*Lock*: Traditional cap or flint
*Stock*: Hardwood
*Barrel*: 9.75 in.
*Sights*: Primitive-style adjustable rear
*Weight*: 2 lb. 14 oz.
*Bore/Caliber*: .50
*Features*: Octagonal blued barrel; double set triggers
**MSRP . . . . . . . . . . . . . . . $316–$355**

TRADITIONS FIREARMS
TRAPPER PISTOL

TRADITIONS FIREARMS
VORTEK PISTOL - HARDWOOD

TRADITIONS FIREARMS
VORTEK ULTRALIGHT LDR

TRADITIONS FIREARMS VORTEK ULTRALIGHT

## VORTEK PISTOL

*Lock*: Hinged breech muzzleloading
*Stock*: Select hardwood, Realtree AP camo, Reaper Buck camo
*Barrel*: 13 in.
*Sights*: Fixed open
*Weight*: 3 lb. 4 oz.
*Bore/Caliber*: .50
*Features*: 209 primer ignition, accelerator breech plug; CeraKote finish on frame and barrel
**Hardwood: . . . . . . . . . . . . . . $383**
**Reaper Buck: . . . . . . . . . . . . . $459**

## VORTEK ULTRALIGHT

*Lock*: Hinged breech muzzleloading
*Stock*: Synthetic black Hogue over-mold, Realtree AP camo, or Reaper Buck camo
*Barrel*: 28 in.
*Sights*: Fixed, green
*Weight*: 6 lb. 4 oz.
*Bore/Caliber*: .50
*Features*: Drop-out trigger assembly; recoil pad; 3-pound factory trigger; frame and barrel have CeraKote finish
**MSRP . . . . . . . . . . . . . . . $430–$515**

## VORTEK ULTRALIGHT LDR

*Lock*: Hinged breech muzzleloading
*Stock*: Synthetic, Reaper Buck camo
*Barrel*: 30 in.
*Sights*: Drilled and tapped for scopes
*Weight*: 6 lb. 13 oz.
*Bore/Caliber*: .50
*Features*: The only break-action muzzle-loader with a 30-inch barrel on the market; accelerator breech plug; LT-1 alloy frame with Premium CeraKote finish; ultralight chromoly tapered, fluted barrel; Hogue comfort grip overmolding; Soft Touch camo stocks
**MSRP . . . . . . . . . . . . . . . $459–$530**

BLACK POWDER

# Uberti

UBERTI 1847 WALKER

UBERTI 1848 DRAGOON

UBERTI 1849 POCKET REVOLVER

UBERTI 1851 NAVY REVOLVER

## 1847 WALKER

*Lock*: Caplock revolver
*Stock*: Walnut
*Barrel*: 9 in.
*Sights*: Fixed, open
*Weight*: 4 lb. 8 oz.
*Bore/Caliber*: .44
*Features*: Case-hardened frame, steel backstrap, brass trigger guard; blued finish
MSRP.....................$439

## 1848 DRAGOON

*Lock*: Caplock revolver
*Stock*: Walnut
*Barrel*: 7.5 in.
*Sights*: Fixed, open
*Weight*: 4 lb. 2 oz.
*Bore/Caliber*: .44
*Features*: Case-hardened frame; steel or brass backstrap and trigger guard; engraved
MSRP.................$429–$439

## 1848–1849 POCKET REVOLVERS

*Lock*: Caplock revolver
*Stock*: Walnut
*Barrel*: 4 in.

*Sights*: Fixed, open
*Weight*: 1 lb. 8 oz.
*Bore/Caliber*: .31
*Features*: Case-hardened frame; brass backstrap and trigger guard; blued octagonal barrel; engraved
MSRP.....................$359

## 1851 NAVY REVOLVER

*Lock*: Caplock revolver
*Stock*: Walnut

*Barrel*: 7.5 in.
*Sights*: Fixed, open
*Weight*: 2 lb. 10 oz.
*Bore/Caliber*: .36
*Features*: Color case-hardened frame; oval or squareback trigger guard; brass or steel backstrap and trigger guard; octagonal barrel (Leech-Rigdon model has round barrel)
MSRP.................$339–$369

**UBERTI 1858 NEW ARMY REVOLVER**

**UBERTI 1860 ARMY REVOLVER**

**UBERTI 1861 NAVY REVOLVER**

**UBERTI 1862 POCKET NAVY REVOLVER**

**UBERTI 1862 POLICE REVOLVER**

### 1858 NEW ARMY REVOLVER

*Lock*: Caplock revolver
*Stock*: Walnut
*Barrel*: 8 in.
*Sights*: Fixed, open
*Weight*: 2 lb. 11 oz.
*Bore/Caliber*: .44
*Features*: Blued or stainless steel frame and backstrap; brass trigger guard; octagonal barrel
**Blued:** . . . . . . . . . . . . . . . . . . **$359**
**Stainless Steel:**. . . . . . . . . . . . **$449**

### 1860 ARMY REVOLVER

*Lock*: Caplock revolver
*Stock*: Walnut
*Barrel*: 7.5 in.
*Sights*: Fixed, open
*Weight*: 2 lb. 10 oz.
*Bore/Caliber*: .44
*Features*: Case-hardened frame, steel backstrap, brass trigger guard; blued, round barrel
**Steel & Brass model:** . . . . . . . . **$349**
**Fluted Steel:** . . . . . . . . . . . . . . **$369**

### 1861 NAVY REVOLVER

*Lock*: Caplock revolver
*Stock*: Walnut
*Barrel*: 7.5 in.
*Sights*: Fixed, open
*Weight*: 2 lb. 10 oz.
*Bore/Caliber*: .36
*Features*: Case-hardened frame, steel or brass backstrap and trigger guard
**Steel:** . . . . . . . . . . . . . . . . . . . **$359**
**Civil Brass:**. . . . . . . . . . . . . . . **$349**

### 1862 POCKET NAVY REVOLVER

*Lock*: Caplock revolver
*Stock*: Walnut
*Barrel*: 5.5 in., 6.5 in.
*Sights*: Fixed, open
*Weight*: 1 lb. 11 oz.
*Bore/Caliber*: .36
*Features*: Case-hardened frame; brass backstrap and trigger guard; octagonal, blued barrel
**MSRP**. . . . . . . . . . . . . . . . . . . **$369**

### 1862 POLICE REVOLVER

*Lock*: Caplock revolver
*Stock*: Walnut
*Barrel*: 5.5 in., 6.5 in.
*Sights*: Fixed, open
*Weight*: 1 lb. 10 oz.
*Bore/Caliber*: .36
*Features*: Case-hardened frame; brass backstrap and trigger guard; fluted round barrel
**MSRP**. . . . . . . . . . . . . . . . . . . **$369**

**BLACK POWDER**

OPTICS

### APEX XP 3-9X40MM

**Weight**: 14 oz.
**Length**: 12.5 in.
**Power**: 3-9X
**Obj. Dia.**: 40mm
**Main Dia.**: 1 in.
**Exit Pupil**: 13-4.5mm
**Field of View**: 35-12 ft @ 100 yds
**Twilight Factor**: 10.95-18.97
**Eye Relief**: 3.5 in.
**Features**: Fully multi-coated lens; WBDC-A reticle; matte black finish; fast-focus; side focus adjust; illuminated red-dot reticle
**MSRP**..................... **$502**

ALPEN APEX
XP 3-9X40MM

### APEX XP 6-24X50MM

**Weight**: 24 oz.
**Length**: 15.5 in.
**Power**: 6-24X
**Obj. Dia.**: 50mm
**Main Dia.**: 30mm
**Exit Pupil**: 8-2mm
**Field of View**: 16-4 ft @ 100 yds
**Twilight Factor**: 17.3-34.6
**Eye Relief**: 3.5 in.
**Features**: Matte black; WBDC-TACT reticle available; also in 1.5-6x42, and in red-dot illuminated-reticle 1.5-6x42, 2.5-10x50, and 4-16x56; 6-24x50 and the 4-16x56 have $\frac{1}{8}$ MOA adjustment increments, while the others have $\frac{1}{4}$ MOA
**MSRP**.................... **$653**

ALPEN APEX XP
6-24X50MM

### KODIAK 3.5-10X50MM

**Weight**: 21 oz.
**Length**: 13.2 in.
**Power**: 3.5-10X
**Obj.Dia.**: 50mm
**Main Dia.**: 1 in.
**Exit Pupil**: 13.5-4.9mm
**Field of View**: 35-12 ft @ 100 yds
**Twilight Factor**: 13.2-22.4
**Eye Relief**: 3 in.
**Features**: Multi-coated optical design; oversized zero-reset windage and elevation dials adjustable in $\frac{1}{4}$ MOA ($\frac{1}{8}$ MOA in the 6-24x50) clicks; AccuPlex Tapered duplex-style reticle; fast-focus eye piece; matte black; also in 1.5-4x32, 3-9x32, 4x32, 3-9x40, 4-12x40, and 6-24x50
**MSRP**..................... **$223**

ALPEN KODIAK
3.5-10X50MM

OPTICS

# British Small Arms Co. (BSA)

## GOLD STAR 2-12X44MM
**Weight**: 18 oz.
**Length**: 13.15 in.
**Power**: 2-12X
**Obj.Dia.**: 44mm
**Main Dia.**: 1 in.
**Exit Pupil**: 22-3.6mm
**Field of View**: 60-10 ft @ 100 yds
**Twilight Factor**: 9.38-22.98
**Eye Relief**: 4 in.
**Features**: The Gold Star line of rifle-scopes represent the pinnacle of BSA performance optics, exceptional clarity and resolution. 6X zoom system; perfected optical design; EZ Hunter reticle; precision W/E adjustment; side parallax available on some models.
**MSRP** . . . . . . . . . . . . . . . . . . .$269.95

BSA GOLD STAR 2-12X44MM

BSA MAJESTIC DX 4-16X44MM

## MAJESTIC DX 4-16X44MM
**Weight**: 17.6 oz.
**Length**: 12.66 in.
**Power**: 4-16X
**Obj. Dia.**: 44mm
**Main Dia.**: 1 in.
**Exit Pupil**: 8-4mm
**Field of View**: 45-7.3 ft @ 100 yds
**Twilight Factor**: 13.27-26.53
**Eye Relief**: 4 in.

**Features**: Newly redesigned one piece tube; fully multi-coated optics; ballistic compensating EZ Hunter reticle; 92 percent light transmission; fast-focus eyepiece
**MSRP** . . . . . . . . . . . . . . . . . .$209.95

# Burris

## FULLFIELD E1 3-9X40MM ILLUMINATED
**Weight**: 12 oz.
**Length**: 11.4 in.
**Power**: 3-9X
**Obj. Dia.**: 40mm
**Main Dia.**: 1 in.
**Exit Pupil**: 17-5mm
**Field of View**: 45-13 ft @ 100 yds
**Twilight Factor**: 10.95-18.97
**Eye Relief**: 3.1-4.1 in.
**Features**: A series of cascading dots to the left and right of the reticle help compensate for crosswinds. The dots represent a 10 mph crosswind (+/- 1.5" at 400 yds) for most hunting cartridges. For a 5 mph crosswind, halve the distance between dot and reticle. For 20 mph crosswind, simply double the distance. Also available in 2-7x35, 3-9x50, 4.5-14x42, and 6.5-20x50
**MSRP** . . . . . . . . . . . . . . . . . . . . . $445

## MTAC 4.5-14X42MM
**Weight**: 17.6 oz.
**Length**: 13 in.
**Power**: 4.5-14X
**Obj. Dia.**: 42mm
**Main Dia.**: 30mm
**Exit Pupil**: 24-6mm
**Field of View**: 22-7.5 ft @ 100 yds
**Twilight Factor**: 13.75-24.25
**Eye Relief**: 3.1-3.8 in.
**Features**: For long-range tactical shooting; adjustable parallax; feature-rich G2B Mil-Dot reticle for precise aiming, distance measurement, holdover, and hold off; new MTAC Mil-Rad knobs with finger-adjustable/resettable dials for windage and elevation; also available in 1-4x-24, 1.5-6x-40, 3.5-10x-42, 6.5-20x-50
**MSRP** . . . . . . . . . . . . . . . . . . . . $828

BURRIS FULLFIELD E1
3-9X40MM

BURRIS MTAC 4.5-14X42MM

# Bushnell Performance Optics

### BONE COLLECTOR 3-9X40MM DOA 600
**Weight**: 13 oz.
**Length**: 12.6 in.
**Power**: 3-9X
**Obj.Dia.**: 40mm
**Main Dia.**: 1 in.
**Exit Pupil**: 13.3-4.4mm
**Field of View**: 33.8-11.5 ft @ 100 yds
**Twilight Factor**: 10.95-18.97
**Eye Relief**: 3.33 in.
**Features**: 90-percent light transmission with the "Ultra Wide Band Coating"; RainGuard HD; one-piece aluminum tube with a fast-focus eyepiece; Bushnell DOA reticle technology–DOA 600 for centerfire rifles and DOA 250 for muzzleloaders; ¼ MOA adjustment increments and a 50 MOA range of adjustment for windage and elevation
**From**:. . . . . . . . . . . . . .$349–$434.95

### ELITE 3-9X40MM MULTI-X
**Weight**: 13 oz.
**Length**: 12.6 in.
**Power**: 3-9X
**Obj.Dia.**: 40mm
**Main Dia.**: 1 in.
**Exit Pupil**: 13.3-4.44mm
**Field of View**: 33.8-11.5 ft @ 100 yds
**Twilight Factor**: 10.95-18.97
**Eye Relief**: 3.4 in.
**Features**: Bushnell's "Ultra Wide Band Coating"; lenses treated with moisture shedding RainGuard HD; fingertip windage and elevation adjustments are audible and resettable and in ¼ MOA increments; also in 1.25-4x24, 2.5-10x40, 2.5-10x50, 4-16x40 Multi-X, 4-16x40 DOA 600, 4-16x50, 6-24x40 Mil-Dot, 6-24x40 Multi-X, 8-32x40 Multi-X, 2-7x 32, 3-10x40, 3-9x40 (Gloss/Silver), 3-9x40 FireFly, 3-9x40 DOA 600, 3-9x50 Multi-X, 3-9x50 DOA 600, 3-9x50 FireFly
**MSRP**. . . . . . . . . . . . . . . . .$423.95

### ELITE 6500 2.5-16X50MM MIL-DOT
**Weight**: 21 oz.
**Length**: 13.5 in.
**Power**: 2.5-16X
**Obj.Dia.**: 50mm
**Main Dia.**: 30mm
**Exit Pupil**: 20-3.12mm
**Field of View**: 42-7 ft @ 100 yds
**Twilight Factor**: 11.18-28.28

BUSHNELL BONE COLLECTOR
3-9X40MM DOA 600

BUSHNELL ELITE
3-9X40MM MULTI-X

BUSHNELL
ELITE TACTICAL
3-12X44MM

BUSHNELL
ELITE TACTICAL
6-24X50MM

BUSHNELL ELITE 6500
2.5-16X50MM MIL-DOT

**Eye Relief**: 3.9 in.
**Features**: Lenses with 60-layer "Ultra Wide Band Coating"; 91-percent total light transmission through the scope; RainGuard HD; windage and elevation adjustments in ¼ MOA audible increments; also in 1.25x-8x32, 2.5-16x42 Fine Multi-X, 2.5-16x42 Mil-Dot, 2.5-16x50 FMX, 4.5-30x50 DOA 600, 4.5-30x50 Fine Multi-X, 4.5-30x50 Mil-Dot
**MSRP**. . . . . . . . . . . . . . . . $1070.95

### ELITE TACTICAL 3-12X44MM
**Weight**: 24.4 oz.
**Length**: 13 in.
**Power**: 3-12X
**Obj.Dia.**: 44mm
**Main Dia.**: 30mm
**Exit Pupil**: 14.66-3.66mm
**Field of View**: 36-10 ft @ 100 yds
**Twilight Factor**: 11.48-22.97
**Eye Relief**: 3.75 in.
**Features**: Tactical treatment of Elite 6500 riflescope; tactical target-adjustment turrets and non-glare black-matte finish as well as "blacked-out" cosmetics for concealment; Bushnell "Ultra Wide Band Coating" optics; RainGuard HD coating; illuminated and non-illuminated Mil-Dot reticles; also in 10x44, 2.5-16x42, 4.5-30x50, 5-15x40, 6-24x50 Mil-Dot, 6-24x50 Illuminated Mil-Dot
**MSRP**. . . . . . . . . . . . . . . . .$1366.95

### ELITE TACTICAL 6-24X50MM
**Weight**: 27 oz.
**Length**: 13.5 in.
**Power**: 6-24X
**Obj.Dia.**: 50mm
**Main Dia.**: 30mm
**Exit Pupil**: 7.5-2.1mm
**Field of View**: 17.5-4.5 ft @ 100 yds
**Twilight Factor**: 17.32-24
**Eye Relief**: 4 in.
**Features**: Exceptional brightness and extended-range magnification with side parallax; RainGuard HD; fully multi-coated optics; ultra-strong, one-piece tube; .1 Mil click value; 3" sunshade; side parallax adjustment; available in Mil-Dot, Illuminated Mil-Dot, G2, and Illuminated BTR-Mil reticles
**MSRP**. . . . . . . . . . . . . . . . .$1192.95

OPTICS

# Bushnell Performance Optics

## ELITE TACTICAL 10X40MM MIL-DOT

**Weight**: 15.9 oz.
**Length**: 11.5 in.
**Power**: 10X
**Obj.Dia.**: 40mm
**Main Dia.**: 1 in.
**Exit Pupil**: 4mm
**Field of View**: 11-3.7 ft @ 100 yds
**Twilight Factor**: 20
**Eye Relief**: 3.5 in.
**Features**: Fixed-power target scope with Mil-Dot reticle and target turret; RainGuard HD; ultra wide band coating; fully multi-coated optics; blacked-out finish; target turrets
**MSRP** . . . . . . . . . . . . . . . . . . **$379.95**

## ELITE TACTICAL HDMR AND DMR 3.5-21X50MM

**Weight**: 32.5 oz.
**Length**: 13.2 in.
**Power**: 3.5-21X
**Obj. Dia.**: 50mm
**Main Dia.**: 34mm
**Exit Pupil**: 10.4-2.4mm
**Field of View**: 25.3 ft @ 100 yds
**Twilight Factor**: 13.23-21.21
**Eye Relief**: 3.74 in.
**Features**: These scopes are part of the Bushnell extended range riflescope (ERS) family designed to give tactical marksmen a powerful optic that works equally well in short or extended range shooting applications. The Bushnell Elite Tactical HDMR is available with the Horus H59 and TreMor 2 reticles, and the Elite Tactical DMR features the G2DMR and Mil-Dot reticles.
**MSRP** . . . . . . . . . . . . . . . . . **$2119.95**

## LEGEND ULTRA HD 1.75-5X32MM DOA 200

**Weight**: 13 oz.
**Length**: 10.25 in.
**Power**: 1.75-5X
**Obj. Dia.**: 32mm
**Main Dia.**: 30mm
**Exit Pupil**: 18.2-6.4mm
**Field of View**: 49-17 ft @ 100 yds
**Twilight Factor**: 7.48-12.65
**Eye Relief**: 4.5 in.
**Features**: The perfect scope for medium range hunting with a shotgun; RainGuard HD; fully multi-coated optics; ultra-strong, one-piece tube; parallax set at 75 yds; waterproof, fog-

BUSHNELL ELITE TACTICAL 10X40MM MIL-DOT

BUSHNELL ELITE TACTICAL HDMR AND DMR 3.5-21X50MM

BUSHNELL LEGEND ULTRA HD 1.75-5X32MM

BUSHNELL TROPHY XLT 3-9X40MM MIL-DOT

proof, and shockproof; fast-focus eye-piece; also in 1.75-5x32 Multi-X/DOA Crossbow, 3-9x40 Multi-X/DOA 600, 3-9x50 Multi-X/DOA 600, 4.5-14x44 Multi-X/Mil-Dot
**MSRP** . . . . . . . . . . . . . . . . . . **$378.95**

## TROPHY XLT 3-9X40MM MIL-DOT

**Weight**: 14.1 oz.
**Length**: 11.9 in.
**Power**: 3-9X
**Obj.Dia.**: 40mm
**Main Dia.**: 1 in.
**Exit Pupil**: 13.3-4.4mm
**Field of View**: 40-13 ft @ 100 yds
**Twilight Factor**: 10.95-18.97

**Eye Relief**: 4 in.
**Features**: 91-percent total light transmission; one-piece tube with integrated saddle; 1/4 MOA fingertip windage and elevation adjustments with range of adjustment of 80 MOA; Butler Creek flip-up scope covers; some scopes available in gloss, matte, silver, or camo finishes; also in 3-9x40 DOA 250, 3-9x40 DOA 600, 3-9x40 Multi-X, 3-9x40 Circle-X, 3-9x50, 4-12x40 DOA 600, 4-12x40 Multi-X, 1-4x24, 1.5-6x42, 1.5-6x44, 3-12x56, 1.75-4x32, 2-6x32, 2-7x36 DOA Crossbow, 2-7x36 DOA 200, 3-9x40 DOA 200, 6-18x50
**MSRP** . . . . . . . . . . . . . . . . . . **$204.95**

# Bushnell Performance Optics

### TROPHY XLT CROSSBOW SCOPE 2-7X36MM

**Weight**: 14.3 oz.
**Length**: 13 in.
**Power**: 2-7X
**Obj.Dia.**: 36mm
**Main Dia.**: 1 in.
**Exit Pupil**: 13.3-4.4mm
**Field of View**: 33-11 ft @ 100 yds
**Twilight Factor**: 8.5-15.9
**Eye Relief**: 5 in.
**Features**: One-piece tube with an integrated mounting saddle; Butler Creek flip-up caps; 91-percent light transmission; DOA Crossbow reticle; ¼ MOA fingertip windage and elevation adjustments allow for extended-range shooting out to 60 yards
**MSRP**.................$227.95

**BUSHNELL TROPHY XLT CROSSBOW SCOPE 2-7X36MM**

# Cabela's

### 30MM TACTICAL CLASSIC 6-18X50MM EXT SF

**Weight**: 17.5 oz.
**Length**: 13.23 in.
**Power**: 6-18X
**Obj.Dia.**: 50mm
**Main Dia.**: 30mm
**Exit Pupil**: 8.33-2.77mm
**Field of View**: 15.88-5.24 ft @ 100 yds
**Twilight Factor**: 17.32-30
**Eye Relief**: 4 in.
**Features**: Tactical-grade 30mm tube; Guidetech broadband lens technology; machined to military-grade tolerances; low-profile turrets with ⅛ MOA click windage and elevation adjustments; hard-blasted anodized finish and moisture- and dust-repelling lenses; also in 2.5-10x50 and 8-32 SFx50 with both EXT and Duplex reticles
**MSRP**.................$439.99

**CABELA'S 30MM TACTICAL CLASSIC 6-18X50MM EXT SF**

**CABELA'S ALASKAN GUIDE 1-INCH EXT 3-10X40MM**

### ALASKAN GUIDE 1-INCH EXT 3-10X40MM

**Weight**: 13.5 oz.
**Length**: 12.8 in.
**Power**: 3-10X
**Obj.Dia.**: 40mm
**Main Dia.**: 1 in.
**Exit Pupil**: 13.33-4mm

**Field of View**: 33.65-10.48 ft @ 100 yds
**Twilight Factor**: 10.95-20
**Eye Relief**: 3.75 in.
**Features**: EXT— "extended range"; "Guidetech" broadband lens coating technology; one-piece tube; components machined to military-grade tolerances; low-profile turrets with ¼ MOA click windage and elevation adjustments; hard-blasted anodized finish for durability and corrosion resistance; moisture- and dust-repelling lenses; also in 4-12x44SF, 6-18x50SF EXT, and 3-10x40, 4-12x44SF, and 6-18x50SF
**MSRP**.................$269.99

OPTICS

## ALASKAN GUIDE 30MM RANGEFINDING 3-12X52MM SF

**Weight**: 21.9 oz.
**Length**: 14 in.
**Power**: 3-12X
**Obj.Dia.**: 52mm
**Main Dia.**: 30mm
**Exit Pupil**: 17.33-4.33mm
**Field of View**: 31.5-7.8 ft @ 100 yds
**Twilight Factor**: 12.48-24.97
**Eye Relief**: 4 in.
**Features**: Also in 4-16SFx52, and both with side-focus parallax adjustment and with Duplex and EXT reticles; 30mm tube and 52mm objective for added light gathering an enhanced field of view with less aberration
**MSRP** . . . . . . . . . . . . . . . . . **$269.99**

## ALASKAN GUIDE PREMIUM RIFLESCOPES

**Weight**: 14.7 oz.–15 oz.
**Length**: 14.3-15.75 in.
**Power**: 4-12X, 6-20X
**Obj.Dia.**: 40mm
**Main Dia.**: 1 in.
**Exit Pupil**: 13.33-4.44mm
**Field of View**: 25.5-8.4 ft @ 100 yds, 16.1 ft @ 100 yds
**Twilight Factor**: 10.95-18.97
**Eye Relief**: 3.5 in.
**Features**: One-piece aluminum tube; rubber coated power adjustment; positive-click increments on the fast-focus eyepiece; metal-to-metal contact between the windage and elevation adjustments and the erector tube; and ½ MOA adjustments; knurled AO ring on higher magnification scopes; adjustable objective–AO
**MSRP** . . . . . . . . . . **$399.99–$449.99**

## CALIBER-SPECIFIC RIFLESCOPES

**Weight**: 14.6 oz.–15.3 oz.
**Length**: 12-13.2 in.
**Power**: 3-9X, 3-12X (.223)
**Obj. Dia.**: 40mm
**Main Dia.**: 1 in.
**Exit Pupil**: 13.33-4.44mm, 13.33-3.33mm (.223)
**Field of View**: 32.3-11.3 ft @ 100 yds, 28.8-7 ft @ 100 yds (.22 Mag.)
**Twilight Factor**: 10.95-18.97
**Eye Relief**: 4.1-3.8 in., 4.3-3.7 in. (.22 Mag.)
**Features**: Precision scopes specifically built to match your favorite target and varmint calibers; caliber-specific EXT bullet-drop reticles (in .17 HMR, .22 LR, .22 Mag., and .223) take the guesswork out of long-range shooting with crosshairs precisely calibrated to the bullet drop of a specific caliber; ¼-MOA adjustments; matte finish
**MSRP** . . . . . . . . . . . **$99.99–$149.99**

CABELA'S ALASKAN GUIDE PREMIUM EXT 3-9X40MM

CABELA'S ALASKAN GUIDE 30MM RANGEFINDING 3-12X52MM SF

CABELA'S CALIBER-SPECIFIC RIFLESCOPES

OPTICS

# Cabela's

### EURO RIFLESCOPE DUPLEX 3-9X42MM

**Weight**: 16 oz.
**Length**: 12.4 in.
**Power**: 3-9X
**Obj.Dia.**: 42mm
**Main Dia.**: 1 in.
**Exit Pupil**: 14-4.66mm
**Field of View**: 36.3-12.1 ft @ 100 yds
**Twilight Factor**: 11.22-19.44
**Eye Relief**: 3.75 in.
**Features**: CNC machined from a single billet of aircraft-aluminum; ELOX (electrolytic oxidation) anodization for a reduced-glare black matte, abrasion-resistant finish; fully multi-coated lenses; fast-focus eyepieces; elevation and windage turrets are finger adjustable in ¼ MOA clicks; also with EXT reticle, and in 4-12x50 and 6-18x50 with EXT and Duplex reticles
**MSRP**................$449.99

### LEVER ACTION 3-9X40MM

**Weight**: 14.64 oz.
**Length**: 13 in.
**Power**: 3-9X
**Obj.Dia.**: 40mm
**Main Dia.**: 1 in.
**Exit Pupil**: 13.33-4.44mm
**Field of View**: 30.55-9.6 ft @ 100 yds
**Twilight Factor**: 10.95-18.97
**Eye Relief**: 5.5 in.
**Features**: Ballistic Glass Reticles specifically engineered for use with a particular Hornady LEVERevolution round; tube is machined aluminum and lenses are multi-coated; windage and elevation are adjustable in ¼ MOA clicks; .30-30 Winchester Reticle (also in .308 Marlin, .338 Marlin Express, .444 Marlin, .35 Rem., and .45-70 Govt. reticles)
**MSRP**................$119.99

### POWDERHORN MUZZLELOADER 3-10X40MM

**Weight**: 11.6 oz.
**Length**: 12.2 in.
**Power**: 3-10X
**Obj.Dia.**: 40mm
**Main Dia.**: 1 in.
**Exit Pupil**: 13.33-4mm
**Field of View**: 31.5-10.5 ft @ 100 yds
**Twilight Factor**: 10.95-20

**Eye Relief**: 3.75 in.
**Features**: Ballistic reticle regulated to match bullet drop; when the scope is sighted in at 100 yards at 10X, the next bar down is calibrated for a drop at 150 yards and the lowest bar down for 250 yards; loading data is based on the 250-grain saboted bullet and 150 grains of Triple Se7en FFg powder; hand-turn ¼ MOA click adjustments; also in silver and camo
**MSRP**................$99.99

CABELA'S EURO RIFLESCOPE DUPLEX 3-9X42MM

CABELA'S LEVER ACTION 3-9X40MM

CABELA'S POWDERHORN MUZZLELOADER 3-10X40MM

**CABELA'S RIMFIRE RIFLESCOPE 3-9X40MM**

## RIMFIRE RIFLESCOPE 3-9X40MM

**Weight**: 13.4 oz.
**Length**: 12 in.
**Power**: 3-9X
**Obj.Dia.**: 40mm
**Main Dia.**: 1 in.
**Exit Pupil**: 13.33-4.44mm
**Field of View**: 37.7-12.4 ft @ 100 yds
**Twilight Factor**: 10.95-18.97
**Eye Relief**: 4 in.
**Features**: For hunting, target shooting, or plinking with a rimfire rifle; parallax-free at 50 yards; multi-coated glass optics; extended eye relief and an expanded exit pupil; low-profile windage and elevation turrets; Duplex reticle; also in 4x32
**MSRP** . . . . . . . . . . . . . . . . . . $79.99

## SHOTGUNS/ BLACKPOWDER 2.5-7X32MM

**Weight**: 12.2 oz.
**Length**: 11.8 in.
**Power**: 2.5-7X
**Obj.Dia.**: 32mm
**Main Dia.**: 1 in.
**Exit Pupil**: 12.8-4.57mm
**Field of View**: 40.03-14.15 ft @ 100 yds
**Twilight Factor**: 8.94-14.96
**Eye Relief**: 4 in.
**Features**: For use with slug guns and muzzleloading rifles; extended eye relief and expanded exit pupil to promote faster target acquisition; rigid machined-aluminum tube; low-profile turrets for windage and elevation adjustments; also available in Seclusion 3D camouflage; Diamond reticle; also with Duplex reticle and in camo, and in 2.5x32 fixed power with Diamond reticle
**MSRP** . . . . . . . . . . . $99.99–$119.99

**CABELA'S SHOTGUNS/ BLACKPOWDER 2.5-7X32MM**

# Carl Zeiss Sports Optics

**CARL ZEISS CONQUEST 3-9X40MM**

## CONQUEST 3-9X40MM

**Weight**: 15.17 oz.
**Length**: 12.9 in.
**Power**: 3-9X
**Obj.Dia.**: 40mm
**Main Dia.**: 1 in.
**Exit Pupil**: 13.3-4.4mm
**Field of View**: 34-11 ft @ 100 yds
**Twilight Factor**: 8.5-19.0
**Eye Relief**: 4 in.
**Features**: Classic, all-purpose scope with excellent light gathering ability; wide fields of view, brilliant contrast and high resolution images; perfect for shotguns, muzzle loaders and centerfire rifles; variety of reticles including the Rapid-Z Ballistic Reticle; featured with #20 reticle, also in 3-9x40; 3.5-10x44, 4.5-14x44, 3-9x50, 3.5-10x50, 4.5-14x50, 6.5-20x50, 3-12x56
**MSRP** . . . . . . . . . . . . . . . . . . $555.54

# Carl Zeiss Sports Optics

### CONQUEST 6.5-20X50MM
*Weight*: 21.83 oz.
*Length*: 15.6 in.
*Power*: 6.5-20X
*Obj.Dia.*: 50mm
*Main Dia.*: 1 in.
*Exit Pupil*: 7.7-2.5mm
*Field of View*: 18-6 ft @ 100 yds
*Twilight Factor*: 18-31.6
*Eye Relief*: 3.5 in.
*Features*: Parallax adjustment for varmints or long-range shooting; available with either target or hunting turret; variety of reticles including the Rapid-Z 800 and Rapid-Z 1000 Ballistic Reticles; featured with #4 or #20 reticles
**MSRP................$1144.43**

### VICTORY DIARANGE 2.5-10X50MM T*
*Weight*: 31.75 oz.
*Length*: 13.2 in.
*Power*: 2.5-10X
*Obj.Dia.*: 56.5mm
*Main Dia.*: 56.5mm
*Exit Pupil*: 15-5mm
*Field of View*: 43.5-12 ft @ 100 yds
*Twilight Factor*: 7.1-22.4
*Eye Relief*: 3.5 in.
*Features*: Laser ranges from 10 yds to 999 yds ± 1 yd at ranges up to 600 yards and ± 0.5% at ranges beyond 600 yards in a measuring time of 0.5 seconds; used in temperatures between -13° to 122°F; illuminated #43 Mil-Dot and illuminated Rapid-Z® 600 & 800 reticles; also in 3-12x56 T*
**MSRP................$4444.43**

### VICTORY DIAVARI 1.5-6X42MM T*
*Weight*: 15.52 oz.
*Length*: 12.25 in.
*Power*: 1.5-6X
*Obj.Dia.*: 42mm
*Main Dia.*: 30mm
*Exit Pupil*: 15-7mm
*Field of View*: 72-23 ft @ 100 yds
*Twilight Factor*: 4.2-15.9
*Eye Relief*: 3.5 in.
*Features*: LotuTec lens coating and ZEISS T* multi-coating; compact, lightweight, low profile scope designed for fast target acquisition; available with rail mount and with illumination on select models; also in 2.5-10x50 T*, 3-12x56 T*, 4-16x50 T* FL, 6-24x56 T* FL, and 6-24x72 T* FL
**MSRP................$1888.88**

CARL ZEISS CONQUEST 6.5-20X50MM

CARL ZEISS VICTORY DIARANGE
2.5-10X50MM T*

CARL ZEISS VICTORY DIAVARI
1.5-6X42MM T*

OPTICS

**CARL ZEISS**
**VICTORY DIAVARI**
**6-24X72MM T\* FL**

## VICTORY DIAVARI 6-24X72MM T\* FL

**Weight**: 37.39 oz.
**Length**: 14.9 in.
**Power**: 6-24X
**Obj.Dia.**: 72mm
**Main Dia.**: 34mm
**Exit Pupil**: 12-3mm
**Field of View**: 18.3-5.1 ft @ 100 yds
**Twilight Factor**: 16.9-41.6
**Eye Relief**: 3.5 in.
**Features**: FL glass objective and LotuTec coating; two ballistic-compensation options—BDC Ballistic Turret and Rapid Z Ballistic reticle; designed for tactical marksmen, varmint or predator hunters, and long-range hunters and shooters; parallax compensation and ¼ MOA lockable windage and elevation turrets; available with illumination
**MSRP** . . . . . . . . . . . . . . . . $3999.99

## VICTORY HT 1.1-4X24MM

**Weight**: 15.5 oz.
**Length**: 11.37 in.
**Power**: 1.1-4X
**Obj. Dia.**: 30mm
**Main Dia.**: 30mm
**Exit Pupil**: 14.8mm
**Field of View**: 114-31.5 ft @ 100 yds
**Twilight Factor**: 3.1-9.8
**Eye Relief**: 3.54 in.
**Features**: With its large exit pupil and wide field of view on low power, this smallest VICTORY HT is perfect for any shooting requiring extremely fast target acquisition; the new reticle #54 with the fine cross on the illuminated dot allows you to shoot with confidence, even when the illuminated red-dot is turned off; also available with reticle #60; LotuTec coating
**MSRP** . . . . . . . . . . . . . . . . $2555.54

**CARL ZEISS VICTORY**
**VARIPOINT 1.1-4X24MM T\***

## VICTORY HT 2.5-10X50MM

**Weight**: 20.2 oz.
**Length**: 13.66 in.
**Power**: 3-12X
**Obj. Dia.**: 63mm
**Main Dia.**: 30mm
**Exit Pupil**: 14.9-4.7mm
**Field of View**: 37.5-25.9 ft @ 100 yds
**Twilight Factor**: 8.5-25.9
**Eye Relief**: 3.54 in.
**Features**: The largest of the VICTORY HT line, this 3-12x56 model makes targets visible in the very last of shooting light; the combination of the advanced HT glass, high-performance 56mm objective lens, the super-fine illuminated dot, and ASV+ turret option makes this scope deadly accurate at any distance, in any light; LotuTec lens coating
**MSRP** . . . . . . . . . . . . . . . . $2666.66

## VICTORY VARIPOINT 1.1-4X24MM T\*

**Weight**: 15.87 oz.
**Length**: 11.8 in.
**Power**: 1.1-4X
**Obj.Dia.**: 24mm
**Main Dia.**: 30mm

**Exit Pupil**: 14.8-6mm
**Field of View**: 108-31 ft @ 100 yds
**Twilight Factor**: 3.1-9.9
**Eye Relief**: 3.5 in.
**Features**: Illuminated red-dot reticle for fast target acquisition; LotuTec "hydrophobic" lens coating; also in 1.5-6x42 T\*, 2.5-10x50 T\*, and 3-12x56 T\*
**MSRP** . . . . . . . . . . . . . . . . $2499.99

## VICTORY VARIPOINT 3-12X56MM T\*

**Weight**: 21.34 oz.
**Length**: 14 in.
**Power**: 3-12X
**Obj.Dia.**: 56mm
**Main Dia.**: 30mm
**Exit Pupil**: 14.7-4.7mm
**Field of View**: 37.5-10.5 ft @ 100 yds
**Twilight Factor**: 8.5-25.9
**Eye Relief**: 3.5 in.
**Features**: The large objective lens of the Victory Varipoint 3-12x56 T\*, is traditional for European scopes that are often used from shooting towers in low light.
**MSRP** . . . . . . . . . . . . . . . . $2666.66

**OPTICS**

**CARL ZEISS VICTORY**
**VARIPOINT 3-12X56MM T\***

**CARL ZEISS VICTORY HT 2.5-10X50MM**

**CARL ZEISS VICTORY**
**HT 1.1-4X24MM**

# Kruger Optical

**KRUGER TACDRIVER T4I 2.5-10X50MM**

### TACDRIVER T4I 2.5-10X50MM
**Weight**: 24 oz.
**Length**: 13 in.
**Power**: 2.5-10X
**Obj. Dia.**: 50mm
**Main Dia.**: 30mm
**Exit Pupil**: 5-12mm
**Field of View**: 38-10.5 ft @ 100 yds
**Twilight Factor**: 11.18-23.36
**Eye Relief**: 3.25 in.
**Features**: These scopes are equipped with proprietary illuminated glass-etched reticles with multiple brightness levels for low-light target engagement. The easy-to-operate 4x magnification system provides a solid zoom range for target acquisition at various distances. Also available in 1-4x24, 1.5-5x32, 6-24x50, and 10-40x56
**MSRP** . . . . . . . . . . . . . . . . . . $399.99

# Leatherwood/Hi-Lux

### CLOSE MEDIUM RANGE (CMR) 1-4X24MM
**Weight**: 16.5 oz.
**Length**: 10.2 in.
**Power**: 1-4X
**Obj.Dia.**: 24mm
**Main Dia.**: 30mm
**Exit Pupil**: 11.1-6mm
**Field of View**: 94.8-26.2 ft @ 100 yds
**Twilight Factor**: 4.89-9.79
**Eye Relief**: 3 in.
**Features**: Zero-locking turrets; large external target-style windage and elevation adjustment knobs; power-ring extended lever handle for power change; CMR ranging reticle for determining range and also BDC hold over value good for .223, .308, and other calibers; green or red illuminated reticle; turrets adjustable in ½ MOA clicks
**MSRP** . . . . . . . . . . . . . . . . . . . $399

**LEATHERWOOD/HI-LUX CMR 1-4X24MM**

### M-1000 AUTO RANGING TRAJECTORY 2.5-10X44MM
**Weight**: 25.2 oz.
**Length**: 13.2 in.
**Power**: 2.5-10X
**Obj.Dia.**: 44mm
**Main Dia.**: 1 in.
**Exit Pupil**: 10.2-4mm
**Field of View**: 47.2-11.9 ft @ 100 yds
**Twilight Factor**: 10.5-21
**Eye Relief**: 3.1 in.
**Features**: Compensates for the bullet

**LEATHERWOOD/HI-LUX M-1000 ART 2.5-10X44MM**

drop automatically by using an external cam system; can be calibrated for most centerfire rifle cartridges–from .223 to .50 BMG; comes with mount and rings; "No-Math Mil-Dot" reticle
**MSRP** . . . . . . . . . . . . . . . . . . . $459

OPTICS

# Leatherwood/Hi-Lux

## MALCOLM 8X USMC SNIPER SCOPE

**Weight**: 25.4 oz.
**Length**: 22.1 in.
**Power**: 8X
**Obj. Dia.**: 31mm
**Main Dia.**: .75 in.
**Exit Pupil**: 4.2mm
**Field of View**: 11 ft @ 100 yds
**Twilight Factor**: 15.75
**Eye Relief**: 3.15 in.
**Features**: Fully multi-coated lens; fine cross reticle; elevation and wind adjustment ¼ MOA per click at the mounts
**MSRP** . . . . . . . . . . . . . . . . . . **$521.55**

## TOBY BRIDGES SERIES HIGH PERFORMANCE MUZZLELOADING 3-9X40MM MATTE BLACK

**Weight**: 15.8 oz.
**Length**: 12.5 in.
**Power**: 3-9X
**Obj.Dia.**: 40mm
**Main Dia.**: 1 in.
**Exit Pupil**: 13.3-4.4mm
**Field of View**: 39-13 ft @ 100 yds
**Twilight Factor**: 10.9-19
**Eye Relief**: 3.25 in.
**Features**: The TB/ML scope is designed for in-line ignition muzzleloaders and saboted bullets. It offers multiple reticles for shooting at ranges out to 250 yards.
**Blue:** . . . . . . . . . . . . . . . . . . . **$179**
**Silver:** . . . . . . . . . . . . . . . . . . **$189**

## TOP ANGLE SERIES 30X50MM

**Weight**: 39.8 oz.
**Length**: 17.2 in.
**Power**: 7-30X
**Obj.Dia.**: 50mm
**Main Dia.**: 30mm
**Exit Pupil**: 6.9-2.3mm
**Field of View**: 10.6-3.5 ft @ 100 yds
**Twilight Factor**: 18.70-38.72
**Eye Relief**: 3.33 in.
**Features**: Larger diameter turret housing offers additional windage-elevation adjustment in ¼ MOA clicks; top-angle objective lens focus rather than adjustment on the objective lens bell; and Mil-Dot reticle for determining range; also in 3-12x50 and 4-16x50
**MSRP** . . . . . . . . . . . . . . . . . . . . **$475**

LEATHERWOOD/HI-LUX MALCOLM 8X USMC SNIPER SCOPE

LEATHERWOOD/HI-LUX TOBY BRIDGES MUZZLELOADING

LEATHERWOOD/HI-LUX TOP ANGLE SERIES 30X50MM

# Leatherwood/Hi-Lux

LEATHERWOOD/HI-LUX WM. MALCOLM SERIES LONG 6X32 INCH

## WM. MALCOLM SERIES LONG 6X32 INCH
**Weight**: 32.5 oz.
**Length**: 30.5 in.
**Power**: 6X
**Obj.Dia.**: 16mm
**Main Dia.**: .75 in.
**Exit Pupil**: 5.8mm
**Field of View**: 10 ft @ 100 yds
**Twilight Factor**: 9.79

**Eye Relief**: 4 in.
**Features**: A modern copy of the Model 1855 W. Malcolm riflescopes; early-style mounts for scoping original and replica 19th century breechloading rifles (Sharps, rolling block, high wall, etc.) or late period long-range percussion muzzleloading bullet rifles; ¾ inch (steel) scope tube; interchangeable front extension tubes to mount on rifles with barrels of 30 to 34 inches; also in 3x17-inch and 6x18-inch short Malcolms
**MSRP** . . . . . . . . . . . . . . . . . . . . . **$439**

# Leupold & Stevens

## FX-3 COMPETITION HUNTER 6X42MM
**Weight**: 15 oz.
**Length**: 12.2 in.
**Power**: 6X
**Obj.Dia.**: 42mm
**Main Dia.**: 1 in.
**Exit Pupil**: 7mm
**Field of View**: 17.3 ft @ 100 yds
**Twilight Factor**: 15.87
**Eye Relief**: 4.4 in.
**Features**: Fixed-power riflescope; Xtended Twilight Lens System; DiamondCoat 2; blackened lens edges; windage and elevation adjustments are ¼ MOA; also available in 12x40 AO, 25x40 AO, 30x40 AO, and 6x42
**MSRP** . . . . . . . . . . . . . . . . . **$589.99**

LEUPOLD FX-3 COMPETITION HUNTER 6X42MM

## MARK 4 CQ/T 1-3X14MM
**Weight**: 17.5 oz.
**Length**: 8.8 in.
**Power**: 1-3X
**Obj.Dia.**: 30mm
**Main Dia.**: 2.9 in.
**Exit Pupil**: 30-10mm
**Field of View**: 112-41 ft @ 100 yds
**Twilight Factor**: 3.74-6.48

LEUPOLD MARK 4 CQ/T 1-3X14MM

**Eye Relief**: 2.8-2 in.
**Features**: Close Quarters/Tactical (CQ/T) riflescope combines a red dot at close range with a variable-power optic; Circle Dot reticle is visible with or without illumination or batteries; eleven reticle-illumination settings; slotted ½ MOA click adjustments for windage and elevation
**MSRP** . . . . . . . . . . . . . . . . . **$1374.99**

# Leupold & Stevens

## MARK 4 MR/T 2.5-8X36MM M1

**Weight**: 16 oz.
**Length**: 11.33 in.
**Power**: 2.5-8X
**Obj.Dia.**: 36mm
**Main Dia.**: 30mm
**Exit Pupil**: 14.4-4.5mm
**Field of View**: 35.5-13.6 ft @ 100 yds
**Twilight Factor**: 9.48-16.97
**Eye Relief**: 3.7-3 in.
**Features**: Xtended Twilight Lens System and DiamondCoat 2; M1 dials are ¼ MOA for windage and elevation; finger-adjustable with audible, tactile clicks; illuminated Mil-Dot, Tactical Milling Reticle (TMR),and non-illuminated TMR versions available; flip-open lens covers; also available in 1.5-5x20, 1.5-5x20 M2, and 2.5-8x36 M2 models
**MSRP** . . . . . . . . . . . . . . . . . **$1189.99**
**IR:** . . . . . . . . . . . . . . . . . **$1374.99**

## MARK AR 3-9X40MM T2

**Weight**: 12.5 oz.
**Length**: 12.4 in.
**Power**: 3-9X
**Obj.Dia.**: 40mm
**Main Dia.**: 1 in.
**Exit Pupil**: 13.33-4.44mm
**Field of View**: 32.3-14.0 ft @ 100 yds
**Twilight Factor**: 10.95-18.97
**Eye Relief**: 4.7-3.7 in.
**Features**: Multi-coated 4 lens system; ½ MOA T2 elevation adjustment includes a pre-engraved Bullet Drop Compensation (BDC) dial to match the ballistics of most 55-grain loads, including the .223 Rem. and 5.56 NATO; large power selector dial with aggressive knurling; also available in 1.5-4x20, 4-12x40 AO T2, and 6-18x40 AO T1 models
**Duplex reticle:** . . . . . . . . . . . **$374.99**
**Mil-Dot:** . . . . . . . . . . . . . . . **$439.99**

## RIFLEMAN 3-9X40MM

**Weight**: 12.6 oz.
**Length**: 12.33 in.
**Power**: 3.3-8.5X (actual)
**Obj.Dia.**: 40mm
**Main Dia.**: 1 in.
**Exit Pupil**: 12-4.7mm
**Field of View**: 329-131 ft @ 1000 yds
**Twilight Factor**: 10.95-18.97
**Eye Relief**: 4.2-3.7 in.
**Features**: Fully coated lenses for excellent low light brightness; durable waterproof construction; also in 2-7x33, 4-12x40, and 3-9x50
**MSRP** . . . . . . . . . . . . . . . . . **$274.99**

**LEUPOLD MARK 4 MR/T 2.5-8X36MM M1**

**LEUPOLD MARK AR 3-9X40MM T2**

**LEUPOLD RIFLEMAN 3-9X40MM**

OPTICS

# Leupold & Stevens

LEUPOLD VX-2 3-9X40MM

### VX-2 3-9X40MM
**Weight**: 12 oz.
**Length**: 12.4 in.
**Power**: 3.3-8.6X (actual)
**Obj.Dia.**: 40mm
**Main Dia.**: 1 in.
**Exit Pupil**: 12-4.6mm
**Field of View**: 323-140 ft @ 1000 yds
**Twilight Factor**: 10.95-18.97
**Eye Relief**: 4.7-3.7 in.
**Features**: Multi-coated 4 Lens System for 92% light transmission; coin click ¼ MOA windage and elevation dials; also in 1-4x20, 4-12x40 AO, 6-18x40 AO and Target, 3-9x50, 4-12x50
**MSRP** . . . . . . . . . . $374.99–$437.99

### VX-3 3.5-10X40MM CDS
**Weight**: 12.6 oz.
**Length**: 12.66 in.
**Power**: 3.3-9.7X (actual)
**Obj.Dia.**: 40mm
**Main Dia.**: 1 in.
**Exit Pupil**: 12.1-4.1mm
**Field of View**: 298-110 ft @ 1000 yds
**Twilight Factor**: 11.83-20
**Eye Relief**: 4.4-3.5 in.
**Features**: X-Tended Twilight Lens System; ¼ MOA windage and elevation dials; Diamond Coat 2 external lens coatings; dual spring erector assembly; available CDS dial options and illuminated reticles; also in 1.5-5x20, 1.5-5x20 IR, 1.75-6x32, 2.5-

8x36, 4.5-14x40, 4.5-14x40 CDS, 4.5-14x40 SF, 4.5-14x40 AO, 6.5-20x40 AO, 6.5-20x40 EFR, 6.5-20x40 SF, 3.5-10x50, 3.5-10x50 CDS, 3.5-10x50 IR, 3.5-10x50 IR Metric, 4.5-14x50, 4.5-14x50 SF, 4.5-14x50 SF IR, 6.5-20x50 SF Target, and 8.5-23x50 SF Target
**MSRP** . . . . . . . . . . $599.99–$664.99

### VX-6 ILLUMINATED 2-12X42MM
**Weight**: 17.8 oz.
**Length**: 12.5 in.
**Power**: 2-12X
**Obj. Dia.**: 42mm
**Main Dia.**: 30mm
**Exit Pupil**: 10-3.5mm
**Field of View**: 112-20.3 ft @ 100 yds
**Twilight Factor**: 9.17-22.45
**Eye Relief**: 3.8 in.
**Features**: Quantum optical system with Xtended Twilight lens coatings; 7 reticle styles include Duplex, Boone &

Crockett, Illum. Duplex, Illum. LR Duplex, and Illum. German #4 Dot; also available in 1-6x24, 3-18x44, 3018x50, 4-24x52
**MSRP** . . . . . . . . . $1124.99–$1249.99

### VX-R 4-12X40MM CDS
**Weight**: 15.1 oz.
**Length**: 12.4 in.
**Power**: 4.4-11.7X (actual)
**Obj.Dia.**: 1.8 in.
**Main Dia.**: 30mm
**Exit Pupil**: 8.6-3.3mm
**Field of View**: 21.5-10 ft @ 100 yds
**Twilight Factor**: 14.2-23.1
**Eye Relief**: 3.7 in.
**Features**: Fire Dot reticle system with fiber optic technology; DiamondCoat lens coatings; finger click adjustments; index matched lens system; proprietary Motion Sensor Technology
**MSRP** . . . . . . . . . . . . . . . . . $789.99

LEUPOLD VX-3 3.5-10X40MM CDS

LEUPOLD VX-R 4-12X40MM CDS

LEUPOLD VX-6 ILLUMINATED 2-12X42MM

## 6-24X50MM ADVANTAGE RIFLE SCOPE

**Weight**: 24.5 oz.
**Length**: 15.5 in.
**Power**: 6-24X
**Obj. Dia.**: 50mm
**Main Dia.**: 30mm
**Exit Pupil**: 8.3-2mm
**Field of View**: 16.5-4.3 ft @ 100 yds
**Twilight Factor**: 17.32-34.64
**Eye Relief**: 4.25-3.25 in.
**Features**: Sniper-style rifle scope with the new L5 reticle; multi-coated lenses; ⅛ MOA turret click value; water-, fog-, and shockproof; matte black finish; available in STRELOK
**MSRP** . . . . . . . . . . . . . . . . . . . . . **$449**

LUCID 6-24X50MM ADVANTAGE RIFLE SCOPE

# Millett Optics

## DMS 1-4X25MM

**Weight**: 18 oz.
**Length**: 11.8 in.
**Power**: 1-4X
**Obj.Dia.**: 25mm
**Main Dia.**: 30mm
**Exit Pupil**: 24-6mm
**Field of View**: 90-23 ft @ 100 yds
**Twilight Factor**: 4.89-9.79
**Eye Relief**: 3.5 in.
**Features**: Designated Marksman Riflescope (DMS) features a Donut Dot illuminated reticle; "donut" subtending 18 MOA for ranges as close as three meters; illuminated dot 1 MOA for medium to extended ranges out to 500 yards; available in matte or ATAC finish
**Matte:** . . . . . . . . . . . . . . . . . **$385.95**
**ATAC:** . . . . . . . . . . . . . . . . . **$429.95**

## LRS 6-25X56MM ILLUMINATED .1 MIL

**Weight**: 35 oz.
**Length**: 18 in.
**Power**: 6-25X
**Obj.Dia.**: 56mm
**Main Dia.**: 35mm
**Exit Pupil**: 9.33-2.24mm
**Field of View**: 45-17 ft @ 100 yds
**Twilight Factor**: 18.33-37.41
**Eye Relief**: 3 in.
**Features**: For extreme-duty and extended-range for calibers such as the .50 BMG and .338 Lapua; one-piece tube; precision controls with 140 MOA range of adjustment; several glass-etched Mil-DotBar reticle and

MILLETT DMS 1-4X24MM

click value configurations; available in a matte or A-TACS finish; also in 6-25x56 Mil-DotBar Reticle .25 or .1 Click Value, 6-25x56 Illuminated Mil-DotBar Reticle A-TACS or Matte Finish
**MSRP** . . . . . . . . . . . . . . . . . . **$813.95**

## TRS 4-16X50MM .1 MIL

**Weight**: 29.5 oz.
**Length**: 16.4 in.
**Power**: 4-16X
**Obj.Dia.**: 50mm
**Main Dia.**: 30mm
**Exit Pupil**: 12.5-3.12mm

**Field of View**: 29-8 ft @ 100 yds
**Twilight Factor**: 14.14-28.28
**Eye Relief**: 3.5 in.
**Features**: Mil-DotBar reticle system functions as a standard Mil-Dot with the addition of a thin line for easier alignment for rangefinding and holdover; illuminated reticle is green and adjustable; scope has side-focus parallax adjustment knob; also in fixed 10x50 model and several 4-16x50 models finished in either matte or A-TACS
**MSRP** . . . . . . . . . . . . . . . . . . **$539.95**

MILLETT LRS 6-25X56MM ILLUMINATED .1 MIL

MILLETT LRS 6-25X56MM ILLUMINATED .1 MIL

# Minox

### ZA 3 3-9X40MM

**Weight**: 13.6 oz.
**Length**: 12.2 in.
**Power**: 3-9X
**Obj. Dia.**: 40mm
**Main Dia.**: 1 in.
**Exit Pupil**: 13.5-4.32mm
**Field of View**: 31.5-10.5 ft @ 100 yds
**Twilight Factor**: 10.95-18.97
**Eye Relief**: 4 in.
**Features**: MINOX M* coating—up to 21 different layers applied to the glass surface to greatly improve light transmission, brightness, contrast, detail, and color rendering; ¼ MOA adjustable windage and elevation; zero-resettable; fast-focus eyepiece; soft-touch rubber variable power ring; Scopecoat protective field cover
**MSRP** . . . . . . . . . . . . . . . . **$479–$499**

MINOX ZA 3 3-9X40MM

### ZA 5 4-20X50MM SF

**Weight**: 19.2 oz.
**Length**: 13.5 in.
**Power**: 4-20X
**Obj.Dia.**: 50mm
**Main Dia.**: 1 in.
**Exit Pupil**: 12.45-2.54mm
**Field of View**: 23.6 ft @ 100 yds
**Twilight Factor**: 14.14-31.62
**Eye Relief**: 4 in.
**Features**: Fully multi-coated Schott-glass lenses with 5-times magnification zoom range; also in 1.5-8x32, 2-10x40, 2-10x50, 3-15x42, 4-20x56, 6-30x56
**MSRP** . . . . . . . . . . . . . . . . **$839–$869**

MINOX ZA 5 4-20X50MM SF

### ZA 5 6-30X56MM SF

**Weight**: 23.6 oz.
**Length**: 14.8 in.
**Power**: 6-30X
**Obj. Dia.**: 55.88mm
**Main Dia.**: 29.97mm
**Exit Pupil**: 9.398-1.778mm
**Field of View**: 15.75-3.16 ft @ 100 yds
**Twilight Factor**: 18.31-40.94
**Eye Relief**: 3.9 in.
**Features**: Side focus parallax adjustment for extreme range shooting; lightweight; waterproof and fogproof; matte-black scope; bullet-drop-compensating reticle available; good in poor light because of 21-layer coating applied
**MSRP** . . . . . . . . . . . . . . . . **$959–$999**

MINOX ZA 5 6-30X56MM SF

**OPTICS**

# Nightforce Optics, Inc.

## 1-4X24MM NXS COMPACT

*Weight*: 17 oz.
*Length*: 8.8 in.
*Power*: 1-4X
*Obj.Dia.*: 24mm
*Main Dia.*: 30mm
*Exit Pupil*: 1-6mm
*Field of View*: 100-25 ft @ 100 yds
*Twilight Factor*: 4.89-9.79
*Eye Relief*: 3.5 in.
*Features*: Ideal for the hunter pursuing dangerous or running game at close quarters; low profile complements big bore bolt action and double rifles; as quick as open sights yet vastly more precise; shooter can keep both eyes open for instant target acquisition in high-stress situations
MSRP................... $1263
ZeroStop: ............... $1450

NIGHTFORCE 1-4X24MM
NXS COMPACT

NIGHTFORCE 2.5-10X32MM
NXS COMPACT

## 2.5-10X32MM NXS COMPACT

*Weight*: 19 oz.
*Length*: 12 in.
*Power*: 2.5-10X
*Obj.Dia.*: 32mm
*Main Dia.*: 30mm
*Exit Pupil*: 13.3-3.3mm
*Field of View*: 44-11 ft @ 100 yds
*Twilight Factor*: 8.94-17.88
*Eye Relief*: 3.4 in.
*Features*: Lightweight, low profile; provides low-light performance that exceeds most optics with much larger objective lenses; large exit pupil for fast target acquisition and no parallax or focusing issues; available with the Nightforce Velocity 600 yard reticle, which provides precise shot placement to 600 yards
MSRP................... $1357
ZeroStop: ............... $1627

## 3.5-15X50MM F1 NXS

*Weight*: 30 oz.
*Length*: 14.8 in.
*Power*: 3.5-15X
*Obj.Dia.*: 50mm
*Main Dia.*: 30mm
*Exit Pupil*: 11.5-3.2mm
*Field of View*: 28-8.7 ft @ 100 yds
*Twilight Factor*: 13.22-27.38
*Eye Relief*: 3.2 in.
*Features*: First focal plane reticle design, applicable to a wide range of targets at various distances; five specialized reticles available to maximize first focal plane design; offered with ¼ MOA or .1 Mil-Radian adjustments; ZeroStop standard; Nightforce Ultralight rings
MSRP................... $2467

## 3.5-15X50MM NXS

*Weight*: 30 oz.
*Length*: 14.8 in.
*Power*: 3.5-15X
*Obj.Dia.*: 50mm
*Main Dia.*: 30mm
*Exit Pupil*: 14.3-3.6mm
*Field of View*: 27.6-7.3 ft @ 100 yds
*Twilight Factor*: 13.22-27.38
*Eye Relief*: 3.9 in.
*Features*: Excellent choice for all-around hunting and professional shooters; low mounting profile; full 110 MOA of internal adjustment; available with ¼ MOA and .1 Mil-Radian adjustments; offered with Nightforce's patented ZeroStop, which provides an instant return to the shooter's chosen zero point under any conditions
MSRP................... $1655
ZeroStop: ............... $1862

NIGHTFORCE 3.5-15X50MM F1 NXS

NIGHTFORCE 3.5-15X50MM NXS

# Nightforce Optics

NIGHTFORCE 5.5-22X50MM NXS

NIGHTFORCE 5.5-22X56MM NXS

### 5.5-22X50MM NXS
**Weight**: 31 oz.
**Length**: 15.1 in.
**Power**: 5.5-22X
**Obj.Dia.**: 50mm
**Main Dia.**: 30mm
**Exit Pupil**: 9.1-2.3mm
**Field of View**: 17.5-4.7 ft @ 100 yds
**Twilight Factor**: 16.58-33.16
**Eye Relief**: 3.8 in.
**Features**: Originally developed for the U.S. military's extreme long range shooting and hard target interdiction; 100 MOA of elevation travel make it ideal for use on the .50 BMG, allowing accurate shots to 2000 yards and beyond; slim profile, easily adaptable to a wide range of mounting systems
**MSRP**. . . . . . . . . . . . . . . . . . **$1821**
**ZeroStop:** . . . . . . . . . . . . . . **$2025**

### 5.5-22X56MM NXS
**Weight**: 32 oz.
**Length**: 15.2 in.
**Power**: 5.5-22X
**Obj.Dia.**: 56mm
**Main Dia.**: 30mm
**Exit Pupil**: 10.2-2.5mm
**Field of View**: 17.5-4.7 ft. @ 100 yds
**Twilight Factor**: 17.54-35.09
**Eye Relief**: 3.9 in.
**Features**: Advanced field tactical riflescope for long-range applications; maximum clarity and resolution across the entire magnification range, exceptional low-light performance; available with ZeroStop technology and 1/8 and 1/4 MOA or .1 Mil-Radian adjustments
**MSRP**. . . . . . . . . . . . . . . . . . **$1766**
**ZeroStop:** . . . . . . . . . . . . . . **$2025**

# Nightforce Optics

**NIGHTFORCE 8-32X56MM BR**

## 8-32X56MM BR

**Weight**: 36 oz.
**Length**: 16.6 in.
**Power**: 8-32X
**Obj.Dia.**: 56mm
**Main Dia.**: 30mm
**Exit Pupil**: 5.6-1.7mm
**Field of View**: 9.4-3.1 ft @ 100 yds
**Twilight Factor**: 21.16-42.33
**Eye Relief**: 2.9 in.
**Features**: Superior resolution; adjustable objective allows extra-fine focus for parallax adjustment from 25 yards to infinity; target adjustments are calibrated in true $1/8$ click) MOA values, and can be re-indexed to zero after sighting in; eyepiece allows for fast reticle focusing and a glass-etched illuminated reticle, with eight different reticles
**MSRP** . . . . . . . . . . . . . . . . . . . $1286

## 8-32X56MM NXS

**Weight**: 34 oz.
**Length**: 15.9 in.
**Power**: 8-32X
**Obj.Dia.**: 56mm
**Main Dia.**: 30mm
**Exit Pupil**: 7-1.8mm
**Field of View**: 12.1-3.1 ft @ 100 yds
**Twilight Factor**: 21.16-42.33
**Eye Relief**: 3.8 in.

**Features**: For long-range hunting, competition, and target shooting; choice of five different reticles for the shooter's chosen application; offered with .125 MOA, .250 MOA or .1 Mil-Radian Hi-Speed adjustments; ZeroStop also available
**MSRP** . . . . . . . . . . . . . . . . . . . $1899
**ZeroStop:** . . . . . . . . . . . . . . . $2092

**NIGHTFORCE 8-32X56MM NXS**

**OPTICS**

# Nikon

NIKON BOLT XR 3X32MM BDC

## BOLT XR 3X32MM BDC
**Weight**: 11.2 oz.
**Length**: 8.1 in.
**Power**: 3-32X
**Obj.Dia.**: 32mm
**Main Dia.**: 1 in.
**Exit Pupil**: 10.7mm
**Field of View**: 35.6 ft @ 100 yds
**Twilight Factor**: 9.79
**Eye Relief**: 3.4 in.
**Features**: 3x Nikon optics; large ocular; quick focus eye-piece with ±4 diopter adjustment; BDC 60 reticle offers aiming points out to 60 yards based upon velocity of approximately 305 fps; ¼ inch at 20 yards adjustments with a 150 MOA adjustment range (at 100 yards); parallax-free at 20 yards.
**MSRP** . . . . . . . . . . . . . . . . . **$218.95**

NIKON BUCKMASTERS
3-9X40MM NIKOPLEX

## BUCKMASTERS 1X20MM BLACKPOWDER MATTE NIKOPLEX
**Weight**: 10.6 oz.
**Length**: 9.1 in.
**Power**: 1X
**Obj.Dia.**: 20mm
**Main Dia.**: 1 in.
**Exit Pupil**: 20mm
**Field of View**: 52.5 ft @ 75 yds
**Twilight Factor**: 4.47
**Eye Relief**: 4.3-13 in.
**Features**: For muzzleloading hunting where only 1X power scopes are allowed; uses Nikon's Brightvue multicoating with a stated 92-percent light transmission; hand-turn ½ MOA positive-click adjustments, plus quick-focus eyepiece
**MSRP** . . . . . . . . . . . . . . . . . **$199.95**

## BUCKMASTERS 3-9X40MM REALTREE APG HD NIKOPLEX
**Weight**: 16.1 oz.
**Length**: 13.1 in.
**Power**: 3-9X
**Obj.Dia.**: 40mm
**Main Dia.**: 1 in.
**Exit Pupil**: 13.3-4.4mm
**Field of View**: 35.7-11.9 ft @ 100 yds
**Twilight Factor**: 10.95-18.97
**Eye Relief**: 3.6-3.6 in.
**Features**: Built for centerfire rifle, muzzleloader, or rimfire, the Buckmasters 3-9x40 has Brightvue multi-coating, quick-focus eyepiece, hand-turn ¼ MOA click adjustments, and is adaptable for a sunshade. Also in 4.5-14x40, 6-18x40, 3-9x50, and 4-12x50, and in matte and silver with BDC, Mil-Dot, and fine crosshair with dot.
**MSRP** . . . . . . . . . . . . . . . . . **$259.95**

NIKON BUCKMASTERS
1X20MM BLACKPOWDER
MATTE NIKOPLEX

OPTICS

## COYOTE SPECIAL 3-9X40MM MOSSY OAK BRUSH BDC PREDATOR

**Weight**: 16 oz.
**Length**: 13.1 in.
**Power**: 3-9X
**Obj.Dia.**: 40mm
**Main Dia.**: 1 in.
**Exit Pupil**: 13.3-4.4mm
**Field of View**: 35.7-11.9 ft @ 100 yds
**Twilight Factor**: 10.95-18.97
**Eye Relief**: 3.6-3.6 in.
**Features**: Utilizes the BDC Predator Reticle for ranges out to 450 yards and beyond; open BDC's ballistic circles don't obscure the target; hand-turn ¼ MOA click adjustments; quick-focus eyepiece and lead- and arsenic-free "Eco-Glass"; ARD (Anti Reflective Device) scope cover to eliminate glare but permit shooting; also in 4.5-14x40 and in matte and RealTree Max-1
**MSRP** . . . . . . . . . . . . . . . . . **$279.95**

## M-223 LASER IRT 3-12X42MM SF RAPID ACTION TURRET NIKOPLEX

**Weight**: 19.93 oz.
**Length**: 13.1 in.
**Power**: 3-12X
**Obj.Dia.**: 42mm
**Main Dia.**: 1 in.
**Exit Pupil**: 14-3.5mm
**Field of View**: 33.6-8.4 ft @ 100 yds
**Twilight Factor**: 11.22-22.44
**Eye Relief**: 4-3.8 in.
**Features**: Side-focus parallax adjustment from zero out to 600 yards; Nikon's Rapid Action Turret technology based on a .223/5.56mm 55-grain polymer tipped bullet; 4-time zoom range, one-piece main body tube and "Ultra ClearCoat optics; variable-magnification reference numbers are viewable from the shooter's position; also in 1-4x20 and 2-8x32 and with BDC 600 reticle)
**MSRP** . . . . . . . . . . . . . . . . . **$459.95**

## M-308 4-16X42MM

**Weight**: 19 oz.
**Length**: 13.5 in.
**Power**: 4-16X
**Obj. Dia.**: 42mm
**Main Dia.**: 1 in.
**Exit Pupil**: 10.5-2.6mm
**Field of View**: 25.2-6.3 ft @ 100 yds
**Twilight Factor**: 12.96-25.92

NIKON COYOTE SPECIAL
3-9X40MM BDC PREDATOR

NIKON M-223 LASER IRT
3-12X42MM SF RAT NIKOPLEX

NIKON M-308 4-16X42MM

NIKON MONARCH 2.5-
10X42MM NIKOPLEX

**Eye Relief**: 4-3.7 in.
**Features**: Available with the all-new BDC 800 reticle or Nikoplex reticle with Rapid Action Turrets; developed specifically for the trajectory of the .308 Winchester/7.62x51 NATO round with 168-grain hollow point boat-tail Match bullet; Ultra ClearCoat optical system; Eye Box technology; smooth zoom control
**MSRP** . . . . . . . . . . . . . . . . . **$529.95**

## MONARCH 2.5-10X42MM NIKOPLEX

**Weight**: 16.6 oz.
**Length**: 12.6 in.
**Power**: 2.5-10X
**Obj.Dia.**: 42mm

**Main Dia.**: 1 in.
**Exit Pupil**: 16.8-4.2mm
**Field of View**: 40.3-10.1 ft @ 100 yds
**Twilight Factor**: 10.24-20.49
**Eye Relief**: 4.0-3.8 in.
**Features**: Enhanced ring spacing for mounting on rifles including magnum-length actions; see-through "ballistic circle" BDC reticle available; Ultra ClearCoat optical system; customized with accessory target-style windage and elevation adjustment knobs and caps; available in 2-8x30, 3-12x42, 4-16x42, 5-20x44, 2.5-10x50, 4-16x50, 6-24x50, and 8-32x50, in matte and silver with ED glass, SF Mil-Dot, and fine crosshair with dot
**MSRP** . . . . . . . . . . . . . . . . . **$419.95**

# Nikon

## MONARCH GOLD 2.5-10X50MM SF BDC

**Weight**: 21.2 oz.
**Length**: 13 in.
**Power**: 2.5-10X
**Obj.Dia.**: 50mm
**Main Dia.**: 30mm
**Exit Pupil**: 19.2-5.2mm
**Field of View**: 38.8-10.5 ft @ 100 yds
**Twilight Factor**: 11.18-22.36
**Eye Relief**: 4.1-4 in.
**Features**: Ultra ClearCoat optical system; larger internal lenses for less spherical aberration; locking side focus adjustment dials out parallax; aircraft grade aluminum; hand-turn ¼ MOA windage and elevation adjustments; also in 1.5-6x42 and 2.5x10x56 and with Nikoplex and German #4 reticles
**MSRP** . . . . . . . . . . . . . . . . . . $709.95

## MONARCH X 2.5-10X44MM SF NIKOPLEX

**Weight**: 23.5 oz.
**Length**: 13.9 in.
**Power**: 2.5-10X
**Obj.Dia.**: 44mm
**Main Dia.**: 30mm
**Exit Pupil**: 17.6-4.4mm
**Field of View**: 42-10.5 ft @ 100 yds
**Twilight Factor**: 10.24-20.49
**Eye Relief**: 3.5-3.8 in.
**Features**: Nikoplex, Mil-Dot, or Dual Illuminated Mil-Dot reticle options; Ultra ClearCoat system; one-piece body tube milled from aircraft grade aluminum; hand-turn ¼ MOA windage and elevation adjustments and side-focus parallax adjustment; also in 4-16x50 with Mil-Dot and dual-illuminated Mil-Dot
**MSRP** . . . . . . . . . . . . . . . . $1299.95

## P-22 2-7X32MM

**Weight**: 13.9 oz.
**Length**: 11.5 in.
**Power**: 2-7X
**Obj. Dia.**: 32mm
**Main Dia.**: 1 in.
**Exit Pupil**: 16-4.6mm
**Field of View**: 33.4-9.5 ft @ 100 yds
**Twilight Factor**: 8-14.97
**Eye Relief**: 3.8-3.8 in.
**Features**: P-22 riflescopes are the rimfire-optimized variant of Nikon's growing line of precision optics for AR rifles; designed for extreme sighting speed and superior accuracy from rimfire AR platform rifles and .22 long rifle cartridges, the P-22 is offered with BDC 150 reticle or 2-7x32 with Nikoplex reticle; Nikon's Rapid Action Turret system
**MSRP** . . . . . . . . . . . . . . . . . . $179.95

## PROSTAFF 3-9X40MM NIKOPLEX

**Weight**: 15 oz.
**Length**: 12.4 in.
**Power**: 3-9X
**Obj.Dia.**: 40mm
**Main Dia.**: 1 in.
**Exit Pupil**: 13.3-4.4mm
**Field of View**: 33.8-11.3 ft @ 100 yds
**Twilight Factor**: 10.95-18.97
**Eye Relief**: 3.6-3.6 in.
**Features**: ¼ MOA hand-turn reticle adjustments with "Zero-Reset" turrets; quick-focus eyepiece; also in 2-7x32– and in Shotgun Hunter with BDC 200 reticle–4-12x40, and 3-9x50 and in silver, RealTree APG and with BDC reticle
**MSRP** . . . . . . . . . . . $179.99–$199.99

NIKON MONARCH GOLD 2.5-10X50MM SF BDC

NIKON MONARCH X 2.5-10X44MM SF

NIKON P-22 2-7X32MM

NIKON PROSTAFF 3-9X40MM NIKOPLEX

OPTICS

## PROSTAFF TARGET EFR 3-9X40MM

**Weight**: 15.7 oz.
**Length**: 12.5 in.
**Power**: 3-9X
**Obj. Dia.**: 40mm
**Main Dia.**: 1 in.
**Exit Pupil**: 13.3-4.4mm
**Field of View**: 16.9-5.7 ft @ 50 yds
**Twilight Factor**: 10.95-18.97
**Eye Relief**: 3.6-3.6 in.
**Features**: Designed and engineered for .22LR, air rifle, and other applications where the versatility of focusing at extended ranges is desired; new Nikon Precision Reticle featuring a fine crosshair with dot; adjustable objective lens that allows parallax adjustments; large ocular with quick focus eyepiece; zero-reset turrets
**MSRP** . . . . . . . . . . . . . . . . . **$189.95**

## SLUGHUNTER 1.65-5X36MM MATTE BDC 200

**Weight**: 13.58 oz.
**Length**: 11.14 in.
**Power**: 1.65-5X
**Obj.Dia.**: 36mm
**Main Dia.**: 1 in.
**Exit Pupil**: 7.2mm (at 5X)

NIKON PROSTAFF TARGET EFR 3-9X40MM

NIKON SLUGHUNTER 1.65-5X36MM MATTE BDC 200

**Field of View**: 45.3-15.1 ft @ 100 yds
**Twilight Factor**: 7.7-13.41
**Eye Relief**: 5 in.
**Features**: Increased exit pupil for low-light performance and a 75-yard parallax setting; BDC 200 trajectory-compensating reticle, with "ballistic circle" aiming points, calibrated for the lower power range and smaller objective; "Eco-Glass" multi-coated optics; hand-turn ¼ MOA click adjustments; also in 3-9x40 and in RealTree APG
**MSRP** . . . . . . . . . . . . . . . . . **$229.95**

# Pentax Imaging Co.

PENTAX GAMESEEKER 30 3-10X40MM

## GAMESEEKER 30 3-10X40MM

**Weight**: 15.2 oz.
**Length**: 13.1 in.
**Power**: 3-10X
**Obj.Dia.**: 40mm
**Main Dia.**: 1 in.
**Exit Pupil**: 13.3-4.44mm
**Field of View**: 35.6-10.5 ft @ 100 yds
**Twilight Factor**: 10.95-20
**Eye Relief**: 3.3-3 in.
**Features**: Variable scope; bullet-drop-compensating "Precision Plex" reticle; also in 4-16x50, 6-24x50, and 8.5-32x50
**MSRP** . . . . . . . . . . . . . . . . . . . **$179**

# Pentax Imaging Co.

## GAMESEEKER II
## 4-16X50MM
**Weight**: 16.1 oz.
**Length**: 13.9 in.
**Power**: 4-16X
**Obj.Dia.**: 50mm
**Main Dia.**: 1 in.
**Exit Pupil**: 12.5-3.125mm
**Field of View**: 26.2-6.8 ft @ 100 yds
**Twilight Factor**: 14.14-28.28
**Eye Relief**: 3 in.
**Features**: One-piece tube; finger-adjustable windage and elevation turrets; also in 2-7x32, 3-9x40, 4-12x40, 3-9x50, and 5-10x56, and P and LPP reticles
**MSRP** . . . . . . . . . . . . . . . . . . . . **$149**

PENTAX GAMESEEKER II 4-16X50MM

## GAMESEEKER III
## 4-12X40MM
**Weight**: 13.4 oz.
**Length**: 13.2 in.
**Power**: 4-12X
**Obj. Dia.**: 40mm
**Main Dia.**: 1 in.
**Exit Pupil**: 9.2-3.4mm
**Field of View**: 27.6-10.6 ft @ 100 yds
**Twilight Factor**: 12.65-21.91
**Eye Relief**: 3.7-3.3 in.
**Features**: New slim line construction and improved optics; fully multi-coated optics; Precision Plex reticle; high quality turrets; one-piece, aluminum construction, waterproof and fogproof; also in 3-9x40, 3-9x50, 4-16x50
**MSRP** . . . . . . . . . . . . . . . . . . . . **$149**

PENTAX GAMESEEKER III 4-12X40MM

## LIGHTSEEKER 30
## 3-10X40MM
**Weight**: 20 oz.
**Length**: 13.1 in.
**Power**: 3-10X
**Obj.Dia.**: 40mm
**Main Dia.**: 30mm
**Exit Pupil**: 13.3-4mm
**Field of View**: 34-14 ft @ 100 yds
**Twilight Factor**: 10.95-20
**Eye Relief**: 3.5-4 in.
**Features**: Finger-adjustable windage and elevation turrets; side parallax adjustment; also in 4-16x50 and 6-24x50, and with Mil-Dot reticle
**MSRP** . . . . . . . . . . . . . . . . . . . . **$519**

## LIGHTSEEKER XL
## 4-16X44MM
**Weight**: 23 oz.
**Length**: 14 in.
**Power**: 4-16X
**Obj.Dia.**: 44mm
**Main Dia.**: 1 in.
**Exit Pupil**: 11-2.8mm
**Field of View**: 24-8 ft @ 100 yds
**Twilight Factor**: 9.4-26.5
**Eye Relief**: 3.5-4 in.
**Features**: Finger-adjustable windage and elevation turrets; "European-style" eyepieces; also in 3-9x40 and 2.5-10x50, and with P and Twilight Plex reticles
**MSRP** . . . . . . . . . . . . . . . . . . . . **$489**

PENTAX LIGHTSEEKER 30 3-10X40MM

PENTAX LIGHTSEEKER XL 4-16X44MM

OPTICS

## REVENGE 3-9X42MM

**Weight**: 14.8 oz.
**Length**: 12.4 in.
**Power**: 3-9X
**Obj. Dia.**: 42mm
**Main Dia.**: 1 in.
**Exit Pupil**: 14.2-4.9mm
**Field of View**: 32.9-11.4 ft @ 100 yds
**Twilight Factor**: 11.22-19.44
**Eye Relief**: 3.5 in.

**Features**: Built-in optical rangefinder means you never need to take your eye off the target; flexible magnification range; available with 4-Plex, Accu-Ranger Hunter, and Accu-Ranger Sabot reticles; also avavilable in 2-7x34, 3-9x52, 4-12x42, and 6-18x44

**MSRP** . . . . . . . . . . . **$199.99–$224.99**

## REVOLUTION 3-9X40MM

**Weight**: 12.6 oz.
**Length**: 12.33 in.
**Power**: 3-9X
**Obj.Dia.**: 40mm
**Main Dia.**: 1 in.
**Exit Pupil**: 12.1-4.7mm
**Field of View**: 32.9-13.1 ft @ 100 yards
**Twilight Factor**: 10.95-18.97
**Eye Relief**: 3.7-4.2 in.
**Features**: Black matte finish and either a 4-Plex or Accu-Range reticle; Illuminator Lens System with premium lenses and vapor-deposition multi-coatings; Accu-Trac windage and elevation adjustment system has resettable stainless steel ¼ MOA finger click adjustments; "Rapid Target Acquisition" (RTA) lockable eyepiece; also available in 2-7x33, 3-9x50, and 4-12x40

**4-Plex:** . . . . . . . . . . . . . . . . **$249.99**
**Accu-Range:** . . . . . . . . . . . . **$264.99**

**REDFIELD REVENGE 3-9X42MM**

**REDFIELD REVOLUTION 3-9X40MM**

# Schmidt & Bender

## 1.1-4X20MM PM SHORT-DOT LOCKING POLICE MARKSMAN

**Weight**: 20.11 oz.
**Length**: 10.6 in.
**Power**: 1.1-4X
**Obj.Dia.**: 20mm
**Main Dia.**: 30mm
**Exit Pupil**: 14-5mm
**Field of View**: 96-30 ft @ 100 yds
**Twilight Factor**: 4.69-8.94
**Eye Relief**: 3.5 in.
**Features**: Includes locking turrets and CQB reticle; M855, 75 gr. TAP, and M118LR calibration rings standard; also in 1.5-6x20 and 1-8x24 Short Dots and 1.1-4x24 PM Zenith Short-Dot LE

**MSRP** . . . . . . . . . . . . . . . . . . . **$2739**

## 1.5-6X42MM ZENITH FLASH-DOT

**Weight**: 21.52 oz.
**Length**: 12.33 in.
**Power**: 1.5-6X
**Obj.Dia.**: 42mm
**Main Dia.**: 30mm
**Exit Pupil**: 28-7mm
**Field of View**: 60-19.5 ft @ 100 yds
**Twilight Factor**: 4.2-15.9
**Eye Relief**: 3.5 in.
**Features**: Flash-Dot reticle in the center of the crosshairs performs like front bead sight on shotgun when illuminated; Flash Dot can also be shut off; click values on the windage and elevation adjustments are ½ MOA on the 1.1-4x24 and ⅓ MOA on the rest; also in 1.1-4x24, 1-8x24, 3-12x50, and 2.5-10x56 with Flash Dot and in 1.1-4x24, 1.5-6x42, 1-8x24, 3-12x50, and 2.5-10x56 with non-illuminated reticle

**MSRP** . . . . . . . . . . . . . . . . . . **$2459**

**SCHMIDT & BENDER 1.1-4X20MM SHORT-DOT LOCKING POLICE MARKSMAN**

**SCHMIDT & BENDER 1.5-6X42MM ZENITH FLASH-DOT**

OPTICS

# Schmidt & Bender

SCHMIDT & BENDER 2.5-10X40MM SUMMIT

## 2.5-10X40MM SUMMIT
**Weight**: 16.8 oz.
**Length**: 13.2 in.
**Power**: 2.5-10X
**Obj.Dia.**: 40mm
**Main Dia.**: 1 in.
**Exit Pupil**: 16-4mm
**Field of View**: 40.4-12.3 ft @ 100 yds
**Twilight Factor**: 14-20
**Eye Relief**: 3.93 in.
**Features**: Built for the American market with its 1 inch tube; adjustments are ¼ MOA
**MSRP** . . . . . . . . . . . . . . . . . . . $1999

## 3-12X42MM PRECISION HUNTER
**Weight**: 19.9 oz.
**Length**: 13.66 in.
**Power**: 3-12X
**Obj.Dia.**: 42mm
**Main Dia.**: 30mm
**Exit Pupil**: 3.5-14mm
**Field of View**: 31.5-11.4 ft @ 100 yds
**Twilight Factor**: 8.5-22.4
**Eye Relief**: 3.5 in.

**Features**: Enhanced model 3-12x42 Klassik designed for longer ranges; P3 reticle with bullet-drop compensated elevation knob; adjustments are in ⅓ MOA; third-turret parallax adjustment; also in 3-12x50 and 4-16x50
**MSRP** . . . . . . . . . . . . . . . . . . . $2399

**SCHMIDT & BENDER 3-12X42MM PRECISION HUNTER**

## 3-12X50MM KLASSIK ILLUMINATED
**Weight**: 21.66 oz.
**Length**: 13.75 in.
**Power**: 3-12X
**Obj.Dia.**: 50mm
**Main Dia.**: 30mm
**Exit Pupil**: 4.2-14.4mm
**Field of View**: 33.3-11.4 ft @ 100 yds
**Twilight Factor**: 8.5-24.5
**Eye Relief**: 3.14 in.
**Features**: All of the Klassik variables have generous objectives for greater light transmission; variety of reticles in illuminated, non-illuminated, and varmint; also in illuminated-reticle 2.5-10x56 and 3-12x42, and in non-illuminated 2.5-10x40, 3-12x42, and 4-16x 50
**MSRP** . . . . . . . . . . . . . . . . . . . $2389

**SCHMIDT & BENDER 3-12X50MM KLASSIK ILLUMINATED**

OPTICS

# Schmidt & Bender

## 4-16X42MM POLICE MARKSMAN II/LP

**Weight**: 30.86 oz.
**Length**: 15.5 in.
**Power**: 4-16X
**Obj.Dia.**: 42mm
**Main Dia.**: 34mm
**Exit Pupil**: 10.5-2.6mm
**Field of View**: 22.5-7 ft @ 100 yds
**Twilight Factor**: 11.3-25.9
**Eye Relief**: 3.5 in.
**Features**: Color coded elevation turret; illuminated reticle and parallax adjustment; LP turret system features a color-coded elevation knob for instant reference to the elevation setting; also in 30mm 10x42 and 34mm 3-12x50 with non-IR, 34mm tube 4-16x42, 3-12x50, 3-20x50, 4-16x50, 5-25x56, and 12-50x56
**MSRP** . . . . . . . . . . . . . . . . . . $3149

## 6X42MM KLASSIK FIXED

**Weight**: 16.67 oz.
**Length**: 13.7 in.
**Power**: 6X
**Obj.Dia.**: 42mm
**Main Dia.**: 1 in.
**Exit Pupil**: 7mm
**Field of View**: 21 ft @ 100 yds
**Twilight Factor**: 15.8
**Eye Relief**: 3.14 in.
**Features**: Fixed 6-power magnification applicable to a wide range of hunting situation; windage and elevation adjustments are in 1/3 MOA increments.; classic European 8x56 configuration offers maximum light transmission; also in 10x42, 7x50, and 8x56
**MSRP** . . . . . . . . . . . . . . . . . . $1239

## 12.5-50X56MM FIELD TARGET

**Weight**: 40.56 oz.
**Length**: 16.4 in.
**Power**: 12.5-50X
**Obj.Dia.**: 56mm
**Main Dia.**: 30mm
**Exit Pupil**: 4.55-1.18mm
**Field of View**: 10.5-2.7 ft @ 100 yds

SCHMIDT & BENDER 12.5-50X56MM FIELD TARGET

SCHMIDT & BENDER 4-16X42 POLICE MARKSMAN II/LP

**Twilight Factor**: 26.5-53
**Eye Relief**: 2.75 in.
**Features**: High-magnification scope has a shallow depth of field, so the parallax side-focus wheel can be used as a reference for gauging the distance to the target and adjusting the trajectory; extra-large focus wheel to range distances from 7-70m; illuminated reticle with brightness settings adjustable from 1 to 11
**MSRP** . . . . . . . . . . . . . . . . . . $3439

SCHMIDT & BENDER 6X42MM KLASSIK FIXED

# Simmons

### .44 MAG. 3-10X44MM

**Weight**: 11.3 oz.
**Length**: 12 in.
**Power**: 3-10X
**Obj.Dia.**: 44mm
**Main Dia.**: 1 in.
**Exit Pupil**: 14.66-4.4mm
**Field of View**: 33-9.4 ft @ 100 yds
**Twilight Factor**: 11.48-20.97
**Eye Relief**: 3.75 in.
**Features**: Wide field of view with brightness delivered via multi-coated optics; QTA (Quick Target Acquisition) eyepiece; TrueZero windage and elevation adjustment system; also in 4-12x44, 6-21x44, 6-24x44
**MSRP** . . . . . . . . . . . . . . . . . **$169.95**

SIMMONS .44 MAG.
3-10X44MM

### PREDATOR QUEST 6-24X50MM

**Weight**: 17 oz.
**Length**: N/A
**Power**: 6-24X
**Obj.Dia.**: 50mm
**Main Dia.**: 30mm

**Exit Pupil**: 8.33-2mm
**Field of View**: 14-4 ft @ 100 yds
**Twilight Factor**: 17.32-35.35
**Eye Relief**: 3.9 in.
**Features**: Inspired by Les Johnson and his popular TV show, the Simmons Predator Quest series; fingertip-adjustable turrets promote quick aim modifications; side focus adjustment for rapid target acquisition; versatile TruPlex reticle; also in 4.5-18x44
**MSRP** . . . . . . . . . . . . . . . . . **$372.95**

### PROHUNTER 3-9X40MM ILLUMINATED TRUPLEX RETICLE

**Weight**: 10.8 oz.
**Length**: 12 in.
**Power**: 3-9X
**Obj.Dia.**: 40mm
**Main Dia.**: 1 in.
**Exit Pupil**: 13.33-4.44mm
**Field of View**: 31.4-11 ft @ 100 yds
**Twilight Factor**: 10.95-18.97
**Eye Relief**: 3.75 in.
**Features**: TrueZero windage and elevation adjustment system for a locked-in zero; raised tab on the power change ring for easy grip and surer adjustments; also in 4x32, 1.5-5x32, 3-9x40 TruPlex Reticle, 4x32, 2-6x32 Matte, 2-6x32 Silver
**MSRP** . . . . . . . . . . . . . . . . . **$190.95**

### PROTARGET 3-9X40MM

**Weight**: 20.4 oz.
**Length**: 12 in.
**Power**: 3-9X
**Obj.Dia.**: 40mm
**Main Dia.**: 1 in.
**Exit Pupil**: 13.33-4.44mm
**Field of View**: 31-10.5 ft @ 100 yds
**Twilight Factor**: 10.95-18.97
**Eye Relief**: 3.9 in.
**Features**: Calibrated for either .22 LR or .17 HMR; mid- to long-range shooting; TruPlex Reticle makes it easier to pinpoint the smallest targets with a rimfire rifle; fingertip-adjustable turrets with a side focus available on the higher magnification models; also in 3-12x40, 6-18x40
**MSRP** . . . . . . . . . . . . . . . . . **$181.95**

SIMMONS PREDATOR
QUEST 6-24X50MM

SIMMONS PROHUNTER
3-9X40MM ILLUMINATED
TRUPLEX RETICLE

SIMMONS PROTARGET
3-9X40MM

## MILITARY/TACTICAL 4-16X50MM

**Weight**: 33.6 oz.
**Length**: 16.1 in.
**Power**: 4-16X
**Obj.Dia.**: 50.8mm
**Main Dia.**: 34.3mm
**Exit Pupil**: 11.9-3.3mm
**Field of View**: 8.7-2.4m @ 100m
**Twilight Factor**: 14.5-27.2
**Eye Relief**: 3.0-3.4 in.
**Features**: Higher magnification range lets you target anything from varmints to big game; side parallax adjustment
**MSRP** . . . . . . . . . . . . . . . . . **$2295.99**

STEINER MILITARY/TACTICAL
4X16-50MM

## MILITARY 5-25X56MM

**Weight**: 36.3 oz.
**Length**: 16.6 in.
**Power**: 5-25X
**Obj. Dia.**: 56mm
**Main Dia.**: 34mm
**Exit Pupil**: 9.8-2.24mm
**Field of View**: 7.23-1.43m @ 100m
**Twilight Factor**: 16.73-37.42
**Eye Relief**: 3.54 in.
**Features**: Extremely high magnification, designed for use on long-range tactical and sniper rifles; high magnification and elevation travel allow to extend the practical shooting range beyond 1,500 meters; broad band anti-reflection coated optic guarantee maximum light transmission; 11 illumination steps; also available in 1-4x24, 3-12x50, 3-12x56, and 4-16x 50
**MSRP** . . . . . . . . . . . . . . . . . **$3095**

STEINER MILITARY
5-25X56MM

## PREDATOR XTREME 3-12X56MM

**Weight**: 24 oz.
**Length**: 14.9 in.
**Power**: 3-12X
**Obj. Dia.**: 56mm
**Main Dia.**: 30mm
**Exit Pupil**: 13-5mm
**Field of View**: 36-9 ft @ 100 yds
**Twilight Factor**: 12.96-25.92
**Eye Relief**: 3.5-4 in.
**Features**: Precision-ground lenses with Steiner's unique CAT (Color Adjusted Transmission) technology; engineered lens coating delivers the highest levels of contrast and light transmission; new Steiner Plex S1 Ballistic etched reticle; features ¼-MOA adjustments for windage and elevation; also in 2.5-10x42 and 4-16x50
**MSRP** . . . . . . . . . . . . . . . . . **$899.99**

STEINER PREDATOR
XTREME 3-12X56MM

**OPTICS**

# Swarovski Optik

### Z3 3-10X42MM

**Weight**: 12.7 oz.
**Length**: 12.6 in.
**Power**: 3-10X
**Obj.Dia.**: 42mm
**Main Dia.**: 1 in.
**Exit Pupil**: 12.6-4.2mm
**Field of View**: 33-11.7 ft @ 1000 yds
**Twilight Factor**: 11.22-20.49
**Eye Relief**: 3.5 in.
**Features**: Z3 riflescopes have a 3X zoom factor and are the lightest riflescopes in the Swarovski Optik line;

perfect fit for many of today's lightweight rifles; reticles for the Z3 include the 4A, Plex, BRX/BRH (3-10x and 4-12x), and ML in the 3-10x
**MSRP** . . . . . . . . . . . . . . . . . . . . **$954**

### Z5 5-25X52MM

**Weight**: 17.5 oz.
**Length**: 14.6 in.
**Power**: 5-25X
**Obj.Dia.**: 52mm
**Main Dia.**: 1 in.
**Exit Pupil**: 9.6-2.1mm

**Field of View**: 21.9-4.5 ft @ 100 yds
**Twilight Factor**: 16.12-36.05
**Eye Relief**: 3.75 in.
**Features**: The Z5 Riflescope line features a 5X zoom factor; a third parallax-adjustment turret; and long eye relief; with reticles available in #4, Plex, Fine in the 5-25x, and BRX/BRH; also available with the ballistic turrets; also in 3.5-18x44
**MSRP** . . . . . . . . . . . . . . . . . . . . **$1777**

### Z6 2-12X50MM

**Weight**: 18.3 oz.
**Length**: 13.4 in.
**Power**: 2-12X
**Obj.Dia.**: 50mm
**Main Dia.**: 30mm
**Exit Pupil**: 25-4.17mm
**Field of View**: 63.0-10.5 ft @100 yds
**Twilight Factor**: 10-24.49
**Eye Relief**: 3.74 in.
**Features**: The Z6 line of riflescopes feature a 6X zoom factor, adjustable parallax, and HD glass on select high magnification models; available with illuminated reticles which have a spare battery stored in the turret cap; wide selection of reticles; also in 1-6x24, 1.7-10x42, 2,5-15x44, 2.5-15x56, 3-18x50, and 5-30x50
**MSRP** . . . . . . . . . . . . . . . . . . . . **$2477**

### Z6I 5-30X50MM P

**Weight**: 22.6 oz.
**Length**: 15.67 in.
**Power**: 5-30X
**Obj. Dia.**: 48.2-50mm
**Main Dia.**: 30mm
**Exit Pupil**: 9.5-1.7mm
**Field of View**: 23.7-3.9 ft @ 100 yds
**Twilight Factor**: 14.1-38.7
**Eye Relief**: 3.74 in.
**Features**: New 2nd Generation scopes feature slimmer design that enables a clearer view of the controls and of the hunting situation; parallax turret also features a lock-in position at the 100 yds mark; more prominent ribbing on the magnification ring; 4A-1, 4W, Plex, and BRH reticles available; also available in 1-6x24, 1-6x24 BRT, 1-6x24 EE, 1.7-10x42, 2-12x50, 2.5-15x44 P, 2.5-15x56 P, 3-18x50 P
**MSRP** . . . . . . . . . . . . . . . . . . . . **$3677**

**SWAROVSKI OPTIK Z3 3-10X42MM**

**SWAROVSKI OPTIK Z5 5-25X52MM**

**SWAROVSKI OPTIK Z6 2-12X50MM**

**SWAROVSKI OPTIK Z6I 5-30X50MM P**

# Trijicon

## ACCUPOINT 3-9X40MM
*Weight*: 13.4 oz.
*Length*: 12.4 in.
*Power*: 3-9X
*Obj.Dia.*: 40mm
*Main Dia.*: 1 in.
*Exit Pupil*: 13.3-4.4mm
*Field of View*: 6.45-2.15 ft @ 100 yds
*Twilight Factor*: 10.95-18.97
*Eye Relief*: 3.6 in.
*Features*: Tritium and fiber battery-free dual-illuminated; manual brightness adjustment override; quick-focus eye-piece; and windage and elevation adjustments; aircraft aluminum with black-matte finish; reticles include BAC Triangle, Standard Cross-Hair with Dot, Mil-Dot Cross-Hair with Dot, and German #4 in red, green, and amber illumination; also in 1-4x24, 1.25-4x24, 5-20x50, and 2.5-10x56
**MSRP** . . . . . . . . . . . . . . . . . . . . **$927**

**TRIJICON ACCUPOINT 3-9X40MM**

## ACOG CROSSBOW SCOPE 3X24MM XB
*Weight*: 5.89 oz.
*Length*: 5 in.
*Power*: 3X
*Obj. Dia.*: 24mm
*Exit Pupil*: 20-3mm
*Field of View*: 25.6 ft @ 100 yds
*Twilight Factor*: 8.49
*Eye Relief*: 1.4 in.
*Features*: The first truly high performance optic designed specifically for crossbows; lightest magnified crossbow optic; illuminated reticle accommodates speeds from 300-340 fps; bolt drop stadia lines out to 80 yds; Bad River Outdoors' patented deer/elk ranging capabilities; ability for ranging and hold-over, all in the field of view; fiber optics and tritium illumination
**MSRP** . . . . . . . . . . . . . . . . . . . **$1148**

**TRIJICON ACOG CROSSBOW SCOPE 3X24 XB**

## TARS 3-15X50MM
*Weight*: 47 oz., 51 oz. with sunshade
*Length*: 13.9in, 16.9 in. with sunshade
*Power*: 3-15X
*Obj. Dia.*: 50mm
*Main Dia.*: 34mm
*Exit Pupil*: 16.8-3.3mm
*Field of View*: 37.5-7.5 ft @ 100 yds
*Twilight Factor*: 10.1-22.6
*Eye Relief*: 3.3 in.
*Features*: Tactical Advanced RifleScope is built for long-range shooting demands; multi-layer coated lenses;

**TRIJICON TARS 3-15X50MM**

aircraft grade hard anodized aluminum; side-focus parallax compensation, powered by 1 CR2032 battery; constant eye relief; available with MOA, Duplex, JW MIL-Square reticles and MOA or MIL adjusters
**MSRP** . . . . . . . . . . . . . . . . . . . **$3990**

**OPTICS**

# Weaver

### 40/44 3-10X44MM

**Weight**: 13.93 oz.
**Length**: 12.09 in.
**Power**: 3-10X
**Obj.Dia.**: 44mm
**Main Dia.**: 1 in.
**Exit Pupil**: 14.7-4.4mm
**Field of View**: 33.5-10.3 ft @ 100 yds
**Twilight Factor**: 11.49-20.98
**Eye Relief**: 3 in.
**Features**: Ballistic-X reticle on some models; one-piece tube construction; aspherical lens system on some models; also available in 2.8-10x44, 3-9x40, 3.8-12x44, 4-12x44, 6.5-20x44; silver finish on some models
**MSRP** . . . . . . . . . . **$223.49–$233.95**

### 40/44 SHOTGUN & MUZZLELOADER

**Weight**: 14-24 oz.
**Length**: 10.31-13.31 in.
**Power**: 2-7X
**Obj.Dia.**: 32mm

**Main Dia.**: 1 in.
**Exit Pupil**: 15-5.4mm
**Field of View**: 44.7-12.7 ft @ 100 yds
**Twilight Factor**: 8-14.97
**Eye Relief**: 3.5 in.
**Features**: Weaver's dedicated shotgun and muzzleloader scopes are engineered specifically for these firearms and give hunters maximum performance out of short to medium-range guns.
**MSRP** . . . . . . . . . . **$185.49–$195.49**

### CLASSIC HANDGUN 2.5-8X28MM

**Weight**: 9.1 oz.
**Length**: 9.29 in.
**Power**: 2.5-8X
**Obj.Dia.**: 28mm

**Main Dia.**: 1 in.
**Exit Pupil**: 11.2-3.5mm
**Field of View**: 11-4.5 ft @ 100 yds
**Twilight Factor**: 8.37-14.97
**Eye Relief**: 24.53 in.
**Features**: Handguns demand a scope that is built to withstand the brutal pounding from today's most powerful revolvers and single-shot pistols. Designed for the tremendous recoil of 1,000 rounds from a .454 Casull revolver; black or silver; also in 1.5-4x20, 2x28, and 4x28.
**MSRP** . . . . . . . . . . . . . . . . . **$348.95**

**WEAVER 40/44 3-10X44MM**

**WEAVER 40/44 SHOTGUN & MUZZLELOADER**

**WEAVER CLASSIC HANDGUN 2.5-8X28MM**

OPTICS

### CLASSIC K SERIES 4X28MM

**Weight**: 14.2 oz.
**Length**: 9.17 in.
**Power**: 4X
**Obj.Dia.**: 38mm
**Main Dia.**: 1 in.
**Exit Pupil**: 7mm
**Field of View**: 8.5 ft @ 100 yds
**Twilight Factor**: 12.33
**Eye Relief**: 9.45 in.
**Features**: Crafted from a one-piece aircraft-grade aluminum tube; built to take heavy recoil punishment and hold zero to 10,000 rounds from a .375 H&H magnum rifle; presents a consistent field of view that's perfect for open field hunting and are among the easiest scopes any instinctive shooter will ever use; also in 4x38, 6x38, 8x56
**MSRP** . . . . . . . . . . . . . . . . . **$273.49**

### CLASSIC RIMFIRE 3-9X32MM

**Weight**: 12 oz.
**Length**: 11.5 in.
**Power**: 3-9X
**Obj.Dia.**: 28mm
**Main Dia.**: 1 in.
**Exit Pupil**: 10.6mm
**Field of View**: 33.2-11 ft @ 100 yds
**Twilight Factor**: 9.17-15.87
**Eye Relief**: 3.58 in.
**Features**: Variable and fixed power models; non-glare lenses that produce edge-sharp, low-light brightness; rugged, aircraft-grade, one-piece aluminum construction; parallax is set at 50 yards; also in 2.5-7x28 (matte, silver) and 4x28
**MSRP** . . . . . . . . . . . . . . . . . **$372.49**

### KASPA TACTICAL SERIES 2.5-10X50MM

**Weight**: 25.04 oz.
**Length**: 12.79 in.
**Power**: 2.5-10X
**Obj. Dia.**: 50mm
**Main Dia.**: 30mm
**Exit Pupil**: 20-5mm
**Field of View**: 37.3 ft @ 100 yds
**Twilight Factor**: 11.18-22.36
**Eye Relief**: 3.74-3.15 in.
**Features**: Rugged one-piece tube construction; nitrogen purged to eliminate internal fogging; fully multi-coated lenses; crisp ¼-inch MOA adjustments; Dual-X, Ballistic-X, TBX, and Tactical Mil-Dot reticles on various models; also in 1x20, 1.5-6x32, 2.5-10x44, 2-7x32, 309x40, 3-12x44, 3-12x50, 4-16x44
**MSRP** . . . . . . . . . . . . . . . . . **$319.99**

**WEAVER CLASSIC K SERIES 4X28MM**

**WEAVER CLASSIC RIMFIRE 3-9X32MM**

**WEAVER KASPA TACTICAL SERIES 2.5-10X50MM**

OPTICS

# Weaver

### SUPER SLAM 4-20X50MM
**Weight**: 24 oz.
**Length**: 13.31 in.
**Power**: 4-20X
**Obj.Dia.**: 50mm
**Main Dia.**: 1 in.
**Exit Pupil**: 10.5-2.44mm
**Field of View**: 24.5-4.9 ft @ 100 yds
**Twilight Factor**: 14.14-31.62
**Eye Relief**: 3.98 in.
**Features**: Line of premier riflescopes designed for the serious big game hunter and shooter; side focus parallax adjustment; pull-up turrets; also in 1-5x24, 2-10x42, 2-10x50, 3-15x42, 3-15x50; in silver or matte black; EBX or Dual-x reticle available
**MSRP** . . . . . . . . . . $968.49–$1039.49

### TACTICAL 1-5X24MM
**Weight**: 14.46 oz.
**Length**: 10.31 in.
**Power**: 1-5X
**Obj.Dia.**: 24mm
**Main Dia.**: 30mm
**Exit Pupil**: 11.4-4.9mm
**Field of View**: 100-19.9 ft @ 100 yds

WEAVER SUPER SLAM 4-20X50MM

WEAVER TACTICAL 1-5X24MM

**Twilight Factor**: 4.9-10.95
**Eye Relief**: 4.25 in.
**Features**: Rugged riflescopes designed specifically for tactical applications; extra hard coating on exterior lenses; first focal plane reticles; side focus

parallax adjustment; reset-to-zero turrets; one-piece tube construction; also in 3-15x50 and 4-20x50; Mil-Dot, CIRT, and EMDR reticles on some scopes
**MSRP** . . . . . . . . . . . . . . . . $1069.95

## SIGHTS
# Aimpoint

### 2 MOA MICRO H-1 AND T-1
**Weight**: 3 oz.
**Length**: 2.4 in.
**Power**: 1X
**Features**: High quality compact red-dot sight; sealed design ensures that no foreign matter will come between the emitter and the lens; can be mounted on nearly any individual weapon platform including: pistols, carbines, personal defense weapons, and sub-machineguns; also available in 4 MOA red-dot
**H-1:** . . . . . . . . . . . . . . . . . . . . . $606
**T-1:** . . . . . . . . . . . . . . . . . . . . . $678

### PATROL RIFLE OPTIC (PRO)
**Weight**: 7.8 oz.
**Length**: 5.1 in.
**Power**: 1X
**Features**: Parallax free optic; 2 MOA

dot for accurate target engagement at all distances; four night vision settings and six daylight settings; modular QRP2 mount includes removable spacer that indexes the sight at optimal height for co-witness with the standard iron sights on AR15/M16/M4 carbine style weapons
**MSRP** . . . . . . . . . . . . . . . . . . . . $405

AIMPOINT 2 MOA MICRO H-1

AIMPOINT PATROL RIFLE OPTIC

OPTICS

# Browning

## BUCK MARK REFLEX SIGHT

**Weight**: N/A
**Power**: 1X
**Field of View**: 47 ft @ 100 yds
**Eye Relief**: Unlimited
**Features**: The Buck Mark has an aluminum housing, four red reticle patterns, a seven-position brightness rheostat powered by a lithium battery, and mounts on a standard Weaver-styled base. Unlimited eye relief.
**MSRP**....................**$64.99**

BROWNING BUCK MARK REFLEX SIGHT

# Burris

## FASTFIRE III RED-DOT REFLEX SIGHT

**Weight**: 0.9 oz.
**Power**: 1.07X
**Features**: Upgraded features such as windage and elevation adjustments that don't require a special tool; 3 or 8 MOA Dot; power button with three levels of brightness; low battery warning indicator and see-through protective cap; ideally suited for use on pistols and AR-15s where fast target acquisition is desired, the FastFire red-dot sight will also match up well with carbines, lever guns, and shotguns; available picatinny mount.
**MSRP**.....................**$372**

BURRIS FASTFIRE III RED-DOT REFLEX SIGHT

# Bushnell

**BUSHNELL 2X MP ELECTRONIC SIGHT**

### 2X MP ELECTRONIC SIGHT
*Weight*: 15.6 oz.
*Length*: 6.75 in.
*Power*: 2X
*Obj. Dia.*: 32mm
*Exit Pupil*: 32mm
*Field of View*: 44 ft @ 100 yds
*Eye Relief*: Unlimited
*Features*: With the ability to display the T-dot reticle in green during low light and red during bright light, the 2X MP offers the versatility shooters demand from electronic sights. With two power magnification and multi-coated optics, the sight is ideal for acquiring close- to mid-range targets.
**MSRP** . . . . . . . . . . . . . . . . . . **$340.95**

# Carl Zeiss Sports Optics

**CARL ZEISS VICTORY COMPACT POINT SIGHT**

### VICTORY COMPACT POINT SIGHT
*Weight*: 2.64 oz.
*Length*: 2.28 in.
*Power*: 1.05X
*Features*: LotuTec protective coating; single button on/off and five level brightness; 25 percent wider than conventional reflex sites for natural viewing with both eyes; Blaser integrated mount allows mounting directly on barrel while standard mount allows mounting on Picatinny/Weaver rail
**Standard:** . . . . . . . . . . . **$577.77**
**Blaser:** . . . . . . . . . . . . . **$799.99**

**CARL ZEISS Z-POINT**

### Z-POINT (RED DOT REFLEX SIGHT)
*Weight*: 5.65 oz.
*Length*: 2.5 in.
*Power*: 1X
*Features*: Acquisition sight for shotguns, rifles, and handguns; dual-source illuminated: a solar cell for daylight hours and battery power for dark; red dot automatically adapts to brightness of surroundings and can be regulated manually; available for Weaver or Picatinny mounts
**MSRP** . . . . . . . . . . . . . . . . . . **$666.66**

OPTICS

## HOLOGRAPHIC HYBRID SIGHT (HHS)

**Power**: 3.25X
**Eye Relief**: 2.2 in.
**Features**: The HHS kits combine the speed of the EXPS holographic weapon sight and the extended range versatility of the new 3.25X G33 magnifier. The HHS1 includes the night vision compatible EXPS3-4 HWS with the 4-dot reticle calibrated for shooting at 0-300, 400, 500 and 600 meters. The HHS2 includes the EXPS2-2 and non-night vision compatible sight with a 2-dot reticle for fast action targeting.
**MSRP** . . . . . . . . . . . . . **$1002–$1069**

**EOTECH HOLOGRAPHIC HYBRID SIGHT**

## XPS2-RF

**Weight**: 7 oz.
**Length**: 3.5 in.
**Power**: 1X
**Eye Relief**: Unlimited
**Features**: Holographic sight specifically for the rimfire rifle; integrated $^3/_8$-inch dovetail mount (not compatible with 1-inch Weaver or 1913 rails); lightweight for smaller platforms; single transverse 123 battery to reduce sight length; shortened base; this model is only intended and warranted for calibers .22LR or smaller
**MSRP** . . . . . . . . . . . . . . . . . . . **$399**

**EOTECH XPS2-RF**

## XPS2-Z ZOMBIE STOPPER

**Features**: 20 brightness settings; 600 hours of run time on one battery; 65 MOA ring with 1 MOA aiming dot; cool biohazard tails to kill zombies deader
**MSRP** . . . . . . . . . . . . . . . . . . . **$588**

**EOTECH XPS2-Z ZOMBIE STOPPER**

# Kruger Optical

**KRUGER DTS 1-8X40MM**

## DUAL TACTICAL SIGHT (DTS) 1-8X40MM

**Weight**: 30 oz.
**Length**: 10 in.
**Power**: 1X, 2-8X

**Obj.Dia.**: 40mm
**Exit Pupil**: 12-4mm
**Field of View**: 126-13 ft @ 100 yds
**Twilight Factor**: 8.94-17.89
**Eye Relief**: Unlimited, 3 in.
**Features**: Switch instantly with no head movement from a close quarter reflex sight to a 2-8x40 Mil-Dot sight; two independently adjustable windage and elevation systems; rapid target technology eye box; lightweight ultra-strong carbon fiber composite shell
**MSRP** . . . . . . . . . . . . . . . . . **$1763.53**

# Leupold & Stevens

## DELTAPOINT REFLEX SIGHT

**Weight**: 0.6 oz.
**Length**: 1.66 in.
**Features**: For use on handguns, shot-guns, and AR-style rifles; includes numerous mounting options; an aspheric lens, motion activation, auto-brightness sensor, locking elevation and windage adjustment system, and a magnesium housing; 7.5 MOA Delta and 3.5 MOA Dot reticles available
**Cross-Slot mount:** . . . . . . . . **$499.99**
**Other mounts:** . . . . . . . . . . **$564.99**

## PRISMATIC HUNTING 1X14MM

**Weight**: 12 oz.
**Length**: 4.5 in.
**Power**: 1X
**Main Dia.**: 30mm
**Field of View**: 83 ft @ 100 yds
**Eye Relief**: 3 in.
**Features**: Fast target acquisition of a non-magnifying red-dot sight with a wide field of view; etched-glass reticle that is visible with or without illumination; ½ MOA finger-adjustable wind-age and elevation dials; focusing eye-piece; black matte finish or dark earth anodized finish and with Circle Plex or DCD reticles
**MSRP** . . . . . . . . . . . . . . . . . **$599.99**

**LEUPOLD DELTAPOINT REFLEX SIGHT**

**LEUPOLD PRISMATIC HUNTING 1X14MM**

# Lucid

**LUCID HD7 RED DOT SIGHT**

## HD7 RED DOT SIGHT
*Weight*: 13 oz.
*Length*: 5.5 in.
*Power*: 1X
*Obj.Dia.*: 34mm
*Field of View*: 44 ft @ 100 yds
*Eye Relief*: Unlimited
*Features*: Third Generation Unit. Integral Picatinny rail and reversible mounting pins for bullpup-style firearms. Manual & Auto-Brightness with 12 brightness settings; 4 operator-selectable reticles based on a 2 MOA dot with ½ MOA click adjustments. Parallax free, it is powered by one AAA battery. The frame is cast aluminum armored in chemical rubber and is available with a 2X screw-in eyepiece. Available in tan.
**MSRP** . . . . . . . . . . . . . . . . . . . **$249**

# Nikon

**NIKON MONARCH DOT SIGHT VSD 1X30MM**

## MONARCH DOT SIGHT VSD 1X30MM
*Weight*: 7.8 oz.
*Length*: 3.8 in.
*Power*: 1X
*Obj.Dia.*: 30mm
*Exit Pupil*: 30mm
*Twilight Factor*: 5.5
*Eye Relief*: Unlimited
*Features*: The Monarch Dot Sight VSD's (Variable Sized Dot) offers selections of 1, 4, 6, 8, or 10 MOA dot size. Includes 11-position rheostat and integral mounting system attachable to any Weaver-style base. Ocular lenses are 30mm. Available in matte, silver, and RealTree APG.
**MSRP** . . . . . . . . . . . . . . . . . **$249.95**

# Pedersoli

## ENGLISH REAR SIGHT, MODEL USA 428

**Features**: Rear sight with convex base, with two adjustable and folding leaves.
**From**: . . . . . . . . . . . . . . . . . . . . **$140**

## FIBER OPTIC FRONT AND REAR SIGHT, MODEL USA 409

**Features**: Front sight and rear sight set for muzzleloading rifles (Model 410 for breechloaders). Front sight with dovetail base; rear sight with base for octagonal barrel.
**From**: . . . . . . . . . . . . . . . . . . . . **$125**

## "GHOST" TANG SIGHT USA 422

**Features**: A tang sight inspired by some models in use in the 1800s, economic, functional, and useful for hunting. Adjustable in elevation and windage, it can fit several gun types. The small eye piece ring enables a quick, instinctive aim at the target; when quickly shouldering the rifle, the open ring provides a clear sight picture with low light condition. Distance between the two mounting holes is 1 ¾ inches.
**From**: . . . . . . . . . . . . . . . . . . . . **$75**

## "SOULE TYPE" MIDDLE RANGE SET, MODEL USA 170

**Features**: Wooden-box set including Soule XL Middle Range Sight; Tunnel Front Sight with a micrometric screw for windage adjustment, spirit level, and fifteen interchangeable inserts; Professional "Hadley Style" Eyepiece with eight varying diameter viewing holes, depending on available light, on a rotating disk which can be selected without disassembling or loosening the eyepiece, and a rubber ring on the eyepiece; six interchangeable glass bubbles (spirit level) with different colors for varying light conditions. 3 in. elevation adjustment.
**From**: . . . . . . . . . . . . . . . . . . . . **$549**

PEDERSOLI ENGLISH REAR SIGHT - 428

PEDERSOLI FIBER OPTIC FRONT AND REAR SIGHT - 409

PEDERSOLI "SOULE TYPE" MIDDLE RANGE SET - 170

PEDERSOLI "GHOST" TANG SIGHT USA 422

OPTICS

# Pedersoli

## SPIRIT LEVEL TUNNEL SIGHT ADJUSTABLE WITH 12 INSERTS SET, MODEL USA 425

**Features**: Spirit level tunnel sight with micrometer adjustment for windage, equipped with twelve interchangeable inserts.

**From:**. . . . . . . . . . . **$29.99–$149.99**

## UNIVERSAL CREEDMOOR SIGHT, MIDDLE AND LONG RANGE, MODELS USA 465 AND 430

**Features**: Tang sight with elevation and windage adjustment in the eye piece. For long-distance target shooting both with muzzle-loading and breech-loading rifles. 2.1875-2.3125 in. between two mounting holes; 2- and 3-inch elevation adjustments

**From:**. . . . . . . . . . **$162.87–$270.67**

## U.S. MODEL 1879 SPRINGFIELD TRAPDOOR REAR SIGHT, MODEL USA 473

**Features**: Sometimes referred to as "Buckhorn" style. Used on Trapdoor rifles from 1874 until superseded by Buffington style in 1884. Side ramps are graduated to 500 yards and the ladder to 1500 yards. Slide has windage adjustment.

**From:**. . . . . . . . . . . . . . . . . . . . **$140**

PEDERSOLI SPIRIT LEVEL TUNNEL
SIGHT ADJUSTABLE - 425

PEDERSOLI UNIVERSAL
CREEDMOOR SIGHT - 430

PEDERSOLI U.S. MODEL 1879
SPRINGFIELD TRAPDOOR REAR
SIGHT - 473

**OPTICS**

# Pentax Imaging Co.

### GAMESEEKER DOT SIGHT HS-20
**Weight**: 3.4 oz.
**Length**: 3.9 in.
**Power**: 1X
**Field of View**: 55-50 ft @ 100 yds
**Features**: 5 MOA dot with 11 brightness settings and 72 hours of continuous battery use; continuous, non-click adjustments; Weaver-style mounting system
**MSRP** . . . . . . . . . . . . . . . . . . . . . **$59**

### GAMESEEKER DOT SIGHT RD-10
**Weight**: 7.07 oz.
**Length**: 3.8 in.
**Power**: 1X
**Obj.Dia.**: 30mm
**Main Dia.**: 39mm
**Field of View**: 54 ft @ 100 yds
**Features**: Reflex sight with a 4 MOA dot; 11 brightness settings; 72 hours continuous battery life; continuous windage and elevation adjustments; Weaver-style mounting system
**MSRP** . . . . . . . . . . . . . . . . . . . . . **$69**

PENTAX GAMESEEKER
DOT SIGHT HS-20

PENTAX GAMESEEKER
DOT SIGHT RD-10

# Trijicon

### RMR ADJUSTABLE LED RM06
**Weight**: 1.2 oz.
**Length**: 1.77 in.
**Power**: 1X
**Features**: LED sight powered by standard CR2032 battery; rugged forged aluminum; adjusters with audible clicks allow for quick windage and elevation adjustments; eight brightness settings; reticle can be manually adjusted; also in Dual-Illuminated RMR with 13.0 MOA dot, 7.0 MOA dot, 9.0 MOA dot, and triangle-reticle RMR LED with 3.25 MOA dot and 6.5 MOA dot
**MSRP** . . . . . . . . . . . . . . . . . . . . . **$696**

TRIJICON RMR
ADJUSTABLE LED RM06

### SRS (SEALED REFLEX SIGHT) 1X38
**Weight**: 13.8 oz.
**Length**: 3.75 in.
**Power**: 1X
**Obj. Dia.**: 38mm
**Features**: Body length of only 3.75 inches virtually eliminates the "tube-effect" common with other, competitive red-dot sights; field of view provides no obstruction to shooters; LED 1.75 MOA aiming point with 10 brightness settings; SRS powered by solar panel and AA battery; parallax-free objective lens; available in Colt-Style flattop mount or Quick Release flattop mount
**MSRP** . . . . . . . . . . . . . . **$1050–$1125**

TRIJICON SRS 1X38

GOLDEN PHEASANT
12 GAUGE - NICKEL PLATED

FIOCCHI
AMMUNITION

AMMUNITION

# Barnes Bullets

### VOR-TX AMMUNITION

**Features**: Provides maximum tissue and bone destruction, pass-through penetration, and devastating energy transfer. Multiple grooves in the bullet's shank reduce pressure and improve accuracy. Bullets open instantly on contact causing the nose to peel back into four sharp-edged copper petals destroying tissue, bone, and vital organs for a quick, humane kill. Handgun, Safari, and Rifle lines. **Available in**: .300 AAC Blackout-110 gr., .35 Whelen-180gr.; Rifle Line: .223 Rem., .243 Win., .25-06, .270 Win., .270 WSM, 7mm-08 Rem., 7mm Rem. Mag., 7x64 Brenneke, .30-30 Win., .308 Win., .30-06 Spfd., .300 WSM, .300 Win. Mag., .300 RUM, 8x57 Mauser, .338 Win. Mag., .35 Whelen, 9.3x62 Mauser, .45-70 Govt.; Safari Line: .375 H&H, .416 Rem. Mag., .416 Rigby, .458 Win. Mag., .458 Lott, .470 Nitro, .500 Nitro; Handgun Line: .375 Mag., .41 Rem. Mag., .44 Mag, .45 Colt, .454 Casull

**MSRP . . . . . . . . . . . $22.99–$146.99**

**BARNES BULLETS VOR-TX AMMUNITION**

# Black Hills Ammunition

## Rifle Ammunition

### BLACK HILLS GOLD

**Features**: Coupling the finest components in the industry with bullets by Barnes, these lead-free non-toxic rounds set a new standard for high-performance hunting ammunition. 20 rounds per box. **Available in**: .22-250, .243 Win., .25-06 Rem., .260 Rem., .270 Win., 6.5-284 Norma, 7mm Rem. Mag., .300 Win. Mag., .308 Win., .30-06 Spfd., .300 WSM

**From: . . . . . . . . . . . . $29.99–$52.99**

### FACTORY NEW RIFLE

**Features**: Coupling the finest components in the industry with bullets by manufacturers such as Hornady, Barnes, and Nosler, these rounds set a new standard for high-performance hunting ammunition. 20 rounds per box. Certain calibers available in Molycoat. **Available in**: .223 Rem., .308 Win. Match, .300 Win. Mag., .338 Lapua, .338 Norma Mag.

**From: . . . . . . . . . . $38.15–$115.99**

### REMANUFACTURED

**Features**: Ammunition designed with the practice shooter in mind, with incredible accuracy for a great price point. It's the same ammunition used by the U.S. Army Marksmanship Unit in 600-yd. matches. It has the capability to produce 2-in. groups at 300m. 50 rounds per box. **Available in**: .223 Rem. (also in Molycoat) and 9mm Luger, .40 S&W, .45 ACP for handguns

**From: . . . . . . . . . . . . $25.99–$39.65**

**BLACK HILLS FACTORY NEW RIFLE**

AMMUNITION

# Black Hills Ammunition

## Handgun Ammunition

### COWBOY ACTION
*Features*: Designed to meet the needs of cowboy-action pistol shooters with its new virgin brass and premium-quality hard-cast bullets. Velocities are moderate to provide low recoil and excellent accuracy.
*Available in*: .32 H&R, .32-20, .38 Long Colt, .38 Spl., .357 Mag., .38-40, .44-40, .44 Russian, .44 Spl., .44 Colt, .45 Schofield, .45 Colt, .38-55, .45-70,
**From:** . . . . . . . . . . . . **$30.66–$38.34**

### FACTORY NEW HANDGUN
*Features*: Used by the U.S. Military in all four branches for its reliability.
*Available in*: .300 Whisper, .32 H&R Mag., .380 Auto, 9mm Luger, .38 Spl., .357 Mag., .40 S&W, .44 Mag., .45 Auto Rim, .45 ACP
**From:** . . . . . . . . . . . . **$34.99–$50.99**

## Brenneke USA

## Shotgun Ammunition Slugs

### 28 GAUGE SLUGS
*Features*: The moderate recoil makes the 28 Ga. a perfect slug for young hunters who will be introduced to slug shooting. 28 gauge is a multi-talent: small game, home defense, and all around shooting.
*Available in*: 28 Ga. (2 ¾ in.)
**MSRP** . . . . . . . . . . . . . **$9.99–$11.99**

### BLACK MAGIC MAGNUM AND SHORT MAGNUM
*Features*: The Black Magic Magnum and Black Magic Short Magnum are two of the most powerful cartridges available on the market, offering tremendous knockdown power up to 100/60 yards. The clean speed coating reduces lead fouling inside the barrel by almost 100 percent.
*Available in*: 12 Ga. (2 ¾ in.), 12 Ga. (3 in.)
**From:** . . . . . . . . . . . . . . **$8.99–$11.99**

### CLASSIC MAGNUM
*Features*: Invented by Wilhelm Brenneke in 1898, the classic is the ancestor of all modern shotgun slugs. Today this state-of-the-art slug provides long-range stopping power, consistently flat trajectories, and a patented B.E.T. wad column.
*Available in*: 12 Ga. (2 ¾ in.), 16 Ga. (2 ¾ in.)
**Box 5:** . . . . . . . . . . . . . . **$8.99–$9.99**

### CLOSE ENCOUNTER
*Features*: The .410 Close Encounter is the perfect choice if you are a fan of 2 ½-inch .410/.45 revolvers. They are powerful without having bad recoil, and they have an incredible frontal area and the legendary Brenneke penetration.
*Available in*: .410 (2 ½ in.)
**MSRP** . . . . . . . . . . . . . . **$6.99–$8.99**

**BRENNEKE CLOSE ENCOUNTER**

# Brenneke USA

### GOLD MAGNUM

*Features*: Designed for long distance and accuracy. Gold Magnum is designed for rifled barrels only; it is one of the heaviest and most accurate slugs on the market. It has broad ribs for optimum guidance in the rifled barrel and a special coating to reduce lead fouling. Range 100+ yards.
*Available in*: 12 Ga. (3 in.)
From:. . . . . . . . . . . . .$8.99–$12.99

### HEAVY FIELD SHORT MAGNUM GREEN LIGHTNING

*Features*: The original "Emerald" slug with patented B.E.T wad and famous stopping power. For all barrel types; range up to 100 yards.
*Available in*: 12 Ga., 20 Ga. (2 ¾ in.)
From:. . . . . . . . . . . . . .$7.99–$9.99

### K.O. SABOT

*Features*: One of the most affordable sabots on the market, it offers 58 percent more frontal area than standard .50-cal. slugs, resulting in massive energy transfer. Deep penetration, expansion up to .9 in. Range up to 100 yards
*Available in*: 12 Ga. (2 ¾ in.), 12 Ga. (3 in.)
From:. . . . . . . . . . . . $10.99–$13.99

### K.O. SLUG

*Features*: The KO is an improved Foster-type slug with excellent penetration. Range up to 60 yards, for all barrel types.
*Available in*: 12 Ga. (2 ¾ in.)
From:. . . . . . . . . . . . . .$4.99–$5.99

### SUPERSABOT

*Features*: The SuperSabot has a movable core, lead free construction and an effective range up to more than 100 yards. It mushrooms up to 1 in.
*Available in*: 12 Ga. (2 ¾ in.), 12 Ga. (3 in.)
From:. . . . . . . . . . . . .$15.99–$17.99

BRENNEKE HEAVY FIELD SHORT MAGNUM GREEN LIGHTNING SLUGS

BRENNEKE K.O. SABOT

# CCI Ammunition

## Rifle Ammunition

### .22 LONG RANGE AR TACTICAL

*Features*: This load is designed specifically for AR-style guns being offered in .22 Long Rifle chambering. These rounds get excellent accuracy including 1.5 in. at 100 yards for 10-shot groups. This target bullet has a copper-plated round nose for smooth feeding. CCI case, priming, and bullet lube combined with clean-burning powder. 375 rounds per box
*Available in*: .22 Long Rifle-40 gr.
From:. . . . . . . . . . . . . . . . . $21.49

### GREEN TAG

*Features*: Our first and still most-popular match rimfire product. Tight manufacturing and accuracy specs mean you get the consistency and accuracy that the unforgiving field of competition demands. The rimfire match ammo leaves the muzzle sub-sonic. That means no buffeting in the transonic zone. Clean-burning propellants keep actions cleaner. Sure-fire CCI priming. Reusable plastic box with dispenser lid
*Available in*: .22LR-40 grain lead round nose
From:. . . . . . . . . . . . . . . . . $16.49

### HMR TNT

*Features*: CCI extends the usefulness of the exciting .17 Hornady Magnum Rimfire by offering the first hollow point loading. A 17-grain Speer TNT hollow point answers requests from varmint hunters and gives explosive performance over the .17's effective range. Clean-burning propellants keep actions cleaner. Sure-fire CCI priming. Reusable plastic box with dispenser lid.
*Available in*: .17 HMR-17 grain TNT hollow point
MSRP. . . . . . . . . . . . . . . . . $16.99

AMMUNITION

## LONG HV AND SHORT HV

**Features**: Designed for rimfire guns that require .22 Long and .22 Short ammunition. Clean-burning propellants keep actions cleaner. Sure-fire CCI priming. Reusable plastic box with dispenser lid.
**Available in**: .22 short-29 gr. solid lead bullet; .22 short-27 gr. hollow point bullet; .22 Long-29 gr. solid lead bullet
**MSRP** . . . . . . . . . . . . . . . . . **$10.95**

## QUIET-22

**Features**: Ideal for bolt-action and single shot .22LR rifles (and perfectly safe in semiautomatics), this new reduced report cartridge generates ¼ the perceived noise level of standard velocity .22LR round.
**Available in**: .22 LR
**From**: . . . . . . . . . . . . **$2.89–$26.99**

## SELECT .22LR

**Features**: The .22 Long Rifle Select is build for semiautomatic competition. Reliable operation, accuracy, and consistency make Select an ideal choice for competition shooters
**Available in**: .22LR
**MSRP** . . . . . . . . . . . . . . . . . **$16.95**

## Handgun and Rifle Ammunition

### .22 WIN. MAG. MAXI MAG

**Features**: A favorite of varmint shooters. 40-gr. TMJ flat nose at 1875 fps, or 40-gr. jacketed HP at 1875 fps. Both loads give over 1400 fps from a 6-in. revolver. Clean-burning propellants keep actions cleaner. Sure-fire CCI priming. Reusable plastic box with dispenser lid.
**Available in**: .22 Win. Mag.
**MSRP** . . . . . . . . . . . . . . . . . **$13.95**

### MINI-MAG. HV

**Features**: CCI's first rimfire product and still most popular. Mini-Mag. hollow points are high-velocity products and offer excellent all-around performance for small game and varmints. Clean-burning propellants keep actions cleaner. Sure-fire CCI priming. Reusable plastic box with dispenser lid

**Available in**: .22 Long Rifle-40 gr. gilded round nose or -36 gr. gilded lead hollow point
**From**: . . . . . . . . . . . . . . . . . **$6.99**

## V-MAX 17 MACH 2

**Features**: The 17 Mach 2 is a .22LR CCI Stinger case necked down to hold a .17-caliber bullet. CCI loads a super accurate 17-grain polymer-tipped bullet, and drives it 60 percent faster than a .22 Long Rifle 40-gr. hollow point. The loaded cartridge is no longer than a .22LR, greatly expanding the gun actions that can accommodate .17-caliber rimfire cartridges. Reusable 50-count plastic box that protects and dispenses five cartridges at a time
**Available in**: .17 Mach 2 (V-Max also available in .17 HMR and .22 Mag. RF)
**MSRP** . . . . . . . . . . . . . . . . . **$9.95**

## PISTOL MATCH

**Features**: Designed expressly for high-ended semiauto match pistols. Singe-die tooling and great care in assembly lets you wring the last bit of accuracy from your precision pistol. Clean-burning propellants keep actions cleaner. Sure-fire CCI priming. Reusable plastic box with dispenser lid
**Available in**: .22LR-40 gr. lead round nose bullet
**From**: . . . . . . . . . . . . . . . . . **$8.29**

CCI GREEN TAG

CCI QUIET-22

CCI MINI-MAG. HV

CCI V-MAX 17 MACH 2

AMMUNITION

# Cor-Bon

## Rifle Ammunition

### .457 WWG

**Features**: Cor-Bon Ammunition and Wild West Guns teemed up to offer the best in a lever gun big game cartridge.

**Available in**: .457 WWG-350, 405, 460 gr.

**From**: . . . . . . . . . . . . . . . . . . . .$69.99

### DPX RIFLE

**Features**: This is an optimum load for Law Enforcement. Lead-free projectile. Reduced recoil due to lighter weight projectile. Deep penetration on soft tissue 12-17 in.

**Available in**: .223 Rem., .22-250 Rem., .243 Win., .25-06 Rem., .257 Wby. Mag., 6x45mm, 6.5-284 Norma, .260 Rem., 6.8mm Rem. SPC, 7.62x39, .270 Win., .270 Wby. Mag., .270 WSM, 7mm RUM, 7mm WSM, 7mm Rem. Mag., 7mm-08 Rem., .284 Win., .30 Carbon, .308 Win., .30-06 Spfd., .300 Win. Mag., .300 RUM, .300 WSM, .30-30 Win., .338 Win. Mag., .338 Lapua, .338 RUM, .340 Wby. Mag., .375 H&H Mag., .375 RUM, .416 Rigby, .444 Marlin, .45/70 Govt., .458 Win. Mag., .458 Socom, .475 Turnbull

**Box 20**: . . . . . . . . . . $33.06–$241.39

### EXPEDITION HUNTER

**Features**: Available with modern DPX lead free X-panding bullet or the legendary Woodleigh bullet. Both field-tested and engineered specifically to take down thick skinned and dangerous game with deep penetration. All partnered with the outstanding reliability that you have come to trust from Cor-Bon Ammunition.

**Available in**: 7mm Rem. Mag., .375 Flanged, .375 H&H Mag., .416 Rem. Mag., .416 Rigby, .404 Jeffery, .458 Win. Mag., .458 Lott, .470 Nitro Express, .505 Gibbs, .577 Nitro Express

**Box 10**: . . . . . . . . . $59.49–$187.13

### GLASER SAFETY SLUG

**Features**: Although slug was originally designed for use by Sky Marshals on airplanes, today the slug is recommended for anyone concerned with over-penetration. The Safety slug uses a copper jacket and is filled with a compressed load of either #12 or #6 lead shot. It is then capped with a round polymer ball that enhances feeding and reloading.

**Available in**: .25 Auto, .32 Auto, .32 NAA, .380 Auto, 9mm Makarov, 9mm Luger +P, .38 Super Auto, .38 Spl. Std., .38 Special +P, .357 Sig, .357 Mag., .40 S&W, 10mm Auto, .400 Corbon, .44 S&W Spl., .44 Mag., .45 Auto +P, .45 Colt +P, .223 (5.56), 7.62x39, .308 Win., .30-06 Spfd.

**Box 6**: . . . . . . . . . . . . $13.39–$28.93

### HUNTER

**Features**: Bonded Core Soft Point ammunition retains optimum weight and integrity and provides reliable expansion coupled with deep penetration. The Penetrator features a heavy full-copper jacket enclosed in a hard linotype lead core. Hard Cast bullets are precision cast from hard linotype lead and have the flat, LBT nose design. Both loads cause a through and through hole, penetrating the thickest hides and breaking the heaviest bone.

**Available in**: .300 Whisper, 7.62x39, .357 Mag., 10mm Auto, .41 Rem. Mag., .44 Auto Mag., .44 Rem. Mag., .440 Corbon, .444 Marlin, .45 Colt +P, .45-70 Govt., .454 Casull, .460 Rowland, .460 S&W Mag., .475 Turnbull, .500 S&W Mag.

**Box 12 or 20**: . . . . . . $30.98–$101.12

## Handgun Ammunition

### DPX HANDGUN

**Features**: DPX is a solid copper hollowpoint bullet that combines the best of the lightweight high-speed JHPs and the heavyweight, deep-penetrating JHPs. The copper bullet construction allows it to conquer hard barriers like auto glass and steel while still maintaining its integrity.

**Available in**: .32 Auto, 9x23 Win., .380 Auto, 9mm Luger, 9mm Luger +P, .38 Super Auto +P, .38 Spl. +P, .357 Sig, .357 Mag., .40 S&W, 10mm Auto, .400 Corbon, .41 Rem. Mag., .44 S&W Special, .44 Rem. Mag., .45 GAP, .45 Auto Rim, .45 Auto, .45 Auto +P, .45 Colt +P, .454 Casull, .480 Ruger, .375 JDJ, .460 S&W Mag., .500 S&W Special, .500 S&W Mag.

**Box 20**: . . . . . . . . . . . . $28.46–$91.17

### GLASER POW'RBALL

**Features**: Designed for finicky feeding pistols, Pow'Rball is a great choice for your semiauto pistols or revolvers. Reliable feeding and consistent reliable expansion; deeper soft tissue penetration; custom scored jacket; proprietary polymer ball and patented lead core

**Available in**: .32 Auto, .380 Auto, 9mm Makarov, 9mm Luger +P, 9x23 Win., .38 Super +P, .38 Spl. +P, .357 Sig, .357 Mag, .40 S&W, 10mm Auto, .400 Corbon, .45 GAP, .45 Auto +P

**Box 20**: . . . . . . . . . . . $21.90–$29.22

**COR-BON
EXPEDITION
HUNTER**

# ENVIRON-Metal

## Shotgun Ammunition

### HEVI-METAL TURKEY
**Features**: HEVI-METAL Turkey is a layered load that combines premium steel shot with HEVI-Shot pellets. Timeless testing of various shot load methods found layering to provide the most pellets on target and the best knockdown performance.
*Available in*: 12 Ga. (3 in., 3 ½ in.), 20 Ga. (3 in.)
**Box 10:** . . . . . . . . . . . $8.99–$12.99

### HEVI-SHOT CLASSIC DOUBLES
**Features**: Optimized for your fixed chokes and fine classic doubles; denser than steel but soft like lead which means you get deeper penetration; USFWS-approved non-toxic shot; 45 percent more on target pellets than steel; belted sphere for maximum pellet mass; buffered and nano-treated pellets for tight patterns; weather-resistant crimp
*Available in*: 12 Ga. (2 ¾ in., 3 in.), 16 Ga. (2 ¾ in.), 20 Ga. (2 ¾ in., 3 in.),
.28 Ga. (2 ¾ in.), .410 Ga. (3 in.)
**Box 10:** . . . . . . . . . . . $30.99–$41.99

### HEVI-SHOT DEAD COYOTE!
**Features**: With these HEVI-Shot T-shot loads, you can be deadly at ranges you never thought possible with a 12 gauge. The 3-in. load pounds out 50 perfectly round pellets at 1,350 fps. 10 percent heavier than lead, 54 percent denser than steel. Every 50 rounds includes a dry-storage box.
*Available in*: 10 Ga. (3 ½ in.), 12 Ga. (2 ¾ in., 3 in., 3 ½ in.)
**Box 10:** . . . . . . . . . . . $49.49–$64.99

### HEVI-SHOT MAGNUM BLEND
**Features**: Put more lethal pellets in your pattern with a combination of No. 5, 6, and 7 HEVI-13 shot, and boost your lethal range by 14 to 17 percent. Buffered and moly-coated pellets produce a denser pattern than conventional shot. HEVI-13 delivers 40 percent more knockdown energy and up to 40 percent longer range than lead shells.
*Available in*: 10 Ga. (3 ½ in.), 12 Ga. (3 in., 3 ½ in.), 20 Ga. (3 in.)
**Box 5:** . . . . . . . . . . . $26.99–$29.99

### SPEED BALL
**Features**: Speed Ball is an elastomeric ball in the base of the wad that accelerates pellets without boosting chamber pressures. An MV² pellet sits in the base of the shell with a HEVI-Shot layer on top, resulting in higher pellet counts in the 30-inch circle than you get with HEVI-Shot. Nearly matches the lethal energy of HEVI-Shot, out to 60 yards (but far exceeds the energy of anything else).
*Available in*: 12 Ga. (3 in., 3 ½ in.) 20 Ga. (3 in.); Shot sizes: BB, 1, 3, 5
**Box 10:** . . . . . . . . . . . $8.99–$14.99

**ENVIRON-METAL SPEED BALL**

**ENVIRON-METAL HEVI-SHOT DEAD COYOTE!**

**ENVIRON-METAL HEVI-METAL TURKEY**

# Federal Fusion Ammunition

## FUSION RIFLE AMMO

**Features**: This specialized deer bullet electrochemically joins pure copper to an extreme pressure-formed core to ensure optimum performance. The result is high terminal energy on impact that radiates lethal shock throughout the target. This energy is optimized through mass weight retention, a top secretive tip-skiving process and superior bullet integrity.
**Available in**: .223 Rem., .22-250 Rem., .243 Win., .25-06 Rem., 6.5x55 Swedish, .260 Rem., .270 Win., .270 WSM, 7mm-08 Rem., .280 Rem., 7mm Rem. Mag., 7mm WSM, 7.62x39mm Soviet, .30-30 Win., .308 Win., .30-06 Spfd., .300 Win. Mag., .300 WSM, .338 Fed., .338 Win. Mag., .35 Whelen, .375 H&H Mag., .416 Rigby, .416 Rem. Mag., .45-70 Govt., .458 Win. Mag., .458 Lott
**Box 20**: . . . . . . . . . . . **$18.99–$89.99**

## FUSION SAFARI

**Features**: Fusion's advanced molecular technique of electro-chemically applying the jacket to the core means consistent toughness. With enhanced aerodynamics, internal skiving, and superb accuracy, these bullets provide great performance on a variety of safari animals. Fusion Safari bullets offer high weight retention to ensure deep penetration.
**Available in**: .375 H&H, .416 Rigby, .416 Rem. Mag., .458 Win. Mag., .458 Lott
**Box 20**: . . . . . . . . . . . **$59.99–$98.95**

## FUSION SHOTGUN SLUGS

**Features**: Fusion slugs have made shotgunners part of the next generation of deer hunters. Slug hunters can now find the same unequaled energy and deer devastation in their favorite rifled-barrel shotgun.

**Available in**: 12, 20 Ga. (2 ¾ in., 3 in.)
**Box 5**: . . . . . . . . . . . . . **$8.19–$24.99**

**FEDERAL FUSION RIFLE AMMO**

# Federal Premium Ammunition

## Rifle Ammunition

### FULL METAL JACKET BOAT-TAIL

**Features**: Accurate, non-expanding bullets. Flat shooting trajectory, leaves small exit holes in game, and put clean holes in paper. Smooth, reliable feeding into semiautomatics too
**Available in**: .223 Rem., .308 Win., .30-06 Spfd. (American Eagle)
**Box 20**: . . . . . . . . . . . . **$9.09–$23.49**

### NOSLER PARTITION

**Features**: Bullet features a partitioned lead core and shank that allows the front half to mushroom while the rear core remains intact for deep penetration and stopping power.
**Available in**: .223 Rem., 22-250 Rem., .243 Win., 6mm Rem., 257 Roberts +P, 25-06 Rem., .270 Win., .270 WSM, 7mm Mauser, 7mm-08 Rem., .280 Rem., 7mm Rem. Mag., 30-30 Win., .308 Win., 30-06 Spfd., 300 H&H Mag.
**Box 20**: . . . . . . . . . . . **$24.99–$57.99**

### SIERRA MATCHKING BOAT-TAIL HP

**Features**: Long ranges are its specialty. Excellent choice for everything from varmints to big game animals. Tapered, boattail design provides extremely flat trajectories. Higher downrange velocity for more energy at the point of impact. Reduced wind drift
**Available in**: .223 Rem., 6.5x55 Swedish, .260 Rem., .308 Win., 30-06 Spfd., .300 Win. Mag., .338 Lapua Mag.
**Box 20**: . . . . . . . . . . **$31.49–$112.99**

### SOFT POINT

**Features**: Proven performer on small game and thin-skinned medium game. Aerodynamic tip for a flat trajectory. Exposed soft point expands rapidly for hard hits, even as velocity slows at longer ranges.
**Available in**: .22 Hornet (V-Shok), .222 Rem., .223 Rem., .22-250 Rem., .243 Win., 6mm Rem., 6.5x55 Swedish, .270 Win., .270 WSM, .280 Rem., 7mm Rem. Mag., 7mm WSM, 7.62x39 Soviet, .300 Savage, .308 Win., .30-06 Spfd., .300 WSM, .303 British, 8mm Mauser, .338 Fed. (Power-Shok, American Eagle), .375 H&H Mag. (Power-Shok)
**Box 20**: . . . . . . . . . . . **$18.99–$51.99**

### SOFT POINT FLAT NOSE

**Features**: Great for thick cover, it expands reliably and penetrates deep on light to medium game. The flat nose prevents accidental discharge.
**Available in**: .30-30 Win., .32 Win. Spl.
**Box 20**: . . . . . . . . . . . **$15.99–$27.49**

### SOFT POINT ROUND NOSE

**Features**: The choice in heavy cover. Large exposed tip, good weight retention and specially tapered jacket provide controlled expansion.
**Available in**: .270 Win., 7mm Mauser, .30 Carbine, .30-30 Win., .35 Rem.
**Box 20**: . . . . . . . . . . . **$15.99–$30.99**

### SPEER TNT GREEN

**Features**: TNT Green brings non-tox technology to the Federal Premium V-Shok varmint hunting line. This is a totally lead-free bullet that couples explosive expansion with match-grade accuracy.
**Available in**: .22 Hornet, .222 Rem., .223 Rem., .22-250 Rem.
**Box 20**: . . . . . . . . . . . **$21.99–$25.99**

### TROPHY BONDED BEAR CLAW

**Features**: Ideal for medium to large dangerous game. The jacket and core are 100% fusion-bonded for reliable bullet expansion from 25 yards to extreme ranges. Bullet retains 95 percent of its weight for deep

# Federal Premium Ammunition

**FEDERAL PREMIUM GUARD DOG HOME DEFENSE**

penetration. Hard solid copper base tapering to a soft, copper nose section for controlled expansion
*Available in*: 7mm Rem. Mag., .30-06 Spfd., .300 Win. Mag., .388 Win. Mag., .35 Whelen (Vital-Shok), .375 H&H Mag., .416 Rigby, .416 Rem. Mag. (Cape-Shok), .45-70 Govt. (Vital-Shok), .458 Win. Mag., .458 Lott, .470 Nitro Express (Cape-Shok)
**Box 20:** . . . . . . . . . . **$33.99–$199.99**

## TROPHY BONDED SLEDGEHAMMER

*Features*: Use it on the largest, most dangerous game in the world. Jack Carter design maximizes stopping power. Bonded bronze solid with a flat nose that minimizes deflection off bone and muscle for a deep straight wound channel.
*Available in*: .375 H&H Mag., .416 Rigby, .416 Rem. Mag., .458 Win. Mag., .458 Lott, .470 Nitro Express (Cape-Shok)
**Box 20:** . . . . . . . . . . **$91.99–$213.99**

## TROPHY BONDED TIP

*Features*: Built on the Trophy Bonded Bear Claw platform to provide deep penetration and high weight retention. Sleek profile, with tapered heel and translucent polymer tip. Nickel-plated. Available as component and in Federal loaded ammunition
*Available in*: .270 Win., .270 WSM, .270 Wby. Mag., 7mm-08 Rem., .280 Rem., 7mm Rem. Mag., 7mm WSM, 7mm Wby. Mag., 7mm STW, .308 Win., .30-06 Spfd., .300 H&H Mag., .300 Win. Mag., .300 WSM, .300 Wby. Mag., .300 Rem. Ultra Mag., .338 Federal, .338 Win. Mag.
**Box 20:** . . . . . . . . . . **$32.99–$59.99**

## VITAL-SHOK TROPHY COPPER

*Features*: Tipped bullet cavity for consistent expansion across a broad range of velocities; grooved bullet shank for increased accuracy across a wider range of firearms; a copper-alloy design that achieves up to 99 percent weight retention; nickel-plated case prevents corrosion and aids in easier, faster extraction from the chamber
*Available in*: .243 Win., .25-06 Rem., .270 Win., .270 WSM, 7mm-08 Rem., .280 Rem., 7mm Rem. Mag., 7mm WSM, .308 Win., .30-06 Spfd., .300 H&H, .300 Win. Mag., .300 WSM, .300 Wby. Mag., .300 Rem. Ultra Mag., .338 Fed., .338 Win. Mag.
**Box 20:** . . . . . . . . . . **$26.99–$56.99**

# Handgun Ammunition

## CASTCORE

*Features*: Heavyweight, flat-nosed, hard cast-lead bullet that smashes through bone
*Available in*: .375 Mag., .41 Rem. Mag., .44 Rem. Mag. (Vital-Shok)
**Box 20:** . . . . . . . . . . **$23.99–$33.99**

## FULL METAL JACKET

*Features*: Good choice for range practice and reducing lead fouling in the barrel. Jacket extends from the nose to the base, preventing bullet expansion and barrel leading. Primarily as military ammunition for recreational shooting.
*Available in*: .25 Auto, .32 Auto, .380 Auto, 9mm Makarov, 9mm Luger, .38 Super +P, .357 Sig, .38 Spl., .40 S&W, 10mm Auto, .45 G.A.P., .45 Auto (American Eagle)
**Box 50:** . . . . . . . . . . **$13.99–$35.99**

**FEDERAL PREMIUM TROPHY BONDED TIP**

## GUARD DOG HOME DEFENSE

*Features*: Protect your home and loved ones with a cartridge designed exclusively for home defense. Guard Dog packs the terminal performance that stops threats while reducing over-penetration through walls.
*Available in*: 9mm Luger, .40 S&W, .45 Auto
**Box 20:** . . . . . . . . . . **$22.99–$26.99**

## HYDRA-SHOK JHP

*Features*: Unique center-post design delivers controlled expansion, and the notched jacket provides efficient energy transfer to penetrate barriers while retaining stopping power. Deep penetration satisfies even the FBI's stringent testing requirements.
*Available in*: .32 Auto, .327 Fed. Mag., .380 Auto, 9mm Luger, .38 Spl., .38 Spl. +P, .357 Mag., .40 S&W, 10mm Auto, .44 Rem. Mag., .45 G.A.P., .45 Auto (Premium Personal Defense)
**Box 20:** . . . . . . . . . . **$20.49–$32.99**

## JACKETED HOLLOW POINT

*Features*: Ideal personal defense round in revolvers and semi-autos. Quick, positive expansion. Jacket ensures smooth feeding into autoloading firearms.
*Available in*: .32 H&R Mag., 9mm Luger (Personal Defense), .38 Super +P (American Eagle), .357 Sig., .357 Mag. (Premium Personal Defense, Power-Shok), .40 S&W (Personal Defense), .41 Rem. Mag., .44 Rem. Mag. (Power-Shok, American Eagle), .45 Auto (Personal Defense)
**Box 20:** . . . . . . . . . . **$18.49-29.99**

## LEAD ROUND NOSE

*Features*: Great training round for practicing at the range. 100 percent lead with no jacket. Excellent accuracy and very economical
*Available in*: .32 S&W Long (Champion), .38 Special (American Eagle)
**MSRP** . . . . . . . . . . . **$14.99–$20.99**

# Federal Premium Ammunition

## LEAD SEMI-WADCUTTER

**Features**: Most popular all-around choice for target and personal defense, a versatile design that cuts clean holes in targets and efficiently transfers energy
**Available in**: .32 H&R Mag. (Champion)
**MSRP**. . . . . . . . . . . . . . . . . **$16.49**

## NYCLAD HP

**Features**: Proven NyClad bullets feature a lead core hollow-point with Nylon coating. Offers great stopping power and penetration—ideal qualities for a personal defense round.
**Available in**: .38 Special-125 gr.
**Box 20:**. . . . . . . . . . . **$16.99–$21.99**

## PREMIUM PERSONAL DEFENSE SHOT SHELLS

**Features**: The Judge from Taurus has emerged as a very popular handgun for Personal Defense. This specialized gun has been without a specialized load—until now.
**Available in**: .410 bore (2 ½ in.); Shot sizes: 000 Buck, 4
**Box 20:**. . . . . . . . . . . . . . . . .**$12.99**

## SEMI-WADCUTTER HP

**Features**: For both small game and personal defense. Hollow point design promotes uniform expansion.
**Available in**: .44 Special, .45 Colt (Champion)
**MSRP**. . . . . . . . . . . **$20.99–$24.99**

## Shotgun Ammunition

### BLACK CLOUD FS STEEL

**Available in**: 10 Ga. (3 ½ in.), 12 Ga. (2 ¾ in., 3 in., 3 ½ in.) 20 Ga. (3 in.); Shot sizes: 2, 3, 4, BB, BBB
**Box 25:**. . . . . . . . . . . **$15.99–$27.49**

### BLACK CLOUD FS STEEL CLOSE RANGE

**Features**: Engineered to put more pellets on targets 20 to 30 yards away, Close Range achieves a full pattern within a very short distance; comprised of 100 percent Flitestopper Steel for the most lethal payload imaginable, Close Range produces more open and optimum patterns; crimp and primer sealed
**Available in**: 12 Ga., 20 Ga. (3 in.)
**Box 25:**. . . . . . . . . . . **$18.99–$20.49**

### BLACK CLOUD HIGH VELOCITY

**Features**: The Black Cloud High Velocity line pumps up the speed and lethal performance for waterfowl hunters everywhere. Boasting higher velocities, increased energy and shorter lead times, the High velocity offerings bring a renewed sense of excitement to the duck blind.
**Available in**: 12 Ga. (3 in.); Shot Sizes: 3, 4
**Box 25:**. . . . . . . . . . . . . . . . .**$20.49**

### GAME-SHOK UPLAND GAME

**Available in**: 12, 16, 20 Ga. (2 ¾ in.); Shot sizes: 6, 8, 7.5
**Box 25:**. . . . . . . . . . . . .**$6.69–$11.99**

FEDERAL PREMIUM BLACK CLOUD FS STEEL

FEDERAL BLACK CLOUD FS STEEL CLOSE RANGE

### GAME-SHOK UPLAND GAME HEAVY FIELD

**Available in**: 12, 20 Ga. (2 ¾ in.); Shot sizes: 4, 5, 6, 7.5
**Box 25:**. . . . . . . . . . . . .**$7.29–$11.49**

### GAME-SHOK UPLAND GAME HI-BRASS

**Available in**: 12, 16, 20 Ga. (2 ¾ in.), .410 bore (2 ½ in., 3 in.); Shot sizes: 4, 5, 6, 7.5
**Box 25:**. . . . . . . . . . . . .**$14.49–$16.79**

FEDERAL PREMIUM NYCLAD HP

# Federal Premium Ammunition

## GOLD MEDAL EXTRA-LITE PAPER (LR)
*Features*: Also available in plastic
*Available in*: 12 Ga. (2 ¾ in.); Shot sizes: 7.5, 8
**Box 25:** . . . . . . . . . . . . **$8.49–$9.99**

## GOLD MEDAL-HANDICAP PAPER HV
*Features*: Also available in plastic
*Available in*: 12 Ga. (2 ¾ in.); Shot sizes: 7.5, 8
**Box 25:** . . . . . . . . . . . . **$8.49–$10.99**

## GOLD MEDAL-INTERNATIONAL PAPER
*Features*: Also available in plastic (with Shot sizes: 7.5, 8)
*Available in*: 12 Ga. (2 ¾ in.); Shot sizes: 7.5
**Box 25:** . . . . . . . . . . . . **$8.99–$10.99**

## GOLD MEDAL-PLASTIC
*Features*: Also available in paper (12 Ga., 2 ¾ in., Shot sizes: 7.5, 8, 9)
*Available in*: 12, 20, 28 Ga. (2 ¾ in.), .410 bore (2 ½ in.); Shot sizes: 7.5, 8, 8.5, 9
**Box 25:** . . . . . . . . . . . . **$7.99–$10.99**

## GOLD MEDAL-SPORTING CLAYS PLASTIC
*Available in*: 12 Ga. (2 ¾ in.); Shot sizes: 7.5, 8, 8.5
**Box 25:** . . . . . . . . . . . . **$8.49–$10.99**

## MAG-SHOK HEAVYWEIGHT TURKEY
*Available in*: 10 Ga. (3 ½ in.), 12 Ga. (2 ¾ in., 3 in., 3 ½ in.), 20 Ga. (2 ¾ in., 3 in.); Shot sizes: 5, 6, 7
**Box 5:** . . . . . . . . . . . . **$14.99–$27.99**

## MAG-SHOK HIGH VELOCITY LEAD WITH FLITECONTROL
*Available in*: 10 Ga. (3 ½ in.), 12 Ga. (2 ¾ in., 3 in., 3 ½ in.) 20 Ga. (3 in.); Shot sizes: 4, 5, 6
**Box 10:** . . . . . . . . . . . **$11.99–$16.99**

## MAG-SHOK LEAD WITH FLITECONTROL
*Available in*: 12 Ga. (3 in., 3 ½ in.); Shot sizes: 4, 5, 6
**Box 10:** . . . . . . . . . . . **$16.99–$19.99**

## PRAIRIE STORM - FS STEEL
*Available in*: 12, 20 Ga. (3 in.); Shot sizes: 3, 4
**Box 25:** . . . . . . . . . . . **$18.29–$20.49**

## SPEED-SHOK WATERFOWL
*Available in*: 10 Ga. (3 ½ in.), 12 Ga. (2 ¾ in., 3 in., 3 ½ in.), 16 Ga. (2 ¾ in.), 20 Ga. (2 ¾ in., 3 in.); Shot sizes: 1, 2, 3, 4, 6, 7, BB, BBB, T
**Box 25:** . . . . . . . . . . . **$7.79–$24.49**

## STRUT-SHOK TURKEY
*Available in*: 12 Ga. (3 in., 3 ½ in.); Shot sizes: 4, 5, 6
**Box 10:** . . . . . . . . . . . **$9.29–$14.49**

## TOP GUN TARGET
*Available in*: 12 Ga., 20 Ga. (2 ¾ in.); Shot sizes: 7.5, 8, 9
**Box 25:** . . . . . . . . . . . **$6.59–$7.69**

## TOP GUN TARGET-STEEL
*Available in*: 12 Ga., 20 Ga. (2 ¾ in.); Shot size: 7
**Box 25:** . . . . . . . . . . . **$7.99–$9.99**

## TOP GUN TARGET-SUBSONIC
*Available in*: 12 Ga. (2 ¾ in.); Shot size: 7.5
**Box 25:** . . . . . . . . . . . **$7.69–$8.99**

## V-SHOK HEAVYWEIGHT COYOTE
*Available in*: 12 Ga. (3 in.); Shot size: BB
**Box 5:** . . . . . . . . . . . **$19.99–$23.99**

## WING-SHOK HIGH VELOCITY
*Features*: Pheasant and Quail Forever versions available
*Available in*: 12 Ga. (2 ¾ in., 3 in.), 28 Ga. (2 ¾ in.); Shot sizes: 4, 5, 6, 7, 7.5, 8
**Box 25:** . . . . . . . . . . . **$15.29–$24.99**

## WING-SHOK MAGNUM
*Available in*: 10 Ga. (3 ½ in.), 12 Ga. (2 ¾ in., 3 in.), 16 Ga. (2 ¾ in.), 20 Ga. (2 ¾ in., 3 in.); Shot sizes: 2, 4, 5, 6, BB
**Box 25:** . . . . . . . . . . . **$24.99-54.99**

# Shotgun Ammunition Slugs

## POWER-SHOK RIFLED SLUG
*Features*: Hollow point slug type
*Available in*: 10 Ga. (3 ½ in.), 12 Ga. (2 ¾ in., 3 in.), 16 Ga. (2 ¾ in.), 20 Ga. (2 ¾ in.), .410 (2 ½ in.)
**Box 5:** . . . . . . . . . . . . **$4.39–$6.19**

## POWER-SHOK SABOT
*Features*: Sabot hollow point slug type
*Available in*: 12 Ga., 20 Ga. (2 ¾ in.)
**Box 5:** . . . . . . . . . . . . **$6.69–$8.49**

FEDERAL PREMIUM PRAIRIE STORM - FS STEEL

# Federal Premium Ammunition

### VITAL-SHOK TROPHY COPPER SABOT SLUG

**Features**: A copper slug that incorporates some of the most advanced technology in the industry; better accuracy, less drop, manageable recoil (similar to a .30-06) and consistent penetration and expansion; unique two-part sabot design achieves accuracy through a clean launch and improved projectile support
**Available in**: 12 Ga., 20 Ga. (2 ¾ in., 3 in.)
**Box 5:** . . . . . . . . . . . $10.99–$12.99

### VITAL-SHOK TRUBALL RIFLED SLUG

**Available in**: 12, 20 Ga. (2 ¾ in., 3 in.)
**Box 5:** . . . . . . . . . . . . . . $4.49–$5.99

**FEDERAL PREMIUM VITAL-SHOK TRUBALL RIFLED SLUG**

# Fiocchi USA

## Rifle Ammunition

### CANNED HEAT CENTERFIRE RIFLE AMMO

**Features**: One of the most innovative and effective ways to store ammunition long term. Canned Heat ammo is packed in an oxygen-free nitrogen gas atmosphere to prevent rust and deterioration over time. The cans have an enamel coating inside and out to insulate against electrolysis and prevent corrosion. They stack and store easily, come with resealable plastic lids, and hold up better over time than conventional cardboard packaging.
**Available in**: .223 Rem., .308 Win., 9x19 Luger, .40 S&W, .45 Auto, .22LR,
**From:** . . . . . . . . . . . . . $8.42–$36.13

### EXTREMA RIFLE HUNTING LINE

**Features**: Combining the best bullets in the business with our precision-drawn brass cases gives you the best combination of value and performance. The Fiocchi Extrema Hunting Line uses bullets like the Hornady SST, V Max, and Sierra Game King to provide a combination of accuracy, high ballistic coefficients, and reliable expansion.
**Available in**: .222 Rem., .204 Ruger, .223 Rem., .22-50 Rem., .243 Win., 6.5x55 Swedish, .270 Win., .308 Win., .30-06 Spfd., .300 Win. Mag.
**From:** . . . . . . . . . . . . $22.49–$34.99

### SHOOTING DYNAMICS RIFLE LINE

**Features**: High-quality reloadable brass cases combined with quality full metal jacket, soft point, or flat soft point (for lever guns) make sure your shooting dollar goes further with Fiocchi. Even our 7.62x39 ammo uses reloadable

**FIOCCHI CANNED HEAT CENTERFIRE RIFLE AMMO**

brass cases, boxer primed (non-corrosive) with copper-jacketed bullets.
**Available in**: .223 Rem., .22-250 Rem., .243 Win., .270 Win., .30-30 Win., .308 Win., .30-06 Spfd., .300 Win. Mag., 7.62x39
**From:** . . . . . . . . . . . . $10.79–$32.99

## Handgun Ammunition

### COWBOY ACTION LINE

**Features**: Loaded with brass reloadable cases, noncorrosive primers, smokeless powders, and lead bullets coated with lube to reduce leading in the barrel. Fiocchi sets the velocity on par with what you would expect from period-correct ammo while keeping the recoil to a minimum for timed Cowboy Action competition and to reduce wear and tear on older guns.
**Available in**: .32 S&W Long, .38 S&W Short, .38 S&W Special, .357 Mag., .44 Special, .44-40, .45 Long Colt
**From:** . . . . . . . . . . . . $19.99–$34.99

**FIOCCHI SHOOTING DYNAMICS PISTOL LINE**

# Fiocchi USA

**FIOCCHI GOLDEN PHEASANT SHOT SHELLS**

**FIOCCHI TUNDRA COMPOSITE**

## EXTREMA XTP HANDGUN LINE

**Features**: Combined with nickel-plated cases for positive feeding and extraction when you need it most, qualified primers and clean powders deliver the maximum performance for the ultimate hunting or self-defense application.
**Available in**: .25 Auto, .32 Auto, .380 Auto, 9mm Luger, .38 Spl., .38 Spl.+P, .357 Mag., .40 S&W, .44 Rem. Mag., .45 Auto,
**From**: . . . . . . . . . . . . **$14.99–$24.99**

## SHOOTING DYNAMICS PISTOL & REVOLVER LINE

**Features**: Combining quality brass cases with consistent primers, clean powders, and full metal jacket, jacketed hollow point, and soft point bullets in many calibers, Fiocchi loads bullets of the same weight to velocities that are comparable with high-quality defensive loads so you get realistic training-recoil impulse and point of aim/impact.
**Available in**: .25 Auto, .32 Auto, .32 S&W Long, .380 Auto, 9mm Luger, 9mm Makarov, 9mm Steyr, 9x21 IMI, .38 Spl., .357 Mag., .38 Super Auto, .40 S&W, .44 Rem. Mag., .44 Spl., .45 Auto
**From**: . . . . . . . . . . . . **$12.99–$34.99**

## Shotgun Ammunition

### CYALUME CHEMICAL TRACER SHOTSHELL

**Features**: The Fiocchi Chemical Tracer powered by Cyalume, provides a daytime visible trace that travels with the cloud of shot as it hits or misses the clay bird. The Chemical Tracer is non-incendiary, non-toxic, and meets EPA and Consumer Safety compliance. It leaves no residue in the barrel and is non-corrosive.
**Available in**: 12 Ga. (2 ¾ in.), Shot size: 8
**From**: . . . . . . . . . . . **$16.45–$44.00**

### EXACTA TARGET LOADS

**Features**: Specifically for competitive shooters. The Target Load Line is the offspring of a 50-year tradition of supporting the world of trap, skeet, and now sporting clays, FITASC, and Compaq.
**Available in**: Steel: 12 Ga., 20 Ga. (2 ¾ in.), Shot size: 7; Helios: 12 Ga. (2 ¾ in.), Shot sizes: 7, 7.5
**From**: . . . . . . . . . . . . . . **$7.99–$8.49**

### GOLDEN PHEASANT LINE

**Features**: Golden Pheasant shot shells utilize a special hard, nickel-plated lead shot, based on Fiocchi's strict ballistic tolerances that ensure proven shot consistency and result in deeper penetration, longer ranges, and much tighter patterns.
**Available in**: 12 Ga. (2 ¾ in., 3 in.), 16 Ga. (2 ¾ in.), 20, 28 Ga. (2 ¾ in., 3 in.); Shot sizes: 4, 5, 6, 7.5
**From**: . . . . . . . . . . . . **$13.99–$18.99**

### GOLDEN TURKEY LINE

**Features**: Copper then nickel-plated shot offers the penetration and patterns you need when you need a turkey for dinner.
**Available in**: 12 Ga. (3 in., 3 ½ in.); Shot sizes: 4, 5, 6
**MSRP** . . . . . . . . . . . . . . . . . . . **N/A**

### NICKEL PLATED BUCKSHOT

**Features**: Harder pellets from the nickel plating mean better patterns, better penetration, and no buffer needed.
**Available in**: 12 Ga. (2 ¾ in.); Shot sizes: 00, 4
**From**: . . . . . . . . . . . . . **$5.00–$11.99**

### OPTIMA SPECIFIC HIGH VELOCITY

**Features**: High brass hulls, one-piece shot cup and cushioned wads, and round shot pellets make sure you get the bang for your buck you have come to expect from Fiocchi.
**Available in**: 12 Ga. (2 ¾ in., 3 in.), 16 Ga. (2 ¾ in.), 20 Ga. (2 ¾ in., 3 in.), 28 Ga. (2 ¾ in., 3 in.), .410 (3 in.); Shot sizes: 4, 5, 6, 7.5, 8, 9
**From**: . . . . . . . . . . . . . **$11.79–$13.46**

### TUNDRA COMPOSITE

**Features**: It's heavier than bismuth for dead-on-delivery performance. Spherical, non-brittle Tundra compound deforms on impact, just like lead. Use with any choke, even full.
**Available in**: 12 Ga. (2 ¾ in., 3 in.), 20, 28 Ga. (3 in.); Shot size 1, 2, 3, 4, 5, 6, BB
**Box 10**: . . . . . . . . . . . **$21.99–$25.49**

### WATERFOWL STEEL HUNTING

**Features**: Treated steel pellets, the correct wad, and powders that perform in the cold conditions often encountered in waterfowl hunting deliver the kills a waterfowl hunter wants.
**Available in**: 12 Ga. (2 ¾ in., 3 in.), 20 Ga. (3 in.); Shot sizes: T, BBB, BB, 1, 2, 3, 4, 5, 6
**From**: . . . . . . . . . . . . . . **$8.85–$15.31**

# Hornady

**HORNADY CRITICAL DUTY**

**HORNADY DANGEROUS GAME**

## Rifle Ammunition

### CUSTOMLITE

**Features**: CustomLite ammunition is recommended for children, women, and anyone new to the game. They offer minimum recoil and a reduced muzzle blast. These are often paired with SST and RN bullets.

**Available in**: .243 Win, .270 Win., 7mm-08 Rem., .30-.30 Win., .308 Win., .30-06 Spfd.

**From:** . . . . . . . . . . . . **$25.99–$27.99**

### DANGEROUS GAME

**Features**: These bullets are among the largest offered by Hornady and feature the DGS (Dangerous Game Solid) and the DGX (Dangerous Game eXpanding). They're made with hard lead/antimony alloy cone and surrounded by a copper-clad steel jacket. Straighter penetration comes from a flat meplat that creates more energy than traditional round bullets.

**Available in**: 9.3X62, 9.3X74R, .376 Steyr., .375 H&H, .375 Ruger, .450-400 Nitro Express, .404 Jeffrey, .416 Rem. Mag., .416 Ruger, .416 Rigby, .458 Win., .450 Nitro Express, .458 Lott, .470 Nitro Express, .500 Nitro Express

**From:** . . . . . . . . . . . . **$38.49–$130.99**

### LEVEREVOLUTION

**Features**: LEVERevolution bullets travel at a speed of 250 fps and have a faster muzzle velocity than most other conventional lever gun loads. They are unbelievably accurate and offer incomparable terminal performance. These bullets are available in FTX and MonoFlex.

**Available in**: .30-.30 Win., .308 Marlin Express, .32 Win. Spl., .338 Marlin Express, .35 Rem., .357 Mag., .44 Mag., .444 Marlin, .45-70 Govt., .450 Marlin

**From:** . . . . . . . . . . . . **$24.49–$38.99**

### MATCH

**Features**: Match bullets feature a boattail hollow point design that provides both accuracy and speed. These bullets' jackets feature near-zero wall thickness, which leads to uniformity throughout the jacket. Case weight and internal capacity are also consistent throughout Match ammunition.

**Available in**: .223 Rem., 6.5 Grendel, 6.5 Creedmoor, .308 Win., .30-06 Springfield, .300 Win. Mag., .338 Lapua, .50 BMG

**From:** . . . . . . . . . . . . **$17.99–$84.99**

### SUPERFORMANCE

**Features**: Superformance bullets are 100 to 200 fps faster than any other traditional type of bullet on the market today. In addition to their speed, they also offer minimal recoil, muzzle blast, temperature sensativity, and inaccuracies. These bullets are versatile and can be paired with all types of firearms, including semi-autos, lever guns, and pump actions.

**Available in**: .223 Rem., .243 Win., .25-06 Rem., .257 Roberts+P, .270 Win., .280 Rem., .30 TC, .30-06 Spfd., .300 RCM., .300 Savage, .300 Win. Mag., .308 Win., .338 RCM, .338 Win. Mag., .35 Whelen, .375 H&H, .375 Ruger, .444 Marlin, .458 Win., 5.56 NATO, 6.5 Creedmoor, 6.5X5.5 Swedish Mauser, 6mm. Rem., 7mm Rem. Mag., 7mm-08 Rem., 7x57 Mauser

**MSRP** . . . . . . . . . . . **$30.27–$118.79**

## Handgun Ammunition

### COWBOY ACTION SHOOTING

**Features**: These swaged bullets flatten instead of fragment when they reach their targets. Their diamond knurling ensures that the entire surface of the bullet is well-lubed.

**Available in**: .44-40, .45 Colt

**Box 20:** . . . . . . . . . . . **$21.93–$24.97**

### CRITICAL DEFENSE

**Features**: Critical Defense bullets are custom-designed for individual loads, and their shiny silver nickel plating prevents bullet corrosion. Heavy clothing such as denim and leather are no match for these bullets. Critical Defense ammunication is cannelured and crimped to avoid bullet setback, and clean burning and stable propellants reduce recoil.

**Available in**: .410, .22 WMR, 32 NAA, 32 H&R Mag., 9x18mm, .380 Auto, 9mm Luger, .38 Spl., .357 Sig., .357 Mag., 40 S&W, 10mm Auto, .44 Special, .44 Mag., .45 Auto, .45 Colt

**From:** . . . . . . . . . . . . **$16.65–$30.35**

# Hornady

## CRITICAL DUTY

**Features**: Critical Duty ammunition features FlexLock Bullets, crimped and nickel-plated cases, interlocking bands, and a core made of high-antimony lead. These bullets are among the top choices of law enforcement and military professionals and highly reliable.
**Available in**: 45 Auto +P, 9mm, 9mm Luger+P, .40 S&W
**Box 20–25:** . . . . . . . . . . . . . .$28.75

## LEVEREVOLUTION

**Features**: LEVERevolution bullets travel at a speed of 250 fps and are unbelievably accurate. These bullets feature Flex Tip Technology and should not be stored for long periods of time, as the tips may become deformed. They deliver 40 percent more energy than traditional bullets.
**Available in**: .357 Mag, .44 Mag, .45 Colt
**From:** . . . . . . . . . . . .$26.05–$28.51

## TAP FPD

**Features**: Police officers, snipers, and military professionals across the world choose TAP FPD ammunition due to reliability and accuracy of these bullets. Silver-nickel cases prevent corrosion and the minimal muzzle flash protects night vision.

**Available in**: .380 Auto, 9mm Luger, 40 S&W, .45 Auto+P
**Box 20–25** . . . . . . . . .$23.17–$29.47

## Shotgun Ammunition

### BUCKSHOT

**Features**: Buckshot ammunition is specially designed for unmodified semiauto and pump shotguns. Made with Versatite wad technology, these reliable bullets offer a tight, accurate shot.
**Available in**: 12 Ga. (2 ¾ in.)
**Box 10:** . . . . . . . . . . .$15.52–$17.08

### HEAVY MAGNUM TURKEY

**Features**: Each 3-inch, 12-gauge shotshell contains 1½ ounces of either #4, #5, or #6 nickel-plated lead. Loads don't require modified shotguns or specialized turkey chokes.
**Available in**: 12 Ga. (3 in.); Shot sizes: 4, 5, 6 nickel
**Box 10:** . . . . . . . . . . . . . . . . .$17.81

### SST SLUGS

**Features**: Sharp points at the end of these slugs allow for faster and more accurate shooting. You'll be able to reach your target from an impressive 200 yards away. Each shot delivers more than 1200 ft.-lbs. of energy. Also available in Superperformance (SPF) Slugs.

**Available in**: 12, 20 Ga. (2 ¾ in)
**Box 5:** . . . . . . . . . . . . .$15.87–$19.81

## Rimfire Ammunition

### 17 HMR

**Features**: The 17 HMR is one of the most accurate rimfire bullets ever made. The polymer tip fragments rapidly and dramatically on impact, and its flat trajectory adds to its accuracy and consistency.
**Available in**: .17 HMR
**Box 50:** . . . . . . . . . . . .$17.04–$17.87

### 17 MACH2

**Features**: These V-MAX bullets are known for their rapid fragmentation and consistent accuracy. These bullets are made in America and hand inspected. Paired with Varmint Express products, ignition is fast and easy.
**Available in**: .17 Mach2
**Box 50:** . . . . . . . . . . . . .$9.91–$11.65

### 22 WMR

**Features**: The .22 WMR guarantees accurate shooting from more than 125 feet. It has a muzzle of 2,200 fps and is one of the most requested products Hornady offers. It's available in 25, 30, and 45 gr.
**Available in**: .22 WMR
**Box 50:** . . . . . . . . . . . .$15.77–$17.53

**HORNADY 17 HMR**

**HORNADY SST SLUGS**

AMMUNITION

# Jarrett Rifles

## TROPHY AMMUNITION

**Features**: Jarrett's high-performance cartridges are in 10-round boxes. The cases are from Norma with Jarrett's headstamp

**Available in**: .243 Win., .270 Win., 7mm Rem. Mag., .30-06 Spfd., .300 WM, .300 Jarrett, .375 H&H, .416 Rem. Mag.

**MSRP** . . . . . . . . . . . **$26.68–$76.05**

JARRETT TROPHY AMMUNITION

# Kynoch Ammunition

KYNOCH RIFLE AMMUNITION

## RIFLE AMMUNITION

**Features**: Kynoch hunting ammunition is now standardized on Woodleigh soft nosed and solid bullets, recognized world wide as the most reliable big game bullets currently manufactured. Kynamco offers virtually the whole range of classic British Nitro Express from its purpose-built factory.

**Available in**: .300 Flanged, .303 British, .318 Westley Richards, 9.5x57 Mannlicher, .333 Jeffery Flanged, .350 Rigby, .400/.360 Westley Richards, .375 Flanged, .400 Purdey, .405 Win., .450/.400, .416 Rigby, .404 Jeffery, .425 Westley Richards, .450 NE, .450 No. 2 NE, .450 Rigby, .577/.450 Martini Henry, .500/.450 NE, .500/.465 NE, .470 NE, .475 No. 2 Eley, .475 No. 2 Jeffery, .476 Westley Richards, .505 Gibbs, .500 Jeffery, .500 NE, .577 NE, .600 NE, .700 NE

**MSRP** . . . . . . . . . . . . . . . . **$30–$250**

AMMUNITION

# Lapua

## Rifle Ammunition

### CENTERFIRE SPORT

**Features**: Lapua's extremely accurate target shooting cartridges are loaded with the best target bullets—Scenar, FMJBT, D46 and Lock Base. Numerous world championships, Olympic championships, and other top competition gold medals, as well as many official world records in different disciplines, are shot with the Lapua cartridges.
**Available in**: .222 Rem., .223 Rem., 6mm BR Norma, 6.5x47 Lapua, 6.5x55 SE, 7.62x39, .308 Win., .30-06 Spfd., 7.62x53R/54R, .338 Lapua Mag.
**Box 20**:. . . . . . . . . . . **$37.99–$59.99**

### MEGA BULLETS

**Features**: Soft point bullet designed for big game hunting; lead core and copper jacket that are mechanically bonded together; long jacket protects core and prevents premature bullet expansion or breakage when bullet goes through light brush or grass cover; up to 97 percent weight retention
**Available in**: 6.5x55 SE, .308 Win., .30-06 Spfd., 7.62x53R/54R, 9.3x62
**MSRP**. . . . . . . . . . . **$43.99–$60.99**

### NATURALIS

**Features**: Bullet mushrooming begins immediately on impact; bullet expands symmetrically and without shattering; gives a maximal shock effect to the hunted game; top premium copper bullet; retains up to 100 percent of its weight after the impact
**Available in**: .243 Win., 6.5x55 SE, .308 Win., .30-06 Spfd., .338 Lapua Mag., 9.3x62
**From**:. . . . . . . . . . . **$77.99–$127.99**

LAPUA CENTERFIRE SPORT

**LAPUA NATURALIS**

# Magtech Ammunition

## Handgun Ammunition

### CLEANRANGE

**Features**: CleanRange ammunition was developed to eliminate airborne lead and the need for lead retrieval at indoor ranges by using a state-of-the-art combination of high-tech, lead-free primers and specially designed Fully Encapsulated Bullets, a unique mix that eliminates lead and heavy metal exposure at the firing point.
**Available in**: .380 Auto, .38 Spl., .40 S&W, .45 Auto, 9mm Luger
**Box 50**:. . . . . . . . . . . **$20.99–$30.99**

### COWBOY ACTION

**Features**: "Old West" Cowboy Action loads were developed specifically for cowboy action shooting enthusiasts. These flat-nose bullets deliver reliable knockdown power that puts steel targets down on the first shot.
**Available in**: .357 Mag., .38 Spl., .44-40 Win., .44 Spl., .45 Colt
**Box 50**:. . . . . . . . . . . **$24.99–$36.99**

### FIRST DEFENSE

**Features**: Magtech First Defense rounds are designed with a 100 percent solid copper bullet, unlike traditional hollow points that contain a lead core covered by a copper jacket. First Defense solid copper bullets have no jacket to split or tear away, ensuring every round you fire meets its target with maximum impact and effectiveness.
**Available in**: 9mm Luger, .38 Spl., .380 Auto, .357 Mag., .40 S&W, .45 Auto
**Box 20**:. . . . . . . . . . . **$17.49–$25.49**

### GUARDIAN GOLD

**Features**: Thanks to its tremendous stopping power, deep penetration, awesome mushrooming, and dead-on accuracy, Guardian Gold is fast-becoming a favorite among those seeking reliable, affordable personal protection.
**Available in**: 9mm Luger, 9mm Luger+P, .38 Spl.+P, .380 Auto+P, .357 Mag., .40 S&W, .45 Auto+P
**Box 20**:. . . . . . . . . . . **$12.79–$19.49**

**MAGTECH AMMUNITION**

### SPORT SHOOTING

**Features**: The 100 percent solid copper hollow-point projectile features a six-petal hollow-point specifically designed to deliver tight groups, superior expansion, virtually 100 percent weight retention, and increased penetration over jacketed lead-core bullets.
**Available in**: .223, .25 Auto, .308, .30 Carbine, .32 Auto, .32 S&W, .357 Mag., .380 Auto, .38 Spl., .38 Super Auto, .38 S&W, .40 S&W, .44-40 Win., .44 Rem. Mag., .454 Casull, .45 Auto, .45 GAP, .500 S&W, .50 BMG, 9mm Luger, 9x21mm
**From**:. . . . . . . . . . . . **$12.99–$47.99**

# Norma Ammunition

## Rifle Ammunition

### AFRICAN PH

*Features*: Based on many generations of experience of reputable African Professional Hunters, this range of cartridges has been developed to optimize ballistic criteria such as bullet momentum, sectional density and deep, straight-line, bone-breaking penetration. Loaded cartridges with Woodleigh softnose and solid bullets
*Available in*: .375 Flanged Mag. NE, .375 H&H Mag., .404 Jeffrey, .416 Rem. Mag., .416 Rigby, .500/.416 NE, .450 Rigby Rimless, .458 Lott, .470 NE, .500 Jeffrey, .500 NE 3, .505 Mag. Gibbs
**Box 10:** . . . . . . . . . **$69.99–$192.99**

### JAKTMATCH

*Features*: Target ammunition should have the same quality as your hunting cartridges. Many hunters also use Jaktmatch to hunt birds and small game so there is no reason to distinguish between hunting and target cartridges. The fired cases provide the reloader with a top quality product to reload.
*Available in*: .222 Rem, .223 Rem, .22-250 Rem., 6mm Norma BR, 6XC, .243 Win., 6.5x55 Swedish Mauser, 6.5-284 Norma, .270 Win., .270 WSM, 7mm Rem. Mag., .308 Win, .30-06 Spfd., .300 WSM, .300 Win. Mag., .338 Win. Mag., .358 Norma Mag., 8x57 JS, 9.3x 57, 9.3x62
**Box 10:** . . . . . . . . . . . **$44.99–$57.99**

### KALAHARI

*Features*: The Kalahari is loaded with selected lots of powder to ensure the highest possible velocity, best possible ballistic coefficient, and lowest wind drift achievable at normal hunting ranges. Bullet expansion is controlled and restricted–only the front third of the bullet will expand into six razor-edged petals, leaving the rear part of the bullet unimpeded, guaranteeing deep penetration.
*Available in*: .270 Win., .270 WSM, .280 Rem., 7x64, 7mm Rem. Mag., .308 Win., .30-06 Spfd., .300 Win. Mag., .300 WSM
**Box 20:** . . . . . . . . . . . **$48.99–$64.99**

### ORYX

*Features*: The Oryx has a thin forward jacket with internal splitting zones. The bonding and the thicker rear jacket wall ensure a high residual weight after impact (often over 90 percent!) and excellent penetration. Norma is in the process of updating the original Oryx design; the boat tail and a better profile provides a 30-percent increase or more in BC.
*Available in*: .222 Rem., .223 Rem., .22-250 Rem., .220 Swift, 6mm Norma BR, 6XC, .243 Win., 6.5x55 Swedish Mauser, .270 Win., .270 WSM, .280 Rem., 7x57 R Mauser, 7x57 Mauser, 7x64, 7x65 R, 7mm Rem. Mag., 7mm Blaser Mag., 7.5x55 Swiss, .308 Win., .30-06 Spfd., .300 Win. Mag., .300 WSM, .300 Blaser Mag., .308 Norma Mag., .338 Blaser Mag., .338 Win. Mag., .35 Whelen, .358 Norma Mag., 8x57 JRS, 8x57 JS, 9.3x57, 9.3x62, 9.3x74 R, .375 Blaser Mag., .375 H&H Mag.
**Box 20:** . . . . . . . . . . **$39.99–$136.99**

NORMA KALAHARI

NORMA ORYX

AMMUNITION

## Rifle Ammunition

### MATCH GRADE

*Features*: Match Grade Ammunition consists of Nosler's precisely-designed Custom Competition bullet along with NoslerCustom Brass. Because of Nosler's unsurpassed quality standards, each piece of brass is checked for correct length, neck-sized, chamfered, trued and flash holes are checked for proper alignment. To further ensure our reputation for quality and consistency, powder charges are meticulously weighed and finished rounds are visually inspected and polished.

*Available in*: .223 Rem.-60, 69, 77 gr., .308 Win.-155, 168, 175 gr.

**Box 20:. . . . . . . . . . . $19.99–$26.99**

### SAFARI

*Features*: For years, hunters around the globe have relied on the quality and consistency of Nosler bullets. That same quality and consistency is now available in Nosler Safari. Loaded with either the Partition or Nosler Solid and designed for the same point of impact with either bullet, Safari Ammunition provides the ultimate versatility for any dangerous game situation.

*Available in*: Available in both Partition and Solid Dangerous Game: .375 Flanged, .375 H&H, .416 Rem. Mag., .416 Rigby, .458 Lott, .458 Win. Mag., 9.3x62mm Mauser; SD only: .470 NE, .500 Jeffery, .500 NE, .505 Gibbs; PT only: .500/.416 NE

**Box 20:. . . . . . . . . . $89.99–$229.99**

**NOSLER TROPHY GRADE VARMINT AMMUNITION**

### TROPHY GRADE HUNTING

*Features*: Manufactured to Nosler's strictest quality standards, Trophy Grade Ammunition uses NoslerCustom Brass and Nosler Bullets to attain optimum performance, no matter where your hunting trip takes you. Whether you want your ammunition loaded with AccuBond, Partition Ballistic Tip or, E-Tip, NoslerCustom Trophy Grade Ammunition will have the right load for the right game.

*Available in*: 243 Win., .25-06 Rem., .257 Roberts +P, .257 Wby., 6.5x55 Mauser, .260 Rem., 6.5x55 Mauser, .260 Rem., 6.5-284 Norma, .264 Win. Mag., .270 Win., .270 WSM, 7mm-08 Rem., .280 Ack. Imp., 7mm SAUM, 7mm Rem. Mag., 7mm STW, 7mm RUM, .308 Win., .30-06 Spfd., .300 H&H Mag., .300 Win. Mag., .300 WSM, .300 SAUM, .300 RUM, .300 Wby., .325 WSM, .338 Lapua Mag., .338 RUM, .338 Win. Mag., .35 Whelen, .375 H&H, .375 H&H Mag.

**Box 20:. . . . . . . . . . . $35.99–$79.99**

### TROPHY GRADE VARMINT

*Features*: Trophy Grade VARMINT Ammunition consists of the venerable Ballistic Tip VARMINT bullet or the frangible Ballistic Tip Lead Free along with NoslerCustom Brass.

*Available in*: .204 Ruger-32 gr.; .223 Rem-35, 40 gr.; .22-250 Rem.-35, 40, 55 gr.

**Box 20:. . . . . . . . . . . $24.99–$34.99**

### VARMAGEDDON

*Features*: Featuring a highly accurate polymer tip or hollow point combined with flat base design, Varmageddon products were created for the high-volume varmint shooter who requires the utmost precision. Loaded with NoslerCustom brass, Varmageddon ammunition provides the highest levels of performance for any varmint hunter. 20 count box.

*Available in*: .17 Rem., .204 Ruger, .221 Rem. Fireball, .222 Rem., .22-250 Rem., .223 Rem., .243 Win.

**Box 20:. . . . . . . . . . . $19.99–$35.49**

**NOSLER SAFARI AMMUNITION**

**NOSLER VARMAGEDDON AMMUNITION & BULLETS**

AMMUNITION

# PMC Ammunition

## Rifle Ammunition

### BRONZE LINE - RIFLE

**Features**: For shooters and hunters who appreciate affordable quality ammunition, the PMC Bronze Line offers reliable performance for every shooting application. Full Metal Jacket (FMJ) bullet types.
*Available in*: .223 Rem, .308 Win., 7.62x39, .50
**Box 20:** . . . . . . . . . . . **$16.99–$39.99**

### FRANGIBLE SINTERFIRE

**Features**: PMC's frangible ammunition combines their incomparable Sinterfire bullet and reduced-hazard primer. Using a lead-free bullet that shatters into non-toxic dust on impact with anything harder than itself, this product virtually eliminates the danger of ricochet from jacket and bullet fragments. Safe for shooting steel plates from any distance or for close-quarters tactical operations.
*Available in*: 5.56mm, 7.62mm, .50
**N/A**

### PRECISION LINE

**Features**: PMC's Precision Line incorporates genuine Hornady bullets with precision-drawn cases loaded to stringent manufacturing standards. The result is unparalleled accuracy and consistent performance. It is available in hunting or target versions.
*Available in*: .223 Rem., .243 Win., .270 Win., 7mm Rem., .300 Win. Mag., .308 Win., .30-06 Spfd., .30-30 Win.
**From:** . . . . . . . . . . . . **$19.30–$24.24**

### X-TAC

**Features**: PMC's exacting adherence to precise specifications of military and law-enforcement organizations assures that X-TAC ammunition will perform perfectly in that fraction of a second when a serious threat arises and your life is on the line. Self-defense depends on reliable, consistent ammunition.
*Available in*: 5.56mm
**Box 20:** . . . . . . . . . . . . . . . . **$21.19**

## Handgun Ammunition

### BRONZE LINE - HANDGUN

**Features**: The same quality and dependability built into our Starfire ammunition is incorporated throughout our extensive line of PMC training ammunition and standard hollow point or soft point ammunition.
*Available in*: .25 Auto, .32 Auto, .380 Auto, .38 Spl., .38 Super +P, 9mm Luger, .357 Mag., 10mm Auto, .40 S&W, .44 S&W Spl., .44 Rem. Mag., .45 Auto
**From:** . . . . . . . . . . . . **$12.99–$21.99**

### GOLD LINE - STARFIRE

**Features**: The secret of Starfire's impressive performance lies in a unique, patented rib-and-flute hollow point cavity design. Upon impact, the pre-notched jacket mouth begins to peel back, separating into five uniform copper petals and allowing expansion to begin.
*Available in*: .380 Auto, .38 Spl. +P, .357 Mag., 9mm Luger, .40 S&W, .44 Rem. Mag., .45 Auto
**From:** . . . . . . . . . . . . **$13.12–$24.78**

### SILVER LINE - ERANGE

**Features**: PMC's eRange environmentally friendly ammunition utilizes a reduced hazard primer that is the first of this type in the industry, an encapsulated metal jacket (EMJ) bullet which completely encloses the surface of the bullet core with precision made copper alloy, and powder with clean-burning characteristics and smooth fire for increased barrel life.
*Available in*: .380 Auto, .38 Spl., .38 Spl. +P, .357 Mag., 9mm Luger, .40 S&W, .44 Rem. Mag., .45 Auto
**From:** . . . . . . . . . . . . **$16.79–$41.15**

## Shotgun Ammunition

### "ONE SHOT" HIGH VELOCITY PHEASANT LOADS

**Features**: These maximum velocity loads deliver a knockout punch of copper plating around extra-hard lead shots. Their specially designed plastic wads incorporate an innovative shot cup that ensures dense, uniform patterns needed to buckle late-season game birds and animals made fat by winter and wary by hunting pressure.
*Available in*: 12, 20 Ga. (2 ¾ in., 3 in.); Shot sizes: 4, 5, 6, 7.5
**From:** . . . . . . . . . . . . **$24.98–$30.48.**

**PMC BRONZE LINE - HANDGUN**

**PMC SILVER LINE - ERANGE**

# Remington Ammunition

## Rifle Ammunition

### .30 REM. AR

**Features**: A short, .30-caliber round whose 125-grain bullets match the speed of .308 150s, for hunting deer-size game with the AR-15 modular repeating rifle. Ammo comes with Core-Lokt and AccuTip bullets (125 grains) and, in UMC loads, with full metal case (123 grains) bullets.
**Available in**: (Exclude Column)
**Box 20**: . . . . . . . . . . **$21.99–$40.99**

### MANAGED RECOIL

**Features**: Managed-Recoil Ammunition delivers Remington Field proven hunting performance out to 200 yards with half the recoil. Bullets provide 2x expansion with over 75 percent weight retention on shots inside 50 yards and out to 200 yards.
**Available in**: .260 Rem., .270 Win., .30-06 Spfd., .300 Rem. Ultra Mag., .30-30 Win., .300 Win. Mag., 7mm Rem. Mag., 7mm-08 Rem., .308 Win.
**Box 20**: . . . . . . . . . . . **$17.99–$35.99**

### POWER LEVEL

**Features**: Power Level Ammunition allows you to incrementally tailor the performance of your 7mm or .300 Ultra Mag. rifle to the species and terrain you're hunting, similar to the way shotgunners use 2 ¾ in., 3 in., and 3 ½ in. shells. Plus, point of impact between Power Levels is within 2 in. at 200 yards.
**Available in**: 7mm Ultra Mag., 7mm Rem. Ultra Mag., .300 Ultra Mag., .300 Rem. Ultra Mag., .375 Rem. Ultra Mag.; three power levels
**Box 20**: . . . . . . . . . . . **$34.99–$67.99**

### PREMIER ACCUTIP

**Features**: Featuring precision-engineered polymer tip bullets designed for match-grade accuracy (sub MOA), Premier AccuTip offers an unprecedented combination of super-flat trajectory and deadly down-range performance.
**Available in**: .30 Rem. AR, .300 Rem. Ultra Mag., .270 WSM, .300 WSM, .223 Rem., .243 Win., .260 Rem., .270 Win., .280 Rem., 7mm Rem. Mag., .30-06 Spfd., .300 Win. Mag., .308 Win., 7mm-08 Rem.,
**Box 20**: . . . . . . . . . . . **$27.99–$49.99**

### PREMIER A-FRAME

**Features**: A-Frame cartridges use dual-core A-Frame bullets, so that you can expect reliable expansion at long-range decreased velocities, but without over-expansion at short-range high velocities. The combination of A-Frame construction and proprietary bonding process produces extremely uniform, controlled expansion to 2x caliber with nearly 100 percent weight retention.
**Available in**: .300 Rem. Ultra Mag. (Power Level III), 7mm STW, 8mm Rem. Mag., 7mm Rem. Mag., .270 Win., .338 Win. Mag., 7mm Rem. Ultra Mag. (Power Level III), .375 H&H Mag., .300 Win. Mag., .30-06 Spfd., .416 Rem. Mag., .338 Rem. Ultra Mag., .375 Rem. Ultra Mag.
**Box 20**: . . . . . . . . . . . **$47.99–$149.20**

### PREMIER COPPER-SOLID

**Features**: This polymer-tipped, lead-free, copper bullet is of boattail design and delivers extremely deep penetration with nearly 100 percent weight retention and has a sleek ogive profile.
**Available in**: .243 Win., .270 Win., 7mm Rem. Mag., .30-30 Win., .30-06 Spfd., .300 Win. Mag., .300 Rem. Ultra Mag., .308 Win.
**Box 20**: . . . . . . . . . . . **$38.99–$66.51**

### PREMIER CORE-LOKT ULTRA BONDED

**Features**: The bonded bullet retains up to 95 percent of its original weight with maximum penetration and energy transfer. Featuring a progressively tapered jacket design, the Core-Lokt Ultra Bonded bullet initiates and controls expansion nearly 2x.
**Available in**: 7mm Rem. SA Ultra Mag., 7mm Rem. Ultra Mag., .300 Ultra Mag., .300 Rem. SA Ultra Mag., .223 Rem., .243 Win., .25-06 Rem., .260 Rem., .270 Win., 7mm Rem. Mag., .30-06 Spfd., .300 Rem. Ultra Mag., .300 Win. Mag., .338 Win. Mag., .308 Win., 6.8mm Rem. SPC
**Box 20**: . . . . . . . . . . . **$23.99–$59.99**

### PREMIER DISINTEGRATOR VARMINT

**Features**: Frangible bullet design with iron/tin bullet core (no lead), designed to disintegrate upon impact on varmints.

**Available in**: .223 Rem., .22-250 Rem.
**Box 20**: . . . . . . . . . . . . . . . . **$25.49**

### PREMIER MATCH

**Features**: Loaded with match-grade bullets, this ammunition employs special loading practices to ensure world-class performance and accuracy with every shot.
**Available in**: .308 Win., .223 Rem., 6.8mm Rem. SPC, .300 Win. Mag., .300 Rem. SA Ultra Mag.
**Box 20**: . . . . . . . . . . . . **$29.99–$43.84**

### PREMIER SCIROCCO BONDED

**Features**: The Swift Scirocco Bonded bullet combines polymer tip ballistics with weight retention. The expansion generating polymer tip and the boattail base defy air resistance at the front end, and reduce drag at the back.
**Available in**: .300 Ultra Mag., .300 Rem. Ultra Mag., 7mm Rem. Mag., .30-06 Spfd., .243 Win., .270 Win., .300 Win. Mag., 7mm Rem. Ultra Mag., .300 WSM
**Box 20**: . . . . . . . . . . . **$43.99–$59.99**

# Remington Ammunition

**REMINGTON GOLDEN SABER HPJ**

## Handgun Ammunition

### DISINTEGRATOR CTF

*Features*: Utilizing jacketless, copper tin frangible bullets, the Disintegrator CTF delivers complete breakup at distances as close as 5 feet with no splash back, no jacket fragments, and absolutely no lead residue.
*Available in*: .38 Spl. (+P), 9mm (+P), .40 S&W, .45 Auto
**Box 20:** . . . . . . . . . . . **$44.49–$49.99**

### EXPRESS PISTOL AND REVOLVER

*Features*: Remington's exceptionally broad line of handgun ammunition covers a comprehensive range of calibers, bullet weights, and bullet styles. Available styles include: Full Metal Case, Lead Round Nose, Jacketed Hollow Point, Lead Hollow Point, Semi-Jacketed Hollow Point, Semi-Wadcutter Lead, Soft Point, and Wadcutter Match
*Available in*: .45 Auto, .25 Auto, .32 S&W, .32 S&W Long, .32 Auto, .357 Mag., 9mm Luger, .380 Auto, .357 Sig., .38 S&W, .38 Spl., .41 Rem. Mag., .40 S&W, .38 Short Colt, .44 S&W Spl., .45 Colt, .44 Rem. Mag,
**From:** . . . . . . . . . . . . **$28.99–$49.99**

### GOLDEN SABER HPJ

*Features*: Designed for law enforcement and personal defense, the Golden Saber High Performance Jacket successfully combines match-type accuracy, deep penetration, maximum expansion, and near 100 percent weight retention. Cases nickel-plated

for reliable feed, function, and extraction.
*Available in*: .357 Mag., .380 Auto, 9mm Luger (+P), .38 Spl. (+P), .40 S&W, .45 Auto (+P)
**Box 25** . . . . . . . . . . . **$25.99–$40.49**

## Rimfire Ammunition

### .22 RIMFIRE TARGET

*Features*: Whether it's getting young shooters started, practice plinking, small-game hunting, or keeping match shooters scoring high, Remington's rimfire quality stands tall. As in their centerfire ammo, they put the maximum level of quality into their .22s so you can get maximum performance out of them.
*Available in*: .22LR
**From:** . . . . . . . . . . . . . **$3.99–$8.99**

### MAGNUM RIMFIRE

*Features*: Premier Gold Box Rimfire ammunition features sleek AccuTip-V bullets. Our standard line of Magnum rimfire ammunition gives shooters the choice of either a Jacketed Hollow Point for quick expansion or a Pointed Soft Point for optimum penetration.
*Available in*: .22 Mag.
**MSRP** . . . . . . . . . . . . . . . . . **$14.22**

### PREMIER GOLD BOX RIMFIRE

*Features*: This ammunition uses the AccuTip-V bullet with precision-engineered polymer tip for match-type accuracy, high on-game energy, and rapid expansion.
*Available in*: .17 HMR, .22 Win. Mag., .17 Mach 2 Rimfire
**From:** . . . . . . . . . . . . **$15.99–$21.99**

### REMINGTON-ELEY COMPETITION RIMFIRE MATCH EPS

*Features*: Remington and Eley offer three grades of their premier .22 Long Rifle ammunition. For the finest performance available Remington/Eley Match EPS offers the ultimate in rimfire accuracy. This match grade load features Eley's innovative Tenex EPS-profile bullet—ideal for aspiring top class shooters and training at the highest level.

*Available in*: .22LR
**Box 50:** . . . . . . . . . . . . . . . . **$21.99**

## Shotgun Ammunition

### TARGET-GUN CLUB TARGET

*Features*: Loaded with Gun Club Grade Shot, Premier STS Primers, and Power Piston One-Piece Wads, these high-quality shells receive the same care in loading as top-of-the-line Premier STS and Nitro .27 shells.
*Available in*: 12, 20 Ga. (2 ¾ in.); Shot sizes: 7.5, 8, 9
**Box 25:** . . . . . . . . . . . . . . . . .**$6.99**

### TARGET-MANAGED RECOIL STS TARGET

*Features*: Managed-Recoil STS target loads offer dramatically reduced recoil (40 percent less in the 12-gauge load) with target-grinding STS consistency and pattern density. Ideal for new shooters and high-volume practice.
*Available in*: 12, 20 Ga. (2 ¾ in.); Shot size: 8.5
**From:** . . . . . . . . . . . . . . **$8.99–$10.50**

### TARGET-PREMIER NITRO 27 TARGET

*Features*: Designed specifically for back-fence trap and long-range sporting clays. Delivers consistent handicap velocity and pattern uniformity. New, improved powder loading significantly reduces felt recoil while retaining high velocity; both factors allow avid trap shooters to stay fresh for the shoot off.
*Available in*: 12 Ga. (2 ¾ in.); Shot Sizes: 7.5, 8
**From:** . . . . . . . . . . . . . . . . . . .**$8.99**

**REMINGTON TARGET-PREMIER NITRO GOLD SPORTING CLAYS**

# Remington Ammunition

## TARGET-PREMIER NITRO GOLD SPORTING CLAYS

**Features**: To meet the special demands of avid sporting clays shooters, Remington developed a new Premier Nitro Gold Sporting Clays target load. At 1300 fps, the extra velocity gives you an added advantage for those long crossers—making target leads closer to normal for ultimate target-crushing satisfaction.
**Available in**: 12, 28 Ga. (2 ¾ in.), .410 (2 ½ in.); Shot sizes: 7.5, 8
**From**:. . . . . . . . . . . . . .$8.99–$12.99

## TARGET-PREMIER STS TARGET

**Features**: STS Target Loads have taken shot-to-shot consistency to a new performance level, setting the standard at all major skeet, trap, and sporting clays shooting across the country, while providing handloaders with unmatched reloading ease and hull longevity. Available in most gauges, Premier STS shells are the most reliable, consistent, and reloadable shells you can shoot.
**Available in**: 12, 20, 28 Ga. (2 ¾ in.), .410 (2 ½ in.); Shot sizes: 7.5, 8, 8.5, 9
**From**:. . . . . . . . . . . . . .$8.99–$12.99

## TURKEY-NITRO MAG. BUFFERED MAGNUM

**Features**: The original buffered magnum shotshells from Remington. The shot charge is packed with a generous amount of shock-absorbing polymer buffering and surrounded by our patented Power Piston wad to protect the specially hardened shot all the way down the barrel for dense, even patterns and uniform shot strings.
**Available in**: 12, 20 Ga. (2 ¾ in., 3 in.); Shot sizes: 2, 4, 6
**Box 25**:. . . . . . . . . . . $26.08–$34.58

## TURKEY-NITRO TURKEY BUFFERED

**Features**: These loads contain Nitro Mag. extra-hard lead shot that is as hard and round as copper-plated shot. Nitro Turkey Magnums will pattern as well as other copper-plated, buffered loads without the higher cost.
**Available in**: 12 Ga. (2 ¾ in., 3 in., 3 ½

in.), 20 Ga. (3 in.); Shot sizes: 4, 5, 6
**Box 10**:. . . . . . . . . . . . .$7.50–$16.99

## TURKEY-PREMIER DUPLEX MAGNUM COPPER-PLATED BUFFERED

**Features**: Shotshell ammunition for the turkey hunter who appreciates dense patterns, deep penetration, and range flexibility. Premier Duplex has No. 4 size shot carefully layered on top of No. 6 shot. When ranges vary, they combine retained energy and penetration from the larger pellets with pattern density from the smaller ones.
**Available in**: 12 Ga. (2 ¾ in., 3 in.); Shot sizes: 4x6
**Box 10**:. . . . . . . . . . . $14.79–$16.79

## TURKEY-PREMIER HIGH-VELOCITY MAGNUM COPPER-PLATED BUFFERED

**Features**: Utilizing a specially-blended powder recipe, Remington's advanced Power Piston one-piece wad, and hardened copper plated shot, these new high-velocity loads result in extremely dense patterns and outstanding knockdown power at effective ranges.
**Available in**: 12 Ga. (3 in., 3 ½ in.); Shot sizes: 4, 5, 6
**From**:. . . . . . . . . . . . . . . .$15.99

## TURKEY-PREMIER MAGNUM COPPER-PLATED BUFFERED

**Features**: Premier Magnum Turkey Loads provide that extra edge to reach out with penetrating power and dense, concentrated patterns. Its magnum-grade, Copper-Lokt shot is protected by our Power Piston wad and cushioned with special polymer buffering.
**Available in**: 10 Ga. (3 ½ in.), 12 Ga. (2 ¾ in., 3 in., 3 ½ in.), 20 Ga. (3 in.).; Shot sizes: 4, 5, 6
**Box 10**:. . . . . . . . . . . $11.29–$19.06

## TURKEY-WINGMASTER HD

**Features**: Comprised of tungsten, bronze, and iron, Wingmaster HD pellets are specifically engineered with a density of 12 grams/cc, 10 percent

denser than lead. Wingmaster HD loads also feature a precise balance of payload and velocity that provide turkey hunters with a shotshell that generates nearly 200 ft.-lbs. more energy at 40 yds. than competitive tungsten based shot. This results in deeper penetrating pellets.
**Available in**: 10 Ga. (3 ½ in.), 12 Ga. (2 ¾ in., 3 in., 3 ½ in.), 20 Ga. (2 ¾ in., 3 in.); Shot sizes: 2, 4, 6, BB, T
**From**:. . . . . . . . . . . . . . . . .$12.99

## UPLAND-EXPRESS EXTRA LONG RANGE

**Features**: Long considered to be some of the best-balanced, best-patterning upland field loads available, our family of shotshells offer great selections for upland bird hunting. The hunter's choice for a wide variety of game-bird applications, from 12-gauge to .410 bore, with shot-size options ranging from BB's all the way down to 9s; suitable for everything from quail to farm predators.
**Available in**: 12, 16, 20, 28 Ga. (2 ¾ in.), .410 (2 ½ in., 3 in.); Shot sizes: 2, 4, 5, 6, 7.5, 9
**From**:. . . . . . . . . . . . .$13.79–$18.99

## UPLAND-LEAD GAME

**Features**: For a wide variety of field gaming, these budget-stretching loads include the same quality components as other Remington shotshells, and are available in four different gauges to match up with your favorite upland shotguns.
**Available in**: 12, 16, 20 Ga. (2 ¾ in.), .410 (2 ½ in.); Shot sizes: 6, 7.5, 8
**From**:. . . . . . . . . . . . . .$6.99–$13.29

## UPLAND-NITRO PHEASANT

**Features**: Uses Remington's own Copper-Lokt copper-plated lead shot with high antimony content. Hard shot stays rounder for truer flight, tighter patterns, and greater penetration. Available in both high-velocity and magnum loadings.
**Available in**: 12, 20 Ga. (2 ¾ in., 3 in.); Shot sizes: 4, 5, 6
**From**:. . . . . . . . . . . . .$17.74–$20.49

# Remington Ammunition

### UPLAND-PHEASANT

**Features**: For the broadest selection in game-specific Upland shotshells, Remington Upland Loads are the perfect choice. Their high-velocity and long-range performance are just right for any pheasant hunting situation. Standard high-base payloads feature Power Piston one-piece wads.
**Available in**: 12, 16, 20 Ga. (2 ¾ in.); Shot sizes: 4, 5, 6, 7.5
**From:** . . . . . . . . . . . . $11.99–$15.99

### UPLAND-SHURSHOT HEAVY DOVE

**Features**: A sure bet for all kinds of upland game, ShurShot loads have earned the reputation as one of the best-balanced, best-pattering upland field loads available. These shells combine an ideal balance of powder charge and shot payload to deliver effective velocities and near-perfect patterns with mild recoil for high-volume upland hunting situations.
**Available in**: 12, 20 Ga. (2 ¾ in.); Shot sizes: 6, 7.5, 8
**From:** . . . . . . . . . . . . $7.99–$11.36

### UPLAND-SHURSHOT HIGH BASE PHEASANT

**Features**: The ShurShot High Base Pheasant loads deliver an ideal combination of velocity and payload. Loaded with our reliable Power Piston Wad and hard lead shot
**Available in**: 12 Ga. (2 ¾ in.); Shot sizes: 4, 5
**From:** . . . . . . . . . . . . . . . . $12.91

### UPLAND-SPORT

**Features**: Remington Sport Loads are an economical, multi-purpose utility load for a variety of shotgunning needs. Loaded with Power Piston wads, and plastic unibody hulls, these shells perform effectively for skeet trap and sporting clays, as well as quail, doves, and woodcock.
**Available in**: 12, 20 Ga. (2 ¾ in.); Shot size: 8
**From:** . . . . . . . . . . . . . . . . .$7.76

### WATERFOWL-HYPERSONIC STEEL

**Features**: The 1,700 fps HyperSonic Steel from Remington. With unprecedented velocity and the highest downrange pattern energies ever achieved, Remington HyperSonic Steel takes lethality to new heights and lengths.
**Available in**: 10 Ga. (3 ½ in.), 12 Ga. (3 in., 3 ½ in.), 20 Ga. (3 in.); Shot sizes: BB, BBB, 1, 2, 3, 4
**From:** . . . . . . . . . . . . $21.99–$31.99

### WATERFOWL-NITRO-STEEL HIGH-VELOCITY

**Features**: Greater hull capacity means heavier charges and larger pellets, which makes these loads ideal for large waterfowl. Nitro-Steel delivers denser patterns for greater lethality and is zinc plated to prevent corrosion.
**Available in**: 10 Ga. (3 ½ in.), 12 Ga. (2 ¾ in., 3 in., 3 ½ in.), 16 Ga. (2 ¾ in.), 20 Ga. (2 ¾ in., 3 in.); Shot sizes: T, BBB, BB, 1, 2, 3, 4
**From:** . . . . . . . . . . . $19.05–$28.38

### WATERFOWL-SPORTSMAN HI-SPEED STEEL

**Features**: Sportsman Hi-Speed Steel's sealed primer, high-quality steel shot, and consistent muzzle velocities combine to provide reliability in adverse weather, while delivering exceptional pattern density and retained energy. A high-speed steel load that is ideal for short-range high-volume shooting during early duck seasons or over decoys.
**Available in**: 10 Ga. (3 ½ in.), 12 Ga. (2 ¾ in., 3 in., 3 ½ in.), 20 Ga. (2 ¾ in.); Shot sizes: BB, 1, 2, 3, 4, 6, 7
**From:** . . . . . . . . . . . . $10.49–$26.91

### WATERFOWL-WINGMASTER HD

**Features**: Wingmaster HD nontoxic shot stretches the kill zone with an ultra-tuned combination of density, shape and energy. At 12 grams/cc, it's 10 percent denser than lead and the scientifically-proven optimum density for pellet count and pattern density. Plus, its smooth, round shape delivers awesome aerodynamics and sustained payload energy.
**Available in**: 10 Ga. (3 ½ in.), 12 Ga. (2 ¾ in., 3 in., 3 ½ in.), 20 Ga (2 ¾ in., 3 in.); Shot sizes: T, BB 2, 4, 6
**From:** . . . . . . . . . . . . $16.99–$36.99

## Shotgun Ammunition–Buckshot

### EXPRESS AND EXPRESS MAGNUM

**Features**: A combination of heavy cushioning behind the shot column and a granulated polymer buffering helps maintain pellet roundness for tight, even patterns.
**Available in**: 12 (2 ¾ in., 3 in., 3 ½ in.), 20 Ga. (2 ¾ in.); Shot sizes: 000, 00, 0, 1, 3, 4
**From:** . . . . . . . . . . . . . . $4.79–$10.79

**REMINGTON WATERFOWL-HYPERSONIC STEEL**

REMINGTON
EXPRESS
BUCKSHOT

# Remington Ammunition

## MANAGED-RECOIL EXPRESS

**Features**: With less felt recoil than full velocity loads, Express Managed-Recoil Buckshot is an ideal close-range performer. Less recoil means second shot recovery is quicker, allowing the user to get back on target more easily. These loads are buffered for dense patterns, allowing for highly effective performance at up to 40 yards.
**Available in**: 12 Ga. (2 ¾ in.); Shot size: 00
**From:** . . . . . . . . . . . . . . . . . . . .$4.99

## Shotgun Ammunition– Slugs

## BUCKHAMMER LEAD

**Features**: Specifically designed for rifled barrels and rifled choke tubes, these high-performance slugs are capable of producing 3-inch or better groups at 100 yards with nearly 100 percent weight retention and controlled expansion to nearly one inch in diameter. Unlike traditional sabot slugs, the BuckHammer's unique attached stabilizer allows for a full bore diameter lead slug that delivers devastating terminal performance with unsurpassed accuracy.
**Available in**: 12, 20 Ga. (2 ¾ in., 3 in.)
**From:** . . . . . . . . . . . . . . . . . . . .$8.79

## MANAGED-RECOIL COPPER SOLID SABOT

**Features**: With 40 percent less recoil, these slugs are perfect for anyone who wants outstanding on-game results without the rearward punch. Or, use them to sight-in, then step up to full loads. There's no finer slug load for young or recoil-sensitive hunters.
**Available in**: 12 Ga. (2 ¾ in.)
**From:** . . . . . . . . . . . . . . . . . . .$17.26

## PREMIER ACCUTIP BONDED SABOT

**Features**: Guided by our new Power Port Tip, the AccuTip Bonded Sabot Slug delivers a degree of accuracy and terminal performance unmatched by any other we tested. It yields over 95 percent weight retention thanks to its spiral nose cuts, bonded construction, and high-strength cartridge brass jacket.

Designed for fully-rifled barrels only.
**Available in**: 12, 20 Ga. (2 ¾ in., 3 in.)
**From:** . . . . . . . . . . . . .$13.79–$15.99

## PREMIER CORE-LOKT ULTRA BONDED SABOT

**Features**: Ultra-high velocities deliver devastating on-game performance and the tightest groups (1.8in) of any shotgun slug with ultra-flat trajectories. Remington patented spiral nose cuts ensure consistent 2x expansion over a wide range of terminal velocities. The 385-grain bonded bullet yields near 100 percent weight retention. Flattest shooting slug in existence—10 percent better than the nearest competition. Designed for use in fully-rifled barrels only.
**Available in**: 12, 20 Ga. (2 ¾ in.)
**From:** . . . . . . . . . . . . . . . . . .$20.49

## SLUGGER HIGH VELOCITY

**Features**: This is the first high-velocity Foster-style lead slug. This higher velocity slug exits the barrel at 1800 fps, 13 percent faster than standard 1-oz. slugs. The ⁷⁄₈ oz. Slugger High Velocity delivers 200 ft.-lbs. more energy at 50 yards with flatter trajectory on deer than standard 1-oz.

slugs. Designed for the avid deer hunter using smooth bore guns.
**Available in**: 12 Ga. (2 ¾ in., 3 in.), 20 Ga. (2 ¾ in.)
**From:** . . . . . . . . . . . . . . .$4.49–$5.89

## SLUGGER MANAGED-RECOIL RIFLED

**Features**: Slugger Managed-Recoil Rifled Slugs offer remarkably effective performance but with 45 percent less felt recoil than full velocity Sluggers. With effective energy out of 80 Yds., these 1-oz. slugs easily handle the majority of shotgun deer hunting ranges.
**Available in**: 12 Ga. (2 ¾ in.)
**From:** . . . . . . . . . . . . . . . . . . . .$4.99

## SLUGGER RIFLED

**Features**: Remington redesigned their 12-gauge Slugger Rifled Slug for a 25 percent improvement in accuracy. Also, at 1760 fps muzzle velocity, the 3-in. 12-ga. Magnum slugs shoot 25 percent flatter than regular 12-Ga. Slugs.
**Available in**: 12 Ga. (2 ¾ in., 3 in.), 16 Ga. (2 ¾ in.), 20 Ga. (2 ¾ in.), .410 (2 ½ in.)
**From:** . . . . . . . . . . . . . . .$4.39–$5.99

**REMINGTON PREMIER ACCUTIP BONDED SABOT**

# RWS

## Centerfire Ammunition

### ID-CLASSIC

**Features**: Penetration and broad effect in the target ideally combine two lead cores of different hardness, which interlock peg-shaped. The soft tip core fragments, the rear core of the ID CLASSIC-bullet strongly mushrooms, the soft steel nickel-plated jacket protects the barrel, and the torpedo-shaped tail of the RWS ID CLASSIC-bullet ensures an especially good flight stability.
**Available in**: .280 Rem., .30-06, .308 Win., 7mm Rem. Mag., 7x57, 7x57 R, 7x64, 7x65 R, 8x57 JRS, 8x57 JS
**Box 20:** . . . . . . . . . . . **$21.99–$27.99**

### SILVER SELECTION HUNT 36 SHOTSHELLS

**Features**: Thanks to the nickel-plated shot pellets, the RWS HUNT 36 stands out due to its good patterning at medium range. The shotshell has a selected powder load, which increases the velocity of the shot and the stopping effect of the game.
**Available in**: 12 Ga.; Shot size: 7
**Price:** . . . . . . . . . . . . . . . . . . . .**N/A**

### SILVER SELECTION WITH UNI PROFESSIONAL

**Features**: A brand-new twin-core bullet with over 18 percent reduced air resistance in comparison to the UNI CLASSIC-bullet ensures a distinctly extended trajectory and longer hunting ranges. With all of these improvements the responding qualities of the bullet were further optimized.
**Available in**: .300 Win. Mag., .30-06, .308 Win.
**Price:** . . . . . . . . . . . . . . . . . . . .**N/A**

**RWS TWIN CORE**   **RWS UNI-CLASSIC**

### TWIN CORE

**Features**: The RWS twin-core-bullet (DK-bullet) consists of two lead cores of different hardness. The front core fragments reliably and ensures high instantaneous effectiveness. To regulate this deformation process, a unique Tombac jacket separates the rear bullet core from the softer tip core.
**Available in**: .30 R Blaser, .300 Win. Mag., .30-06, .308 Win., 6.5x55, 6.5x57, 6.5x57 R, 7x64, 7x65 R, 8x57 JRS, 8x57 JS, 8x68 S, 9.3x62, 9.3x64, 9.3x74 R
**Box 20:** . . . . . . . . . . . **$21.97–$33.00**

### UNI-CLASSIC

**Features**: The harder and heavier tail core of the bullet has a tendency to mushroom a little bit less, which increases its penetration even more. The front tip core, which fragments reliably, ensures the especially high instantaneous effectiveness. The inceased flight stability of the UNI CLASSIC-bullet is achieved by the torpedo-shaped tail.
**Available in**: .30 R Blaser, .300 Win. Mag., .30-06, .308 Win., .375 H&H Mag., 9.3x62, 9.3x64, 9.3x74 R
**Box 20:** . . . . . . . . . . . **$21.99–$27.99**

## Rimfire Ammunition

### MAGNUM FULL METAL JACKET

**Features**: The RWS Magnum FMJ reaches an extremely high velocity. This guarantees an extended trajectory of up to 100m for hunting and high

energy release in the target. For this reason, this small-caliber ammunition is very good for hunting small game. In addition, it causes very little damage to the games meat because it only minimally perforates the pelt.
**Available in**: .22 Mag.
**Box 50:** . . . . . . . . . . . . . **$9.99–$31.99**

### R 50

**Features**: For competitive shooters demanding the ultimate in precision. This cartridge has been used to establish several world records and is used by Olympic Gold Medalists. Now available in R 50 SC.
**Available in**: .22LR
**From:** . . . . . . . . . . . . . . **$18.99**

### RIFLE MATCH

**Features**: Perfect for the club-level target competitor. Accurate and affordable.
**Available in**: .22LR
**From:** . . . . . . . . . . . . . . . . **$11.29**

### SUBSONIC HOLLOW POINT

**Features**: The RWS Subsonic HP is a special cartridge for low-noise shooting. The bullet velocity stays distinctly below the sound barrier—consequently, there is no sonic boom. For this reason, this rimfire cartridge is very well suited for weapons with silencers.
**Available in**: .22LR
**From:** . . . . . . . . . . . . . . . . **$8.69**

### TARGET RIFLE

**Features**: An ideal training and field cartridge, the .22 Long Rifle Target also excels in informal competitions. The target .22 provides the casual shooter with accuracy at an economical price.
**Available in**: .22LR
**From:** . . . . . . . . . . . . . . . . **$7.99**

**RWS SILVER SELECTION WITH UNI PROFESSIONAL**

**RWS ID-CLASSIC**

# Weatherby

**WEATHERBY MAGNUM**

## WEATHERBY MAGNUM
**Features**: Weatherby Magnum cartridges are loaded with a variety of popular bullet types for a wide range of shooting purposes.
***Available in***: .224, .240, .257, .270, 7mm, .300, .340, .30-378, .338-378, .375, .378, .416, .460
**MSRP**................**$43–$193**

# Winchester Ammunition

## Rifle Ammunition

### ACCUBOND CT
**Features**: Fully-bonded lead alloy core, high weight retention, pinpoint accuracy, boattail design, Lubalox coating/red polymer tip.
***Available in***: .25-06 Rem., .25 WSSM, .270 Win., .270 WSM, .30-06 Spfd., .300 Win. Mag., .300 WSM, .325 WSM, .338 Win. Mag., .338 Lapua Mag., 7mm Rem. Mag., 7mm WSM
**From:**.............**$39.99–$87.99**

### BALLISTIC SILVERTIP
**Features**: Solid-based boattail design delivers excellent long-range accuracy. In .22 calibers, the ballistic plastic polycarbonate Silvertip bullet initiates rapid fragmentation. In medium to larger calibers, special jacket contours extend range and reduce cross-wind drift. Harder lead core ensures proper bullet expansion.
***Available in***: .22-250 Rem., .223 Rem., .204 Ruger, .223 WSSM, .243 Win., .243 WSSM, .25-06 Rem., .25 WSSM, .270 Win., .270 WSM, .280 Rem., .300 Win. Mag., .30-06 Spfd., .300 WSM, .30-30 Win., .308 Win., .325 WSM, .338 Win. Mag., 7mm Rem. Mag., 7mm-08 Rem., 7mm WSM
**Box 20:**...........**$21.49–$56.99**

### E-TIP LEAD-FREE
**Features**: The E-Tip lead-free bullet is developed for big-game hunters and complies with current state non-toxic regulations. Co-developed with Nosler, the bullet features an E2 energy

expansion cavity, which promotes consistent upset, and is made of gliding metal instead of pure copper, which helps prevent barrel fouling.
***Available in***: .270 WSM, .270 Win., .30-06 Spfd., .300 WSM, .300 Win. Mag., .308 Win., 7mm Rem. Mag.
**From: .** . . . . . . . . . **$39.39–$65.99**

### PDX1 DEFENDER CENTERFIRE RIFLE
**Features**: Given the recent popularity of modern sporting rifles (MSR) among shooters and hunters, Winchester has designed a product using Split Core Technology (SCT) for personal defense. The SCT technology, using a quick expansion front lead core and a deep driving bonded rear lead core, creates the ultimate .223 Rem. Home Defense load.

***Available in***: .223 Rem.,.308 Win., 7.62x39mm
**Box 20:** . . . . . . . . . . **$29.99–$39.99**

### POWER MAX BONDED BULLETS
**Features**: Key features of the Super-X bullet include: protected hollow point PHP design, lead core bonded to jacket with proprietary process, massive frontal area of mushroom is more than double original diameter, lead remains bonded to jacket after impact.
***Available in***: .223 Rem., .243 Win., .270 Win., .270 WSM, .30-06 Spfd., .300 WSM, .30-30 Win., .308 Win., .300 Win. Mag., .325 WSM. .338 Win. Mag., 7mm Rem. Mag., .338 Lapua Mag., 7mm WSM
**From: .** . . . . . . . . **$39.99–$55.99**

**WINCHESTER ACCUBOND CT**

# Winchester Ammunition

## RAZORBACK XT

*Features*: Razorback XT is designed specifically for the rugged demands of boar hunting. It drives through thick hide and bone to deliver lethal force. This lead-free bullet has a beveled profile and is made of solid gilding metal with a hollow point for delayed expansion on extremely tough wild hogs. Flash suppressed powders make Razorback XT perfect for use in low light or after dark with night vision technology.
*Available in*: .223 Rem., .270 Win., .30-06 Spfd., .308 Win., 7.62x39mm
**Box 20:** . . . . . . . . . **$25.99–$37.99**

## SUPER-X HOLLOW POINT

*Available in*: .204 Ruger, .218 Bee, .22 Hornet, .30-30 Win.
**From:** . . . . . . . . . . **$18.99–$77.99**

## SUPER-X HOLLOW SOFT POINT

*Available in*: .30 Carbine, .44 Rem. Mag.
**From:** . . . . . . . . . . . . . . . .**$22.99**

## SUPER-X JACKETED SOFT POINT

*Available in*: .357 Mag.
**Box 50:** . . . . . . . . . . . . . . . .**$53.93**

## SUPER-X JHP

*Available in*: .45-70 Govt.
**Box 20:** . . . . . . . . . . . . . .**$32.99**

## SUPER-X LEAD

*Available in*: .32-20 Win.
**Box 20:** . . . . . . . . . . . . . . . .**$43.49**

## SUPER-X POSITIVE EXPANDING POINT

*Available in*: .25-06 Rem., .25 WSSM
**From:** . . . . . . . . . . . .**$30.99–$32.99**

## SUPER-X POWER CORE 95/5

*Features*: Start with a 95/5 copper alloy, integrate a highly engineered contoured cavity—and you have a new benchmark in lead-free big-game cartridges. Featuring a devastating effective bullet with massive initial impact shock plus deep penetration and virtually 100 percent retained weight to assure maximum trauma to bone and vitals.

*Available in*: .223 Rem., .243 Win., .270 Win., .270 WSM, .30-06 Spfd., .300 Win. Mag., .300 WSM, .30-30 Win., .308 Win., 7mm-08 Rem., 7mm Rem. Mag., 7mm WSM
**Box 20:** . . . . . . . . . . **$23.99–$46.999**

## SUPER-X POWER-POINT

*Available in*: .22-250 Rem., .223 Rem., .223 WSSM, .243 Win., .243 WSSM, .257 Roberts +P, .264 Win. Mag., .270 Win., .270 WSM, .284 Win., .300 Savage, .30-06 Spfd., .300 WSM, .30-30 Win., .303 British, .30-40 Krag, .307 Win., .308 Win., .300 Win. Mag., .325 WSM, .32 Win. Spl., .338 Win. Mag., .356 Win., 35 Rem., .375 Win., 6mm Rem., 7mm-08 Rem., 7mm Mauser (7 x 57), 7mm Rem. Mag., 7mm WSM, 8mm Mauser (8 x 57)
**Box 20:** . . . . . . . . . . **$15.99–$52.99**

## SUPER-X SILVERTIP HOLLOW POINT

*Available in*: 44 Rem. Mag.
**Box 20:** . . . . . . . . . . . . . . . .**$26.99**

## SUPER-X SOFT POINT

*Available in*: .22 Hornet, .25-20 Win., .25-35 Win., .38-40 Win., .38-55 Win., .44-40 Win., .458 Win., 6.5x55 Swedish, 7.62x39mm Russian
**Box 20:** . . . . . . . . . . **$25.99–$71.99**

## SUPREME HOLLOW POINT BOATTAIL MATCH

*Features*: (Exclude Column)
*Available in*: .308 Win. Match, .338 Lapua Mag.
**From:** . . . . . . . . . . . . . . .**$36.99**

## XP3

*Features*: The XP3 bullet delivers precision accuracy, awesome knockdown power, and deep penetration all in one package—and it's as effective on thin-skinned game, like deer and antelope, as it is on tough game, like elk, moose, bear, and African animals, at short and long ranges.
*Available in*: .243 Win., .243 WSSM, .270 WSM, .270 Win., .30-06 Spfd., .300 WSM, .300 Win. Mag., .308 Win., .325 WSM, 7mm Rem. Mag., 7mm WSM
**Box 20:** . . . . . . . . . . **$39.99–$64.99**

## Handgun Ammunition

## DUAL BOND

*Features*: Dual Bond offers a large hollow point cavity, which provides consistent upsets at a variety of ranges and impact velocities. The heavy outer jacket is mechanically bonded to the inner bullet. The inner bullet utilizes a proprietary bonding process for a combination of knockdown power, solid penetration, and significant tissue damage.
*Available in*: .44 Rem. Mag., .454 Cassull, .460 S&W Mag., .500 S&W Mag.
**Box 20:** . . . . . . . . . . **$35.99–$60.99**

## FULL METAL JACKET

*Available in*: .45 Auto, .38 Spl., 9mm Luger, .25 Auto, .38 Super Auto +P, .380 Auto, .40 S&W, .32 Auto, .45 G.A.P., 9mm Luger
**From:** . . . . . . . . . . . . **$13.99–$48.99**

**WINCHESTER RAZORBACK XT**

**WINCHESTER DUAL BOND**

# Winchester Ammunition

## LEAD FLATNOSE
*Available in*: .38 Spl., .44-40 Win., .44 S&W Spl., .45 Colt
**Box 50:** . . . . . . . . . . $30.99–$39.99

## PDX1 DEFENDER
*Features*: The new Winchester Supreme Elite Bonded PDX1, which was chosen by the FBI as their primary service round, is engineered to maximize terminal ballistics, as defined by the demanding FBI test protocol, which simulates real-world threats.
*Available in*: .357 Mag., .357 Sig., .380 Auto, .38 Spl., +P, .40 S&W, .45 Colt, .45 Auto, 9mm Luger +P, 9mm Luger
**From:** . . . . . . . . . . . $17.79–$25.99

## PLATINUM TIP HOLLOW POINT
*Features*: Patented notched reserve taper bullet jacket, plated heavy wall jacket, and two-part hollow point cavity for uniform bullet expansion, massive energy depot.
*Available in*: .41 Rem. Mag., .44 Rem. Mag., .454 Casull, .500 S&W
**Box 20:** . . . . . . . . . . $28.49–$59.99

## SUPER-X BLANK-BLACK POWDER
*Available in*: .32 S&W
**Box 50:** . . . . . . . . . . $31.49–$32.99

## SUPER-X BLANK-SMOKELESS
*Available in*: .38 Special
**Box 50:** . . . . . . . . . . $37.49–$39.99

## SUPER-X EXPANDING POINT
*Available in*: .25 Auto
**Box 50:** . . . . . . . . . . . $38.99

## SUPER-X HOLLOW SOFT POINT
*Available in*: .30 Carbine, .44 Rem. Mag.
**From:** . . . . . . . . . . . . . $22.99

## SUPER-X JACKETED SOFT POINT
*Available in*: .357 Mag., .38 Spl.
**From:** . . . . . . . . . . . $23.99–$45.49

## SUPER-X JHP
*Available in*: .357 Mag., .38 Spl. +P, .454 Casull, .45 Win. Mag., .460 S&W

**WINCHESTER PLATINUM TIP HOLLOW POINT**

**WINCHESTER SUPER-X SILVERTIP HOLLOW POINT**

**WINCHESTER DYNA POINT - PLATED**

Mag.
**Box 20:** . . . . . . . . . $33.99–$50.99

## SUPER-X LEAD ROUND NOSE
*Available in*: .32 Short Colt, .32 S&W Long, .32 S&W, .38 Spl., .38 S&W, .44 S&W Spl., .45 Colt
**From:** . . . . . . . . . . . $18.99–$43.99

## SUPER-X LEAD SEMI-WAD CUTTER
*Available in*: .38 Spl.
**Box 50:** . . . . . . . . . . . $34.99

## SUPER-X LEAD SEMI-WAD CUTTER HP
*Available in*: .38 Spl. +P
**Box 50:** . . . . . . . . . . . $35.49

## SUPER-X MATCH
*Available in*: .38 Spl. Super Match
**Box 50:** . . . . . . . . . . . . . $30.99

## SUPER-X SILVERTIP HOLLOW POINT
*Available in*: 10mm Auto, .32 Auto, .357 Mag., .380 Auto, .38 Super Auto +P, .38 Spl. +P, .38 Spl., .40 S&W, .41 Rem. Mag., .44 Rem. Mag., .44 S&W Spl., .45 Auto, .45 Colt, .45 G.A.P., 9x23 Win., 9mm Luger
**From:** . . . . . . . . . . . $20.49–$50.99

## Rimfire Ammunition

## DYNA POINT - PLATED
*Available in*: .22 Win. Mag.
**Box 50:** . . . . . . . . . . . . . $8.99

# Winchester Ammunition

### SUPER-X #12 SHOT
*Available in*: .22LR
From:...................$8.99

### SUPER-X BLANK
*Available in*: .22 Short
Box 50:.............$8.49

### SUPER-X FULL METAL JACKET
*Available in*: .22 Win. Mag.
Box 50:.............$10.99

### SUPER-X JHP
*Available in*: .17 HMR, .17 Win. Super Mag., .22 Win. Mag.
From:...........$10.99–$13.99

### SUPER-X LEAD HOLLOW POINT
*Available in*: .22LR
From:.............$2.99–$7.89

### SUPER-X LEAD ROUND NOSE
*Available in*: .22LR, .22 Long, .22 Short
From:.............$2.99–$3.49

### SUPER-X LEAD ROUND NOSE, STANDARD VELOCITY
*Available in*: .22LR
From:.............$3.39–$5.99

### SUPER-X POWER-POINT, LEAD HOLLOW POINT
*Available in*: .22LR
From:.............$3.49–$7.89

### XPERT LEAD HOLLOW POINT
*Available in*: .22LR
Box 500:..........$29.99

### VARMINT HIGH ENERGY
*Available in*: .22LR, .22 Win. Mag., .17 Win. Super Mag.
From:.............$6.49–$15.99

### VARMINT HIGH VELOCITY
*Available in*: .22 Win. Mag., .17 HMR, .17 Win. Super Mag.
Box 50:...........$13.99–$14.99

### VARMINT LEAD FREE
*Available in*: .22 Mag., .22LR
From:.............$7.59–$13.19

### WILDCAT 22 LEAD ROUND NOSE
*Available in*: .22LR
Box 50:..............$2.19

## Shotgun Ammunition– Loads

### AA FEATHERLITE
*Features*: 20-gauge Featherlite AA shotshells are high-performance, low-recoil training loads for sporting clays, trap, and skeet. This new Featherlite load was designed to address recoil. AA loads use Winchester proprietary one-piece plastic wads, clean burning powder, and hard shot for consistent pattern performance.
*Available in*: 20 Ga. (2 ¾ in.)
Box 25:................$8.89

### AA TARGET LOADS
*Features*: The hunter's choice for a wide variety of game bird applications, available in an exceptionally broad selection of loadings, from 12-gauge to .410 bore, with shot size options ranging from BBs all the way down to 9s—suitable for everything from quail to farm predators.
*Available in*: 12, 20, 28 Ga. (2 ¾ in.), .410 (2½ in.); Shot sizes: 7.5, 8, 8.5, 9
From:.............$8.49–$9.99

### BLIND SIDE
*Features*: Blind Side ammunition combines ground-breaking, stacked HEX Shot technology and the Diamond Cut Wad in the most deadly Winchester waterfowl load available. Loaded with 100 percent HEX Shot, you get more pellets on target, a larger kill zone, and more trauma inducing pellets than ever before, meaning quick kill shots.
*Available in*: 12 Ga. (2 ¾ in., 3 in., 3 ½ in.), 20 Ga. (3 in.); Shot size: BB, 1, 2, 3, 5, 6
From:.............$19.99–$26.99

### SUPER TARGET LOADS
*Available in*: 12, 20 Ga. (2 ¾ in.); Shot sizes: 7, 7.5, 8, 9
From:.............$5.70–$9.99

### SUPER PHEASANT LOADS
*Available in*: 12 Ga. (2 ¾ in., 3 in.), 20 Ga. (3 in.); Shot sizes: 4, 5, 6
From:.............$12.79–$21.49

AMMUNITION

WINCHESTER VARMINT LEAD FREE

**WINCHESTER AA FEATHERLITE**

**WINCHESTER BLIND SIDE**

# Winchester Ammunition

## SUPER PHEASANT STEEL LOADS
*Available in*: 12 Ga. (3 in.); Shot size: 4
**From:** . . . . . . . . . . . . . . . . . .**$21.49**

## SUPER-X TRIALS AND BLANKS
*Available in*: 10 Ga. (2 $^7/_8$ in.), 12 Ga. (2 ¾ in.)
**From:** . . . . . . . . . . . . . . . . . .**$35.49**

## SUPER-X TURKEY LOADS
*Available in*: 12 Ga. (2 ¾ in., 3 in.); Shot sizes: 4, 5, 6
**Box 10:** . . . . . . . . . . . . . $8.79–$10.39

## SUPER-X XPERT HI-VELOCITY STEEL LOADS
*Available in*: 12 Ga. (2 ¾ in., 3 in.), 20 Ga. (3 in.); Shot sizes: BB, 1, 2, 3, 4
**From:** . . . . . . . . . . . . . **$11.49–$12.99**

## SUPER-X XPERT STEEL LOADS
*Available in*: 12, 28 Ga., .410 bore (2 ¾ in.); Shot sizes: 6, 7
**From:** . . . . . . . . . . . . . **$7.39–$13.59**

## XTENDED RANGE HD COYOTE
*Available in*: 12 Ga. (3 in.); Shot size: B
**Box 5:** . . . . . . . . . . . . . . . **$13.99**

## XTENDED RANGE HD TURKEY
*Available in*: 12 Ga. (2 ¾ in., 3 in., 3 ½ in.), 20 Ga. (3 in.); Shot sizes: 4, 5, 6
**From:** . . . . . . . . . . . . . **$22.39–$41.99**

## XTENDED RANGE HD WATERFOWL
*Available in*: 12 Ga. (2 ¾ in., 3 in., 3 ½ in.), 20 Ga. (3 in.); Shot sizes: 2, 4, B
**From:** . . . . . . . . . . . . . **$22.39–$30.59**

## Shotgun Ammunition– Slugs

## SUPER-X BUCKSHOT
*Available in*: 12 Ga. (2 ¾ in., 3 in., 3½ in.), 20 Ga. (2 ¾ in.), .410 (2½ in., 3 in.); Shot sizes: 4, 3, 1, 00, 000
**From:** . . . . . . . . . . . . . **$4.79–$16.79**

## PDX1 12 AND BUCK
*Features*: The 12-gauge PDX1 Defender ammunition features a distinctive black hull, black oxide high-base head and three pellets of Grex buffered 00 plated buckshot nested on top of a 1 oz. rifled slug. The result is the ideal, tight patterning personal defense load. The slug/buckshot combination provides optimum performance at short and long ranges while compensating for aim error.
*Available in*: 12 Ga. (2 ¾ in.)
**From:** . . . . . . . . . . . . . . . . . .**$13.99**

## PDX1 DEFENDER SEGMENTING SLUG
*Features*: The uniquely designed slug segments into three pieces when fired into FBI protocol barriers such as bare, light cloth, and heavy cloth covered ballistic gelatin. The round is designed to compensate for aim error over traditional slugs.
*Available in*: 12 Ga. ( 2 ¾ in.)
**Box 10:** . . . . . . . . . . . . . . . .**$14.99**

## RACKMASTER RIFLED SLUGS
*Features*: The RackMaster system design consists of a hard-hitting lead nose and the innovative WinGlide rear projectile stabilizer, engineered specifically to improve in-bore alignment and enhance down-range accuracy. RackMaster delivers high accuracy, hard-hitting knockdown performance to hunters shooting shotguns with either smooth bore, rifled choke tube or fully-rifled barrels.
*Available in*: 12 Ga. (2 ¾ in., 3 in.), 20 Ga. (2 ¾ in.)
**From:** . . . . . . . . . . . . . **$6.79–$8.99**

## SUPER-X
*Available in*: 12, 20 Ga. (2 ¾ in., 3 in.), .410 (2½ in., 3 in.)
**From:** . . . . . . . . . . . . . **$4.59–$14.17**

## XP3 SABOT SHOTGUN
*Available in*: 12 Ga. (2 ¾ in., 3 in.)
**Box 5:** . . . . . . . . . . . . . **$11.99–$15.49**

**WINCHESTER XP3 SABOT SHOTGUN**

**WINCHESTER PDX1 DEFENDER SEGMENTING SLUG**

**WINCHESTER SUPER-X BUCKSHOT**

# MUZZLELOADING BULLETS

## Barnes Bullets

### EXPANDER MZ
**Features**: 100 percent copper with a large, hollow cavity; six copper petals with double-diameter expansion; full weight retention.
**Available in**: .45 (195 gr.), .50 (250, 300 gr.), .54 (275, 325 gr.)
**Box 24**:. . . . . . . . . . . . $34.15–$77.67

### SPIT-FIRE MZ
**Features**: A streamlined semi-spitzer give, boattail base and tack-driving accuracy; six razor-sharp copper petals create massive shock, deep penetration, and double-diameter expansion; retains virtually 100 percent of its original weight; available in 15-and 24-bullet packs
**Available in**: .50 (245, 285 gr.)
**Box 24**:. . . . . . . . . . . . $36.02–$37.26

### SPIT-FIRE TMZ
**Features**: 100 percent copper boattail design with streamlined polymer tip for faster expansion; expands at 1050 fps.; remains intact at extreme velocities; redesigned sabot loads faster while retaining tight gas seal
**Available in**: .50 (250, 290 gr.)
**Box 24**:. . . . . . . . . . . . $39.75–$42.23

**BARNES BULLETS SPIT-FIRE MZ**

**BARNES BULLETS SPIT-FIRE TMZ**

**BARNES BULLETS EXPANDER MZ**

## Federal Fusion Ammunition

### FUSION MUZZLELOADING SLUGS
**Features**: Now you can harness the energy of Fusion muzzleloader sabot slugs. Fusion technology gives .50-caliber crush-rib sabots reason to seat themselves at the breech of your T/C.
**Available in**: .50 (240, 260, 300 gr.)
**Box 12**:. . . . . . . . . . . . $12.49–$16.99

**FEDERAL FUSION MUZZLELOADING SLUGS**

AMMUNITION

www.skynorsepublishing.com

## SABER TOOTH BELTED

**Features**: Copper-clad belted bullets in Harvester Crush Rib Sabot.
**Available in**: .50 (250, 270, 300, 350 gr.)
**MSRP**....................**$11.99**

## SCORPION FUNNEL POINT MAG

**Features**: Electroplated copper plating does not separate from lead core. Loaded in Harvester Crush Rib Sabots.
**Available in**: .50 (240, 260, 300 gr.); .54 (240, 260, 300 gr.)
**MSRP**..............**$8.99–$11.49**

## SCORPION PT GOLD

**Features**: Scorpion PT Gold Ballistic Tip Bullets are electroplated with copper plating that does not separate from lead core. The PT Gold offers greater accuracy at longer ranges than

**HARVESTER SABER TOOTH BELTED**

**HARVESTER SCORPION FUNNEL POINT MAG**

**HARVESTER SCORPION PT GOLD**

a hollow point. The 3 percent antimony makes the bullet harder than pure lead.
**Available in**: .45 (240, 260, 300 gr.); .50 ((240, 260, 300 gr.)
**MSRP**.............**$10.99–$21.99**

# Hornady

## GREAT PLAINS - PA CONICAL

**Features**: Hornady's PA Conical bullets deliver greater accuracy and more knock-down power. PA bullets are prelubed with special knurled grooves on the bearing surface to hold the lubricant on the bullet—no need for a patch or sabot.
**Available in**: .50 (240, 385 gr.); .54 (425 gr.)
**MSRP**.............**$11.41–$14.64**

## HP/XTP BULLET/SABOT

**Features**: Hornady XTP bullet/sabot combination with controlled expansion XTP bullet.
**Available in**: .50 cal. sabot with .44 (240 gr.) or .45 (240, 300 gr.) bullet
**MSRP**.............**$12.72–$15.01**

**HORNADY GREAT PLAINS - PA CONICAL**

**HORNADY HP/XTP BULLET/SABOT**

AMMUNITION

# Knight Rifles

### FTX BULLETS
*Features*: Copper bullet with patented Flex Tip Design and Sabot; 18 pack
*Available in*: .52 (325 gr.)
**MSRP** . . . . . . . . . . . . . . . . . .**$19.99**

### JACKETED BULLETS WITH SABOTS
*Features*: Copper jacketed, hollow point bullet with sabot; 20 pack
*Available in*: .50 (240, 260, 300 gr.)
**MSRP** . . . . . . . . . . . . **$14.99–$15.99**

### LEAD BULLETS WITH SABOTS
*Features*: Pure lead bullet with sabot; 20 pack
*Available in*: .50 (260, 310 gr.)
**MSRP** . . . . . . . . . . . . **$14.99–$15.99**

### POLYMER-TIP BOAT-TAIL BULLETS
*Features*: Sabot with all copper polymer tip bullet; expands into six razor-sharp copper petals while retaining 100 percent of original

**KNIGHT RIFLES FTX BULLETS**

weight; 18 pack
*Available in*: .50 (250, 290 gr.)
**MSRP** . . . . . . . . . . . . **$25.99–$31.49**

### RED HOT BULLETS
*Features*: Saboted Barnes solid copper bullet with superior expansion.

**KNIGHT RIFLES JACKETED BULLETS WITH SABOTS**
*Available in*: .45 (175 gr.); .50 (250, 300 gr.); .52 (275, 350, 375 gr.)
**MSRP** . . . . . . . . . . . . **$22.99–$31.49**

### SPITZER BOAT-TAIL BULLETS
*Features*: Sabot loaded with Barnes Spitzer Boat-tail bullet; 18 pack
*Available in*: .50 (245 gr.)
**MSRP** . . . . . . . . . . . . . . . . . .**$25.99**

# PowerBelt

### AEROLITE
*Features*: Designed specifically for use with standard 100-grain loads. The AeroLite's shape is noticeably longer and more aerodynamic than other PowerBelts of similar weight. This longer length is made possible by the massive hollow point cavity that is filled by an oversized polycarbonate point.
*Available in*: .50 (250, 300 gr.)
**MSRP** . . . . . . . . . . . . **$29.95–$31.95**

### COPPER
*Features*: Thin copper plating reduces bore friction while allowing for optimal bullet expansion. Available in four tip designs: Hollow Point, AeroTip, Flat Point, and Steel Tip.
*Available in*: .45 (175, 195, 225, 275 gr.); .50 (223, 245, 295, 348, 405, 444 gr.); .54 (295, 348, 405, 444 gr.)
**MSRP** . . . . . . . . . . . . **$21.95–$64.95**

**POWERBELT AEROLITE**

**POWERBELT COPPER**

**POWERBELT PLATINUM AEROTIP**

**POWERBELT PURE LEAD HOLLOW POINT**

### PLATINUM AEROTIP
*Features*: Proprietary hard plating and aggressive bullet taper design for improved ballistic coefficient. A large-size fluted gas check produces higher and more consistent pressures.
*Available in*: .45 (223, 300 gr.); .50 (270, 300, 338 gr.)
**MSRP** . . . . . . . . . . . . **$28.95–$30.95**

### PURE LEAD
*Features*: Pure lead, available in four different grain weights in Hollow Point and 444 in Flat Point.
*Available in*: .50 (295, 348, 405, 444 gr.); .54 (295, 348 , 405, 444 gr.)
**MSRP** . . . . . . . . . . . . **$21.95–$22.95**

AMMUNITION

# Thompson/Center

## MAG EXPRESS SABOTS
***Features***: Mag Express Sabots separate from the projectile quickly. Sabots are preassembled with XTP bullets, but also available separately.
***Available in***: .50 (240, 300 gr.); .54 (250 gr.)
**Box 30:** . . . . . . . . . . . **$26.38–$28.41**

## MAXI-BALL SUPERIOR PENETRATION
***Features***: An exceptionally accurate bullet and the preferred bullet for penetration needed for large game like elk. Lubricating grooves (maxi wide grooves)
***Available in***: .50 (320, 370 gr.)
**Box 20:** . . . . . . . . . . . **$27.39–$28.41**

## MAXI-HUNTER CONICAL ALL LEAD
***Features***: Maximum expansion on deer-sized game. Lubricating grooves (maxi hunter multiple grooves)
***Available in***: .50 (275, 350 gr.)
**Box 20:** . . . . . . . . . . . **$26.38–$29.42**

## SHOCK WAVE SABOTS
***Features***: Polymer tip spire point bullet with sabot. Incorporates harder lead core with walls interlocked with the jacket for maximum weight retention and expansion. Available with spire point or bonded bullets
***Available in***: .45 (200 gr.); .50 (200, 250, 300 gr.)
**Box 15:** . . . . . . . . . . . **$21.30–$31.45**

**THOMPSON/CENTER MAXI-BALL
SUPERIOR PENETRATION**

**THOMPSON/CENTER MAXI-HUNTER
CONICAL ALL LEAD**

**THOMPSON/CENTER SHOCK
WAVE SABOTS**

# Winchester Ammunition

## SUPREME PLATINUM TIP BULLETS & SABOTS
***Features***: The Platinum Tip Hollow Point bullet includes Winchester's patented reverse taper jacket and notching technology that delivers expansion and on-target energy delivery.
***Available in***: .50 (260 gr.); .54 (400 gr.)
**Box 30:** . . . . . . . . . . . . . . . . **$34.49**

**WINCHESTER SUPREME PLATINUM TIP
BULLETS & SABOTS**

AMMUNITION

# BULLETS

## Barnes Bullets

Barnes continues to develop leading-edge products with a wide range of workability and functionality using an incredibly broad range of purpose-built components and ammunition. Barnes's most popular hunting bullets, the all-copper TSX line, also comes with a streamlined polymer tip. The Barnes Buster line can be used for both rifles and handguns.

## Rifle Bullets

| Caliber & Description | "223 S BT" | 6MM S BT | 25 S BT | 6.5MM S BT | 270 S BT | 7MM S BT | 30 S BT | 338 FN | 338 RN | 9.3mm FN | 9.3mm FN | 9.3MM RN | 9.3MM RN | 375 RN | 375 FN | 375 RN |
|---|---|---|---|---|---|---|---|---|---|---|---|---|---|---|---|---|
| Diameter, Inches | .224 | .243 | .257 | .264 | .277 | .284 | .308 | .338 | .338 | .366 | .366 | .366 | .366 | .375 | .375 | .375 |
| Weight, Grains | 45 | 75 | 90 | 110 | 120 | 140 | 165 | 250 | 250 | 250 | 286 | 250 | 286 | 270 | 270 | 300 |
| Density | .128 | .181 | .195 | .225 | .223 | .248 | .248 | .313 | .313 | .267 | .305 | .267 | .305 | .274 | .274 | .305 |
| Ballistic Coefficient | .195 | .341 | .325 | .452 | .438 | .464 | .438 | .208 | .247 | .222 | .258 | .214 | .247 | .207 | .284 | .230 |
| Catalog Number | 22425 | 24375 | 25793 | 26422 | 27763 | 28464 | 30816 | 33824 | 33825 | 36602 | 36604 | 36611 | 36612 | 37512 | 37513 | 37525 |

| Caliber & Description | 375 FN | 375 RN | 375 FN | 450/400 FN | 416 FN | 416 RN | 416 FN | 416 RN | 404 JEFF FN | 404 JEFF RN | 458 SOCOM FN | 458 FN | 458 RN | 458 FN | 458 RN | 470 NITRO FN |
|---|---|---|---|---|---|---|---|---|---|---|---|---|---|---|---|---|
| Diameter, Inches | .375 | .375 | .375 | .410 | .416 | .416 | .416 | .416 | .422 | .422 | .458 | .458 | .458 | .458 | .458 | .474 |
| Weight, Grains | 300 | 350 | 350 | 400 | 350 | 350 | 400 | 400 | 400 | 400 | 330 | 450 | 450 | 500 | 500 | 500 |
| Density | .305 | .356 | .356 | .340 | .289 | .289 | .330 | .330 | .319 | .321 | .226 | .306 | .306 | .341 | .341 | .318 |
| Ballistic Coefficient | .307 | .283 | - | .292 | .364 | - | .388 | .261 | .236 | .261 | .191 | .362 | .267 | .394 | .301 | .243 |
| Catalog Number | 37526 | 37527 | 37528 | 40935 | 41629 | 41628 | 41635 | 41660 | 42320 | 42330 | 45861 | 45828 | 45840 | 45856 | 45855 | 47455 |

| Caliber & Description | 505 GIBBS RN | 505 Gibbs FN | 500 NITRO FN | 500 JEFF RN | 500 JEFF FN | 50 BMG BORE RIDER | 50 BMG BORE RIDER | 577 NITRO FN | 600 NITRO FN |
|---|---|---|---|---|---|---|---|---|---|
| Diameter, Inches | .504 | .504 | .509 | .510 | .510 | .510 | .510 | .583 | .618 |
| Weight, Grains | 525 | 525 | 570 | 535 | 535 | 750 | 800 | 750 | 900 |
| Density | .295 | .294 | .314 | .294 | .294 | .412 | .439 | .315 | .337 |
| Ballistic Coefficient | .267 | .226 | .243 | - | .219 | 1.070 | 1.095 | .257 | .380 |
| Catalog Number | 50505 | 50525 | 50950 | 51003 | 51053 | 510750A | 510800A | 58525 | 62025 |

**From: $20.74–$61.91**

# Barnes Bullets

## BARNES BUSTER

| Caliber & Description | "44 MAG. FN FB" | 454 CASULL FN FB | 45/70 FN FB | 500 S&W FN FB |
|---|---|---|---|---|
| Diameter, Inches | .429 | .451 | .458 | .500 |
| Weight, Grains | 300 | 325 | 400 | 400 |
| Density | .233 | .228 | .272 | .229 |
| Ballistic Coefficient | .241 | .206 | .242 | .220 |
| Catalog Number | 42982 | 45135 | 45884 | 50040 |

**Box 50: $52.14–$63.31**

## BARNES ORIGINAL

| Caliber & Description | "348 WIN FN SP" | 348 WIN FN SP | 375 WIN FN SP | 38/55 FN SP | 38/55 FN SP | "45/70 SSSP" | 45/70 FN SP | 45/70 SSSP | 45/70 FN SP | 50/110 WIN FN SP | 50/110 WIN FN SP |
|---|---|---|---|---|---|---|---|---|---|---|---|
| Diameter, Inches | .348 | .348 | .375 | .375 | .377 | .458 | .458 | .458 | .458 | .510 | .510 |
| Weight, Grains | 220 | 250 | 255 | 255 | 255 | 300 | 300 | 400 | 400 | 300 | 450 |
| Jckt. | .032 | .032 | .032 | .032 | .032 | .032 | .032 | .032 | .032 | .032 | .032 |
| Density | .260 | .295 | .259 | .259 | .256 | .204 | .204 | .272 | .272 | .165 | .247 |
| Ballistic Coefficient | .301 | .327 | .290 | .290 | .290 | .291 | .227 | .389 | .302 | .183 | .274 |
| Catalog Number | 34805 | 34810 | 375w20 | 38/5510 | 38/5520 | 457010 | 457020 | 457030 | 457040 | 5011010 | 5011020 |

**From: $20.85–$58.86**

## LRX BULLETS

| Caliber & Description | "6.5MM BT" | 270 BT | 7MM BT | 7MM BT | 30 BT | 30 BT | 338 LAPUA BT | 338 LAPUA BT |
|---|---|---|---|---|---|---|---|---|
| Diameter, Inches | .264 | .277 | .284 | .284 | .308 | .308 | .338 | .338 |
| Weight, Grains | 127 | 129 | 145 | 168 | 175 | 200 | 265 | 280 |
| Density | .257 | .240 | .257 | .257 | .264 | .301 | .331 | .350 |
| Ballistic Coefficient | .468 | .463 | .486 | .550 | .508 | .546 | .575 | .667 |
| Catalog Number | 26403 | 27740 | 28404 | 28407 | 30807 | 30880 | 33882 | 33881 |

**Box 50: $39.02–$50.83**

## MATCH BURNER BULLETS

| Caliber & Description | "22 FB" | 22 BT | 22 BT | 6MM FB | 6MM BT | 6.5MM BT | 7MM BT | "30 PALMA FB" | 30 BT |
|---|---|---|---|---|---|---|---|---|---|
| Diameter, Inches | .224 | .224 | .224 | .243 | .243 | .264 | .284 | .308 | .308 |
| Weight, Grains | 52 | 69 | 85 | 68 | 105 | 140 | 171 | 155 | 175 |
| Density | .148 | .196 | .242 | .165 | .254 | .287 | .303 | .233 | .264 |
| Ballistic Coefficient | .224 | .339 | .410 | .267 | .511 | .586 | .645 | .467 | .521 |
| Catalog Number | 22413 | 22415 | 22417 | 24313 | 24316 | 26404 | 28414 | 30892 | 30896 |

**Box 100: $20.91–$34.69**

**AMMUNITION**

# Barnes Bullets

## M/LE Reduced Ricochet, Limited Penetration (RRLP) Bullets

| Caliber & Description | "223/5.56 FB" | 6.8MM FB | 30 FB | 7.62X39 FB |
|---|---|---|---|---|
| Diameter, Inches | .224 | .277 | .308 | .310 |
| Weight, Grains | 55 | 85 | 150 | 108 |
| Density | .157 | .158 | .226 | .161 |
| Ballistic Coefficient | .225 | .229 | .357 | .243 |
| Catalog Number | 22414 | 27711 | 30802 | 31010 |

From: $20.74–$31.92

## M/LE TAC-TX Bullets

| Caliber & Description | 300 AAC Blackout | 6.5mm BT | 6.5mm BT | 6.8mm BT | 30 FB | 30 BT | 338 BT | 338 BT | 458 SOCOM BT |
|---|---|---|---|---|---|---|---|---|---|
| Diameter, Inches | - | .264 | .264 | .277 | .308 | .308 | .338 | .338 | .458 |
| Weight, Grains | 110 | 100 | 120 | 95 | 110 | 168 | 225 | 265 | 300 |
| Density | .166 | .205 | .246 | .177 | .166 | .253 | .281 | .331 | .204 |
| Ballistic Coefficient | .289 | - | .443 | .292 | .295 | .470 | .514 | .575 | .236 |
| Catalog Number | 30811 | 26412 | 26414 | 27721 | 30851 | 30856 | 33858 | 33856 | 45863 |

From: $35.01–$54.69

## Multi-Purpose Green (MPG) Bullets

| Caliber & Description | "223 FB" | 6.8MM FB | 30 FB | 7.62X39 FB |
|---|---|---|---|---|
| Diameter, Inches | .224 | .277 | .308 | .310 |
| Weight, Grains | 55 | 85 | 150 | 108 |
| Density | .157 | .158 | .226 | .161 |
| Ballistic Coefficient | .225 | .229 | .357 | .243 |
| Catalog Number | 22476 | 27701 | 30817 | 31008 |

From: $20.74–$285.00

## TSX Bullets

| Caliber & Description | "22 FB" | 22 FB | 22 FB | 22 FB | 22 BT | 22 BT | 6MM BT | 25 BT | 25 FB | 6.5MM BT | 6.5MM FB | 6.8MM FB | 6.8MM BT | 270 BT | 270 BT |
|---|---|---|---|---|---|---|---|---|---|---|---|---|---|---|---|
| Diameter, Inches | .224 | .224 | .224 | .224 | .224 | .224 | .243 | .257 | .257 | .264 | .264 | .277 | .277 | .277 | .277 |
| Weight, Grains | 45 | 50 | 53 | 55 | 62 | 70 | 85 | 100 | 115 | 120 | 130 | 85 | 110 | 130 | 140 |
| Density | .128 | .142 | .151 | .157 | .177 | .199 | .206 | .216 | .249 | .246 | .266 | .158 | .205 | .242 | .261 |
| Ballistic Coefficient | .188 | .197 | .204 | .209 | .287 | .314 | .333 | .336 | .335 | .381 | .365 | .246 | .323 | .374 | .404 |
| Catalog Number | 22441 | 22440 | 22443 | 22444 | 22460 | 22470 | 24341 | 25742 | 25743 | 26441 | 26442 | 27732 | 27738 | 27742 | 27744 |

| Caliber & Description | 270 FB | 7MM BT | 7MM BT | 7MM BT | 7MM FB | 7MM FB | 30 FN FB | 30 FB | 30 BT | 30 BT | 30 BT | 30 BT | 30 BT | 30 FB | 7.62X39 BT |
|---|---|---|---|---|---|---|---|---|---|---|---|---|---|---|---|
| Diameter, Inches | .277 | .284 | .284 | .284 | .284 | .284 | .308 | .308 | .308 | .308 | .308 | .308 | .308 | .308 | .310 |
| Weight, Grains | 150 | 120 | 140 | 150 | 160 | 175 | 150 | 110 | 130 | 150 | 165 | 168 | 180 | 200 | 123 |
| Density | .279 | .213 | .248 | .266 | .283 | .310 | .226 | .166 | .196 | .226 | .248 | .253 | .271 | .301 | .183 |
| Ballistic Coefficient | .386 | .349 | .394 | .408 | .392 | .417 | .184 | .264 | .340 | .369 | .398 | .404 | .453 | .423 | .275 |
| Catalog Number | 27746 | 28442 | 28444 | 28447 | 28446 | 28448 | 30820 | 30835 | 30838 | 30841 | 30843 | 30844 | 30846 | 30848 | 31012 |

# Barnes Bullets

| Caliber & Description | 303/7.65MM FB | 8MM BT | 8MM BT | 338 BT | 338 BT | 338 FB | 338 FB | 338 LAPUA BT | 35 FB | 35 FB | 9.3MM FB | 9.3MM FB | 375 FB | 375 FB | 375 FB |
|---|---|---|---|---|---|---|---|---|---|---|---|---|---|---|---|
| Diameter, Inches | .311 | .323 | .323 | .338 | .338 | .338 | .338 | .338 | .358 | .358 | .366 | .366 | .375 | .375 | .375 |
| Weight, Grains | 150 | 180 | 200 | 185 | 210 | 225 | 250 | 285 | 200 | 225 | 250 | 286 | 235 | 270 | 300 |
| Density | .222 | .246 | .274 | .231 | .263 | .281 | .313 | .356 | .223 | .251 | .267 | .305 | .239 | .274 | .305 |
| Ballistic Coefficient | .322 | .381 | .421 | .352 | .404 | .386 | .425 | .585 | .284 | .359 | .361 | .411 | .270 | .326 | .357 |
| Catalog Number | 31115 | 32306 | 32320 | 33843 | 33845 | 33846 | 33848 | 33850 | 35820 | 35824 | 36625 | 36628 | 37552 | 37556 | 37558 |

| Caliber & Description | 375 FB | 405 WIN FB | 416 FB | 416 FB | 416 FB | 404 JEFFREY FB | 458 FB | 458 FB | 458 FB | 458 FB | 45/70 FN | 45/70 FN | 470 NITRO FB |
|---|---|---|---|---|---|---|---|---|---|---|---|---|---|
| Diameter, Inches | .375 | .411 | .416 | .416 | .416 | .422 | .458 | .458 | .458 | .458 | .458 | .458 | .474 |
| Weight, Grains | 350 | 300 | 300 | 350 | 400 | 400 | 300 | 350 | 450 | 500 | 250 | 300 | 500 |
| Density | .356 | .254 | .248 | .289 | .330 | .321 | .204 | .238 | .306 | .341 | .170 | .204 | .318 |
| Ballistic Coefficient | .425 | .281 | .298 | .345 | .392 | .378 | .234 | .278 | .369 | .412 | .136 | .163 | .363 |
| Catalog Number | 37560 | 41130 | 41683 | 41686 | 41689 | 42340 | 45814 | 45816 | 45819 | 45821 | 45841 | 45843 | 47452 |

| Caliber & Description | 505 GIBBS FB | 500 NITRO FB | 50 BMG BT | 577 NITRO FB |
|---|---|---|---|---|
| Diameter, Inches | .505 | .509 | .510 | .583 |
| Weight, Grains | 525 | 570 | 647 | 750 |
| Density | .294 | .314 | .355 | .315 |
| Ballistic Coefficient | .320 | .369 | .572 | .402 |
| Catalog Number | 50553 | 50958 | 51062 | 58472 |

**From: $19.68–$64.91**

## VARMIN-A-TOR

| Caliber & Description | 20 FB | 22 FB | 22 FB | 6mm FB | 6mm FB |
|---|---|---|---|---|---|
| Diameter, Inches | .204 | .224 | .224 | .243 | .243 |
| Weight, Grains | 32 | 40 | 50 | 58 | 72 |
| Density | .110 | .114 | .142 | .140 | .174 |
| Ballistic Coefficient | .159 | .153 | .192 | .173 | .208 |
| Catalog Number | 20432 | 22429 | 22442 | 24329 | 24339 |

**From: $20.96–$23.52**

## VARMINT GRENADE

| Caliber & Description | "20 FB" | 22 HORNET FB | 22 FB | 223 FB | 6MM FB |
|---|---|---|---|---|---|
| Diameter, Inches | .204 | .224 | .224 | .224 | .243 |
| Weight, Grains | 26 | 30 | 36 | 50 | 62 |
| Density | .089 | .085 | .102 | .142 | .150 |
| Ballistic Coefficient | .131 | .101 | .149 | .183 | .199 |
| Catalog Number | 20426 | 22430 | 22436 | 22486 | 24372 |

**Box 100: $18.91–$25.59**

# Handgun Bullets

## M/LE TAC-XP PISTOL BULLETS

| Caliber & Description | 380 ACP | 9MM | 9MM | .357 SIG | 38 SPL. | 357 MAG. | 10MM/40 S&W | 10MM/40 S&W | 10MM/40 S&W | 44 SPL. | 45 ACP/45 GAP | 45 ACP |
|---|---|---|---|---|---|---|---|---|---|---|---|---|
| Diameter, Inches | .355 | .355 | .355 | .355 | .355 | .357 | .400 | .400 | .400 | .429 | .451 | .451 |
| Weight, Grains | 80 | 95 | 115 | 125 | 110 | 125 | 125. | 140 | 155 | 200 | 160 | 185 |
| Density | .091 | .108 | .130 | .142 | .123 | .140 | .112 | .125 | .138 | .155 | .112 | .130 |
| Ballistic Coefficient | .107 | .120 | .167 | .159 | .156 | .160 | - | .128 | .189 | .138 | .133 | .167 |
| Catalog Number | 35500 | 35502 | 35501 | 35503 | 35703 | 35713 | 40003 | 40005 | 40006 | 42912 | 45106 | 45108 |

**Box 40: $26.60–$36.17**

# Barnes Bullets

### XPB Pistol Bullets

| Caliber & Description | 357 Mag. | 41 Mag. | 44 Mag. | 44 Mag. | 45 Colt | 45 Colt | 454 Casull | 460 S&W | 460 S&W | 480 Ruger | 500 S&W XPB | 500 S&W XPB | 500 S&W XPB |
|---|---|---|---|---|---|---|---|---|---|---|---|---|---|
| Diameter, Inches | .357 | .410 | .429 | .429 | .451 | .451 | .451 | .451 | .451 | .475 | .500 | .500 | .500 |
| Weight, Grains | 140 | 180 | 200 | 225 | 200 | 225 | 250 | 200 | 275 | 275 | 275 | 325 | 375 |
| Density | .157 | .153 | .155 | .175 | .140 | .158 | .176 | .140 | .193 | .174 | .157 | .186 | .214 |
| Ballistic Coefficient | .150 | .126 | .138 | .166 | - | .146 | .141 | .160 | .215 | .155 | .141 | .228 | .261 |
| Catalog Number | 35714 | 41018 | 42920 | 42922 | 45116 | 45120 | 45123 | 45115 | 45105 | 48010 | 50025 | 50026 | 50028 |

**Box 20: $16.49–$26.60**

# Berger Bullets

Famous for their superior performance in benchrest matches, Berger bullets also include hunting designs. From .17 to .30, all Bergers feature fourteen jackets with a wall concentricity tolerance of .0003. Lead cores are 99.9 percent pure and swaged in dies to within .0001 of a round. Berger's line includes several profiles: Match, Low Drag, Very Low Drag, Length Tolerant, and Maximum-Expansion, besides standard flat-base and boattail.

### HUNTING

| Caliber & Description | 6mm VLD | 6mm VLD | 6mm | 6mm VLD | 6mm VLD | 25 VLD" | 6.5mm VLD | 6.5mm VLD | 270 VLD | 270 Classic | 270 VLD | 270 VLD | 7mm VLD | 7mm VLD | 7mm Classic | 7mm VLD | 30 VLD | 30 VLD | 30 Classic | 30 VLD | 30 VLD | 30 Classic | 30 VLD | 30 VLD | 338 Elite | 338 Elite |
|---|---|---|---|---|---|---|---|---|---|---|---|---|---|---|---|---|---|---|---|---|---|---|---|---|---|---|
| Diameter, Inches | .243 | .243 | .243 | .243 | .243 | .257 | .264 | .264 | .277 | .277 | .277 | .277 | .284 | .284 | .284 | .284 | .308 | .308 | .308 | .308 | .308 | .308 | .308 | .308 | .338 | .338 |
| Weight, Grains | 87 | 95 | 95 | 105 | 115 | 115 | 130 | 140 | 130 | 130 | 140 | 150 | 140 | 168 | 168 | 180 | 155 | 168 | 168 | 175 | 185 | 185 | 190 | 210 | 250 | 300 |
| Density | .210 | .230 | - | .254 | .278 | .249 | .266 | .287 | .241 | - | .260 | .279 | .248 | .298 | - | .319 | .233 | .253 | - | .264 | .279 | - | .286 | .316 | - | - |
| Ballistic Coefficient | .412 | .480 | .427 | .532 | .545 | .466 | .552 | .612 | .452 | .497 | .487 | .531 | .510 | .617 | .604 | .659 | .439 | .473 | .496 | .498 | .549 | .547 | .570 | .631 | .682 | .818 |
| Catalog Number | 24524 | 24527 | 24570 | 24528 | 24530 | 25513 | 26503 | 26504 | 27501 | 27570 | 27502 | 27503 | 28503 | 28501 | 28570 | 28502 | 30508 | 30510 | 30570 | 30512 | 30513 | 30571 | 30514 | 30515 | 33554 | 33556 |

**From: $38.18–$88.40**

### TARGET

| Caliber & Description | 22 FBHP | 22 FBHP | 22 VLD | 22 BTHP | 22 VLD | 22 VLD | 22 VLD | 22 LRBTHP | 22 VLD | 6mm FBHP | 6mm BR | 6mm BTHP | 6mm FBHP | 6mm FBHP | 6mm BTHP | 6mm VLD |
|---|---|---|---|---|---|---|---|---|---|---|---|---|---|---|---|---|
| Diameter, Inches | .224 | .224 | .224 | .224 | .224 | .224 | .224 | .224 | .224 | .243 | .243 | .243 | .243 | .243 | .243 | .243 |
| Weight, Grains | 52 | 55 | 70 | 73 | 75 | 80 | 80.5 | 82 | 90 | 62 | - | 65 | 65 | 68 | 90 | 95 |
| Density | .148 | .157 | .199 | .208 | .214 | .228 | .229 | .233 | .256 | .150 | - | .157 | .157 | .165 | .218 | .230 |
| Ballistic Coefficient | .242 | .262 | .371 | .343 | .423 | .445 | .436 | .444 | .551 | .253 | .277 | .270 | .265 | .280 | .411 | .480 |
| Catalog Number | 22408 | 22410 | 22418 | 22420 | 22421 | 22422 | 22427 | 22424 | 22423 | 24404 | 24407 | 24408 | 24409 | 24411 | 24425 | 24427 |

# Berger Bullets

| Caliber & Description | 6mm BTHP | 6mm VLD | 6mm Hybrid | 6mm BTHP | 6mm VLD | 6.5mm BTHP | 6.5mm VLD | 6.5mm VLD | 6.5mm LRBTHP | 6.5mm Hybrid | 7mm VLD | 7mm VLD | 7mm Hybrid |
|---|---|---|---|---|---|---|---|---|---|---|---|---|---|
| Diameter, Inches | .243 | .243 | .243 | .243 | .243 | .264 | .264 | .264 | .264 | .264 | .284 | .284 | .284 |
| Weight, Grains | 105 | 105 | 105 | 108 | 115 | 120 | 130 | 140 | 140 | 140 | 168 | 180 | 180 |
| Density | .254 | .254 | .254 | .261 | .278 | .245 | .266 | .287 | .287 | .287 | .298 | .319 | .319 |
| Ballistic Coefficient | .493 | .495 | .547 | .551 | .545 | .453 | .552 | .612 | .592 | .618 | .617 | .659 | .674 |
| Catalog Number | 24428 | 24429 | 24433 | 24431 | 24430 | 26402 | 26403 | 26401 | 26409 | 26414 | 28401 | 28405 | 28407 |

| Caliber & Description | 30 FBHP | 30 FBHP | 30 VLD | 30 Hybrid | 30 LRBTHP | 30 VLD | 30 Hybrid | 30 LRBTHP | 30 VLD | 30 Juggernaut | 30 VLD | 30 Hybrid |
|---|---|---|---|---|---|---|---|---|---|---|---|---|
| Diameter, Inches | .308 | .308 | .308 | .308 | .308 | .308 | .308 | .308 | .308 | .308 | .308 | .308 |
| Weight, Grains | 115 | 150 | 155 | 155 | 155.5 | 168 | 168 | 175 | 175 | 185 | 185 | 185 |
| Density | .183 | .226 | .233 | .233 | .234 | .253 | .253 | .264 | .264 | .279 | .279 | .279 |
| Ballistic Coefficient | .296 | .398 | .439 | .483 | .464 | .473 | .519 | .515 | .498 | .560 | .549 | .569 |
| Catalog Number | 30421 | 30407 | 30408 | 30426 | 30416 | 30410 | 30425 | 30420 | 30412 | 30418 | 30413 | 30424 |

| Caliber & Description | 30 Hybrid | 30 LRBTHP | 30 VLD | 30 Hybrid | 30 Hybrid |
|---|---|---|---|---|---|
| Diameter, Inches | .308 | .308 | .308 | .308 | .308 |
| Weight, Grains | 200 | 210 | 210 | 215 | 230 |
| Density | .301 | .316 | .316 | - | - |
| Ballistic Coefficient | .624 | .626 | .631 | .696 | .743 |
| Catalog Number | 30427 | 30419 | 30415 | 30429 | 30430 |

**From: $28.52–$67.54**

| LEGEND | |
|---|---|
| **Type of Bullet** | **HP** – Hollow Point |
| **BT** – Boattail | **LD** – Low Drag |
| **FB** – Flat Base | **LR** – Long Range |
| | **VLD** – Very Low Drag |

## VARMINT

| Caliber & Description | 17 FBHP | 20 FBHP | 20 BTHP | 20 LRBTHP | 22 FBHP | 22 FBHP | 22 FBHP | 22 FBHP | 22 FBHP | 6mm LDHP | 6mm FBHP | 6mm LDHP |
|---|---|---|---|---|---|---|---|---|---|---|---|---|
| Diameter, Inches | .172 | .204 | .204 | .204 | .224 | .224 | .224 | .224 | .224 | .243 | .243 | .243 |
| Weight, Grains | 25 | 35 | 40 | 55 | 40 | 52 | 55 | 60 | 64 | 69 | 80 | 88 |
| Density | .121 | .120 | .137 | .188 | .114 | .148 | .157 | .171 | .182 | .167 | .194 | .213 |
| Ballistic Coefficient | .150 | .176 | .225 | .381 | .155 | .197 | .210 | .278 | .294 | .291 | .306 | .391 |
| Catalog Number | 17308 | 20303 | 20304 | 20306 | 22303 | 22309 | 22311 | 22312 | 22316 | 24313 | 24321 | 24323 |

**From: $28.35–$56.52**

AMMUNITION

# Hornady Bullets

Hornady's product line includes over 300 bullets, ranging from .17 caliber all the way up to the .50 caliber AMAX bullet for the .50 BMG. Hornady is always working to originate the next technological innovation. From prairie dogs to dangerous game, they have the perfect bullet to meet every hunting and shooting need.

## Rifle Bullets

### FMJ Bullets

| Caliber & Description | 22 FMJ-BT | 30 FMJ | 30 FMJ-BT | 303 FMJ-BT | 375 FMJ |
|---|---|---|---|---|---|
| Diameter, Inches | .224 | .308 | .308 | .3105 | .375 |
| Weight, Grains | 55 | 110 | 150 | 174 | 300 |
| Density | .157 | .166 | .226 | .255 | .305 |
| Ballistic Coefficient | .243 | .178 | .398 | .470 | .275 |
| Catalog Number | 2267 | 3017 | 3037 | 3131 | 37277 |

**MSRP $18.98–$57.24**

### InterBond

| Caliber & Description | 6mm | 25 | 6.5mm | 270 | 270 | 7mm | 7mm | 30 | 30 | 30 | 338 | 416 RN |
|---|---|---|---|---|---|---|---|---|---|---|---|---|
| Diameter, Inches | .243 | .257 | .264 | .277 | .277 | .284 | .284 | .308 | .308 | .308 | .338 | .416 |
| Weight, Grains | 85 | 110 | 129 | 130 | 150 | 139 | 154 | 150 | 165 | 180 | 225 | 400 |
| Density | .206 | .238 | .264 | .242 | .279 | .246 | .525 | .226 | .248 | .271 | .281 | .330 |
| Ballistic Coefficient | .395 | .390 | .485 | .460 | .525 | .486 | .273 | .415 | .447 | .480 | .515 | .311 |
| Catalog Number | 24539 | 25419 | 26209 | 27309 | 27409 | 28209 | 28309 | 30309 | 30459 | 30709 | 33209 | 41659 |

**MSRP $60.87–$88.75**

### InterLock

| Caliber & Description | 22 SP" | 6mm SP | 6mm BT SP | 25 SP" | 25 BTSP | 25 RN | 25 HP | 6.5mm SP | 6.5mm SP | 6.5mm RN | 6.5mm Carcano RN | 270 SP | 270 BTSP | 270 SP | 7mm BTSP | 7mm SP | 7mm SP | 7mm BTSP | 7mm RN | 7mm SP" |
|---|---|---|---|---|---|---|---|---|---|---|---|---|---|---|---|---|---|---|---|---|
| Diameter, Inches | .227 | .243 | .243 | .257 | .257 | .257 | .257 | .264 | .264 | .264 | .268 | .277 | .277 | .277 | .284 | .284 | .284 | .284 | .284 | .284 |
| Weight, Grains | 70 | 100 | 100 | 100 | 117 | 117 | 120 | 129 | 140 | 160 | 160 | 130 | 140 | 150 | 139 | 139 | 154 | 162 | 175 | 175 |
| Density | .194 | .242 | .242 | .216 | .253 | .253 | .260 | .264 | .287 | .328 | .321 | .242 | .261 | .279 | .246 | .246 | .273 | .287 | .310 | .310 |
| Ballistic Coefficient | .296 | .381 | .405 | .357 | .391 | .243 | .394 | .445 | .465 | .283 | .275 | .409 | .486 | .462 | .453 | .392 | .433 | .514 | .285 | .462 |
| Catalog Number | 2280 | 2450 | 2453 | 2540 | 2552 | 2550 | 2560 | 2620 | 2630 | 2640 | 2645 | 2730 | 2735 | 2740 | 2825 | 2820 | 2830 | 2845 | 2855 | 2850 |

| Caliber & Description | 30 BTSP | 30 RN | 30 SP | 30 BTSP | 30 SP | 30 FP | 30 BTSP | 30 RN | 30 SP | 30 BTSP | 30 RN | 7.62 SP | 303 SP | 303 RN | 32 FP | 8mm SP |
|---|---|---|---|---|---|---|---|---|---|---|---|---|---|---|---|---|
| Diameter, Inches | .308 | .308 | .308 | .308 | .308 | .308 | .308 | .308 | .308 | .308 | .308 | .310 | .312 | .312 | .321 | .323 |
| Weight, Grains | 150 | 150 | 150 | 165 | 165 | 170 | 180 | 180 | 180 | 190 | 220 | 123 | 150 | 174 | 170 | 150 |
| Density | .226 | .226 | .226 | .248 | .248 | .256 | .271 | .271 | .271 | .286 | .331 | .183 | .220 | .255 | .236 | .205 |
| Ballistic Coefficient | .349 | .186 | .338 | .435 | .387 | .189 | .452 | .241 | .425 | .491 | .300 | .252 | .361 | .262 | .249 | .290 |
| Catalog Number | 3033 | 3035 | 3031 | 3045 | 3040 | 3060 | 3072 | 3075 | 3070 | 3085 | 3090 | 3140 | 3120 | 3130 | 3210 | 3232 |

| Caliber & Description | 8mm RN | 8mm SP | 338 SP-RP | 338 SP-RP | 338 RN | 338 SP-RP | 348 FP | 35 RN | 35 SP-RP | 35 RN | 35 SP-RP | 9.3 SP-RP | 375 FP | 375 SP-RP | 375 SP-RP | 375 BTSP | 375 RN |
|---|---|---|---|---|---|---|---|---|---|---|---|---|---|---|---|---|---|
| Diameter, Inches | .323 | .323 | .338 | .338 | .338 | .338 | .348 | .358 | .358 | .358 | .358 | .366 | .375 | .375 | .375 | .375 | .375 |
| Weight, Grains | 170 | 195 | 200 | 225 | 250 | 250 | 200 | 200 | 200 | 250 | 250 | 286 | 220 | 225 | 270 | 300 | 300 |
| Density | .233 | .267 | .250 | .281 | .313 | .313 | .236 | .223 | .223 | .279 | .279 | .305 | .223 | .229 | .229 | .305 | .305 |
| Ballistic Coefficient | .217 | .410 | .361 | .397 | .291 | .431 | .246 | .195 | .282 | .271 | .375 | .410 | .217 | .320 | .380 | .460 | .250 |
| Catalog Number | 3235 | 3236 | 3310 | 3320 | 3330 | 3335 | 3410 | 3515 | 3510 | 3525 | 3520 | 3560 | 3705 | 3706 | 3711 | 3725 | 3720 |

| Caliber & Description | 405 FP | 405 SP | 416 RN | 44 FP | 45 HP | 45 FP | 45 RN | 45 RN |
|---|---|---|---|---|---|---|---|---|
| Diameter, Inches | .411 | .411 | .416 | .430 | .458 | .458 | .458 | .458 |
| Weight, Grains | 300 | 300 | 400 | 265 | 300 | 350 | 350 | 500 |
| Density | .251 | .251 | .330 | .205 | .204 | .238 | .238 | .341 |
| Ballistic Coefficient | .215 | .250 | .311 | .186 | .197 | .195 | .189 | .287 |
| Catalog Number | 41050 | 41051 | 4165 | 4300 | 4500 | 4503 | 4502 | 4504 |

**MSRP $28.20–$66.65**

## Match A-Max

| Caliber & Description | 6.5mm | 22 | 22 MOLY | 22 | 22 | 6mm | 6mm MOLY | 6.5mm | 6.5mm | 6.5mm | 7mm | 30 | 30 MOLY | 30 | 30 MOLY | 30 | 30 | 50 |
|---|---|---|---|---|---|---|---|---|---|---|---|---|---|---|---|---|---|---|
| Diameter, Inches | .264 | .224 | .224 | .224 | .224 | .243 | .243 | .264 | .264 | .264 | .284 | .308 | .308 | .308 | .308 | .308 | .308 | .510 |
| Weight, Grains | 100 | 52 | 75 | 75 | 80 | 105 | 105 | 120 | 123 | 140 | 162 | 155 | 155 | 168 | 168 | 178 | 208 | 750 |
| Density | .246 | .148 | .214 | .214 | .228 | .254 | .254 | .246 | .252 | .287 | .287 | .233 | .233 | .253 | .253 | .268 | .313 | .412 |
| Ballistic Coefficient | .390 | .247 | .435 | .435 | .453 | .500 | .500 | .465 | .510 | .585 | .625 | .435 | .435 | .475 | .475 | .495 | .325 | 1.050 |
| Catalog Number | 26101 | 22492 | 22794 | 22792 | 22832 | 24562 | 24564 | 26172 | 26171 | 26332 | 28402 | 30312 | 30314 | 30502 | 30504 | 30712 | 30732 | 5165 |

**MSRP $25.47–$61.80**

# Hornady Bullets

## SST

| Caliber & Description | 6mm | 25 | 6.5mm | 6.5mm | 6.5mm | 270 | 270 | 270 | 270 | 7mm SST | 7mm SST | 7mm SST | 30 | 30 | 30 | 30 |
|---|---|---|---|---|---|---|---|---|---|---|---|---|---|---|---|---|
| Diameter, Inches | .243 | .257 | .264 | .264 | .264 | .277 | .277 | .277 | .277 | .284 | .284 | .284 | .308 | .308 | .308 | .308 |
| Weight, Grains | 95 | 117 | 123 | 129 | 140 | 120 | 130 | 140 | 150 | 139 | 154 | 162 | 125 | 150 | 150 | 165 |
| Density | .230 | .253 | .252 | .264 | .287 | .223 | .242 | .261 | .279 | .246 | .273 | .287 | .185 | .226 | N/A | .248 |
| Ballistic Coefficient | .355 | .390 | .510 | .485 | .520 | .400 | .460 | .495 | .525 | .486 | .525 | .550 | .305 | .415 | N/A | .447 |
| Catalog Number | 24532 | 25522 | 26173 | 26202 | 26302 | 2716 | 27302 | 27352 | 27402 | 28202 | 28302 | 28452 | 3019 | 30302 | 30303 | 30452 |

| Caliber & Description | 30 | 7.62 | 338 | 338 |
|---|---|---|---|---|
| Diameter, Inches | .308 | .310 | .338 | .338 |
| Weight, Grains | 180 | 123 | 200 | 225 |
| Density | .271 | .183 | .250 | .281 |
| Ballistic Coefficient | .480 | .260 | .455 | .515 |
| Catalog Number | 30702 | 3142 | 33102 | 33202 |

**LEGEND**

**Type of Bullet**

| | | |
|---|---|---|
| BT | – | Boat Tail |
| CT | – | Combat Target |
| FMJ | – | Full Metal Jacket |
| FP | – | Flat Point |
| HB | – | Hollow Base |
| L | – | Lead |
| RN | – | Round Nose |
| SP | – | Spire Point |
| SX | – | Super Explosive |
| SWC | – | Semi-Wadcutter |
| WC | – | Wadcutter |

**MSRP $39.20–$50.85**

## TRADITIONAL VARMINT

| Caliber & Description | 17 HP | 20 SP | 22 JET | 22 Hornet | 22 Hornet | 22 HP BEE | 22 SP | 22 SP SX | 22 SP | 22 SP | 22 SP SX | 22 HP | 22 SP | 6mm HP |
|---|---|---|---|---|---|---|---|---|---|---|---|---|---|---|
| Diameter, Inches | .172 | .204 | .222 | .223 | .224 | .224 | .224 | .224 | .224 | .224 | .224 | .224 | .224 | .243 |
| Weight, Grains | 25 | 45 | 40 | 45 | 45 | 45 | 50 | 50 | 55 | 55 | 55 | 60 | 60 | 75 |
| Density | .121 | .155 | .116 | .129 | .128 | .128 | .142 | .142 | .157 | .157 | .157 | .171 | .171 | .181 |
| Ballistic Coefficient | .187 | .245 | .104 | .202 | .202 | .108 | .214 | .214 | .235 | .235 | .235 | .271 | .264 | .294 |
| Catalog Number | 1710 | 22008 | 2210 | 2220 | 2230 | 2229 | 2245 | 2240 | 2265 | 2266 | 2260 | 2275 | 2270 | 2420 |

| Caliber & Description | 6mm BTHP | 6mm SP | 25 FP | 25 HP | 25 SP | 6.5mm SP | 270 SP | 270 HP | 270 BTHP | 7mm HP | 30 Short Jacket | 30 SP | 30 RN | 30 SP |
|---|---|---|---|---|---|---|---|---|---|---|---|---|---|---|
| Diameter, Inches | .243 | .243 | .257 | .257 | .257 | .264 | .277 | .277 | .277 | .284 | .308 | .308 | .308 | .308 |
| Weight, Grains | 87 | 87 | 60 | 75 | 87 | 100 | 100 | 110 | 110 | 120 | 100 | 110 | 110 | 130 |
| Density | .210 | .210 | .130 | .162 | .188 | .205 | .186 | .205 | .205 | .213 | .151 | .166 | .166 | .196 |
| Ballistic Coefficient | .376 | .327 | .101 | .257 | .322 | .358 | .307 | .352 | .360 | .334 | .152 | .256 | .150 | .295 |
| Catalog Number | 2442 | 2440 | 2510 | 2520 | 2530 | 2610 | 2710 | 2720 | 27200 | 2815 | 3005 | 3010 | 3015 | 3020 |

**MSRP $18.17–$37.31**

AMMUNITION

# Hornady Bullets

## V-Max

| Caliber & Description | 17 | 17 | 20 | 20 | 22 | 22 | 22 | 22 MOLY | 22 | 22 | 22 | 22 MOLY | 22 | 6mm |
|---|---|---|---|---|---|---|---|---|---|---|---|---|---|---|
| Diameter, Inches | .172 | .172 | .204 | .204 | .224 | .224 | .224 | .224 | .224 | .224 | .224 | .224 | .224 | .243 |
| Weight, Grains | 20 | 25 | 32 | 40 | 35 | 40 | 50 | 50 | 53 | 55 | 55 | 55 | 60 | 58 |
| Density | .097 | .121 | .110 | .137 | .100 | .114 | .142 | .142 | .151 | .157 | .157 | .157 | .171 | .140 |
| Ballistic Coefficient | .185 | .230 | .210 | .275 | .109 | .200 | .242 | .242 | .290 | .255 | .255 | .255 | .265 | .250 |
| Catalog Number | 21710 | 17105 | 22004 | 22006 | 22252 | 22241 | 22261 | 22613 | 22265 | 22272 | 22271 | 22713 | 22281 | 22411 |

| Caliber & Description | 6mm | 6mm | 6mm | 25 | 6.5mm | 270 | 7mm | 30 |
|---|---|---|---|---|---|---|---|---|
| Diameter, Inches | .243 | .243 | .243 | .257 | .264 | .277 | .284 | .308 |
| Weight, Grains | 65 | 75 | 87 | 75 | 95 | 110 | 120 | 110 |
| Density | .157 | .181 | .210 | .162 | .195 | .205 | .213 | .166 |
| Ballistic Coefficient | .280 | .330 | .400 | .290 | .365 | .370 | .365 | .290 |
| Catalog Number | 22415 | 22420 | 22440 | 22520 | 22601 | 22721 | 22810 | 23010 |

> **LEGEND**
> **Type of Bullet**
> **BT** – Boat Tail
> **CT** – Combat Target
> **FMJ** – Full Metal Jacket
> **FP** – Flat Point
> **HB** – Hollow Base
> **L** – Lead
> **RN** – Round Nose
> **SP** – Spire Point
> **SX** – Super Explosive
> **SWC** – Semi-Wadcutter
> **WC** – Wadcutter

**MSRP $22.32–$37.28**

## Handgun Bullets

### FMJ BULLETS

| Caliber & Description | 9mm FMJ-RN | 9mm FMJ-RN | 10mm FMJ- FP | 45 SWC | 45 FMJ-RN | 45 FMJ-FP | 9mm FMJ | 9mm FMJ-FP | 9mm FMJ-RN | 10mm FMJ-FP | "45 FMJ-CT" |
|---|---|---|---|---|---|---|---|---|---|---|---|
| Diameter, Inches | .355 | .355 | .400 | .451 | .451 | .451 | .355 | .355 | .355 | .400 | .451 |
| Weight, Grains | 115 | 124 | 180 | 185 | 230 | 230 | 100 | 124 | 147 | 200 | 200 |
| Density | .130 | .141 | N/A | .130 | .162 | .162 | .141 | .141 | .167 | .179 | .140 |
| Ballistic Coefficient | .140 | .145 | N/A | .068 | .184 | .168 | .158 | .160 | .212 | .182 | .115 |
| Catalog Number | 35557 | 355771 | 400471 | 45137 | 45177 | 451871 | 35527B | 35567B | 35597B | 40077B | 45157B |

**MSRP $22.52–$451.12**

### FRONTIER/LEAD BULLETS

| Caliber & Description | 32 HBWC | 32 SWC | 38 | 38 HBWC | 38 LRN | 38 SWC | 38 SWC HP | 44 Cowboy | 44 Cowboy |
|---|---|---|---|---|---|---|---|---|---|
| Diameter, Inches | .314 | .314 | .358 | .358 | .358 | .358 | .358 | .427 | .430 |
| Weight, Grains | 90 | 90 | 140 | 148 | 158 | 158 | 158 | 205 | 180 |
| Density | .130 | .130 | .157 | .165 | .176 | .176 | .176 | .161 | .139 |
| Ballistic Coefficient | .040 | .096 | .127 | .047 | .159 | .135 | .139 | .123 | .114 |
| Catalog Number | 10028 | 10008 | 10078 | 10208 | 10508 | 10408 | 10428 | 11208 | 11058 |

# Hornady Bullets

## FRONTIER/LEAD BULLETS (CONT.)

| Caliber & Description | 44 SWC | 44 SWC HP | "45 L-C/T" | 45 SWC | 45 LRN | 45 FP Cowboy |
|---|---|---|---|---|---|---|
| Diameter, Inches | .430 | .430 | .452 | .452 | .452 | .454 |
| Weight, Grains | 240 | 240 | 200 | 200 | 230 | 255 |
| Density | .185 | .185 | .140 | .140 | .162 | .177 |
| Ballistic Coefficient | .182 | .204 | .081 | .070 | .207 | .117 |
| Catalog Number | 11108 | 11118 | 12208 | 12108 | 12308 | 12458 |

**MSRP $31.79–$50.24**

## HAP BULLETS

| Caliber & Description | 9mm | 9mm | 9mm | 10mm | 45 | 45 | 10mm |
|---|---|---|---|---|---|---|---|
| Diameter, Inches | .356 | .356 | .356 | .400 | .451 | .451 | .400 |
| Weight, Grains | 115 | 125 | 121 | 180 | 185 | 230 | 200 |
| Density | .130 | .141 | .136 | .161 | .130 | .162 | .179 |
| Ballistic Coefficient | .129 | .158 | .147 | .164 | .139 | .188 | .199 |
| Catalog Number | 355281 | 355721 | 35530B | 400421 | 451051 | 451611 | 40061B |

**MSRP $77.65–$327.15**

### LEGEND

**Type of Bullet**

| | | |
|---|---|---|
| BT | – | Boat Tail |
| CT | – | Combat Target |
| FMJ | – | Full Metal Jacket |
| FP | – | Flat Point |
| HB | – | Hollow Base |
| L | – | Lead |
| RN | – | Round Nose |
| SP | – | Spire Point |
| SX | – | Super Explosive |
| SWC | – | Semi-Wadcutter |
| WC | – | Wadcutter |

## XTP BULLETS

| Caliber & Description | 30 RN | 30 HP | 32 HP | 32 HP | 32 HP | 9mm HP | 9mm HP | 38 HP | 9mm HP | 38 FP | 9mm HP | 38 HP | 38 HP | 38 FP | 38 HP | 38 HP | 9x18mm HP | 10mm HP | 10mm HP |
|---|---|---|---|---|---|---|---|---|---|---|---|---|---|---|---|---|---|---|---|
| Diameter, Inches | .308 | .309 | .312 | .312 | .312 | .355 | .355 | .357 | .355 | .357 | .355 | .357 | .357 | .357 | .357 | .357 | .365 | .400 | .400 |
| Weight, Grains | 86 | 90 | 60 | 85 | 100 | 90 | 115 | 110 | 124 | 125 | 147 | 125 | 140 | 158 | 158 | 180 | 95 | 155 | 180 |
| Density | .130 | .136 | .088 | .125 | .147 | .102 | .130 | .123 | .141 | .140 | .167 | .140 | .157 | .177 | .177 | .202 | .102 | .138 | .161 |
| Ballistic Coefficient | .105 | .115 | .090 | .145 | .170 | .099 | .129 | .131 | .165 | .148 | .212 | .151 | .169 | .199 | .206 | .230 | .127 | .137 | .164 |
| Catalog Number | 3100 | 31000 | 32010 | 32050 | 32070 | 35500 | 35540 | 35700 | 35571 | 35730 | 35580 | 35710 | 35740 | 35780 | 35750 | 35771 | 36500 | 40000 | 40040 |

| Caliber & Description | 10mm HP | 41 HP | 44 HP | 44 HP | 44 CL-SIL | 44 HP | 44 HP | 45 HP | 45 HP | 45 HP | 45 | 45 HP | 45 HP | 45 | 475 MAG | 475 | 50 | 500 MAG | 500 FP |
|---|---|---|---|---|---|---|---|---|---|---|---|---|---|---|---|---|---|---|---|
| Diameter, Inches | .400 | .410 | .430 | .430 | .430 | .430 | .300 | .451 | .451 | .451 | .452 | .452 | .452 | .452 | .475 | .475 | .500 | .500 | .500 |
| Weight, Grains | 200 | 210 | 180 | 200 | 240 | 240 | 300 | 185 | 200 | 230 | 240 | 250 | 300 | 300 | 325 | 400 | 300 | 350 | 500 |
| Density | .179 | .178 | .139 | .155 | .185 | .185 | .232 | .130 | .140 | .162 | .168 | .175 | .210 | .210 | .206 | .253 | .171 | .192 | .275 |
| Ballistic Coefficient | .199 | .182 | .138 | .170 | .174 | .205 | .245 | .139 | .151 | .188 | .160 | .146 | .180 | .200 | .150 | .182 | .120 | .145 | .185 |
| Catalog Number | 40060 | 41000 | 44050 | 44100 | 4425 | 44200 | 44280 | 45100 | 45140 | 45160 | 45220 | 45200 | 45230 | 45235 | 47500 | 47550 | 50101 | 50100 | 50105 |

**MSRP $21.13–$57.97**

## Rifle Bullets

Lapua precision bullets are made from the best raw materials and meet the toughest precision specifications. Each bullet is subject to visual inspection and tested with advanced measurement devices.

### D46

The D46 bullet is manufactured to the strictest tolerances for concentricity, uniformity of shape, and weight.
**From: $41.00–$45.99**

### D166

The Lapua's unique D166 construction has remained the same since the late 1930s: superb accurate FMJBT bullet for 7.62mm (.311) cartridges.
**From: $51.99**

### FMJ

Ten rounds loaded with Lapua's .30 S374 8.0/123gr FMJ bullet from 100m can easily achieve groupings less than 30mm.
**From: $27.99–$80.99**

### HOLLOW POINT

This HPCE bullet cuts a clean and easily distinguishable hole in your target. With ten rounds (G477 in .308 Win.) fired at 100m, this bullet typically achieves groupings of under 25mm—sometimes even less than 15mm.
**From: $43.99–$89.99**

### LOCK BASE

A distinctive Full Metal Jacket Boat Tail bullet that has many applications from sport shooting to battlefield. Streamlined ballistic shape combined with patented base design
**From: $49.99–$79.99**

### MEGA

This soft point bullet with a protective copper jacket bullet is at its best in the field and typically more than duplicates on impact. The mechanical bonding locks the lead alloy in place.
**From: $50.99–$60.99**

### SCENAR

Scenar Hollow Point Boat Tail bullets have the IBS World Record in 600-yard Heavy Gun 5-shot group (.404") and hold the official world ISSF record of 600 out of 600 possible. Also available in Coated Silver Jacket version
**From: $43.99–$89.99**

### SCENAR-L

The next generation Scenar, the Scenar-L is a refinement in all manufacturing steps that has resulted in closer weight tolerances, tighter jacket wall concentricity standards, and greater uniformity in every dimension, including the gilding metal cup, lead wire and jacket forming, ending up to core-jacket assembly, boat tail pressing, and tipping.
**From: $50.99–$59.99**

LAPUA D46

LAPUA D166

LAPUA FMJ S

LAPUA HP

LAPUA LOCK BASE

LAPUA MEGA

LAPUA SCENAR

LAPUA SCENAR-L

**AMMUNITION**

# Nosler Bullets

## Rifle Bullets

### ACCUBOND

| Caliber & Description | 6mm S | 25 SWT | 6.5mm SWT | 6.5mm | 270 SWT | 270 SWT | 7mm SWT | 7mm SWT | 30 SWT | 30 SWT | 30 S | 30 SWT | 30 SWT |
|---|---|---|---|---|---|---|---|---|---|---|---|---|---|
| Diameter, inches | .243 | .257 | .264 | .264 | .277 | .277 | .277 | .277 | .284 | .284 | .308 | .308 | .308 |
| Weight, Grains | 90 | 110 | 130 | 140 | 100 | 110 | 130 | 140 | 140 | 160 | 125 | 150 | 165 |
| Density | .218 | .238 | .266 | .287 | .186 | .205 | .242 | .261 | .248 | .283 | .188 | .226 | .248 |
| Ballistic Coefficient | .376 | .418 | .488 | .509 | .323 | .370 | .435 | .496 | .485 | .531 | .366 | .435 | .475 |
| Catalog Number | 56357 | 53742 | 56902 | 57873 | 57845 | 54382 | 54987 | 54765 | 59992 | 54932 | 52165 | 56719 | 55602 |

| Caliber & Description | 30 S | 30 S | 8mm S | 338 S | 338 S | 338 S | 338 S | 338 S | 35 Whelen S | 35 Whelen S | 9.3mm S | 375 S | 375 S |
|---|---|---|---|---|---|---|---|---|---|---|---|---|---|
| Diameter, inches | .308 | .308 | .323 | .338 | .338 | .338 | .338 | .338 | .358 | .358 | .366 | .375 | .375 |
| Weight, Grains | 180 | 200 | 200 | 180 | 200 | 225 | 250 | 300 | 200 | 225 | 250 | 260 | 300 |
| Density | .271 | .301 | .274 | .225 | .250 | .281 | .313 | .375 | .223 | .251 | .267 | .264 | .305 |
| Ballistic Coefficient | .507 | .588 | .450 | .372 | .414 | .550 | .575 | .720 | .365 | .421 | .494 | .473 | .485 |
| Catalog Number | 54825 | 54618 | 54374 | 57625 | 56382 | 54357 | 57287 | 54851 | 54425 | 50712 | 59756 | 54413 | 53662 |

**MSRP $28.00–$57.00**

### BALLISTIC TIP HUNTING

| Caliber & Description | 6mm S | 6mm S | 25 S | 25 S | 6.5mm S | 6.5mm S | 6.5mm S | 270 S | 270 S | 270 S | 7mm S | 7mm S |
|---|---|---|---|---|---|---|---|---|---|---|---|---|
| Diameter, inches | .243 | .243 | .257 | .257 | .264 | .264 | .264 | .277 | .277 | .277 | .284 | .284 |
| Weight, Grains | 90 | 95 | 100 | 115 | 100 | 120 | 140 | 130 | 140 | 150 | 120 | 140 |
| Density | .218 | .230 | .216 | .249 | .205 | .246 | .287 | .242 | .261 | .279 | .213 | .248 |
| Ballistic Coefficient | .365 | .379 | .393 | .453 | .350 | .458 | .509 | .433 | .456 | .496 | .417 | .485 |
| Catalog Number | 24090 | 24095 | 25100 | 25115 | 26100 | 26120 | 26140 | 27130 | 27140 | 27150 | 28120 | 28140 |

| Caliber & Description | 7mm S | 30 S | 30 S | 30 S | 30 S | 30 S | 8mm S |
|---|---|---|---|---|---|---|---|
| Diameter, inches | .284 | .308 | .308 | .308 | .308 | .308 | .323 |
| Weight, Grains | 150 | 125 | 150 | 165 | 168 | 180 | 180 |
| Density | .266 | .188 | .226 | .248 | .253 | .271 | .247 |
| Ballistic Coefficient | .493 | .366 | .435 | .475 | .490 | .507 | .394 |
| Catalog Number | 28150 | 30125 | 30150 | 30165 | 30168 | 30180 | 32180 |

**MSRP $19.00–$26.00**

**LEGEND**

| Type of Bullet | | Type of Tip | |
|---|---|---|---|
| BT | – Boat Tail | PT | – Purple Tip |
| HP | – Hollow Point | BT | – Blue Tip |
| J | – Jacketed | BrT | – Brown Tip |
| PP | – Protected Point | BuT | – Buckskin Tip |
| RN | – Round Nose | GT | – Green Tip |
| S | – Spitzer | GuT | – Gunmetal Tip |
| SS | – Semi Spitzer | MT | – Maroon Tip |
| W | – Whelen | OT | – Olive Tip |
| | | RT | – Red Tip |
| | | SLT | – Soft Lead Tip |
| | | YT | – Yellow Tip |

AMMUNITION

# Nosler Bullets

## BALLISTIC TIP VARMINT

| Caliber & Description | 204 S | 204 S | 22 S | 22 S | 22 S | 22 S | 6mm S | 6mm S | 6mm S | 25 S |
|---|---|---|---|---|---|---|---|---|---|---|
| Diameter, inches | .204 | .204 | .224 | .224 | .224 | .224 | .243 | .243 | .243 | .257 |
| Weight, Grains | 32 | 40 | 40 | 50 | 55 | 60 | 55 | 70 | 80 | 85 |
| Density | .110 | .137 | .114 | .142 | .157 | .171 | .133 | .169 | .194 | .184 |
| Ballistic Coefficient | .206 | .239 | .221 | .238 | .27 | .270 | .276 | .310 | .329 | .329 |
| Catalog Number | 35216 | 52111 | 39510 | 39522 | 39526 | 34992 | 24055 | 39532 | 24080 | 43004 |

**MSRP $25.00–$33.00**

## CT BALLISTIC SILVERTIP HUNTING

| Caliber & Description | 6mm S | 25 S | 270 S | 270 S | 7mm S | 7mm S | 30 S | 30 RN | 30 S | 30 S | 8mm S | 45-70 RN | 338 S |
|---|---|---|---|---|---|---|---|---|---|---|---|---|---|
| Diameter, inches | .243 | .257 | .277 | .277 | .284 | .284 | .308 | .308 | .308 | .308 | .323 | .458 | .338 |
| Weight, Grains | 95 | 115 | 130 | 150 | 140 | 150 | 150 | 150 | 168 | 180 | 180 | 300 | 200 |
| Density | .230 | .249 | .242 | .279 | .248 | .266 | .226 | .226 | .253 | .271 | .247 | .204 | .250 |
| Ballistic Coefficient | .379 | .453 | .433 | .496 | .485 | .493 | .435 | .232 | .490 | .507 | .394 | .191 | .414 |
| Catalog Number | 51040 | 51050 | 51075 | 51100 | 51105 | 51110 | 51150 | 51165 | 51160 | 51170 | 51693 | 51834 | 51200 |

**MSRP $23.00–$38.00**

## CUSTOM COMPETITION

| Caliber & Description | 22 HPBT | 22 HPBT | 22 HPBT | 22 HPBT | 6mm HPBT | 6mm HPBT | 6.5mm HPBT | 6.5mm HPBT | 6.8mm HPBT | 7mm HPBT | 30 HPBT | 30 HPBT | 30 HPBT | 30 HPBT | 30 HPBT | 8mm HPBT | 45 JHP |
|---|---|---|---|---|---|---|---|---|---|---|---|---|---|---|---|---|---|
| Diameter, inches | .224 | .224 | .224 | .224 | .243 | .243 | .264 | .264 | .277 | .284 | .308 | .308 | .308 | .308 | .308 | .323 | .451 |
| Weight, Grains | 52 | 69 | 77 | 80 | 105 | 107 | 123 | 140 | 115 | 168 | 140 | 155 | 168 | 175 | 190 | 200 | 185 |
| Density | .148 | .196 | .219 | .228 | .254 | .259 | .252 | .287 | .214 | .298 | .211 | .233 | .253 | .264 | .286 | .274 | .130 |
| Ballistic Coefficient | .220 | .305 | .340 | .415 | .517 | .525 | .510 | .529 | .375 | .520 | .396 | .450 | .462 | .505 | .530 | .520 | .142 |
| Catalog Number | 53294 | 17101 | 22421 | 25116 | 53614 | 49742 | 53415 | 26725 | 45357 | 53418 | 53152 | 53155 | 53164 | 53952 | 53412 | 49524 | 44847 |

**MSRP $24.00–$57.00**

## E-TIP

| Caliber & Description | 6mm S | 25 S | 6.8mm S | 270 S | 7mm S | 7mm S | 30 S | 30 S | 30 S | 8mm S | 338 S |
|---|---|---|---|---|---|---|---|---|---|---|---|
| Diameter, inches | .243 | .257 | .277 | .277 | .284 | .284 | .308 | .308 | .308 | .323 | .338 |
| Weight, Grains | 90 | 100 | 85 | 130 | 140 | 150 | 150 | 168 | 180 | 180 | 200 |
| Density | .218 | .216 | .158 | .242 | .248 | .266 | .226 | .253 | .271 | .246 | .250 |
| Ballistic Coefficient | .403 | .409 | .273 | .459 | .489 | .498 | .469 | .503 | .523 | .427 | .425 |
| Catalog Number | 59165 | 59456 | 59543 | 59298 | 59955 | 59426 | 59378 | 59415 | 59180 | 59265 | 59186 |

**MSRP $29.00–$45.00**

# Nosler Bullets

## PARTITION

| Caliber & Description | 22 S | 6mm S | 6mm S | 6mm S | 25 S | 25 S | 25 S | 6.5mm S | 6.5mm S | 6.5mm S | 270 S | 270 S | 270 S | 270 SS |
|---|---|---|---|---|---|---|---|---|---|---|---|---|---|---|
| Diameter, Inches | .224 | .243 | .243 | .243 | .257 | .257 | .257 | .264 | .264 | .264 | .277 | .277 | .277 | .277 |
| Weight, Grains | 60 | 85 | 95 | 100 | 100 | 115 | 120 | 100 | 125 | 140 | 130 | 140 | 150 | 160 |
| Density | .171 | .206 | .230 | .242 | .216 | .249 | .260 | .205 | .256 | .287 | .242 | .261 | .279 | .298 |
| Ballistic Coefficient | .228 | .315 | .365 | .384 | .377 | .389 | .391 | .326 | .4479 | .490 | .416 | .432 | .465 | .434 |
| Catalog Number | 16316 | 16314 | 16315 | 35642 | 16317 | 16318 | 35643 | 16319 | 16320 | 16321 | 16322 | 35200 | .16323 | 16324 |

| Caliber & Description | 7mm S | 7mm S | 7mm S | 7mm S | 30 S | 30 S | 30 RN | 30 PP | 30 S | 30 S | 30 SS | 8mm S | 338 S | 338 S |
|---|---|---|---|---|---|---|---|---|---|---|---|---|---|---|
| Diameter, Inches | .284 | .284 | .284 | .284 | .308 | .308 | .308 | .308 | .308 | .308 | .308 | .323 | .338 | .338 |
| Weight, Grains | 140 | 150 | 160 | 175 | 150 | 165 | 170 | 180 | 180 | 200 | 220 | 200 | 210 | 225 |
| Density | .248 | .266 | .283 | .310 | .226 | .248 | .256 | .271 | .271 | .301 | .331 | .274 | .263 | .281 |
| Ballistic Coefficient | .434 | .456 | .475 | .519 | .387 | .410 | .252 | .361 | .474 | .481 | .351 | .426 | .400 | .454 |
| Catalog Number | 16325 | 16326 | 16327 | 35645 | 16329 | 16330 | 16333 | 25396 | 16331 | 35626 | 16332 | 35277 | 16337 | 16336 |

| Caliber & Description | 338 S | 35 S | 35 S | 9.3mm S | 375 S | 375 S | 416 S | 458 PP |
|---|---|---|---|---|---|---|---|---|
| Diameter, Inches | .338 | .358 | .358 | .366 | .375 | .375 | .416 | .458 |
| Weight, Grains | 250 | 225 | 250 | 286 | 260 | 300 | 400 | 500 |
| Density | .313 | .251 | .279 | .307 | .264 | .305 | .330 | .389 |
| Ballistic Coefficient | .473 | .430 | .446 | .482 | .314 | .398 | .390 | .341 |
| Catalog Number | 35644 | 44800 | 44801 | 44750 | 44850 | 44845 | 45200 | 44745 |

**MSRP $29.00–$80.60**

### LEGEND

| Type of Bullet | | Type of Tip | |
|---|---|---|---|
| BT | – Boat Tail | PT | – Purple Tip |
| HP | – Hollow Point | BT | – Blue Tip |
| J | – Jacketed | BrT | – Brown Tip |
| PP | – Protected Point | BuT | – Buckskin Tip |
| RN | – Round Nose | GT | – Green Tip |
| S | – Spitzer | GuT | – Gunmetal Tip |
| SS | – Semi Spitzer | MT | – Maroon Tip |
| W | – Whelen | OT | – Olive Tip |
| | | RT | – Red Tip |
| | | SLT | – Soft Lead Tip |
| | | YT | – Yellow Tip |

## SOLID

| Caliber & Description | 9.3mm Solid | 375 Solid | 375 Solid | 416 Solid | 458 Solid | 470 NE Solid |
|---|---|---|---|---|---|---|
| Diameter, Inches | .366 | .375 | .375 | .416 | .458 | .474 |
| Weight, Grains | 286 | 260 | 300 | 400 | 500 | 500 |
| Density | .305 | .264 | .305 | .330 | .341 | .318 |
| Ballistic Coefficient | .350 | .254 | .300 | .289 | .246 | .237 |
| Catalog Number | 29825 | 29755 | 28451 | 23654 | 27452 | 28455 |

### LEGEND

| Type of Bullet | | | |
|---|---|---|---|
| BT | – Boattail | J | – Jacketed |
| FMJ | – Full Metal Jacket | PP | – Protected Point |
| | | RN | – Round Nose |
| | | S | – Spitzer |

**MSRP $70.00–$89.00**

# Nosler Bullets

## VARMAGEDDON

| Caliber & Description | 17 FBHP | 17 FB Tipped | 20 FBHP | 20 FB Tipped | 22 FB Tipped | 22 FBHP | 22 FB Tipped | 22 FBHP | 22 FB Tipped | 22 FBHP | 6mm FBHP | 6mm FB Tipped | 6mm FB Tipped | 30 FB Tipped |
|---|---|---|---|---|---|---|---|---|---|---|---|---|---|---|
| Diameter, Inches | .172 | .172 | .204 | .204 | .224 | .224 | .224 | .224 | .224 | .224 | .243 | .243 | .243 | .308 |
| Weight, Grains | 20 | 20 | 32 | 32 | 35 | 40 | 40 | 55 | 55 | 62 | 55 | 55 | 70 | 110 |
| Density | .097 | .097 | .110 | .110 | .100 | .114 | .114 | .157 | .157 | .176 | .133 | .133 | .169 | .166 |
| Ballistic Coefficient | .119 | .183 | .131 | .204 | .120 | .158 | .211 | .210 | .218 | .251 | .192 | .252 | .334 | .293 |
| Catalog Number | 17205 | 17210 | 17215 | 17220 | 36763 | 17225 | 17230 | 17235 | 17240 | 35631 | 17245 | 17250 | 26123 | 34057 |

**From: $13.99–$22.99**

# Handgun Bullets

## SPORTING HANDGUN-PISTOL

| Caliber & Description | 9mm JHP | 9mm JHP | 10mm JHP | 10mm JHP | 10mm JHP | 10mm JHP | 45 JHP | 45 FMJ |
|---|---|---|---|---|---|---|---|---|
| Diameter, Inches | .355 | .355 | .400 | .400 | .400 | .400 | .451 | .451 |
| Weight, Grains | 115 | 124 | 135 | 150 | 180 | 200 | 230 | 230 |
| Density | .109 | .141 | .093 | .106 | .161 | .179 | .1625 | .162 |
| Ballistic Coefficient | .130 | .118 | .121 | .134 | .147 | .163 | .175 | .183 |
| Catalog Number | 44848 | 43123 | 44852 | 44860 | 44885 | 44952 | 44922 | 44964 |

**MSRP $45.00–$62.00**

## SPORTING HANDGUN

| Caliber & Description | 38 JHP | 41 JHP | 44 JHP | 44 JHP | 44 JHP | 44 JHP | 45 Colt JHP |
|---|---|---|---|---|---|---|---|
| Diameter, Inches | .357 | .410 | .429 | .429 | .429 | .429 | .451 |
| Weight, Grains | 158 | 210 | 200 | 240 | 240 | 300 | 250 |
| Density | .182 | .170 | .151 | .173 | .177 | .206 | .177 |
| Ballistic Coefficient | .177 | .178 | 155 | .186 | .186 | .233 | .176 |
| Catalog Number | 44841 | 43012 | 44846 | 44842 | 44868 | 42069 | 43013 |

**MSRP $32.00–$62.00**

# Sierra Bullets

## Rifle Bullets

### BLITZKING

| Caliber & Description | 20 | 20 | 224 | 224 | 224 | 6mm | 6mm | 257 | 257 |
|---|---|---|---|---|---|---|---|---|---|
| Diameter, Inches | .204 | .204 | .224 | .224 | .224 | .243 | .243 | .257 | .257 |
| Weight, Grains | 32 | 39 | 40 | 50 | 55 | 55 | 70 | 70 | 90 |
| Density | .110 | .134 | .114 | .142 | .157 | .133 | .169 | .151 | .195 |
| Ballistic Coefficient | .221 | .287 | .196 | .248 | .185 | .225 | .299 | .260 | .388 |
| Catalog Number | 1032 | 1039 | 1440 | 1450 | 1455 | 1502 | 1507 | 1605 | 1616 |

**From: $26.45–$32.09**

# Sierra Bullets

## GameKing

| Caliber & Description | 22 FMJBT | 22 SBT | 22 HPBT | 22 SBT | 6mm HPBT | 6mm FMJBT | 6mm SBT | 25 HPBT | 25 SBT | 25 SBT | 25 HPBT | 6.5mm HPBT |
|---|---|---|---|---|---|---|---|---|---|---|---|---|
| Diameter, Inches | .224 | .224 | .224 | .224 | .243 | .243 | .243 | .257 | .257 | .257 | .257 | .264 |
| Weight, Grains | 55 | 55 | 55 | 65 | 85 | 90 | 100 | 90 | 100 | 117 | 120 | 130 |
| Density | .157 | .257 | .157 | .185 | .206 | .218 | .242 | .195 | .216 | .253 | .260 | .266 |
| Ballistic Coefficient | .272 | .250 | .185 | .303 | .282 | .387 | .430 | .250 | .355 | .410 | .350 | .355 |
| Catalog Number | 1355 | 1365 | 1390 | 1395 | 1530 | 1535 | 1560 | 1615 | 1625 | 1630 | 1650 | 1728 |

| Caliber & Description | 6.5mm SBT | 270 SBT | 270 HPBT | 270 SBT | 270 SBT | 7mm HPBT | 7mm SBT | 7mm SBT | 7mm SBT | 7mm HPBT | 7mm SBT | 30 FMJBT |
|---|---|---|---|---|---|---|---|---|---|---|---|---|
| Diameter, Inches | .264 | .277 | .277 | .277 | .277 | .284 | .274 | .284 | .284 | .284 | .284 | .308 |
| Weight, Grains | 140 | 130 | 140 | 140 | 150 | 140 | 140 | 150 | 160 | 160 | 175 | 150 |
| Density | .287 | .242 | .261 | .261 | .279 | .248 | .248 | .266 | .283 | .283 | .310 | .226 |
| Ballistic Coefficient | .495 | .436 | .337 | .457 | .483 | .375 | .416 | .436 | .455 | .384 | .533 | .408 |
| Catalog Number | 1730 | 1820 | 1835 | 1845 | 1840 | 1912 | 1905 | 1913 | 1920 | 1925 | 1940 | 2115 |

| Caliber & Description | 30 SBT | 30 HPBT | 30 SBT | 30 SBT | 30 SBT | 8mm SBT | 338 SBT | 338 SBT | 35 SBT | 375 SBT | 375 SBT |
|---|---|---|---|---|---|---|---|---|---|---|---|
| Diameter, Inches | .308 | .308 | .308 | .308 | .308 | .323 | .338 | .338 | .358 | .375 | .375 |
| Weight, Grains | 150 | 165 | 165 | 180 | 200 | 220 | 215 | 250 | 225 | 250 | 300 |
| Density | .226 | .248 | .248 | .271 | .301 | .301 | .269 | .313 | .251 | .254 | .305 |
| Ballistic Coefficient | .380 | .363 | .404 | .501 | .560 | .521 | .485 | .565 | .370 | .353 | .475 |
| Catalog Number | 2125 | 2140 | 2145 | 2160 | 2165 | 2420 | 2610 | 2600 | 2850 | 2950 | 3000 |

From: $19.40–$41.93

## MatchKing

| Caliber & Description | 22 HPBT | 22 HP | 22 HPBT | 22 HPBT | 22 HPBT | 22 HPBT | 22 HPBT | 6mm HPBT | 6mm HPBT | 6mm HPBT | 25 HPBT | 6.5mm HPBT | 6.5mm HPBT | 6.5mm HPBT | 6.5mm HPBT |
|---|---|---|---|---|---|---|---|---|---|---|---|---|---|---|---|
| Diameter, Inches | .224 | .224 | .224 | .224 | .224 | .224 | .224 | .243 | .243 | .243 | .257 | .264 | .264 | .264 | .264 |
| Weight, Grains | 52 | 53 | 69 | 77 | 77 | 80 | 90 | 70 | 107 | 95 | 100 | 107 | 120 | 123 | 140 |
| Density | .148 | .151 | .196 | .219 | .219 | .228 | .256 | .169 | .259 | .230 | .216 | .219 | .246 | .252 | .287 |
| Ballistic Coefficient | .225 | .224 | .301 | .372 | .372 | .420 | .504 | .259 | .527 | .480 | .394 | .430 | .421 | .510 | .535 |
| Catalog Number | 1410 | 1400 | 1380 | 9377T | 9378T | 9390T | 9290T | 1505 | 1570 | 1537 | 1628 | 1715 | 1725 | 1727 | 1740 |

AMMUNITION

# Sierra Bullets

## MatchKing

| Caliber & Description | 6.5mm HPBT | 270 HPBT | 270 HPBT | 7mm HPBT | 7mm HPBT | 7mm HPBT | 7mm HPBT | 7mm HPBT | 30 HP | 30 HPBT | 30 HPBT | 30 HPBT | 30 HPBT | 30 HPBT | 30 HPBT |
|---|---|---|---|---|---|---|---|---|---|---|---|---|---|---|---|
| Diameter, Inches | .264 | .277 | .277 | .284 | .284 | .284 | .284 | .284 | .308 | .308 | .308 | .308 | .308 | .308 | .308 |
| Weight, Grains | 142 | 115 | 135 | 130 | 150 | 168 | 175 | 180 | 125 | 135 | 150 | 155 | 168 | 175 | 180 |
| Density | .291 | .214 | .251 | .230 | .266 | .298 | .310 | .319 | .188 | .203 | .226 | .233 | .253 | .264 | .271 |
| Ballistic Coefficient | .595 | .318 | .488 | .395 | .429 | .488 | .608 | .660 | .349 | .390 | .417 | .450 | .462 | .505 | .475 |
| Catalog Number | 1742 | 1815 | 1833 | 1903 | 1915 | 1930 | 1975 | 1980 | 2121 | 2123 | 2190 | 2155 | 2200 | 2275 | 2220 |

| Caliber & Description | 30 HPBT | 30 HPBT | 30 HPBT | 30 HPBT | 30 HPBT | 303 HPBT | 8mm HPBT | 338 HPBT | 338 HPBT | 375 HPBT |
|---|---|---|---|---|---|---|---|---|---|---|
| Diameter, Inches | .308 | .308 | .308 | .308 | .308 | .311 | .323 | .338 | .338 | .375 |
| Weight, Grains | 190 | 200 | 210 | 220 | 240 | 174 | 200 | 250 | 300 | 350 |
| Density | .286 | .301 | .316 | .331 | .361 | .257 | .274 | .313 | .375 | .355 |
| Ballistic Coefficient | .533 | .565 | .645 | .629 | .711 | .499 | .520 | .587 | .768 | .805 |
| Catalog Number | 2210 | 2230 | 9240T | 2240 | 9245T | 2315 | 2415 | 2650 | 9300T | 9350T |

**LEGEND**
- **BT** – Boattail
- **FMJ** – Full Metal Jacket
- **FN** – Flat Nose
- **HC** – Hollow Cavity
- **HP** – Hollow Point
- **J** – Jacketed
- **RN** – Round Nose
- **S** – Spitzer
- **SMP** – Semi-Pointed
- **SP** – Soft Point

**From: $17.36–$54.85**

## Pro-Hunter

| Caliber & Description | 6mm S | 25 S | 25 S | 6.5mm S | 270 S | 270 S | 7mm S | 7mm S | 30 HP/FN | 30 FN | 30 FN |
|---|---|---|---|---|---|---|---|---|---|---|---|
| Diameter, Inches | .243 | .257 | .257 | .264 | .277 | .277 | .284 | .284 | .308 | .308 | .308 |
| Weight, Grains | 100 | 100 | 117 | 120 | 110 | 130 | 120 | 140 | 125 | 150 | 170 |
| Density | .242 | .216 | .253 | .246 | .205 | .242 | .213 | .248 | .188 | .226 | .256 |
| Ballistic Coefficient | .373 | .330 | .388 | .356 | .318 | .370 | .328 | .377 | .119 | .185 | .205 |
| Catalog Number | 1540 | 1620 | 1640 | 1720 | 1810 | 1830 | 1900 | 1910 | 2020 | 2000 | 2010 |

| Caliber & Description | 30 RN | 30 FMJ | 30 S | 30 S | 30 RN | 30 S | 30 RN | 30 RN |
|---|---|---|---|---|---|---|---|---|
| Diameter, Inches | .308 | .308 | .308 | .308 | .308 | .308 | .308 | .308 |
| Weight, Grains | 110 | 110 | 125 | 150 | 150 | 180 | 180 | 220 |
| Density | .166 | .166 | .188 | .226 | .226 | .271 | .271 | .331 |
| Ballistic Coefficient | .144 | .144 | .279 | .336 | .200 | .407 | .240 | .310 |
| Catalog Number | 2100 | 2105 | 2120 | 2130 | 2135 | 2150 | 2170 | 2180 |

# Sierra Bullets

## Pro-Hunter (cont.)

| Caliber & Description | 303 S | 303 S | 303 S | 8mm S | 8mm S | 338 S | 35 RN | 375 FN | 45-70 HP/FN |
|---|---|---|---|---|---|---|---|---|---|
| Diameter, Inches | .311 | .311 | .311 | .323 | .323 | .338 | .358 | .375 | .458 |
| Weight, Grains | 125 | 150 | 180 | 150 | 175 | 225 | 200 | 200 | 300 |
| Density | .185 | .222 | .266 | .205 | .240 | .281 | .223 | .203 | .204 |
| Ballistic Coefficient | .274 | .344 | .411 | .336 | .381 | .462 | .148 | .195 | .120 |
| Catalog Number | 2305 | 2300 | 2310 | 2400 | 2410 | 2620 | 2800 | 2900 | 8900 |

### Varminter

| Caliber & Description | 22 Hornet | 22 Hornet | 22 Hornet | 22 Hornet | 22 HP |
|---|---|---|---|---|---|
| Diameter, Inches | .223 | .223 | .224 | .224 | .224 |
| Weight, Grains | 40 | 45 | 40 | 45 | 40 |
| Density | .115 | .129 | .114 | .128 | .114 |
| Ballistic Coefficient | .117 | .132 | .116 | .131 | .155 |
| Catalog Number | 1100 | 1110 | 1200 | 1210 | 1385 |

**From: $19.17–$34.83**

| Caliber & Description | 22 S | 22 S | 22 S | 22 Blitz | 22 Blitz | 22 SMP | 22 S | 22 HP | 22 SMP | 6mm HP | 6mm HP | 6mm SBT Blitz | 6mm S | 25 HP | 25 S | 6.5mm HP | 6.5mm HP | 270 HP | 7mm HP | 30 HP |
|---|---|---|---|---|---|---|---|---|---|---|---|---|---|---|---|---|---|---|---|---|
| Diameter, Inches | .224 | .224 | .224 | .224 | .224 | .224 | .224 | .224 | .224 | .243 | .243 | .243 | .243 | .257 | .257 | .264 | .264 | .277 | .284 | .308 |
| Weight, Grains | 45 | 50 | 50 | 50 | 55 | 55 | 55 | 60 | 63 | 60 | 75 | 80 | 85 | 75 | 87 | 85 | 100 | 90 | 100 | 110 |
| Density | .128 | .142 | .142 | .142 | .157 | .157 | .157 | .171 | .179 | .145 | .181 | .194 | .206 | .162 | .188 | .174 | .205 | .168 | .177 | .166 |
| Ballistic Coefficient | .210 | .192 | .222 | .222 | .237 | .204 | .237 | .246 | .231 | .182 | .217 | .319 | .315 | .189 | .293 | .225 | .259 | .195 | .209 | .177 |
| Catalog Number | 1310 | 1320 | 1330 | 1340 | 1345 | 1350 | 1360 | 1375 | 1370 | 1500 | 1510 | 1515 | 1520 | 1600 | 1610 | 1700 | 1710 | 1800 | 1895 | 2110 |

**From: $18.85–$30.59**

## Handgun Bullets

### Sports Master

| Caliber & Description | 30 RN | 32 JHC | 9mm JHP | 9mm JHP | 9mm JHP | 38 JHP Blitz | 38 JHP | 38 JSP | 38 JHP | 38 JHC | 38 JSP | 10mm JHP | 10mm JHP |
|---|---|---|---|---|---|---|---|---|---|---|---|---|---|
| Diameter, Inches | .308 | .312 | .355 | .355 | .355 | .357 | .357 | .357 | .357 | .357 | .357 | .400 | .400 |
| Weight, Grains | 85 | 90 | 90 | 115 | 125 | 110 | 125 | 125 | 140 | 158 | 158 | 135 | 150 |
| Density | .128 | .132 | .102 | .130 | .142 | .123 | .140 | .140 | .157 | .177 | .177 | .121 | .134 |
| Ballistic Coefficient | .102 | .125 | .095 | .107 | .124 | .120 | .133 | .133 | .0776 | .100 | .100 | .105 | .120 |
| Catalog Number | 8005 | 8030 | 8100 | 8110 | 8125 | 8300 | 8320 | 8310 | 8325 | 8360 | 8340 | 8425 | 8430 |

| Caliber & Description | 10mm JHP | 10mm JHP | 41 JHC | 41 JHC | 44 JHC | 44 JHC | 44 JHC | 44 JSP | 45 JHP | 45 JHP | 45 JHC | 45 JSP | 50 JHP | 50 JSP |
|---|---|---|---|---|---|---|---|---|---|---|---|---|---|---|
| Diameter, Inches | .400 | .400 | .410 | .410 | .4295 | .4295 | .4295 | .4295 | .4515 | .4515 | .4515 | .4515 | .500 | .500 |
| Weight, Grains | 165 | 180 | 170 | 210 | 180 | 210 | 240 | 300 | 185 | 230 | 240 | 300 | 350 | 400 |
| Density | .147 | .161 | .144 | .178 | .139 | .163 | .186 | .232 | .130 | .161 | .168 | .210 | .200 | .229 |
| Ballistic Coefficient | .130 | .140 | .123 | .165 | .130 | .160 | .185 | .230 | .100 | .145 | .150 | .192 | .155 | .185 |
| Catalog Number | 8445 | 8460 | 8500 | 8520 | 8600 | 8620 | 8610 | 8630 | 8800 | 8805 | 8820 | 8830 | 5350 | 5400 |

**From: $17.58–$34.49**

# Speer Bullets

## Rifle Bullets

### DeepCurl

This new line offers big game hunters of all types a consistent, tough, and accurate bullet, utilizing Speer's ability to bond bullets at the chemical level. Designed with a flat base for uniform bullet heel, DeepCurl is stable, accurate, and offers good weight retention.

Also available in handgun loads.
***Available in***: 6mm (80 Gr., 90 Gr.); 25 (120 Gr.); 6.5mm (140 Gr.); .270 (150 Gr.); 7mm (160 Gr., 175 Gr.); 30 (110 Gr., 150 Gr., 165 Gr., 170 Gr., 180 Gr.); .338 (225 Gr.).
**From:** . . . . . . . . . . . . . **$19.79–$32.99**

### Boat Tail Bullets

| Caliber & Description | 22 Match* HP | 6mm SSP | 6mm SSP | 25 SHP | 25 SSP | 270 SSP | 270 SSP | 7mm SSP |
|---|---|---|---|---|---|---|---|---|
| Diameter, Inches | .224 | .243 | .243 | .257 | .257 | .277 | .277 | .284 |
| Weight, Grains | 52 | 85 | 100 | 100 | 120 | 130 | 150 | 130 |
| Density | .148 | .206 | .242 | .216 | .260 | .242 | .279 | .230 |
| Ballistic Coefficient | .253 | .380 | .446 | .393 | .480 | .412 | .489 | .424 |
| Catalog Number | 1036 | 1213 | 1220 | 1408 | 1410 | 1458 | 1604 | 1624 |

*Match bullets are not recommended for use on game animals.

| Caliber & Description | 7mm SSP | 7mm Match* HP | 7mm SSP | 30 SSP | 30 SSP | 30 Match* HP | 30 SSP | 338 SSP | 375 SSP |
|---|---|---|---|---|---|---|---|---|---|
| Diameter, Inches | .284 | .284 | .284 | .308 | .308 | .308 | .308 | .338 | .375 |
| Weight, Grains | 145 | 145 | 160 | 150 | 165 | 168 | 180 | 225 | 270 |
| Density | .257 | .257 | .284 | .226 | .248 | .253 | .271 | .281 | .274 |
| Ballistic Coefficient | .472 | .468 | .519 | .417 | .520 | .534 | .545 | .497 | .478 |
| Catalog Number | 1628 | 1631 | 1634 | 2022 | 2034 | 2040 | 2052 | 2406 | 2472 |

*Match bullets are not recommended for use on game animals.

**From: $19.29–$33.99**

### Grand Slam

| Caliber & Description | 6mm SP | 25 HCSP | 270 HCSP | 270 HCSP | 7mm HCSP | 7mm HCSP | 7mm HCSP | 30 HCSP | 30 HCSP | 30 HCSP | 338 HCSP | 375 HCSP |
|---|---|---|---|---|---|---|---|---|---|---|---|---|
| Diameter, Inches | .243 | .257 | .277 | .277 | .284 | .284 | .284 | .308 | .308 | .308 | .338 | .375 |
| Weight, Grains | 100 | 120 | 130 | 150 | 145 | 160 | 175 | 150 | 165 | 180 | 250 | 285 |
| Density | .242 | .260 | .242 | .279 | .257 | .283 | .310 | .226 | .248 | .271 | .313 | .290 |
| Ballistic Coefficient | .327 | .356 | .332 | .378 | .353 | .389 | .436 | .295 | .354 | .374 | .436 | .354 |
| Catalog Number | 1222 | 1415 | 1465 | 1608 | 1632 | 1638 | 1643 | 2026 | 2038 | 2063 | 2408 | 2473 |

**From: $27.99–$59.99**

**LEGEND**

| | | |
|---|---|---|
| BT | – | Boat Tail |
| FB | – | Fusion Bonded |
| FMJ | – | Full Metal Jacket |
| FN | – | Flat Nose |
| GD | – | Gold Dot® |
| HC | – | Hot-Cor® |
| HP | – | Hollow Point |
| L | – | Lead |
| MHP™ | – | Molybdenum Disulfide Impregnated |
| S | – | Spitzer |
| SS | – | Semi-Spitzer |
| SB™ | – | For Short-Barrel Firearms |
| SP | – | Soft Point |
| TMJ® | – | Encased-Core Full Jacket |
| RN | – | Round Nose |
| SWC | – | Semi-Wadcutter |
| UC | – | Uni-Cor® |
| WC | – | Wadcutter |

**AMMUNITION**

# Speer Bullets

## Hot-Cor Bullets*

| Caliber & Description | 6mm SSP | 25 SPFN | 25 SSP | 25 SSP | 25 SSP | 6.5mm SSP | 6.5mm SSP | 270 SSP | 270 SSP | 7mm SSP | 7mm SPFN | 7mm SSP |
|---|---|---|---|---|---|---|---|---|---|---|---|---|
| Diameter, Inches | .243 | .257 | .257 | .257 | .257 | .264 | .264 | .277 | .277 | .284 | .284 | .284 |
| Weight, Grains | 90 | 75 | 87 | 100 | 120 | 120 | 140 | 130 | 150 | 130 | 130 | 145 |
| Density | .218 | .162 | .188 | .216 | .260 | .246 | .287 | .242 | .279 | .230 | .230 | .257 |
| Ballistic Coefficient | .365 | .135 | .300 | .334 | .405 | .392 | .498 | .383 | .455 | .394 | .257 | .416 |
| Catalog Number | 1217 | 1237 | 1241 | 1405 | 1411 | 1435 | 1441 | 1459 | 1605 | 1623 | 1625 | 1629 |

*Not recommended for lever-action rifles.*

| Caliber & Description | 7mm SSP | 30 Spire SP | 30 FNSP | "30 SPFN" | 30 RNSP | 30 SSP | 30 Mag-Tip | 30 SSP | 30 SSP | 30 SPRN | 30 SSP | 30 SSP | 7.62x39 SSP |
|---|---|---|---|---|---|---|---|---|---|---|---|---|---|
| Diameter, Inches | .284 | .308 | .308 | .308 | .308 | .308 | .308 | .308 | .308 | .308 | .308 | .308 | .310 |
| Weight, Grains | 160 | 110 | 130 | 150 | 150 | 150 | 150 | 165 | 170 | 180 | 180 | 200 | 123 |
| Density | .283 | .166 | .196 | .226 | .226 | .226 | .226 | .248 | .256 | .271 | .271 | .301 | .183 |
| Ballistic Coefficient | .504 | .245 | .213 | .255 | .235 | .377 | .301 | .444 | .298 | .304 | .441 | .478 | .283 |
| Catalog Number | 1635 | 1855 | 2007 | 2011 | 2017 | 2023 | 2025 | 2035 | 2041 | 2047 | 2053 | 2211 | 2213 |

*Not recommended for lever-action rifles.*

| Caliber & Description | 303 SSP | 303 RNSP | 32 FNSP | 8mm SSP | 8mm SSSP | 8mm SSP | 338 SSP | 358 FNSP | 358 FNSP | 358 SSP | 9.3mm SSSP | 375 SSSP | 416 Mag-Tip | 45 FNSP |
|---|---|---|---|---|---|---|---|---|---|---|---|---|---|---|
| Diameter, Inches | .311 | .311 | .321 | .323 | .323 | .323 | .338 | .358 | .358 | .358 | .366 | .375 | .416 | .458 |
| Weight, Grains | 150 | 180 | 170 | 150 | 170 | 200 | 200 | 180 | 220 | 250 | 270 | 235 | 350 | 350 |
| Density | .222 | .266 | .236 | .205 | .233 | .274 | .250 | .201 | .245 | .279 | .288 | .239 | .289 | .238 |
| Ballistic Coefficient | .351 | .299 | .283 | .343 | .311 | .440 | .426 | .236 | .286 | .422 | .361 | .301 | .332 | .218 |
| Catalog Number | 2217 | 2223 | 2259 | 2277 | 2283 | 2285 | 2405 | 2435 | 2439 | 2453 | 2459 | 2471 | 2477 | 2478 |

**From: $17.49–$36.49**

## Jacketed HP Bullets

| Caliber & Description | 22 Hornet | 45 |
|---|---|---|
| Diameter, Inches | .224 | .458 |
| Weight, Grains | 33 | 300 |
| Density | .094 | .204 |
| Ballistic Coefficient | .080 | .206 |
| Catalog Number | 1014 | 2482 |

**From: $16.79–$29.49**

## Special Purpose Bullets*

| Caliber & Description | 30 SPRN | 30 HP | 45 SPFN |
|---|---|---|---|
| Diameter, Inches | .308 | .308 | .458 |
| Weight, Grains | 100 | 110 | 400 |
| Density | .151 | .166 | .272 |
| Ballistic Coefficient | .144 | .128 | .259 |
| Catalog Number | 1805 | 1835 | 2479 |

**From: $17.79–$30.99**

# Speer Bullets

## TNT BULLETS

| Caliber & Description | 204 HP | 22 HP | 22 HP | 6mm HP | 25 HP | 6.5mm HP | 270 HP | 7mm HP | 30 HP |
|---|---|---|---|---|---|---|---|---|---|
| Diameter, Inches | .204 | .224 | .224 | .243 | .247 | .264 | .277 | .284 | .308 |
| Weight, Grains | 39 | 50 | 55 | 70 | 87 | 90 | 90 | 110 | 125 |
| Density | .134 | .142 | .157 | .169 | .188 | .184 | .168 | .195 | .188 |
| Ballistic Coefficient | .202 | .228 | .233 | .279 | .337 | .281 | .303 | .384 | .341 |
| Catalog Number | 1015 | 1030 | 1032 | 1206 | 1246 | 1445 | 1446 | 1616 | 1986 |

**From: $15.79–$26.99**

## Handgun Bullets

### GOLD DOT BULLETS

| Caliber & Description | 25 HP | 32 Auto HP | 327 Fed. Mag. HP | 327 Fed. Mag. HP | 380 Auto HP | 9mm HP | 9mm HP | 9mm HP | 357 SIG HP | 38 Spl. HPSB | 38 HPSB | 357 Mag. HP | 40/10mm HP |
|---|---|---|---|---|---|---|---|---|---|---|---|---|---|
| Diameter, Inches | .251 | .312 | .312 | .312 | .355 | .355 | .355 | .355 | .355 | .357 | .357 | .357 | .400 |
| Weight, Grains | 35 | 60 | 100 | 115 | 90 | 115 | 124 | 147 | 125 | 110 | 135 | 125 | 155 |
| Density | .079 | .088 | .147 | .168 | .102 | .130 | .141 | .167 | .142 | .123 | .151 | .177 | .138 |
| Ballistic Coefficient | .091 | .118 | .137 | .180 | .101 | .125 | .134 | .164 | .141 | .117 | .141 | .140 | .123 |
| Catalog Number | 3985 | 3986 | 3990 | 3988 | 3992 | 3994 | 3998 | 4002 | 4360 | 4009 | 4014 | 4012 | 4400 |

| Caliber & Description | 40/10mm HP | 40/10mm HP | 40/10mm HPSB | 44 Spl. HP | 44 Mag. HP | 45 Auto HP | 45 Auto HP | 45 Auto HP | 45 HPSB |
|---|---|---|---|---|---|---|---|---|---|
| Diameter, Inches | .400 | .400 | .400 | .429 | .429 | .451 | .451 | .451 | .451 |
| Weight, Grains | 165 | 180 | 180 | .200 | 210 | 185 | 200 | 230 | 230 |
| Density | .147 | .161 | .161 | .155 | .163 | .130 | .140 | .162 | .162 |
| Ballistic Coefficient | .138 | .143 | .148 | .145 | .154 | .109 | .138 | .143 | .148 |
| Catalog Number | 4397 | 4406 | 4401 | 4427 | 4428 | 4470 | 4478 | 4483 | 4482 |

**From: $17.79–$29.99**

### LEGEND

| | | | |
|---|---|---|---|
| BT | – Boat Tail | S | – Spitzer |
| FB | – Fusion Bonded | SS | – Semi-Spitzer |
| FMJ | – Full Metal Jacket | SB™ | – For Short-Barrel Firearms |
| FN | – Flat Nose | SP | – Soft Point |
| GD | – Gold Dot® | TMJ® | – Encased-Core Full Jacket |
| HC | – Hot-Cor® | RN | – Round Nose |
| HP | – Hollow Point | SWC | – Semi-Wadcutter |
| L | – Lead | UC | – Uni-Cor® |
| MHP™ | – Molybdenum Disulfide Impregnated | WC | – Wadcutter |

# Speer Bullets

## Jacketed Bullets

| Caliber & Description | 9mm Luger FN JSP | 38 Spl./357 Mag. JHP | 38 Spl./357 Mag. JSP | 38 Spl./357 Mag. JHP | 38 Spl./357 Mag. JHP | 38 Spl./357 Mag. JHP | 38 Spl./357 Mag. JSP | 38 Spl./357 Mag. JSP |
|---|---|---|---|---|---|---|---|---|
| Diameter, Inches | .355 | .357 | .357 | .357 | .357 | .357 | .357 | .357 |
| Weight, Grains | 124 | 110 | 125 | 125 | 140 | 158 | 158 | 158 |
| Density | .141 | .123 | .140 | .140 | .157 | .177 | .177 | .177 |
| Ballistic Coefficient | .115 | .113 | .129 | .129 | .145 | .163 | .164 | .163 |
| Catalog Number | 3997 | 4007 | 4011 | 4013 | 4203 | 4211 | 4217 | 4732 |

| Caliber & Description | 44 Mag. JSP | 44 Mag. JSP | 45 Colt/460 S&W JHP | 45 Colt/460 S&W JSP | 50 Action Express JHP |
|---|---|---|---|---|---|
| Diameter, Inches | .429 | .429 | .451 | .451 | .186 |
| Weight, Grains | 240 | 300 | 260 | 300 | 325 |
| Density | .186 | .233 | .183 | .211 | .186 |
| Ballistic Coefficient | .169 | .213 | .183 | .199 | .169 |
| Catalog Number | 4454 | 4463 | 4481 | 4485 | 4495 |

**From: $14.99–$27.49**

**LEGEND**

| | | | |
|---|---|---|---|
| FN | – Flat Nose | S | – Spitzer |
| HB | – Hollow Base | SP | – Soft Point |
| HC | – Hot-Cor® | SS | – Semi-Spitzer |
| HP | – Hollow Point | SWC | – Semi-Wadcutter |
| J | – Jacketed | WC | – Wadcutter |
| RN | – Round Nose | | |

## Lead Handgun Bullets

| Caliber & Description | 32 S&W HBWC | 9mm Luger RN | 38 HBWC | 38 SWC | 38 SWC HP | 38 RN | 44 SWC | 45 Auto SWC | 45 Auto RN | 45 Colt SWC |
|---|---|---|---|---|---|---|---|---|---|---|
| Diameter, Inches | .314 | .356 | .358 | .358 | .358 | .358 | .430 | .452 | .452 | .452 |
| Weight, grains | 98 | 125 | 148 | 158 | 158 | 158 | 240 | 200 | 230 | 250 |
| Density | .142 | .141 | .165 | .176 | .176 | .176 | .185 | .140 | .161 | .175 |
| Ballistic Coefficient | .044 | .155 | .050 | .123 | .121 | .170 | .151 | .078 | .160 | .117 |
| Bulk Part No. | 4600 | 4602 | 4618 | 4624 | 4628 | 4648 | 4661 | 4678 | 4691 | 4684 |
| Bulk Count | 1000 | 500 | 500 | 500 | 500 | 500 | 500 | 500 | 500 | 500 |

**From: $38.99–$70.99**

# Swift Bullets

## Rifle Bullets

The Scirocco II rifle bullet starts with a tough, pointed polymer tip that reduces air resistance, prevents tip deformation, and blends into the radius of its secant ogive nose section. The Scirocco II has a bonded core construction with a pure lead core encased in a tapered, progressively thickening jacket of pure copper. The Swift A-Frame bullet with its midsection wall of copper is less aerodynamic than the Scirocco, but it produces a broad mushroom while carrying almost all its weight through muscle and bone.

# Swift Bullets

## A-Frame

| Caliber & Description | 25 SS | 25 SS | 6.5mm SS | 6.5mm SS | 270 SS | 270 SS | 270 SS | 7mm SS | 7mm SS | 7mm SS | 30-30 FN | 30 SS | 30-30 FN | 30 SS | 30 SS |
|---|---|---|---|---|---|---|---|---|---|---|---|---|---|---|---|
| Diameter, Inches | .257 | .257 | .264 | .264 | .277 | .277 | .277 | .284 | .284 | .284 | .308 | .308 | .308 | .308 | .308 |
| Weight, Grains | 100 | 120 | 120 | 140 | 130 | 140 | 150 | 140 | 160 | 175 | 150 | 165 | 170 | 180 | 200 |
| Density | .216 | .260 | .246 | .287 | .242 | .261 | .279 | .248 | .283 | .310 | .226 | .248 | .256 | .271 | .301 |
| Ballistic Coefficient | .318 | .382 | .344 | .401 | .323 | .414 | .444 | .335 | .450 | .493 | .220 | .367 | .266 | .400 | .444 |

| Caliber & Description | 338 SS | 338 SS | 338 SS | 348 FN | 35 SS | 35 SS | 35 SS | 9.3mm SS | 9.3mm SS | 9.3mm SS | 375 SS | 375 SS | 375 SS | 400 SS | 400 SS |
|---|---|---|---|---|---|---|---|---|---|---|---|---|---|---|---|
| Diameter, Inches | .338 | .338 | .338 | .348 | .358 | .358 | .358 | .366 | .366 | .366 | .375 | .375 | .375 | .410 | .410 |
| Weight, Grains | 225 | 250 | 275 | 200 | 225 | 250 | 280 | 250 | 286 | 300 | 250 | 270 | 300 | 350 | 400 |
| Density | .281 | .313 | .344 | .236 | .251 | .279 | .312 | .267 | .305 | .320 | .254 | .274 | .305 | .297 | .339 |
| Ballistic Coefficient | .384 | .427 | .469 | .245 | .312 | .347 | .388 | .285 | .385 | .342 | .271 | .349 | .325 | .321 | .367 |

| Caliber & Description | 416 SS | 416 SS | 404 SS | 45-70 FN | 458 FN | 458 SS | 458 SS | 470 RN | 505 RN | 505 RN | 50 FN | 500 RN | 500 RN |
|---|---|---|---|---|---|---|---|---|---|---|---|---|---|
| Diameter, Inches | .416 | .416 | .423 | .457 | .458 | .458 | .458 | .475 | .505 | .505 | .509 | .509 | .509 |
| Weight, Grains | 350 | 400 | 400 | 350 | 400 | 450 | 500 | 500 | 535 | 570 | 450 | 535 | 570 |
| Density | .289 | .330 | .319 | .238 | .272 | .307 | .341 | .329 | .300 | .319 | .247 | .294 | .313 |
| Ballistic Coefficient | .321 | .367 | .375 | .172 | .258 | .325 | .361 | .364 | .285 | .306 | .180 | .285 | .306 |

**MSRP $55.00–$114.50**

## Scirocco

| Caliber & Description | 224 BTS | 224 BTS | 6mm BTS | 25 BTS | 6.5mm BTS | 270 BTS | 7mm BTS | 30 BTS | 30 BTS | 30 BTS | 338 BTS |
|---|---|---|---|---|---|---|---|---|---|---|---|
| Diameter, Inches | .224 | .224 | .243 | .257 | .264 | .277 | .284 | .308 | .308 | .308 | .338 |
| Weight, Grains | 62 | 75 | 90 | 100 | 130 | 130 | 150 | 150 | 165 | 180 | 210 |
| Density | .177 | .214 | .218 | .216 | .266 | .242 | .266 | .226 | .248 | .271 | .263 |
| Ballistic Coefficient | .307 | .419 | .419 | .429 | .571 | .450 | .515 | .430 | .470 | .520 | .507 |

**MSRP $52.25–$69.00**

**LEGEND**
- **BT** – Boattail
- **FN** – Flat Nose
- **HP** – Hollow Point
- **RN** – Round Nose
- **S** – Spitzer
- **SS** – Semi-Spitzer

AMMUNITION

# Swift Bullets

## Handgun Bullets

| A-FRAME<br>HUNTING<br>REVOLVER<br>BULLETS | | | | | | | | | | |
|---|---|---|---|---|---|---|---|---|---|---|
| Caliber &<br>Description | 357<br>HP | 357<br>HP | 41<br>HP | 44<br>HP | 44<br>HP | 44<br>HP | 45<br>HP | 45<br>HP | 45<br>HP | 50<br>HP |
| Diameter, Inches | .357 | .357 | .410 | .430 | .430 | .430 | .452 | .452 | .452 | .499 |
| Weight, Grains | 158 | 180 | 210 | 240 | 280 | 300 | 265 | 300 | 325 | 325 |
| Density | .177 | .202 | .178 | .185 | .216 | .232 | .185 | .210 | .227 | .186 |
| Ballistic Coefficient | .183 | .189 | .159 | .119 | .139 | .147 | .129 | .153 | .171 | .135 |

**LEGEND**
- **BT** – Boattail
- **FN** – Flat Nose
- **HP** – Hollow Point
- **RN** – Round Nose
- **S** – Spitzer
- **SS** – Semi-Spitzer

**MSRP $54.00**

# Woodleigh Bullets

## HYDROSTATICALLY STABILIZED

Hydrostatic stabilization is a method of producing pierced hollow bars to very precise concentricity to produce a bullet that resists deflection and achieves deep straight-line penetration. It's non-toxic and environmentally sensitive. It can be used in most nitro double and magazine rifles.
**From: $35.49–$79.99**

| Caliber | Diameter | "Weight, Grains" | Catalog Number | Caliber | Diameter | "Weight, Grains" | Catalog Number |
|---|---|---|---|---|---|---|---|
| 7mm | .308 | 140 | H7mm | 416 | .416 | 400 | H416 |
| 308 | .308 | 150 | H308A | 404 Jeffery | .422 | 400 | H404 |
| 308 | .308 | 180 | H308 | 450 | .458 | 325 | H450BPE |
| 303 | .312 | 215 | H303 | 45/70 | .458 | 400 | H45/70 |
| 8mm | .323 | 170 | H8mm | 458 | .458 | 450 | H458A |
| 338 | .338 | 185 | H338A | 458 | .458 | 480 | H458 |
| 338 | .338 | 225 | H338 | 465 | .468 | 480 | H465 |
| 358 | .358 | 225 | H358 | 470 | .474 | 500 | H470 |
| 9.3 | .366 | "232 286" | "H9.3A H9.3" | 500 | .510 | 570 | H500 |
| 375 Win. | .375 | 235 | H375A | 50 Alaskan | .510 | 400 | H50 Alaskan |
| 375 | .375 | 300 | H375 | 505 | .505 | 525 | H505 |
| 450/400 3" | .410 | 400 | H450/400 | 577 | .585 | 750 | H577 |

**98% & 95%
RETAINED WEIGHT
300 WIN MAG
180GR PP**

**458 X 500GN SN
RECOVERED FROM
BUFFALO**

**270 WIN 150GN PP
86% RETAINED
WEIGHT**

**94% RETAINED
WEIGHT
300 WIN MAG
180GR PP**

**500/465 RECOVERED
FROM BUFFALO**

**AMMUNITION**

# Woodleigh Bullets

**TRADITIONAL BULLETS**
Fashioned from gilding-metal-clad steel 2mm thick, jackets on FMJ bullets are heavy at the nose for extra impact resistance. The jacket then tapers toward the base to assist rifling engraving. Woodleigh Weldcore Soft Nose bullets are made from 90/100 gilding metal (90 percent copper; 10 percent zinc) 1.6 mm thick.
**From: $30.49–$91.99**

| Caliber Diameter | Type | "Weight, Grains" | SD | BC | Catalog Number |
|---|---|---|---|---|---|
| 6.5mm .264 | PP SN | 140 | .287 | .444 | 80 |
| | PP SN | 160 | .328 | .509 | 80A |
| | RN SN | 160 | .328 | .285 | 80B |
| 270 Win .277 | PP SN | 130 | .242 | .409 | 72 |
| | PP SN | 150 | .279 | .463 | 73 |
| | PP SN | 180 | .334 | .513 | 73A |
| 7mm .284 | PP SN | 140 | .248 | .436 | 74 |
| | PP SN | 160 | .283 | .486 | 75 |
| | PP SN | 175 | .310 | .510 | 76 |
| 275 H&H .287 | PP SN | 160 | .277 | .474 | 77 |
| | PP SN | 175 | .304 | .509 | 78 |
| 308 .308 | "PP SN | 130 | .189 | .302 | 65I |
| | PP SN | 150 | .226 | .310 | 65F |
| | PP SN | 165 | .248 | .320 | 65A |
| | PP SN | 180 | .271 | .376 | 65B |
| | RN SN | 220 | .331 | .367 | 65C |
| | FMJ | 220 | .331 | .359 | 65 |
| 30-30 .308 | FN SN | 150 | .226 | .246 | 65H |
| 30/06 .308 | PP SN | 240 | .361 | .401 | 65G |
| 300 Win. Mag. .308 | PP SN | 180 | .271 | .435 | 65D |
| | PP SN | 200 | .301 | .450 | 65E |
| 303 British .312 | PP SN | 174 | .255 | .362 | 68A |
| | RN SN | 215 | .316 | .359 | 68 |
| 303/ 7.62mmx-39mm .312 | PP SN | 130 | .312 | .347 | 68B |
| 8mm .323 | RN SN | 196 | .268 | .315 | 64B |
| | RN SN | 220 | .301 | .355 | 64C |
| | RN SN | 250 | .343 | .403 | 64D |
| 325 Win. (8mm) .323 | PP SN | 200 | .274 | .406 | 64F |
| | PP SN | 220 | .301 | .448 | 64G |
| 8x57 .318 | RN SN | 200 | .283 | .331 | 64E |
| 318 WR .330 | RN SN | 250 | .328 | .420 | 63 |
| | FMJ | 250 | .328 | .364 | 64 |
| 333 Jeffery .333 | RN SN | 250 | .322 | .335 | 60 |
| | RN SN | 300 | .386 | .418 | 61 |
| | FMJ | 300 | .386 | .418 | 62 |
| 338 Fed .338 | PP SN | 180 | .226 | .361 | 56C |
| | PP SN | 200 | .251 | .401 | 56D |
| 33 Win. .338 | FN SN | 200 | .246 | .234 | 56E |
| 338 Mag .338 | PP SN | 225 | .281 | .425 | 56A |
| | RN SN | 250 | .313 | .332 | 56 |
| | PP SN | 250 | .313 | .431 | 56B |
| | FMJ | 250 | .313 | .326 | 57 |
| | RN SN | 300 | .375 | .416 | 58 |
| | FMJ | 300 | .375 | .414 | 59 |
| 348 Win. .348 | FN SN | 250 | .295 | .281 | 348 |

| Caliber Diameter | Type | "Weight, Grains" | SD | BC | Catalog Number |
|---|---|---|---|---|---|
| 358 .358 | RN SN | 225 | .251 | .263 | 51 |
| | PP SN | 225 | .251 | .372 | 51A |
| | FMJ | 225 | .251 | .263 | 52 |
| | RN SN | 250 | .279 | .300 | 53 |
| | PP SN | 250 | .279 | .400 | 53A |
| | PP SN | 275 | .307 | .450 | 53B |
| | RN SN | 310 | .346 | .458 | 54 |
| | FMJ | 310 | .346 | .458 | 55 |
| 9.3 .366 | RN SN | 250 | .267 | .281 | 47A |
| | PP SN | 250 | .267 | .381 | 47C |
| | RN SN | 286 | .305 | .321 | 47 |
| | PP SN | 286 | .305 | .396 | 47B |
| | FMJ | 286 | .305 | .305 | 48 |
| | RN SN | 320 | .341 | .359 | 49 |
| | PP SN | 320 | .341 | .457 | 49A |
| | FMJ | 320 | .341 | .341 | 50 |
| 375 Mag. .375 | PP SN | 235 | .239 | .310 | 42A |
| | RN SN | 270 | .274 | .250 | 42 |
| | PP SN | 270 | .274 | .370 | 43A |
| | RN SN | 300 | .305 | .277 | 44HD |
| | RN SN | 300 | .305 | .277 | 44 |
| | PP SN | 300 | .305 | .380 | 45A |
| | FMJ | 300 | .305 | .275 | 46 |
| | RN SN | 350 | .356 | .321 | 46B |
| | RN SN | 350 | .356 | .323 | 46BHD |
| | PP SN | 350 | .356 | .400 | 46C |
| | FMJ | 350 | .356 | .307 | 46D |
| 400 Purdey .405 | RN SN | 230 | .200 | .181 | 81 |
| 450/400 Nitro .408 | RN SN | 400 | .344 | .307 | 40A |
| 450/400 Nitro .411" | RN SN | 400 | .338 | .307 | 40 |
| 450/400 Ruger .410 | RN SN | 400 | .338 | .307 | 40B |
| 450/400 Ruger .408" | FMJ | 400 | .344 | .300 | 41A |
| .410 Ruger | FMJ | 400 | .338 | .300 | 41 |
| 405 Win. .412 | RN SN | 300 | .252 | .194 | 71 |
| 416 Rigby .416 | PP SN | 340 | .281 | .330 | 39 |
| | RN SN | 410 | .338 | .307 | 37A |
| | FMJ | 410 | .338 | .300 | 38 |
| | RN SN | 450 | .371 | .338 | 37B |
| | FMJ | 450 | .371 | .330 | 38B" |
| 416 Rem. .416 | RN SN | 400 | .330 | .305 | 37C |
| | FMJ | 400 | .330 | .300 | 38C |
| | RN SN | 450 | .371 | .338 | 37N |
| | FMJ | 450 | .371 | .330 | 38N |
| 404 Jeffery .422 | RN SN | 350 | .281 | .293 | 35 |
| | RN SN | 400 | .321 | .335 | 33A |
| | FMJ | 400 | .321 | .330 | 34 |
| | RN SN | 450 | .361 | .360 | 33B |
| | FMJ | 450 | .361 | .355 | 34B |
| 10.75x68mm .423 | RN SN | 347 | .277 | .290 | 36 |
| | FMJ | 347 | .277 | .288 | 36A |
| 444 Marlin .430 | FN SN | 280 | .216 | .186 | 444 |

# Woodleigh Bullets

| Caliber Diameter | Type | "Weight, Grains" | SD | BC | Catalog Number |
|---|---|---|---|---|---|
| 425 WR .435 | RN SN | 410 | .310 | .222 | 31 |
| | FMJ | 410 | .310 | .221 | 32 |
| 11.2 Schuler .440 | RN SN | 401 | .296 | .325 | 67 |
| 458 Mag. .458 | PP SN | 400 | .272 | .340 | 30 |
| | RN SN | 480 | .327 | .328 | 24A |
| | FMJ | 480 | .327 | .325 | 25A |
| | RN SN | 500 | .341 | .310 | 26 |
| | PP SN | 500 | .341 | .378 | 26A |
| | FMJ | 500 | .341 | .310 | 28 |
| | RN SN | 550 | .375 | .340 | 27 |
| | FMJ | 550 | .375 | .326 | 29 |
| 450 BPE .458 | RN SN | 350 | .238 | .250 | 30A |
| 45/70 .458 | FN SN | 405 | .276 | .204 | 30B |
| | FN SN | 300 | .205 | .196 | 30C |
| 450 Nitro .458 | RN SN | 480 | .327 | .328 | 24 |
| | FMJ | 480 | .327 | .325 | 25 |
| 465 Nitro .468 | RN SN | 480 | .313 | .334 | 22 |
| | FMJ | 480 | .313 | .330 | 23 |
| 470 Nitro .474 | RN SN | 500 | .318 | .374 | 20 |
| | FMJ | 500 | .318 | .370 | 21 |
| 476 WR .476 | RN SN | 520 | .328 | .385 | 18 |
| | FMJ | 520 | .328 | .380 | 19 |
| 475 No. 2 .483 | RN SN | 480 | .294 | .309 | 15 |
| | FMJ | 480 | .294 | .300 | 16 |
| 475 No. 2 Jeffery .488 | RN SN | 500 | .300 | .315 | 13 |
| | FMJ | 500 | .300 | .300 | 14 |

| Caliber Diameter | Type | "Weight, Grains" | SD | BC | Catalog Number |
|---|---|---|---|---|---|
| 500 S&W MAG .500 | FN SN | 400 | .229 | .182 | 83 |
| 505 Gibbs .505 | RN SN | 525 | .294 | .345 | 11 |
| | FMJ | 525 | .294 | .340 | 12 |
| | PP SN | 600 | .336 | .360 | 11A |
| | FMJ | 600 | .336 | .360 | 12A |
| 500 Jeffery .510 | RN SN | 535 | .294 | .350 | 9 |
| | PP SN | 535 | .294 | .310 | 9A |
| | FMJ | 535 | .294 | .340 | 10 |
| | PP SN | 600 | .330 | .350 | 10B |
| | FMJ | 600 | .330 | .355 | 10A |
| 500 BP .510 | RN SN | 440 | .242 | .255 | 8 |
| 50 Alaskan & 50/110 Win. .510 | FN SN | 500 | .275 | .219 | 82 |
| 500 Nitro .510 | RN SN | 450 | .247 | .257 | 06A |
| | RN SN | 570 | .313 | .368 | 6 |
| | FMJ | 570 | .313 | .350 | 7 |
| 577 BP Express .585 | RN SN | 650 | .271 | .292 | 5 |
| 577 Nitro .585 | RN SN | 650 | .271 | .292 | 3A |
| | RN SN | 750 | .313 | .346 | 3 |
| 577 Nitro .584 | FMJ | 650 | .272 | .292 | 4A |
| | FMJ | 750 | .314 | .351 | 4 |
| 600 Nitro .620 | RN SN | 900 | .334 | .371 | 1 |
| | FMJ | 900 | .334 | .334 | 2 |
| 700 Nitro .700 | RN SN | 1000 | .292 | .340 | A |
| | FMJ | 1000 | .292 | .340 | B |

## POWDERS

## RELOADING TOOLS

# POWDERS

## Accurate Powder

### Rifle

#### 1680
Extremely fast burning, double-base, spherical rifle powder well suited for large-capacity, high-performance handgun cartridges as well as low capacity rifle cartridges.
1lb: . . . . . . . . . . . . . . . . . . . . .$19.25
8lbs: . . . . . . . . . . . . . . . . . . .$138.00

#### 2015
Fast-burning, single-base, extruded rifle powder that performs very well in small to medium varmint calibers.
1lb: . . . . . . . . . . . . . . . . . . . . .$21.05
8lbs: . . . . . . . . . . . . . . . . . . . $157.00

#### 2200
High-performance, small caliber propellant; double-base, spherical propellant.
1lb: . . . . . . . . . . . . . . . . . . . . .$19.25
8lbs: . . . . . . . . . . . . . . . . . . .$138.00

#### 2230
Fast-burning, double-base, spherical rifle propellant. Excellent flow characteristics and grain size are ideal for progressive loading.
1lb: . . . . . . . . . . . . . . . . . . . . .$19.25
8lbs: . . . . . . . . . . . . . . . . . . .$138.00

#### 2460
Fast-burning, double-base, spherical rifle powder; slower derivative of the AA2230 powder; suitable for small and medium sized calibers.
1lb: . . . . . . . . . . . . . . . . . . . . .$19.25
8lbs: . . . . . . . . . . . . . . . . . . .$138.00

#### 2495
Single-base, extruded rifle powder that was developed for the .308 Win. and can be used over a wide range of rifle calibers.
1lb: . . . . . . . . . . . . . . . . . . . . .$21.05
8lbs: . . . . . . . . . . . . . . . . . . .$157.00

#### 2520
Medium-burning, double-base, spherical rifle propellant designed around the .308 Win.
1lb: . . . . . . . . . . . . . . . . . . . . .$19.25
8lbs: . . . . . . . . . . . . . . . . . . .$138.00

#### 2700
Medium-burning, double-base, spherical rifle powder that is suited for the .30-06 Spfd.
1lb: . . . . . . . . . . . . . . . . . . . . .$19.25
8lbs: . . . . . . . . . . . . . . . . . . .$138.00

#### 4064
Intermediate-burning, single-base, short cut extruded rifle powder designed around the .30-06 Spfd.
1lb: . . . . . . . . . . . . . . . . . . . . .$21.05
8lbs: . . . . . . . . . . . . . . . . . . .$157.00

#### 4350
Short-cut, single-base, extruded rifle powder in the extremely popular 4350 burn range.
1lb: . . . . . . . . . . . . . . . . . . . . .$21.05
8lbs: . . . . . . . . . . . . . . . . . . .$157.00

#### 5744
Low, bulky density and superior ignition characteristics; many rifle calibers and large-capacity black-powder cartridges
1lb: . . . . . . . . . . . . . . . . . . . . .$24.85
8lbs: . . . . . . . . . . . . . . . . . . .$185.00

#### MAGPRO
Slow-burning, double-base, spherical rifle powder developed specifically for the short magnums of both Winchester and Remington.
1lb: . . . . . . . . . . . . . . . . . . . . .$19.25
8lbs: . . . . . . . . . . . . . . . . . . .$138.00

### Handgun

#### 4100
Slow-burning with exceptional metering characteristics. Excellent choice for high-performance, full-power loads in magnum handgun cartridges.
1lb: . . . . . . . . . . . . . . . . . . . . .$19.99
4lbs: . . . . . . . . . . . . . . . . . . . .$74.99
8lbs: . . . . . . . . . . . . . . . . . . .$139.99

#### NO. 2
Extremely fast-burning, double-base, spherical powder. Low recoil and low flash; well suited for use in short barrel, concealed carry applications.
1lb: . . . . . . . . . . . . . . . . . . . . .$16.80
5lbs: . . . . . . . . . . . . . . . . . . . .$75.00

#### NO. 5
Wide performance range from target and Cowboy Action applications to full-power defense loads. Strikes a balance between ballistics and cost efficiency.
1lb: . . . . . . . . . . . . . . . . . . . . .$18.10
8lbs: . . . . . . . . . . . . . . . . . . .$130.50

#### NO. 7
Intermediate-burning, double-base, spherical powder suitable for a wide range of handgun calibers, especially high performance semi-auto handguns.
1lb: . . . . . . . . . . . . . . . . . . . . .$18.10
8lbs: . . . . . . . . . . . . . . . . . . .$130.50

#### NO. 9
Ideal for high power loads in traditional magnums such as the .357 Mag., .41 Rem. Mag., and .44 Rem. Mag.
1lb: . . . . . . . . . . . . . . . . . . . . .$18.10
8lbs: . . . . . . . . . . . . . . . . . . .$130.50

## Shotshell

### NITRO 100

Fast-burning, flattened spherical, double-base shotshell powder that is a clean burning, cost-effective choice for all 12-gauge target applications.

12oz: . . . . . . . . . . . . . . . . . .$14.95
4lbs: . . . . . . . . . . . . . . . . . . .$70.99
8lbs: . . . . . . . . . . . . . . . . . .$116.25

### SOLO 1000

Ultra clean burning powder that is well suited for target handgun loads in .45 ACP and Cowboy Action cartridges.

12oz: . . . . . . . . . . . . . . . . . .$15.10
4lbs: . . . . . . . . . . . . . . . . . .$69.99
8lbs: . . . . . . . . . . . . . . . . .$118.75

# Alliant Powder

## ALLIANT SMOKELESS POWDERS

### 20/28 SMOKELESS SHOTSHELL POWDER

Powder designed to deliver competition-grade performance to 20 and 28 Ga. clay target shooters. Extremely clean burning with proven lot-to-lot consistency.

1lb: $16.25
4lbs: $60.15
8lbs: $112.50

### 410

Cleanest .410 bore powder on the market.

1lb: $16.25
4lbs: $60.15
8lbs: $112.50

### 2400

Legendary for its performance in .44 Mag. and other magnum pistol loads. Originally developed for the .22 Hornet, it's also the shooter's choice for .410 bore.

1lb: $16.25
4lbs: $60.15
8lbs:$112.50

### AMERICAN SELECT

This ultra-clean burning premium powder makes a versatile target load and superior 1 oz. load for improved clay target scores. Great for Cowboy Action handgun loading, too.

1lb: $15.65
4lbs: $65.99
8lbs: $106.80

### AR-COMP

Developed specifically for AR-style rifles and ideally suited for heavy .223 and .308 match bullets, AR-Comp delivers high-performance ignition each and every time.

1lb: $19.40
8lbs: $144.50

### BLACK MZ

Designed for shooters of all disciplines, Black MZ is an ideal choice for hunters as well as Cowboy Action shooters, reenactment shooters and the recent rise in .45-70, .45-90, and, .45-100 shooters.

1lb: $19.60

# Alliant Powder

### BLUE DOT
The powder of choice for magnum lead shotshell loads. 10, 12, 16, 20, and 28 Ga. Consistent and accurate. Doubles as magnum handgun powder.
**1lb: $15.55**
**5lbs: $68.45**

### BULL'S-EYE
America's best known pistol powder. Unsurpassed for .45 ACP target loads.
**1lb: $15.20**
**4lbs: $56.00**
**8lbs: $104.80**

### E3
The first of a new generation of high performance powders.
**1lb: $15.65**
**4lb: $58.70**
**8lbs: $106.80**

### GREEN DOT
It delivers precise burn rates for uniformly tight patterns and you'll appreciate the lower felt recoil. Versatile for target and field.
**1lb: $15.65**
**4lbs: $58.70**
**8lbs: $106.80**

### HERCO
Since 1920, a proven powder for heavy shotshell loads, including 10, 12, 16, 20, and 28 Ga. target loads. The ultimate in 12 Ga., 1¼ oz. upland game loads.
**1lb: $15.65**
**4lbs: $58.70**
**8lbs: $106.80**

### POWER PISTOL
Designed for high performance in semi-automatic pistols (9mm, .40 S&W, and .357 SIG).
**1lb: $15.20**
**4lbs: $55.90**

### RED DOT
America's #1 choice for clay target loads, now 50 percent cleaner. Since 1932, more 100 straights than any other powder.
**1lb: $15.65**
**4lbs: $58.70**
**8lbs: $106.80**

### RELOADER 7
Designed for small caliber varmint loads, it meters consistently and meets the needs of the most demanding bench rest shooter. Great in .45-70 and .450 Marlin.
**1lb: $19.15**
**5lbs: $89.40**

### RELOADER 10X
Best choice for light bullet applications in .222 Rem., .223 Rem., .22-250 Rem., and key benchrest calibers, as well as .308 Win. loads.
**1lb: $19.15**
**5lbs: $89.40**

# Alliant Powder

### RELOADER 15
An all-around medium speed rifle powder. It provides excellent .223 and .308 performance. Selected as the powder for U.S. Military's M118 Special Ball Long Range Sniper Round.
**1lb: $19.15**
**5lbs: $89.40**

### RELOADER 19
Provides superb accuracy in most medium and heavy rifle loads and is the powder of choice for .30-06 and .338 calibers.
**1lb: $19.15**
**5lbs: $89.40**

### RELOADER 22
This top performing powder for big-game loads provides excellent metering and is the powder of choice for .270, 7mm Mag., and .300 Win. Mag.
**1lb: $19.15**
**5lbs: $89.40**

### RELOADER 25
This powder for big game hunting features improved slower burning and delivers the high-energy, heavy magnum loads needed.
**1lb: $19.15**
**5lbs: $89.40**

### STEEL
Designed for waterfowl shotshells. Gives steel shot high velocity within safe pressure limits for 10 and 12 Ga. loads.
**1lb: $15.70**
**4lbs: $58.00**

### UNIQUE
Shotgun/handgun powder for 12, 16, 20, and 28 Ga. loads. Use with most hulls, primers, and wads.
**1lb: $15.65**
**4lbs: $58.70**
**8lbs: $106.80**

# Hodgdon

## Smokeless Powders

### CLAYS
Tailored for use in 12 Ga., 7/8 oz., 1 oz., and 1 1/8 oz. loads. Performs well in many handgun applications, including .38 Spl., .40 S&W, and .45 ACP.
14oz: . . . . . . . . . . . . . . . . . .$15.25
4lbs: . . . . . . . . . . . . . . . . . .$65.20
8lbs: . . . . . . . . . . . . . . . . . .$121.70

### CLAYS, INTERNATIONAL
Ideal for 12 and 20 Ga. autoloaders who want reduced recoil.
14oz: . . . . . . . . . . . . . . . . . .$15.25
4lbs: . . . . . . . . . . . . . . . . . .$65.20
8lbs: . . . . . . . . . . . . . . . . . .$121.70

### CLAYS, UNIVERSAL
Loads nearly all the straight-wall pistol cartridges as well as 12 Ga. 1 1/4 oz. thru 28 Ga. 3/4 oz. target loads.
1lb: . . . . . . . . . . . . . . . . . .$18.25
4lbs: . . . . . . . . . . . . . . . . . .$68.50
8lbs: . . . . . . . . . . . . . . . . . .$128.35

### COPPER FOULING ERASER (CFE) 223
Versatile spherical rifle propellant incorporates in its formula Copper Fouling Eraser, an ingredient used in military propellant that deters copper fouling. It contributes to longer periods of top accuracy with less barrel clean-ing time. Top velocities in .204 Ruger, .223 Rem./5.56mm NATO, .22-250 Rem., .308 Win./7.62mm NATO
1lb: . . . . . . . . . . . . . . . . . .$18.65
8lbs: . . . . . . . . . . . . . . . . . .$136.35

### EXTREME BENCHMARK
A fine choice for small rifle cases like the .223 Rem. and PPC competition rounds. Appropriate also for the .30-30 and 7x57.
1lb: . . . . . . . . . . . . . . . . . .$21.35
8lbs: . . . . . . . . . . . . . . . . . .$152.00

### EXTREME H50 BMG
Designed for the .50 BMG cartridge. Highly insensitive to extreme tempera-ture changes.
1lb: . . . . . . . . . . . . . . . . . .$21.35
8lbs: . . . . . . . . . . . . . . . . . .$152.00

### EXTREME H322
This powder fills the gap between H4198 and BL-C9(2). Performs best in small to medium capacity cases.
1lb: . . . . . . . . . . . . . . . . . .$21.35
8lbs: . . . . . . . . . . . . . . . . . .$152.00

### EXTREME H1000 EXTRUDED POWDER
Fills the gap between H4831 and H87. Works especially well in overbore capacity cartridges (1,000-yd. shooters take note).
1lb: . . . . . . . . . . . . . . . . . .$21.35
8lbs: . . . . . . . . . . . . . . . . . .$152.00

### EXTREME H4198
H4198 was developed especially for small and medium capacity cartridges.
1lb: . . . . . . . . . . . . . . . . . .$21.35
8lbs: . . . . . . . . . . . . . . . . . .$152.00

### EXTREME H4350
Gives superb accuracy at optimum velocity for many large capacity metal-lic rifle cartridges.
1lb: . . . . . . . . . . . . . . . . . .$25.49
8lbs: . . . . . . . . . . . . . . . . . .$173.99

### EXTREME H4831
Outstanding performance with medi-um and heavy bullets in the 6mm, .25-06, .270, and Magnum calibers. Also available with shortened grains (H4831SC) for easy metering.
1lb: . . . . . . . . . . . . . . . . . .$21.35
8lbs: . . . . . . . . . . . . . . . . . .$152.00

### EXTREME H4895
4895 gives desirable performance in almost all cases from .222 Rem. to .458 Win. Reduced loads to as low as 3/5 maximum still give target accuracy.
1lb: . . . . . . . . . . . . . . . . . .$21.35
8lbs: . . . . . . . . . . . . . . . . . .$152.00

### EXTREME RETUMBO
Designed for such cartridges as the .300 Rem. Ultra Mag., .30-378 Weatherby, the 7mm STW, and other cases with large capacities and small bores. Expect up to 40-100 fps more velocity than other magnum powders.
1lb: . . . . . . . . . . . . . . . . . .$21.35
8lbs: . . . . . . . . . . . . . . . . . .$152.00

### EXTREME VARGET
Features small extruded grain powder for uniform metering, plus higher velocities/normal pressures in such calibers as .223, .22-250, .306, .30-06, and .375 H&H.
1lb: . . . . . . . . . . . . . . . . . .$21.35
8lbs: . . . . . . . . . . . . . . . . . .$152.00

### H110
A spherical powder made especially for the .30 M1 carbine. H110 also does very well in .357, .44 Spl., .44 Mag., or .410 shotshell. Recommended for consistent ignition.
1lb: . . . . . . . . . . . . . . . . . .$18.10
8lbs: . . . . . . . . . . . . . . . . . .$133.30

### HP-38
A fast pistol powder for most pistol loading. Especially recommended for mid-range .38 Spl.
1lb: . . . . . . . . . . . . . . . . . .$16.30
8lbs: . . . . . . . . . . . . . . . . . .$117.00

### HS-6
HS-6 for magnum field loads is unsur-passed. Delivers uniform charges and is dense to allow sufficient wad col-umn for best patterns.
1lb: . . . . . . . . . . . . . . . . . .$18.70
8lbs: . . . . . . . . . . . . . . . . . .$136.35

### LONGSHOT
Spherical powder for heavy shotgun loads.
1lb: . . . . . . . . . . . . . . . . . .$18.05
4lbs: . . . . . . . . . . . . . . . . . .$69.35
8lbs: . . . . . . . . . . . . . . . . . .$133.30

## PYRODEX PELLETS

Both rifle and pistol pellets eliminate powder measures, speeds shooting for black powder enthusiasts.
**From:** . . . . . . . . . . . . **$10.79–$26.49**

## SPHERICAL BL-C(2)

Best performance is in the .222, .308, other cases smaller than .30-06.
**1lb:** . . . . . . . . . . . . . . . . . .**$18.65**
**8lbs:** . . . . . . . . . . . . . . . . .**$136.35**

## SPHERICAL H335

H335 is popular for its performance in medium capacity cases, especially in .222 and .308 Win.
**1lb:** . . . . . . . . . . . . . . . . . .**$18.65**
**8lbs:** . . . . . . . . . . . . . . . . .**$136.35**

## SPHERICAL H380

H380 is a superb performer in the .220 Swift, .243, .257 Roberts, and other fine varmint cartridges.
**1lb:** . . . . . . . . . . . . . . . . . .**$18.65**
**8lbs:** . . . . . . . . . . . . . . . . .**$136.35**

## SPHERICAL H414

In many popular medium to medium large calibers, pressure velocity relationship is better.
**1lb:** . . . . . . . . . . . . . . . . . .**$18.65**
**8lbs:** . . . . . . . . . . . . . . . . .**$136.35**

## SPHERICAL LEVEREVOLUTION

Same spherical propellant used in Hornady's high-performance factory ammunition. This fabulous propellant meters flawlessly and makes lever-action cartridges like the .30-30 Win. yield velocities in excess of 100 fps over any published handloads.
**1lb:** . . . . . . . . . . . . . . . . . .**$19.20**
**8lbs:** . . . . . . . . . . . . . . . . .**$138.50**

## SPHERICAL SUPERFORMANCE

Superformance delivers striking velocities in Hornady cartridges like the .22-250 Rem., .243 Win. and .300 Win. Short Mag.
**1lb:** . . . . . . . . . . . . . . . . . .**$19.20**
**8lbs:** . . . . . . . . . . . . . . . . .**$138.50**

## TITEGROUP

Excellent for most straight-walled pistol cartridges, including .38 Spl., .44 Spl., .45 ACP. Low charge weights, clean burning, position insensitive, and flawless ignition.
**1lb:** . . . . . . . . . . . . . . . . . .**$18.99**
**4lbs:** . . . . . . . . . . . . . . . . .**$68.99**
**8lbs:** . . . . . . . . . . . . . . . . .**$130.99**

## TITEWAD

This 12 Ga. flattened spherical shotgun powder is ideal for 7/8 oz., 1 oz. and 1 1/8 oz. loads, with minimum recoil and mild muzzle report. The fastest fuel in Hodgdon's line.
**1lb:** . . . . . . . . . . . . . . . . . .**$16.29**
**4lbs:** . . . . . . . . . . . . . . . . .**$63.99**
**8lbs:** . . . . . . . . . . . . . . . . .**$116.99**

## TRIPLE SEVEN PELLETS

Sulfur-free Triple Seven powder in 50-grain pellets. Formulated for use with 209 shotshell primers, Triple Seven leaves no rotten-egg smell, and the residue is easy to clean from the bore with only water. The pellets are sized for .50-caliber muzzleloaders and can be used singly (for target shooting or small game) as well as two at a time.
**From:** . . . . . . . . . . . . **$10.79–$29.49**

# IMR

### IMR 3031

A propellant with many uses, IMR 3031 is a favorite of .308 match shooters using 168 gr. match bullets. It is equally effective in small-capacity varmint cartridges from .223 Rem. to .22-250 Rem. and a great .30–30 Win. powder.

**1lb:** . . . . . . . . . . . . . . . . . . . . .**$20.60**
**8lbs:** . . . . . . . . . . . . . . . . . . . . .**$147.80**

### IMR 4007 SSC

Powder that is made to be versatile. Perfect for a wide range of calibers (.17 to .416) and cut super short for smooth, even metering and more consistency.

**1lb:** . . . . . . . . . . . . . . . . . . . . .**$20.60**
**8lbs:** . . . . . . . . . . . . . . . . . . . . .**$147.80**

### IMR 4198

This fast burning rifle powder gives outstanding performance in cartridges like the .222 Rem., .221 Fireball, .45-70 and .450 Marlin.

**1lb:** . . . . . . . . . . . . . . . . . . . . .**$20.60**
**8lbs:** . . . . . . . . . . . . . . . . . . . . .**$147.80**

### IMR 4227

The choice for true magnum velocities and performance. In rifles, this powder delivers excellent velocity and accuracy in such cartridges as the .22 Hornet and .221 Fireball.

**1lb:** . . . . . . . . . . . . . . . . . . . . .**$20.60**
**8lbs:** . . . . . . . . . . . . . . . . . . . . .**$147.80**

### IMR 4320

Short granulation, easy metering, and perfect for the .223 Remington, .22-250 Remington, .250 Savage, and other medium burn rate cartridges. It has long been a top choice for the vintage .300 Savage cartridge.

**1lb:** . . . . . . . . . . . . . . . . . . . . .**$20.60**
**8lbs:** . . . . . . . . . . . . . . . . . . . . .**$147.80**

### IMR 4350

The No. 1 choice for the new short magnums, both Remington and Winchester versions. For magnums with light to medium bullet weights, IMR 4350 is the best choice.

**1lb:** . . . . . . . . . . . . . . . . . . . . .**$20.60**
**8lbs:** . . . . . . . . . . . . . . . . . . . . .**$147.80**

### IMR 4895

Originally a military powder featured in the .30-06, IMR 4895 is extremely versatile. From .17 Rem. to the .243 Win. to the .375 H&H Mag., accuracy and performance are excellent. In addition, it is a longtime favorite of match shooters.

**1lb:** . . . . . . . . . . . . . . . . . . . . .**$20.60**
**8lbs:** . . . . . . . . . . . . . . . . . . . . .**$147.80**

### IMR 7828

The big magnum powder. This slow burner gives real magnum performance to the large overbored magnums, such as the .300 Rem. Ultra Mag., the .30-378 Wby. Mag., and 7mm Rem. Ultra Mag.

**1lb:** . . . . . . . . . . . . . . . . . . . . .**$20.60**
**8lbs:** . . . . . . . . . . . . . . . . . . . . .**$147.80**

### IMR 8208 XBR

Accurate metering, super short grained extruded rifle powder was designed expressly for match, varmint, and AR sniper cartridges. Ideally suited for cartridges like the .223 Rem./5.56mm, .308 Win./7.62mm NATO, and the 6mm PPC.

**1lb:** . . . . . . . . . . . . . . . . . . . . .**$20.60**
**8lbs:** . . . . . . . . . . . . . . . . . . . . .**$147.80**

## Handguns & Shotgun Powders

### HI-SKOR 700-X

This extruded flake type powder is ideally suited for shotshells in 12 and 16 Ga. where clay target and light field loads are the norm. It doubles as an excellent pistol target powder for such cartridges as the .38 Spl., .45 ACP, and many more.

**1lb:** . . . . . . . . . . . . . . . . . . . . .**$14.35**
**4lbs:** . . . . . . . . . . . . . . . . . . . . .**$60.85**
**8lbs:** . . . . . . . . . . . . . . . . . . . . .**$115.25**

### HI-SKOR 800-X

This large-grained flake powder is at its best when used in heavy field loads from 10 Ga. to 28 Ga. In handgun cartridges, 800-X performs superbly in cartridges such as the 10mm Auto, .357 Mag., and .44 Rem. Mag.

**1lb:** . . . . . . . . . . . . . . . . . . . . .**$16.50**
**4lbs:** . . . . . . . . . . . . . . . . . . . . .**$62.15**
**8lbs:** . . . . . . . . . . . . . . . . . . . . .**$116.35**

### PB

Named for the porous base structure of its grains by which the burning rate is controlled, PB is an extremely clean burning, single-base powder. It gives very low pressure in 12 and 20 Ga.

shotshell target loads and performs well in a wide variety of handgun loads.

**14oz:** . . . . . . . . . . . . . . . . . . .**$19.30**
**8lbs:** . . . . . . . . . . . . . . . . . . .**$160.00**

## SR 4756

This fine-grained, easy-metering propellant has long been a favorite of upland and waterfowl handloaders. SR4756 performs extremely well in big handgun cartridges.

**1lb:** . . . . . . . . . . . . . . . . . . .**$20.05**
**8lbs:** . . . . . . . . . . . . . . . . . . .**$138.20**

## SR 4759

This bulky handgun powder works great in the magnums, but really shines as a reduced load propellant for rifle cartridges. Its large grain size gives good loading density for reduced loads, enhancing velocity uniformity.

**1lb:** . . . . . . . . . . . . . . . . . . . . .**$20.05**
**8lbs:** . . . . . . . . . . . . . . . . . . . . .**$138.20**

## SR 7625

SR7625 covers the wide range of shotshells from 10 Ga. to 28 Ga. in both target and field loadings. This versatile powder is equally useful in a large array of handgun cartridges for target, self-defense, and hunting loads.

**1lb:** . . . . . . . . . . . . . . . . . . . .**$22.25**
**8lbs:** . . . . . . . . . . . . . . . . . . . .**$162.30**

# Ramshot

Ramshot (Western Powders, Inc.) powders are all double-base propellants, meaning they contain nitrocellulose and nitroglycerine. While some spherical or ball powders are known for leaving plenty of residue in barrels, these fuels burn very clean. They meter easily, as do all ball powders. Plastic canisters are designed for spill-proof use and include basic loading data on the labels.

## BIG GAME

A versatile propellant for cartridges as diverse as the .30-06 and the .338 Win. and for light-bullet loads in small-bore magnums.

**1lb:** . . . . . . . . . . . . . . . . . . .**$18.50**
**8lbs:** . . . . . . . . . . . . . . . . . . .**$132.80**

## COMPETITION

For the clay target shooter. A fast-burning powder comparable to 700-X or Red Dot, it performs well in a variety of 12 Ga. target loads, offering low recoil, consistent pressures, and clean combustion.

**1lb:** . . . . . . . . . . . . . . . . . . .**$15.30**
**4lbs:** . . . . . . . . . . . . . . . . . . .**$66.50**
**8lbs:** . . . . . . . . . . . . . . . . . . .**$116.40**

# Ramshot

### ENFORCER

A match for high-performance handgun hulls like the .40 S&W. It is designed for full-power loading and high velocities. A fast burning rifle powder, it excels in small-caliber, medium-capacity cartridges.

1lb: . . . . . . . . . . . . . . . . . . . .$18.10
4lbs: . . . . . . . . . . . . . . . . . . . .$65.60

### HUNTER

A double-base, clean-burning, high-performance propellant that is perfect for elk country cartridges such as the .270 Win., .300 WSM. and .338 Win. Mag.

1lb: . . . . . . . . . . . . . . . . . . . .$18.50
8lbs: . . . . . . . . . . . . . . . . . . . .$132.80

### MAGNUM

The slowest powder of the Western line does its best work in cartridges with lots of case volume and small to medium bullet diameter. It is the powder of choice in 7mm and .30 magnums.

1lb: . . . . . . . . . . . . . . . . . . . .$18.50
8lbs: . . . . . . . . . . . . . . . . . . . .$132.80

### SILHOUETTE

Ideal for the 9mm handgun cartridge, from light to heavy loads. It also works well in the .40 S&W and combat loads for the .45 Auto.

1lb: . . . . . . . . . . . . . . . . . . . .$18.10
4lbs: . . . . . . . . . . . . . . . . . . . .$65.60

### TAC

Formulated for tactical rifle cartridges, specifically the .223 and .308. It has produced exceptional accuracy with a variety of bullets and charge weights.

1lb: . . . . . . . . . . . . . . . . . . . .$18.50
8lbs: . . . . . . . . . . . . . . . . . . . .$132.80

### TRUE BLUE

Designed for small-to medium-size handgun cartridges. Similar to Win. 231 and Hodgdon HP-38, it has enough bulk to nearly fill most cases, thereby better positioning the powder for ignition.

1lb: . . . . . . . . . . . . . . . . . . . .$18.10
4lbs: . . . . . . . . . . . . . . . . . . . .$65.60

### X-TERMINATOR

A clean-burning powder designed for the .222 Rem., .223 Rem., and .22 Benchrest calibers.

1lb: . . . . . . . . . . . . . . . . . . . .$18.50
8lbs: . . . . . . . . . . . . . . . . . . . .$132.80

### ZIP

A fast-burning target powder for cartridges like the .38 Spl. and .45 ACP, gives competitors uniform velocities.

1lb: . . . . . . . . . . . . . . . . . . . .$18.10
4lbs: . . . . . . . . . . . . . . . . . . . .$65.60

# VihtaVuori

### N100 SERIES RELOADING POWDERS

The N100 series powders are single-base powders used mainly in rifle calibers. There are ten N100 series powders with different burning rates and suitability from the .17 Rem. up to the .458 Win. Mag. and two special powders for .50 BMG

1lb: . . . . . . . . . . . . . . . . . . . .$29.15
8lbs: . . . . . . . . . . . . . . . . . . . .$189.00

### N300 SERIES RELOADING POWDERS

The N300 series powders are single-base porous powders for handguns. There are altogether nine handgun powders with different kinds of shooting properties and suitable applications.

1lb: . . . . . . . . . . . . . . . . . . . .$29.95
4lbs: . . . . . . . . . . . . . . . . . . . .$100.50

## N500 SERIES RELOADING POWDERS

The N500 series powders are impregnated extruded rifle powders with Nitroglycerol added as an extra energy component. If higher loading densities and more energy are needed, N500 series powders are competent alternatives for the N100 series powders.

N500 series High Energy powders are available in five different burning rates.
**1lb:** .................... **$33.50**

## TIN STAR PREMIUM POWDER

Intended for Cowboy Action Shooters. The primary benefit of Tin Star is its exceptionally high loading volume.

This porous powder fills the case much better than most conventional smokeless propellants, providing the loading density needed for those classic black powder cartridges.
**From:** .................... **$29.95**

# Reloading Tools

# Dillon Precision Reloaders

## RL 550B 4 STATION PROGRESSIVE LOADER

Able to load rifle as well as pistol cartridges; uses standard 7/8 by 14 thread per inch dies, as long as they deprime in the size die; manually indexed shellplate; manually fed cases and bullets; capable of loading 400 to 600 rounds per hour. It has 4 stations and includes a caliber conversion kit, powder measure with large and small powder bars, one tool head, one prime system and small priming parts, and one loaded cartridge catch bin.
**MSRP** .................. **$439.95**

## SL 900 SHOT SHELL RELOADER

This shot shell reloader reloads 12, 20, and 28 Ga. loaders. It has automatic indexing, auto powder and priming systems. Features easily adjustable, case-activated powder and shot systems that eliminate troublesome bushing changes along with spilled powder and shot. Adjustable shot dispenser uses the same design principle, with an extra large hopper that holds 25 pounds of shot. The frame is a heavy duty O-frame design, precision CNC machined to exacting tolerances. The tool head assembly slides out of the frame, keeping all your critical die and measurement adjustments intact and comes with factory adjusted dies.
**MSRP** .................. **$919.95**

## SQUARE DEAL B AUTO-INDEXING RELOADER

Designed to produce up to 400 or 500 handgun rounds per hour; comes with a factory-adjusted carbide die set; change from one caliber to another in minutes with a Square Deal B caliber conversion kit; automatic indexing; auto powder/priming systems; available in 14 handgun calibers; loading dies standard
**MSRP** .................. **$379.95**

## XL 650 5 STATION PROGRESSIVE LOADER

The XL 650 loads virtually every popular pistol and rifle cartridge utilizing standard dies. The optional powder charge check die on the third station sounds an alarm if the powder charge in a round is out of limits either high or low. An exclusive primer system uses a rotary indexing plate that positively controls each primer and keeps a steel shield between the primers and the operator. Features: automatic indexing; five-station interchangeable tool-head; auto powde/priming systems; uses standard 7/8-in. x 14-in. dies;rotary indexing plate for primers.
**MSRP** .................. **$566.95**

**FORSTER RELOADING 3-IN-1 CASE MOUTH CUTTER**

# Forster Reloading

## 3-IN-1 CASE MOUTH CUTTER

This carbide case trimmer accessory performs three functions simultaneously: It trims the case to length, chamfers the inside of the case to an angle of 14 degrees, and the outside of the mouth at 30 degrees. Blades never need sharpening if used on brass only. Currently available for three bullet diameters: .224, .243, .308.
**MSRP** .................... **$86.00**

## .50 BMG CASE TRIMMER

The .50 BMG Case Trimmer is designed specifically for the reloading needs of .50 BMG shooters. It does not require a collet, but it comes complete with a #510 pilot and rim holder.
**MSRP** .................. **$132.00**

# Forster Reloading

## BENCH REST POWDER MEASURE

The superior design of our Bench Rest Powder Measure throws uniform charges. The charge arm/operating handle meters the powder and dispenses a flow of powder that is free from extremes in variation while minimizing powder shearing. The powder hopper's built-in baffle feeds powder into the charge arm very uniformly. Our Bench Rest measure can throw consistent charges from 2½ grains of Bulls-Eye to 95 grains of 432. Convenient and simple to use.

MSRP . . . . . . . . . . . . . . . . . $155.00

## BENCHREST SEATER DIES

Bench Rest Rifle Dies are glass-hard and polished mirror-smooth with special attention given to headspace, tapers, and diameters. Sizing die has an elevated expander button to ensure better alignment of case and neck.

**Original Bench Rest**
**Seater Die:** . . . . . . . . . . . . . . $67.00
**Ultra Micrometer**
 **Seater Die:** . . . . . . . . . . . . $102.00
**Custom:** . . . . . . . . . . . . . . . $92–$127

## CLASSIC CASE TRIMMER

Case Trimmer Classic (collet and pilot not included). Suitable for more than three hundred different big bore calibers from popular big-game rifles to classic black powder calibers. The Classic trims case lengths from 1$^{7}$/$_{8}$ in. long through 4$^{1}$/$_{8}$ in. long; shorter cases can be trimmed by mounting on a standard length base.

MSRP . . . . . . . . . . . . . . . . . $122.00

## CO-AX CASE AND CARTRIDGE INSPECTOR

Forster's exclusive Co-Ax Case and Cartridge Inspector provides you with the ability to ensure uniformity by measuring three critical dimensions: neck wall thickness, case neck concentricity, and bullet runout. The Inspector is unique because it checks both the bullet and case alignment in relation to the centerline (axis) of the entire cartridge or case.

MSRP . . . . . . . . . . . . . . . . . $122.00

## CO-AX PRIMER SEATER

Unlike other seaters, ours is designed so the operator can eliminate all slop when working with a specific cartridge. That translates into perfect seating, reliable ignition, and reduced misfires. The E-Z-Just jaws close to securely grip most modern rifle and pistol cases with a rim thickness of .045 in. to .072 in. Other features include a built-in primer flipper tray. Large and small primer tubes have an open slot and primers stack sideways for added safety.

MSRP . . . . . . . . . . . . . . . . . $104.00

**FORSTER BENCHREST SEATER DIE**

**FORSTER CO-AX CASE AND CARTRIDGE INSPECTOR**

**FORSTER CO-AX PRIMER SEATER**

# Forster Reloading

## CO-AX RELOADING PRESS

Designed to make reloading easier and more accurate, this press offers the following features: snap-in and snap-out die change, positive spent primer catcher, automatic self-acting shell holder, floating guide rod, top priming device seats primers to factory specification, uses any standard $^7/_8$ in x 14 in dies; short-throw handle.

**MSRP** . . . . . . . . . . . . . . . . **$440.00**

**FORSTER CO-AX RELOADING PRESS**

## UNIVERSAL SIGHT MOUNTING FIXTURE

To drill and tap holes for the mounting of scope mounts, receiver sights, and shotgun beads. The fixture will accommodate any single-barrel long gun including bolt actions, lever actions, and pump actions as long as the barrel can be laid into the "V" blocks of the fixture. Tubular mag guns can be drilled. The two "V" blocks are made from hardened steel accurately ground on the "V" as well as the shaft. The blocks are adjustable for height. Universal Site Mounting Fixture includes 6-48 bushings.

**MSRP** . . . . . . . . . . . . . . . . . **$488.00**

# Frankford Arsenal

**FRANKFORD ARSENAL DIGITAL RELOADING SCALE**

**FRANKFORD ARSENAL EZ SONIC CLEANER**

**FRANKFORD ARSENAL MAGNUM SONIC CLEANER**

## DS-750 DIGITAL RELOADING SCALE

A light, accurate, portable scale, the unit is suitable for use on the reloading bench, yet is at home on the shooting range or in the field. It weighs objects up to 750 grains. Accurate within ± .1 grains, it can be set to read in grains, grams, ounces, ct, or dwt. It comes with a protective sleeve and is small enough to fit in your shirt pocket. A calibration weight and batteries are also included.

**MSRP** . . . . . . . . . . . . . . . . . . **$59.99**

## EZ SONIC CLEANER

*Features*: High frequency ultrasonic agitation quickly and quietly cleans the exterior and interior of brass without a mess, even breaking down the stubborn carbon build up found in primer pockets. Tank size of 5.8" x 4.8" x 1.9" gives it a capacity of .75L; capable of cleaning approximately 125 pieces of .223 brass per batch; 30 watt unit at 42KHz

**MSRP** . . . . . . . . . . . . . . . . . . **$76.99**

## MAGNUM SONIC CLEANER

*Features*: Tank size of 7.7" x 6.5" x 2.6" gives it a capacity of 2L; capable of cleaning approximately 350 pieces of .223 brass per batch; provides added cleaning power with a heating function; offers a digital display and time controls; 100 watt unit at 42KHz

**MSRP** . . . . . . . . . . . . . . . . . . **$161.99**

# Hornady

## 366 AUTO PROGRESSIVE RELOADER

The 366 Auto features full-length resizing with each stroke, automatic primer feed, swing-out wad guide, three-state crimping featuring Taper-Loc for factory-tapered crimp, automatic advance to the next station, and automatic ejection. The turntable holds 8 shells for 8 operations with each stroke. Automatic charge bar loads shot and powder, dies and crimp starters for 6 point, 8 point, and paper crimps.

**12, 20, 28 Ga.:** . . . . . . . . . . . **$716.83**
**.410:** . . . . . . . . . . . . . . . . . . **$844.93**

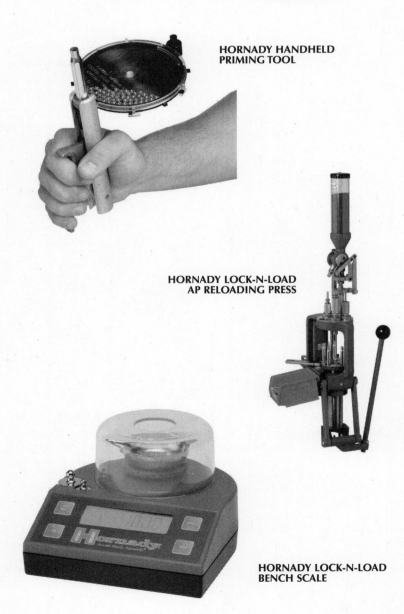

HORNADY 366 AUTO
PROGRESSIVE RELOADER

## HANDHELD PRIMING TOOL

This portable tool primes new or cleaned cases—no need to use your press. Very useful for priming large quantities of cases before processing through a loader. The pliers-style design gives you more leverage, less fatigue, and a better feel than thumb-operated styles. Holds both small and large primers right side up for proper feeding. Uses standard Hornady shell holders, and a converter is available for RCBS shells.

**MSRP** . . . . . . . . . . . . . . . . . **$48.60**

HORNADY HANDHELD
PRIMING TOOL

## LOCK-N-LOAD AP RELOADING PRESS

Dies and powder measure are inserted into Lock-N-Load die bushings. The bushings remain with the die and powder measure and can be removed in seconds. Other features include: deluxe powder measure, automatic indexing, off-set handle, power-pac linkage, case ejector, five die bushings, shellplate, primer catcher, Positive Priming System, powder drop, Deluxe Powder Measure, and automatic primer feed.

**MSRP** . . . . . . . . . . . . . . . . . **$520.16**

HORNADY LOCK-N-LOAD
AP RELOADING PRESS

## LOCK-N-LOAD BENCH SCALE

Made from the same high-quality, precision load cell found on the Lock-N-Load Auto Charge. With a capacity of 1500 grains, you can weigh powder, bullets, cases, cartridges, and more. The large LCD display is easy to read and weighs precisely to one-tenth (.1) of a grain. Included are two calibration weights, AC adaptor, 220V adaptor, and metal powder pan.

**MSRP** . . . . . . . . . . . . . . . . . **$122.72**

HORNADY LOCK-N-LOAD
BENCH SCALE

HORNADY LOCK-N-LOAD
BULLET FEEDER

HORNADY LOCK-N-LOAD CASE
PREP TRIO

HORNADY LOCK-N-
LOAD QUICK
TRICKLE

## LOCK-N-LOAD BULLET FEEDER

The Lock-N-Load Bullet Feeder can be used with any press with ⁷/₈ in.–14 in. die threads. The bullet feeder die is case activated, which means the bullet will only feed upon contact with a case. The collets are made of solid steel. The setup and caliber change-overs are quick and easy and there are no special tools required for adjustments. The easy-feed bullet hopper holds up to 200 pistol bullets and features an adjustable center plate and bullet feed-wipers to ensure smooth feeding.
**MSRP**..................**$363.52**

## LOCK-N-LOAD CASE PREP TRIO

*Features*: Durable brushed aluminum housing and high torque, low speed motor. 3-tool capacity and onboard storage for optional accessories like our primer pocket cleaners, primer pocket reamers, case neck brushes, and any other 8-32 thread tools. With three active stations, you can chamfer, deburr, and clean primer pockets without having to change tools. Both inside diameter and outside diameter chamfer and deburr tools. Unit is compatible with 110V or 220V power.
**MSRP**..................**$129.38**

## LOCK-N-LOAD CLASSIC LOADER

Lock-N-Load is available on Hornady's single stage and progressive reloader models. This bushing system locks the die into the press like a rifle bolt. Instead of threading dies in and out of the press, you simply lock and unlock them with a slight twist. Dies are held firmly in a die bushing that stays with the die and retains the die setting. Features: Easygrip handle and O-style high-strength
**MSRP**..................**$146.50**
**Lock-N-Load Classic Kit:** ...**$383.06**

## MATCH GRADE RIFLE DIES

The neck-size die features interchangeable, self-centering neck-size bushings (available in .002 in. increments) that eliminate the chance of oversizing your case necks and overworking the brass. Some calibers are available in two styles: full-length sizing and shoulder bump neck-size. Both styles feature interchangeable neck-sizing bushings.
**MSRP**...........**$53.20–$100.00**

## LOCK-N-LOAD QUICK TRICKLE

*Features*: This versatile powder trickler features hand-operated high and low speeds with up to a three-to-one gear ratio. Combined with double-sided, sealed ball bearings that prevent stray

powder from impeding operation, the Quick Trickle is the smoothest operating powder dispensing tool for your reloading bench.
**MSRP**..................**$115.84**

## LOCK-N-LOAD SONIC CLEANER 2L

*Features*: Features an 80 watt ceramic heater. Large 2L stainless steel tank holds up to three hundred .223 cases or one hundred fifty .308 cases. Microjet action of the Cleaner 2L removes carbon residue and other debris from cartridge cases, small gun parts, and other small metal equipment and it cleans internal and external surfaces of cartridge cases and primer pockets. 5 to 30 minute timer. 110V or 220V.
**MSRP**..................**$142.84**

HORNADY LOCK-N-LOAD SONIC
CLEANER 2L

# Lyman Reloading Tools

### 3-DIE CARBIDE PISTOL DIE SETS

Lyman originated the Tungsten Carbide (T-C) sizing die and the addition of extra seating screws for pistol die sets and the two-step neck expanding die. Multi-Deluxe Die sets offer these features: a one-piece hardened steel decapping rod, extra seating screws for all popular bullet-nose shapes, and all-steel construction.

**MSRP** . . . . . . . . . . . . . . . . . . . . **$63.95**

### 50 BMG CASE PREP MULTI-TOOL

**Features**: Lyman has engineered full-sized .50 caliber tools and put them together in a handy double ended storage handle—always ready and all in one place. The unique knurled handle unthreads in the middle to store all the parts. Both ends of the handle are threaded to allow a tool head to be mounted on each end. In addition to the double ended storage handle, the set includes: .50 cal. Outside Deburring Tool, .50 cal. VLD Inside Deburring Tool, .50 BMG Primer Pocket Reamer, Cleaner, and Uniformer

**MSRP** . . . . . . . . . . . . . . . . . . . . **$59.99**

### 55 CLASSIC BLACK POWDER MEASURE

Lyman's 55 Classic Powder Measure is ideal for the Cowboy Action Competition or black powder cartridge shooters. The one-pound-capacity aluminum reservoir and brass powder meter eliminate static. The internal powder baffle assures highly accurate and consistent charges. The 24 in. powder compacting drop tube allows the maximum charge in each cartridge. Drop tube works on calibers .38 through .50 and mounts easily to the bottom of the measure.

**Model with tubes:** . . . . . . . . **$174.95**
**Powder Drop Tubes only:** . . . **$37.50**

### 1200 CLASSIC TUMBLER

This case tumbler features an improved base and drive system, plus a stronger suspension system and built-in exciters for better tumbling action and faster cleaning.

**1200 Classic:** . . . . . **$109.95–$117.50**
**Auto-Flo:** . . . . . . . . **$113.95–$124.00**

**LYMAN 3-DIE CARBIDE PISTOL DIE SET**

**LYMAN 50 BMG CASE PREP MULTI-TOOL**

**LYMAN 1200 CLASSIC TUMBLER**

**LYMAN 55 CLASSIC BLACK POWDER MEASURE**

# Lyman Reloading Tools

## 1200 DPS 3 (DIGITAL POWER SYSTEM)

Imagine precisely weighing every charge you load nearly as fast as using a measure. With Lyman's new DPS 3, it can be a reality. This is the fastest powder system ever. In addition, the auto-repeat setting throws a precise charge automatically each time the pan is put in place. The DPS 3 is weighing your next charge while you're seating the bullet on your last charge. Now change powders faster and easier. Automatically throws the next charge each time the pan is put in place.
MSRP . . . . . . . . . . . . .$374.95–$385

**LYMAN 1200 DPS 3 (DIGITAL POWER SYSTEM)**

## 2500 PRO MAGNUM TUMBLER

The Lyman 2500 Pro Magnum tumbler handles up to 900 .38 Spl. cartridges at once.
MSRP . . . . . . . . . . . $99.95–$117.50
Auto-Flo: . . . . . . . . $147.95–$148.00

## ACCU-TRIMMER

Lyman's Accu-Trimmer can be used for all rifle and pistol cases from .22 to .458 Win. Mag. Standard shell holders are used to position the case, and the trimmer incorporates standard Lyman cutter heads and pilots. Mounting options include bolting to a bench, C-clamp, or vise.
MSRP . . . . . . . . . . . . . . . . . . .$66.95

**LYMAN 2500 PRO MAGNUM TUMBLER**

## CASE PREP MULTI-TOOL

The unique new case prep accessory provides the reloader with all the essential Case Prep accessories in one compact, double-ended storage handle. Both ends of the handle are threaded to allow two tool heads to be mounted simultaneously. Plus the hollow, knurled handle unthreads in the center to store all parts and function equally well as two separate handles. The compact aluminum storage handle contains: an outside deburring tool, a VLD inside deburring tool, both large and small primer pocket cleaners, and reamers.
MSRP . . . . . . . . . . . . . . . . . . .$27.95

**LYMAN ACCU-TRIMMER**

**LYMAN CASE PREP MULTI-TOOL**

# Lyman Reloading Tools

### CASE PREP XPRESS

Lyman introduces one of the most complete electric case prep systems yet developed. It features all the most popular case prep accessories driven by a high torque gear motor. The Case Prep Xpress allows the reloader to have five different case prep tools mounted vertically and powered, ready to instantly perform the desired operation. Every commonly-used case prep tool is included with the substantial five-position power base. In addition, a side-mounted, inside neck lube station is also part of the base with four neck brushes and Mica lube. For easy cleanup of fouling and brass shavings, a convenient removable dump pan is built in.

**115 V Model:** . . . . . . . . . . . **$157.50**
**230 V Model:** . . . . . . . . . . . **$162.50**

### CLASSIC DIE SETS

Lyman Products offers new reloading dies sets for .40-60 Win., .45-65 Win., and .45-75 Win. cartridges. These cartridges have become popular with the introduction of the new '76 Win. lever action reproductions. Most importantly, these new dies have been carefully engineered to modern standards to provide precise reloads with either black or smokeless powder.

**MSRP** . . . . . . . . . . . . . . . . . **$66.50**

### CRUSHER II PRO KIT

Includes Crusher II press, loading block, case lube kit, primer tray, Model 500 Pro scale, powder funnel, and Lyman Reloading Handbook.

**MSRP** . . . . . . . . . . . . . . . . . **$269.95**

### CRUSHER II RELOADING PRESS

Our new Crusher II is the ideal press for reloading both rifle and pistol cartridges. The Crusher starts with a 1 in. diameter ram, compound linkage and a 4½ in. press opening, which makes even the largest magnum cartridges easy to load. Its classic "O" frame design takes all standard ⅞ in. x 14 in. dies. The Crusher II is equipped with hardened and ground linkage pins and retaining rings for a smooth and tight operation. The new base design has 14 square inches of "machined flat" surface area with three mounting bolt holes (vs. two slots for Rock ChuckerT) for perfect rigid mounting.

**MSRP** . . . . . . . . . . . . . . . . . **$179.95**

**LYMAN CLASSIC DIE SETS**

**LYMAN CASE PREP XPRESS**

**LYMAN CRUSHER II RELOADING PRESS**

## DEBURRING TOOL

Bevels and removes burrs from both inside and outside of case mouth. Precision machined and hardened, fits all cases from .17 to .45 caliber.

**MSRP** . . . . . . . . . . . . . . . . . . . .**$19.95**

## DELUXE CARBIDE EXPANDER & DECAP DIE ROD COMPLETE

*Features*: The Lyman Deluxe Carbide expander and decapping rod assembly features a super hard and slick carbide expander button with an adjustable positioning sleeve. The carbide button will offer easier extraction through case necks, which will help prevent case stretching and lessen case trimming. The carbide button also floats free on the rod to allow for self-centering in the case neck. It will also allow the user to adjust when the button pulls through the case neck so the press linkage can be positioned for better leverage. Includes adapter for use with RCBS dies.

**MSRP** . . . . . . . . . . . . . . . . . . . .**$29.95**

## E-ZEE CASE GAUGE

This improved version measures the case length of over 70 popular rifle and pistol cases. Many new cartridges are included like the Winchester Short Mags, .204 Ruger, .500 S&W, and others. Precisely made, this rugged metal

gauge makes sorting cases quick, easy, and accurate.

**MSRP** . . . . . . . . . . . . . . . . . . . .**$21.50**

## MAGNUM INERTIA BULLET PULLER

Safely strips loaded rounds in seconds without damage to bullet or case. Features newly-engineered head design that allows use on full range of calibers from tiny 5.7x28FN to the largest Magnums. New "full-size" ergonomic molded handle with rubber insert for comfort and sure grip. Traps components with just a few raps on the bench.

**MSRP** . . . . . . . . . . . . . . . . . . . .**$22.98**

## MASTER CASTING KIT

Designed especially to meet the needs of blackpowder shooters, this kit features Lyman's combination round ball and maxi ball mould blocks. It also contains a combination double cavity mould, mould handle, mini-mag furnace, lead dipper, bullet lube, a user's manual, and a cast bullet guide. Kits

are available in .45, .50, and .54 caliber.

**MSRP** . . . . . . . . . . **$254.95–$265.00**

## MASTER RELOADING KIT

The complete reloading kit compares in price to other starter kits but is the first one that includes a state-of-the-art digital scale like the Lyman 1000 Grain. The new reloader can choose the turret T-Mag or single stage Crusher press kit and get all the high-end Lyman tools and accessories needed to start turning out top quality reloads. The only additional items needed are the dies and shellholder. Lyman's Trimmer Plus Case Conditioning Kit makes a perfect addition once the reloader is ready to further improve the performance of his reloads. The Lyman Master Reloading Kit includes a $7/8$ in. x 14 in. Adapter, 1000 grain electronic scale, #55 powder measure, a universal priming arm, a powder funnel, and an auto primer feed system.

**T-Mag Master Kit:** . . . . . . . . **$489.95**
**Crusher Master Kit:** . . . . . . . **$429.95**

**LYMAN DEBURRING TOOL**

**LYMAN DELUXE CARBIDE EXPANDER & DECAP DIE ROD COMPLETE**

**LYMAN E-ZEE CASE GAUGE**

**LYMAN MASTER RELOADING KIT**

**LYMAN MAGNUM INTERTIA BULLET PULLER**

# Lyman Reloading Tools

**LYMAN MICRO-TOUCH 1500 ELECTRONIC RELOADING SCALE**

**LYMAN OUTSIDE NECK TURNING TOOL**

**LYMAN PISTOL E-ZEE CASE GAUGE**

## MICRO-TOUCH 1500 ELECTRONIC RELOADING SCALE

*Features*: Lyman's newest electronic scale, the Micro-Touch 1500 has all the features of much larger models combined with state-of-the-art touch screen controls. Just 3.25" wide by 5.375" long and 1.25" tall with the dust cover in place, this scale has a full 1500 grain capacity. It is powered by an included AC adapter, but can also function on battery power when at the range or camp. The Micro-Touch 1500 also includes its own powder pan and calibration weight.
**From:**..................**$69.95**

## OUTSIDE NECK TURNING TOOL

For both Lyman's Universal Trimmer and AccuTrimmer. Provides the user with a simple-to-operate tool that guarantees neck wall thickness and outside neck diameter. Essential for case reforming. Improves accuracy. Adjustable cutter (for length of cut and rate of feed) removes minimum brass to attain uniformity. Cutter blade can be adjusted to any diameter from .195 in. to .405 in. Comes with two extra cutting blades. Mandrels from .22 to .375. Includes six mandrel Multi-Pack (for .22, .243, .25, .270, 7mm, and .30 calibers). (Not adaptable to Power Trimmer.) Replacement parts and additional mandrels also available.
**MSRP**..................**$42.50**

## PISTOL E-ZEE CASE GAUGE

*Features*: Here's Lyman's popular E-Zee Case Gauge in a smaller, more convenient size yet covering virtually any pistol case. The precise metal "no-go" gauge makes judging case length fast, easy, and accurate.
**MSRP**..................**$14.95**

## POWER DEBURRING TOOL KIT

Features a high-torque, rechargeable power driver plus a complete set of accessories, including inside and outside deburr tools, large and small reamers, and cleaners, and case neck brushes. No threading or chucking required. Set also includes battery recharger and standard flat and Phillips driver bits.
**MSRP**..................**$66.50**

## PREMIUM CARBIDE 4-DIE SETS FOR PISTOLS

Lyman 4-Die Sets feature a separate taper crimp die and powder charge/expanding die. The powder charge/expand die has a special hollow two-step neck expanding plug which allows powder to flow through the die from a powder measure directly into the case. The powder charge/expanding die has a standard 7/8 in. x 14 in. thread and will accept Lyman's 55 Powder Measure, or most other powder measures.
**MSRP**..................**$84.95**

## PRO 1000 & 500 RELOADING SCALES

Features include improved platform system; hi-tech base design of high impact styrene; extra-large, smooth leveling wheel; dual agate bearings; larger damper for fast zeroing; built-in counter weight compartment; easy-tread beam.
**Pro 1000 Scale:**...........**$87.50**
**Pro 500 Scale:**...........**$72.50**

**LYMAN POWER DEBURRING TOOL KIT**

**LYMAN PRO 1000 RELOADING SCALE**

## REVOLUTION ROTATING GUN VISE

This versatile gun vise is engineered with a full range of adjustments; it tilts, clamps, and has inserts to securely hold any firearm. The padded contact points protect the firearm during cleaning, maintenance, or gunsmithing, even bore sighting.

**MSRP** . . . . . . . . . . . . . . . . . . . . **$95.95**

## RIFLE DIE SETS

Lyman precision rifle dies feature fine adjustment threads on the bullet seating stem to allow for precision adjustments of bullet seating depth. Lyman dies fit all popular presses using industry standard $7/8$ in. x 14 in. threads, including RCBS, Lee, Hornady, Dillon, Redding and others. Each sizing die for bottle-necked rifle cartridges is carefully vented. Each sizing die is polished and heat treated for toughness.

**MSRP** . . . . . . . . . . . . . . . . . . . . **$22.50**

## RIFLE 2-DIE SETS

Set consists of a full-length resizing die with decapping stem and neck expanding button and a bullet-seating die for loading jacketed bullets in bottlenecked rifle cases. For those who load cast bullets, use a neck-expanding die, available separately.

**MSRP** . . . . . . . . . . . . . . . . . . . **$43.75**

## RIFLE 3-DIE SETS

Straight wall rifle cases require these three-die sets consisting of a full-length resizing die with decapping stem, a two-step neck expanding (M) die, and a bullet-seating die. These sets are ideal for loading cast bullets due to the inclusion of the neck-expanding die.

**MSRP** . . . . . . . . . . . . . . . . . . . **$56.95**

**LYMAN RIFLE 3-DIE SET**

## T-MAG II RELOADING PRESS

The T-Mag II has a hi-tech iron frame with state-of-the-art silver hammertone powder coat finish for guaranteed durability. Lyman's improved Turret Retention System allows smooth indexing while maintaining rock solid turret support. The T-Mag II's six station turret head lets the reloader mount up to six different reloading dies at one time. Like more expensive progressive presses the turret head detaches to easily change calibers while retaining precise setup. The turret handle doubles as a turret-removing wrench. Obtain extra turret heads and have all your favorite calibers set up to reload. The T-Mag II features a "flat machined" base that mounts easily to a wood or metal bench. Compound leverage assures a powerful and smooth operation. The handle mounts for either right or left hand use. The T-Mag II uses standard $7/8$ in. x 14 in. dies and can be used for reloading rifle or pistol cases. It comes with universal priming arm, primer catcher, and turret handle.

**MSRP** . . . . . . . . . . . . . . . . . . . **$260.00**

**LYMAN T-MAG II RELOADING PRESS**

**LYMAN REVOLUTION ROTATING GUN VISE**

## TURBO SONIC 700

**Features**: Ultrasonic cleaning that allows the reloader to clean cases inside and out in less than 10 minutes. Used with Lyman's specially formulated cleaning solutions, these machines deliver superior cleaning of cases, steel and stainless steel gun frames and parts, tools, and even jewelry. The ultrasonic cavitation lifts and dissolves carbon, dirt, and residue. Cleans up to 100 9mm cases; uses advanced oscillation circuitry; two color LED display with five timed cleaning cycles; simple, push button digital controls; stainless tank with plastic parts basket; includes watch stand and CD holder

**115V:** . . . . . . . . . . . . . . . . . . . . **$79.95**
**230V:** . . . . . . . . . . . . . . . . . . . . **$82.50**

**LYMAN TURBO SONIC 700**

# Lyman Reloading Tools

**LYMAN TURBO SONIC 6000**

**LYMAN TURBO TWIN TUMBLER**

**LYMAN UNIVERSAL CASE PREP ACCESSORY SET**

**LYMAN UNIVERSAL POWER TRIMMER**

**LYMAN UNIVERSAL TRIMMER**

### TURBO SONIC 6000

**Features**: 6.3 quart tank (12.8"x8"x3.9") fits the biggest handguns or multiple pistol frames. Cleans up to 1300 9mm cases or four handgun frames. Powered by two industrial grade ultrasonic transducers. Tank has a built-in drain and hose for easy solution changes; comes with a large plastic parts basket with convenient handles; heated tank for optimum cleaning performance; two color LED display with five timed cleaning cycles.

**115V:** . . . . . . . . . . . . . . . . . . .$349.95
**230V:** . . . . . . . . . . . . . . . . . . . $360

### TURBO TWIN TUMBLER

The Twin features Lyman 1200 Pro Tumbler with an extra 600 bowl system. Reloaders may use each bowl interchangeably for small or large capacity loads. 1200 Pro Bowl System has a built-in sifter lid for easy sifting of cases and media at the end of the polishing cycle. The Twin Tumbler features the Lyman Hi-Profile base design with built-in exciters and anti-rotation

pads for faster, more consistent tumbling action.

**115V:** . . . . . . . . . . . . . . . . . . .$91.95
**230V:** . . . . . . . . . . . . . . . . . . .$95.00

### UNIVERSAL CASE PREP ACCESSORY SET

This accessory features all the items necessary for quality case preparation in one deluxe set. Includes both large and small primer pocket reamers, primer pocket cleaners, outside deburring tool, inside (VLD) chamfer tool, and large and small primer pocket uniformer tools. All individual items have their own molded handle with rubber insert for sure grip. Includes custom zippered case for storage or easy transport to the range.

**MSRP** . . . . . . . . . . . . . . . . . . .$69.95

### UNIVERSAL POWER TRIMMER

The Universal Power Trimmer has all the accuracy and fast cartridge case lock/unlock of the original trimmer. Plus, the powerful 175 RPM motor adds real ease, speed, and powered

primer pocket cleaning to the process. Trimming is rapid and uniform with precise, fully-adjustable settings for overall trim length. The replaceable cutter head accepts all Lyman pilots. Includes 9 pilot multi-pack and carbide cutter. Power Trimmer is available for 110 or 220 volt systems.

**MSRP** . . . . . . . . . . . . . . . . . . .$349.95
**230 Volt Model:** . . . . . . . . . .$355.00

### UNIVERSAL TRIMMER

This trimmer with patented chuckhead accepts all metallic rifle or pistol cases, regardless of rim thickness. To change calibers, simply change the case head pilot. Other features include coarse and fine cutter adjustments, an oil-impregnated bronze bearing, and a rugged cast base to assure precision alignment. Optional carbide cutter available.

**MSRP** . . . . . . . . . . . . . . . . . . .$105.00
**Universal Trimmer Power Pack Combo:** . . . . . .$124.95
**Universal Trimmer Power Adapter:** . . . . . . . . . .$28.00

# MEC Reloaders

### 600 JR. MARK 5

This single-stage reloader features a cam-action crimp die to ensure that each shell returns to its original condition. MEC's 600 Jr. Mark 5 can load six to eight boxes per hour and can be updated with the 285 CA primer feed. Press is adjustable for 3 in. shells.

**MSRP** . . . . . . . . . . $192.96–$208.45

**MEC 600 JR. MARK 5**

## 650N

This reloader works on six shells at once. A reloaded shell is completed with every stroke. The MEC 650 does not resize except as a separate operation. Automatic primer feed is standard. Simply fill it with a full box of primers and it will do the rest. Reloader has three crimping stations: the first one starts the crimp, the second closes the crimp and the third places a taper on the shell. Available in 12, 16, 20 and 28 Ga. and .410 bore. No die sets available.

**MSRP . . . . . . . . . . $350.70–$379.98**

**MEC 650N**

## 8567N GRABBER

This reloader features twelve different operations at all six stations, producing finished shells with each stroke of the handle. It includes a fully automatic primer feed and Auto-Cycle charging, plus MEC's exclusive three-stage crimp. The "Power Ring" resizer ensures consistent, accurately-sized shells without interrupting the reloading sequence. Simply put in the wads and shell casings, then remove the loaded shells with each pull of the handle. Available in 12, 16, 20, 28 Ga., and .410 bore.

**MSRP . . . . . . . . . . $483.11–$524.80**

## 9000 SERIES

Automatic indexing and finished shell ejection for quicker and easier reloading. The factory set speed provides uniform movement through every reloading stage. The reloader requires only a minimal adjustment from low to high brass domestic shells, any one of which can be removed for inspection from any station. Can be set up for automatic or manual indexing. Available in 12, 16, 20, 28 Ga., and .410 bore. No die sets are available.

**9000GN: . . . . . . . . $591.58–$642.60**
**9001HN without**
**P&H: . . . . . . . . . . $663.45–$705.63**
**9000HN: . . . . . . . .$1231.50–$1246.50**

**MEC 8567N
GRABBER**

**MEC 9000 SERIES**

## SIZEMASTER

Sizemaster's "Power Ring" collet resizer returns each base to factory specifications. This resizing station handles brass or steel heads, both high and low base. An eight-fingered collet squeezes the base back to original dimensions, then opens up to release the shell easily. The E-Z Prime auto primer feed is standard equipment (not offered in .410 bore). Press is adjustable for 3 in. shells and is available in 10, 12, 16, 20, 28 Ga. and .410 bore.

**MSRP . . . . . . . . . . $278.88–$299.50**

## STEELMASTER

Equipped to load steel shotshells as well as lead ones. Every base is resized to factory specs by a precision "power ring" collet. Handles brass or steel heads in high or low base. The E-Z prime auto primer feed dispenses primers automatically and is standard equipment. Separate presses are available for 12 Ga. 2¾ in., 3 in., 3½ in. and 10 Ga.

**MSRP . . . . . . . . . . $319.02–$334.50**

**MEC STEELMASTER**

# MTM Case-Gard

## DS-750 MINI DIGITAL RELOADING SCALE

Scale features a powder pan, custom designed to facilitate bullet, powder, and arrow weighing. It has up to a 750-grain capacity. It measures in grains, grams, carats, and ounces. The high-impact, plastic sensory cover doubles as a large powder pan.
**MSRP** . . . . . . . . . . . . . . . . . . . .**$42.49**

MTM CASE-GARD DS-750 MINI DIGITAL
RELOADING SCALE

# Nosler

## CUSTOM BRASS

With uncompromising attention to detail, each round of NoslerCustom cartridge brass is made to precise dimensional standards and tolerances using top-grade materials to maximize accuracy, consistency, and enhance case life. Flash holes are deburred, necks are deburred and chamfered.
**MSRP** . . . . . . . . . . . . **$34.00–$77.00**

NOSLER CUSTOM BRASS

# RCBS
## Reloading Presses

### AMMOMASTER-2 SINGLE STAGE PRESS

The AmmoMaster offers handloaders the freedom to configure a press to particular needs and preferences. It covers the complete spectrum of reloading, from single-stage through fully-automatic progressive reloading, from .25 Auto to .50 caliber. The AmmoMaster Auto has all the features of a five-station press.
**MSRP** . . . . . . . . . . . . . . . . . .**$362.95**

### AMMOMASTER .50 BMG PACK

The Pack includes the press, dies, and accessory items needed, all in one box. The press is the Ammo Master Single Stage rigged for 1½ in. dies. It has a 1½ in. solid steel ram and plenty of height for the big .50. The kit also has a set of RCBS .50 BMG , 1½ in. reloading dies, including both full-length sizer and seater. Other items are a shell holder, ram priming unit, and a trim die.
**MSRP** . . . . . . . . . . . . . . . . . .**$787.95**

RCBS AMMOMASTER-2
SINGLE STAGE PRESS

RCBS AMMOMASTER .50
BMG PACK

# RCBS

## GRAND SHOTSHELL PRESS

The combination of the powder system, shot system, and case holders allows the user to reload shells without fear of spillage. The powder system is case-actuated: no hull, no powder. Cases are easily removed with universal 12 and 20 Ga. case holders allowing cases to be sized down to the rim. Only one primer feeds at a time. Steel size ring provides complete resizing of high and low base hulls. Holds 25 lbs. of shot and 1½ lbs. of powder.

**MSRP** . . . . . . . . . . . . . . . . **$1,025.95**
**Grand Conversion Kit:** . . . . . **$489.95**

## MINI-GRAND SHOTSHELL PRESS

The Mini-Grand shotgun press, a seven-station single-stage press, loads 12 and 20 Ga. hulls, from 2¾ in. to 3½ in. in length. It utilizes RCBS, Hornady, and Ponsness Warren powder and shot bushings, with a half-pound capacity powder hopper and 12½ lb. capacity shot hopper. The machine will load both lead and steel shot.

**From:** . . . . . . . . . . . . . . . . . . **$128.99**

## PARTNER PRESS

Easy-to-use, durable press in a compact package. Features compound linkage, durable steel links, priming arm. Reloads most standard calibers.
**Partner Press:** . . . . . . . . . . . **$96.95**
**Partner Standard Reloading Kit:** . . . **$243.95**

## PIGGYBACK 3 CONVERSION KIT

The Piggyback 3 conversion unit moves from single-stage reloading to five-station, manual-indexing, progressive reloading in one step. The Piggyback 3 will work with the RCBS Rock Chucker, Reloader Special-3, and Reloader Special-5.

**MSRP** . . . . . . . . . . . . . . . . . . **$523.95**

## PRO 2000 PROGRESSIVE PRESS

Constructed of cast iron, the Pro-2000 features five reloading stations. The case-actuated powder measure assures repeatability of dispensing powder. A Micrometer Adjustment Screw allows precise return to previously recorded charges. All dies are standard ⅞ in. x 14 in., including the Expander Die. The press incorporates the APS Priming System. Allows full-length sizing in calibers from .32 Auto to .460 Wby Mag.

**MSRP** . . . . . . . . . . . . . . . . . . **$693.95**

## RELOADER SPECIAL-5 PRESS

The Reloader Special press features a ball handle and primer arm so that cases can be primed and resized at the same time. Other features include a compound leverage system; solid aluminum "O" frame offset; corrosion resistant baked-powder finish; ⅞ in. x 14 in. thread for all standard reloading dies and accessories; optional Piggyback 2 conversion unit.

**MSRP** . . . . . . . . . . . . . . . . . . **$165.95**

**RCBS MINI-GRAND SHOTSHELL PRESS**

**RCBS PIGGYBACK 3 CONVERSION KIT**

**RCBS GRAND SHOTSHELL PRESS**

**RCBS PARTNER PRESS**

**RCBS RELOADER SPECIAL-5 PRESS**

# RCBS

### ROCK CHUCKER SUPREME MASTER RELOADING KIT

Kit includes all the tools and accessories needed to start handloading: Rock Chucker Press; RCBS 505 Reloading Scale; Speer Manual #13; Uniflow Powder Measure; deburring tool; case loading block; Primer Tray-2; hand priming tool; powder funnel; case lube pad; case neck brushes; fold-up hex key set; Trim Pro Manual Case Trimmer Kit.

**MSRP** . . . . . . . . . . . . . . . . . . **$472.95**

### ROCK CHUCKER SUPREME PRESS

With its easy operation, outstanding strength and versatility, a Rock Chucker Supreme press serves beginner and pro alike. Heavy-duty cast iron for easy case resizing; larger window opening to accommodate longer cartridges; 1 in. ram held in place by 12½ sq. in. of ram bearing surface; ambidextrous handle; compound leverage system; 7/8 in. x 14 in. thread for all standard reloading dies and accessories

**MSRP** . . . . . . . . . . . . . . . . . . **$202.95**

### TURRET PRESS

With pre-set dies in the six-station turret head, the Turret Press can increase production from 50 to 200 rounds per hour. The frame, links, and toggle block are constructed of cast iron and the handle offers compound leverage for full-length sizing of any caliber from .25 ACP to .460 Wby. Mag. Six stations allow for custom setup. The quick-change turret head makes caliber changes fast and easy. This press accepts all standard 7/8 in. x 14 in. dies and shell holders.

**MSRP** . . . . . . . . . . . . . . . . . . **$293.95**
**Turret Press Deluxe**
**Reloading Kit:** . . . . . . . . . . . **$576.95**

## Scales and Measures

### 505 RELOADING SCALE

This 511-grain capacity scale has a three-poise system with widely-spaced, deep-beam notches. Two smaller poises on right side adjust from .1 to 10 grains, larger one on left side adjusts in full 10-grain steps. The scale uses magnetic dampening to eliminate beam oscillation. The 5-0-5 also has a sturdy diecast base with large leveling legs. Self-aligning agate bearings support the hardened steel beam pivots for a guaranteed sensitivity to .1 grains.

**MSRP** . . . . . . . . . . . . . . . . . . **$119.95**

### 1010 RELOADING SCALE

Normal capacity is 510 grains, which can be increased without loss of sensitivity by attaching the included extra weight up to 1010 grains. Features include micrometer poise for quick, precise weighing, special approach-to weight indicator, easy-to-read graduation, magnetic dampener, agate bearings, anti-tip pan, and a dustproof lid snaps on to cover scale for storage. Sensitivity is guaranteed to .1 grains.

**MSRP** . . . . . . . . . . . . . . . . . . **$201.95**

### CHARGEMASTER 1500 SCALE

High-performance reloading scale with 1500-grain capacity. Scale reads in grains or grams; calibration weights included. Available in 110 or 220 volt—AC adaptor included. Can be upgraded to an automatic dispensing system with the RCBS ChargeMaster.

**MSRP** . . . . . . . . . . . . . . . . . . **$254.95**

### CHARGEMASTER COMBO

Performs as a scale or as a complete powder dispensing system. Scale can be removed and used separately. Dispenses from 2 to 300 grains. Reads and dispenses in grains or grams. Stores up to 30 charges in memory for quick recall of favorite loads. 110-volt or 220-volt adaptor included.

**MSRP** . . . . . . . . . . . . . . . . . . **$484.95**

**RCBS 1010 RELOADING SCALE**

**RCBS 505 RELOADING SCALE**

**RCBS CHARGEMASTER COMBO**

# RCBS

## RANGEMASTER 750 SCALE

Compact, lightweight, and portable with 750-grain capacity. Scale reads in grams or grains; calibration weights included. Accurate to ± .1 of a grain; fast calibration; Powered by AC or 9-volt battery—AC adaptor included. 110- or 220-volt model available.

**MSRP** . . . . . . . . . . . . . . . . . . **$161.95**

## RC-130 MECHANICAL SCALE

The RC130 features a 130-grain capacity and maintenance-free movement, plus a magnetic dampening system for fast readings. A three-poise design incorporates easy adjustments with a beam that is graduated in increments of 10 grains and 1 grain. A micrometer poise measures in .1-grain increments with accuracy to ±.1 grain.

**MSRP** . . . . . . . . . . . . . . . . . . **$56.95**

**RCBS RANGEMASTER 750 SCALE**

## Reloading Tools

## APS PRIMER STRIP LOADER

For those who keep a supply of CCI primers in conventional packaging, the APS primer strip loader allows quick filling of empty strips. Each push of the handle seats 25 primers.

**From:** . . . . . . . . . . . . . . . . . . **$31.99**

## AR SERIES DIES

The RCBS AR Series is a must for the progressive reloader. It features a Small Base sizing die and a new Taper Crimp seating die. This combination makes reloading easier for AR-style or semi-auto shooters. The Small Base sizer guarantees that the cartridge will rechamber. The Taper Crimp Seater is more forgiving when various case lengths are loaded at the same time. Case neck crimp bulges and buckled shoulders are virtually eliminated when Taper crimping is used with cannelured bullets.

**From:** . . . . . . . . . . . . . $34.99–$69.99

## BULLET FEED DIE-PISTOL

RCBS's Pistol Bullet Feed Die allows the progressive pistol loader to leave the feed die set up on the removable die plate for quick caliber change-overs. The popular RCBS Bullet Feeder shortens reloading sessions while increasing load rates by approximately 50 percent. Rather than reinstalling on die plates and adjusting Bullet Fingers and Guides, simply install another Bullet Feed Die to save even more time during caliber changeovers. Includes one set of Bullet Fingers and retaining clip.

**MSRP** . . . . . . . . . . . . . . . . . . **$30.95**

**RCBS APS PRIMER STRIP LOADER**

**RCBS BULLET FEED DIE-PISTOL**

**RCBS AR SERIES DIE**

# RCBS

### BULLET FEEDER

Designed to fit most progressive presses with 7/8 in. x 14 in. Platform holes, this automatic unit features a rotating collator that orients the bullets to drop into the feed mechanism/ eat die. Choose .22 or .3. The hopper holds 250 .22 caliber bullets over .30s. Powdered by 110-240 VAC, the unit comes with plug adapters for foreign outlets.

**Rifle:** . . . . . . . . . . . . . . . . . . .$632.95
**Pistol:** . . . . . . . . . . . . . . . . . .$541.95

### CARBIDE REPLACEMENT TOOLS

Replacement carbide tipped cutters for your Case Trimmer, 3-Way Cutter and Trim Mate Chamfer, or Debur tool. These carbide tipped tools cut clean and stay sharp for a lifetime of use.

**MSRP** . . . . . . . . . . . . . . . . . . .$44.95

### ELECTRONIC DIGITAL MICROMETER

Instant reading; large, easy-to-read numbers for error reduction with instant inch/millimeter conversion; zero adjust at any position; thimble lock for measuring like objects; replaceable silver oxide cell—1.55 Volt; auto off after five minutes for longer battery life; adjustment wrench included; fitted wooden storage cases.

**MSRP** . . . . . . . . . . . . . . . . . .$161.95

### HAND PRIMING TOOL

A patented safety mechanism separates the seating operation from the primer supply, virtually eliminating the possibility of tray detonation. Fits in your hand for portable primer seating. Primer tray installation requires no contact with the primers. Uses the same RCBS shell holders as RCBS presses. Made of cast metal.

**MSRP** . . . . . . . . . . . . . . . . . . .$51.95

### POWDER TRICKLER-2

Today's trend is to use electronic scales to measure powder charges. Many of these scales have scale pans that are positioned out of reach of existing powder tricklers. The Powder Trickler-2 solves this problem by adding a height adjustable, non-skid base and powder tube extension.

**MSRP** . . . . . . . . . . . . . . . . . .$23.95

### POW'R PULL BULLET PULLER KIT

The RCBS Pow'r Pull bullet puller features a three-jaw chuck that grips the case rim—just rap it on any solid surface like a hammer, and powder and bullet drop into the main chamber for reuse. A soft cushion protects bullets from damage. Works with most centerfire cartridges from .22 to .45 (not for use with rimfire cartridges).

**From:** . . . . . . . . . . . . . . . . . . .$19.99

**RCBS CARBIDE CHAMFER REPLACEMENT TOOL**

**RCBS ELECTRONIC DIGITAL MICROMETER**

**RCBS POWDER TRICKLER-2**

**RCBS CARBIDE CUTTER HEAD REPLACEMENT TOOL**

**RCBS HAND PRIMING TOOL**

**RCBS POW'R PULL BULLET PULLER KIT**

**RCBS CARBIDE CUTTER REPLACEMENT TOOL**

## PRECISION BIPOD

Quick-adjust telescoping legs of 6061 T6 alloy secure your rifle for accurate shooting on uneven ground. Range of movement: 7 to 10 inches, with 25 degrees of cant. Skid-resistant polyurethane feet grip slick surfaces. Tool-free mounting adapts this bipod to any Picatinny rail. Paddle locks make for quick, easy deployment. Hard-coating anodizing ensures tough use.

**MSRP** . . . . . . . . . . . . . . . . . . **$219.95**

## PRIMER POCKET SWAGER - BENCH TOOL

*Features*: Simplifies removal of staked primer pockets and requires 35 percent less force than other tools; rugged construction and foam padded handle; comes with hardened steel swaging heads and rods for small and large pockets; accommodates cases .22-caliber and larger

**MSRP** . . . . . . . . . . . . . . . . . . **$105.95**

## SHELL HOLDER RACK

Twelve positions that hold two shell holders on each post; room to store six Trim Pro Shell Holders as well; clear cover keeps out the dust and dirt; mounted on the wall or used on the bench; wall mount spacing allows it to be hung off of standard 1-in. pegboard hooks; support legs angle the bottom out for wall mounting or the top up for bench use; Shell Holder Racks can be snapped together if more shell holder storage is needed; sticker labels are included

**MSRP** . . . . . . . . . . . . . . . . . . **$15.95**

## TRIM PRO CASE TRIMMER

Cases are trimmed quickly and easily. The lever-type handle is more accurate to use than draw collet systems. A flat plate shell holder keeps cases locked in place and aligned. A micrometer fine adjustment bushing offers trimming accuracy to within .001 in. Made of diecast metal with hardened cutting blades.

**120V:** . . . . . . . . . . . . . . . . . **$369.95**
**240V:** . . . . . . . . . . . . . . . . . **$397.95**
**Manual Kit:** . . . . . . . . . . . . . **$133.95**

## TUBE PISTOL BULLET FEEDER

*Features*: Caliber specific; tube fed; allows use of jacketed, plated, cast or swaged lead bullets; compatible with any 7/8" x 14" threaded press; increase load rate up to 50 percent

**MSRP** . . . . . . . . . . . . . . . . . . **$35.95**

## UNIVERSAL PRIMER ARM 2

Designed for fast and accurate primer seating. Primer plugs and sleeves included for large and small rifle and pistol primers. Universal primer for Rock Chucker Press.

**MSRP** . . . . . . . . . . . . . . . . . . **$16.95**

**RCBS TUBE PISTOL BULLET FEEDER**

**RCBS PRIMER POCKET SWAGER - BENCH TOOL**

**RCBS TRIM PRO CASE TRIMMER**

**RCBS SHELL HOLDER RACK**

**RCBS UNIVERSAL PRIMER ARM 2**

# Redding Reloading Tools

## Handloading Presses

### BIG BOSS RELOADING PRESS

A larger version of the Boss reloading press built on a heavier frame with a longer ram stroke for reloading magnum cartridges. It features a 1 in. diameter ram with over 3.8 in. of stroke; smart primer arm; offset ball handle; heavy-duty cast iron frame; heavy-duty compound linkage; steel adapter bushing accepts all standard ⁷/₈ in. x 14 in. threaded dies.

| | |
|---|---|
| Big Boss II: | $297.00 |
| Big Boss: | $266.00 |
| Big Boss II Ram Only | $52.50 |
| Big Boss II Kit: | $360.00 |
| Big Boss Kit: | $329.00 |

### BOSS RELOADING PRESS

This "O" type reloading press features a rigid cast iron frame whose 36-degree offset provides the best visibility and access of comparable presses. Its "Smart" primer arm moves in and out of position automatically with ram travel. The priming arm is positioned at the bottom of ram travel for lowest leverage and best feel. Model 721 accepts all standard ⁷/₈ in. x 14 in. threaded dies and universal shell holders.

| | |
|---|---|
| MSRP | $211.00 |
| Boss Reloading Kit: | $274.00 |

### T-7 TURRET PRESS

The Redding T-7 Turret Press has a 7-station turret head that is easily turned to set the next die in place. With the addition of additional turret heads (sold separately) a reloader can switch between calibers without readjusting depth. The cast iron construction and stout compound linkage allow for reloading magnum cartridges with ease.

| | |
|---|---|
| MSRP | $462.00 |
| Turret Kit: | $525.00 |

### ULTRAMAG RELOADING PRESS

Highly recommended for the reloader needing a large frame press. The leverage system on this press (unlike most others) is connected to the top of the press frame which gives it literally tons of pressure without the usual concerns of press frame deflection or misalignment.

| | |
|---|---|
| MSRP | $480.00 |
| Kit: | $543.00 |

**REDDING BIG BOSS RELOADING PRESS**

**REDDING T-7 TURRET PRESS**

## Case Trimmers

### MODEL 1400-XT CASE TRIMMING LATHE

The frame is cast iron with storage holes in the base for extra pilots. Coarse and fine adjustments are provided for case length. Also features: six pilots (.22, 6mm, .25, .270, 7mm, and .30); universal collet; two neck cleaning brushes (.22 through .30 cal.); two primer pocket cleaners; tin coated replaceable cutter; accessory power screwdriver adaptor.

| | |
|---|---|
| Case Trimming Lathe: | $149.00 |
| Pilots: | $6.75 |

**HANDLOADING**

# Redding Reloading Tools

## Dies & Bushings

### BODY DIES
Designed to resize the case body and bump the shoulder position for proper chambering without disturbing the case neck. They are intended for use only to resize cases that have become increasingly difficult to chamber after repeated firing and neck sizing. Small Base Body Dies are available in .223 Rem., 6mm P.P.C, 6mm B. R. Rem., 6mm/284 Win., .260 Rem., 6.5mm/284 Win., .284 Win., .308 Win., and .30-06.

Category I:. . . . . . . . . . . . . . .$43.00
Category II: . . . . . . . . . . . . . .$53.00
Category III: . . . . . . . . . . . .$65.00

### COMPETITION BULLET SEATER DIE FOR HANDGUN & STRAIGHT-WALL RIFLE CARTRIDGES
The precision seating stem moves well down into the die chamber to accomplish early bullet contact. The seating stem's spring loading provides positive alignment bias between the tapered nose and the bullet ogive. The Competition Bullet Seating Die features dial-in micrometer adjustment calibrated in .001-in. increments.

MSRP . . . . . . . . . . . . . . . . . .$123.00

### FORM & TRIM DIES
Redding trim dies file trim cases without unnecessary resizing because they are made to chamber dimensions. For case forming and necking brass down from another caliber, Redding trim dies can be the perfect intermediate step before full-length resizing.

Series A: . . . . . . . . . . . . . . . .$43.00
Series B: . . . . . . . . . . . . . . . .$58.00
Series C: . . . . . . . . . . . . . . . .$72.50
Series D: . . . . . . . . . . . . . . . .$80.00

### G-RX PUSH THRU BASE SIZING DIE
The G-Rx Carbide Push Thru Base Sizing Die is designed to restore fired cases from .40 S&W autoloading pistols that exhibit a bulge near the base without the need for case lube. By passing the case completely through the new G-Rx Carbide Die, the bulge is removed and the case may be returned to service.

MSRP . . . . . . . . . . . . . . . . . .$56.00

### NATIONAL MATCH DIE SET
Redding now offers a specialized die set for the military match shooter. Available in 6.8 SPC, .223 Rem., .308 Win., .30-06 Spfd., and .300 Blackout, the set includes a Full-Length Sizing Die a Competition Bullet Seating Die and a Taper Crimp Die.

MSRP . . . . . . . . . . . . . . . . . .$228.00

**REDDING G-RX PUSH THRU BASE SIZING DIE**

**REDDING BODY DIE**

**REDDING COMPETITION BULLET SEATER DIE**

**REDDING NATIONAL MATCH DIE SET**

# Redding Reloading Tools

**REDDING NECK SIZING BUSHINGS**

## NECK SIZING BUSHINGS

Redding Neck Sizing Bushings are available in two styles. Both share the same external dimensions (1/2 in. O.D. x 3/8 in. long) and freely interchange in all Redding Bushing style Neck Sizing Dies. They are available in .001 in. size increments throughout the range of .185 in. through .365 in., covering all calibers from .17 to .338.

**Heat Treated Steel:** ........$21.00
**Titanium Nitride Treatment:** .$36.00
**Storage Box:** ..............$3.72

## NECK SIZING DIES

These dies size only the necks of bottleneck cases to prolong brass life and improve accuracy. These dies size only the neck and not the shoulder or body, fired cases should not be interchanged between rifles of the same caliber. Available individually or in Deluxe Die Sets.

**Series A:** ................$48.00
**Series B:** ................$64.50
**Series C:** ................$82.00
**Series D:** ................$92.50

## PROFILE CRIMP DIES

For cartridges without head-space on the case mouth. These dies were designed for those who want the best possible crimp. Profile crimp dies provide a tighter, more uniform roll type crimp, and require the bullet to be seated to the correct depth in a previous operation.

**Series A:** ................$38.00
**Series B:** ................$38.00
**Series C:** ................$58.00
**Series D:** ...............$64.50

## TAPER & CRIMP DIES

Designed for cartridges with head-space on the case mouth where con-

ventional roll crimping is undesirable. Available in the following rifle calibers: .223 Rem., 7.62MM x 39, .30-30, .308 Win, .30-06, .300 Win. Mag.

**Series A:** ................$38.00
**Series B:** ................$38.00
**Series C:** ................$58.00
**Series D:** ...............$64.50

## TRIM DIES

Redding trim dies allow trimming cases without excessive resizing. Trim dies require extended shell holders.

**Series A:** ................$43.00
**Series B:** ................$43.00
**Series C:** ................$72.50
**Series D:** ...............$80.00

## TYPE S-BUSHING STYLE DIES

The new Type S-Bushing Style Neck Sizing Die provides reloaders with a simple means to precisely control case neck size and tension. The Type-S features: interchangeable sizing bushings available in .001 in. increments; adjustable decapping rod with standard size button; self-centering resizing bushing; decapping pin retainer. All dies are supplied without bushings.

**Category I:** ...............$84.00
**Category II:** ............$102.00
**Category III:** ...........$126.00

**REDDING PROFILE CRIMP DIE**

## Handloading Accessories

### CARBIDE SIZE BUTTON KITS

Make inside neck sizing smoother and easier without lubrication. Now die sets can be upgraded with a carbide size button kit. Available for bottleneck cartridges .22 through .338 cal. The carbide size button is free-floating on the decap rod, allowing it to self-center in the case neck. Kits contain: carbide size button, retainer, and spare decapping pin.

**MSRP** . . . . . . . . . . . . . . . . . . . .**$43.00**

### COMPETITION MODEL 10X-PISTOL AND SMALL RIFLE POWDER MEASURE

This powder measure uses all of the special features of the Competition Model BR-30 combined with a drum and metering unit designed to provide the most uniform metering of small charge weights.

**MSRP** . . . . . . . . . . . . . . . . . . . .**$294.00**

### COMPETITION MODEL BR-30 POWDER MEASURE

Combines all of the features of Competition Model BR-30, with a drum and metering unit designed to provide uniform metering of small charge weights. The diameter of the metering cavity is reduced and the metering plunger is given a hemispherical shape. Charge range: 1 to 25 grains.

**MSRP** . . . . . . . . . . . . . . . . .**$294.00**

### DROP TUBE ADAPTER

*Features*: The adapter is a simple friction fit and works with all Redding powder measures and the Redding powder funnel. Not simply a reducer, this adapter is manufactured with an integral chamber, engineered and tested to provide smooth powder flow and reduced bridging as the powder flows through the smaller orifice for the .17- and .20-caliber case necks.

**From:** . . . . . . . . . . . . . . . . . . . .**$8.39**

### IMPERIAL BIO-GREEN CASE LUBE

*Features*: Redding now introduces a new plant, based sizing lube, which is highly effective, completely bio degradable, and totally renewable. Imperial Bio Green Case Lubricant sets a new standard for pad applied resizing lubricants. It will not stain your brass and offers easy water cleanup making it perfect for use with ultrasonic case cleaners.

**From:** . . . . . . . . . . . . . . . . . . . .**$6.99**

### INSTANT INDICATOR HEADSPACE & BULLET COMPARATOR

The Instant Indicator checks the headspace from the case shoulder to the base. Bullet seating depths can be compared and bullets can be sorted by checking the base of bullets to give dimension. Case length can be measured. Available for 33 cartridges from .222 Rem to .338 Win. Mag., including WSSM cartridges.

**With Dial Indicator:** . . . . . . .**$184.50**
**Without Dial Indicator:** . . . .**$144.00**
**1-in. Dial Indicator:** . . . . . . . .**$46.00**

**REDDING CARBIDE SIZE BUTTON**

**REDDING DROP TUBE ADAPTER**

**REDDING IMPERIAL BIO-GREEN CASE LUBE**

# Redding Reloading Tools

### MATCH-GRADE MODEL 3BR POWDER MEASURE

Interchangeable universal-or pistol-metering chambers. Measures charges up to 100 grains. Unit is fitted with lock ring for fast dump with large clear plastic reservoir. See-through drop tube accepts all calibers from .22 to .6. Precision-fitted rotating drum is critically honed to prevent powder escape. Knife-edged powder chamber shears coarse-grained powders with ease, ensuring accurate charges.

**Powder measure:**. . . . . . . . . **$249.00**
**Measure with
both chambers:** . . . . . . . . . **$306.00**

### MODEL 3 POWDER MEASURE

The Model 3 has a micrometer metering chamber in front. The frame is precision-machined cast iron with hand honed fit between the frame and hard surfaced drum to easily cut and meter powders. The Model 3 features a large capacity clear powder reservoir; see-through drop tube; body with standard 7/8 in. x 14 in. thread to fit mounting bracket and optional bench stand; cast mounting bracket included.

**MSRP** . . . . . . . . . . . . . . . . . **$197.00**

### VERSA PAK RELOADING KIT

Offers all of the products a serious handloader needs (without the press and dies), at a substantial savings over the cost of the individual items. The Versa Pak includes all the items listed in the Pro Pak (less press and dies) plus a Model 3 Master Powder Measure, a 1400 XT Case Trimmer, Imperial Dry Neck Lube in Application Media, a starter size of Imperial Sizing Die Wax and our DVD, "Advanced Handloading, Beyond the Basics."

**MSRP** . . . . . . . . . . . . . . . . . **$600.00**

**REDDING MATCH-GRADE MODEL 3BR POWDER MEASURE**

**REDDING VERSA PAK RELOADING KIT**

## Powder Scales

### MODEL NO. 2 POWDER AND BULLET SCALE

Model No. 2 features 505-grain capacity and .1-grain accuracy, a dampened beam, and hardened knife edges, and milled stainless bearing seats for smooth, consistent operation and a high level of durability.

**MSRP** . . . . . . . . . . . . . . . . . **$132.00**

## Shellholders

### EXTENDED SHELLHOLDERS

Extended shell holders are required when trimming short cases under 1½ in. O.A.L. They are machined to the same tolerances as standard shell holders, except they're longer.

**MSRP** . . . . . . . . . . . . . . . . . **$21.00**

### EZ FEED SHELLHOLDERS

Redding shell holders are of a universal "snap-in" design recommended for use with all Redding dies and presses, as well as all other popular brands. They are precision-machined to very close tolerances and heat-treated to fit cases and eliminate potential resizing problems. The outside knurling makes them easier to handle and change.

**MSRP** . . . . . . . . . . . . . . . . . **$12.00**

**REDDING MODEL NO. 2 POWDER AND BULLET SCALE**

**REDDING EXTENDED SHELLHOLDER**

**REDDING EZ FEED SHELLHOLDER**

# Centerfire Rifle Ballistics

Updated for 2013–2014

## Comprehensive Ballistics Tables for Currently Manufactured Sporting Rifle Cartridges

No more collecting catalogs and peering at microscopic print to find out what ammunition is offered for a cartridge, and how it performs relative to other factory loads! *Shooter's Bible* has assembled the data for you, in easy-to-read tables, by cartridge.

Data is taken from manufacturers' charts; your chronograph readings may vary. Listings are not intended as recommendations. For example, the data for the .44 Magnum at 400 yards shows its effective range is much shorter. The lack of data for a 285-grain .375 H&H bullet beyond 300 yards does not mean the bullet has no authority farther out. Besides ammunition, the rifle, sights, conditions and shooter ability all must be considered when contemplating a long shot. Accuracy and bullet energy both matter when big game is in the offing.

Barrel length affects velocity, and at various rates depending on the load. As a rule, figure 50 fps per inch of barrel, plus or minus, if your barrel is longer or shorter than 22 inches.

Bullets are given by make, weight (in grains) and type. Most type abbreviations are self-explanatory: BT=Boat-Tail, FMJ=Full Metal Jacket, HP=Hollow Point, SP=Soft Point—except in Hornady listings, where SP is the firm's Spire Point. TNT and TXP are trademarked designations of Speer and Norma. XLC identifies a coated Barnes X bullet. HE indicates a Federal High Energy load, similar to the Hornady LM (Light Magnum) and HM (Heavy Magnum) cartridges.

Arc (trajectory) is based on a zero range published by the manufacturer, from 100 to 300 yards. If a zero does not fall in a yardage column, it lies halfway between—at 150 yards, for example, if the bullet's strike is "+" at 100 yards and "-" at 200.

## .17 HORNET TO .22 HORNET

| CARTRIDGE BULLET | RANGE, YARDS: | 0 | 100 | 200 | 300 | 400 |
|---|---|---|---|---|---|---|
| **.17 HORNET** | | | | | | |
| Hornady 15.5 NXT SPF | | 0 | 100 | 200 | 300 | 400 |
| | velocity, fps: | 3860 | 2924 | 2159 | 1531 | 1108 |
| | energy, ft-lb: | 513 | 294 | 160 | 81 | 42 |
| | arc, inches: | -1.5 | +1.4 | 0 | -9.1 | -33.7 |
| Hornady 20 V-MAX | | 0 | 100 | 200 | 300 | 400 |
| | velocity, fps: | 3650 | 3077 | 2574 | 2122 | 1721 |
| | energy, ft-lb: | 592 | 420 | 294 | 200 | 132 |
| | arc, inches: | -1.5 | +1.1 | 0 | -6.4 | -20.7 |
| **.17 REMINGTON** | | | | | | |
| Rem. 20 AccuTip BT | velocity, fps: | 4250 | 3594 | 3028 | 2529 | 2081 |
| | energy, ft-lb: | 802 | 574 | 407 | 284 | 192 |
| | arc, inches: | | +1.3 | +1.3 | -2.5 | -11.8 |
| Rem. 20 Fireball | velocity, fps | 4000 | 3380 | 2840 | 2360 | 1930 |
| | energy, ft-lb: | 710 | 507 | 358 | 247 | 165 |
| | arc, inches | | +1.6 | +1.5 | -2.8 | -13.5 |
| Rem. 25 HP Power-Lokt | velocity, fps: | 4040 | 3284 | 2644 | 2086 | 1606 |
| | energy, ft-lb: | 906 | 599 | 388 | 242 | 143 |
| | arc, inches: | | +1.8 | 0 | -3.3 | -16.6 |
| **.204 RUGER** | | | | | | |
| Federal 32 Nosler Ballistic Tip | velocity, fps | 4030 | 3465 | 2968 | 2523 | 2119 |
| | arc, inches | | +0.7 | 0 | -4.7 | -14.9 |
| Hornady 32 V-Max | velocity, fps: | 4225 | 3632 | 3114 | 2652 | 2234 |
| | energy, ft-lb: | 1268 | 937 | 689 | 500 | 355 |
| | arc, inches: | | +0.6 | 0 | -4.2 | -13.4 |
| Hornady 40 V-Max | velocity, fps: | 3900 | 3451 | 3046 | 2677 | 2335 |
| | energy, ft-lb: | 1351 | 1058 | 824 | 636 | 485 |
| | arc, inches: | | +0.7 | 0 | -4.5 | -13.9 |
| Rem. 32 AccuTip | velocity, fps: | 4225 | 3632 | 3114 | 2652 | 2234 |
| | Energy, ft-lb: | 1268 | 937 | 689 | 500 | 355 |
| | Arc, inches: | | +0.6 | 0 | -4.1 | -13.1 |

| CARTRIDGE BULLET | RANGE, YARDS: | 0 | 100 | 200 | 300 | 400 |
|---|---|---|---|---|---|---|
| Rem. 40 AccuTip | velocity, fps: | 3900 | 3451 | 3046 | 2677 | 2336 |
| | energy, ft-lb: | 1351 | 1058 | 824 | 636 | 485 |
| | arc, inches: | | +0.7 | 0 | -4.3 | -13.2 |
| Win. 32 Ballistic Silver Tip | velocity, fps | 4050 | 3482 | 2984 | 2537 | 2132 |
| | energy, ft-lb | 1165 | 862 | 632 | 457 | 323 |
| | arc, inches | | +0.7 | 0 | -4.6 | -14.7 |
| Win. 34 HP | velocity, fps: | 4025 | 3339 | 2751 | 2232 | 1775 |
| | energy, ft-lb: | 1223 | 842 | 571 | 376 | 238 |
| | arc, inches: | | +0.8 | 0 | -5.5 | -18.1 |
| **.218 BEE** | | | | | | |
| Win. 46 Hollow Point | velocity, fps: | 2760 | 2102 | 1550 | 1155 | 961 |
| | energy, ft-lb: | 778 | 451 | 245 | 136 | 94 |
| | arc, inches: | | 0 | -7.2 | -29.4 | |
| **.22 HORNET** | | | | | | |
| Hornady 35 V-Max | velocity, fps: | 3100 | 2278 | 1601 | 1135 | 929 |
| | energy, ft-lb: | 747 | 403 | 199 | 100 | 67 |
| | arc, inches: | | +2.8 | 0 | -16.9 | -60.4 |
| Rem. 35 AccuTip | velocity, fps: | 3100 | 2271 | 1591 | 1127 | 924 |
| | energy, ft-lb: | 747 | 401 | 197 | 99 | 66 |
| | arc, inches: | | +1.5 | -3.5 | -22.3 | -68.4 |
| Rem. 45 Pointed Soft Point | velocity, fps: | 2690 | 2042 | 1502 | 1128 | 948 |
| | energy, ft-lb: | 723 | 417 | 225 | 127 | 90 |
| | arc, inches: | | 0 | -7.1 | -30.0 | |
| Rem. 45 Hollow Point | velocity, fps: | 2690 | 2042 | 1502 | 1128 | 948 |
| | energy, ft-lb: | 723 | 417 | 225 | 127 | 90 |
| | arc, inches: | | 0 | -7.1 | -30.0 | |
| Win. 34 Jacketed HP | velocity, fps: | 3050 | 2132 | 1415 | 1017 | 852 |
| | energy, ft-lb: | 700 | 343 | 151 | 78 | 55. |
| | arc, inches: | | 0 | -6.6 | -29.9 | |
| Win. 45 Soft Point | velocity, fps: | 2690 | 2042 | 1502 | 1128 | 948. |
| | energy, ft-lb: | 723 | 417 | 225 | 127 | 90 |
| | arc, inches: | | 0 | -7.7 | -31.3 | |

BALLISTICS

| CARTRIDGE BULLET | RANGE, YARDS: | 0 | 100 | 200 | 300 | 400 |
|---|---|---|---|---|---|---|
| Win. 46 Hollow Point | velocity, fps: | 2690 | 2042 | 1502 | 1128 | 948. |
| | energy, ft-lb: | 739 | 426 | 230 | 130 | 92 |
| | arc, inches: | | 0 | -7.7 | -31.3 | |

### .221 REMINGTON FIREBALL

| CARTRIDGE BULLET | RANGE, YARDS: | 0 | 100 | 200 | 300 | 400 |
|---|---|---|---|---|---|---|
| Rem. 50 AccuTip BT | velocity, fps: | 2995 | 2605 | 2247 | 1918 | 1622 |
| | energy, ft-lb: | 996 | 753 | 560 | 408 | 292 |
| | arc, inches: | | +1.8 | 0 | -8.8 | -27.1 |

### .222 REMINGTON

| CARTRIDGE BULLET | RANGE, YARDS: | 0 | 100 | 200 | 300 | 400 |
|---|---|---|---|---|---|---|
| Federal 50 Hi-Shok | velocity, fps: | 3140 | 2600 | 2120 | 1700 | 1350 |
| | energy, ft-lb: | 1095 | 750 | 500 | 320 | 200 |
| | arc, inches: | | +1.9 | 0 | -9.7 | -31.6 |
| Federal 55 FMJ boat-tail | velocity, fps: | 3020 | 2740 | 2480 | 2230 | 1990 |
| | energy, ft-lb: | 1115 | 915 | 750 | 610 | 484. |
| | arc, inches: | | +1.6 | 0 | -7.3 | -21.5 |
| Hornady 40 V-Max | velocity, fps: | 3600 | 3117 | 2673 | 2269 | 1911 |
| | energy, ft-lb: | 1151 | 863 | 634 | 457 | 324 |
| | arc, inches: | | +1.1 | 0 | -6.1 | -18.9 |
| Hornady 50 V-Max | velocity, fps: | 3140 | 2729 | 2352 | 2008 | 1710. |
| | energy, ft-lb: | 1094 | 827 | 614 | 448 | 325 |
| | arc, inches: | | +1.7 | 0 | -7.9 | -24.4 |
| Norma 50 Soft Point | velocity, fps: | 3199 | 2667 | 2193 | 1771 | |
| | energy, ft-lb: | 1136 | 790 | 534 | 348 | |
| | arc, inches: | | +1.7 | 0 | -9.1 | |
| Norma 50 FMJ | velocity, fps: | 2789 | 2326 | 1910 | 1547 | |
| | energy, ft-lb: | 864 | 601 | 405 | 266 | |
| | arc, inches: | | +2.5 | 0 | -12.2 | |
| Norma 62 Soft Point | velocity, fps: | 2887 | 2457 | 2067 | 1716 | |
| | energy, ft-lb: | 1148 | 831 | 588 | 405 | |
| | arc, inches: | | +2.1 | 0 | -10.4 | |
| PMC 50 Pointed Soft Point | velocity, fps: | 3044 | 2727 | 2354 | 2012 | 1651 |
| | energy, ft-lb: | 1131 | 908 | 677 | 494 | 333 |
| | arc, inches: | | +1.6 | 0 | -7.9 | -24.5 |
| PMC 55 Pointed Soft Point | velocity, fps: | 2950 | 2594 | 2266 | 1966 | 1693 |
| | energy, ft-lb: | 1063 | 822 | 627 | 472 | 350 |
| | arc, inches: | | +1.9 | 0 | -8.7 | -26.3 |
| Rem. 50 Pointed Soft Point | velocity, fps: | 3140 | 2602 | 2123 | 1700 | 1350. |
| | energy, ft-lb: | 1094 | 752 | 500 | 321 | 202 |
| | arc, inches: | | +1.9 | 0 | -9.7 | -31.7 |
| Rem. 50 HP Power-Lokt | velocity, fps: | 3140 | 2635 | 2182 | 1777 | 1432. |
| | energy, ft-lb: | 1094 | 771 | 529 | 351 | 228 |
| | arc, inches: | | +1.8 | 0 | -9.2 | -29.6 |
| Rem. 50 AccuTip BT | velocity, fps: | 3140 | 2744 | 2380 | 2045 | 1740 |
| | energy, ft-lb: | 1094 | 836 | 629 | 464 | 336. |
| | arc, inches: | | +1.6 | 0 | -7.8 | -23.9 |
| Win. 40 Ballistic Silvertip | velocity, fps: | 3370 | 2915 | 2503 | 2127 | 1786 |
| | energy, ft-lb: | 1009 | 755 | 556 | 402 | 283 |
| | arc, inches: | | +1.3 | 0 | -6.9 | -21.5 |
| Win. 50 Pointed Soft Point | velocity, fps: | 3140 | 2602 | 2123 | 1700 | 1350 |
| | energy, ft-lb: | 1094 | 752 | 500 | 321 | 202 |
| | arc, inches: | | +2.2 | 0 | -10.0 | -32.3 |

### .222 REMINGTON MAGNUM

| CARTRIDGE BULLET | RANGE, YARDS: | 0 | 100 | 200 | 300 | 400 |
|---|---|---|---|---|---|---|
| Nosler 40 BT | velocity, fps: | 3600 | 3140 | 2726 | 2347 | 2000 |
| | energy, ft-lb: | 1150 | 876 | 660 | 489 | 355 |
| | arc, inches: | -1.5 | +1.0 | 0 | -5.7 | -17.8 |
| Nosler 50 BT | velocity, fps: | 3340 | 2917 | 2533 | 2179 | 1855 |
| | energy, ft-lb: | 1238 | 945 | 712 | 527 | 382 |
| | arc, inches: | -1.5 | +1.3 | 0 | -6.8 | -20.9 |

### .223 REMINGTON

| CARTRIDGE BULLET | RANGE, YARDS: | 0 | 100 | 200 | 300 | 400 |
|---|---|---|---|---|---|---|
| Black Hills 40 Nosler B. Tip | velocity, fps: | 3600 | | | | |
| | energy, ft-lb: | 1150 | | | | |
| | arc, inches: | | | | | |
| Black Hills 50 V-Max | velocity, fps: | 3300 | | | | |
| | energy, ft-lb: | 1209 | | | | |
| | arc, inches: | | | | | |
| Black Hills 52 Match HP | velocity, fps: | 3300 | | | | |
| | energy, ft-lb: | 1237 | | | | |
| | arc, inches: | | | | | |
| Black Hills 55 Softpoint | velocity, fps: | 3250 | | | | |
| | energy, ft-lb: | 1270 | | | | |
| | arc, inches: | | | | | |
| Black Hills 60 SP or V-Max | velocity, fps: | 3150 | | | | |
| | energy, ft-lb: | 1322 | | | | |
| | arc, inches: | | | | | |
| Black Hills 60 Partition | velocity, fps: | 3150 | | | | |
| | energy, ft-lb: | 1322 | | | | |
| | arc, inches: | | | | | |
| Black Hills 68 Heavy Match | velocity, fps: | 2850 | | | | |
| | energy, ft-lb: | 1227 | | | | |
| | arc, inches: | | | | | |
| Black Hills 69 Sierra MK | velocity, fps: | 2850 | | | | |
| | energy, ft-lb: | 1245 | | | | |
| | arc, inches: | | | | | |
| Black Hills 73 Berger BTHP | velocity, fps: | 2750 | | | | |
| | energy, ft-lb: | 1226 | | | | |
| | arc, inches: | | | | | |
| Black Hills 75 Heavy Match | velocity, fps: | 2750 | | | | |
| | energy, ft-lb: | 1259 | | | | |
| | arc, inches: | | | | | |
| Black Hills 77 Sierra MKing | velocity, fps: | 2750 | | | | |
| | energy, ft-lb: | 1293 | | | | |
| | arc, inches: | | | | | |
| Federal 50 Jacketed HP | velocity, fps: | 3400 | 2910 | 2460 | 2060 | 1700 |
| | energy, ft-lb: | 1285 | 940 | 675 | 470 | 320 |
| | arc, inches: | | +1.3 | 0 | -7.1 | -22.7 |
| Federal 50 Speer TNT HP | velocity, fps: | 3300 | 2860 | 2450 | 2080 | 1750 |
| | energy, ft-lb: | 1210 | 905 | 670 | 480 | 340 |
| | arc, inches: | | +1.4 | 0 | -7.3 | -22.6 |
| Federal 52 Sierra MatchKing BTHP | velocity, fps: | 3300 | 2860 | 2460 | 2090 | 1760 |
| | energy, ft-lb: | 1255 | 945 | 700 | 505 | 360 |
| | arc, inches: | | +1.4 | 0 | -7.2 | -22.4 |
| Federal 55 Hi-Shok | velocity, fps: | 3240 | 2750 | 2300 | 1910 | 1550 |
| | energy, ft-lb: | 1280 | 920 | 650 | 445 | 295 |
| | arc, inches: | | +1.6 | 0 | -8.2 | -26.1 |
| Federal 55 FMJ boat-tail | velocity, fps: | 3240 | 2950 | 2670 | 2410 | 2170 |
| | energy, ft-lb: | 1280 | 1060 | 875 | 710 | 575 |
| | arc, inches: | | +1.3 | 0 | -6.1 | -18.3 |
| Federal 55 Sierra GameKing BTHP | velocity, fps: | 3240 | 2770 | 2340 | 1950 | 1610 |
| | energy, ft-lb: | 1280 | 935 | 670 | 465 | 315 |
| | arc, inches: | | +1.5 | 0 | -8.0 | -25.3 |
| Federal 55 Trophy Bonded | velocity, fps: | 3100 | 2630 | 2210 | 1830 | 1500. |
| | energy, ft-lb: | 1175 | 845 | 595 | 410 | 275 |
| | arc, inches: | | +1.8 | 0 | -8.9 | -28.7 |
| Federal 55 Nosler Bal. Tip | velocity, fps: | 3240 | 2870 | 2530 | 2220 | 1920 |
| | energy, ft-lb: | 1280 | 1005 | 780 | 600 | 450 |
| | arc, inches: | | +1.4 | 0 | -6.8 | -20.8 |
| Federal 55 Sierra BlitzKing | velocity, fps: | 3240 | 2870 | 2520 | 2200 | 1910 |
| | energy, ft-lb: | 1280 | 1005 | 775 | 590 | 445 |
| | arc, inches: | | +-1.4 | 0 | -6.9 | -20.9 |

BALLISTICS

# Centerfire Rifle Ballistics

## .223 REMINGTON TO 5.6X52 R

| CARTRIDGE BULLET | RANGE, YARDS: | 0 | 100 | 200 | 300 | 400 |
|---|---|---|---|---|---|---|
| Federal 62 FMJ | velocity, fps: | 3020 | 2650 | 2310 | 2000 | 1710 |
| | energy, ft-lb: | 1225 | 970 | 735 | 550 | 405 |
| | arc, inches: | | +1.7 | 0 | -8.4 | -25.5 |
| Federal 64 Hi-Shok SP | velocity, fps: | 3090 | 2690 | 2325 | 1990 | 1680 |
| | energy, ft-lb: | 1360 | 1030 | 770 | 560 | 400 |
| | arc, inches: | | +1.7 | 0 | -8.2 | -25.2 |
| Federal 69 Sierra MatchKing BTHP | velocity, fps: | 3000 | 2720 | 2460 | 2210 | 1980 |
| | energy, ft-lb: | 1380 | 1135 | 925 | 750 | 600 |
| | arc, inches: | | +1.6 | 0 | -7.4 | -21.9 |
| Hornady 40 V-Max | velocity, fps: | 3800 | 3305 | 2845 | 2424 | 2044 |
| | energy, ft-lb: | 1282 | 970 | 719 | 522 | 371 |
| | arc, inches: | | +0.8 | 0 | -5.3 | -16.6 |
| Hornady 53 Hollow Point | velocity, fps: | 3330 | 2882 | 2477 | 2106 | 1710 |
| | energy, ft-lb: | 1305 | 978 | 722 | 522 | 369 |
| | arc, inches: | | +1.7 | 0 | -7.4 | -22.7 |
| Hornady 55 V-Max | velocity, fps: | 3240 | 2859 | 2507 | 2181 | 1891. |
| | energy, ft-lb: | 1282 | 998 | 767 | 581 | 437 |
| | arc, inches: | | +1.4 | 0 | -7.1 | -21.4 |
| Hornady 55 TAP-FPD | velocity, fps: | 3240 | 2854 | 2500 | 2172 | 1871 |
| | energy, ft-lb: | 1282 | 995 | 763 | 576 | 427 |
| | arc, inches: | | +1.4 | 0 | -7.0 | -21.4 |
| Hornady 55 Urban Tactical | velocity, fps: | 2970 | 2626 | 2307 | 2011 | 1739 |
| | energy, ft-lb: | 1077 | 842 | 650 | 494 | 369 |
| | arc, inches: | | +1.5 | 0 | -8.1 | -24.9 |
| Hornady 60 Soft Point | velocity, fps: | 3150 | 2782 | 2442 | 2127 | 1837. |
| | energy, ft-lb: | 1322 | 1031 | 795 | 603 | 450 |
| | arc, inches: | | +1.6 | 0 | -7.5 | -22.5 |
| Hornady 60 TAP-FPD | velocity, fps: | 3115 | 2754 | 2420 | 2110 | 1824 |
| | energy, ft-lb: | 1293 | 1010 | 780 | 593 | 443 |
| | arc, inches: | | +1.6 | 0 | -7.5 | -22.9 |
| Hornady 60 Urban Tactical | velocity, fps: | 2950 | 2619 | 2312 | 2025 | 1762 |
| | energy, ft-lb: | 1160 | 914 | 712 | 546 | 413 |
| | arc, inches: | | +1.6 | 0 | -8.1 | -24.7 |
| Hornady 75 BTHP Match | velocity, fps: | 2790 | 2554 | 2330 | 2119 | 1926 |
| | energy, ft-lb: | 1296 | 1086 | 904 | 747 | 617 |
| | arc, inches: | | +2.4 | 0 | -8.8 | -25.1 |
| Hornacy 75 TAP-FPD | velocity, fps: | 2790 | 2582 | 2383 | 2193 | 2012 |
| | energy, ft-lb: | 1296 | 1110 | 946 | 801 | 674 |
| | arc, inches: | | +1.9 | 0 | -8.0 | -23.2 |
| Hornady 75 BTHP Tactical | velocity, fps: | 2630 | 2409 | 2199 | 2000 | 1814 |
| | energy, ft-lb: | 1152 | 966 | 805 | 666 | 548 |
| | arc, inches: | | +2.0 | 0 | -9.2 | -25.9 |
| PMC 40 non-toxic | velocity, fps: | 3500 | 2606 | 1871 | 1315 | |
| | energy, ft-lb: | 1088 | 603 | 311 | 154 | |
| | arc, inches: | | +2.6 | 0 | -12.8 | |
| PMC 50 Sierra BlitzKing | velocity, fps: | 3300 | 2874 | 2484 | 2130 | 1809 |
| | energy, ft-lb: | 1209 | 917 | 685 | 504 | 363 |
| | arc, inches: | | +1.4 | 0 | -7.1 | -21.8 |
| PMC 52 Sierra HPBT Match | velocity, fps: | 3200 | 2808 | 2447 | 2117 | 1817 |
| | energy, ft-lb: | 1182 | 910 | 691 | 517 | 381 |
| | arc, inches: | | +1.5 | 0 | -7.3 | -22.5. |
| PMC 53 Barnes XLC | velocity, fps: | 3200 | 2815 | 2461 | 2136 | 1840 |
| | energy, ft-lb: | 1205 | 933 | 713 | 537 | 398. |
| | arc, inches: | | +1.5 | 0 | -7.2 | -22.2 |
| PMC 55 HP boat-tail | velocity, fps: | 3240 | 2717 | 2250 | 1832 | 1473 |
| | energy, ft-lb: | 1282 | 901 | 618 | 410 | 265 |
| | arc, inches: | | +1.6 | 0 | -8.6 | -27.7 |
| PMC 55 FMJ boat-tail | velocity, fps: | 3195 | 2882 | 2525 | 2169 | 1843 |
| | energy, ft-lb: | 1246 | 1014 | 779 | 574 | 415 |
| | arc, inches: | | +1.4 | 0 | -6.8 | -21.1 |
| PMC 55 Pointed Soft Point | velocity, fps: | 3112 | 2767 | 2421 | 2100 | 1806 |
| | energy, ft-lb: | 1182 | 935 | 715 | 539 | 398 |
| | arc, inches: | | +1.5 | 0 | -7.5 | -22.9 |
| PMC 64 Pointed Soft Point | velocity, fps: | 2775 | 2511 | 2261 | 2026 | 1806. |
| | energy, ft-lb: | 1094 | 896 | 726 | 583 | 464 |
| | arc, inches: | | +2.0 | 0 | -8.8 | -26.1 |
| PMC 69 Sierra BTHP Match | velocity, fps: | 2900 | 2591 | 2304 | 2038 | 1791 |
| | energy, ft-lb: | 1288 | 1029 | 813 | 636 | 492 |
| | arc, inches: | | +1.9 | 0 | -8.4 | -25.3 |
| Rem. 50 AccuTip BT | velocity, fps: | 3300 | 2889 | 2514 | 2168 | 1851 |
| | energy, ft-lb: | 1209 | 927 | 701 | 522 | 380 |
| | arc, inches: | | +1.4 | 0 | -6.9 | -21.2 |
| Rem. 55 Pointed Soft Point | velocity, fps: | 3240 | 2747 | 2304 | 1905 | 1554 |
| | energy, ft-lb: | 1282 | 921 | 648 | 443 | 295 |
| | arc, inches: | | +1.6 | 0 | -8.2 | -26.2 |
| Rem. 55 HP Power-Lokt | velocity, fps: | 3240 | 2773 | 2352 | 1969 | 1627 |
| | energy, ft-lb: | 1282 | 939 | 675 | 473 | 323 |
| | arc, inches: | | +1.5 | 0 | -7.9 | -24.8 |
| Rem. 55 AccuTip BT | velocity, fps: | 3240 | 2854 | 2500 | 2172 | 1871 |
| | energy, ft-lb: | 1282 | 995 | 763 | 576 | 427 |
| | arc, inches: | | +1.5 | 0 | -7.1 | -21.7 |
| Rem. 55 Metal Case | velocity, fps: | 3240 | 2759 | 2326 | 1933 | 1587 |
| | energy, ft-lb: | 1282 | 929 | 660 | 456 | 307 |
| | arc, inches: | | +1.6 | 0 | -8.1 | -25.5 |
| Rem. 62 HP Match | velocity, fps: | 3025 | 2572 | 2162 | 1792 | 1471 |
| | energy, ft-lb: | 1260 | 911 | 643 | 442 | 298 |
| | arc, inches: | | +1.9 | 0 | -9.4 | -29.9 |
| Rem. 69 BTHP Match | velocity, fps: | 3000 | 2720 | 2457 | 2209 | 1975 |
| | energy, ft-lb: | 1379 | 1133 | 925 | 747 | 598 |
| | arc, inches: | | +1.6 | 0 | -7.4 | -21.9 |
| Win. 40 Ballistic Silvertip | velocity, fps: | 3700 | 3166 | 2693 | 2265 | 1879. |
| | energy, ft-lb: | 1216 | 891 | 644 | 456 | 314 |
| | arc, inches: | | +1.0 | 0 | -5.8 | -18.4 |
| Win. 45 JHP | velocity, fps: | 3600 | | | | |
| | energy, ft-lb: | 1295 | | | | |
| | arc, inches: | | | | | |
| Win. 50 Ballistic Silvertip | velocity, fps: | 3410 | 2982 | 2593 | 2235 | 1907. |
| | energy, ft-lb: | 1291 | 987 | 746 | 555 | 404 |
| | arc, inches: | | +1.2 | 0 | -6.4 | -19.8 |
| Win. 53 Hollow Point | velocity, fps: | 3330 | 2882 | 2477 | 2106 | 1770 |
| | energy, ft-lb: | 1305 | 978 | 722 | 522 | 369 |
| | arc, inches: | | +1.7 | 0 | -7.4 | -22.7 |
| Win. 55 Pointed Soft Point | velocity, fps: | 3240 | 2747 | 2304 | 1905 | 1554. |
| | energy, ft-lb: | 1282 | 921 | 648 | 443 | 295 |
| | arc, inches: | | +1.9 | 0 | -8.5 | -26.7 |
| Win. 55 Super Clean NT | velocity, fps: | 3150 | 2520 | 1970 | 1505 | 1165 |
| | energy, ft-lb: | 1212 | 776 | 474 | 277 | 166 |
| | arc, inches: | | +2.8 | 0 | -11.9 | -38.9 |
| Win. 55 FMJ | velocity, fps: | 3240 | 2854 | | | |
| | energy, ft-lb: | 1282 | 995 | | | |
| | arc, inches: | | | | | |
| Win. 55 Ballistic Silvertip | velocity, fps: | 3240 | 2871 | 2531 | 2215 | 1923 |
| | energy, ft-lb: | 1282 | 1006 | 782 | 599 | 451 |
| | arc, inches: | | +1.4 | 0 | -6.8 | -20.8 |
| Win. 64 Power-Point | velocity, fps: | 3020 | 2656 | 2320 | 2009 | 1724 |
| | energy, ft-lb: | 1296 | 1003 | 765 | 574 | 423 |
| | arc, inches: | | +1.7 | 0 | -8.2 | -25.1 |
| Win. 64 Power-Point Plus | velocity, fps: | 3090 | 2684 | 2312 | 1971 | 1664 |
| | energy, ft-lb: | 1357 | 1024 | 760 | 552 | 393 |
| | arc, inches: | | +1.7 | 0 | -8.2 | -25.4 |

## 5.6 x 52 R

| CARTRIDGE BULLET | RANGE, YARDS: | 0 | 100 | 200 | 300 | 400 |
|---|---|---|---|---|---|---|
| Norma 71 Soft Point | velocity, fps: | 2789 | 2446 | 2128 | 1835 | |
| | energy, ft-lb: | 1227 | 944 | 714 | 531 | |
| | arc, inches: | | +2.1 | 0 | -9.9 | |

| CARTRIDGE BULLET | RANGE, YARDS: | 0 | 100 | 200 | 300 | 400 |
|---|---|---|---|---|---|---|
| **.22 PPC** | | | | | | |
| A-Square 52 Berger | velocity, fps: | 3300 | 2952 | 2629 | 2329 | 2049 |
| | energy, ft-lb: | 1257 | 1006 | 798 | 626 | 485 |
| | arc, inches: | | +1.3 | 0 | -6.3 | -19.1 |
| **.225 WINCHESTER** | | | | | | |
| Win. 55 Pointed Soft Point | velocity, fps: | 3570 | 3066 | 2616 | 2208 | 1838. |
| | energy, ft-lb: | 1556 | 1148 | 836 | 595 | 412 |
| | arc, inches: | | +2.4 | +2.0 | -3.5 | -16.3 |
| **.224 WEATHERBY MAGNUM** | | | | | | |
| Wby. 55 Pointed Expanding | velocity, fps: | 3650 | 3192 | 2780 | 2403 | 2056 |
| | energy, ft-lb: | 1627 | 1244 | 944 | 705 | 516 |
| | arc, inches: | | +2.8 | +3.7 | 0 | -9.8 |
| **.22-250 REMINGTON** | | | | | | |
| Black Hills 50 Nos. Bal. Tip | velocity, fps: | 3700 | | | | |
| | energy, ft-lb: | 1520 | | | | |
| | arc, inches: | | | | | |
| Black Hills 60 Nos. Partition | velocity, fps: | 3550 | | | | |
| | energy, ft-lb: | 1679 | | | | |
| | arc, inches: | | | | | |
| Federal 40 Nos. Bal. Tip | velocity, fps: | 4150 | 3610 | 3130 | 2700 | 2300 |
| | energy, ft-lb: | 1530 | 1155 | 870 | 645 | 470 |
| | arc, inches: | | +0.6 | 0 | -4.2 | -13.2 |
| Federal 40 Sierra Varminter | velocity, fps: | 4000 | 3320 | 2720 | 2200 | 1740 |
| | energy, ft-lb: | 1420 | 980 | 660 | 430 | 265 |
| | arc, inches: | | +0.8 | 0 | -5.6 | -18.4 |
| Federal 55 Hi-Shok | velocity, fps: | 3680 | 3140 | 2660 | 2220 | 1830 |
| | energy, ft-lb: | 1655 | 1200 | 860 | 605 | 410 |
| | arc, inches: | | +1.0 | 0 | -6.0 | -19.1 |
| Federal 55 Sierra BlitzKing | velocity, fps: | 3680 | 3270 | 2890 | 2540 | 2220 |
| | energy, ft-lb: | 1655 | 1300 | 1020 | 790 | 605 |
| | arc, inches: | | +0.9 | 0 | -5.1 | -15.6 |
| Federal 55 Sierra GameKing BTHP | velocity, fps: | 3680 | 3280 | 2920 | 2590 | 2280 |
| | energy, ft-lb: | 1655 | 1315 | 1040 | 815 | 630 |
| | arc, inches: | | +0.9 | 0 | -5.0 | -15.1 |
| Federal 55 Trophy Bonded | velocity, fps: | 3600 | 3080 | 2610 | 2190 | 1810. |
| | energy, ft-lb: | 1585 | 1155 | 835 | 590 | 400. |
| | arc, inches: | | +1.1 | 0 | -6.2 | -19.8 |
| Hornady 40 V-Max | velocity, fps: | 4150 | 3631 | 3147 | 2699 | 2293 |
| | energy, ft-lb: | 1529 | 1171 | 879 | 647 | 467 |
| | arc, inches: | | +0.5 | 0 | -4.2 | -13.3 |
| Hornady 50 V-Max | velocity, fps: | 3800 | 3349 | 2925 | 2535 | 2178 |
| | energy, ft-lb: | 1603 | 1245 | 950 | 713 | 527 |
| | arc, inches: | | +0.8 | 0 | -5.0 | -15.6 |
| Hornady 53 Hollow Point | velocity, fps: | 3680 | 3185 | 2743 | 2341 | 1974. |
| | energy, ft-lb: | 1594 | 1194 | 886 | 645 | 459 |
| | arc, inches: | | +1.0 | 0 | -5.7 | -17.8 |
| Hornady 55 V-Max | velocity, fps: | 3680 | 3265 | 2876 | 2517 | 2183 |
| | energy, ft-lb: | 1654 | 1302 | 1010 | 772 | 582 |
| | arc, inches: | | +0.9 | 0 | -5.3 | -16.1 |
| Hornady 60 Soft Point | velocity, fps: | 3600 | 3195 | 2826 | 2485 | 2169 |
| | energy, ft-lb: | 1727 | 1360 | 1064 | 823 | 627 |
| | arc, inches: | | +1.0 | 0 | -5.4 | -16.3 |
| Norma 53 Soft Point | velocity, fps: | 3707 | 3234 | 2809 | 1716 | |
| | energy, ft-lb: | 1618 | 1231 | 928 | 690 | |
| | arc, inches: | | +0.9 | 0 | -5.3 | |
| PMC 50 Sierra BlitzKing | velocity, fps: | 3725 | 3264 | 2641 | 2455 | 2103 |
| | energy, ft-lb: | 1540 | 1183 | 896 | 669 | 491 |
| | arc, inches: | | +0.9 | 0 | -5.2 | -16.2 |
| PMC 50 Barnes XLC | velocity, fps: | 3725 | 3280 | 2871 | 2495 | 2152 |
| | energy, ft-lb: | 1540 | 1195 | 915 | 691 | 514. |
| | arc, inches: | | +0.9 | 0 | -5.1 | -15.9 |

| CARTRIDGE BULLET | RANGE, YARDS: | 0 | 100 | 200 | 300 | 400 |
|---|---|---|---|---|---|---|
| PMC 55 HP boat-tail | velocity, fps: | 3680 | 3104 | 2596 | 2141 | 1737 |
| | energy, ft-lb: | 1654 | 1176 | 823 | 560 | 368 |
| | arc, inches: | | +1.1 | 0 | -6.3 | -20.2 |
| PMC 55 Pointed Soft Point | velocity, fps: | 3586 | 3203 | 2852 | 2505 | 2178 |
| | energy, ft-lb: | 1570 | 1253 | 993 | 766 | 579 |
| | arc, inches: | | +1.0 | 0 | -5.2 | -16.0 |
| Rem. 50 AccuTip BT (also in EtronX) | velocity, fps: | 3725 | 3272 | 2864 | 2491 | 2147 |
| | energy, ft-lb: | 1540 | 1188 | 910 | 689 | 512 |
| | arc, inches: | | +1.7 | +1.6 | -2.8 | -12.8 |
| Rem. 55 Pointed Soft Point | velocity, fps: | 3680 | 3137 | 2656 | 2222 | 1832 |
| | energy, ft-lb: | 1654 | 1201 | 861 | 603 | 410 |
| | arc, inches: | | +1.9 | +1.8 | -3.3 | -15.5 |
| Rem. 55 HP Power-Lokt | velocity, fps: | 3680 | 3209 | 2785 | 2400 | 2046. |
| | energy, ft-lb: | 1654 | 1257 | 947 | 703 | 511 |
| | arc, inches: | | +1.8 | +1.7 | -3.0 | -13.7 |
| Rem. 60 Nosler Partition (also in EtronX) | velocity, fps: | 3500 | 3045 | 2634 | 2258 | 1914 |
| | energy, ft-lb: | 1632 | 1235 | 924 | 679 | 488 |
| | arc, inches: | | +2.1 | +1.9 | -3.4 | -15.5 |
| Win. 40 Ballistic Silvertip | velocity, fps: | 4150 | 3591 | 3099 | 2658 | 2257 |
| | energy, ft-lb: | 1530 | 1146 | 853 | 628 | 453 |
| | arc, inches: | | +0.6 | 0 | -4.2 | -13.4 |
| Win. 50 Ballistic Silvertip | velocity, fps: | 3810 | 3341 | 2919 | 2536 | 2182 |
| | energy, ft-lb: | 1611 | 1239 | 946 | 714 | 529. |
| | arc, inches: | | +0.8 | 0 | -4.9 | -15.2 |
| Win. 55 Pointed Soft Point | velocity, fps: | 3680 | 3137 | 2656 | 2222 | 1832 |
| | energy, ft-lb: | 1654 | 1201 | 861 | 603 | 410 |
| | arc, inches: | | +2.3 | +1.9 | -3.4 | -15.9 |
| Win. 55 Ballistic Silvertip | velocity, fps: | 3680 | 3272 | 2900 | 2558 | 2240 |
| | energy, ft-lb: | 1654 | 1307 | 1027 | 799 | 613 |
| | arc, inches: | | +0.9 | 0 | -5.0 | -15.4 |
| Win. 64 Power-Point | velocity, fps: | 3500 | 3086 | 2708 | 2360 | 2038 |
| | energy, ft-lb: | 1741 | 1353 | 1042 | 791 | 590 |
| | arc, inches: | | +1.1 | 0 | -5.9 | -18.0 |
| **.220 SWIFT** | | | | | | |
| Federal 52 Sierra MatchKing BTHP | velocity, fps: | 3830 | 3370 | 2960 | 2600 | 2230 |
| | energy, ft-lb: | 1690 | 1310 | 1010 | 770 | 575 |
| | arc, inches: | | +0.8 | 0 | -4.8 | -14.9 |
| Federal 55 Sierra BlitzKing | velocity, fps: | 3800 | 3370 | 2990 | 2630 | 2310. |
| | energy, ft-lb: | 1765 | 1390 | 1090 | 850 | 650 |
| | arc, inches: | | +0.8 | 0 | -4.7 | -14.4 |
| Federal 55 Trophy Bonded | velocity, fps: | 3700 | 3170 | 2690 | 2270 | 1880 |
| | energy, ft-lb: | 1670 | 1225 | 885 | 625 | 430 |
| | arc, inches: | | +1.0 | 0 | -5.8 | -18.5 |
| Hornady 40 V-Max | velocity, fps: | 4200 | 3678 | 3190 | 2739 | 2329 |
| | energy, ft-lb: | 1566 | 1201 | 904 | 666 | 482 |
| | arc, inches: | | +0.5 | 0 | -4.0 | -12.9 |
| Hornady 50 V-Max | velocity, fps: | 3850 | 3396 | 2970 | 2576 | 2215. |
| | energy, ft-lb: | 1645 | 1280 | 979 | 736 | 545 |
| | arc, inches: | | +0.7 | 0 | -4.8 | -15.1 |
| Hornady 50 SP | velocity, fps: | 3850 | 3327 | 2862 | 2442 | 2060. |
| | energy, ft-lb: | 1645 | 1228 | 909 | 662 | 471 |
| | arc, inches: | | +0.8 | 0 | -5.1 | -16.1 |
| Hornady 55 V-Max | velocity, fps: | 3680 | 3265 | 2876 | 2517 | 2183 |
| | energy, ft-lb: | 1654 | 1302 | 1010 | 772 | 582 |
| | arc, inches: | | +0.9 | 0 | -5.3 | -16.1 |
| Hornady 60 Hollow Point | velocity, fps: | 3600 | 3199 | 2824 | 2475 | 2156 |
| | energy, ft-lb: | 1727 | 1364 | 1063 | 816 | 619 |
| | arc, inches: | | +1.0 | 0 | -5.4 | -16.3 |
| Norma 50 Soft Point | velocity, fps: | 4019 | 3380 | 2826 | 2335 | |
| | energy, ft-lb: | 1794 | 1268 | 887 | 605 | |
| | arc, inches: | | +0.7 | 0 | -5.1 | |

# Centerfire Rifle Ballistics

## .220 SWIFT TO .243 WINCHESTER

| CARTRIDGE BULLET | RANGE, YARDS: | 0 | 100 | 200 | 300 | 400 |
|---|---|---|---|---|---|---|
| Rem. 50 Pointed Soft Point | velocity, fps: | 3780 | 3158 | 2617 | 2135 | 1710 |
| | energy, ft-lb: | 1586 | 1107 | 760 | 506 | 325 |
| | arc, inches: | | +0.3 | -1.4 | -8.2 | |
| Rem. 50 V-Max boat-tail | velocity, fps: | 3780 | 3321 | 2908 | 2532 | 2185 |
| (also in EtronX) | energy, ft-lb: | 1586 | 1224 | 939 | 711 | 530 |
| | arc, inches: | | +0.8 | 0 | -5.0 | -15.4 |
| Win. 40 Ballistic Silvertip | velocity, fps: | 4050 | 3518 | 3048 | 2624 | 2238. |
| | energy, ft-lb: | 1457 | 1099 | 825 | 611 | 445 |
| | arc, inches: | | +0.7 | 0 | -4.4 | -13.9 |
| Win. 50 Pointed Soft Point | velocity, fps: | 3870 | 3310 | 2816 | 2373 | 1972 |
| | energy, ft-lb: | 1663 | 1226 | 881 | 625 | 432 |
| | arc, inches: | | +0.8 | 0 | -5.2 | -16.7 |

### .223 WSSM

| CARTRIDGE BULLET | RANGE, YARDS: | 0 | 100 | 200 | 300 | 400 |
|---|---|---|---|---|---|---|
| Win. 55 Ballistic Silvertip | velocity, fps: | 3850 | 3438 | 3064 | 2721 | 2402 |
| | energy, ft-lb: | 1810 | 1444 | 1147 | 904 | 704 |
| | arc, inches: | | +0.7 | 0 | -4.4 | -13.6 |
| Win. 55 Pointed Softpoint | velocity, fps: | 3850 | 3367 | 2934 | 2541 | 2181 |
| | energy, ft-lb: | 1810 | 1384 | 1051 | 789 | 581 |
| | arc, inches: | | +0.8 | 0 | -4.9 | -15.1 |
| Win. 64 Power-Point | velocity, fps: | 3600 | 3144 | 2732 | 2356 | 2011 |
| | energy, ft-lb: | 1841 | 1404 | 1061 | 789 | 574 |
| | arc, inches: | | +1.0 | 0 | -5.7 | -17.7 |

### 6MM PPC

| CARTRIDGE BULLET | RANGE, YARDS: | 0 | 100 | 200 | 300 | 400 |
|---|---|---|---|---|---|---|
| A-Square 68 Berger | velocity, fps: | 3100 | 2751 | 2428 | 2128 | 1850 |
| | energy, ft-lb: | 1451 | 1143 | 890 | 684 | 516 |
| | arc, inches: | | +1.5 | 0 | -7.5 | -22.6 |

### 6X70 R

| CARTRIDGE BULLET | RANGE, YARDS: | 0 | 100 | 200 | 300 | 400 |
|---|---|---|---|---|---|---|
| Norma 95 Nosler Bal. Tip | velocity, fps: | 2461 | 2231 | 2013 | 1809 | |
| | energy, ft-lb: | 1211 | 995 | 810 | 654 | |
| | arc, inches: | | +2.7 | 0 | -11.3 | |

### .243 WINCHESTER

| CARTRIDGE BULLET | RANGE, YARDS: | 0 | 100 | 200 | 300 | 400 |
|---|---|---|---|---|---|---|
| Black Hills 55 Nosler B. Tip | velocity, fps: | 3800 | | | | |
| | energy, ft-lb: | 1763 | | | | |
| | arc, inches: | | | | | |
| Black Hills 95 Nosler B. Tip | velocity, fps: | 2950 | | | | |
| | energy, ft-lb: | 1836 | | | | |
| | arc, inches: | | | | | |
| Federal 70 Nosler Bal. Tip | velocity, fps: | 3400 | 3070 | 2760 | 2470 | 2200 |
| | energy, ft-lb: | 1795 | 1465 | 1185 | 950 | 755. |
| | arc, inches: | | +1.1 | 0 | -5.7 | -17.1 |
| Federal 70 Speer TNT HP | velocity, fps: | 3400 | 3040 | 2700 | 2390 | 2100 |
| | energy, ft-lb: | 1795 | 1435 | 1135 | 890 | 685 |
| | arc, inches: | | +1.1 | 0 | -5.9 | -18.0 |
| Federal 80 Sierra Pro-Hunter | velocity, fps: | 3350 | 2960 | 2590 | 2260 | 1950 |
| | energy, ft-lb: | 1995 | 1550 | 1195 | 905 | 675 |
| | arc, inches: | | +1.3 | 0 | -6.4 | -19.7 |
| Federal 85 Sierra GameKing BTHP | velocity, fps: | 3320 | 3070 | 2830 | 2600 | 2380 |
| | energy, ft-lb: | 2080 | 1770 | 1510 | 1280 | 1070 |
| | arc, inches: | | +1.1 | 0 | -5.5 | -16.1 |
| Federal 90 Trophy Bonded | velocity, fps: | 3100 | 2850 | 2610 | 2380 | 2160. |
| | energy, ft-lb: | 1920 | 1620 | 1360 | 1130 | 935 |
| | arc, inches: | | +1.4 | 0 | -6.1 | -19.2 |
| Federal 100 Hi-Shok | velocity, fps: | 2960 | 2700 | 2450 | 2220 | 1990 |
| | energy, ft-lb: | 1945 | 1615 | 1330 | 1090 | 880 |
| | arc, inches: | | +1.6 | 0 | -7.5 | -22.0 |
| Federal 100 Sierra GameKing BTSP | velocity, fps: | 2960 | 2760 | 2570 | 2380 | 2210 |
| | energy, ft-lb: | 1950 | 1690 | 1460 | 1260 | 1080 |
| | arc, inches: | | +1.5 | 0 | -6.8 | -19.8 |
| Federal 100 Nosler Partition | velocity, fps: | 2960 | 2730 | 2510 | 2300 | 2100 |
| | energy, ft-lb: | 1945 | 1650 | 1395 | 1170 | 975. |
| | arc, inches: | | +1.6 | 0 | -7.1 | -20.9 |

| CARTRIDGE BULLET | RANGE, YARDS: | 0 | 100 | 200 | 300 | 400 |
|---|---|---|---|---|---|---|
| Hornady 58 V-Max | velocity, fps: | 3750 | 3319 | 2913 | 2539 | 2195 |
| | energy, ft-lb: | 1811 | 1418 | 1093 | 830 | 620 |
| | arc, inches: | | +1.2 | 0 | -5.5 | -16.4 |
| Hornady 75 Hollow Point | velocity, fps: | 3400 | 2970 | 2578 | 2219 | 1890 |
| | energy, ft-lb: | 1926 | 1469 | 1107 | 820 | 595 |
| | arc, inches: | | +1.2 | 0 | -6.5 | -20.3 |
| Hornady 100 BTSP | velocity, fps: | 2960 | 2728 | 2508 | 2299 | 2099 |
| | energy, ft-lb: | 1945 | 1653 | 1397 | 1174 | 979 |
| | arc, inches: | | +1.6 | 0 | -7.2 | -21.0 |
| Hornady 100 BTSP LM | velocity, fps: | 3100 | 2839 | 2592 | 2358 | 2138 |
| | energy, ft-lb: | 2133 | 1790 | 1491 | 1235 | 1014 |
| | arc, inches: | | +1.5 | 0 | -6.8 | -19.8 |
| Norma 80 FMJ | velocity, fps: | 3117 | 2750 | 2412 | 2098 | |
| | energy, ft-lb: | 1726 | 1344 | 1034 | 782 | |
| | arc, inches: | | +1.5 | 0 | -7.5 | |
| Norma 100 FMJ | velocity, fps: | 3018 | 2747 | 2493 | 2252 | |
| | energy, ft-lb: | 2023 | 1677 | 1380 | 1126 | |
| | arc, inches: | | +1.5 | 0 | -7.1 | |
| Norma 100 Soft Point | velocity, fps: | 3018 | 2748 | 2493 | 2252 | |
| | energy, ft-lb: | 2023 | 1677 | 1380 | 1126 | |
| | arc, inches: | | +1.5 | 0 | -7.1 | |
| Norma 100 Oryx | velocity, fps: | 3018 | 2653 | 2316 | 2004 | |
| | energy, ft-lb: | 2023 | 1563 | 1191 | 892 | |
| | arc, inches: | | +1.7 | 0 | -8.3 | |
| PMC 80 Pointed Soft Point | velocity, fps: | 2940 | 2684 | 2444 | 2215 | 1999 |
| | energy, ft-lb: | 1535 | 1280 | 1060 | 871 | 709 |
| | arc, inches: | | +1.7 | 0 | -7.5 | -22.1 |
| PMC 85 Barnes XLC | velocity, fps: | 3250 | 3022 | 2805 | 2598 | 2401 |
| | energy, ft-lb: | 1993 | 1724 | 1485 | 1274 | 1088 |
| | arc, inches: | | +1.6 | 0 | -5.6 | 16.3 |
| PMC 85 HP boat-tail | velocity, fps: | 3275 | 2922 | 2596 | 2292 | 2009 |
| | energy, ft-lb: | 2024 | 1611 | 1272 | 991 | 761 |
| | arc, inches: | | +1.3 | 0 | -6.5 | -19.7 |
| PMC 100 Pointed Soft Point | velocity, fps: | 2743 | 2507 | 2283 | 2070 | 1869 |
| | energy, ft-lb: | 1670 | 1395 | 1157 | 951 | 776 |
| | arc, inches: | | +2.0 | 0 | -8.7 | -25.5 |
| PMC 100 SP boat-tail | velocity, fps: | 2960 | 2742 | 2534 | 2335 | 2144 |
| | energy, ft-lb: | 1945 | 1669 | 1425 | 1210 | 1021 |
| | arc, inches: | | +1.6 | 0 | -7.0 | -20.5 |
| Rem. 75 AccuTip BT | velocity, fps: | 3375 | 3065 | 2775 | 2504 | 2248 |
| | energy, ft-lb: | 1897 | 1564 | 1282 | 1044 | 842 |
| | arc, inches: | | +2.0 | +1.8 | -3.0 | -13.3 |
| Rem. 80 Pointed Soft Point | velocity, fps: | 3350 | 2955 | 2593 | 2259 | 1951 |
| | energy, ft-lb: | 1993 | 1551 | 1194 | 906 | 676 |
| | arc, inches: | | +2.2 | +2.0 | -3.5 | -15.8 |
| Rem. 80 HP Power-Lokt | velocity, fps: | 3350 | 2955 | 2593 | 2259 | 1951 |
| | energy, ft-lb: | 1993 | 1551 | 1194 | 906 | 676 |
| | arc, inches: | | +2.2 | +2.0 | -3.5 | -15.8 |
| Rem. 90 Nosler Bal. Tip (also in EtronX) or Scirocco | velocity, fps: | 3120 | 2871 | 2635 | 2411 | 2199 |
| | energy, ft-lb: | 1946 | 1647 | 1388 | 1162 | 966 |
| | arc, inches: | | +1.4 | 0 | -6.4 | -18.8 |
| Rem. 95 AccuTip | velocity, fps: | 3120 | 2847 | 2590 | 2347 | 2118 |
| | energy, ft-lb: | 2053 | 1710 | 1415 | 1162 | 946 |
| | arc, inches: | | +1.5 | 0 | -6.6 | -19.5 |
| Rem. 100 PSP Core-Lokt (also in EtronX) | velocity, fps: | 2960 | 2697 | 2449 | 2215 | 1993 |
| | energy, ft-lb: | 1945 | 1615 | 1332 | 1089 | 882 |
| | arc, inches: | | +1.6 | 0 | -7.5 | -22.1 |
| Rem. 100 PSP boat-tail | velocity, fps: | 2960 | 2720 | 2492 | 2275 | 2069 |
| | energy, ft-lb: | 1945 | 1642 | 1378 | 1149 | 950 |
| | arc, inches: | | +2.8 | +2.3 | -3.8 | -16.6 |
| Speer 100 Grand Slam | velocity, fps: | 2950 | 2684 | 2434 | 2197 | |
| | energy, ft-lb: | 1932 | 1600 | 1315 | 1072 | |

| CARTRIDGE BULLET | RANGE, YARDS: | 0 | 100 | 200 | 300 | 400 |
|---|---|---|---|---|---|---|
| | arc, inches: | | +1.7 | 0 | -7.6 | -22.4 |
| Win. 55 Ballistic Silvertip | velocity, fps: | 4025 | 3597 | 3209 | 2853 | 2525 |
| | energy, ft-lb: | 1978 | 1579 | 1257 | 994 | 779 |
| | arc, inches: | | +0.6 | 0 | -4.0 | -12.2 |
| Win. 80 Pointed Soft Point | velocity, fps: | 3350 | 2955 | 2593 | 2259 | 1951. |
| | energy, ft-lb: | 1993 | 1551 | 1194 | 906 | 676 |
| | arc, inches: | | +2.6 | +2.1 | -3.6 | -16.2 |
| Win. 95 Ballistic Silvertip | velocity, fps: | 3100 | 2854 | 2626 | 2410 | 2203 |
| | energy, ft-lb: | 2021 | 1719 | 1455 | 1225 | 1024 |
| | arc, inches: | | +1.4 | 0 | -6.4 | -18.9 |
| Win. 95 Supreme Elite XP3 | velocity, fps | 3100 | 2864 | 2641 | 2428 | 2225 |
| | energy, ft-lb | 2027 | 1730 | 1471 | 1243 | 1044 |
| | a rc, inches: | | +1.4 | 0 | -6.4 | -18.7 |
| Win. 100 Power-Point | velocity, fps: | 2960 | 2697 | 2449 | 2215 | 1993 |
| | energy, ft-lb: | 1945 | 1615 | 1332 | 1089 | 882 |
| | arc, inches: | | +1.9 | 0 | -7.8 | -22.6. |
| Win. 100 Power-Point Plus | velocity, fps: | 3090 | 2818 | 2562 | 2321 | 2092 |
| | energy, ft-lb: | 2121 | 1764 | 1458 | 1196 | 972 |
| | arc, inches: | | +1.4 | 0 | -6.7 | -20.0 |

## 6MM REMINGTON

| CARTRIDGE BULLET | RANGE, YARDS: | 0 | 100 | 200 | 300 | 400 |
|---|---|---|---|---|---|---|
| Federal 80 Sierra Pro-Hunter | velocity, fps: | 3470 | 3060 | 2690 | 2350 | 2040 |
| | energy, ft-lb: | 2140 | 1665 | 1290 | 980 | 735 |
| | arc, inches: | | +1.1 | 0 | -5.9 | -18.2 |
| Federal 100 Hi-Shok | velocity, fps: | 3100 | 2830 | 2570 | 2330 | 2100 |
| | energy, ft-lb: | 2135 | 1775 | 1470 | 1205 | 985 |
| | arc, inches: | | +1.4 | 0 | -6.7 | -19.8 |
| Federal 100 Nos. Partition | velocity, fps: | 3100 | 2860 | 2640 | 2420 | 2220 |
| | energy, ft-lb: | 2135 | 1820 | 1545 | 1300 | 1090 |
| | arc, inches: | | +1.4 | 0 | -6.3 | -18.7 |
| Hornady 100 SP boat-tail | velocity, fps: | 3100 | 2861 | 2634 | 2419 | 2231 |
| | energy, ft-lb: | 2134 | 1818 | 1541 | 1300 | 1088 |
| | arc, inches: | | +1.3 | 0 | -6.5 | -18.9 |
| Hornady 100 SPBT LM | velocity, fps: | 3250 | 2997 | 2756 | 2528 | 2311 |
| | energy, ft-lb: | 2345 | 1995 | 1687 | 1418 | 1186 |
| | arc, inches: | | +1.6 | 0 | -6.3 | -18.2 |
| Rem. 75 V-Max boat-tail | velocity, fps: | 3400 | 3088 | 2797 | 2524 | 2267 |
| | energy, ft-lb: | 1925 | 1587 | 1303 | 1061 | 856 |
| | arc, inches: | | +1.9 | +1.7 | -3.0 | -13.1 |
| Rem. 100 PSP Core-Lokt | velocity, fps: | 3100 | 2829 | 2573 | 2332 | 2104. |
| | energy, ft-lb: | 2133 | 1777 | 1470 | 1207 | 983 |
| | arc, inches: | | +1.4 | 0 | -6.7 | -19.8 |
| Rem. 100 PSP boat-tail | velocity, fps: | 3100 | 2852 | 2617 | 2394 | 2183. |
| | energy, ft-lb: | 2134 | 1806 | 1521 | 1273 | 1058 |
| | arc, inches: | | +1.4 | 0 | -6.5 | -19.1 |
| Win. 100 Power-Point | velocity, fps: | 3100 | 2829 | 2573 | 2332 | 2104 |
| | energy, ft-lb: | 2133 | 1777 | 1470 | 1207 | 983 |
| | arc, inches: | | +1.7 | 0 | -7.0 | -20.4 |

## .243 WSSM

| CARTRIDGE BULLET | RANGE, YARDS: | 0 | 100 | 200 | 300 | 400 |
|---|---|---|---|---|---|---|
| Win. 55 Ballistic Silvertip | velocity, fps: | 4060 | 3628 | 3237 | 2880 | 2550 |
| | energy, ft-lb: | 2013 | 1607 | 1280 | 1013 | 794 |
| | arc, inches: | | +0.6 | 0 | -3.9 | -12.0 |
| Win. 95 Ballistic Silvertip | velocity, fps: | 3250 | 3000 | 2763 | 2538 | 2325 |
| | energy, ft-lb: | 2258 | 1898 | 1610 | 1359 | 1140 |
| | arc, inches: | | +1.2 | 0 | 5.7 | 16.9 |
| Win. 95 Supreme Elite XP3 | velocity, fps | 3150 | 2912 | 2686 | 2471 | 2266 |
| | energy, ft-lb | 2093 | 1788 | 1521 | 1287 | 1083 |
| | arc, inches | 1.3 | 0 | -6.1 | -18.0 | |
| Win. 100 Power Point | velocity, fps: | 3110 | 2838 | 2583 | 2341 | 2112 |
| | energy, ft-lb: | 2147 | 1789 | 1481 | 1217 | 991 |
| | arc, inches: | | +1.4 | 0 | -6.6 | -19.7 |

## .240 WEATHERBY MAGNUM

| CARTRIDGE BULLET | RANGE, YARDS: | 0 | 100 | 200 | 300 | 400 |
|---|---|---|---|---|---|---|
| Wby. 87 Pointed Expanding | velocity, fps: | 3523 | 3199 | 2898 | 2617 | 2352 |
| | energy, ft-lb: | 2397 | 1977 | 1622 | 1323 | 1069 |
| | arc, inches: | | +2.7 | +3.4 | 0 | -8.4 |
| Wby. 90 Barnes-X | velocity, fps: | 3500 | 3222 | 2962 | 2717 | 2484 |
| | energy, ft-lb: | 2448 | 2075 | 1753 | 1475 | 1233 |
| | arc, inches: | | +2.6 | +3.3 | 0 | -8.0 |
| Wby. 95 Nosler Bal. Tip | velocity, fps: | 3420 | 3146 | 2888 | 2645 | 2414 |
| | energy, ft-lb: | 2467 | 2087 | 1759 | 1475 | 1229 |
| | arc, inches: | | +2.7 | +3.5 | 0 | -8.4 |
| Wby. 100 Pointed Expanding | velocity, fps: | 3406 | 3134 | 2878 | 2637 | 2408 |
| | energy, ft-lb: | 2576 | 2180 | 1839 | 1544 | 1287 |
| | arc, inches: | | +2.8 | +3.5 | 0 | -8.4 |
| Wby. 100 Partition | velocity, fps: | 3406 | 3136 | 2882 | 2642 | 2415 |
| | energy, ft-lb: | 2576 | 2183 | 1844 | 1550 | 1294 |
| | arc, inches: | | +2.8 | +3.5 | 0 | -8.4 |

## .25-20 WINCHESTER

| CARTRIDGE BULLET | RANGE, YARDS: | 0 | 100 | 200 | 300 | 400 |
|---|---|---|---|---|---|---|
| Rem. 86 Soft Point | velocity, fps: | 1460 | 1194 | 1030 | 931 | 858 |
| | energy, ft-lb: | 407 | 272 | 203 | 165 | 141 |
| | arc, inches: | | 0 | -22.9 | -78.9 | -173.0 |
| Win. 86 Soft Point | velocity, fps: | 1460 | 1194 | 1030 | 931 | 858. |
| | energy, ft-lb: | 407 | 272 | 203 | 165 | 141 |
| | arc, inches: | | 0 | -23.5 | -79.6 | -175.9 |

## .25-35 WINCHESTER

| CARTRIDGE BULLET | RANGE, YARDS: | 0 | 100 | 200 | 300 | 400 |
|---|---|---|---|---|---|---|
| Win. 117 Soft Point | velocity, fps: | 2230 | 1866 | 1545 | 1282 | 1097 |
| | energy, ft-lb: | 1292 | 904 | 620 | 427 | 313 |
| | arc, inches: | | +2.1 | -5.1 | -27.0 | -70.1 |

## .250 SAVAGE

| CARTRIDGE BULLET | RANGE, YARDS: | 0 | 100 | 200 | 300 | 400 |
|---|---|---|---|---|---|---|
| Rem. 100 Pointed SP | velocity, fps: | 2820 | 2504 | 2210 | 1936 | 1684. |
| | energy, ft-lb: | 1765 | 1392 | 1084 | 832 | 630 |
| | arc, inches: | | +2.0 | 0 | -9.2 | -27.7 |
| Win. 100 Silvertip | velocity, fps: | 2820 | 2467 | 2140 | 1839 | 1569 |
| | energy, ft-lb: | 1765 | 1351 | 1017 | 751 | 547 |
| | arc, inches: | | +2.4 | 0 | -10.1 | -30.5 |

## .257 ROBERTS

| CARTRIDGE BULLET | RANGE, YARDS: | 0 | 100 | 200 | 300 | 400 |
|---|---|---|---|---|---|---|
| Federal 120 Nosler Partition | velocity, fps: | 2780 | 2560 | 2360 | 2160 | 1970 |
| | energy, ft-lb: | 2060 | 1750 | 1480 | 1240 | 1030 |
| | arc, inches: | | +1.9 | 0 | -8.2 | -24.0 |
| Hornady 117 SP boat-tail | velocity, fps: | 2780 | 2550 | 2331 | 2122 | 1925 |
| | energy, ft-lb: | 2007 | 1689 | 1411 | 1170 | 963 |
| | arc, inches: | | +1.9 | 0 | -8.3 | -24.4 |
| Hornady 117 SP boat-tail LM | velocity, fps: | 2940 | 2694 | 2460 | 2240 | 2031 |
| | energy, ft-lb: | 2245 | 1885 | 1572 | 1303 | 1071 |
| | arc, inches: | | +1.7 | 0 | -7.6 | -21.8 |
| Rem. 117 SP Core-Lokt | velocity, fps: | 2650 | 2291 | 1961 | 1663 | 1404 |
| | energy, ft-lb: | 1824 | 1363 | 999 | 718 | 512 |
| | arc, inches: | | +2.6 | 0 | -11.7 | -36.1 |
| Win. 117 Power-Point | velocity, fps: | 2780 | 2411 | 2071 | 1761 | 1488 |
| | energy, ft-lb: | 2009 | 1511 | 1115 | 806 | 576. |
| | arc, inches: | | +2.6 | 0 | -10.8 | -33.0 |

## .25-06 REMINGTON

| CARTRIDGE BULLET | RANGE, YARDS: | 0 | 100 | 200 | 300 | 400 |
|---|---|---|---|---|---|---|
| Black Hills 100 Nos. Bal. Tip | velocity, fps: | 3200 | | | | |
| | energy, ft-lb: | 2273 | | | | |
| | arc, inches: | | | | | |
| Black Hills 100 Barnes XLC | velocity, fps: | 3200 | | | | |
| | energy, ft-lb: | 2273 | | | | |
| | arc, inches: | | | | | |
| Black Hills 115 Barnes X | velocity, fps: | 2975 | | | | |

## .25-06 REMINGTON TO 6.5X55 SWEDISH

| CARTRIDGE BULLET | RANGE, YARDS: | 0 | 100 | 200 | 300 | 400 |
|---|---|---|---|---|---|---|
| | energy, ft-lb: | 2259 | | | | |
| | arc, inches: | | | | | |
| Federal 90 Sierra Varminter | velocity, fps: | 3440 | 3040 | 2680 | 2340 | 2030 |
| | energy, ft-lb: | 2365 | 1850 | 1435 | 1100 | 825 |
| | arc, inches: | | +1.1 | 0 | -6.0 | -18.3 |
| Federal 100 Barnes XLC | velocity, fps: | 3210 | 2970 | 2750 | 2540 | 2330 |
| | energy, ft-lb: | 2290 | 1965 | 1680 | 1430 | 1205 |
| | arc, inches: | | +1.2 | 0 | -5.8 | -17.0 |
| Federal 100 Nosler Bal. Tip | velocity, fps: | 3210 | 2960 | 2720 | 2490 | 2280 |
| | energy, ft-lb: | 2290 | 1940 | 1640 | 1380 | 1150. |
| | arc, inches: | | +1.2 | 0 | -6.0 | -17.5 |
| Federal 115 Nosler Partition | velocity, fps: | 2990 | 2750 | 2520 | 2300 | 2100 |
| | energy, ft-lb: | 2285 | 1930 | 1620 | 1350 | 1120 |
| | arc, inches: | | +1.6 | 0 | -7.0 | -20.8 |
| Federal 115 Trophy Bonded | velocity, fps: | 2990 | 2740 | 2500 | 2270 | 2050 |
| | energy, ft-lb: | 2285 | 1910 | 1590 | 1310 | 1075 |
| | arc, inches: | | +1.6 | 0 | -7.2 | -21.1 |
| Federal 117 Sierra Pro Hunt. | velocity, fps: | 2990 | 2730 | 2480 | 2250 | 2030 |
| | energy, ft-lb: | 2320 | 1985 | 1645 | 1350 | 1100 |
| | arc, inches: | | +1.6 | 0 | -7.2 | -21.4 |
| Federal 117 Sierra GameKing BTSP | velocity, fps: | 2990 | 2770 | 2570 | 2370 | 2190 |
| | energy, ft-lb: | 2320 | 2000 | 1715 | 1465 | 1240 |
| | arc, inches: | | +1.5 | 0 | -6.8 | -19.9 |
| Hornady 117 SP boat-tail | velocity, fps: | 2990 | 2749 | 2520 | 2302 | 2096 |
| | energy, ft-lb: | 2322 | 1962 | 1649 | 1377 | 1141 |
| | arc, inches: | | +1.6 | 0 | -7.0 | -20.7 |
| Hornady 117 SP boat-tail LM | velocity, fps: | 3110 | 2855 | 2613 | 2384 | 2168 |
| | energy, ft-lb: | 2512 | 2117 | 1774 | 1476 | 1220 |
| | arc, inches: | | +1.8 | 0 | -7.1 | -20.3 |
| PMC 100 SPBT | velocity, fps: | 3200 | 2925 | 2650 | 2395 | 2145 |
| | energy, ft-lb: | 2273 | 1895 | 1561 | 1268 | 1019 |
| | arc, inches: | | +1.3 | 0 | -6.3 | -18.6 |
| PMC 117 PSP | velocity, fps: | 2950 | 2706 | 2472 | 2253 | 2047 |
| | energy, ft-lb: | 2261 | 1900 | 1588 | 1319 | 1088 |
| | arc, inches: | | +1.6 | 0 | -7.3 | -21.5 |
| Rem. 100 PSP Core-Lokt | velocity, fps: | 3230 | 2893 | 2580 | 2287 | 2014 |
| | energy, ft-lb: | 2316 | 1858 | 1478 | 1161 | 901 |
| | arc, inches: | | +1.3 | 0 | -6.6 | -19.8 |
| Rem. 115 Core-Lokt Ultra | velocity, fps: | 3000 | 2751 | 2516 | 2293 | 2081 |
| | energy, ft-lb: | 2298 | 1933 | 1616 | 1342 | 1106 |
| | arc, inches: | | +1.6 | 0 | -7.1 | -20.7 |
| Rem. 120 PSP Core-Lokt | velocity, fps: | 2990 | 2730 | 2484 | 2252 | 2032 |
| | energy, ft-lb: | 2382 | 1985 | 1644 | 1351 | 1100 |
| | arc, inches: | | +1.6 | 0 | -7.2 | -21.4 |
| Speer 120 Grand Slam | velocity, fps: | 3130 | 2835 | 2558 | 2298 | |
| | energy, ft-lb: | 2610 | 2141 | 1743 | 1407 | |
| | arc, inches: | | +1.4 | 0 | -6.8 | -20.1 |
| Win. 85 Ballistic Silvertip | velocity, fps | 3470 | 3156 | 2863 | 2589 | 2331 |
| | energy, ft-lb: | 2273 | 1880 | 1548 | 1266 | 1026 |
| | arc, inches: | | +1.0 | 0 | -5.2 | -15.7 |
| Win. 90 Pos. Exp. Point | velocity, fps: | 3440 | 3043 | 2680 | 2344 | 2034 |
| | energy, ft-lb: | 2364 | 1850 | 1435 | 1098 | 827 |
| | arc, inches: | | +2.4 | +2.0 | -3.4 | -15.0 |
| Win. 110 AccuBond CT | velocity, fps: | 3100 | 2870 | 2651 | 2442 | 2243 |
| | energy, ft-lb: | 2347 | 2011 | 1716 | 1456 | 1228 |
| | arc, inches: | | +1.4 | 0 | -6.3 | -18.5 |
| Win. 115 Ballistic Silvertip | velocity, fps: | 3060 | 2825 | 2603 | 2390 | 2188 |
| | energy, ft-lb: | 2391 | 2038 | 1729 | 1459 | 1223 |
| | arc, inches: | | +1.4 | 0 | -6.6 | -19.2 |
| Win. 120 Pos. Pt. Exp. | velocity, fps: | 2990 | 2717 | 2459 | 2216 | 1987 |
| | energy, ft-lb: | 2382 | 1967 | 1612 | 1309 | 1053 |
| | arc, inches: | | +1.6 | 0 | -7.4 | -21.8 |

### .25 WINCHESTER SUPER SHORT MAGNUM

| CARTRIDGE BULLET | RANGE, YARDS: | 0 | 100 | 200 | 300 | 400 |
|---|---|---|---|---|---|---|
| Win. 85 Ballistic Silvertip | velocity, fps: | 3470 | 3156 | 2863 | 2589 | 2331 |
| | energy, ft-lb: | 2273 | 1880 | 1548 | 1266 | 1026 |
| | arc, inches: | | +1.0 | 0 | -5.2 | -15.7 |
| Win. 110 AccuBond CT | velocity, fps: | 3100 | 2870 | 2651 | 2442 | 2243. |
| | energy, ft-lb: | 2347 | 2011 | 1716 | 1456 | 1228 |
| | arc, inches: | | +1.4 | 0 | -6.3 | -18.5 |
| Win. 115 Ballistic Silvertip | velocity, fps: | 3060 | 2844 | 2639 | 2442 | 2254 |
| | energy, ft-lb: | 2392 | 2066 | 1778 | 1523 | 1298 |
| | arc, inches: | | +1.4 | 0 | -6.4 | -18.6 |
| Win. 120 Pos. Pt. Exp. | velocity, fps: | 2990 | 2717 | 2459 | 2216 | 1987 |
| | energy, ft-lb: | 2383 | 1967 | 1612 | 1309 | 1053 |
| | arc, inches: | | +1.6 | 0 | -7.4 | -21.8 |

### .257 WEATHERBY MAGNUM

| CARTRIDGE BULLET | RANGE, YARDS: | 0 | 100 | 200 | 300 | 400 |
|---|---|---|---|---|---|---|
| Federal 115 Nosler Partition | velocity, fps: | 3150 | 2900 | 2660 | 2440 | 2220. |
| | energy, ft-lb: | 2535 | 2145 | 1810 | 1515 | 1260 |
| | arc, inches: | | +1.3 | 0 | -6.2 | -18.4 |
| Federal 115 Trophy Bonded | velocity, fps: | 3150 | 2890 | 2640 | 2400 | 2180 |
| | energy, ft-lb: | 2535 | 2125 | 1775 | 1470 | 1210 |
| | arc, inches: | | +1.4 | 0 | -6.3 | -18.8 |
| Wby. 87 Pointed Expanding | velocity, fps: | 3825 | 3472 | 3147 | 2845 | 2563 |
| | energy, ft-lb: | 2826 | 2328 | 1913 | 1563 | 1269 |
| | arc, inches: | | +2.1 | +2.8 | 0 | -7.1 |
| Wby. 100 Pointed Expanding | velocity, fps: | 3602 | 3298 | 3016 | 2750 | 2500 |
| | energy, ft-lb: | 2881 | 2416 | 2019 | 1680 | 1388 |
| | arc, inches: | | +2.4 | +3.1 | 0 | -7.7 |
| Wby. 115 Nosler Bal. Tip | velocity, fps: | 3400 | 3170 | 2952 | 2745 | 2547 |
| | energy, ft-lb: | 2952 | 2566 | 2226 | 1924 | 1656. |
| | arc, inches: | | +3.0 | +3.5 | 0 | -7.9 |
| Wby. 115 Barnes X | velocity, fps: | 3400 | 3158 | 2929 | 2711 | 2504 |
| | energy, ft-lb: | 2952 | 2546 | 2190 | 1877 | 1601 |
| | arc, inches: | | +2.7 | +3.4 | 0 | -8.1 |
| Wby. 117 RN Expanding | velocity, fps: | 3402 | 2984 | 2595 | 2240 | 1921 |
| | energy, ft-lb: | 3007 | 2320 | 1742 | 1302 | 956 |
| | arc, inches: | | +3.4 | +4.31 | 0 | -11.1 |
| Wby. 120 Nosler Partition | velocity, fps: | 3305 | 3046 | 2801 | 2570 | 2350 |
| | energy, ft-lb: | 2910 | 2472 | 2091 | 1760 | 1471 |
| | arc, inches: | | +3.0 | +3.7 | 0 | -8.9 |

### 6.53 (.257) SCRAMJET

| CARTRIDGE BULLET | RANGE, YARDS: | 0 | 100 | 200 | 300 | 400 |
|---|---|---|---|---|---|---|
| Lazzeroni 85 Nosler Bal. Tip | velocity, fps: | 3960 | 3652 | 3365 | 3096 | 2844 |
| | energy, ft-lb: | 2961 | 2517 | 2137 | 1810 | 1526 |
| | arc, inches: | | +1.7 | +2.4 | 0 | -6.0 |
| Lazzeroni 100 Nosler Part. | velocity, fps: | 3740 | 3465 | 3208 | 2965 | 2735 |
| | energy, ft-lb: | 3106 | 2667 | 2285 | 1953 | 1661. |
| | arc, inches: | | +2.1 | +2.7 | 0 | -6.7 |

### 6.5x50 JAPANESE

| CARTRIDGE BULLET | RANGE, YARDS: | 0 | 100 | 200 | 300 | 400 |
|---|---|---|---|---|---|---|
| Norma 156 Alaska | velocity, fps: | 2067 | 1832 | 1615 | 1423 | |
| | energy, ft-lb: | 1480 | 1162 | 904 | 701 | |
| | arc, inches: | | +4.4 | 0 | -17.8 | |

### 6.5x52 CARCANO

| CARTRIDGE BULLET | RANGE, YARDS: | 0 | 100 | 200 | 300 | 400 |
|---|---|---|---|---|---|---|
| Norma 156 Alaska | velocity, fps: | 2428 | 2169 | 1926 | 1702 | |
| | energy, ft-lb: | 2043 | 1630 | 1286 | 1004 | |
| | arc, inches: | | +2.9 | 0 | -12.3 | |

### 6.5x55 SWEDISH

| CARTRIDGE BULLET | RANGE, YARDS: | 0 | 100 | 200 | 300 | 400 |
|---|---|---|---|---|---|---|
| Federal 140 Hi-Shok | velocity, fps: | 2600 | 2400 | 2220 | 2040 | 1860 |
| | energy, ft-lb: | 2100 | 1795 | 1525 | 1285 | 1080 |

| CARTRIDGE BULLET | RANGE, YARDS: | 0 | 100 | 200 | 300 | 400 |
|---|---|---|---|---|---|---|
| Federal 140 Trophy Bonded | arc, inches: | | +2.3 | 0 | -9.4 | -27.2 |
| | velocity, fps: | 2550 | 2350 | 2160 | 1980 | 1810 |
| | energy, ft-lb: | 2020 | 1720 | 1450 | 1220 | 1015 |
| Federal 140 Sierra MatchKg. BTHP | arc, inches: | | +2.4 | 0 | -9.8 | -28.4 |
| | velocity, fps: | 2630 | 2460 | 2300 | 2140 | 2000 |
| | energy, ft-lb: | 2140 | 1880 | 1640 | 1430 | 1235 |
| Hornady 129 SP LM | arc, inches: | | +16.4 | +28.8 | +33.9 | +31.8 |
| | velocity, fps: | 2770 | 2561 | 2361 | 2171 | 1994 |
| | energy, ft-lb: | 2197 | 1878 | 1597 | 1350 | 1138 |
| Hornady 140 SP Interlock | arc, inches: | | +2.0 | 0 | -8.2 | -23.2 |
| | velocity, fps: | 2525 | 2341 | 2165 | 1996 | 1836 |
| | energy, ft-lb: | 1982 | 1704 | 1457 | 1239 | 1048 |
| Hornady140 SP LM | arc, inches: | | +2.4 | 0 | -9.9 | -28.5 |
| | velocity, fps: | 2740 | 2541 | 2351 | 2169 | 1999 |
| | energy, ft-lb: | 2333 | 2006 | 1717 | 1463 | 1242 |
| Norma 120 Nosler Bal. Tip | arc, inches: | | +2.4 | 0 | -8.7 | -24.0 |
| | velocity, fps: | 2822 | 2609 | 2407 | 2213 | |
| | energy, ft-lb: | 2123 | 1815 | 1544 | 1305 | |
| Norma 139 Vulkan | arc, inches: | | +1.8 | 0 | -7.8 | |
| | velocity, fps: | 2854 | 2569 | 2302 | 2051 | |
| | energy, ft-lb: | 2515 | 2038 | 1636 | 1298 | |
| Norma 140 Nosler Partition | arc, inches: | | +1.8 | 0 | -8.4 | |
| | velocity, fps: | 2789 | 2592 | 2403 | 2223 | |
| | energy, ft-lb: | 2419 | 2089 | 1796 | 1536 | |
| Norma 156 TXP Swift A-Fr. | arc, inches: | | +1.8 | 0 | -7.8 | |
| | velocity, fps: | 2526 | 2276 | 2040 | 1818 | |
| | energy, ft-lb: | 2196 | 1782 | 1432 | 1138 | |
| Norma 156 Alaska | arc, inches: | | +2.6 | 0 | -10.9 | |
| | velocity, fps: | 2559 | 2245 | 1953 | 1687 | |
| | energy, ft-lb: | 2269 | 1746 | 1322 | 986 | |
| Norma 156 Vulkan | arc, inches: | | +2.7 | 0 | -11.9 | |
| | velocity, fps: | 2644 | 2395 | 2159 | 1937 | |
| | energy, ft-lb: | 2422 | 1987 | 1616 | 1301 | |
| Norma 156 Oryx | arc, inches: | | +2.2 | 0 | -9.7 | |
| | velocity, fps: | 2559 | 2308 | 2070 | 1848 | |
| | energy, ft-lb: | 2269 | 1845 | 1485 | 1183 | |
| PMC 139 Pointed Soft Point | arc, inches: | | +2.5 | 0 | -10.6 | |
| | velocity, fps: | 2850 | 2560 | 2290 | 2030 | 1790 |
| | energy, ft-lb: | 2515 | 2025 | 1615 | 1270 | 985 |
| PMC 140 HP boat-tail | arc, inches: | | +2.2 | 0 | -8.9 | -26.3 |
| | velocity, fps: | 2560 | 2398 | 2243 | 2093 | 1949 |
| | energy, ft-lb: | 2037 | 1788 | 1563 | 1361 | 1181 |
| PMC 140 SP boat-tail | arc, inches: | | +2.3 | 0 | -9.2 | -26.4 |
| | velocity, fps: | 2560 | 2386 | 2218 | 2057 | 1903 |
| | energy, ft-lb: | 2037 | 1769 | 1529 | 1315 | 1126 |
| PMC 144 FMJ | arc, inches: | | +2.3 | 0 | -9.4 | -27.1 |
| | velocity, fps: | 2650 | 2370 | 2110 | 1870 | 1650 |
| | energy, ft-lb: | 2425 | 1950 | 1550 | 1215 | 945 |
| Rem. 140 PSP Core-Lokt | arc, inches: | | +2.7 | 0 | -10.5 | -30.9 |
| | velocity, fps: | 2550 | 2353 | 2164 | 1984 | 1814 |
| | energy, ft-lb: | 2021 | 1720 | 1456 | 1224 | 1023 |
| Speer 140 Grand Slam | arc, inches: | | +2.4 | 0 | -9.8 | -27.0 |
| | velocity, fps: | 2550 | 2318 | 2099 | 1892 | |
| | energy, ft-lb: | 2021 | 1670 | 1369 | 1112 | |
| Win. 140 Soft Point | arc, inches: | | +2.5 | 0 | -10.4 | -30.6 |
| | velocity, fps: | 2550 | 2359 | 2176 | 2002 | 1836 |
| | energy, ft-lb: | 2022 | 1731 | 1473 | 1246 | 1048. |
| | arc, inches: | | +2.4 | 0 | -9.7 | -28.1 |

## 6.5 GRENDEL

| CARTRIDGE BULLET | RANGE, YARDS: | 0 | 100 | 200 | 300 | 400 |
|---|---|---|---|---|---|---|
| Hornady 123 A-MAX | velocity, fps: | 2590 | 2420 | 2256 | 2099 | 1948 |
| | energy, ft-lb: | 1832 | 1599 | 1390 | 1203 | 1037 |
| | arc, inches: | -2.4 | +1.8 | 0 | -8.6 | -25.1 |

| CARTRIDGE BULLET | RANGE, YARDS: | 0 | 100 | 200 | 300 | 400 |
|---|---|---|---|---|---|---|
| Hornady 123 SST | velocity, fps: | 2620 | 2449 | 2284 | 2126 | 1974 |
| | energy, ft-lb: | 1875 | 1638 | 1425 | 1234 | 1064 |
| | arc, inches: | -2.4 | +1.7 | 0 | -8.4 | -24.5 |

## 6.5 CREEDMOOR

| CARTRIDGE BULLET | RANGE, YARDS: | 0 | 100 | 200 | 300 | 400 |
|---|---|---|---|---|---|---|
| Hornady 120 GMX | velocity, fps: | 3050 | 2850 | 2659 | 2476 | 2300 |
| | energy, ft-lb: | 2479 | 2164 | 1884 | 1634 | 1410 |
| | arc, inches: | -1.5 | +1.4 | 0 | -6.3 | -18.3 |
| Hornady 129 SST | velocity, fps: | 2950 | 2756 | 2571 | 2394 | 2223 |
| | energy, ft-lb: | 2493 | 2176 | 1894 | 1641 | 1415 |
| | arc, inches: | -1.5 | +1.5 | 0 | -6.8 | -19.7 |
| Hornady 140 A-MAX | velocity, fps: | 2710 | 2557 | 2410 | 2267 | 2129 |
| | energy, ft-lb: | 2283 | 2033 | 1805 | 1598 | 1410 |
| | arc, inches: | -1.5 | +1.9 | 0 | -7.9 | -22.6 |
| Nosler 140 BT | velocity, fps: | 2550 | 2380 | 2217 | 2060 | 1910 |
| | energy, ft-lb: | 2021 | 1761 | 1527 | 1319 | 1134 |
| | arc, inches: | -1.5 | +2.3 | 0 | -9.4 | -27.0 |

## .260 REMINGTON

| CARTRIDGE BULLET | RANGE, YARDS: | 0 | 100 | 200 | 300 | 400 |
|---|---|---|---|---|---|---|
| Federal 140 Sierra GameKing BTSP | velocity, fps: | 2750 | 2570 | 2390 | 2220 | 2060 |
| | energy, ft-lb: | 2350 | 2045 | 1775 | 1535 | 1315 |
| | arc, inches: | | +1.9 | 0 | -8.0 | -23.1 |
| Federal 140 Trophy Bonded | velocity, fps: | 2750 | 2540 | 2340 | 2150 | 1970 |
| | energy, ft-lb: | 2350 | 2010 | 1705 | 1440 | 1210 |
| | arc, inches: | | +1.9 | 0 | -8.4 | -24.1 |
| Rem. 120 Nosler Bal. Tip | velocity, fps: | 2890 | 2688 | 2494 | 2309 | 2131 |
| | energy, ft-lb: | 2226 | 1924 | 1657 | 1420 | 1210 |
| | arc, inches: | | +1.7 | 0 | -7.3 | -21.1 |
| Rem. 120 AccuTip | velocity, fps: | 2890 | 2697 | 2512 | 2334 | 2163 |
| | energy, ft-lb: | 2392 | 2083 | 1807 | 1560 | 1340 |
| | arc, inches: | | +1.6 | 0 | -7.2 | -20.7 |
| Rem. 125 Nosler Partition | velocity, fps: | 2875 | 2669 | 2473 | 2285 | 2105. |
| | energy, ft-lb: | 2294 | 1977 | 1697 | 1449 | 1230 |
| | arc, inches: | +1.71 | 0 | -7.4 | -21.4 | |
| Rem. 140 PSP Core-Lokt (and C-L Ultra) | velocity, fps: | 2750 | 2544 | 2347 | 2158 | 1979 |
| | energy, ft-lb: | 2351 | 2011 | 1712 | 1448 | 1217 |
| | arc, inches: | | +1.9 | 0 | -8.3 | -24.0 |
| Speer 140 Grand Slam | velocity, fps: | 2750 | 2518 | 2297 | 2087 | |
| | energy, ft-lb: | 2351 | 1970 | 1640 | 1354 | |
| | arc, inches: | | +2.3 | 0 | -8.9 | -25.8 |

## 6.5/284

| CARTRIDGE BULLET | RANGE, YARDS: | 0 | 100 | 200 | 300 | 400 |
|---|---|---|---|---|---|---|
| Norma 120 Nosler Bal. Tip | velocity, fps: | 3117 | 2890 | 2674 | 2469 | |
| | energy, ft-lb: | 2589 | 2226 | 1906 | 1624 | |
| | arc, inches: | | +1.3 | 0 | -6.2 | |
| Norma 140 Nosler Part. | velocity, fps: | 2953 | 2750 | 2557 | 2371 | |
| | energy, ft-lb: | 2712 | 2352 | 2032 | 1748 | |
| | arc, inches: | | +1.5 | 0 | -6.8 | |

## 6.5/284 NORMA

| CARTRIDGE BULLET | RANGE, YARDS: | 0 | 100 | 200 | 300 | 400 |
|---|---|---|---|---|---|---|
| Nosler 120 Ballistic Tip | velocity, fps: | 3000 | 2792 | 2594 | 2404 | 2223 |
| | energy, ft-lb: | 2398 | 2077 | 1793 | 1540 | 1316 |
| | arc, inches: | -1.5 | +1.4 | 0 | -6.6 | -17.1 |
| Nosler 125 PT | velocity, fps: | 3000 | 2788 | 2585 | 2392 | 2207 |
| | energy, ft-lb: | 2497 | 2157 | 1855 | 1588 | 1352 |
| | arc, inches: | -1.5 | +1.5 | 0 | -6.7 | -19.5 |
| Nosler 130 AccuBond | velocity, fps: | 2900 | 2709 | 2526 | 2351 | 2182 |
| | energy, ft-lb: | 2427 | 2118 | 1842 | 1595 | 1374 |
| | arc, inches: | -1.5 | +1.5 | 0 | -6.9 | -18.4 |

## 6.5 REMINGTON MAGNUM

| CARTRIDGE BULLET | RANGE, YARDS: | 0 | 100 | 200 | 300 | 400 |
|---|---|---|---|---|---|---|
| Nosler 125 PT | velocity, fps: | 3025 | 2811 | 2608 | 2414 | 2228 |
| | energy, ft-lb: | 2539 | 2194 | 1888 | 1617 | 1377 |
| | arc, inches: | -1.5 | +1.5 | 0 | -6.6 | -19.1 |

# Centerfire Rifle Ballistics

## 6.5 REMINGTON MAGNUM TO .270 WINCHESTER

| CARTRIDGE BULLET | RANGE, YARDS: | 0 | 100 | 200 | 300 | 400 |
|---|---|---|---|---|---|---|
| Rem. 120 Core-Lokt PSP | velocity, fps: | 3210 | 2905 | 2621 | 2353 | 2102 |
| | energy, ft-lb: | 2745 | 2248 | 1830 | 1475 | 1177 |
| | arc, inches: | | +2.7 | +2.1 | -3.5 | -15.5 |

### .264 WINCHESTER MAGNUM

| CARTRIDGE BULLET | RANGE, YARDS: | 0 | 100 | 200 | 300 | 400 |
|---|---|---|---|---|---|---|
| Nosler 100 Ballistic Tip | velocity, fps: | 3400 | 3105 | 2829 | 2569 | 2324 |
| | energy, ft-lb: | 2567 | 2141 | 1777 | 1465 | 1199 |
| | arc, inches: | -1.5 | +1.0 | 0 | -5.5 | -16.1 |
| Nosler 130 AccuBond | velocity, fps: | 3100 | 2900 | 2709 | 2527 | 2351 |
| | energy, ft-lb: | 2774 | 2428 | 2119 | 1843 | 1595 |
| | arc, inches: | -1.5 | +1.2 | 0 | -6.0 | -17.5 |
| Rem. 140 PSP Core-Lokt | velocity, fps: | 3030 | 2782 | 2548 | 2326 | 2114 |
| | energy, ft-lb: | 2854 | 2406 | 2018 | 1682 | 1389 |
| | arc, inches: | | +1.5 | 0 | -6.9 | -20.2 |
| Win. 140 Power-Point | velocity, fps: | 3030 | 2782 | 2548 | 2326 | 2114. |
| | energy, ft-lb: | 2854 | 2406 | 2018 | 1682 | 1389 |
| | arc, inches: | | +1.8 | 0 | -7.2 | -20.8 |

### 6.8MM REMINGTON SPC

| CARTRIDGE BULLET | RANGE, YARDS: | 0 | 100 | 200 | 300 | 400 |
|---|---|---|---|---|---|---|
| Hornady 110 BTHP | velocity, fps: | 2570 | 2332 | 2107 | 1895 | 1697 |
| | energy, ft-lb: | 1613 | 1328 | 1084 | 877 | 703 |
| | arc, inches: | -2.4 | +2.0 | 0 | -9.9 | -29.5 |
| Hornady 120 SST | velocity, fps: | 2460 | 2250 | 2051 | 1863 | 1687 |
| | energy, ft-lb: | 1612 | 1349 | 1121 | 925 | 758 |
| | arc, inches: | -2.4 | +2.3 | 0 | -10.5 | -31.1 |
| Rem. 115 Open Tip Match | velocity, fps: | 2800 | 2535 | 2285 | 2049 | 1828 |
| (and HPBT Match) | energy, ft-lb: | 2002 | 1641 | 1333 | 1072 | 853 |
| | arc, inches: | | +2.0 | 0 | -8.8 | -26.2 |
| Rem. 115 Metal Case | velocity, fps: | 2800 | 2523 | 2262 | 2017 | 1789 |
| | energy, ft-lb: | 2002 | 1625 | 1307 | 1039 | 817 |
| | arc, inches: | | +2.0 | 0 | -8.8 | -26.2 |
| Rem. 115 Sierra HPBT | velocity, fps: | 2775 | 2511 | 2263 | 2028 | 1809 |
| (2005; all vel. @ 2775) | energy, ft-lb: | 1966 | 1610 | 1307 | 1050 | 835 |
| | arc, inches: | | +2.0 | 0 | -8.8 | -26.2. |
| Rem. 115 CL Ultra | velocity, fps: | 2775 | 2472 | 2190 | 1926 | 1683 |
| | energy, ft-lb: | 1966 | 1561 | 1224 | 947 | 723 |
| | arc, inches: | | +2.1 | 0 | -9.4 | -28.2 |

### .270 WINCHESTER

| CARTRIDGE BULLET | RANGE, YARDS: | 0 | 100 | 200 | 300 | 400 |
|---|---|---|---|---|---|---|
| Black Hills 130 Nos. Bal. T. | velocity, fps: | 2950 | | | | |
| | energy, ft-lb: | 2512 | | | | |
| | arc, inches: | | | | | |
| Black Hills 130 Barnes XLC | velocity, ft-lb: | 2950 | | | | |
| | energy, ft-lb: | 2512 | | | | |
| | arc, inches: | | | | | |
| Federal 130 Hi-Shok | velocity, fps: | 3060 | 2800 | 2560 | 2330 | 2110 |
| | energy, ft-lb: | 2700 | 2265 | 1890 | 1565 | 1285 |
| | arc, inches: | | +1.5 | 0 | -6.8 | -20.0 |
| Federal 130 Sierra Pro-Hunt. | velocity, fps: | 3060 | 2830 | 2600 | 2390 | 2190 |
| | energy, ft-lb: | 2705 | 2305 | 1960 | 1655 | 1390 |
| | arc, inches: | | +1.4 | 0 | -6.4 | -19.0 |
| Federal 130 Sierra GameKing | velocity, fps: | 3060 | 2830 | 2620 | 2410 | 2220. |
| | energy, ft-lb: | 2700 | 2320 | 1980 | 1680 | 1420 |
| | arc, inches: | | +1.4 | 0 | -6.5 | -19.0 |
| Federal 130 Nosler Bal. Tip | velocity, fps: | 3060 | 2840 | 2630 | 2430 | 2230 |
| | energy, ft-lb: | 2700 | 2325 | 1990 | 1700 | 1440 |
| | arc, inches: | | +1.4 | 0 | -6.5 | -18.8 |
| Federal 130 Nos. Partition | velocity, fps: | 3060 | 2830 | 2610 | .2400 | 2200 |
| And Solid Base | energy, ft-lb: | 2705 | 2310 | 1965 | 1665 | 1400 |
| | arc, inches: | | +1.4 | 0 | -6.5 | -19.1. |
| Federal 130 Barnes XLC | velocity, fps: | 3060 | 2840 | 2620 | 2420 | 2220 |
| And Triple Shock | energy, ft-lb: | 2705 | 2320 | 1985 | 1690 | 1425 |
| | arc, inches: | | +1.4 | 0 | -6.4 | -18.9 |

| CARTRIDGE BULLET | RANGE, YARDS: | 0 | 100 | 200 | 300 | 400 |
|---|---|---|---|---|---|---|
| Federal 130 Trophy Bonded | velocity, fps: | 3060 | 2810 | 2570 | 2340 | 2130 |
| | energy, ft-lb: | 2705 | 2275 | 1905 | 1585 | 1310 |
| | arc, inches: | | +1.5 | 0 | -6.7 | -19.8 |
| Federal 140 Trophy Bonded | velocity, fps: | 2940 | 2700 | 2480 | 2260 | 2060 |
| | energy, ft-lb: | 2685 | 2270 | 1905 | 1590 | 1315 |
| | arc, inches: | | +1.6 | 0 | -7.3 | -21.5 |
| Federal 140 Tr. Bonded HE | velocity, fps: | 3100 | 2860 | 2620 | 2400 | 2200. |
| | energy, ft-lb: | 2990 | 2535 | 2140 | 1795 | 1500 |
| | arc, inches: | | +1.4 | 0 | -6.4 | -18.9 |
| Federal 140 Nos. AccuBond | velocity, fps: | 2950 | 2760 | 2580 | 2400 | 2230 |
| | energy, ft-lb: | 2705 | 2365 | 2060 | 1790 | 1545 |
| | arc, inches: | | +1.5 | 0 | -6.7 | -19.6 |
| Federal 150 Hi-Shok RN | velocity, fps: | 2850 | 2500 | 2180 | 1890 | 1620 |
| | energy, ft-lb: | 2705 | 2085 | 1585 | 1185 | 870 |
| | arc, inches: | | +2.0 | 0 | -9.4 | -28.6 |
| Federal 150 Sierra GameKing | velocity, fps: | 2850 | 2660 | 2480 | 2300 | 2130 |
| | energy, ft-lb: | 2705 | 2355 | 2040 | 1760 | 1510 |
| | arc, inches: | | +1.7 | 0 | -7.4 | -21.4 |
| Federal 150 Sierra GameKing HE | velocity, fps: | 3000 | 2800 | 2620 | 2430 | 2260 |
| | energy, ft-lb: | 2995 | 2615 | 2275 | 1975 | 1700 |
| | arc, inches: | | +1.5 | 0 | -6.5 | -18.9 |
| Federal 150 Nosler Partition | velocity, fps: | 2850 | 2590 | 2340 | 2100 | 1880. |
| | energy, ft-lb: | 2705 | 2225 | 1815 | 1470 | 1175 |
| | arc, inches: | | +1.9 | 0 | -8.3 | -24.4 |
| Hornady 130 SST (or Interbond) | velocity, fps: | 3060 | 2845 | 2639 | 2442 | 2254 |
| | energy, ft-lb: | 2700 | 2335 | 2009 | 1721 | 1467 |
| | arc, inches: | | +1.4 | 0 | -6.6 | -19.1 |
| Hornady 130 SST LM (or Interbond) | velocity, fps: | 3215 | 2998 | 2790 | 2590 | 2400 |
| | energy, ft-lb: | 2983 | 2594 | 2246 | 1936 | 1662 |
| | arc, inches: | | +1.2 | 0 | -5.8 | -17.0 |
| Hornady 140 SP boat-tail | velocity, fps: | 2940 | 2747 | 2562 | 2385 | 2214 |
| | energy, ft-lb: | 2688 | 2346 | 2041 | 1769 | 1524 |
| | arc, inches: | | +1.6 | 0 | -7.0 | -20.2 |
| Hornady 140 SP boat-tail LM | velocity, fps: | 3100 | 2894 | 2697 | 2508 | 2327. |
| | energy, ft-lb: | 2987 | 2604 | 2261 | 1955 | 1684 |
| | arc, inches: | | +1.4 | 0 | 6.3 | -18.3 |
| Hornady 150 SP | velocity, fps: | 2800 | 2684 | 2478 | 2284 | 2100 |
| | energy, ft-lb: | 2802 | 2400 | 2046 | 1737 | 1469 |
| | arc, inches: | | +1.7 | 0 | -7.4 | -21.6 |
| Norma 130 SP | velocity, fps: | 3140 | 2862 | 2601 | 2354 | |
| | energy, ft-lb: | 2847 | 2365 | 1953 | 1600 | |
| | arc, inches: | | +1.3 | 0 | -6.5 | |
| Norma 130 FMJ | velocity, fps: | 2887 | 2634 | 2395 | 2169 | |
| | energy, ft-lb: | | | | | |
| | arc, inches: | | +1.8 | 0 | -7.8 | |
| Norma 150 SP | velocity, fps: | 2799 | 2555 | 2323 | 2104 | |
| | energy, ft-lb: | 2610 | 2175 | 1798 | 1475 | |
| | arc, inches: | | +1.9 | 0 | -8.3 | |
| Norma 150 Oryx | velocity, fps: | 2854 | 2608 | 2376 | 2155 | |
| | energy, ft-lb: | 2714 | 2267 | 1880 | 1547 | |
| | arc, inches: | | +1.8 | 0 | -8.0 | |
| PMC 130 Barnes X | velocity, fps: | 2910 | 2717 | 2533 | 2356 | 2186 |
| | energy, ft-lb: | 2444 | 2131 | 1852 | 1602 | 1379 |
| | arc, inches: | | +1.6 | 0 | -7.1 | -20.4 |
| PMC 130 SP boat-tail | velocity, fps: | 3050 | 2830 | 2620 | 2421 | 2229 |
| | energy, ft-lb: | 2685 | 2312 | 1982 | 1691 | 1435 |
| | arc, inches: | | +1.5 | 0 | -6.5 | -19.0 |
| PMC 130 Pointed Soft Point | velocity, fps: | 2950 | 2691 | 2447 | 2217 | 2001 |
| | energy, ft-lb: | 2512 | 2090 | 1728 | 1419 | 1156 |
| | arc, inches: | | +1.6 | 0 | -7.5 | -22.1 |
| PMC 150 Barnes X | velocity, fps: | 2700 | 2541 | 2387 | 2238 | 2095 |
| | energy, ft-lb: | 2428 | 2150 | 1897 | 1668 | 1461 |
| | arc, inches: | | +2.0 | 0 | -8.1 | -23.1 |

BALLISTICS

## .270 WINCHESTER TO .270 WINCHESTER SHORT MAGNUM

| CARTRIDGE BULLET | RANGE, YARDS: | 0 | 100 | 200 | 300 | 400 |
|---|---|---|---|---|---|---|
| PMC 150 SP boat-tail | velocity, fps: | 2850 | 2660 | 2477 | 2302 | 2134 |
| | energy, ft-lb: | 2705 | 2355 | 2043 | 1765 | 1516. |
| | arc, inches: | | +1.7 | 0 | -7.4 | -21.4 |
| PMC 150 Pointed Soft Point | velocity, fps: | 2750 | 2530 | 2321 | 2123 | 1936 |
| | energy, ft-lb: | 2519 | 2131 | 1794 | 1501 | 1248 |
| | arc, inches: | | +2.0 | 0 | -8.4 | -24.6 |
| Rem. 100 Pointed Soft Point | velocity, fps: | 3320 | 2924 | 2561 | 2225 | 1916 |
| | energy, ft-lb: | 2448 | 1898 | 1456 | 1099 | 815 |
| | arc, inches: | | +2.3 | +2.0 | -3.6 | -16.2 |
| Rem. 115 PSP Core-Lokt mr | velocity, fps: | 2710 | 2412 | 2133 | 1873 | 1636 |
| | energy, ft-lb: | 1875 | 1485 | 1161 | 896 | 683 |
| | arc, inches: | | +1.0 | -2.7 | -14.2 | -35.6 |
| Rem. 130 PSP Core-Lokt | velocity, fps: | 3060 | 2776 | 2510 | 2259 | 2022 |
| | energy, ft-lb: | 2702 | 2225 | 1818 | 1472 | 1180 |
| | arc, inches: | | +1.5 | 0 | -7.0 | -20.9 |
| Rem. 130 Bronze Point | velocity, fps: | 3060 | 2802 | 2559 | 2329 | 2110 |
| | energy, ft-lb: | 2702 | 2267 | 1890 | 1565 | 1285 |
| | arc, inches: | | +1.5 | 0 | -6.8 | -20.0 |
| Rem. 130 Swift Scirocco | velocity, fps: | 3060 | 2838 | 2677 | 2425 | 2232 |
| | energy, ft-lb: | 2702 | 2325 | 1991 | 1697 | 1438 |
| | arc, inches: | | +1.4 | 0 | -6.5 | -18.8 |
| Rem. 130 AccuTip BT | velocity, fps: | 3060 | 2845 | 2639 | 2442 | 2254 |
| | energy, ft-lb: | 2702 | 2336 | 2009 | 1721 | 1467 |
| | arc, inches: | | +1.4 | 0 | -6.4 | -18.6 |
| Rem. 140 Swift A-Frame | velocity, fps: | 2925 | 2652 | 2394 | 2152 | 1923 |
| | energy, ft-lb: | 2659 | 2186 | 1782 | 1439 | 1150 |
| | arc, inches: | | +1.7 | 0 | -7.8 | -23.2 |
| Rem. 140 PSP boat-tail | velocity, fps: | 2960 | 2749 | 2548 | 2355 | 2171 |
| | energy, ft-lb: | 2723 | 2349 | 2018 | 1724 | 1465 |
| | arc, inches: | | +1.6 | 0 | -6.9 | -20.1 |
| Rem. 140 Nosler Bal. Tip | velocity, fps: | 2960 | 2754 | 2557 | 2366 | 2187 |
| | energy, ft-lb: | 2724 | 2358 | 2032 | 1743 | 1487 |
| | arc, inches: | | +1.6 | 0 | -6.9 | -20.0 |
| Rem. 140 PSP C-L Ultra | velocity, fps: | 2925 | 2667 | 2424 | 2193 | 1975 |
| | energy, ft-lb: | 2659 | 2211 | 1826 | 1495 | 1212 |
| | arc, inches: | | +1.7 | 0 | -7.6 | -22.5 |
| Rem. 150 SP Core-Lokt | velocity, fps: | 2850 | 2504 | 2183 | 1886 | 1618 |
| | energy, ft-lb: | 2705 | 2087 | 1587 | 1185 | 872 |
| | arc, inches: | | +2.0 | 0 | -9.4 | -28.6 |
| Rem. 150 Nosler Partition | velocity, fps: | 2850 | 2652 | 2463 | 2282 | 2108 |
| | energy, ft-lb: | 2705 | 2343 | 2021 | 1734 | 1480 |
| | arc, inches: | | +1.7 | 0 | -7.5 | -21.6 |
| Speer 130 Grand Slam | velocity, fps: | 3050 | 2774 | 2514 | 2269 | |
| | energy, ft-lb: | 2685 | 2221 | 1824 | 1485 | |
| | arc, inches: | | +1.5 | 0 | -7.0 | -20.9 |
| Speer 150 Grand Slam | velocity, fps: | 2830 | 2594 | 2369 | 2156 | |
| | energy, ft-lb: | 2667 | 2240 | 1869 | 1548 | |
| | arc, inches: | | +1.8 | 0 | -8.1 | -23.6 |
| Win. 130 Power-Point | velocity, fps: | 3060 | 2802 | 2559 | 2329 | 2110 |
| | energy, ft-lb: | 2702 | 2267 | 1890 | 1565 | 1285. |
| | arc, inches: | | +1.8 | 0 | -7.1 | -20.6 |
| Win. 130 Power-Point Plus | velocity, fps: | 3150 | 2881 | 2628 | 2388 | 2161 |
| | energy, ft-lb: | 2865 | 2396 | 1993 | 1646 | 1348 |
| | arc, inches: | | +1.3 | 0 | -6.4 | -18.9 |
| Win. 130 Silvertip | velocity, fps: | 3060 | 2776 | 2510 | 2259 | 2022. |
| | energy, ft-lb: | 2702 | 2225 | 1818 | 1472 | 1180 |
| | arc, inches: | | +1.8 | 0 | -7.4 | -21.6 |
| Win. 130 Ballistic Silvertip | velocity, fps: | 3050 | 2828 | 2618 | 2416 | 2224 |
| | energy, ft-lb: | 2685 | 2309 | 1978 | 1685 | 1428 |
| | arc, inches: | | +1.4 | 0 | -6.5 | -18.9 |
| Win. 140 AccuBond | velocity, fps: | 2950 | 2751 | 2560 | 2378 | 2203 |
| | energy, ft-lb: | 2705 | 2352 | 2038 | 1757 | 1508 |
| | arc, inches: | | +1.6 | 0 | -6.9 | -19.9 |
| Win. 140 Fail Safe | velocity, fps: | 2920 | 2671 | 2435 | 2211 | 1999 |
| | energy, ft-lb: | 2651 | 2218 | 1843 | 1519 | 1242 |
| | arc, inches: | | +1.7 | 0 | -7.6 | -22.3 |
| Win. 150 Power-Point | velocity, fps: | 2850 | 2585 | 2336 | 2100 | 1879 |
| | energy, ft-lb: | 2705 | 2226 | 1817 | 1468 | 1175 |
| | arc, inches: | | +2.2 | 0 | -8.6 | -25.0 |
| Win. 150 Power-Point Plus | velocity, fps: | 2950 | 2679 | 2425 | 2184 | 1957 |
| | energy, ft-lb: | 2900 | 2391 | 1959 | 1589 | 1276 |
| | arc, inches: | | +1.7 | 0 | -7.6 | -22.6 |
| Win. 150 Partition Gold | velocity, fps: | 2930 | 2693 | 2468 | 2254 | 2051 |
| | energy, ft-lb: | 2860 | 2416 | 2030 | 1693 | 1402 |
| | arc, inches: | | +1.7 | 0 | -7.4 | -21.6 |
| Win. 150 Supreme Elite XP3 | velocity, fps: | 2950 | 2763 | 2583 | 2411 | 2245 |
| | energy, ft-lb: | 2898 | 2542 | 2223 | 1936 | 1679 |
| | arc, inches: | | +1.5 | 0 | -6.9 | -15.5 |

### .270 WINCHESTER SHORT MAGNUM

| CARTRIDGE BULLET | RANGE, YARDS: | 0 | 100 | 200 | 300 | 400 |
|---|---|---|---|---|---|---|
| Black Hills 140 AccuBond | velocity, fps: | 3100 | | | | |
| | energy, ft-lb: | 2987 | | | | |
| | arc, inches: | | | | | |
| Federal 130 Nos. Bal. Tip | velocity, fps: | 3300 | 3070 | 2840 | 2630 | 2430 |
| | energy, ft-lb: | 3145 | 2710 | 2335 | 2000 | 1705 |
| | arc, inches: | | +1.1 | 0 | -5.4 | -15.8 |
| Federal 130 Nos. Partition And Nos. Solid Base And Barnes TS | velocity, fps: | 3280 | 3040 | 2810 | 2590 | 2380 |
| | energy, ft-lb: | 3105 | 2665 | 2275 | 1935 | 1635 |
| | arc, inches: | | +1.1 | 0 | -5.6 | -16.3 |
| Federal 140 Nos. AccuBond | velocity, fps | 3200 | 3000 | 2810 | 2630 | 2450 |
| | energy, ft-lb: | 3185 | 2795 | 2455 | 2145 | 1865 |
| | arc, inches: | | +1.2 | 0 | -5.6 | -16.2 |
| Federal 140 Trophy Bonded | velocity, fps: | 3130 | 2870 | 2640 | 2410 | 2200 |
| | energy, ft-lb: | 3035 | 2570 | 2160 | 1810 | 1500 |
| | arc, inches: | | +1.4 | 0 | -6.3 | 18.7 |
| Federal 150 Nos. Partition | velocity, fps: | 3160 | 2950 | 2750 | 2550 | 2370 |
| | energy, ft-lb: | 3325 | 2895 | 2515 | 2175 | 1870 |
| | arc, inches: | | +1.3 | 0 | -5.9 | -17.0 |
| Norma 130 FMJ | velocity, fps: | 3150 | 2882 | 2630 | 2391 | |
| | energy, ft-lb: | | | | | |
| | arc, inches: | | +1.5 | 0 | -6.4 | |
| Norma 130 Ballistic ST | velocity, fps: | 3281 | 3047 | 2825 | 2614 | |
| | energy, ft-lb: | 3108 | 2681 | 2305 | 1973 | |
| | arc, inches: | | +1.1 | 0 | -5.5 | |
| Norma 140 Barnes X TS | velocity, fps: | 3150 | 2952 | 2762 | 2580 | |
| | energy, ft-lb: | 3085 | 2709 | 2372 | 2070 | |
| | arc, inches: | | +1.3 | 0 | -5.8 | |
| Norma 150 Nosler Bal. Tip | velocity, fps: | 3280 | 3046 | 2824 | 2613 | |
| | energy, ft-lb: | 3106 | 2679 | 2303 | 1972 | |
| | arc, inches: | | +1.1 | 0 | -5.4 | |
| Norma 150 Oryx | velocity, fps: | 3117 | 2856 | 2611 | 2378 | |
| | energy, ft-lb: | 3237 | 2718 | 2271 | 1884 | |
| | arc, inches: | | +1.4 | 0 | -6.5 | |
| Win. 130 Bal. Silvertip | velocity, fps: | 3275 | 3041 | 2820 | 2609 | 2408 |
| | energy, ft-lb: | 3096 | 2669 | 2295 | 1964 | 1673 |
| | arc, inches: | | +1.1 | 0 | -5.5 | -16.1 |
| Win. 140 AccuBond | velocity, fps: | 3200 | 2989 | 2789 | 2597 | 2413 |
| | energy, ft-lb: | 3184 | 2779 | 2418 | 2097 | 1810 |
| | arc, inches: | | +1.2 | 0 | -5.7 | -16.5 |
| Win. 140 Fail Safe | velocity, fps: | 3125 | 2865 | 2619 | 2386 | 2165 |
| | energy, ft-lb: | 3035 | 2550 | 2132 | 1769 | 1457 |
| | arc, inches: | | +1.4 | 0 | -6.5 | -19.0 |
| Win. 150 Ballistic Silvertip | velocity, fps: | 3120 | 2923 | 2734 | 2554 | 2380. |
| | energy, ft-lb: | 3242 | 2845 | 2490 | 2172 | 1886. |
| | arc, inches: | | +1.3 | 0 | -5.9 | -17.2 |

**BALLISTICS**

# Centerfire Rifle Ballistics

## .270 WINCHESTER SHORT MAGNUM TO 7MM-08 REMINGTON

| CARTRIDGE BULLET | RANGE, YARDS: | 0 | 100 | 200 | 300 | 400 |
|---|---|---|---|---|---|---|
| Win. 150 Power Point | velocity, fps: | 3150 | 2867 | 2601 | 2350 | 2113 |
| | energy, ft-lb: | 3304 | 2737 | 2252 | 1839 | 1487 |
| | arc, inches: | | +1.4 | 0 | -6.5 | -19.4 |
| Win. 150 Supreme Elite XP3 | velocity, fps: | 3120 | 2926 | 2740 | 2561 | 2389 |
| | energy, ft-lb: | 3242 | 2850 | 2499 | 2184 | 1901 |
| | arc, inches: | | +1.3 | 0 | -5.9 | -17.1 |

### .270 WEATHERBY MAGNUM

| CARTRIDGE BULLET | RANGE, YARDS: | 0 | 100 | 200 | 300 | 400 |
|---|---|---|---|---|---|---|
| Federal 130 Nosler Partition | velocity, fps: | 3200 | 2960 | 2740 | 2520 | 2320 |
| | energy, ft-lb: | 2955 | 2530 | 2160 | 1835 | 1550 |
| | arc, inches: | | +1.2 | 0 | -5.9 | -17.3 |
| Federal 130 Sierra GameKing BTSP | velocity, fps: | 3200 | 2980 | 2780 | 2580 | 2400 |
| | energy, ft-lb: | 2955 | 2570 | 2230 | 1925 | 1655 |
| | arc, inches: | | +1.2 | 0 | -5.7 | -16.6 |
| Federal 140 Trophy Bonded | velocity, fps: | 3100 | 2840 | 2600 | 2370 | 2150. |
| | energy, ft-lb: | 2990 | 2510 | 2100 | 1745 | 1440 |
| | arc, inches: | | +1.4 | 0 | -6.6 | -19.3 |
| Wby. 100 Pointed Expanding | velocity, fps: | 3760 | 3396 | 3061 | 2751 | 2462 |
| | energy, ft-lb: | 3139 | 2560 | 2081 | 1681 | 1346 |
| | arc, inches: | | +2.3 | +3.0 | 0 | -7.6 |
| Wby. 130 Pointed Expanding | velocity, fps: | 3375 | 3123 | 2885 | 2659 | 2444 |
| | energy, ft-lb: | 3288 | 2815 | 2402 | 2041 | 1724 |
| | arc, inches: | | +2.8 | +3.5 | 0 | -8.4 |
| Wby. 130 Nosler Partition | velocity, fps: | 3375 | 3127 | 2892 | 2670 | 2458. |
| | energy, ft-lb: | 3288 | 2822 | 2415 | 2058 | 1744 |
| | arc, inches: | | +2.8 | +3.5 | 0 | -8.3 |
| Wby. 140 Nosler Bal. Tip | velocity, fps: | 3300 | 3077 | 2865 | 2663 | 2470. |
| | energy, ft-lb: | 3385 | 2943 | 2551 | 2204 | 1896 |
| | arc, inches: | | +2.9 | +3.5 | 0 | -8.4 |
| Wby. 140 Barnes X | velocity, fps: | 3250 | 3032 | 2825 | 2628 | 2438 |
| | energy, ft-lb: | 3283 | 2858 | 2481 | 2146 | 1848 |
| | arc, inches: | | +3.0 | +3.7 | 0 | -8.7 |
| Wby. 150 Pointed Expanding | velocity, fps: | 3245 | 3028 | 2821 | 2623 | 2434 |
| | energy, ft-lb: | 3507 | 3053 | 2650 | 2292 | 1973 |
| | arc, inches: | | +3.0 | +3.7 | 0 | -8.7 |
| Wby. 150 Nosler Partition | velocity, fps: | 3245 | 3029 | 2823 | 2627 | 2439. |
| | energy, ft-lb: | 3507 | 3055 | 2655 | 2298 | 1981 |
| | arc, inches: | | +3.0 | +3.7 | 0 | -8. |

### 7-30 WATERS

| CARTRIDGE BULLET | RANGE, YARDS: | 0 | 100 | 200 | 300 | 400 |
|---|---|---|---|---|---|---|
| Federal 120 Sierra GameKing BTSP | velocity, fps: | 2700 | 2300 | 1930 | 1600 | 1330. |
| | energy, ft-lb: | 1940 | 1405 | 990 | 685 | 470 |
| | arc, inches: | | +2.6 | 0 | -12.0 | -37.6 |

### 7MM MAUSER (7X57)

| CARTRIDGE BULLET | RANGE, YARDS: | 0 | 100 | 200 | 300 | 400 |
|---|---|---|---|---|---|---|
| Federal 140 Sierra Pro-Hunt. | velocity, fps: | 2660 | 2450 | 2260 | 2070 | 1890. |
| | energy, ft-lb: | 2200 | 1865 | 1585 | 1330 | 1110 |
| | arc, inches: | | +2.1 | 0 | -9.0 | -26.1 |
| Federal 140 Nosler Partition | velocity, fps: | 2660 | 2450 | 2260 | 2070 | 1890. |
| | energy, ft-lb: | 2200 | 1865 | 1585 | 1330 | 1110 |
| | arc, inches: | | +2.1 | 0 | -9.0 | -26.1 |
| Federal 175 Hi-Shok RN | velocity, fps: | 2440 | 2140 | 1860 | 1600 | 1380 |
| | energy, ft-lb: | 2315 | 1775 | 1340 | 1000 | 740 |
| | arc, inches: | | +3.1 | 0 | -13.3 | -40.1 |
| Hornady 139 SP boat-tail | velocity, fps: | 2700 | 2504 | 2316 | 2137 | 1965 |
| | energy, ft-lb: | 2251 | 1936 | 1656 | 1410 | 1192 |
| | arc, inches: | | +2.0 | 0 | -8.5 | -24.9 |
| Hornady 139 SP Interlock | velocity, fps: | 2680 | 2455 | 2241 | 2038 | 1846 |
| | energy, ft-lb: | 2216 | 1860 | 1550 | 1282 | 1052 |
| | arc, inches: | | +2.1 | 0 | -9.1 | -26.6 |
| Hornady 139 SP boat-tail LM | velocity, fps: | 2830 | 2620 | 2450 | 2250 | 2070 |
| | energy, ft-lb: | 2475 | 2135 | 1835 | 1565 | 1330 |
| | arc, inches: | | +1.8 | 0 | -7.6 | -22.1 |

| CARTRIDGE BULLET | RANGE, YARDS: | 0 | 100 | 200 | 300 | 400 |
|---|---|---|---|---|---|---|
| Hornady 139 SP LM | velocity, fps: | 2950 | 2736 | 2532 | 2337 | 2152. |
| | energy, ft-lb: | 2686 | 2310 | 1978 | 1686 | 1429 |
| | arc, inches: | | +2.0 | 0 | -7.6 | -21.5 |
| Norma 150 Soft Point | velocity, fps: | 2690 | 2479 | 2278 | 2087 | |
| | energy, ft-lb: | 2411 | 2048 | 1729 | 1450 | |
| | arc, inches: | | +2.0 | 0 | -8.8 | |
| PMC 140 Pointed Soft Point | velocity, fps: | 2660 | 2450 | 2260 | 2070 | 1890 |
| | energy, ft-lb: | 2200 | 1865 | 1585 | 1330 | 1110. |
| | arc, inches: | | +2.4 | 0 | -9.6 | -27.3 |
| PMC 175 Soft Point | velocity, fps: | 2440 | 2140 | 1860 | 1600 | 1380 |
| | energy, ft-lb: | 2315 | 1775 | 1340 | 1000 | 740 |
| | arc, inches: | | +1.5 | -3.6 | -18.6 | -46.8 |
| Rem. 140 PSP Core-Lokt | velocity, fps: | 2660 | 2435 | 2221 | 2018 | 1827 |
| | energy, ft-lb: | 2199 | 1843 | 1533 | 1266 | 1037 |
| | arc, inches: | | +2.2 | 0 | -9.2 | -27.4 |
| Win. 145 Power-Point | velocity, fps: | 2660 | 2413 | 2180 | 1959 | 1754 |
| | energy, ft-lb: | 2279 | 1875 | 1530 | 1236 | 990 |
| | arc, inches: | | +1.1 | -2.8 | -14.1 | -34.4 |

### 7x57 R

| CARTRIDGE BULLET | RANGE, YARDS: | 0 | 100 | 200 | 300 | 400 |
|---|---|---|---|---|---|---|
| Norma 150 FMJ | velocity, fps: | 2690 | 2489 | 2296 | 2112 | |
| | energy, ft-lb: | 2411 | 2063 | 1756 | 1486 | |
| | arc, inches: | | +2.0 | 0 | -8.6 | |
| Norma 154 Soft Point | velocity, fps: | 2625 | 2417 | 2219 | 2030 | |
| | energy, ft-lb: | 2357 | 1999 | 1684 | 1410 | |
| | arc, inches: | | +2.2 | 0 | -9.3 | |
| Norma 156 Oryx | velocity, fps: | 2608 | 2346 | 2099 | 1867 | |
| | energy, ft-lb: | 2357 | 1906 | 1526 | 1208 | |
| | arc, inches: | | +2.4 | 0 | -10.3 | |

### 7MM-08 REMINGTON

| CARTRIDGE BULLET | RANGE, YARDS: | 0 | 100 | 200 | 300 | 400 |
|---|---|---|---|---|---|---|
| Black Hills 140 AccuBond | velocity, fps: | 2700 | | | | |
| | energy, ft-lb: | | | | | |
| | arc, inches: | | | | | |
| Federal 140 Nosler Partition | velocity, fps: | 2800 | 2590 | 2390 | 2200 | 2020 |
| | energy, ft-lb: | 2435 | 2085 | 1775 | 1500 | 1265 |
| | arc, inches: | | +1.8 | 0 | -8.0 | -23.1 |
| Federal 140 Nosler Bal. Tip And AccuBond | velocity, fps: | 2800 | 2610 | 2430 | 2260 | 2100 |
| | energy, ft-lb: | 2440 | 2135 | 1840 | 1590 | 1360. |
| | arc, inches: | | +1.8 | 0 | -7.7 | -22.3 |
| Federal 140 Tr. Bonded HE | velocity, fps: | 2950 | 2660 | 2390 | 2140 | 1900 |
| | energy, ft-lb: | 2705 | 2205 | 1780 | 1420 | 1120 |
| | arc, inches: | | +1.7 | 0 | -7.9 | -23.2 |
| Federal 150 Sierra Pro-Hunt. | velocity, fps: | 2650 | 2440 | 2230 | 2040 | 1860 |
| | energy, ft-lb: | 2340 | 1980 | 1660 | 1390 | 1150 |
| | arc, inches: | | +2.2 | 0 | -9.2 | -26.7 |
| Hornady 139 SP boat-tail LM | velocity, fps: | 3000 | 2790 | 2590 | 2399 | 2216 |
| | energy, ft-lb: | 2777 | 2403 | 2071 | 1776 | 1515 |
| | arc, inches: | | +1.5 | 0 | -6.7 | -19.4 |
| Norma 140 Ballistic ST | velocity, fps: | 2822 | 2633 | 2452 | 2278 | |
| | energy, ft-lb: | 2476 | 2156 | 1870 | 1614 | |
| | arc, inches: | | +1.8 | 0 | -7.6 | |
| PMC 139 PSP | velocity, fps: | 2850 | 2610 | 2384 | 2170 | 1969 |
| | energy, ft-lb: | 2507 | 2103 | 1754 | 1454 | 1197 |
| | arc, inches: | | +1.8 | 0 | -7.9 | -23.3 |
| Rem. 120 Hollow Point | velocity, fps: | 3000 | 2725 | 2467 | 2223 | 1992 |
| | energy, ft-lb: | 2398 | 1979 | 1621 | 1316 | 1058 |
| | arc, inches: | | +1.6 | 0 | -7.3 | -21.7 |
| Rem. 140 PSP Core-Lokt | velocity, fps: | 2860 | 2625 | 2402 | 2189 | 1988 |
| | energy, ft-lb: | 2542 | 2142 | 1793 | 1490 | 1228 |
| | arc, inches: | | +1.8 | 0 | -7.8 | -22.9 |
| Rem. 140 PSP boat-tail | velocity, fps: | 2860 | 2656 | 2460 | 2273 | 2094 |
| | energy, ft-lb: | 2542 | 2192 | 1881 | 1606 | 1363 |
| | arc, inches: | | +1.7 | 0 | -7.5 | -21.7 |

BALLISTICS

| CARTRIDGE BULLET | RANGE, YARDS: | 0 | 100 | 200 | 300 | 400 |
|---|---|---|---|---|---|---|
| Rem. 140 AccuTip BT | velocity, fps: | 2860 | 2670 | 2488 | 2313 | 2145 |
| | energy, ft-lb: | 2543 | 2217 | 1925 | 1663 | 1431 |
| | arc, inches: | | +1.7 | 0 | -7.3 | -21.2 |
| Rem. 140 Nosler Partition | velocity, fps: | 2860 | 2648 | 2446 | 2253 | 2068 |
| | energy, ft-lb: | 2542 | 2180 | 1860 | 1577 | 1330 |
| | arc, inches: | | +1.7 | 0 | -7.6 | -22.0 |
| Speer 145 Grand Slam | velocity, fps: | 2845 | 2567 | 2305 | 2059 | |
| | energy, ft-lb: | 2606 | 2121 | 1711 | 1365 | |
| | arc, inches: | | +1.9 | 0 | -8.4 | -25.5 |
| Win. 140 Power-Point | velocity, fps: | 2800 | 2523 | 2268 | 2027 | 1802 |
| | energy, ft-lb: | 2429 | 1980 | 1599 | 1277 | 1010 |
| | arc, inches: | | +2.0 | 0 | -8.8 | -26.0 |
| Win. 140 Power-Point Plus | velocity, fps: | 2875 | 2597 | 2336 | 2090 | 1859 |
| | energy, ft-lb: | 2570 | 1997 | 1697 | 1358 | 1075 |
| | arc, inches: | | +2.0 | 0 | -8.8 | 26.0 |
| Win. 140 Fail Safe | velocity, fps: | 2760 | 2506 | 2271 | 2048 | 1839 |
| | energy, ft-lb: | 2360 | 1953 | 1603 | 1304 | 1051 |
| | arc, inches: | | +2.0 | 0 | -8.8 | -25.9 |
| Win. 140 Ballistic Silvertip | velocity, fps: | 2770 | 2572 | 2382 | 2200 | 2026 |
| | energy, ft-lb: | 2386 | 2056 | 1764 | 1504 | 1276 |
| | arc, inches: | | +1.9 | 0 | -8.0 | -23.8 |

## 7x64 BRENNEKE

| CARTRIDGE BULLET | RANGE, YARDS: | 0 | 100 | 200 | 300 | 400 |
|---|---|---|---|---|---|---|
| Federal 160 Nosler Partition | velocity, fps: | 2650 | 2480 | 2310 | 2150 | 2000 |
| | energy, ft-lb: | 2495 | 2180 | 1895 | 1640 | 1415 |
| | arc, inches: | | +2.1 | 0 | -8.7 | -24.9 |
| Norma 140 AccuBond | velocity, fps: | 2953 | 2759 | 2572 | 2394 | |
| | energy, ft-lb: | 2712 | 2366 | 2058 | 1782 | |
| | arc, inches: | | +1.5 | 0 | -6.8 | |
| Norma 154 Soft Point | velocity, fps: | 2821 | 2605 | 2399 | 2203 | |
| | energy, ft-lb: | 2722 | 2321 | 1969 | 1660 | |
| | arc, inches: | | +1.8 | 0 | -7.8 | |
| Norma 156 Oryx | velocity, fps: | 2789 | 2516 | 2259 | 2017 | |
| | energy, ft-lb: | 2695 | 2193 | 1768 | 1410 | |
| | arc, inches: | | +2.0 | 0 | -8.8 | |
| Norma 170 Vulkan | velocity, fps: | 2756 | 2501 | 2259 | 2031 | |
| | energy, ft-lb: | 2868 | 2361 | 1927 | 1558 | |
| | arc, inches: | | +2.0 | 0 | -8.8 | |
| Norma 170 Oryx | velocity, fps: | 2756 | 2481 | 2222 | 1979 | |
| | energy, ft-lb: | 2868 | 2324 | 1864 | 1478 | |
| | arc, inches: | | +2.1 | 0 | -9.2 | |
| Norma 170 Plastic Point | velocity, fps: | 2756 | 2519 | 2294 | 2081 | |
| | energy, ft-lb: | 2868 | 2396 | 1987 | 1635 | |
| | arc, inches: | | +2.0 | 0 | -8.6 | |
| PMC 170 Pointed Soft Point | velocity, fps: | 2625 | 2401 | 2189 | 1989 | 1801 |
| | energy, ft lb: | 2601 | 2175 | 1808 | 1493 | 1224 |
| | arc, inches: | | +2.3 | 0 | -9.6 | -27.9 |
| Rem. 175 PSP Core-Lokt | velocity, fps: | 2650 | 2445 | 2248 | 2061 | 1883 |
| | energy, ft-lb: | 2728 | 2322 | 1964 | 1650 | 1378 |
| | arc, inches: | | +2.2 | 0 | -9.1 | -26.4 |
| Speer 160 Grand Slam | velocity, fps: | 2600 | 2376 | 2164 | 1962 | |
| | energy, ft-lb: | 2401 | 2006 | 1663 | 1368 | |
| | arc, inches: | | +2.3 | 0 | -9.8 | -28.6 |
| Speer 175 Grand Slam | velocity, fps: | 2650 | 2461 | 2280 | 2106 | |
| | energy, ft-lb: | 2728 | 2353 | 2019 | 1723 | |
| | arc, inches: | | +2.4 | 0 | -9.2 | -26.2 |

## 7x65 R

| CARTRIDGE BULLET | RANGE, YARDS: | 0 | 100 | 200 | 300 | 400 |
|---|---|---|---|---|---|---|
| Norma 150 FMJ | velocity, fps: | 2756 | 2552 | 2357 | 2170 | |
| | energy, ft-lb: | 2530 | 2169 | 1850 | 1569 | |
| | arc, inches: | | +1.9 | 0 | -8.2 | |
| Norma 156 Oryx | velocity, fps: | 2723 | 2454 | 2200 | 1962 | |
| | energy, ft-lb: | 2569 | 2086 | 1678 | 1334 | |
| | arc, inches: | | +2.1 | 0 | -9.3 | |

| CARTRIDGE BULLET | RANGE, YARDS: | 0 | 100 | 200 | 300 | 400 |
|---|---|---|---|---|---|---|
| Norma 170 Plastic Point | velocity, fps: | 2625 | 2390 | 2167 | 1956 | |
| | energy, ft-lb: | 2602 | 2157 | 1773 | 1445 | |
| | arc, inches: | | +2.3 | 0 | -9.7 | |
| Norma 170 Vulkan | velocity, fps: | 2657 | 2392 | 2143 | 1909 | |
| | energy, ft-lb: | 2666 | 2161 | 1734 | 1377 | |
| | arc, inches: | | +2.3 | 0 | -9.9 | |
| Norma 170 Oryx | velocity, fps: | 2657 | 2378 | 2115 | 1871 | |
| | energy, ft-lb: | 2666 | 2135 | 1690 | 1321 | |
| | arc, inches: | | +2.3 | 0 | -10.1 | |

## .284 WINCHESTER

| CARTRIDGE BULLET | RANGE, YARDS: | 0 | 100 | 200 | 300 | 400 |
|---|---|---|---|---|---|---|
| Win. 150 Power-Point | velocity, fps: | 2860 | 2595 | 2344 | 2108 | 1886 |
| | energy, ft-lb: | 2724 | 2243 | 1830 | 1480 | 1185 |
| | arc, inches: | | +2.1 | 0 | -8.5 | -24.8 |

## .280 REMINGTON

| CARTRIDGE BULLET | RANGE, YARDS: | 0 | 100 | 200 | 300 | 400 |
|---|---|---|---|---|---|---|
| Federal 140 Sierra Pro-Hunt. | velocity, fps: | 2990 | 2740 | 2500 | 2270 | 2060 |
| | energy, ft-lb: | 2770 | 2325 | 1940 | 1605 | 1320 |
| | arc, inches: | | +1.6 | 0 | -7.0 | -20.8 |
| Federal 140 Trophy Bonded | velocity, fps: | 2990 | 2630 | 2310 | 2040 | 1730 |
| | energy, ft-lb: | 2770 | 2155 | 1655 | 1250 | 925 |
| | arc, inches: | | +1.6 | 0 | -8.4 | -25.4 |
| Federal 140 Tr. Bonded HE | velocity, fps: | 3150 | 2850 | 2570 | 2300 | 2050 |
| | energy, ft-lb: | 3085 | 2520 | 2050 | 1650 | 1310 |
| | arc, inches: | | +1.4 | 0 | -6.7 | -20.0 |
| Federal 140 Nos. AccuBond And Bal. Tip And Solid Base | velocity, fps: | 3000 | 2800 | 2620 | 2440 | 2260 |
| | energy, ft-lb: | 2800 | 2445 | 2130 | 1845 | 1590 |
| | arc, inches: | | +1.5 | 0 | -6.5 | -18.9 |
| Federal 150 Hi-Shok | velocity, fps: | 2890 | 2670 | 2460 | 2260 | 2060 |
| | energy, ft-lb: | 2780 | 2370 | 2015 | 1695 | 1420 |
| | arc, inches: | | +1.7 | 0 | -7.5 | -21.8 |
| Federal 150 Nosler Partition | velocity, fps: | 2890 | 2690 | 2490 | 2310 | 2130 |
| | energy, ft-lb: | 2780 | 2405 | 2070 | 1770 | 1510. |
| | arc, inches: | | +1.7 | 0 | -7.2 | -21.1 |
| Federal 150 Nos. AccuBond | velocity, fps | 2800 | 2630 | 2460 | 2300 | 2150 |
| | energy, ft-lb: | 2785 | 2455 | 2155 | 1885 | 1645 |
| | arc, inches: | | +1.8 | 0 | -7.5 | -21.5 |
| Federal 160 Trophy Bonded | velocity, fps: | 2800 | 2570 | 2350 | 2140 | 1940 |
| | energy, ft-lb: | 2785 | 2345 | 1960 | 1625 | 1340 |
| | arc, inches: | | +1.9 | 0 | -8.3 | -24.0 |
| Hornady 139 SPBT LMmoly | velocity, fps: | 3110 | 2888 | 2675 | 2473 | 2280. |
| | energy, ft-lb: | 2985 | 2573 | 2209 | 1887 | 1604 |
| | arc, inches: | | +1.4 | 0 | -6.5 | -18.6 |
| Norma 156 Oryx | velocity, fps: | 2789 | 2516 | 2259 | 2017 | |
| | energy, ft-lb: | 2695 | 2193 | 1768 | 1410 | |
| | arc, inches: | | +2.0 | 0 | -8.8 | |
| Norma 170 Plastic Point | velocity, fps: | 2707 | 2468 | 2241 | 2026 | |
| | energy, ft-lb: | 2767 | 2299 | 1896 | 1550 | |
| | arc, inches: | | +2.1 | 0 | -9.1 | |
| Norma 170 Vulkan | velocity, fps: | 2592 | 2346 | 2113 | 1894 | |
| | energy, ft-lb: | 2537 | 2078 | 1686 | 1354 | |
| | arc, inches: | | +2.4 | 0 | -10.2 | |
| Norma 170 Oryx | velocity, fps: | 2690 | 2416 | 2159 | 1918 | |
| | energy, ft-lb: | 2732 | 2204 | 1760 | 1389 | |
| | arc, inches: | | +2.2 | 0 | -9.7 | |
| Rem. 140 PSP Core-Lokt | velocity, fps: | 3000 | 2758 | 2528 | 2309 | 2102 |
| | energy, ft-lb: | 2797 | 2363 | 1986 | 1657 | 1373 |
| | arc, inches: | | +1.5 | 0 | -7.0 | -20.5 |
| Rem. 140 PSP boat-tail | velocity, fps: | 2860 | 2656 | 2460 | 2273 | 2094 |
| | energy, ft-lb: | 2542 | 2192 | 1881 | 1606 | 1363 |
| | arc, inches: | | +1.7 | 0 | -7.5 | -21.7 |
| Rem. 140 Nosler Bal. Tip | velocity, fps: | 3000 | 2804 | 2616 | 2436 | 2263 |
| | energy, ft-lb: | 2799 | 2445 | 2128 | 1848 | 1593 |
| | arc, inches: | | +1.5 | 0 | -6.8 | -19.0 |

BALLISTICS

# Centerfire Rifle Ballistics

## .280 REMINGTON TO 7MM REMINGTON MAGNUM

| CARTRIDGE BULLET | RANGE, YARDS: | 0 | 100 | 200 | 300 | 400 |
|---|---|---|---|---|---|---|
| Rem. 140 AccuTip | velocity, fps: | 3000 | 2804 | 2617 | 2437 | 2265 |
| | energy, ft-lb: | 2797 | 2444 | 2129 | 1846 | 1594 |
| | arc, inches: | | +1.5 | 0 | -6.8 | -19.0 |
| Rem. 150 PSP Core-Lokt | velocity, fps: | 2890 | 2624 | 2373 | 2135 | 1912 |
| | energy, ft-lb: | 2781 | 2293 | 1875 | 1518 | 1217 |
| | arc, inches: | | +1.8 | 0 | -8.0 | -23.6 |
| Rem. 165 SP Core-Lokt | velocity, fps: | 2820 | 2510 | 2220 | 1950 | 1701 |
| | energy, ft-lb: | 2913 | 2308 | 1805 | 1393 | 1060. |
| | arc, inches: | | +2.0 | 0 | -9.1 | -27.4 |
| Speer 145 Grand Slam | velocity, fps: | 2900 | 2619 | 2354 | 2105 | |
| | energy, ft-lb: | 2707 | 2207 | 1784 | 1426 | |
| | arc, inches: | | +2.1 | 0 | -8.4 | -24.7 |
| Speer 160 Grand Slam | velocity, fps: | 2890 | 2652 | 2425 | 2210 | |
| | energy, ft-lb: | 2967 | 2497 | 2089 | 1735 | |
| | arc, inches: | | +1.7 | 0 | -7.7 | -22.4 |
| Win. 140 Fail Safe | velocity, fps: | 3050 | 2756 | 2480 | 2221 | 1977 |
| | energy, ft-lb: | 2893 | 2362 | 1913 | 1533 | 1216 |
| | arc, inches: | | +1.5 | 0 | -7.2 | -21.5 |
| Win. 140 Ballistic Silvertip | velocity, fps: | 3040 | 2842 | 2653 | 2471 | 2297 |
| | energy, ft-lb: | 2872 | 2511 | 2187 | 1898 | 1640 |
| | arc, inches: | | +1.4 | 0 | -6.3 | -18.4 |

## .280 ACKLEY IMPROVED

| CARTRIDGE BULLET | RANGE, YARDS: | 0 | 100 | 200 | 300 | 400 |
|---|---|---|---|---|---|---|
| Nosler 140 AccuBond | velocity, fps: | 3150 | 2947 | 2753 | 2567 | 2389 |
| | energy, ft-lb: | 3084 | 2700 | 2355 | 2048 | 1774 |
| | arc, inches: | -1.5 | +1.1 | 0 | -5.0 | -16.8 |
| Nosler 150 ABLR | velocity, fps: | 2930 | 2775 | 2626 | 2482 | 2342 |
| | energy, ft-lb: | 2858 | 2565 | 2297 | 2052 | 1827 |
| | arc, inches: | -1.5 | +1.5 | 0 | -6.6 | -18.7 |
| Nosler 160 Partition | velocity, fps: | 2950 | 2752 | 2562 | 2380 | 2206 |
| | energy, ft-lb: | 3091 | 2690 | 2332 | 2013 | 1729 |
| | arc, inches: | -1.5 | +1.5 | 0 | -6.7 | -19.4 |

## 7MM REMINGTON MAGNUM

| CARTRIDGE BULLET | RANGE, YARDS: | 0 | 100 | 200 | 300 | 400 |
|---|---|---|---|---|---|---|
| A-Square 175 Monolithic Solid | velocity, fps: | 2860 | 2557 | 2273 | 2008 | 1771 |
| | energy, ft-lb: | 3178 | 2540 | 2008 | 1567 | 1219 |
| | arc, inches: | | +1.92 | 0 | -8.7 | -25.9 |
| Black Hills 140 Nos. Bal. Tip | velocity, fps: | 3150 | | | | |
| | energy, ft-lb: | 3084 | | | | |
| | arc, inches: | | | | | |
| Black Hills 140 Barnes XLC | velocity, fps: | 3150 | | | | |
| | energy, ft-lb: | 3084 | | | | |
| | arc, inches: | | | | | |
| Black Hills 140 Nos. Partition | velocity, fps: | 3150 | | | | |
| | energy, ft-lb: | 3084 | | | | |
| | arc, inches: | | | | | |
| Federal 140 Nosler Bal. Tip And AccuBond | velocity, fps: | 3110 | 2910 | 2720 | 2530 | 2360. |
| | energy, ft-lb: | 3005 | 2630 | 2295 | 1995 | 1725 |
| | arc, inches: | | +1.3 | 0 | -6.0 | -17.4 |
| Federal 140 Nosler Partition | velocity, fps: | 3150 | 2930 | 2710 | 2510 | 2320 |
| | energy, ft-lb: | 3085 | 2660 | 2290 | 1960 | 1670 |
| | arc, inches: | | +1.3 | 0 | -6.0 | -17.5 |
| Federal 140 Trophy Bonded | velocity, fps: | 3150 | 2910 | 2680 | 2460 | 2250. |
| | energy, ft-lb: | 3085 | 2630 | 2230 | 1880 | 1575 |
| | arc, inches: | | +1.3 | 0 | -6.1 | -18.1 |
| Federal 150 Hi-Shok | velocity, fps: | 3110 | 2830 | 2570 | 2320 | 2090 |
| | energy, ft-lb: | 3220 | 2670 | 2200 | 1790 | 1450 |
| | arc, inches: | | +1.4 | 0 | -6.7 | -19.9 |
| Federal 150 Sierra GameKing BTSP | velocity, fps: | 3110 | 2920 | 2750 | 2580 | 2410 |
| | energy, ft-lb: | 3220 | 2850 | 2510 | 2210 | 1930 |
| | arc, inches: | | +1.3 | 0 | -5.9 | -17.0 |
| Federal 150 Nosler Bal. Tip | velocity, fps: | 3110 | 2910 | 2720 | 2540 | 2370 |
| | energy, ft-lb: | 3220 | 2825 | 2470 | 2150 | 1865 |
| | arc, inches: | | +1.3 | 0 | -6.0 | -17.4 |

| CARTRIDGE BULLET | RANGE, YARDS: | 0 | 100 | 200 | 300 | 400 |
|---|---|---|---|---|---|---|
| Federal 150 Nos. Solid Base | velocity, fps: | 3100 | 2890 | 2690 | 2500 | 2310 |
| | energy, ft-lb: | 3200 | 2780 | 2405 | 2075 | 1775 |
| | arc, inches: | | +1.3 | 0 | -6.2 | -17.8 |
| Federal 160 Barnes XLC | velocity, fps: | 2940 | 2760 | 2580 | 2410 | 2240 |
| | energy, ft-lb: | 3070 | 2695 | 2360 | 2060 | 1785 |
| | arc, inches: | | +1.5 | 0 | -6.8 | -19.6 |
| Federal 160 Sierra Pro-Hunt. | velocity, fps: | 2940 | 2730 | 2520 | 2320 | 2140 |
| | energy, ft-lb: | 3070 | 2640 | 2260 | 1920 | 1620 |
| | arc, inches: | | +1.6 | 0 | -7.1 | -20.6 |
| Federal 160 Nosler Partition | velocity, fps: | 2950 | 2770 | 2590 | 2420 | 2250. |
| | energy, ft-lb: | 3090 | 2715 | 2375 | 2075 | 1800 |
| | arc, inches: | | +1.5 | 0 | -6.7 | -19.4 |
| Federal 160 Nos. AccuBond | velocity, fps: | 2950 | 2770 | 2600 | 2440 | 2280. |
| | energy, ft-lb: | 3090 | 2730 | 2405 | 2110 | 1845 |
| | arc, inches: | | +1.5 | 0 | -6.6 | -19.1 |
| Federal 160 Trophy Bonded | velocity, fps: | 2940 | 2660 | 2390 | 2140 | 1900 |
| | energy, ft-lb: | 3070 | 2505 | 2025 | 1620 | 1280. |
| | arc, inches: | | +1.7 | 0 | -7.9 | -23.3 |
| Federal 165 Sierra GameKing BTSP | velocity, fps: | 2950 | 2800 | 2650 | 2510 | 2370. |
| | energy, ft-lb: | 3190 | 2865 | 2570 | 2300 | 2050 |
| | arc, inches: | | +1.5 | 0 | -6.4 | -18.4 |
| Federal 175 Hi-Shok | velocity, fps: | 2860 | 2650 | 2440 | 2240 | 2060 |
| | energy, ft-lb: | 3180 | 2720 | 2310 | 1960 | 1640 |
| | arc, inches: | | +1.7 | 0 | -7.6 | -22.1 |
| Federal 175 Trophy Bonded | velocity, fps: | 2860 | 2600 | 2350 | 2120 | 1900 |
| | energy, ft-lb: | 3180 | 2625 | 2150 | 1745 | 1400 |
| | arc, inches: | | +1.8 | 0 | -8.2 | -24.0 |
| Hornady 139 SPBT | velocity, fps: | 3150 | 2933 | 2727 | 2530 | 2341 |
| | energy, ft-lb: | 3063 | 2656 | 2296 | 1976 | 1692 |
| | arc, inches: | | +1.2 | 0 | -6.1 | -17.7 |
| Hornady 139 SST (or Interbond) | velocity, fps: | 3150 | 2948 | 2754 | 2569 | 2391 |
| | energy, ft-lb: | 3062 | 2681 | 2341 | 2037 | 1764 |
| | arc, inches: | | +1.1 | 0 | -5.7 | -16.7 |
| Hornady 139 SST LM (or Interbond) | velocity, fps: | 3250 | 3044 | 2847 | 2657 | 2475 |
| | energy, ft-lb: | 3259 | 2860 | 2501 | 2178 | 1890 |
| | arc, inches: | | +1.1 | 0 | -5.5 | -16.2 |
| Hornady 139 SPBT HMmoly | velocity, fps: | 3250 | 3041 | 2822 | 2613 | 2413 |
| | energy, ft-lb: | 3300 | 2854 | 2458 | 2106 | 1797. |
| | arc, inches: | | +1.1 | 0 | -5.7 | -16.6 |
| Hornady 154 Soft Point | velocity, fps: | 3035 | 2814 | 2604 | 2404 | 2212 |
| | energy, ft-lb: | 3151 | 2708 | 2319 | 1977 | 1674 |
| | arc, inches: | | +1.3 | 0 | -6.7 | -19.3 |
| Hornady 154 SST (or Interbond) | velocity, fps: | 3035 | 2850 | 2672 | 2501 | 2337 |
| | energy, ft-lb: | 3149 | 2777 | 2441 | 2139 | 1867 |
| | arc, inches: | | +1.4 | 0 | -6.5 | -18.7 |
| Hornady 162 SP boat-tail | velocity, fps: | 2940 | 2757 | 2582 | 2413 | 2251 |
| | energy, ft-lb: | 3110 | 2735 | 2399 | 2095 | 1823 |
| | arc, inches: | | +1.6 | 0 | -6.7 | -19.7 |
| Hornady 175 SP | velocity, fps: | 2860 | 2650 | 2440 | 2240 | 2060. |
| | energy, ft-lb: | 3180 | 2720 | 2310 | 1960 | 1640 |
| | arc, inches: | | +2.0 | 0 | -7.9 | -22.7 |
| Norma 140 Nosler Bal. Tip | velocity, fps: | 3150 | 2936 | 2732 | 2537 | |
| | energy, ft-lb: | 3085 | 2680 | 2320 | 2001 | |
| | arc, inches: | | +1.2 | 0 | -5.9 | |
| Norma 140 Barnes X TS | velocity, fps: | 3117 | 2912 | 2716 | 2529 | |
| | energy, ft-lb: | 3021 | 2637 | 2294 | 1988 | |
| | arch, inches: | | +1.3 | 0 | -6.0 | |
| Norma 150 Scirocco | velocity, fps: | 3117 | 2934 | 2758 | 2589 | |
| | energy, ft-lb: | 3237 | 2869 | 2535 | 2234 | |
| | arc, inches: | | +1.2 | 0 | -5.8 | |
| Norma 156 Oryx | velocity, fps: | 2953 | 2670 | 2404 | 2153 | |
| | energy, ft-lb: | 3021 | 2470 | 2002 | 1607 | |
| | arc, inches: | | +1.7 | 0 | -7.7 | |

BALLISTICS

## 7MM REMINGTON MAGNUM TO 7MM WINCHESTER SHORT MAGNUM

| CARTRIDGE BULLET | RANGE, YARDS: | 0 | 100 | 200 | 300 | 400 |
|---|---|---|---|---|---|---|
| Norma 170 Vulkan | velocity, fps: | 3018 | 2747 | 2493 | 2252 | |
| | energy, ft-lb: | 3439 | 2850 | 2346 | 1914 | |
| | arc, inches: | | +1.5 | 0 | -2.8 | |
| Norma 170 Oryx | velocity, fps: | 2887 | 2601 | 2333 | 2080 | |
| | energy, ft-lb: | 3147 | 2555 | 2055 | 1634 | |
| | arc, inches: | | +1.8 | 0 | -8.2 | |
| Norma 170 Plastic Point | velocity, fps: | 3018 | 2762 | 2519 | 2290 | |
| | energy, ft-lb: | 3439 | 2880 | 2394 | 1980 | |
| | arc, inches: | | +1.5 | 0 | -7.0 | |
| PMC 140 Barnes X | velocity, fps: | 3000 | 2808 | 2624 | 2448 | 2279 |
| | energy, ft-lb: | 2797 | 2451 | 2141 | 1863 | 1614 |
| | arc, inches: | | +1.5 | 0 | -6.6 | 18.9 |
| PMC 140 Pointed Soft Point | velocity, fps: | 3099 | 2878 | 2668 | 2469 | 2279 |
| | energy, ft-lb: | 2984 | 2574 | 2212 | 1895 | 1614 |
| | arc, inches: | | +1.4 | 0 | -6.2 | -18.1 |
| PMC 140 SP boat-tail | velocity, fps: | 3125 | 2891 | 2669 | 2457 | 2255 |
| | energy, ft-lb: | 3035 | 2597 | 2213 | 1877 | 1580 |
| | arc, inches: | | +1.4 | 0 | -6.3 | -18.4 |
| PMC 160 Barnes X | velocity, fps: | 2800 | 2639 | 2484 | 2334 | 2189 |
| | energy, ft-lb: | 2785 | 2474 | 2192 | 1935 | 1703 |
| | arc, inches: | | +1.8 | 0 | -7.4 | -21.2 |
| PMC 160 Pointed Soft Point | velocity, fps: | 2914 | 2748 | 2586 | 2428 | 2276 |
| | energy, ft-lb: | 3016 | 2682 | 2375 | 2095 | 1840 |
| | arc, inches: | | +1.6 | 0 | -6.7 | -19.4 |
| PMC 160 SP boat-tail | velocity, fps: | 2900 | 2696 | 2501 | 2314 | 2135 |
| | energy, ft-lb: | 2987 | 2582 | 2222 | 1903 | 1620 |
| | arc, inches: | | +1.7 | 0 | -7.2 | -21.0 |
| PMC 175 Pointed Soft Point | velocity, fps: | 2860 | 2645 | 2442 | 2244 | 2957 |
| | energy, ft-lb: | 3178 | 2718 | 2313 | 1956 | 1644 |
| | arc, inches: | | +2.0 | 0 | -7.9 | -22.7 |
| Rem. 140 PSP Core-Lokt mr | velocity, fps: | 2710 | 2482 | 2265 | 2059 | 1865 |
| | energy, ft-lb: | 2283 | 1915 | 1595 | 1318 | 1081 |
| | arc, inches: | | +1.0 | -2.5 | -12.8 | -31.3 |
| Rem. 140 PSP Core-Lokt | velocity, fps: | 3175 | 2923 | 2684 | 2458 | 2243 |
| | energy, ft-lb: | 3133 | 2655 | 2240 | 1878 | 1564 |
| | arc, inches: | | +2.2 | +1.9 | -3.2 | -14.2 |
| Rem. 140 PSP boat-tail | velocity, fps: | 3175 | 2956 | 2747 | 2547 | 2356 |
| | energy, ft-lb: | 3133 | 2715 | 2345 | 2017 | 1726 |
| | arc, inches: | | +2.2 | +1.6 | -3.1 | -13.4 |
| Rem. 150 AccuTip | velocity, fps: | 3110 | 2926 | 2749 | 2579 | 2415 |
| | energy, ft-lb: | 3221 | 2850 | 2516 | 2215 | 1943 |
| | arc, inches: | | +1.3 | 0 | -5.9 | -17.0 |
| Rem. 150 PSP Core-Lokt | velocity, fps: | 3110 | 2830 | 2568 | 2320 | 2085 |
| | energy, ft-lb: | 3221 | 2667 | 2196 | 1792 | 1448 |
| | arc, inches: | | +1.3 | 0 | -6.6 | -20.2 |
| Rem. 150 Nosler Bal. Tip | velocity, fps: | 3110 | 2912 | 2723 | 2542 | 2367 |
| | energy, ft-lb: | 3222 | 2825 | 2470 | 2152 | 1867 |
| | arc, inches: | | +1.2 | 0 | -5.9 | -17.3 |
| Rem. 150 Swift Scirocco | velocity, fps: | 3110 | 2927 | 2751 | 2582 | 2419 |
| | energy, ft-lb: | 3221 | 2852 | 2520 | 2220 | 1948 |
| | arc, inches: | | +1.3 | 0 | -5.9 | -17.0 |
| Rem. 160 Swift A-Frame | velocity, fps: | 2900 | 2659 | 2430 | 2212 | 2006 |
| | energy, ft-lb: | 2987 | 2511 | 2097 | 1739 | 1430 |
| | arc, inches: | | +1.7 | 0 | -7.6 | -22.4 |
| Rem. 160 Nosler Partition | velocity, fps: | 2950 | 2752 | 2563 | 2381 | 2207 |
| | energy, ft-lb: | 3091 | 2690 | 2333 | 2014 | 1730 |
| | arc, inches: | | +0.6 | -1.9 | -9.6 | -23.6 |
| Rem. 175 PSP Core-Lokt | velocity, fps: | 2860 | 2645 | 2440 | 2244 | 2057 |
| | energy, ft-lb: | 3178 | 2718 | 2313 | 1956 | 1644 |
| | arc, inches: | | +1.7 | 0 | -7.6 | -22.1 |
| Speer 145 Grand Slam | velocity, fps: | 3140 | 2843 | 2565 | 2304 | |
| | energy, ft-lb: | 3174 | 2602 | 2118 | 1708 | |
| | arc, inches: | | +1.4 | 0 | -6.7 | |
| Speer 175 Grand Slam | velocity, fps: | 2850 | 2653 | 2463 | 2282 | |
| | energy, ft-lb: | 3156 | 2734 | 2358 | 2023 | |
| | arc, inches: | | +1.7 | 0 | -7.5 | -21.7 |
| Win. 140 Fail Safe | velocity, fps: | 3150 | 2861 | 2589 | 2333 | 2092 |
| | energy, ft-lb: | 3085 | 2544 | 2085 | 1693 | 1361 |
| | arc, inches: | | +1.4 | 0 | -6.6 | -19.5 |
| Win. 140 Ballistic Silvertip | velocity, fps: | 3100 | 2889 | 2687 | 2494 | 2310 |
| | energy, ft-lb: | 2988 | 2595 | 2245 | 1934 | 1659. |
| | arc, inches: | | +1.3 | 0 | -6.2 | -17.9 |
| Win. 140 AccuBond CT | velocity, fps: | 3180 | 2965 | 2760 | 2565 | 2377 |
| | energy, ft-lb: | 3143 | 2733 | 2368 | 2044 | 1756 |
| | arc, inches: | | +1.2 | 0 | -5.8 | -16.9 |
| Win. 150 Power-Point | velocity, fps: | 3090 | 2812 | 2551 | 2304 | 2071 |
| | energy, ft-lb: | 3181 | 2634 | 2167 | 1768 | 1429 |
| | arc, inches: | | +1.5 | 0 | -6.8 | -20.2 |
| Win. 150 Power-Point Plus | velocity, fps: | 3130 | 2849 | 2586 | 2337 | 2102 |
| | energy, ft-lb: | 3264 | 2705 | 2227 | 1819 | 1472 |
| | arc, inches: | | +1.4 | 0 | -6.6 | -19.6 |
| Win. 150 Ballistic Silvertip | velocity, fps: | 3100 | 2903 | 2714 | 2533 | 2359 |
| | energy, ft-lb: | 3200 | 2806 | 2453 | 2136 | 1853 |
| | arc, inches: | | +1.3 | 0 | -6.0 | -17.5 |
| Win. 160 AccuBond | velocity, fps: | 2950 | 2766 | 2590 | 2420 | 2257 |
| | energy, ft-lb: | 3091 | 2718 | 2382 | 2080 | 1809 |
| | arc, inches: | | +1.5 | 0 | -6.7 | -19.4 |
| Win. 160 Partition Gold | velocity, fps: | 2950 | 2743 | 2546 | 2357 | 2176 |
| | energy, ft-lb: | 3093 | 2674 | 2303 | 1974 | 1682 |
| | arc, inches: | | +1.6 | 0 | -6.9 | -20.1 |
| Win. 160 Fail Safe | velocity, fps: | 2920 | 2678 | 2449 | 2331 | 2025 |
| | energy, ft-lb: | 3030 | 2549 | 2131 | 1769 | 1457 |
| | arc, inches: | | +1.7 | 0 | -7.5 | -22.0 |
| Win. 175 Power-Point | velocity, fps: | 2860 | 2645 | 2440 | 2244 | 2057 |
| | energy, ft-lb: | 3178 | 2718 | 2313 | 1956 | 1644 |
| | arc, inches: | | +2.0 | 0 | -7.9 | -22.7 |

### 7MM REMINGTON SHORT ULTRA MAGNUM

| CARTRIDGE BULLET | RANGE, YARDS: | 0 | 100 | 200 | 300 | 400 |
|---|---|---|---|---|---|---|
| Rem. 140 PSP C-L Ultra | velocity, fps: | 3175 | 2934 | 2707 | 2490 | 2283 |
| | energy, ft-lb: | 3133 | 2676 | 2277 | 1927 | 1620. |
| | arc, inches: | | +1.3 | 0 | -6.0 | -17.7 |
| Rem. 150 PSP Core-Lokt | velocity, fps: | 3110 | 2828 | 2563 | 2313 | 2077 |
| | energy, ft-lb: | 3221 | 2663 | 2188 | 1782 | 1437 |
| | arc, inches: | | +2.5 | +2.1 | -3.6 | -15.8 |
| Rem. 160 Partition | velocity, fps: | 2960 | 2762 | 2572 | 2390 | 2215 |
| | energy, ft-lb: | 3112 | 2709 | 2350 | 2029 | 1744 |
| | arc, inches: | | +2.6 | +2.2 | -3.6 | -15.4 |
| Rem. 160 PSP C-L Ultra | velocity, fps: | 2960 | 2733 | 2518 | 2313 | 2117 |
| | energy, ft-lb: | 3112 | 2654 | 2252 | 1900 | 1592 |
| | arc, inches: | | +2.7 | +2.2 | -3.7 | -16.2 |

### 7MM WINCHESTER SHORT MAGNUM

| CARTRIDGE BULLET | RANGE, YARDS: | 0 | 100 | 200 | 300 | 400 |
|---|---|---|---|---|---|---|
| Federal 140 Nos. AccuBond | velocity, fps: | 3250 | 3040 | 2840 | 2660 | 2470 |
| | energy, ft-lb: | 3285 | 2875 | 2515 | 2190 | 1900 |
| | arc, inches: | | +1.1 | 0 | -5.5 | -15.8 |
| Federal 140 Nos. Bal. Tip | velocity, fps: | 3310 | 3100 | 2900 | 2700 | 2520 |
| | energy, ft-lb: | 3405 | 2985 | 2610 | 2270 | 1975 |
| | arc, inches: | | +1.1 | 0 | -5.2 | 15.2 |
| Federal 150 Nos. Solid Base | velocity, fps: | 3230 | 3010 | 2800 | 2600 | 2410 |
| | energy, ft-lb: | 3475 | 3015 | 2615 | 2255 | 1935 |
| | arc, inches: | | +1.3 | 0 | -5.6 | -16.3 |
| Federal 160 Nos. AccuBond | velocity, fps: | 3120 | 2940 | 2760 | 2590 | 2430 |
| | energy, ft-lb: | 3460 | 3065 | 2710 | 2390 | 2095 |
| | arc, inches: | | +1.3 | 0 | -5.9 | -16.8 |
| Federal 160 Nos. Partition | velocity, fps: | 3160 | 2950 | 2750 | 2560 | 2380. |
| | energy, ft-lb: | 3545 | 3095 | 2690 | 2335 | 2015. |
| | arc, inches: | | +1.2 | 0 | -5.9 | -16.9 |

# Centerfire Rifle Ballistics

## 7MM WINCHESTER SHORT MAGNUM TO 7MM REMINGTON ULTRA MAGNUM

| CARTRIDGE BULLET | RANGE, YARDS: | 0 | 100 | 200 | 300 | 400 |
|---|---|---|---|---|---|---|
| Federal 160 Barnes TS | velocity, fps: | 2990 | 2780 | 2590 | 2400 | 2220 |
| | energy, ft-lb: | 3175 | 2755 | 2380 | 2045 | 1750 |
| | arc, inches: | | +1.5 | 0 | -6.6 | -19.4 |
| Federal 160 Trophy Bonded | velocity, fps: | 3120 | 2880 | 2650 | 2440 | 2230 |
| | energy, ft-lb: | 3460 | 2945 | 2500 | 2105 | 1765 |
| | arc, inches: | | +1.4 | 0 | -6.3 | -18.5 |
| Win. 140 Bal. Silvertip | velocity, fps: | 3225 | 3008 | 2801 | 2603 | 2414 |
| | energy, ft-lb: | 3233 | 2812 | 2438 | 2106 | 1812 |
| | arc, inches: | | +1.2 | 0 | -5.6 | -16.4 |
| Win. 140 AccuBond CT | velocity, fps: | 3225 | 3008 | 2801 | 2604 | 2415 |
| | energy, ft-lb: | 3233 | 2812 | 2439 | 2107 | 1812 |
| | arc, inches: | | +1.2 | 0 | -5.6 | -16.4 |
| Win. 150 Power Point | velocity, fps: | 3200 | 2915 | 2648 | 2396 | 2157 |
| | energy, ft-lb: | 3410 | 2830 | 2335 | 1911 | 1550 |
| | arc, inches: | | +1.3 | 0 | -6.3 | -18.6 |
| Win. 160 AccuBond | velocity, fps: | 3050 | 2862 | 2682 | 2509 | 2342 |
| | energy, ft-lb: | 3306 | 2911 | 2556 | 2237 | 1950 |
| | arc, inches: | | 1.4 | 0 | -6.2 | -17.9 |
| Win. 160 Fail Safe | velocity, fps: | 2990 | 2744 | 2512 | 2291 | 2081 |
| | energy, ft-lb: | 3176 | 2675 | 2241 | 1864 | 1538 |
| | arc, inches: | | +1.6 | 0 | -7.1 | -20.8 |

### 7MM WEATHERBY MAGNUM

| CARTRIDGE BULLET | RANGE, YARDS: | 0 | 100 | 200 | 300 | 400 |
|---|---|---|---|---|---|---|
| Federal 160 Nosler Partition | velocity, fps: | 3050 | 2850 | 2650 | 2470 | 2290 |
| | energy, ft-lb: | 3305 | 2880 | 2505 | 2165 | 1865 |
| | arc, inches: | | +1.4 | 0 | -6.3 | -18.4 |
| Federal 160 Sierra GameKing BTSP | velocity, fps: | 3050 | 2880 | 2710 | 2560 | 2400 |
| | energy, ft-lb: | 3305 | 2945 | 2615 | 2320 | 2050 |
| | arc, inches: | | +1.4 | 0 | -6.1 | -17.4 |
| Federal 160 Trophy Bonded | velocity, fps: | 3050 | 2730 | 2420 | 2140 | 1880. |
| | energy, ft-lb: | 3305 | 2640 | 2085 | 1630 | 1255 |
| | arc, inches: | | +1.6 | 0 | -7.6 | -22.7 |
| Hornady 154 Soft Point | velocity, fps: | 3200 | 2971 | 2753 | 2546 | 2348. |
| | energy, ft-lb: | 3501 | 3017 | 2592 | 2216 | 1885 |
| | arc, inches: | | +1.2 | 0 | -5.8 | -17.0 |
| Hornady 154 SST (or Interbond) | velocity, fps: | 3200 | 3009 | 2825 | 2648 | 2478 |
| | energy, ft-lb: | 3501 | 3096 | 2729 | 2398 | 2100 |
| | arc, inches: | | +1.2 | 0 | -5.7 | -16.5 |
| Hornady 175 Soft Point | velocity, fps: | 2910 | 2709 | 2516 | 2331 | 2154 |
| | energy, ft-lb: | 3290 | 2850 | 2459 | 2111 | 1803 |
| | arc, inches: | | +1.6 | 0 | -7.1 | -20.6 |
| Wby. 139 Pointed Expanding | velocity, fps: | 3340 | 3079 | 2834 | 2601 | 2380. |
| | energy, ft-lb: | 3443 | 2926 | 2478 | 2088 | 1748 |
| | arc, inches: | | +2.9 | +3.6 | 0 | -8.7 |
| Wby. 140 Nosler Partition | velocity, fps: | 3303 | 3069 | 2847 | 2636 | 2434 |
| | energy, ft-lb: | 3391 | 2927 | 2519 | 2159 | 1841 |
| | arc, inches: | | +2.9 | +3.6 | 0 | -8.5 |
| Wby. 150 Nosler Bal. Tip | velocity, fps: | 3300 | 3093 | 2896 | 2708 | 2527 |
| | energy, ft-lb: | 3627 | 3187 | 2793 | 2442 | 2127 |
| | arc, inches: | | +2.8 | +3.5 | 0 | -8.2 |
| Wby. 150 Barnes X | velocitiy, fps: | 3100 | 2901 | 2710 | 2527 | 2352 |
| | energy, ft-lb: | 3200 | 2802 | 2446 | 2127 | 1842 |
| | arc, inches: | | +3.3 | +4.0 | 0 | -9.4 |
| Wby. 154 Pointed Expanding | velocity, fps: | 3260 | 3028 | 2807 | 2597 | 2397 |
| | energy, ft-lb: | 3634 | 3134 | 2694 | 2307 | 1964 |
| | arc, inches: | | +3.0 | +3.7 | 0 | -8.8 |
| Wby. 160 Nosler Partition | velocity, fps: | 3200 | 2991 | 2791 | 2600 | 2417 |
| | energy, ft-lb: | 3638 | 3177 | 2767 | 2401 | 2075. |
| | arc, inches: | | +3.1 | +3.8 | 0 | -8.9 |
| Wby. 175 Pointed Expanding | velocity, fps: | 3070 | 2861 | 2662 | 2471 | 2288 |
| | energy, ft-lb: | 3662 | 3181 | 2753 | 2373 | 2034 |
| | arc, inches: | | +3.5 | +4.2 | 0 | -9.9 |

| CARTRIDGE BULLET | RANGE, YARDS: | 0 | 100 | 200 | 300 | 400 |
|---|---|---|---|---|---|---|

### 7MM DAKOTA

| CARTRIDGE BULLET | | 0 | 100 | 200 | 300 | 400 |
|---|---|---|---|---|---|---|
| Dakota 140 Barnes X | velocity, fps: | 3500 | 3253 | 3019 | 2798 | 2587 |
| | energy, ft-lb: | 3807 | 3288 | 2833 | 2433 | 2081 |
| | arc, inches: | | +2.0 | +2.1 | -1.5 | -9.6 |
| Dakota 160 Barnes X | velocity, fps: | 3200 | 3001 | 2811 | 2630 | 2455 |
| | energy, ft-lb: | 3637 | 3200 | 2808 | 2456 | 2140 |
| | arc, inches: | | +2.1 | +1.9 | -2.8 | -12.5 |

### 7MM STW

| CARTRIDGE BULLET | | 0 | 100 | 200 | 300 | 400 |
|---|---|---|---|---|---|---|
| A-Square 140 Nos. Bal. Tip | velocity, fps: | 3450 | 3254 | 3067 | 2888 | 2715 |
| | energy, ft-lb: | 3700 | 3291 | 2924 | 2592 | 2292 |
| | arc, inches: | | +2.2 | +3.0 | 0 | -7.3 |
| A-Square 160 Nosler Part. | velocity, fps: | 3250 | 3071 | 2900 | 2735 | 2576. |
| | energy, ft-lb: | 3752 | 3351 | 2987 | 2657 | 2357 |
| | arc, inches: | | +2.8 | +3.5 | 0 | -8.2 |
| A-Square 160 SP boat-tail | velocity, fps: | 3250 | 3087 | 2930 | 2778 | 2631 |
| | energy, ft-lb: | 3752 | 3385 | 3049 | 2741 | 2460 |
| | arc, inches: | | +2.8 | +3.4 | 0 | -8.0 |
| Federal 140 Trophy Bonded | velocity, fps: | 3330 | 3080 | 2850 | 2630 | 2420 |
| | energy, ft-lb: | 3435 | 2950 | 2520 | 2145 | 1815 |
| | arc, inches: | | +1.1 | 0 | -5.4 | -15.8 |
| Federal 150 Trophy Bonded | velocity, fps: | 3250 | 3010 | 2770 | 2560 | 2350. |
| | energy, ft-lb: | 3520 | 3010 | 2565 | 2175 | 1830 |
| | arc, inches: | | +1.2 | 0 | -5.7 | -16.7 |
| Federal 160 Sierra GameKing BTSP | velocity, fps: | 3200 | 3020 | 2850 | 2670 | 2530. |
| | energy, ft-lb: | 3640 | 3245 | 2890 | 2570 | 2275 |
| | arc, inches: | | +1.1 | 0 | -5.5 | -15.7 |
| Nosler 175 ABLR | velocity, fps: | 2900 | 2760 | 2625 | 2493 | 2366 |
| | energy, ft-lb: | 3267 | 2960 | 2677 | 2416 | 2175 |
| | arc, inches: | -1.5 | +1.5 | 0 | -6.6 | -18.8 |
| Rem. 140 PSP Core-Lokt | velocity, fps: | 3325 | 3064 | 2818 | 2585 | 2364 |
| | energy, ft-lb: | 3436 | 2918 | 2468 | 2077 | 1737 |
| | arc, inches: | | +2.0 | +1.7 | -2.9 | -12.8 |
| Rem. 140 Swift A-Frame | velocity, fps: | 3325 | 3020 | 2735 | 2467 | 2215 |
| | energy, ft-lb: | 3436 | 2834 | 2324 | 1892 | 1525 |
| | arc, inches: | | +2.1 | +1.8 | -3.1 | -13.8 |
| Speer 145 Grand Slam | velocity, fps: | 3300 | 2992 | 2075 | 2435 | |
| | energy, ft-lb: | 3506 | 2882 | 2355 | 1909 | |
| | arc, inches: | | +1.2 | 0 | -6.0 | -17.8 |
| Win. 140 Ballistic Silvertip | velocity, fps: | 3320 | 3100 | 2890 | 2690 | 2499 |
| | energy, ft-lb: | 3427 | 2982 | 2597 | 2250 | 1941 |
| | arc, inches: | | +1.1 | 0 | -5.2 | -15.2 |
| Win. 150 Power-Point | velocity, fps: | 3250 | 2957 | 2683 | 2424 | 2181 |
| | energy, ft-lb: | 3519 | 2913 | 2398 | 1958 | 1584 |
| | arc, inches: | | +1.2 | 0 | -6.1 | -18.1 |
| Win. 160 Fail Safe | velocity, fps: | 3150 | 2894 | 2652 | 2422 | 2204 |
| | energy, ft-lb: | 3526 | 2976 | 2499 | 2085 | 1727 |
| | arc, inches: | | +1.3 | 0 | -6.3 | -18.5 |

### 7MM REMINGTON ULTRA MAGNUM

| CARTRIDGE BULLET | | 0 | 100 | 200 | 300 | 400 |
|---|---|---|---|---|---|---|
| Nosler 175 ABLR | velocity, fps: | 3040 | 2896 | 2756 | 2621 | 2490 |
| | energy, ft-lb: | 3590 | 3258 | 2952 | 2669 | 2409 |
| | arc, inches: | -1.5 | +1.3 | 0 | -5.9 | -16.9 |
| Rem. 140 PSP Core-Lokt | velocity, fps: | 3425 | 3158 | 2907 | 2669 | 2444 |
| | energy, ft-lb: | 3646 | 3099 | 2626 | 2214 | 1856 |
| | arc, inches: | | +1.8 | +1.6 | -2.7 | -11.9 |
| Rem. 140 Nosler Partition | velocity, fps: | 3425 | 3184 | 2956 | 2740 | 2534 |
| | energy, ft-lb: | 3646 | 3151 | 2715 | 2333 | 1995 |
| | arc, inches: | | +1.7 | +1.6 | -2.6 | -11.4 |
| Rem. 160 Nosler Partition | velocity, fps: | 3200 | 2991 | 2791 | 2600 | 2417 |
| | energy, ft-lb: | 3637 | 3177 | 2767 | 2401 | 2075 |
| | arc, inches: | | +2.1 | +1.8 | -3.0 | -12.9 |

| CARTRIDGE BULLET | RANGE, YARDS: | 0 | 100 | 200 | 300 | 400 |
|---|---|---|---|---|---|---|
| **7.21 (.284) FIREHAWK** | | | | | | |
| Lazzeroni 140 Nosler Part. | velocity, fps: | 3580 | 3349 | 3130 | 2923 | 2724 |
| | energy, ft-lb: | 3985 | 3488 | 3048 | 2656 | 2308 |
| | arc, inches: | | +2.2 | +2.9 | 0 | -7.0 |
| Lazzeroni 160 Swift A-Fr. | velocity, fps: | 3385 | 3167 | 2961 | 2763 | 2574 |
| | energy, ft-lb: | 4072 | 3565 | 3115 | 2713 | 2354 |
| | arc, inches: | | +2.6 | +3.3 | 0 | -7.8 |
| **7.5x55 SWISS** | | | | | | |
| Norma 180 Soft Point | velocity, fps: | 2651 | 2432 | 2223 | 2025 | |
| | energy, ft-lb: | 2810 | 2364 | 1976 | 1639 | |
| | arc, inches: | | +2.2 | 0 | -9.3 | |
| Norma 180 Oryx | velocity, fps: | 2493 | 2222 | 1968 | 1734 | |
| | energy, ft-lb: | 2485 | 1974 | 1549 | 1201 | |
| | arc, inches: | | +2.7 | 0 | -11.8 | |
| **7.62x39 RUSSIAN** | | | | | | |
| Federal 123 Hi-Shok | velocity, fps: | 2300 | 2030 | 1780 | 1550 | 1350 |
| | energy, ft-lb: | 1445 | 1125 | 860 | 655 | 500. |
| | arc, inches: | | 0 | -7.0 | -25.1 | |
| Federal 124 FMJ | velocity, fps: | 2300 | 2030 | 1780 | 1560 | 1360 |
| | energy, ft-lb: | 1455 | 1135 | 875 | 670 | 510 |
| | arc, inches: | | +3.5 | 0 | -14.6 | -43.5 |
| PMC 123 FMJ | velocity, fps: | 2350 | 2072 | 1817 | 1583 | 1368 |
| | energy, ft-lb: | 1495 | 1162 | 894 | 678 | 507 |
| | arc, inches: | | 0 | -5.0 | -26.4 | -67.8 |
| PMC 125 Pointed Soft Point | velocity, fps: | 2320 | 2046 | 1794 | 1563 | 1350 |
| | energy, ft-lb: | 1493 | 1161 | 893 | 678 | 505. |
| | arc, inches: | | 0 | -5.2 | -27.5 | -70.6 |
| Rem. 125 Pointed Soft Point | velocity, fps: | 2365 | 2062 | 1783 | 1533 | 1320 |
| | energy, ft-lb: | 1552 | 1180 | 882 | 652 | 483 |
| | arc, inches: | | 0 | -6.7 | -24.5 | |
| Win. 123 Soft Point | velocity, fps: | 2365 | 2033 | 1731 | 1465 | 1248 |
| | energy, ft-lb: | 1527 | 1129 | 818 | 586 | 425 |
| | arc, inches: | | +3.8 | 0 | -15.4 | -46.3 |
| **.30 CARBINE** | | | | | | |
| Federal 110 Hi-Shok RN | velocity, fps: | 1990 | 1570 | 1240 | 1040 | 920 |
| | energy, ft-lb: | 965 | 600 | 375 | 260 | 210 |
| | arc, inches: | | 0 | -12.8 | -46.9 | |
| Federal 110 FMJ | velocity, fps: | 1990 | 1570 | 1240 | 1040 | 920 |
| | energy, ft-lb: | 965 | 600 | 375 | 260 | 210 |
| | arc, inches: | | 0 | -12.8 | -46.9 | |
| Magtech 110 FMC | velocity, fps: | 1990 | 1654 | | | |
| | energy, ft-lb: | 965 | 668 | | | |
| | arc, inches: | | 0 | | | |
| PMC 110 FMJ | (and RNSP)velocity, fps: | 1927 | 1548 | 1248 | | |
| | energy, ft-lb: | 906 | 585 | 380 | | |
| | arc, inches: | | 0 | -14.2 | | |
| Rem. 110 Soft Point | velocity, fps: | 1990 | 1567 | 1236 | 1035 | 923 |
| | energy, ft-lb: | 967 | 600 | 373 | 262 | 208 |
| | arc, inches: | | 0 | -12.9 | -48.6 | |
| Win. 110 Hollow Soft Point | velocity, fps: | 1990 | 1567 | 1236 | 1035 | 923 |
| | energy, ft-lb: | 967 | 600 | 373 | 262 | 208 |
| | arc, inches: | | 0 | -13.5 | -49.9 | |
| **.30 T/C HORNADAY** | | | | | | |
| Hornady 150 | velocity, fps | 3000 | 2772 | 2555 | 2348 | |
| | energy, ft-lb | 2997 | 2558 | 2176 | 1836 | |
| | arc, inches | -1.5 | +1.5 | 0 | -6.9 | |
| Hornady 165 | velocity, fps | 2850 | 2644 | 2447 | 2258 | |
| | energy, ft-lb | 2975 | 2560 | 2193 | 1868 | |
| | arc, inches | -1.5 | +1.7 | 0 | -7.6 | |

| CARTRIDGE BULLET | RANGE, YARDS: | 0 | 100 | 200 | 300 | 400 |
|---|---|---|---|---|---|---|
| **.30-30 WINCHESTER** | | | | | | |
| Federal 125 Hi-Shok HP | velocity, fps: | 2570 | 2090 | 1660 | 1320 | 1080 |
| | energy, ft-lb: | 1830 | 1210 | 770 | 480 | 320 |
| | arc, inches: | | +3.3 | 0 | -16.0 | -50.9 |
| Federal 150 Hi-Shok FN | velocity, fps: | 2390 | 2020 | 1680 | 1400 | 1180 |
| | energy, ft-lb: | 1900 | 1355 | 945 | 650 | 460 |
| | arc, inches: | | +3.6 | 0 | -15.9 | -49.1 |
| Federal 170 Hi-Shok RN | velocity, fps: | 2200 | 1900 | 1620 | 1380 | 1190 |
| | energy, ft-lb: | 1830 | 1355 | 990 | 720 | 535 |
| | arc, inches: | | +4.1 | 0 | -17.4 | -52.4 |
| Federal 170 Sierra Pro-Hunt. | velocity, fps: | 2200 | 1820 | 1500 | 1240 | 1060 |
| | energy, ft-lb: | 1830 | 1255 | 845 | 575 | 425 |
| | arc, inches: | | +4.5 | 0 | -20.0 | -63.5 |
| Federal 170 Nosler Partition | velocity, fps: | 2200 | 1900 | 1620 | 1380 | 1190 |
| | energy, ft-lb: | 1830 | 1355 | 990 | 720 | 535 |
| | arc, inches: | | +4.1 | 0 | -17.4 | -52.4 |
| Hornady 150 Round Nose | velocity, fps: | 2390 | 1973 | 1605 | 1303 | 1095 |
| | energy, ft-lb: | 1902 | 1296 | 858 | 565 | 399 |
| | arc, inches: | | 0 | -8.2 | -30.0 | |
| Hornady 160 Evolution | velocity, fps: | 2400 | 2150 | 1916 | 1699 | |
| | energy, ft-lb: | 2046 | 1643 | 1304 | 1025 | |
| | arc, inches: | | +3.0 | 0.2 | -12.1 | |
| Hornady 170 Flat Point | velocity, fps: | 2200 | 1895 | 1619 | 1381 | 1191 |
| | energy, ft-lb: | 1827 | 1355 | 989 | 720 | 535 |
| | arc, inches: | | 0 | -8.9 | -31.1 | |
| Norma 150 Soft Point | velocity, fps: | 2329 | 2008 | 1716 | 1459 | |
| | energy, ft-lb: | 1807 | 1344 | 981 | 709 | |
| | arc, inches: | | +3.6 | 0 | -15.5 | |
| PMC 150 Starfire HP | velocity, fps: | 2100 | 1769 | 1478 | | |
| | energy, ft-lb: | 1469 | 1042 | 728 | | |
| | arc, inches: | | 0 | -10.8 | | |
| PMC 150 Flat Nose | velocity, fps: | 2300 | 1943 | 1627 | | |
| | energy, ft-lb: | 1762 | 1257 | 881 | | |
| | arc, inches: | | 0 | -7.8 | | |
| PMC 170 Flat Nose | velocity, fps: | 2150 | 1840 | 1566 | | |
| | energy, ft-lb: | 1745 | 1277 | 926 | | |
| | arc, inches: | | 0 | -8.9 | | |
| Rem. 55 PSP (sabot) "Accelerator" | velocity, fps: | 3400 | 2693 | 2085 | 1570 | 1187 |
| | energy, ft-lb: | 1412 | 886 | 521 | 301 | 172 |
| | arc, inches: | | +1.7 | 0 | -9.9 | -34.3 |
| Rem. 150 SP Core-Lokt | velocity, fps: | 2390 | 1973 | 1605 | 1303 | 1095 |
| | energy, ft-lb: | 1902 | 1296 | 858 | 565 | 399 |
| | arc, inches: | | 0 | -7.6 | -28.8 | |
| Rem. 170 SP Core-Lokt | velocity, fps: | 2200 | 1895 | 1619 | 1381 | 1191 |
| | energy, ft-lb: | 1827 | 1355 | 989 | 720 | 535 |
| | arc, inches: | | 0 | -8.3 | -29.9 | |
| Rem. 170 HP Core-Lokt | velocity, fps: | 2200 | 1895 | 1619 | 1381 | 1191. |
| | energy, ft-lb: | 1827 | 1355 | 989 | 720 | 535 |
| | arc, inches: | | 0 | -8.3 | -29.9 | |
| Speer 150 Flat Nose | velocity, fps: | 2370 | 2067 | 1788 | 1538 | |
| | energy, ft-lb: | 1870 | 1423 | 1065 | 788 | |
| | arc, inches: | | +3.3 | 0 | -14.4 | -43.7 |
| Win. 150 Hollow Point | velocity, fps: | 2390 | 2018 | 1684 | 1398 | 1177 |
| | energy, ft-lb: | 1902 | 1356 | 944 | 651 | 461 |
| | arc, inches: | | 0 | -7.7 | -27.9 | |
| Win. 150 Power-Point | velocity, fps: | 2390 | 2018 | 1684 | 1398 | 1177 |
| | energy, ft-lb: | 1902 | 1356 | 944 | 651 | 461 |
| | arc, inches: | | 0 | -7.7 | -27.9 | |
| Win. 150 Silvertip | velocity, fps: | 2390 | 2018 | 1684 | 1398 | 1177 |
| | energy, ft-lb: | 1902 | 1356 | 944 | 651 | 461 |
| | arc, inches: | | 0 | -7.7 | -27.9 | |

**BALLISTICS**

# Centerfire Rifle Ballistics

## .30-30 WINCHESTER TO .308 WINCHESTER

| CARTRIDGE BULLET | RANGE, YARDS: | 0 | 100 | 200 | 300 | 400 |
|---|---|---|---|---|---|---|
| Win. 150 Power-Point Plus | velocity, fps: | 2480 | 2095 | 1747 | 1446 | 1209 |
| | energy, ft-lb: | 2049 | 1462 | 1017 | 697 | 487 |
| | arc, inches: | | 0 | -6.5 | -24.5 | |
| Win. 170 Power-Point | velocity, fps: | 2200 | 1895 | 1619 | 1381 | 1191 |
| | energy, ft-lb: | 1827 | 1355 | 989 | 720 | 535. |
| | arc, inches: | | 0 | -8.9 | -31.1 | |
| Win. 170 Silvertip | velocity, fps: | 2200 | 1895 | 1619 | 1381 | 1191 |
| | energy, ft-lb: | 1827 | 1355 | 989 | 720 | 535 |
| | arc, inches: | | 0 | -8.9 | -31.1 | |

### .300 SAVAGE

| CARTRIDGE BULLET | RANGE, YARDS: | 0 | 100 | 200 | 300 | 400 |
|---|---|---|---|---|---|---|
| Federal 150 Hi-Shok | velocity, fps: | 2630 | 2350 | 2100 | 1850 | 1630 |
| | energy, ft-lb: | 2305 | 1845 | 1460 | 1145 | 885 |
| | arc, inches: | | +2.4 | 0 | -10.4 | -30.9 |
| Federal 180 Hi-Shok | velocity, fps: | 2350 | 2140 | 1940 | 1750 | 1570 |
| | energy, ft-lb: | 2205 | 1825 | 1495 | 1215 | 985 |
| | arc, inches: | | +3.1 | 0 | -12.4 | -36.1 |
| Rem. 150 PSP Core-Lokt | velocity, fps: | 2630 | 2354 | 2095 | 1853 | 1631 |
| | energy, ft-lb: | 2303 | 1845 | 1462 | 1143 | 806. |
| | arc, inches: | | +2.4 | 0 | -10.4 | -30.9 |
| Rem. 180 SP Core-Lokt | velocity, fps: | 2350 | 2025 | 1728 | 1467 | 1252 |
| | energy, ft-lb: | 2207 | 1639 | 1193 | 860 | 626 |
| | arc, inches: | | 0 | -7.1 | -25.9 | |
| Win. 150 Power-Point | velocity, fps: | 2630 | 2311 | 2015 | 1743 | 1500 |
| | energy, ft-lb: | 2303 | 1779 | 1352 | 1012 | 749 |
| | arc, inches: | | +2.8 | 0 | -11.5 | -34.4 |

### .307 WINCHESTER

| CARTRIDGE BULLET | RANGE, YARDS: | 0 | 100 | 200 | 300 | 400 |
|---|---|---|---|---|---|---|
| Win. 180 Power-Point | velocity, fps: | 2510 | 2179 | 1874 | 1599 | 1362 |
| | energy, ft-lb: | 2519 | 1898 | 1404 | 1022 | 742 |
| | arc, inches: | | +1.5 | -3.6 | -18.6 | -47.1 |

### .30-40 KRAG

| CARTRIDGE BULLET | RANGE, YARDS: | 0 | 100 | 200 | 300 | 400 |
|---|---|---|---|---|---|---|
| Rem. 180 PSP Core-Lokt | velocity, fps: | 2430 | 2213 | 2007 | 1813 | 1632. |
| | energy, ft-lb: | 2360 | 1957 | 1610 | 1314 | 1064 |
| | arc, inches, s: | | 0 | -5.6 | -18.6 | |
| Win. 180 Power-Point | velocity, fps: | 2430 | 2099 | 1795 | 1525 | 1298 |
| | energy, ft-lb: | 2360 | 1761 | 1288 | 929 | 673 |
| | arc, inches, s: | | 0 | -7.1 | -25.0 | |

### 7.62x54R RUSSIAN

| CARTRIDGE BULLET | RANGE, YARDS: | 0 | 100 | 200 | 300 | 400 |
|---|---|---|---|---|---|---|
| Norma 150 Soft Point | velocity, fps: | 2953 | 2622 | 2314 | 2028 | |
| | energy, ft-lb: | 2905 | 2291 | 1784 | 1370 | |
| | arc, inches: | | +1.8 | 0 | -8.3 | |
| Norma 180 Alaska | velocity, fps: | 2575 | 2362 | 2159 | 1967 | |
| | energy, ft-lb: | 2651 | 2231 | 1864 | 1546 | |
| | arc, inches: | | +2.9 | 0 | -12.9 | |
| Winchester 180 FMJ | velocity, fps: | 2580 | 2401 | 2230 | 2066 | 1909 |
| | energy, ft-lb: | 2658 | 2304 | 1987 | 1706 | 1457 |
| | arc, inches: | -1.5 | +2.6 | 0 | -9.6 | -27.3 |
| Winchester 180 SP | velocity, fps: | 2625 | 2302 | 2003 | 1729 | 1485 |
| | energy, ft-lb: | 2751 | 2117 | 1603 | 1195 | 882 |
| | arc, inches: | -1.5 | +2.9 | 0 | -11.6 | -34.9 |

### .308 MARLIN EXPRESS

| CARTRIDGE BULLET | RANGE, YARDS: | 0 | 100 | 200 | 300 | 400 |
|---|---|---|---|---|---|---|
| Hornady 160 | velocity, fps | 2660 | 2438 | 2226 | 2026 | 1836 |
| | energy, ft-lb | 2513 | 2111 | 1761 | 1457 | 1197 |
| | arc, inches | -1.5 | +3.0 | +1.7 | -6.7 | -23.5 |
| Hornady 140 MonoFlex | velocity, fps: | 2800 | 2532 | 2279 | 2040 | 1818 |
| | energy, ft-lb: | 2437 | 1992 | 1614 | 1294 | 1027 |
| | arc, inches: | -1.5 | +2.0 | 0 | -8.7 | -25.8 |

### .308 WINCHESTER

| CARTRIDGE BULLET | RANGE, YARDS: | 0 | 100 | 200 | 300 | 400 |
|---|---|---|---|---|---|---|
| Black Hills 150 Nosler B. Tip | velocity, fps: | 2800 | | | | |
| | energy, ft-lb: | 2611 | | | | |
| | arc, inches: | | | | | |
| Black Hills 165 Nosler B. Tip (and SP) | velocity, fps: | 2650 | | | | |
| | energy, ft-lb: | 2573 | | | | |
| | arc, inches: | | | | | |
| Black Hills 168 Barnes X (and Match) | velocity, fps: | 2650 | | | | |
| | energy, ft-lb: | 2620 | | | | |
| | arc, inches: | | | | | |
| Black Hills 175 Match | velocity, fps: | 2600 | | | | |
| | energy, ft-lb: | 2657 | | | | |
| | arc, inches: | | | | | |
| Black Hills 180 AccuBond | velocity, fps: | 2600 | | | | |
| | energy, ft-lb: | 2701 | | | | |
| | arc, inches: | | | | | |
| Federal 150 Hi-Shok | velocity, fps: | 2820 | 2530 | 2260 | 2010 | 1770 |
| | energy, ft-lb: | 2650 | 2140 | 1705 | 1345 | 1050 |
| | arc, inches: | | +2.0 | 0 | -8.8 | -26.3 |
| Federal 150 Nosler Bal. Tip. | velocity, fps: | 2820 | 2610 | 2410 | 2220 | 2040 |
| | energy, ft-lb: | 2650 | 2270 | 1935 | 1640 | 1380 |
| | arc, inches: | | +1.8 | 0 | -7.8 | -22.7 |
| Federal 150 FMJ boat-tail | velocity, fps: | 2820 | 2620 | 2430 | 2250 | 2070 |
| | energy, ft-lb: | 2650 | 2285 | 1965 | 1680 | 1430 |
| | arc, inches: | | +1.8 | 0 | -7.7 | -22.4 |
| Federal 150 Barnes XLC | velocity, fps: | 2820 | 2610 | 2400 | 2210 | 2030 |
| | energy, ft-lb: | 2650 | 2265 | 1925 | 1630 | 1370 |
| | arc, inches: | | +1.8 | 0 | -7.8 | -22.9 |
| Federal 155 Sierra MatchKg. BTHP | velocity, fps: | 2950 | 2740 | 2540 | 2350 | 2170 |
| | energy, ft-lb: | 2995 | 2585 | 2225 | 1905 | 1620 |
| | arc, inches: | | +1.9 | 0 | -8.9 | -22.6 |
| Federal 165 Sierra GameKing BTSP | velocity, fps: | 2700 | 2520 | 2330 | 2160 | 1990 |
| | energy, ft-lb: | 2670 | 2310 | 1990 | 1700 | 1450 |
| | arc, inches: | | +2.0 | 0 | -8.4 | -24.3 |
| Federal 165 Trophy Bonded | velocity, fps: | 2700 | 2440 | 2200 | 1970 | 1760 |
| | energy, ft-lb: | 2670 | 2185 | 1775 | 1425 | 1135 |
| | arc, inches: | | +2.2 | 0 | -9.4 | -27.7 |
| Federal 165 Tr. Bonded HE | velocity, fps: | 2870 | 2600 | 2350 | 2120 | 1890 |
| | energy, ft-lb: | 3020 | 2485 | 2030 | 1640 | 1310 |
| | arc, inches: | | +1.8 | 0 | -8.2 | -24.0 |
| Federal 168 Sierra MatchKg. BTHP | velocity, fps: | 2600 | 2410 | 2230 | 2060 | 1890 |
| | energy, ft-lb: | 2520 | 2170 | 1855 | 1580 | 1340. |
| | arc, inches: | | +2.1 | 0 | +8.9 | +25.9 |
| Federal 180 Hi-Shok | velocity, fps: | 2620 | 2390 | 2180 | 1970 | 1780 |
| | energy, ft-lb: | 2745 | 2290 | 1895 | 1555 | 1270 |
| | arc, inches: | | +2.3 | 0 | -9.7 | -28.3 |
| Federal 180 Sierra Pro-Hunt. | velocity, fps: | 2620 | 2410 | 2200 | 2010 | 1820 |
| | energy, ft-lb: | 2745 | 2315 | 1940 | 1610 | 1330 |
| | arc, inches: | | +2.3 | 0 | -9.3 | -27.1 |
| Federal 180 Nosler Partition | velocity, fps: | 2620 | 2430 | 2240 | 2060 | 1890 |
| | energy, ft-lb: | 2745 | 2355 | 2005 | 1700 | 1430. |
| | arc, inches: | | +2.2 | 0 | -9.2 | -26.5 |
| Federal 180 Nosler Part. HE | velocity, fps: | 2740 | 2550 | 2370 | 2200 | 2030 |
| | energy, ft-lb: | 3000 | 2600 | 2245 | 1925 | 1645 |
| | arc, inches: | | +1.9 | 0 | -8.2 | -23.5 |
| Hornady 110 TAP-FPD | velocity, fps: | 3165 | 2830 | 2519 | 2228 | 1957 |
| | energy, ft-lb: | 2446 | 1956 | 1649 | 1212 | 935 |
| | arc, inches: | | +1.4 | 0 | -6.9 | -20.9 |
| Hornady 110 Urban Tactical | velocity, fps: | 3170 | 2825 | 2504 | 2206 | 1937 |
| | energy, ft-lb: | 2454 | 1950 | 1532 | 1189 | 916 |
| | arc, inches: | | +1.5 | 0 | -7.2 | -21.2 |

BALLISTICS

| CARTRIDGE BULLET | RANGE, YARDS: | 0 | 100 | 200 | 300 | 400 |
|---|---|---|---|---|---|---|
| Hornady 150 SP boat-tail | velocity, fps: | 2820 | 2560 | 2315 | 2084 | 1866 |
| | energy, ft-lb: | 2648 | 2183 | 1785 | 1447 | 1160 |
| | arc, inches: | | +2.0 | 0 | -8.5 | -25.2 |
| Hornady 150 SST | velocity, fps: | 2820 | 2593 | 2378 | 2174 | 1984 |
| (or Interbond) | energy, ft-lb: | 2648 | 2240 | 1884 | 1574 | 1311 |
| | arc, inches: | | +1.9 | 0 | -8.1 | -22.9 |
| Hornady 150 SST LM | velocity, fps: | 3000 | 2765 | 2541 | 2328 | 2127 |
| (or Interbond) | energy, ft-lb: | 2997 | 2545 | 2150 | 1805 | 1506. |
| | arc, inches: | | +1.5 | 0 | -7.1 | -20.6 |
| Hornady 150 SP LM | velocity, fps: | 2980 | 2703 | 2442 | 2195 | 1964 |
| | energy, ft-lb: | 2959 | 2433 | 1986 | 1606 | 1285 |
| | arc, inches: | | +1.6 | 0 | -7.5 | -22.2 |
| Hornady 155 A-Max | velocity, fps: | 2815 | 2610 | 2415 | 2229 | 2051 |
| | energy, ft-lb: | 2727 | 2345 | 2007 | 1709 | 1448 |
| | arc, inches: | | +1.9 | 0 | -7.9 | -22.6 |
| Hornady 155 TAP-FPD | velocity, fps: | 2785 | 2577 | 2379 | 2189 | 2008 |
| | energy, ft-lb: | 2669 | 2285 | 1947 | 1649 | 1387 |
| | arc, inches: | | +1.9 | 0 | -8.0 | -23.3 |
| Hornady 165 SP boat-tail | velocity, fps: | 2700 | 2496 | 2301 | 2115 | 1937 |
| | energy, ft-lb: | 2670 | 2283 | 1940 | 1639 | 1375 |
| | arc, inches: | | +2.0 | 0 | -8.7 | -25.2 |
| Hornady 165 SPBT LM | velocity, fps: | 2870 | 2658 | 2456 | 2283 | 2078 |
| | energy, ft-lb: | 3019 | 2589 | 2211 | 1877 | 1583 |
| | arc, inches: | | +1.7 | 0 | -7.5 | -21.8 |
| Hornady 165 SST LM | velocity, fps: | 2880 | 2672 | 2474 | 2284 | 2103 |
| (or Interbond) | energy, ft-lb: | 3038 | 2616 | 2242 | 1911 | 1620 |
| | arc, inches: | | +1.6 | 0 | -7.3 | -21.2 |
| Hornady 168 BTHP Match | velocity, fps: | 2700 | 2524 | 2354 | 2191 | 2035. |
| | energy, ft-lb: | 2720 | 2377 | 2068 | 1791 | 1545 |
| | arc, inches: | | +2.0 | 0 | -8.4 | -23.9 |
| Hornady 168 BTHP Match LM | velocity, fps: | 2640 | 2630 | 2429 | 2238 | 2056 |
| | energy, ft-lb: | 3008 | 2579 | 2201 | 1868 | 1577 |
| | arc, inches: | | +1.8 | 0 | -7.8 | -22.4 |
| Hornady 168 A-Max Match | velocity, fps: | 2620 | 2446 | 2280 | 2120 | 1972 |
| | energy, ft-lb: | 2560 | 2232 | 1939 | 1677 | 1450 |
| | arc, inches: | | +2.6 | 0 | -9.2 | -25.6 |
| Hornady 168 A-Max | velocity, fps: | 2700 | 2491 | 2292 | 2102 | 1921 |
| | energy, ft-lb: | 2719 | 2315 | 1959 | 1648 | 1377 |
| | arc, inches: | | +2.4 | 0 | -9.0 | -25.9 |
| Hornady 168 TAP-FPD | velocity, fps: | 2700 | 2513 | 2333 | 2161 | 1996 |
| | energy, ft-lb: | 2719 | 2355 | 2030 | 1742 | 1486 |
| | arc, inches: | | +2.0 | 0 | -8.4 | -24.3 |
| Hornady 178 A-Max | velocity, fps: | 2965 | 2778 | 2598 | 2425 | 2259 |
| | energy, ft-lb: | 3474 | 3049 | 2666 | 2323 | 2017 |
| | arc, inches: | | +1.6 | 0 | -6.9 | -19.8 |
| Hornady 180 A-Max Match | velocity, fps: | 2550 | 2397 | 2249 | 2106 | 1974 |
| | energy, ft-lb: | 2598 | 2295 | 2021 | 1773 | 1557 |
| | arc, inches: | | +2.7 | 0 | -9.5 | -26.2 |
| Norma 150 Nosler Bal. Tip | velocity, fps: | 2822 | 2588 | 2365 | 2154 | |
| | energy, ft-lb: | 2653 | 2231 | 1864 | 1545 | |
| | arc, inches: | | +1.6 | 0 | -7.1 | |
| Norma 150 Soft Point | velocity, fps: | 2861 | 2537 | 2235 | 1954 | |
| | energy, ft-lb: | 2727 | 2144 | 1664 | 1272 | |
| | arc, inches: | | +2.0 | 0 | -9.0 | |
| Norma 165 TXP Swift A-Fr. | velocity, fps: | 2700 | 2459 | 2231 | 2015 | |
| | energy, ft-lb: | 2672 | 2216 | 1824 | 1488 | |
| | arc, inches: | | +2.1 | 0 | -9.1 | |
| Norma 180 Plastic Point | velocity, fps: | 2612 | 2365 | 2131 | 1911 | |
| | energy, ft-lb: | 2728 | 2235 | 1815 | 1460 | |
| | arc, inches: | | +2.4 | 0 | -10.1 | |
| Norma 180 Nosler Partition | velocity, fps: | 2612 | 2414 | 2225 | 2044 | |
| | energy, ft-lb: | 2728 | 2330 | 1979 | 1670 | |
| | arc, inches: | | +2.2 | 0 | -9.3 | |

| CARTRIDGE BULLET | RANGE, YARDS: | 0 | 100 | 200 | 300 | 400 |
|---|---|---|---|---|---|---|
| Norma 180 Alaska | velocity, fps: | 2612 | 2269 | 1953 | 1667 | |
| | energy, ft-lb: | 2728 | 2059 | 1526 | 1111 | |
| | arc, inches: | | +2.7 | 0 | -11.9 | |
| Norma 180 Vulkan | velocity, fps: | 2612 | 2325 | 2056 | 1806 | |
| | energy, ft-lb: | 2728 | 2161 | 1690 | 1304 | |
| | arc, inches: | | +2.5 | 0 | -10.8 | |
| Norma 180 Oryx | velocity, fps: | 2612 | 2305 | 2019 | 1755 | |
| | energy, ft-lb: | 2728 | 2124 | 1629 | 1232 | |
| | arc, inches: | | +2.5 | 0 | -11.1 | |
| Norma 200 Vulkan | velocity, fps: | 2461 | 2215 | 1983 | 1767 | |
| | energy, ft-lb: | 2690 | 2179 | 1747 | 1387 | |
| | arc, inches: | | +2.8 | 0 | -11.7 | |
| PMC 147 FMJ boat-tail | velocity, fps: | 2751 | 2473 | 2257 | 2052 | 1859 |
| | energy, ft-lb: | 2428 | 2037 | 1697 | 1403 | 1150 |
| | arc, inches: | | +2.3 | 0 | -9.3 | -27.3 |
| PMC 150 Barnes X | velocity, fps: | 2700 | 2504 | 2316 | 2135 | 1964 |
| | energy, ft-lb: | 2428 | 2087 | 1786 | 1518 | 1284 |
| | arc, inches: | | +2.0 | 0 | -8.6 | -24.7 |
| PMC 150 Pointed Soft Point | velocity, fps: | 2750 | 2478 | 2224 | 1987 | 1766 |
| | energy, ft-lb: | 2519 | 2045 | 1647 | 1315 | 1039 |
| | arc, inches: | | +2.1 | 0 | -9.2 | -27.1 |
| PMC 150 SP boat-tail | velocity, fps: | 2820 | 2581 | 2354 | 2139 | 1935 |
| | energy, ft-lb: | 2648 | 2218 | 1846 | 1523 | 1247. |
| | arc, inches: | | +1.9 | 0 | -8.2 | -24.0 |
| PMC 168 Barnes X | velocity, fps: | 2600 | 2425 | 2256 | 2095 | 1940 |
| | energy, ft-lb: | 2476 | 2154 | 1865 | 1608 | 1379 |
| | arc, inches: | | +2.2 | 0 | -9.0 | -26.0 |
| PMC 168 HP boat-tail | velocity, fps: | 2650 | 2460 | 2278 | 2103 | 1936 |
| | energy, ft-lb: | 2619 | 2257 | 1935 | 1649 | 1399 |
| | arc, inches: | | +2.1 | 0 | -8.8 | -25.6 |
| PMC 168 Pointed Soft Point | velocity, fps: | 2559 | 2354 | 2160 | 1976 | 1803 |
| | energy, ft-lb: | 2443 | 2067 | 1740 | 1457 | 1212 |
| | arc, inches: | | +2.4 | 0 | -9.9 | -28.7 |
| PMC 168 Pointed Soft Point | velocity, fps: | 2600 | 2404 | 2216 | 2037 | 1866 |
| | energy, ft-lb: | 2476 | 2064 | 1709 | 1403 | 1142 |
| | arc, inches: | | +2.3 | 0 | -9.8 | -28.7 |
| PMC 180 Pointed Soft Point | velocity, fps: | 2550 | 2335 | 2132 | 1940 | 1760 |
| | energy, ft-lb: | 2599 | 2179 | 1816 | 1504 | 1238. |
| | arc, inches: | | +2.5 | 0 | -10.1 | -29.5 |
| PMC 180 SP boat-tail | velocity, fps: | 2620 | 2446 | 2278 | 2117 | 1962 |
| | energy, ft-lb: | 2743 | 2391 | 2074 | 1790 | 1538 |
| | arc, inches: | | +2.2 | 0 | -8.9 | -25.4 |
| Rem. 125 PSP C-L MR | velocity, fps: | 2660 | 2348 | 2057 | 1788 | 1546 |
| | energy, ft-lb: | 1964 | 1529 | 1174 | 887 | 663 |
| | arc, inches: | | +1.1 | -2.7 | -14.3 | -35.8 |
| Rem. 150 PSP Core-Lokt | velocity, fps: | 2820 | 2533 | 2263 | 2009 | 1774 |
| | energy, ft-lb: | 2648 | 2137 | 1705 | 1344 | 1048 |
| | arc, inches: | | +2.0 | 0 | -8.8 | -26.2 |
| Rem. 150 PSP C-L Ultra | velocity, fps: | 2620 | 2404 | 2198 | 2002 | 1818 |
| | energy, ft-lb: | 2743 | 2309 | 1930 | 1601 | 1320 |
| | arc, inches: | | +2.3 | 0 | -9.5 | -26.4 |
| Rem. 150 Swift Scirocco | velocity, fps: | 2820 | 2611 | 2410 | 2219 | 2037 |
| | energy, ft-lb: | 2648 | 2269 | 1935 | 1640 | 1381 |
| | arc, inches: | | +1.8 | 0 | -7.8 | -22.7 |
| Rem. 165 AccuTip | velocity, fps: | 2700 | 2501 | 2311 | 2129 | 1958. |
| | energy, ft-lb: | 2670 | 2292 | 1957 | 1861 | 1401. |
| | arc, inches: | | +2.0 | 0 | -8.6 | -24.8 |
| Rem. 165 PSP boat-tail | velocity, fps: | 2700 | 2497 | 2303 | 2117 | 1941. |
| | energy, ft-lb: | 2670 | 2284 | 1942 | 1642 | 1379 |
| | arc, inches: | | +2.0 | 0 | -8.6 | -25.0 |
| Rem. 165 Nosler Bal. Tip | velocity, fps: | 2700 | 2613 | 2333 | 2161 | 1996 |
| | energy, ft-lb: | 2672 | 2314 | 1995 | 1711 | 1460 |
| | arc, inches: | | +2.0 | 0 | -8.4 | -24.3 |

# Centerfire Rifle Ballistics

## .308 WINCHESTER TO .30-06 SPRINGFIELD

| CARTRIDGE BULLET | RANGE, YARDS: | 0 | 100 | 200 | 300 | 400 |
|---|---|---|---|---|---|---|
| Rem. 165 Swift Scirocco | velocity, fps: | 2700 | 2513 | 2233 | 2161 | 1996 |
| | energy, fps: | 2670 | 2313 | 1994 | 1711 | 1459 |
| | arc, inches: | | +2.0 | 0 | -8.4 | -24.3 |
| Rem. 168 HPBT Match | velocity, fps: | 2680 | 2493 | 2314 | 2143 | 1979 |
| | energy, ft-lb: | 2678 | 2318 | 1998 | 1713 | 1460 |
| | arc, inches: | | +2.1 | 0 | -8.6 | -24.7 |
| Rem. 180 SP Core-Lokt | velocity, fps: | 2620 | 2274 | 1955 | 1666 | 1414 |
| | energy, ft-lb: | 2743 | 2066 | 1527 | 1109 | 799 |
| | arc, inches: | | +2.6 | 0 | -11.8 | -36.3 |
| Rem. 180 PSP Core-Lokt | velocity, fps: | 2620 | 2393 | 2178 | 1974 | 1782 |
| | energy, ft-lb: | 2743 | 2288 | 1896 | 1557 | 1269 |
| | arc, inches: | | +2.3 | 0 | -9.7 | -28.3 |
| Rem. 180 Nosler Partition | velocity, fps: | 2620 | 2436 | 2259 | 2089 | 1927. |
| | energy, ft-lb: | 2743 | 2371 | 2039 | 1774 | 1485 |
| | arc, inches: | | +2.2 | 0 | -9.0 | -26.0 |
| Speer 150 Grand Slam | velocity, fps: | 2900 | 2599 | 2317 | 2053 | |
| | energy, ft-lb: | 2800 | 2249 | 1788 | 1404 | |
| | arc, inches: | | +2.1 | 0 | -8.6 | -24.8 |
| Speer 165 Grand Slam | velocity, fps: | 2700 | 2475 | 2261 | 2057 | |
| | energy, ft-lb: | 2670 | 2243 | 1872 | 1550 | |
| | arc, inches: | | +2.1 | 0 | -8.9 | -25.9 |
| Speer 180 Grand Slam | velocity, fps: | 2620 | 2420 | 2229 | 2046 | |
| | energy, ft-lb: | 2743 | 2340 | 1985 | 1674 | |
| | arc, inches: | | +2.2 | 0 | -9.2 | -26.6 |
| Win. 150 Power-Point | velocity, fps: | 2820 | 2488 | 2179 | 1893 | 1633 |
| | energy, ft-lb: | 2648 | 2061 | 1581 | 1193 | 888 |
| | arc, inches: | | +2.4 | 0 | -9.8 | -29.3 |
| Win. 150 Power-Point Plus | velocity, fps: | 2900 | 2558 | 2241 | 1946 | 1678 |
| | energy, ft-lb: | 2802 | 2180 | 1672 | 1262 | 938 |
| | arc, inches: | | +1.9 | 0 | -8.9 | -27.0 |
| Win. 150 Partition Gold | velocity, fps: | 2900 | 2645 | 2405 | 2177 | 1962 |
| | energy, ft-lb: | 2802 | 2332 | 1927 | 1579 | 1282. |
| | arc, inches: | | +1.7 | 0 | -7.8 | -22.9 |
| Win. 150 Ballistic Silvertip | velocity, fps: | 2810 | 2601 | 2401 | 2211 | 2028 |
| | energy, ft-lb: | 2629 | 2253 | 1920 | 1627 | 1370. |
| | arc, inches: | | +1.8 | 0 | -7.8 | -22.8 |
| Win. 150 Fail Safe | velocity, fps: | 2820 | 2533 | 2263 | 2010 | 1775 |
| | energy, ft-lb: | 2649 | 2137 | 1706 | 1346 | 1049 |
| | arc, inches: | | +2.0 | 0 | -8.8 | -26.2 |
| Win. 150 Supreme Elite XP3 | velocity, fps: | 2825 | 2616 | 2417 | 2226 | 2044 |
| | energy, ft-lb: | 2658 | 2279 | 1945 | 1650 | 1392 |
| | arc, inches: | | +1.8 | 0 | -7.8 | -22.6 |
| Win. 168 Ballistic Silvertip | velocity, fps: | 2670 | 2484 | 2306 | 2134 | 1971 |
| | energy, ft-lb: | 2659 | 2301 | 1983 | 1699 | 1449 |
| | arc, inches: | | +2.1 | 0 | -8.6 | -24.8 |
| Win. 168 HP boat-tail Match | velocity, fps: | 2680 | 2485 | 2297 | 2118 | 1948 |
| | energy, ft-lb: | 2680 | 2303 | 1970 | 1674 | 1415 |
| | arc, inches: | | +2.1 | 0 | -8.7 | -25.1 |
| Win. 180 Power-Point | velocity, fps: | 2620 | 2274 | 1955 | 1666 | 1414 |
| | energy, ft-lb: | 2743 | 2066 | 1527 | 1109 | 799 |
| | arc, inches: | | +2.9 | 0 | -12.1 | -36.9 |
| Win. 180 Silvertip | velocity, fps: | 2620 | 2393 | 2178 | 1974 | 1782 |
| | energy, ft-lb: | 2743 | 2288 | 1896 | 1557 | 1269 |
| | arc, inches: | | +2.6 | 0 | -9.9 | -28.9 |

## .30-06 SPRINGFIELD

| CARTRIDGE BULLET | RANGE, YARDS: | 0 | 100 | 200 | 300 | 400 |
|---|---|---|---|---|---|---|
| A-Square 180 M & D-T | velocity, fps: | 2700 | 2365 | 2054 | 1769 | 1524 |
| | energy, ft-lb: | 2913 | 2235 | 1687 | 1251 | 928 |
| | arc, inches: | | +2.4 | 0 | -10.6 | -32.4 |
| A-Square 220 Monolythic Solid | velocity, fps: | 2380 | 2108 | 1854 | 1623 | 1424 |
| | energy, ft-lb: | 2767 | 2171 | 1679 | 1287 | 990 |
| | arc, inches: | | +3.1 | 0 | -13.6 | -39.9 |

| CARTRIDGE BULLET | RANGE, YARDS: | 0 | 100 | 200 | 300 | 400 |
|---|---|---|---|---|---|---|
| Black Hills 150 Nosler B. Tip | velocity, fps: | 2900 | | | | |
| | energy, ft-lb: | 2770 | | | | |
| | arc, inches: | | | | | |
| Black Hills 165 Nosler B. Tip | velocity, fps: | 2750 | | | | |
| | energy, ft-lb: | 2770 | | | | |
| | arc, inches: | | | | | |
| Black Hills 168 Hor. Match | velocity, fps: | 2700 | | | | |
| | energy, ft-lb: | 2718 | | | | |
| | arc, inches: | | | | | |
| Black Hills 180 Barnes X | velocity, fps: | 2650 | | | | |
| | energy, ft-lb: | 2806 | | | | |
| | arc, inches: | | | | | |
| Black Hills 180 AccuBond | velocity, ft-lb: | 2700 | | | | |
| | energy, ft-lb: | | | | | |
| | arc, inches: | | | | | |
| Federal 125 Sierra Pro-Hunt. | velocity, fps: | 3140 | 2780 | 2450 | 2140 | 1850 |
| | energy, ft-lb: | 2735 | 2145 | 1660 | 1270 | 955 |
| | arc, inches: | | +1.5 | 0 | -7.3 | -22.3 |
| Federal 150 Hi-Shok | velocity, fps: | 2910 | 2620 | 2340 | 2080 | 1840 |
| | energy, ft-lb: | 2820 | 2280 | 1825 | 1445 | 1130 |
| | arc, inches: | | +1.8 | 0 | -8.2 | -24.4 |
| Federal 150 Sierra Pro-Hunt. | velocity, fps: | 2910 | 2640 | 2380 | 2130 | 1900 |
| | energy, ft-lb: | 2820 | 2315 | 1880 | 1515 | 1205 |
| | arc, inches: | | +1.7 | 0 | -7.9 | -23.3 |
| Federal 150 Sierra GameKing BTSP | velocity, fps: | 2910 | 2690 | 2480 | 2270 | 2070 |
| | energy, ft-lb: | 2820 | 2420 | 2040 | 1710 | 1430 |
| | arc, inches: | | +1.7 | 0 | -7.4 | -21.5 |
| Federal 150 Nosler Bal. Tip | velocity, fps: | 2910 | 2700 | 2490 | 2300 | 2110 |
| | energy, ft-lb: | 2820 | 2420 | 2070 | 1760 | 1485 |
| | arc, inches: | | +1.6 | 0 | -7.3 | -21.1 |
| Federal 150 FMJ boat-tail | velocity, fps: | 2910 | 2710 | 2510 | 2320 | 2150 |
| | energy, ft-lb: | 2820 | 2440 | 2100 | 1800 | 1535 |
| | arc, inches: | | +1.6 | 0 | -7.1 | -20.8 |
| Federal 165 Sierra Pro-Hunt. | velocity, fps: | 2800 | 2560 | 2340 | 2130 | 1920 |
| | energy, ft-lb: | 2875 | 2410 | 2005 | 1655 | 1360 |
| | arc, inches: | | +1.9 | 0 | -8.3 | -24.3 |
| Federal 165 Sierra GameKing BTSP | velocity, fps: | 2800 | 2610 | 2420 | 2240 | 2070. |
| | energy, ft-lb: | 2870 | 2490 | 2150 | 1840 | 1580 |
| | arc, inches: | | +1.8 | 0 | -7.8 | -22.4 |
| Federal 165 Sierra GameKing HE | velocity, fps: | 3140 | 2900 | 2670 | 2450 | 2240 |
| | energy, ft-lb: | 3610 | 3075 | 2610 | 2200 | 1845 |
| | arc, inches: | | +1.5 | 0 | -6.9 | -20.4 |
| Federal 165 Nosler Bal. Tip | velocity, fps: | 2800 | 2610 | 2430 | 2250 | 2080 |
| | energy, ft-lb: | 2870 | 2495 | 2155 | 1855 | 1585 |
| | arc, inches: | | +1.8 | 0 | -7.7 | -22.3 |
| Federal 165 Trophy Bonded | velocity, fps: | 2800 | 2540 | 2290 | 2050 | 1830. |
| | energy, ft-lb: | 2870 | 2360 | 1915 | 1545 | 1230 |
| | arc, inches: | | +2.0 | 0 | -8.7 | -25.4 |
| Federal 165 Tr. Bonded HE | velocity, fps: | 3140 | 2860 | 2590 | 2340 | 2100 |
| | energy, ft-lb: | 3610 | 2990 | 2460 | 2010 | 1625. |
| | arc, inches: | | +1.6 | 0 | -7.4 | -21.9 |
| Federal 168 Sierra MatchKg. BTHP | velocity, fps: | 2700 | 2510 | 2320 | 2150 | 1980 |
| | energy, ft-lb: | 2720 | 2350 | 2010 | 1720 | 1460 |
| | arc, inches: | | +16.2 | +28.4 | +34.1 | +32.3 |
| Federal 180 Hi-Shok | velocity, fps: | 2700 | 2470 | 2250 | 2040 | 1850 |
| | energy, ft-lb: | 2915 | 2435 | 2025 | 1665 | 1360 |
| | arc, inches: | | +2.1 | 0 | -9.0 | -26.4 |
| Federal 180 Sierra Pro-Hunt. RN | velocity, fps: | 2700 | 2350 | 2020 | 1730 | 1470 |
| | energy, ft-lb: | 2915 | 2200 | 1630 | 1190 | 860 |
| | arc, inches: | | +2.4 | 0 | -11.0 | -33.6 |
| Federal 180 Nosler Partition | velocity, fps: | 2700 | 2500 | 2320 | 2140 | 1970 |
| | energy, ft-lb: | 2915 | 2510 | 2150 | 1830 | 1550 |
| | arc, inches: | | +2.0 | 0 | -8.6 | -24.6 |

BALLISTICS

| CARTRIDGE BULLET | RANGE, YARDS: | 0 | 100 | 200 | 300 | 400 |
|---|---|---|---|---|---|---|
| Federal 180 Nosler Part. HE | velocity, fps: | 2880 | 2690 | 2500 | 2320 | 2150 |
| | energy, ft-lb: | 3315 | 2880 | 2495 | 2150 | 1845 |
| | arc, inches: | | +1.7 | 0 | -7.2 | -21.0 |
| Federal 180 Sierra GameKing BTSP | velocity, fps: | 2700 | 2540 | 2380 | 2220 | 2080 |
| | energy, ft-lb: | 2915 | 2570 | 2260 | 1975 | 1720 |
| | arc, inches: | | +1.9 | 0 | -8.1 | -23.1 |
| Federal 180 Barnes XLC | velocity, fps: | 2700 | 2530 | 2360 | 2200 | 2040. |
| | energy, ft-lb: | 2915 | 2550 | 2220 | 1930 | 1670 |
| | arc, inches: | | +2.0 | 0 | -8.3 | -23.8 |
| Federal 180 Trophy Bonded | velocity, fps: | 2700 | 2460 | 2220 | 2000 | 1800 |
| | energy, ft-lb: | 2915 | 2410 | 1975 | 1605 | 1290 |
| | arc, inches: | | +2.2 | 0 | -9.2 | -27.0 |
| Federal 180 Tr. Bonded HE | velocity, fps: | 2880 | 2630 | 2380 | 2160 | 1940 |
| | energy, ft-lb: | 3315 | 2755 | 2270 | 1855 | 1505 |
| | arc, inches: | | +1.8 | 0 | -8.0 | -23.3 |
| Federal 220 Sierra Pro-Hunt. RN | velocity, fps: | 2410 | 2130 | 1870 | 1630 | 1420 |
| | energy, ft-lb: | 2835 | 2215 | 1705 | 1300 | 985 |
| | arc, inches: | | +3.1 | 0 | -13.1 | -39.3 |
| Hornady 150 SP | velocity, fps: | 2910 | 2617 | 2342 | 2083 | 1843 |
| | energy, ft-lb: | 2820 | 2281 | 1827 | 1445 | 1131 |
| | arc, inches: | | +2.1 | 0 | -8.5 | -25.0 |
| Hornady 150 SP LM | velocity, fps: | 3100 | 2815 | 2548 | 2295 | 2058 |
| | energy, ft-lb: | 3200 | 2639 | 2161 | 1755 | 1410 |
| | arc, inches: | | +1.4 | 0 | -6.8 | -20.3 |
| Hornady 150 SP boat-tail | velocity, fps: | 2910 | 2683 | 2467 | 2262 | 2066. |
| | energy, ft-lb: | 2820 | 2397 | 2027 | 1706 | 1421 |
| | arc, inches: | | +2.0 | 0 | -7.7 | -22.2 |
| Hornady 150 SST (or Interbond) | velocity, fps: | 2910 | 2802 | 2599 | 2405 | 2219 |
| | energy, ft-lb: | 3330 | 2876 | 2474 | 2118 | 1803 |
| | arc, inches: | | +1.5 | 0 | -6.6 | -19.3 |
| Hornady 150 SST LM | velocity, fps: | 3100 | 2860 | 2631 | 2414 | 2208 |
| | energy, ft-lb: | 3200 | 2724 | 2306 | 1941 | 1624 |
| | arc, inches: | | +1.4 | 0 | -6.6 | -19.2 |
| Hornady 165 SP boat-tail | velocity, fps: | 2800 | 2591 | 2392 | 2202 | 2020 |
| | energy, ft-lb: | 2873 | 2460 | 2097 | 1777 | 1495 |
| | arc, inches: | | +1.8 | 0 | -8.0 | -23.3 |
| Hornady 165 SPBT LM | velocity, fps: | 3015 | 2790 | 2575 | 2370 | 2176 |
| | energy, ft-lb: | 3330 | 2850 | 2428 | 2058 | 1734 |
| | arc, inches: | | +1.6 | 0 | -7.0 | -20.1 |
| Hornady 165 SST (or Interbond) | velocity, fps: | 2800 | 2598 | 2405 | 2221 | 2046 |
| | energy, ft-lb: | 2872 | 2473 | 2119 | 1808 | 1534 |
| | arc, inches: | | +1.9 | 0 | -8.0 | -22.8 |
| Hornady 165 SST LM | velocity, fps: | 3015 | 2802 | 2599 | 2405 | 2219 |
| | energy, ft-lb: | 3330 | 2878 | 2474 | 2118 | 1803. |
| | arc, inches: | | +1.5 | 0 | -6.5 | -19.3 |
| Hornady 168 HPBT Match | velocity, fps: | 2790 | 2620 | 2447 | 2280 | 2120. |
| | energy, ft-lb: | 2925 | 2561 | 2234 | 1940 | 1677. |
| | arc, inches: | | +1.7 | 0 | -7.7 | -22.2 |
| Hornady 180 SP | velocity, fps: | 2700 | 2469 | 2258 | 2042 | 1846 |
| | energy, ft-lb: | 2913 | 2436 | 2023 | 1666 | 1362 |
| | arc, inches: | | +2.4 | 0 | -9.3 | -27.0 |
| Hornady 180 SPBT LM | velocity, fps: | 2880 | 2676 | 2480 | 2293 | 2114 |
| | energy, ft-lb: | 3316 | 2862 | 2459 | 2102 | 1786 |
| | arc, inches: | | +1.7 | 0 | -7.3 | -21.3 |
| Norma 150 Nosler Bal. Tip | velocity, fps: | 2936 | 2713 | 2502 | 2300 | |
| | energy, ft-lb: | 2872 | 2453 | 2085 | 1762 | |
| | arc, inches: | | +1.6 | 0 | -7.1 | |
| Norma 150 Soft Point | velocity, fps: | 2972 | 2640 | 2331 | 2043 | |
| | energy, ft-lb: | 2943 | 2321 | 1810 | 1390 | |
| | arc, inches: | | +1.8 | 0 | -8.2 | |
| Norma 180 Alaska | velocity, fps: | 2700 | 2351 | 2028 | 1734 | |
| | energy, ft-lb: | 2914 | 2209 | 1645 | 1202 | |
| | arc, inches: | | +2.4 | 0 | -11.0 | |

| CARTRIDGE BULLET | RANGE, YARDS: | 0 | 100 | 200 | 300 | 400 |
|---|---|---|---|---|---|---|
| Norma 180 Nosler Partition | velocity, fps: | 2700 | 2494 | 2297 | 2108 | |
| | energy, ft-lb: | 2914 | 2486 | 2108 | 1777 | |
| | arc, inches: | | +2.1 | 0 | -8.7 | |
| Norma 180 Plastic Point | velocity, fps: | 2700 | 2455 | 2222 | 2003 | |
| | energy, ft-lb: | 2914 | 2409 | 1974 | 1603 | |
| | arc, inches: | | +2.1 | 0 | -9.2 | |
| Norma 180 Vulkan | velocity, fps: | 2700 | 2416 | 2150 | 1901 | |
| | energy, ft-lb: | 2914 | 2334 | 1848 | 1445 | |
| | arc, inches: | | +2.2 | 0 | -9.8 | |
| Norma 180 Oryx | velocity, fps: | 2700 | 2387 | 2095 | 1825 | |
| | energy, ft-lb: | 2914 | 2278 | 1755 | 1332 | |
| | arc, inches: | | +2.3 | 0 | -10.2 | |
| Norma 180 TXP Swift A-Fr. | velocity, fps: | 2700 | 2479 | 2268 | 2067 | |
| | energy, ft-lb: | 2914 | 2456 | 2056 | 1708 | |
| | arc, inches: | | +2.0 | 0 | -8.8 | |
| Norma 180 AccuBond | velocity, fps: | 2674 | 2499 | 2331 | 2169 | |
| | energy, ft-lb: | 2859 | 2497 | 2172 | 1881 | |
| | arc, inches: | | +2.0 | 0 | -8.5 | |
| Norma 200 Vulkan | velocity, fps: | 2641 | 2385 | 2143 | 1916 | |
| | energy, ft-lb: | 3098 | 2527 | 2040 | 1631 | |
| | arc, inches: | | +2.3 | 0 | -9.9 | |
| Norma 200 Oryx | velocity, fps: | 2625 | 2362 | 2115 | 1883 | |
| | energy, ft-lb: | 3061 | 2479 | 1987 | 1575 | |
| | arc, inches: | | +2.3 | 0 | -10.1 | |
| PMC 150 X-Bullet | velocity, fps: | 2750 | 2552 | 2361 | 2179 | 2005 |
| | energy, ft-lb: | 2518 | 2168 | 1857 | 1582 | 1339 |
| | arc, inches: | | +2.0 | 0 | -8.2 | -23.7 |
| PMC 150 Pointed Soft Point | velocity, fps: | 2773 | 2542 | 2322 | 2113 | 1916 |
| | energy, ft-lb: | 2560 | 2152 | 1796 | 1487 | 1222. |
| | arc, inches: | | +1.9 | 0 | -8.4 | -24.6 |
| PMC 150 SP boat-tail | velocity, fps: | 2900 | 2657 | 2427 | 2208 | 2000 |
| | energy, ft-lb: | 2801 | 2351 | 1961 | 1623 | 1332 |
| | arc, inches: | | +1.7 | 0 | -7.7 | -22.5 |
| PMC 150 FMJ | velocity, fps: | 2773 | 2542 | 2322 | 2113 | 1916 |
| | energy, ft-lb: | 2560 | 2152 | 1796 | 1487 | 1222 |
| | arc, inches: | | +1.9 | 0 | -8.4 | -24.6 |
| PMC 168 Barnes X | velocity, fps: | 2750 | 2569 | 2395 | 2228 | 2067 |
| | energy, ft-lb: | 2770 | 2418 | 2101 | 1818 | 1565 |
| | arc, inches: | | +1.9 | 0 | -8.0 | -23.0 |
| PMC 180 Barnes X | velocity, fps: | 2650 | 2487 | 2331 | 2179 | 2034 |
| | energy, ft-lb: | 2806 | 2472 | 2171 | 1898 | 1652 |
| | arc, inches: | | +2.1 | 0 | -8.5 | -24.3 |
| PMC 180 Pointed Soft Point | velocity, fps: | 2650 | 2430 | 2221 | 2024 | 1839 |
| | energy, ft-lb: | 2807 | 2359 | 1972 | 1638 | 1351 |
| | arc, inches: | | +2.2 | 0 | -9.3 | -27.0 |
| PMC 180 SP boat-tail | velocity, fps: | 2700 | 2523 | 2352 | 2188 | 2030 |
| | energy, ft-lb: | 2913 | 2543 | 2210 | 1913 | 1646 |
| | arc, inches: | | +2.0 | 0 | -8.3 | -23.9 |
| PMC 180 HPBT Match | velocity, fps: | 2800 | 2622 | 2456 | 2302 | 2158 |
| | energy, ft-lb: | 3133 | 2747 | 2411 | 2118 | 1861 |
| | arc, inches: | | +1.8 | 0 | -7.6 | -21.7 |
| Rem. 55 PSP (sabot) "Accelerator" | velocity, fps: | 4080 | 3484 | 2964 | 2499 | 2080 |
| | energy, ft-lb: | 2033 | 1482 | 1073 | 763 | 528. |
| | arc, inches: | | +1.4 | +1.4 | -2.6 | -12.2 |
| Rem. 125 PSP C-L MR | velocity, fps: | 2660 | 2335 | 2034 | 1757 | 1509 |
| | energy, ft-lb: | 1964 | 1513 | 1148 | 856 | 632 |
| | arc, inches: | | +1.1 | -3.0 | -15.5 | -37.4 |
| Rem. 125 Pointed Soft Point | velocity, fps: | 3140 | 2780 | 2447 | 2138 | 1853 |
| | energy, ft-lb: | 2736 | 2145 | 1662 | 1269 | 953. |
| | arc, inches: | | +1.5 | 0 | -7.4 | -22.4 |
| Rem. 150 AccuTip | velocity, fps: | 2910 | 2686 | 2473 | 2270 | 2077 |
| | energy, ft-lb: | 2820 | 2403 | 2037 | 1716 | 1436 |
| | arc, inches: | | +1.8 | 0 | -7.4 | -21.5 |

BALLISTICS

# Centerfire Rifle Ballistics

## .30-06 SPRINGFIELD TO .300 BLACKOUT

| CARTRIDGE BULLET | RANGE, YARDS: | 0 | 100 | 200 | 300 | 400 |
|---|---|---|---|---|---|---|
| Rem. 150 PSP Core-Lokt | velocity, fps: | 2910 | 2617 | 2342 | 2083 | 1843 |
| | energy, ft-lb: | 2820 | 2281 | 1827 | 1445 | 1131 |
| | arc, inches: | | +1.8 | 0 | -8.2 | -24.4 |
| Rem. 150 Bronze Point | velocity, fps: | 2910 | 2656 | 2416 | 2189 | 1974 |
| | energy, ft-lb: | 2820 | 2349 | 1944 | 1596 | 1298 |
| | arc, inches: | | +1.7 | 0 | -7.7 | -22.7 |
| Rem. 150 Nosler Bal. Tip | velocity, fps: | 2910 | 2696 | 2492 | 2298 | 2112. |
| | energy, ft-lb: | 2821 | 2422 | 2070 | 1769 | 1485 |
| | arc, inches: | | +1.6 | 0 | -7.3 | -21.1 |
| Rem. 150 Swift Scirocco | velocity, fps: | 2910 | 2696 | 2492 | 2298 | 2111 |
| | energy, ft-lb: | 2820 | 2421 | 2069 | 1758 | 1485 |
| | arc, inches: | | +1.6 | 0 | -7.3 | -21.1 |
| Rem. 165 AccuTip | velocity, fps: | 2800 | 2597 | 2403 | 2217 | 2039 |
| | energy, ft-lb: | 2872 | 2470 | 2115 | 1800 | 1523 |
| | arc, inches: | | +1.8 | 0 | -7.9 | -22.8 |
| Rem. 165 PSP Core-Lokt | velocity, fps: | 2800 | 2534 | 2283 | 2047 | 1825. |
| | energy, ft-lb: | 2872 | 2352 | 1909 | 1534 | 1220 |
| | arc, inches: | | +2.0 | 0 | -8.7 | -25.9 |
| Rem. 165 PSP boat-tail | velocity, fps: | 2800 | 2592 | 2394 | 2204 | 2023 |
| | energy, ft-lb: | 2872 | 2462 | 2100 | 1780 | 1500 |
| | arc, inches: | | +1.8 | 0 | -7.9 | -23.0 |
| Rem. 165 Nosler Bal. Tip | velocity, fps: | 2800 | 2609 | 2426 | 2249 | 2080. |
| | energy, ft-lb: | 2873 | 2494 | 2155 | 1854 | 1588 |
| | arc, inches: | | +1.8 | 0 | -7.7 | -22.3 |
| Rem. 168 PSP C-L Ultra | velocity, fps: | 2800 | 2546 | 2306 | 2079 | 1866 |
| | energy, ft-lb: | 2924 | 2418 | 1984 | 1613 | 1299 |
| | arc, inches: | | +1.9 | 0 | -8.5 | -25.1 |
| Rem. 180 SP Core-Lokt | velocity, fps: | 2700 | 2348 | 2023 | 1727 | 1466 |
| | energy, ft-lb: | 2913 | 2203 | 1635 | 1192 | 859 |
| | arc, inches: | | +2.4 | 0 | -11.0 | -33.8 |
| Rem. 180 PSP Core-Lokt | velocity, fps: | 2700 | 2469 | 2250 | 2042 | 1846 |
| | energy, ft-lb: | 2913 | 2436 | 2023 | 1666 | 1362 |
| | arc, inches: | | +2.1 | 0 | -9.0 | -26.3 |
| Rem. 180 PSP C-L Ultra | velocity, fps: | 2700 | 2480 | 2270 | 2070 | 1882 |
| | energy, ft-lb: | 2913 | 2457 | 2059 | 1713 | 1415 |
| | arc, inches: | | +2.1 | 0 | -8.9 | -25.8 |
| Rem. 180 Bronze Point | velocity, fps: | 2700 | 2485 | 2280 | 2084 | 1899. |
| | energy, ft-lb: | 2913 | 2468 | 2077 | 1736 | 1441 |
| | arc, inches: | | +2.1 | 0 | -8.8 | -25.5 |
| Rem. 180 Swift A-Frame | velocity, fps: | 2700 | 2465 | 2243 | 2032 | 1833 |
| | energy, ft-lb: | 2913 | 2429 | 2010 | 1650 | 1343 |
| | arc, inches: | | +2.1 | 0 | -9.1 | -26.6 |
| Rem. 180 Nosler Partition | velocity, fps: | 2700 | 2512 | 2332 | 2160 | 1995 |
| | energy, ft-lb: | 2913 | 2522 | 2174 | 1864 | 1590 |
| | arc, inches: | | +2.0 | 0 | -8.4 | -24.3 |
| Rem. 220 SP Core-Lokt | velocity, fps: | 2410 | 2130 | 1870 | 1632 | 1422 |
| | energy, ft-lb: | 2837 | 2216 | 1708 | 1301 | 988 |
| | arc, inches, s: | | 0 | -6.2 | -22.4 | |
| Speer 150 Grand Slam | velocity, fps: | 2975 | 2669 | 2383 | 2114 | |
| | energy, ft-lb: | 2947 | 2372 | 1891 | 1489 | |
| | arc, inches: | | +2.0 | 0 | -8.1 | -24.1 |
| Speer 165 Grand Slam | velocity, fps: | 2790 | 2560 | 2342 | 2134 | |
| | energy, ft-lb: | 2851 | 2401 | 2009 | 1669 | |
| | arc, inches: | | +1.9 | 0 | -8.3 | -24.1 |
| Speer 180 Grand Slam | velocity, fps: | 2690 | 2487 | 2293 | 2108 | |
| | energy, ft-lb: | 2892 | 2472 | 2101 | 1775 | |
| | arc, inches: | | +2.1 | 0 | -8.8 | -25.1 |
| Win. 125 Pointed Soft Point | velocity, fps: | 3140 | 2780 | 2447 | 2138 | 1853 |
| | energy, ft-lb: | 2736 | 2145 | 1662 | 1269 | 953 |
| | arc, inches: | | +1.8 | 0 | -7.7 | -23.0 |
| Win. 150 Power-Point | velocity, fps: | 2920 | 2580 | 2265 | 1972 | 1704 |
| | energy, ft-lb: | 2839 | 2217 | 1708 | 1295 | 967 |
| | arc, inches: | | +2.2 | 0 | -9.0 | -27.0 |

| CARTRIDGE BULLET | RANGE, YARDS: | 0 | 100 | 200 | 300 | 400 |
|---|---|---|---|---|---|---|
| Win. 150 Power-Point Plus | velocity, fps: | 3050 | 2685 | 2352 | 2043 | 1760 |
| | energy, ft-lb: | 3089 | 2402 | 1843 | 1391 | 1032 |
| | arc, inches: | | +1.7 | 0 | -8.0 | -24.3 |
| Win. 150 Silvertip | velocity, fps: | 2910 | 2617 | 2342 | 2083 | 1843 |
| | energy, ft-lb: | 2820 | 2281 | 1827 | 1445 | 1131 |
| | arc, inches: | | +2.1 | 0 | -8.5 | -25.0 |
| Win. 150 Partition Gold | velocity, fps: | 2960 | 2705 | 2464 | 2235 | 2019 |
| | energy, ft-lb: | 2919 | 2437 | 2022 | 1664 | 1358. |
| | arc, inches: | | +1.6 | 0 | -7.4 | -21.7 |
| Win. 150 Ballistic Silvertip | velocity, fps: | 2900 | 2687 | 2483 | 2289 | 2103 |
| | energy, ft-lb: | 2801 | 2404 | 2054 | 1745 | 1473 |
| | arc, inches: | | +1.7 | 0 | -7.3 | -21.2 |
| Win. 150 Fail Safe | velocity, fps: | 2920 | 2625 | 2349 | 2089 | 1848 |
| | energy, ft-lb: | 2841 | 2296 | 1838 | 1455 | 1137 |
| | arc, inches: | | +1.8 | 0 | -8.1 | -24.3 |
| Win. 165 Pointed Soft Point | velocity, fps: | 2800 | 2573 | 2357 | 2151 | 1956 |
| | energy, ft-lb: | 2873 | 2426 | 2036 | 1696 | 1402 |
| | arc, inches: | | +2.2 | 0 | -8.4 | -24.4 |
| Win. 165 Fail Safe | velocity, fps: | 2800 | 2540 | 2295 | 2063 | 1846 |
| | energy, ft-lb: | 2873 | 2365 | 1930 | 1560 | 1249 |
| | arc, inches: | | +2.0 | 0 | -8.6 | -25.3 |
| Win. 168 Ballistic Silvertip | velocity, fps: | 2790 | 2599 | 2416 | 2240 | 2072 |
| | energy, ft-lb: | 2903 | 2520 | 2177 | 1872 | 1601 |
| | arc, inches: | | +1.8 | 0 | -7.8 | -22.5 |
| Win. 180 Ballistic Silvertip | velocity, fps: | 2750 | 2572 | 2402 | 2237 | 2080 |
| | energy, ft-lb: | 3022 | 2644 | 2305 | 2001 | 1728 |
| | arc, inches: | | +1.9 | 0 | -7.9 | -22.8 |
| Win. 180 Power-Point | velocity, fps: | 2700 | 2348 | 2023 | 1727 | 1466 |
| | energy, ft-lb: | 2913 | 2203 | 1635 | 1192 | 859 |
| | arc, inches: | | +2.7 | 0 | -11.3 | -34.4 |
| Win. 180 Power-Point Plus | velocity, fps: | 2770 | 2563 | 2366 | 2177 | 1997 |
| | energy, ft-lb: | 3068 | 2627 | 2237 | 1894 | 1594 |
| | arc, inches: | | +1.9 | 0 | -8.1 | -23.6 |
| Win. 180 Silvertip | velocity, fps: | 2700 | 2469 | 2250 | 2042 | 1846 |
| | energy, ft-lb: | 2913 | 2436 | 2023 | 1666 | 1362 |
| | arc, inches: | | +2.4 | 0 | -9.3 | -27.0 |
| Win. 180 AccuBond | velocity, fps: | 2750 | 2573 | 2403 | 2239 | 2082 |
| | energy, ft-lb: | 3022 | 2646 | 2308 | 2004 | 1732 |
| | arc, inches: | | +1.9 | 0 | -7.9 | -22.8 |
| Win. 180 Partition Gold | velocity, fps: | 2790 | 2581 | 2382 | 2192 | 2010 |
| | energy, ft-lb: | 3112 | 2664 | 2269 | 1920 | 1615 |
| | arc, inches: | | +1.9 | 0 | -8.0 | -23.2 |
| Win. 180 Fail Safe | velocity, fps: | 2700 | 2486 | 2283 | 2089 | 1904 |
| | energy, ft-lb: | 2914 | 2472 | 2083 | 1744 | 1450 |
| | arc, inches: | | +2.1 | 0 | -8.7 | -25.5 |
| Win. 150 Supreme Elite XP3 | velocity, fps: | 2925 | 2712 | 2508 | 2313 | 2127 |
| | energy, ft-lb: | 2849 | 2448 | 2095 | 1782 | 1507 |
| | arc, inches: | | +1.6 | 0 | -7.2 | -20.8 |
| Win. 180 Supreme Elite XP3 | velocity, fps: | 2750 | 2579 | 2414 | 2256 | 2103 |
| | energy, ft-lb: | 3022 | 2658 | 2330 | 2034 | 1768 |
| | arc, inches: | | +1.9 | 0 | -7.8 | -22.5 |

### .300 BLACKOUT (.300 WHISPER)

| CARTRIDGE BULLET | RANGE, YARDS: | 0 | 100 | 200 | 300 | 400 |
|---|---|---|---|---|---|---|
| Barnes 110 Tac/TX | velocity, fps: | 2350 | 1810 | 1369 | | |
| | energy, ft-lb: | 1349 | 800 | 458 | | |
| | arc, inches: | -1.5 | -6.7 | -55.5 | | |
| Hornady 110 V-MAX | velocity, fps: | 2375 | 2094 | 1834 | 1597 | |
| | energy, ft-lb: | 1378 | 1071 | 821 | 623 | |
| | arc, inches: | -1.5 | +3.2 | 0 | -13.7 | |
| Hornady 208 A-MAX | velocity, fps: | 1020 | 987 | 959 | | |
| | energy, ft-lb: | 480 | 450 | 424 | | |
| | arc, inches: | -1.5 | 0 | -34.1 | | |

BALLISTICS

| CARTRIDGE BULLET | RANGE, YARDS: | 0 | 100 | 200 | 300 | 400 |
|---|---|---|---|---|---|---|
| **.300 H&H MAGNUM** | | | | | | |
| Handload, 165 Sierra HP | velocity, fps: | 3000 | 2784 | 2579 | 2382 | 2195 |
| | energy, ft-lb: | 3297 | 2840 | 2436 | 2079 | 1764 |
| | arc, inches: | -1.5 | +1.5 | 0 | -6.7 | -19.5 |
| Federal 180 Barnes TSX | velocity, fps: | 2880 | 2680 | 2480 | 2290 | 2120 |
| | energy, ft-lb: | 3315 | 2860 | 2460 | 2105 | 1790 |
| | arc, inches: | -1.5 | +1.7 | 0 | -7.3 | -21.3 |
| Hornady 180 InterBond | velocity, fps: | 2870 | 2678 | 2493 | 2316 | 2146 |
| | energy, ft-lb: | 3292 | 2865 | 2484 | 2144 | 1841 |
| | arc, inches: | -1.5 | +1.7 | 0 | -7.3 | -21.0 |
| Federal 180 Nosler Partition | velocity, fps: | 2880 | 2620 | 2380 | 2150 | 1930 |
| | energy, ft-lb: | 3315 | 2750 | 2260 | 1840 | 1480 |
| | arc, inches: | | +1.8 | 0 | -8.0 | -23.4 |
| Win. 180 Fail Safe | velocity, fps: | 2880 | 2628 | 2390 | 2165 | 1952 |
| | energy, ft-lb: | 3316 | 2762 | 2284 | 1873 | 1523 |
| | arc, inches: | | +1.8 | 0 | -7.9 | -23.2 |
| Handload, 190 Hornady | velocity, fps: | 2800 | 2615 | 2437 | 2266 | 2102 |
| | energy, ft-lb: | 3307 | 2884 | 2505 | 2166 | 1864 |
| | arc, inches: | -1.5 | +1.8 | 0 | -7.7 | -22.1 |
| **.308 NORMA MAGNUM** | | | | | | |
| Norma 180 TXP Swift A-Fr. | velocity, fps: | 2953 | 2704 | 2469 | 2245 | |
| | energy, ft-lb: | 3486 | 2924 | 2437 | 2016 | |
| | arc, inches: | | +1.6 | 0 | -7.3 | |
| Norma 180 Oryx | velocity, fps: | 2953 | 2630 | 2330 | 2049 | |
| | energy, ft-lb: | 3486 | 2766 | 2170 | 1679 | |
| | arc, inches: | | +1.8 | 0 | -8.2 | |
| Norma 200 Vulkan | velocity, fps: | 2903 | 2624 | 2361 | 2114 | |
| | energy, ft-lb: | 3744 | 3058 | 2476 | 1985 | |
| | arc, inches: | 0 | +1.8 | 0 | -8.0 | |
| Nosler 180 AB | velocity, fps: | 2975 | 2787 | 2608 | 2435 | 2269 |
| | energy, ft-lb: | 3536 | 3105 | 2718 | 2371 | 2058 |
| | arc, inches: | -1.5 | +1.5 | 0 | -6.6 | -19.1 |
| **.300 WINCHESTER MAGNUM** | | | | | | |
| A-Square 180 Dead Tough | velocity, fps: | 3120 | 2756 | 2420 | 2108 | 1820 |
| | energy, ft-lb: | 3890 | 3035 | 2340 | 1776 | 1324 |
| | arc, inches: | | +1.6 | 0 | -7.6 | -22.9 |
| Black Hills 180 Nos. Bal. Tip | velocity, fps: | 3100 | | | | |
| | energy, ft-lb: | 3498 | | | | |
| | arc, inches: | | | | | |
| Black Hills 180 Barnes X | velocity, fps: | 2950 | | | | |
| | energy, ft-lb: | 3498 | | | | |
| | arc, inches: | | | | | |
| Black Hills 180 AccuBond | velocity, fps: | 3000 | | | | |
| | energy, ft-lb: | 3597 | | | | |
| | arc, inches: | | | | | |
| Black Hills 190 Match | velocity, fps: | 2950 | | | | |
| | energy, ft-lb: | 3672 | | | | |
| | arc, inches: | | | | | |
| Federal 150 Sierra Pro Hunt. | velocity, fps: | 3280 | 3030 | 2800 | 2570 | 2360. |
| | energy, ft-lb: | 3570 | 3055 | 2600 | 2205 | 1860 |
| | arc, inches: | | +1.1 | 0 | -5.6 | -16.4 |
| Federal 150 Trophy Bonded | velocity, fps: | 3280 | 2980 | 2700 | 2430 | 2190 |
| | energy, ft-lb: | 3570 | 2450 | 2420 | 1970 | 1590 |
| | arc, inches: | | +1.2 | 0 | -6.0 | -17.9 |
| Federal 180 Sierra Pro Hunt. | velocity, fps: | 2960 | 2750 | 2540 | 2340 | 2160 |
| | energy, ft-lb: | 3500 | 3010 | 2580 | 2195 | 1860 |
| | arc, inches: | | +1.6 | 0 | -7.0 | -20.3 |
| Federal 180 Barnes XLC | velocity, fps: | 2960 | 2780 | 2600 | 2430 | 2260 |
| | energy, ft-lb: | 3500 | 3080 | 2700 | 2355 | 2050 |
| | arc, inches: | | +1.5 | 0 | -6.6 | -19.2 |

| CARTRIDGE BULLET | RANGE, YARDS: | 0 | 100 | 200 | 300 | 400 |
|---|---|---|---|---|---|---|
| Federal 180 Trophy Bonded | velocity, fps: | 2960 | 2700 | 2460 | 2220 | 2000 |
| | energy, ft-lb: | 3500 | 2915 | 2410 | 1975 | 1605 |
| | arc, inches: | | +1.6 | 0 | -7.4 | -21.9 |
| Federal 180 Tr. Bonded HE | velocity, fps: | 3100 | 2830 | 2580 | 2340 | 2110 |
| | energy, ft-lb: | 3840 | 3205 | 2660 | 2190 | 1790 |
| | arc, inches: | | +1.4 | 0 | -6.6 | -19.7 |
| Federal 180 Nosler Partition | velocity, fps: | 2960 | 2700 | 2450 | 2210 | 1990 |
| | energy, ft-lb: | 3500 | 2905 | 2395 | 1955 | 1585 |
| | arc, inches: | | +1.6 | 0 | -7.5 | -22.1 |
| Federal 190 Sierra MatchKg. BTHP | velocity, fps: | 2900 | 2730 | 2560 | 2400 | 2240 |
| | energy, ft-lb: | 3550 | 3135 | 2760 | 2420 | 2115 |
| | arc, inches: | | +12.9 | +22.5 | +26.9 | +25.1 |
| Federal 200 Sierra GameKing BTSP | velocity, fps: | 2830 | 2680 | 2530 | 2380 | 2240 |
| | energy, ft-lb: | 3560 | 3180 | 2830 | 2520 | 2230 |
| | arc, inches: | | +1.7 | 0 | -7.1 | -20.4 |
| Federal 200 Nosler Part. HE | velocity, fps: | 2930 | 2740 | 2550 | 2370 | 2200 |
| | energy, ft-lb: | 3810 | 3325 | 2885 | 2495 | 2145 |
| | arc, inches: | | +1.6 | 0 | -6.9 | -20.1 |
| Federal 200 Trophy Bonded | velocity, fps: | 2800 | 2570 | 2350 | 2150 | 1950 |
| | energy, ft-lb: | 3480 | 2935 | 2460 | 2050 | 1690 |
| | arc, inches: | | +1.9 | 0 | -8.2 | -23.9 |
| Hornady 150 SP boat-tail | velocity, fps: | 3275 | 2988 | 2718 | 2464 | 2224 |
| | energy, ft-lb: | 3573 | 2974 | 2461 | 2023 | 1648 |
| | arc, inches: | | +1.2 | 0 | -6.0 | -17.8 |
| Hornady 150 SST (and Interbond) | velocity, fps: | 3275 | 3027 | 2791 | 2565 | 2352 |
| | energy, ft-lb: | 3572 | 3052 | 2593 | 2192 | 1842 |
| | arc, inches: | | +1.2 | 0 | -5.8 | -17.0 |
| Hornady 165 SP boat-tail | velocity, fps: | 3100 | 2877 | 2665 | 2462 | 2269. |
| | energy, ft-lb: | 3522 | 3033 | 2603 | 2221 | 1887 |
| | arc, inches: | | +1.3 | 0 | -6.5 | -18.5 |
| Hornady 165 SST | velocity, fps: | 3100 | 2885 | 2680 | 2483 | 2296 |
| | energy, ft-lb: | 3520 | 3049 | 2630 | 2259 | 1930 |
| | arc, inches: | | +1.4 | 0 | -6.4 | -18.6 |
| Hornady 180 SP boat-tail | velocity, fps: | 2960 | 2745 | 2540 | 2344 | 2157 |
| | energy, ft-lb: | 3501 | 3011 | 2578 | 2196 | 1859 |
| | arc, inches: | | +1.9 | 0 | -7.3 | -20.9 |
| Hornady 180 SST | velocity, fps: | 2960 | 2764 | 2575 | 2395 | 2222 |
| | energy, ft-lb: | 3501 | 3052 | 2650 | 2292 | 1974 |
| | arc, inches: | | +1.6 | 0 | -7.0 | -20.1. |
| Hornady 180 SPBT HM | velocity, fps: | 3100 | 2879 | 2668 | 2467 | 2275 |
| | energy, ft-lb: | 3840 | 3313 | 2845 | 2431 | 2068 |
| | arc, inches: | | +1.4 | 0 | -6.4 | -18.7 |
| Hornady 190 SP boat-tail | velocity, fps: | 2900 | 2711 | 2529 | 2355 | 2187 |
| | energy, ft-lb: | 3549 | 3101 | 2699 | 2340 | 2018 |
| | arc, inches: | | +1.6 | 0 | -7.1 | -20.4 |
| Norma 150 Nosler Bal. Tip | velocity, fps: | 3250 | 3014 | 2791 | 2578 | |
| | energy, ft-lb: | 3519 | 3027 | 2595 | 2215 | |
| | arc, inches: | | +1.1 | 0 | -5.6 | |
| Norma 150 Barnes TS | velocity, fps: | 3215 | 2982 | 2761 | 2550 | |
| | energy, ft-lb: | 3444 | 2962 | 2539 | 2167 | |
| | arc, inches: | | +1.2 | 0 | -5.8 | |
| Norma 165 Scirocco | velocity, fps: | 3117 | 2921 | 2734 | 2554 | |
| | energy, ft-lb: | 3561 | 3127 | 2738 | 2390 | |
| | arc, inches: | | +1.2 | 0 | -5.9 | |
| Norma 180 Soft Point | velocity, fps: | 3018 | 2780 | 2555 | 2341 | |
| | energy, ft-lb: | 3641 | 3091 | 2610 | 2190 | |
| | arc, inches: | | +1.5 | 0 | -7.0 | |
| Norma 180 Plastic Point | velocity, fps: | 3018 | 2755 | 2506 | 2271 | |
| | energy, ft-lb: | 3641 | 3034 | 2512 | 2062 | |
| | arc, inches: | | +1.6 | 0 | -7.1 | |
| Norma 180 TXP Swift A-Fr. | velocity, fps: | 2920 | 2688 | 2467 | 2256 | |
| | energy, ft-lb: | 3409 | 2888 | 2432 | 2035 | |
| | arc, inches: | | +1.7 | 0 | -7.4 | |

# Centerfire Rifle Ballistics

## .300 WINCHESTER MAGNUM TO .300 REMINGTON SHORT ULTRA MAGNUM

| CARTRIDGE BULLET | RANGE, YARDS: | 0 | 100 | 200 | 300 | 400 |
|---|---|---|---|---|---|---|
| Norma 180 AccuBond | velocity, fps: | 2953 | 2767 | 2588 | 2417 | |
| | energy, ft-lb: | 3486 | 3061 | 2678 | 2335 | |
| | arc, inches: | | +1.5 | 0 | -6.7 | |
| Norma 180 Oryx | velocity, fps: | 2920 | 2600 | 2301 | 2023 | |
| | energy, ft-lb: | 3409 | 2702 | 2117 | 1636 | |
| | arc, inches: | | +1.8 | 0 | -8.4 | |
| Norma 200 Vulkan | velocity, fps: | 2887 | 2609 | 2347 | 2100 | |
| | energy, ft-lb: | 3702 | 3023 | 2447 | 1960 | |
| | arc, inches: | | +1.8 | 0 | -8.2 | |
| Norma 200 Oryx | velocity, fps: | 2789 | 2510 | 2248 | 2002 | |
| | energy, ft-lb: | 3455 | 2799 | 2245 | 1780 | |
| | arc, inches: | | +2.0 | 0 | -8.9 | |
| PMC 150 Barnes X | velocity, fps: | 3135 | 2918 | 2712 | 2515 | 2327 |
| | energy, ft-lb: | 3273 | 2836 | 2449 | 2107 | 1803 |
| | arc, inches: | | +1.3 | 0 | -6.1 | -17.7 |
| PMC 150 Pointed Soft Point | velocity, fps: | 3150 | 2902 | 2665 | 2438 | 2222 |
| | energy, ft-lb: | 3304 | 2804 | 2364 | 1979 | 1644. |
| | arc, inches: | | +1.3 | 0 | -6.2 | -18.3 |
| PMC 150 SP boat-tail | velocity, fps: | 3250 | 2987 | 2739 | 2504 | 2281 |
| | energy, ft-lb: | 3517 | 2970 | 2498 | 2088 | 1733 |
| | arc, inches: | | +1.2 | 0 | -6.0 | -17.4 |
| PMC 180 Barnes X | velocity, fps: | 2910 | 2738 | 2572 | 2412 | 2258 |
| | energy, ft-lb: | 3384 | 2995 | 2644 | 2325 | 2037 |
| | arc, inches: | | +1.6 | 0 | -6.9 | -19.8 |
| PMC 180 Pointed Soft Point | velocity, fps: | 2853 | 2643 | 2446 | 2258 | 2077 |
| | energy, ft-lb: | 3252 | 2792 | 2391 | 2037 | 1724 |
| | arc, inches: | | +1.7 | 0 | -7.5 | -21.9 |
| PMC 180 SP boat-tail | velocity, fps: | 2900 | 2714 | 2536 | 2365 | 2200 |
| | energy, ft-lb: | 3361 | 2944 | 2571 | 2235 | 1935 |
| | arc, inches: | | +1.6 | 0 | -7.1 | -20.3 |
| PMC 180 HPBT Match | velocity, fps: | 2950 | 2755 | 2568 | 2390 | 2219 |
| | energy, ft-lb: | 3478 | 3033 | 2636 | 2283 | 1968 |
| | arc, inches: | | +1.5 | 0 | -6.8 | -19.7 |
| Rem. 150 PSP Core-Lokt | velocity, fps: | 3290 | 2951 | 2636 | 2342 | 2068 |
| | energy, ft-lb: | 3605 | 2900 | 2314 | 1827 | 1859 |
| | arc, inches: | | +1.6 | 0 | -7.0 | -20.2 |
| Rem. 150 PSP C-L MR | velocity, fps: | 2650 | 2373 | 2113 | 1870 | 1646 |
| | energy, ft-lb: | 2339 | 1875 | 1486 | 1164 | 902 |
| | arc, inches: | | +1.0 | -2.7 | -14.3 | -35.8 |
| Rem. 150 PSP C-L Ultra | velocity, fps: | 3290 | 2967 | 2666 | 2384 | 2120 |
| | energy, ft-lb: | 3065 | 2931 | 2366 | 1893 | 1496 |
| | arc, inches: | | +1.2 | 0 | -6.1 | -18.4 |
| Rem. 180 AccuTip | velocity, fps: | 2960 | 2764 | 2577 | 2397 | 2224 |
| | energy, ft-lb: | 3501 | 3053 | 2653 | 2295 | 1976 |
| | arc, inches: | | +1.5 | 0 | -6.8 | -19.6 |
| Rem. 180 PSP Core-Lokt | velocity, fps: | 2960 | 2745 | 2540 | 2344 | 2157 |
| | energy, ft-lb: | 3501 | 3011 | 2578 | 2196 | 1424 |
| | arc, inches: | | +2.2 | +1.9 | -3.4 | -15.0 |
| Rem. 180 PSP C-L Ultra | velocity, fps: | 2960 | 2727 | 2505 | 2294 | 2093 |
| | energy, ft-lb: | 3501 | 2971 | 2508 | 2103 | 1751 |
| | arc, inches: | | +2.7 | +2.2 | -3.8 | -16.4 |
| Rem. 180 Nosler Partition | velocity, fps: | 2960 | 2725 | 2503 | 2291 | 2089 |
| | energy, ft-lb: | 3501 | 2968 | 2503 | 2087 | 1744 |
| | arc, inches: | | +1.6 | 0 | -7.2 | -20.9 |
| Rem. 180 Nosler Bal. Tip | velocity, fps: | 2960 | 2774 | 2595 | 2424 | 2259. |
| | energy, ft-lb: | 3501 | 3075 | 2692 | 2348 | 2039 |
| | arc, inches: | | +1.5 | 0 | -6.7 | -19.3 |
| Rem. 180 Swift Scirocco | velocity, fps: | 2960 | 2774 | 2595 | 2424 | 2259 |
| | energy, ft-lb: | 3501 | 3075 | 2692 | 2348 | 2039 |
| | arc, inches: | | +1.5 | 0 | -6.7 | -19.3 |
| Rem. 190 PSP boat-tail | velocity, fps: | 2885 | 2691 | 2506 | 2327 | 2156 |
| | energy, ft-lb: | 3511 | 3055 | 2648 | 2285 | 1961 |
| | arc, inches: | | +1.6 | 0 | -7.2 | -20.8 |

| CARTRIDGE BULLET | RANGE, YARDS: | 0 | 100 | 200 | 300 | 400 |
|---|---|---|---|---|---|---|
| Rem. 190 HPBT Match | velocity, fps: | 2900 | 2725 | 2557 | 2395 | 2239 |
| | energy, ft-lb: | 3547 | 3133 | 2758 | 2420 | 2115 |
| | arc, inches: | | +1.6 | 0 | -6.9 | -19.9 |
| Rem. 200 Swift A-Frame | velocity, fps: | 2825 | 2595 | 2376 | 2167 | 1970 |
| | energy, ft-lb: | 3544 | 2989 | 2506 | 2086 | 1722 |
| | arc, inches: | | +1.8 | 0 | -8.0 | -23.5 |
| Speer 180 Grand Slam | velocity, fps: | 2950 | 2735 | 2530 | 2334 | |
| | energy, ft-lb: | 3478 | 2989 | 2558 | 2176 | |
| | arc, inches: | — | +1.6 | 0 | -7.0 | -20.5 |
| Speer 200 Grand Slam | velocity, fps: | 2800 | 2597 | 2404 | 2218 | |
| | energy, ft-lb: | 3481 | 2996 | 2565 | 2185 | |
| | arc, inches: | | +1.8 | 0 | -7.9 | -22.9 |
| Win. 150 Power-Point | velocity, fps: | 3290 | 2951 | 2636 | 2342 | 2068. |
| | energy, ft-lb: | 3605 | 2900 | 2314 | 1827 | 1424 |
| | arc, inches: | | +2.6 | +2.1 | -3.5 | -15.4 |
| Win. 150 Fail Safe | velocity, fps: | 3260 | 2943 | 2647 | 2370 | 2110 |
| | energy, ft-lb: | 3539 | 2884 | 2334 | 1871 | 1483 |
| | arc, inches: | | +1.3 | 0 | -6.2 | -18.7 |
| Win. 165 Fail Safe | velocity, fps: | 3120 | 2807 | 2515 | 2242 | 1985 |
| | energy, ft-lb: | 3567 | 2888 | 2319 | 1842 | 1445 |
| | arc, inches: | | +1.5 | 0 | -7.0 | -20.0 |
| Win. 180 Power-Point | velocity, fps: | 2960 | 2745 | 2540 | 2344 | 2157 |
| | energy, ft-lb: | 3501 | 3011 | 2578 | 2196 | 1859 |
| | arc, inches: | | +1.9 | 0 | -7.3 | -20.9 |
| Win. 180 Power-Point Plus | velocity, fps: | 3070 | 2846 | 2633 | 2430 | 2236 |
| | energy, ft-lb: | 3768 | 3239 | 2772 | 2361 | 1999 |
| | arc, inches: | | +1.4 | 0 | -6.4 | -18.7 |
| Win. 180 Ballistic Silvertip | velocity, fps: | 2950 | 2764 | 2586 | 2415 | 2250 |
| | energy, ft-lb: | 3478 | 3054 | 2673 | 2331 | 2023 |
| | arc, inches: | | +1.5 | 0 | -6.7 | -19.4 |
| Win. 180 AccuBond | velocity, fps: | 2950 | 2765 | 2588 | 2417 | 2253 |
| | energy, ft-lb: | 3478 | 3055 | 2676 | 2334 | 2028 |
| | arc, inches: | | +1.5 | 0 | -6.7 | -19.4 |
| Win. 180 Fail Safe | velocity, fps: | 2960 | 2732 | 2514 | 2307 | 2110 |
| | energy, ft-lb: | 3503 | 2983 | 2528 | 2129 | 1780 |
| | arc, inches: | | +1.6 | 0 | -7.1 | -20.7 |
| Win. 180 Partition Gold | velocity, fps: | 3070 | 2859 | 2657 | 2464 | 2280 |
| | energy, ft-lb: | 3768 | 3267 | 2823 | 2428 | 2078 |
| | arc, inches: | | +1.4 | 0 | -6.3 | -18.3 |
| Win. 150 Supreme Elite XP3 | velocity, fps: | 3260 | 3030 | 2811 | 2603 | 2404 |
| | energy, ft-lb: | 3539 | 3057 | 2632 | 2256 | 1925 |
| | arc, inches: | | +1.1 | 0 | -5.6 | -16.2 |
| Win. 180 Supreme Elite XP3 | velocity, fps: | 3000 | 2819 | 2646 | 2479 | 2318 |
| | energy, ft-lb: | 3597 | 3176 | 2797 | 2455 | 2147 |
| | arc, inches: | | +1.4 | 0 | -6.4 | -18.5 |

## .300 REMINGTON SHORT ULTRA MAGNUM

| CARTRIDGE BULLET | RANGE, YARDS: | 0 | 100 | 200 | 300 | 400 |
|---|---|---|---|---|---|---|
| Rem. 150 PSP C-L Ultra | velocity, fps: | 3200 | 2901 | 2672 | 2359 | 2112 |
| | energy, ft-lb: | 3410 | 2803 | 2290 | 1854 | 1485 |
| | arc, inches: | | +1.3 | 0 | -6.4 | -19.l |
| Rem. 165 PSP Core-Lokt | velocity, fps: | 3075 | 2792 | 2527 | 2276 | 2040 |
| | energy, ft-lb: | 3464 | 2856 | 2339 | 1828 | 1525 |
| | arc, inches: | | +1.5 | 0 | -7.0 | -20.7 |
| Rem. 180 Partition | velocity, fps: | 2960 | 2761 | 2571 | 2389 | 2214 |
| | energy, ft-lb: | 3501 | 3047 | 2642 | 2280 | 1959 |
| | arc, inches: | | +1.5 | 0 | -6.8 | -19.7 |
| Rem. 180 PSP C-L Ultra | velocity, fps: | 2960 | 2727 | 2506 | 2295 | 2094 |
| | energy, ft-lb: | 3501 | 2972 | 2509 | 2105 | 1753 |
| | arc, inches: | | +1.6 | 0 | -7.1 | -20.9 |
| Rem. 190 HPBT Match | velocity, fps: | 2900 | 2725 | 2557 | 2395 | 2239 |
| | energy, ft-lb: | 3547 | 3133 | 2758 | 2420 | 2115 |
| | arc, inches: | | +1.6 | 0 | -6.9 | -19.9 |

BALLISTICS

| CARTRIDGE BULLET | RANGE, YARDS: | 0 | 100 | 200 | 300 | 400 |
|---|---|---|---|---|---|---|
| **.300 WINCHESTER SHORT MAGNUM** | | | | | | |
| Black Hills 175 Sierra MKing | velocity, fps: | 2950 | | | | |
| | energy, ft-lb: | 3381 | | | | |
| | arc, inches: | | | | | |
| Black Hills 180 AccuBond | velocity, fps: | 2950 | | | | |
| | energy, ft-lb: | 3478 | | | | |
| | arc, inches: | | | | | |
| Federal 150 Nosler Bal. Tip | velocity, fps: | 3200 | 2970 | 2755 | 2545 | 2345 |
| | energy, ft-lb: | 3410 | 2940 | 2520 | 2155 | 1830. |
| | arc, inches: | | +1.2 | 0 | -5.8 | -17.0 |
| Federal 165 Nos. Partition | velocity, fps: | 3130 | 2890 | 2670 | 2450 | 2250 |
| | energy, ft-lb: | 3590 | 3065 | 2605 | 2205 | 1855. |
| | arc, inches: | | +1.3 | 0 | -6.2 | -18.2 |
| Federal 165 Nos. Solid Base | velocity, fps: | 3130 | 2900 | 2690 | 2490 | 2290 |
| | energy, ft-lb: | 3590 | 3090 | 2650 | 2265 | 1920 |
| | arc, inches: | | +1.3 | 0 | -6.1 | -17.8 |
| Federal 180 Barnes TS And Nos. Solid Base | velocity, fps: | 2980 | 2780 | 2580 | 2400 | 2220 |
| | energy, ft-lbs: | 3550 | 3085 | 2670 | 2300 | 1970 |
| | arc, inches: | | +1.5 | 0 | -6.7 | -19.5 |
| Federal 180 Grand Slam | velocity, fps: | 2970 | 2740 | 2530 | 2320 | 2130 |
| | energy, ft-lb: | 3525 | 3010 | 2555 | 2155 | 1810 |
| | arc, inches: | | +1.5 | 0 | -7.0 | -20.5 |
| Federal 180 Trophy Bonded | velocity, fps: | 2970 | 2730 | 2500 | 2280 | 2080 |
| | energy, ft-lb: | 3525 | 2975 | 2500 | 2085 | 1725 |
| | arc, inches: | | +1.5 | 0 | -7.2 | -21.0 |
| Federal 180 Nosler Partition | velocity, fps: | 2975 | 2750 | 2535 | 2290 | 2126 |
| | energy, ft-lb: | 3540 | 3025 | 2570 | 2175 | 1825 |
| | arc, inches: | | +1.5 | 0 | -7.0 | -20.3 |
| Federal 180 Nos. AccuBond | velocity, fps: | 2960 | 2780 | 2610 | 2440 | 2280 |
| | energy, ft-lb: | 3500 | 3090 | 2715 | 2380 | 2075 |
| | arc, inches: | | +1.5 | 0 | -6.6 | -19.0 |
| Federal 180 Hi-Shok SP | velocity, fps: | 2970 | 2520 | 2115 | 1750 | 1430 |
| | energy, ft-lb: | 3525 | 2540 | 1785 | 1220 | 820 |
| | arc, inches: | | +2.2 | 0 | -9.9 | -31.4 |
| Norma 150 FMJ | velocity, fps: | 2953 | 2731 | 2519 | 2318 | |
| | energy, ft-lb: | | | | | |
| | arc, inches: | | +1.6 | 0 | -7.1 | |
| Norma 150 Barnes X TS | velocity, fps: | 3215 | 2982 | 2761 | 2550 | |
| | energy, ft-lb: | 3444 | 2962 | 2539 | 2167 | |
| | arc, inches: | | +1.2 | 0 | -5.7 | |
| Norma 180 Nosler Bal. Tip | velocity, fps: | 3215 | 2985 | 2767 | 2560 | |
| | energy, ft-lb: | 3437 | 2963 | 2547 | 2179 | |
| | arc, inches: | | +1.2 | 0 | -5.7 | |
| Norma 180 Oryx | velocity, fps: | 2936 | 2542 | 2180 | 1849 | |
| | energy, ft-lb: | 3446 | 2583 | 1900 | 1368 | |
| | arc, inches: | | +1.9 | 0 | -8.9 | |
| Win. 150 Power-Point | velocity, fps: | 3270 | 2903 | 2565 | 2250 | 1958 |
| | energy, ft-lb: | 3561 | 2807 | 2190 | 1686 | 1277 |
| | arc, inches: | | +1.3 | 0 | -6.6 | -20.2 |
| Win. 150 Ballistic Silvertip | velocity, fps: | 3300 | 3061 | 2834 | 2619 | 2414 |
| | energy, ft-lb: | 3628 | 3121 | 2676 | 2285 | 1941 |
| | arc, inches: | | +1.1 | 0 | -5.4 | -15.9 |
| Win. 165 Fail Safe | velocity, fps: | 3125 | 2846 | 2584 | 2336 | 2102 |
| | energy, ft-lb: | 3577 | 2967 | 2446 | 1999 | 1619 |
| | arc, inches: | | +1.4 | 0 | -6.6 | -19.6 |
| Win. 180 Ballistic Silvertip | velocity, fps: | 3010 | 2822 | 2641 | 2468 | 2301. |
| | energy, ft-lb: | 3621 | 3182 | 2788 | 2434 | 2116 |
| | arc, inches: | | +1.4 | 0 | -6.4 | -18.6 |
| Win. 180 AccuBond | velocity, fps: | 3010 | 2822 | 2643 | 2470 | 2304 |
| | energy, ft-lb: | 3622 | 3185 | 2792 | 2439 | 2121 |
| | arc, inches: | | +1.4 | 0 | -6.4 | -18.5 |

| CARTRIDGE BULLET | RANGE, YARDS: | 0 | 100 | 200 | 300 | 400 |
|---|---|---|---|---|---|---|
| Win. 180 Fail Safe | velocity, fps: | 2970 | 2741 | 2524 | 2317 | 2120 |
| | energy, ft-lb: | 3526 | 3005 | 2547 | 2147 | 1797 |
| | arc, inches: | | +1.6 | 0 | -7.0 | -20.5 |
| Win. 180 Power Point | velocity, fps: | 2970 | 2755 | 2549 | 2353 | 2166 |
| | energy, ft-lb: | 3526 | 3034 | 2598 | 2214 | 1875 |
| | arc, inches: | | +1.5 | 0 | -6.9 | -20.1 |
| Win. 150 Supreme Elite XP3 | velocity, fps: | 3300 | 3068 | 2847 | 2637 | 2437 |
| | energy, ft-lb: | 3626 | 3134 | 2699 | 2316 | 1978 |
| | arc, inches: | | +1.1 | 0 | -5.4 | -15.8 |
| Win. 180 Supreme Elite XP3 | velocity, fps: | 3010 | 2829 | 2655 | 2488 | 2326 |
| | energy, ft-lb: | 3621 | 3198 | 2817 | 2473 | 2162 |
| | arc, inches: | | +1.4 | 0 | -6.4 | -18.3 |
| **.300 RUGER COMPACT MAGNUM** | | | | | | |
| Hornady 150 SST | velocity, fps: | 3310 | 3065 | 2833 | 2613 | 2404 |
| | energy, ft-lb: | 3648 | 3128 | 2673 | 2274 | 1924 |
| | arc, inches: | -1.5 | +1.1 | 0 | -5.4 | -16.0 |
| Hornady 165 GMX | velocity, fps: | 3130 | 2911 | 2703 | 2504 | 2314 |
| | energy, ft-lb: | 3589 | 3105 | 2677 | 2297 | 1963 |
| | arc, inches: | -1.5 | +1.3 | 0 | -6.1 | -17.7 |
| Hornady 180 SST | velocity, fps: | 3040 | 2840 | 2649 | 2466 | 2290 |
| | energy, ft-lb: | 3693 | 3223 | 2804 | 2430 | 2096 |
| | arc, inches: | -1.5 | +1.4 | 0 | -6.4 | -18.5 |
| **.300 WEATHERBY MAGNUM** | | | | | | |
| A-Square 180 Dead Tough | velocity, fps: | 3180 | 2811 | 2471 | 2155 | 1863. |
| | energy, ft-lb: | 4041 | 3158 | 2440 | 1856 | 1387 |
| | arc, inches: | | +1.5 | 0 | -7.2 | -21.8 |
| A-Square 220 Monolythic Solid | velocity, fps: | 2700 | 2407 | 2133 | 1877 | 1653 |
| | energy, ft-lb: | 3561 | 2830 | 2223 | 1721 | 1334 |
| | arc, inches: | | +2.3 | 0 | -9.8 | -29.7 |
| Federal 180 Sierra GameKing BTSP | velocity, fps: | 3190 | 3010 | 2830 | 2660 | 2490 |
| | energy, ft-lb: | 4065 | 3610 | 3195 | 2820 | 2480 |
| | arc, inches: | | +1.2 | 0 | -5.6 | -16.0 |
| Federal 180 Trophy Bonded | velocity, fps: | 3190 | 2950 | 2720 | 2500 | 2290 |
| | energy, ft-lb: | 4065 | 3475 | 2955 | 2500 | 2105 |
| | arc, inches: | | +1.3 | 0 | -5.9 | -17.5 |
| Federal 180 Tr. Bonded HE | velocity, fps: | 3330 | 3080 | 2850 | 2750 | 2410 |
| | energy, ft-lb: | 4430 | 3795 | 3235 | 2750 | 2320 |
| | arc, inches: | | +1.1 | 0 | -5.4 | -15.8 |
| Federal 180 Nosler Partition | velocity, fps: | 3190 | 2980 | 2780 | 2590 | 2400 |
| | energy, ft-lb: | 4055 | 3540 | 3080 | 2670 | 2305 |
| | arc, inches: | | +1.2 | 0 | -5.7 | -16.7 |
| Federal 180 Nosler Part. HE | velocity, fps: | 3330 | 3110 | 2810 | 2710 | 2520 |
| | energy, ft-lb: | 4430 | 3875 | 3375 | 2935 | 2540 |
| | arc, inches: | | +1.0 | 0 | -5.2 | -15.1 |
| Federal 200 Trophy Bonded | velocity, fps: | 2900 | 2670 | 2440 | 2230 | 2030 |
| | energy, ft-lb: | 3735 | 3150 | 2645 | 2200 | 1820 |
| | arc, inches: | | +1.7 | 0 | -7.6 | -22.2 |
| Hornady 150 SST (or Interbond) | velocity, fps: | 3375 | 3123 | 2882 | 2652 | 2434 |
| | energy, ft-lb: | 3793 | 3248 | 2766 | 2343 | 1973 |
| | arc, inches: | | +1.0 | 0 | -5.4 | -15.8 |
| Hornady 180 SP | velocity, fps: | 3120 | 2891 | 2673 | 2466 | 2268. |
| | energy, ft-lb: | 3890 | 3340 | 2856 | 2430 | 2055 |
| | arc, inches: | | +1.3 | 0 | -6.2 | -18.1 |
| Hornady 180 SST | velocity, fps: | 3120 | 2911 | 2711 | 2519 | 2335 |
| | energy, ft-lb: | 3890 | 3386 | 2936 | 2535 | 2180 |
| | arc, inches: | | +1.3 | 0 | -6.2 | -18.1 |
| Rem. 180 PSP Core-Lokt | velocity, fps: | 3120 | 2866 | 2627 | 2400 | 2184 |
| | energy, ft-lb: | 3890 | 3284 | 2758 | 2301 | 1905 |
| | arc, inches: | | +2.4 | +2.0 | -3.4 | -14.9 |

BALLISTICS

# Centerfire Rifle Ballistics

## .300 WEATHERBY MAGNUM TO .303 BRITISH

| CARTRIDGE BULLET | RANGE, YARDS: | 0 | 100 | 200 | 300 | 400 |
|---|---|---|---|---|---|---|
| Rem. 190 PSP boat-tail | velocity, fps: | 3030 | 2830 | 2638 | 2455 | 2279 |
| | energy, ft-lb: | 3873 | 3378 | 2936 | 2542 | 2190. |
| | arc, inches: | | +1.4 | 0 | -6.4 | -18.6 |
| Rem. 200 Swift A-Frame | velocity, fps: | 2925 | 2690 | 2467 | 2254 | 2052 |
| | energy, ft-lb: | 3799 | 3213 | 2701 | 2256 | 1870 |
| | arc, inches: | | +2.8 | +2.3 | -3.9 | -17.0 |
| Speer 180 Grand Slam | velocity, fps: | 3185 | 2948 | 2722 | 2508 | |
| | energy, ft-lb: | 4054 | 3472 | 2962 | 2514 | |
| | arc, inches: | | +1.3 | 0 | -5.9 | -17.4 |
| Wby. 150 Pointed Expanding | velocity, fps: | 3540 | 3225 | 2932 | 2657 | 2399 |
| | energy, ft-lb: | 4173 | 3462 | 2862 | 2351 | 1916 |
| | arc, inches: | | +2.6 | +3.3 | 0 | -8.2 |
| Wby. 150 Nosler Partition | velocity, fps: | 3540 | 3263 | 3004 | 2759 | 2528 |
| | energy, ft-lb: | 4173 | 3547 | 3005 | 2536 | 2128 |
| | arc, inches: | | +2.5 | +3.2 | 0 | -7.7 |
| Wby. 165 Pointed Expanding | velocity, fps: | 3390 | 3123 | 2872 | 2634 | 2409 |
| | energy, ft-lb: | 4210 | 3573 | 3021 | 2542 | 2126 |
| | arc, inches: | | +2.8 | +3.5 | 0 | -8.5 |
| Wby. 165 Nosler Bal. Tip | velocity, fps: | 3350 | 3133 | 2927 | 2730 | 2542 |
| | energy, ft-lb: | 4111 | 3596 | 3138 | 2730 | 2367 |
| | arc, inches: | | +2.7 | +3.4 | 0 | -8.1 |
| Wby. 180 Pointed Expanding | velocity, fps: | 3240 | 3004 | 2781 | 2569 | 2366 |
| | energy, ft-lb: | 4195 | 3607 | 3091 | 2637 | 2237 |
| | arc, inches: | | +3.1 | +3.8 | 0 | -9.0 |
| Wby. 180 Barnes X | velocity, fps: | 3190 | 2995 | 2809 | 2631 | 2459 |
| | energy, ft-lb: | 4067 | 3586 | 3154 | 2766 | 2417 |
| | arc, inches: | | +3.1 | +3.8 | 0 | -8.7 |
| Wby. 180 Bal. Tip | velocity, fps: | 3250 | 3051 | 2806 | 2676 | 2503 |
| | energy, ft-lb: | 4223 | 3721 | 3271 | 2867 | 2504 |
| | arc, inches: | | +2.8 | +3.6 | 0 | -8.4 |
| Wby. 180 Nosler Partition | velocity, fps: | 3240 | 3028 | 2826 | 2634 | 2449 |
| | energy, ft-lb: | 4195 | 3665 | 3193 | 2772 | 2396 |
| | arc, inches: | | +3.0 | +3.7 | 0 | -8.6 |
| Wby. 200 Nosler Partition | velocity, fps: | 3060 | 2860 | 2668 | 2485 | 2308 |
| | energy, ft-lb: | 4158 | 3631 | 3161 | 2741 | 2366 |
| | arc, inches: | | +3.5 | +4.2 | 0 | -9.8 |
| Wby. 220 RN Expanding | velocity, fps: | 2845 | 2543 | 2260 | 1996 | 1751. |
| | energy, ft-lb: | 3954 | 3158 | 2495 | 1946 | 1497 |
| | arc, inches: | | +4.9 | +5.9 | 0 | -14.6 |

### .300 DAKOTA

| CARTRIDGE BULLET | RANGE, YARDS: | 0 | 100 | 200 | 300 | 400 |
|---|---|---|---|---|---|---|
| Dakota 165 Barnes X | velocity, fps: | 3200 | 2979 | 2769 | 2569 | 2377 |
| | energy, ft-lb: | 3751 | 3251 | 2809 | 2417 | 2070 |
| | arc, inches: | | +2.1 | +1.8 | -3.0 | -13.2 |
| Dakota 200 Barnes X | velocity, fps: | 3000 | 2824 | 2656 | 2493 | 2336 |
| | energy, ft-lb: | 3996 | 3542 | 3131 | 2760 | 2423 |
| | arc, inches: | | +2.2 | +1.5 | -4.0 | -15.2 |

### .300 PEGASUS

| CARTRIDGE BULLET | RANGE, YARDS: | 0 | 100 | 200 | 300 | 400 |
|---|---|---|---|---|---|---|
| A-Square 180 SP boat-tail | velocity, fps: | 3500 | 3319 | 3145 | 2978 | 2817 |
| | energy, ft-lb: | 4896 | 4401 | 3953 | 3544 | 3172 |
| | arc, inches: | | +2.3 | +2.9 | 0 | -6.8 |
| A-Square 180 Nosler Part. | velocity, fps: | 3500 | 3295 | 3100 | 2913 | 2734 |
| | energy, ft-lb: | 4896 | 4339 | 3840 | 3392 | 2988 |
| | arc, inches: | | +2.3 | +3.0 | 0 | -7.1 |
| A-Square 180 Dead Tough | velocity, fps: | 3500 | 3103 | 2740 | 2405 | 2095 |
| | energy, ft-lb: | 4896 | 3848 | 3001 | 2312 | 1753 |
| | arc, inches: | | +1.1 | 0 | -5.7 | -17.5 |

### .300 REMINGTON ULTRA MAGNUM

| CARTRIDGE BULLET | RANGE, YARDS: | 0 | 100 | 200 | 300 | 400 |
|---|---|---|---|---|---|---|
| Federal 180 Trophy Bonded | velocity, fps: | 3250 | 3000 | 2770 | 2550 | 2340 |
| | energy, ft-lb: | 4220 | 3605 | 3065 | 2590 | 2180 |
| | arc, inches: | | +1.2 | 0 | -5.7 | -16.8 |

| CARTRIDGE BULLET | RANGE, YARDS: | 0 | 100 | 200 | 300 | 400 |
|---|---|---|---|---|---|---|
| Rem. 150 Swift Scirocco | velocity, fps: | 3450 | 3208 | 2980 | 2762 | 2556 |
| | energy, ft-lb: | 3964 | 3427 | 2956 | 2541 | 2175 |
| | arc, inches: | | +1.7 | +1.5 | -2.6 | -11.2 |
| Rem. 180 Nosler Partition | velocity, fps: | 3250 | 3037 | 2834 | 2640 | 2454 |
| | energy, ft-lb: | 4221 | 3686 | 3201 | 2786 | 2407 |
| | arc, inches: | | +2.4 | +1.8 | -3.0 | -12.7 |
| Rem. 180 Swift Scirocco | velocity, fps: | 3250 | 3048 | 2856 | 2672 | 2495 |
| | energy, ft-lb: | 4221 | 3714 | 3260 | 2853 | 2487 |
| | arc, inches: | | +2.0 | +1.7 | -2.8 | -12.3 |
| Rem. 180 PSP Core-Lokt | velocity, fps: | 3250 | 2988 | 2742 | 2508 | 2287 |
| | energy, ft-lb: | 3517 | 2974 | 2503 | 2095 | 1741 |
| | arc, inches: | | +2.1 | +1.8 | -3.1 | -13.6 |
| Rem. 200 Nosler Partition | velocity, fps: | 3025 | 2826 | 2636 | 2454 | 2279 |
| | energy, ft-lb: | 4063 | 3547 | 3086 | 2673 | 2308 |
| | arc, inches: | | +2.4 | +2.0 | -3.4 | -14.6 |

### .30-378 WEATHERBY MAGNUM

| CARTRIDGE BULLET | RANGE, YARDS: | 0 | 100 | 200 | 300 | 400 |
|---|---|---|---|---|---|---|
| Nosler 210 ABLR | velocity, fps: | 3040 | 2907 | 2778 | 2653 | 2531 |
| | energy, ft-lb: | 4308 | 3940 | 3599 | 3282 | 2987 |
| | arc, inches: | -1.5 | +1.3 | 0 | -5.8 | -16.6 |
| Wby. 165 Nosler Bal. Tip | velocity, fps: | 3500 | 3275 | 3062 | 2859 | 2665 |
| | energy, ft-lb: | 4488 | 3930 | 3435 | 2995 | 2603 |
| | arc, inches: | | +2.4 | +3.0 | 0 | -7.4 |
| Wby. 180 Nosler Bal. Tip | velocity, fps: | 3420 | 3213 | 3015 | 2826 | 2645 |
| | energy, ft-lb: | 4676 | 4126 | 3634 | 3193 | 2797 |
| | arc, inches: | | +2.5 | +3.1 | 0 | -7.5 |
| Wby. 180 Barnes X | velocity, fps: | 3450 | 3243 | 3046 | 2858 | 2678 |
| | energy, ft-lb: | 4757 | 4204 | 3709 | 3264 | 2865 |
| | arc, inches: | | +2.4 | +3.1 | 0 | -7.4 |
| Wby. 200 Nosler Partition | velocity, fps: | 3160 | 2955 | 2759 | 2572 | 2392. |
| | energy, ft-lb: | 4434 | 3877 | 3381 | 2938 | 2541 |
| | arc, inches: | | +3.2 | +3.9 | 0 | -9.1 |

### 7.82 (.308) WARBIRD

| CARTRIDGE BULLET | RANGE, YARDS: | 0 | 100 | 200 | 300 | 400 |
|---|---|---|---|---|---|---|
| Lazzeroni 150 Nosler Part. | velocity, fps: | 3680 | 3432 | 3197 | 2975 | 2764 |
| | energy, ft-lb: | 4512 | 3923 | 3406 | 2949 | 2546. |
| | arc, inches: | | +2.1 | +2.7 | 0 | -6.6 |
| Lazzeroni 180 Nosler Part. | velocity, fps: | 3425 | 3220 | 3026 | 2839 | 2661 |
| | energy, ft-lb: | 4689 | 4147 | 3661 | 3224 | 2831 |
| | arc, inches: | | +2.5 | +3.2 | 0 | -7.5 |
| Lazzeroni 200 Swift A-Fr. | velocity, fps: | 3290 | 3105 | 2928 | 2758 | 2594. |
| | energy, ft-lb: | 4808 | 4283 | 3808 | 3378 | 2988 |
| | arc, inches: | | +2.7 | +3.4 | 0 | -7.9 |

### 7.65x53 ARGENTINE

| CARTRIDGE BULLET | RANGE, YARDS: | 0 | 100 | 200 | 300 | 400 |
|---|---|---|---|---|---|---|
| Norma 174 Soft Point | velocity, fps: | 2493 | 2173 | 1878 | 1611 | |
| | energy, ft-lb: | 2402 | 1825 | 1363 | 1003 | |
| | arc, inches: | | +2.0 | 0 | -9.5 | |
| Norma 180 Soft Point | velocity, fps: | 2592 | 2386 | 2189 | 2002 | |
| | energy, ft-lb: | 2686 | 2276 | 1916 | 1602 | |
| | arc, inches: | | +2.3 | 0 | -9.6 | |

### .303 BRITISH

| CARTRIDGE BULLET | RANGE, YARDS: | 0 | 100 | 200 | 300 | 400 |
|---|---|---|---|---|---|---|
| Federal 150 Hi-Shok | velocity, fps: | 2690 | 2440 | 2210 | 1980 | 1780 |
| | energy, ft-lb: | 2400 | 1980 | 1620 | 1310 | 1055 |
| | arc, inches: | | +2.2 | 0 | -9.4 | -27.6 |
| Federal 180 Sierra Pro-Hunt. | velocity, fps: | 2460 | 2230 | 2020 | 1820 | 1630 |
| | energy, ft-lb: | 2420 | 1995 | 1625 | 1315 | 1060 |
| | arc, inches: | | +2.8 | 0 | -11.3 | -33.2 |
| Federal 180 Tr. Bonded HE | velocity, fps: | 2590 | 2350 | 2120 | 1900 | 1700 |
| | energy, ft-lb: | 2680 | 2205 | 1795 | 1445 | 1160 |
| | arc, inches: | | +2.4 | 0 | -10.0 | -30.0 |
| Hornady 150 Soft Point | velocity, fps: | 2685 | 2441 | 2210 | 1992 | 1787 |
| | energy, ft-lb: | 2401 | 1984 | 1627 | 1321 | 1064 |
| | arc, inches: | | +2.2 | 0 | -9.3 | -27.4 |

BALLISTICS

### .303 British (continued)

| CARTRIDGE BULLET | RANGE, YARDS: | 0 | 100 | 200 | 300 | 400 |
|---|---|---|---|---|---|---|
| Hornady 150 SP LM | velocity, fps: | 2830 | 2570 | 2325 | 2094 | 1884. |
| | energy, ft-lb: | 2667 | 2199 | 1800 | 1461 | 1185 |
| | arc, inches: | | +2.0 | 0 | -8.4 | -24.6 |
| Norma 150 Soft Point | velocity, fps: | 2723 | 2438 | 2170 | 1920 | |
| | energy, ft-lb: | 2470 | 1980 | 1569 | 1228 | |
| | arc, inches: | | +2.2 | 0 | -9.6 | |
| PMC 174 FMJ (and HPBT) | velocity, fps: | 2400 | 2216 | 2042 | 1876 | 1720 |
| | energy, ft-lb: | 2225 | 1898 | 1611 | 1360 | 1143 |
| | arc, inches: | | +2.8 | 0 | -11.2 | -32.2 |
| PMC 180 SP boat-tail | velocity, fps: | 2450 | 2276 | 2110 | 1951 | 1799 |
| | energy, ft-lb: | 2399 | 2071 | 1779 | 1521 | 1294 |
| | arc, inches: | | +2.6 | 0 | -10.4 | -30.1 |
| Rem. 180 SP Core-Lokt | velocity, fps: | 2460 | 2124 | 1817 | 1542 | 1311 |
| | energy, ft-lb: | 2418 | 1803 | 1319 | 950 | 687 |
| | arc, inches, s: | | 0 | -5.8 | -23.3 | |
| Win. 180 Power-Point | velocity, fps: | 2460 | 2233 | 2018 | 1816 | 1629 |
| | energy, ft-lb: | 2418 | 1993 | 1627 | 1318 | 1060 |
| | arc, inches, s: | | 0 | -6.1 | -20.8 | |

### 7.7x58 Japanese Arisaka

| CARTRIDGE BULLET | RANGE, YARDS: | 0 | 100 | 200 | 300 | 400 |
|---|---|---|---|---|---|---|
| Norma 174 Soft Point | velocity, fps: | 2493 | 2173 | 1878 | 1611 | |
| | energy, ft-lb: | 2402 | 1825 | 1363 | 1003 | |
| | arc, inches: | | +2.0 | 0 | -9.5 | |
| Norma 180 Soft Point | velocity, fps: | 2493 | 2291 | 2099 | 1916 | |
| | energy, ft-lb: | 2485 | 2099 | 1761 | 1468 | |
| | arc, inches: | | +2.6 | 0 | -10.5 | |

### .32-20 Winchester

| CARTRIDGE BULLET | RANGE, YARDS: | 0 | 100 | 200 | 300 | 400 |
|---|---|---|---|---|---|---|
| Rem. 100 Lead | velocity, fps: | 1210 | 1021 | 913 | 834 | 769 |
| | energy, ft-lb: | 325 | 231 | 185 | 154 | 131 |
| | arc, inches: | | 0 | -31.6 | -104.7 | |
| Win. 100 Lead | velocity, fps: | 1210 | 1021 | 913 | 834 | 769 |
| | energy, ft-lb: | 325 | 231 | 185 | 154 | 131 |
| | arc, inches: | | 0 | -32.3 | -106.3 | |

### .32 Winchester Special

| CARTRIDGE BULLET | RANGE, YARDS: | 0 | 100 | 200 | 300 | 400 |
|---|---|---|---|---|---|---|
| Federal 170 Hi-Shok | velocity, fps: | 2250 | 1920 | 1630 | 1370 | 1180 |
| | energy, ft-lb: | 1910 | 1395 | 1000 | 710 | 520 |
| | arc, inches: | | 0 | -8.0 | -29.2 | |
| Hornady 165 FTX | velocity, fps: | 2410 | 2145 | 1897 | 1669 | |
| | energy, ft-lb: | 2128 | 1685 | 1318 | 1020 | |
| | arc, inches: | -1.5 | +3.0 | 0 | -12.8 | |
| Rem. 170 SP Core-Lokt | velocity, fps: | 2250 | 1921 | 1626 | 1372 | 1175 |
| | energy, ft-lb: | 1911 | 1393 | 998 | 710 | 521 |
| | arc, inches: | | 0 | -8.0 | -29.3 | |
| Win. 170 Power-Point | velocity, fps: | 2250 | 1870 | 1537 | 1267 | 1082 |
| | energy, ft-lb: | 1911 | 1320 | 892 | 606 | 442 |
| | arc, inches: | | 0 | -9.2 | -33.2 | |

### 8mm Mauser (8x57)

| CARTRIDGE BULLET | RANGE, YARDS: | 0 | 100 | 200 | 300 | 400 |
|---|---|---|---|---|---|---|
| Federal 170 Hi-Shok | velocity, fps: | 2360 | 1970 | 1620 | 1330 | 1120 |
| | energy, ft-lb: | 2100 | 1465 | 995 | 670 | 475 |
| | arc, inches: | | 0 | -7.6 | -28.5 | |
| Hornady 195 SP | velocity, fps: | 2550 | 2343 | 2146 | 1959 | 1782 |
| | energy, ft-lb: | 2815 | 2377 | 1994 | 1861 | 1375 |
| | arc, inches: | | +2.3 | 0 | -9.9 | -28.8. |
| Hornady 195 SP (2005) | velocity, fps: | 2475 | 2269 | 2074 | 1888 | 1714 |
| | energy, ft-lb: | 2652 | 2230 | 1861 | 1543 | 1271 |
| | arc, inches: | | +2.6 | 0 | -10.7 | -31.3 |
| Norma 123 FMJ | velocity, fps: | 2559 | 2121 | 1729 | 1398 | |
| | energy, ft-lb: | 1789 | 1228 | 817 | 534 | |
| | arc, inches: | | +3.2 | 0 | -15.0 | |
| Norma 196 Oryx | velocity, fps: | 2395 | 2146 | 1912 | 1695 | |
| | energy, ft-lb: | 2497 | 2004 | 1591 | 1251 | |
| | arc, inches: | | +3 | 0 | -12.6 | |

### 8mm Mauser (8x57) (continued)

| CARTRIDGE BULLET | RANGE, YARDS: | 0 | 100 | 200 | 300 | 400 |
|---|---|---|---|---|---|---|
| Norma 196 Vulkan | velocity, fps: | 2395 | 2156 | 1930 | 1720 | |
| | energy, ft-lb: | 2497 | 2023 | 1622 | 1289 | |
| | arc, inches: | | 3.0 | 0 | -12.3 | |
| Norma 196 Alaska | velocity, fps: | 2395 | 2112 | 1850 | 1611 | |
| | energy, ft-lb: | 2714 | 2190 | 1754 | 1399 | |
| | arc, inches: | | 0 | -6.3 | -22.9 | |
| Norma 196 Soft Point (JS) | velocity, fps: | 2526 | 2244 | 1981 | 1737 | |
| | energy, ft-lb: | 2778 | 2192 | 1708 | 1314 | |
| | arc, inches: | | +2.7 | 0 | -11.6 | |
| Norma 196 Alaska (JS) | velocity, fps: | 2526 | 2248 | 1988 | 1747 | |
| | energy, ft-lb: | 2778 | 2200 | 1720 | 1328 | |
| | arc, inches: | | +2.7 | 0 | -11.5 | |
| Norma 196 Vulkan (JS) | velocity, fps: | 2526 | 2276 | 2041 | 1821 | |
| | energy, ft-lb: | 2778 | 2256 | 1813 | 1443 | |
| | arc, inches: | | +2.6 | 0 | -11.0 | |
| Norma 196 Oryx (JS) | velocity, fps: | 2526 | 2269 | 2027 | 1802 | |
| | energy, ft-lb: | 2778 | 2241 | 1789 | 1413 | |
| | arc, inches: | | +2.6 | 0 | -11.1 | |
| PMC 170 Pointed Soft Point | velocity, fps: | 2360 | 1969 | 1622 | 1333 | 1123 |
| | energy, ft-lb: | 2102 | 1463 | 993 | 671 | 476 |
| | arc, inches: | | +1.8 | -4.5 | -24.3 | -63.8 |
| Rem. 170 SP Core-Lokt | velocity, fps: | 2360 | 1969 | 1622 | 1333 | 1123 |
| | energy, ft-lb: | 2102 | 1463 | 993 | 671 | 476 |
| | arc, inches: | | +1.8 | -4.5 | -24.3 | -63.8. |
| Win. 170 Power-Point | velocity, fps: | 2360 | 1969 | 1622 | 1333 | 1123 |
| | energy, ft-lb: | 2102 | 1463 | 993 | 671 | 476 |
| | arc, inches: | | +1.8 | -4.5 | -24.3 | -63.8 |

### .325 WSM

| CARTRIDGE BULLET | RANGE, YARDS: | 0 | 100 | 200 | 300 | 400 |
|---|---|---|---|---|---|---|
| Win. 180 Ballistic ST | velocity, fps: | 3060 | 2841 | 2632 | 2432 | 2242 |
| | energy, ft-lb: | 3743 | 3226 | 2769 | 2365 | 2009 |
| | arc, inches: | | +1.4 | 0 | -6.4 | -18.7 |
| Win. 200 AccuBond CT | velocity, fps: | 2950 | 2753 | 2565 | 2384 | 2210 |
| | energy, ft-lb: | 3866 | 3367 | 2922 | 2524 | 2170 |
| | arc, inches: | | +1.5 | 0 | -6.8 | -19.8 |
| Win. 220 Power-Point | velocity, fps: | 2840 | 2605 | 2382 | 2169 | 1968 |
| | energy, ft-lb: | 3941 | 3316 | 2772 | 2300 | 1893 |
| | arc, inches: | | +1.8 | 0 | -8.0 | -23.3 |

### 8mm Remington Magnum

| CARTRIDGE BULLET | RANGE, YARDS: | 0 | 100 | 200 | 300 | 400 |
|---|---|---|---|---|---|---|
| A-Square 220 Monolythic Solid | velocity, fps: | 2800 | 2501 | 2221 | 1959 | 1718 |
| | energy, ft-lb: | 3829 | 3055 | 2409 | 1875 | 1442 |
| | arc, inches: | | +2.1 | 0 | -9.1 | -27.6 |
| Nosler 180 BT | velocity, fps: | 3200 | 2923 | 2662 | 2416 | 2183 |
| | energy, ft-lb: | 4092 | 3414 | 2832 | 2333 | 1905 |
| | arc, inches: | -1.5 | +1.3 | 0 | -6.2 | -18.4 |
| Rem. 200 Swift A-Frame | velocity, fps: | 2900 | 2623 | 2361 | 2115 | 1885 |
| | energy, ft-lb: | 3734 | 3054 | 2476 | 1987 | 1577 |
| | arc, inches: | | +1.8 | 0 | -8.0 | -23.9 |

### .338 Federal

| CARTRIDGE BULLET | RANGE, YARDS: | 0 | 100 | 200 | 300 | 400 |
|---|---|---|---|---|---|---|
| Federal 180 AccuBond | velocity, fps: | 2830 | 2590 | 2350 | 2130 | 1930 |
| | energy, ft-lb: | 3200 | 2670 | 2215 | 1820 | 1480 |
| | arc, inches: | -1.5 | +1.8 | 0 | -8.2 | -23.9 |
| Federal 185 Barnes TSX | velocity, fps: | 2750 | 2500 | 2260 | 2030 | 1820 |
| | energy, ft-lb: | 3105 | 2560 | 2090 | 1695 | 1355 |
| | arc, inches: | -1.5 | +2.0 | 0 | -8.9 | -26.2 |
| Federal 200 Tr. Bonded T | velocity, fps: | 2630 | 2430 | 2240 | 2060 | 1890 |
| | energy, ft-lb: | 3070 | 2625 | 2230 | 1885 | 1580 |
| | arc, inches: | -1.5 | +2.2 | 0 | -9.2 | -26.3 |
| Federal 210 Partition | velocity, fps: | 2630 | 2410 | 2200 | 2010 | 1820 |
| | energy, ft-lb: | 3225 | 2710 | 2265 | 1880 | 1545 |
| | arc, inches: | -1.5 | +2.3 | 0 | -9.4 | -27.3 |

# Centerfire Rifle Ballistics

## .338 MARLIN EXPRESS TO .340 WEATHERBY MAGNUM

| CARTRIDGE BULLET | RANGE, YARDS: | 0 | 100 | 200 | 300 | 400 |
|---|---|---|---|---|---|---|
| **.338 MARLIN EXPRESS** | | | | | | |
| Hornady 200 FTX | velocity, fps: | 2565 | 2365 | 2174 | 1992 | `1820 |
| | energy, ft-lb: | 2922 | 2484 | 2099 | 1762 | 1471 |
| | arc, inches: | -1.5 | +3.0 | +1.2 | -7.9 | -25.9 |
| **.338-06** | | | | | | |
| A-Square 200 Nos. Bal. Tip | velocity, fps: | 2750 | 2553 | 2364 | 2184 | 2011 |
| | energy, ft-lb: | 3358 | 2894 | 2482 | 2118 | 1796 |
| | arc, inches: | | +1.9 | 0 | -8.2 | -23.6 |
| A-Square 250 SP boat-tail | velocity, fps: | 2500 | 2374 | 2252 | 2134 | 2019 |
| | energy, ft-lb: | 3496 | 3129 | 2816 | 2528 | 2263 |
| | arc, inches: | | +2.4 | 0 | -9.3 | -26.0 |
| A-Square 250 Dead Tough | velocity, fps: | 2500 | 2222 | 1963 | 1724 | 1507 |
| | energy, ft-lb: | 3496 | 2742 | 2139 | 1649 | 1261 |
| | arc, inches: | | +2.8 | 0 | -11.9 | -35.5 |
| Nosler 180 AB | velocity, fps: | 2950 | 2698 | 2460 | 2234 | 2020 |
| | energy, ft-lb: | 3477 | 2909 | 2418 | 1994 | 1631 |
| | arc, inches: | -1.5 | +1.6 | 0 | -7.4 | -21.8 |
| Nosler 225 AB | velocity, fps: | 2600 | 2441 | 2287 | 2139 | 1997 |
| | energy, ft-lb: | 3376 | 2976 | 2614 | 2286 | 1992 |
| | arc, inches: | -1.5 | +2.2 | 0 | -8.8 | -25.3 |
| Wby. 210 Nosler Part. | velocity, fps: | 2750 | 2526 | 2312 | 2109 | 1916 |
| | energy, ft-lb: | 3527 | 2975 | 2403 | 2074 | 1712 |
| | arc, inches: | | +4.8 | +5.7 | 0 | -13.5 |
| **.338 RUGER COMPACT MAGNUM** | | | | | | |
| Hornady 185 GMX | velocity, fps: | 2980 | 2755 | 2542 | 2338 | 2143 |
| | energy, ft-lb: | 3647 | 3118 | 2653 | 2242 | 1887 |
| | arc, inches: | -1.5 | +1.5 | 0 | -6.9 | -20.3 |
| Hornady 200 SST | velocity, fps: | 2950 | 2744 | 2547 | 2358 | 2177 |
| | energy, ft-lb: | 3846 | 3342 | 2879 | 2468 | 2104 |
| | arc, inches: | -1.5 | +1.6 | 0 | -6.9 | -20.1 |
| Hornady 225 SST | velocity, fps: | 2750 | 2575 | 2407 | 2245 | 2089 |
| | energy, ft-lb: | 3778 | 3313 | 2894 | 2518 | 2180 |
| | arc, inches: | -1.5 | +1.9 | 0 | -7.9 | -22.7 |
| **.338 WINCHESTER MAGNUM** | | | | | | |
| A-Square 250 SP boat-tail | velocity, fps: | 2700 | 2568 | 2439 | 2314 | 2193 |
| | energy, ft-lb: | 4046 | 3659 | 3302 | 2972 | 2669 |
| | arc, inches: | | +4.4 | +5.2 | 0 | -11.7 |
| A-Square 250 Triad | velocity, fps: | 2700 | 2407 | 2133 | 1877 | 1653 |
| | energy, ft-lb: | 4046 | 3216 | 2526 | 1956 | 1516 |
| | arc, inches: | | +2.3 | 0 | -9.8 | -29.8 |
| Federal 210 Nosler Partition | velocity, fps: | 2830 | 2600 | 2390 | 2180 | 1980 |
| | energy, ft-lb: | 3735 | 3160 | 2655 | 2215 | 1835 |
| | arc, inches: | | +1.8 | 0 | -8.0 | -23.3 |
| Federal 225 Sierra Pro-Hunt. | velocity, fps: | 2780 | 2570 | 2360 | 2170 | 1980 |
| | energy, ft-lb: | 3860 | 3290 | 2780 | 2340 | 1960 |
| | arc, inches: | | +1.9 | 0 | -8.2 | -23.7 |
| Federal 225 Trophy Bonded | velocity, fps: | 2800 | 2560 | 2330 | 2110 | 1900 |
| | energy, ft-lb: | 3915 | 3265 | 2700 | 2220 | 1800 |
| | arc, inches: | | +1.9 | 0 | -8.4 | -24.5 |
| Federal 225 Tr. Bonded HE | velocity, fps: | 2940 | 2690 | 2450 | 2230 | 2010 |
| | energy, ft-lb: | 4320 | 3610 | 3000 | 2475 | 2025 |
| | arc, inches: | | +1.7 | 0 | -7.5 | -22.0 |
| Federal 225 Barnes XLC | velocity, fps: | 2800 | 2610 | 2430 | 2260 | 2090 |
| | energy, ft-lb: | 3915 | 3405 | 2950 | 2545 | 2190 |
| | arc, inches: | | +1.8 | 0 | -7.7 | -22.2 |
| Federal 250 Nosler Partition | velocity, fps: | 2660 | 2470 | 2300 | 2120 | 1960 |
| | energy, ft-lb: | 3925 | 3395 | 2925 | 2505 | 2130. |
| | arc, inches: | | +2.1 | 0 | -8.8 | -25.1 |
| Federal 250 Nosler Part HE | velocity, fps: | 2800 | 2610 | 2420 | 2250 | 2080 |
| | energy, ft-lb: | 4350 | 3775 | 3260 | 2805 | 2395 |
| | arc, inches: | | +1.8 | 0 | -7.8 | -22.5 |
| Hornady 225 Soft Point HM | velocity, fps: | 2920 | 2678 | 2449 | 2232 | 2027 |
| | energy, ft-lb: | 4259 | 3583 | 2996 | 2489 | 2053 |
| | arc, inches: | | +1.8 | 0 | -7.6 | -22.0 |
| Norma 225 TXP Swift A-Fr. | velocity, fps: | 2740 | 2507 | 2286 | 2075 | |
| | energy, ft-lb: | 3752 | 3141 | 2611 | 2153 | |
| | arc, inches: | | +2.0 | 0 | -8.7 | |
| Norma 230 Oryx | velocity, fps: | 2756 | 2514 | 2284 | 2066 | |
| | energy, ft-lb: | 3880 | 3228 | 2665 | 2181 | |
| | arc, inches: | | +2.0 | 0 | -8.7 | |
| Norma 250 Nosler Partition | velocity, fps: | 2657 | 2470 | 2290 | 2118 | |
| | energy, ft-lb: | 3920 | 3387 | 2912 | 2490 | |
| | arc, inches: | | +2.1 | 0 | -8.7 | |
| PMC 225 Barnes X | velocity, fps: | 2780 | 2619 | 2464 | 2313 | 2168 |
| | energy, ft-lb: | 3860 | 3426 | 3032 | 2673 | 2348. |
| | arc, inches: | | +1.8 | 0 | -7.6 | -21.6 |
| Rem. 200 Nosler Bal. Tip | velocity, fps: | 2950 | 2724 | 2509 | 2303 | 2108 |
| | energy, ft-lb: | 3866 | 3295 | 2795 | 2357 | 1973 |
| | arc, inches: | | +1.6 | 0 | -7.1 | -20.8 |
| Rem. 210 Nosler Partition | velocity, fps: | 2830 | 2602 | 2385 | 2179 | 1983 |
| | energy, ft-lb: | 3734 | 3157 | 2653 | 2214 | 1834 |
| | arc, inches: | | +1.8 | 0 | -7.9 | -23.2 |
| Rem. 225 PSP Core-Lokt | velocity, fps: | 2780 | 2572 | 2374 | 2184 | 2003 |
| | energy, ft-lb: | 3860 | 3305 | 2815 | 2383 | 2004 |
| | arc, inches: | | +1.9 | 0 | -8.1 | -23.4 |
| Rem. 225 PSP C-L Ultra | velocity, fps: | 2780 | 2582 | 2392 | 2210 | 2036 |
| | energy, ft-lb: | 3860 | 3329 | 2858 | 2440 | 2071 |
| | arc, inches: | | +1.9 | 0 | -7.9 | -23.0 |
| Rem. 225 Swift A-Frame | velocity, fps: | 2785 | 2517 | 2266 | 2029 | 1808 |
| | energy, ft-lb: | 3871 | 3165 | 2565 | 2057 | 1633 |
| | arc, inches: | | +2.0 | 0 | -8.8 | -25.2 |
| Rem. 250 PSP Core-Lokt | velocity, fps: | 2660 | 2456 | 2261 | 2075 | 1898 |
| | energy, ft-lb: | 3927 | 3348 | 2837 | 2389 | 1999 |
| | arc, inches: | | +2.1 | 0 | -8.9 | -26.0 |
| Speer 250 Grand Slam | velocity, fps: | 2645 | 2442 | 2247 | 2062 | |
| | energy, ft-lb: | 3883 | 3309 | 2803 | 2360 | |
| | arc, inches: | | +2.2 | 0 | -9.1 | -26.2 |
| Win. 200 Power-Point | velocity, fps: | 2960 | 2658 | 2375 | 2110 | 1862 |
| | energy, ft-lb: | 3890 | 3137 | 2505 | 1977 | 1539 |
| | arc, inches: | | +2.0 | 0 | -8.2 | -24.3 |
| Win. 200 Ballistic Silvertip | velocity, fps: | 2950 | 2724 | 2509 | 2303 | 2108 |
| | energy, ft-lb: | 3864 | 3294 | 2794 | 2355 | 1972 |
| | arc, inches: | | +1.6 | 0 | -7.1 | -20.8 |
| Win. 225 AccuBond | velocity, fps: | 2800 | 2634 | 2474 | 2319 | 2170 |
| | energy, ft-lb: | 3918 | 3467 | 3058 | 2688 | 2353 |
| | arc, inches: | | +1.8 | 0 | -7.4 | -21.3 |
| Win. 230 Fail Safe | velocity, fps: | 2780 | 2573 | 2375 | 2186 | 2005 |
| | energy, ft-lb: | 3948 | 3382 | 2881 | 2441 | 2054 |
| | arc, inches: | | +1.9 | 0 | -8.1 | -23.4 |
| Win. 250 Partition Gold | velocity, fps: | 2650 | 2467 | 2291 | 2122 | 1960 |
| | energy, ft-lb: | 3899 | 3378 | 2914 | 2520 | 2134 |
| | arc, inches: | | +2.1 | 0 | -8.7 | -25.2 |
| **.340 WEATHERBY MAGNUM** | | | | | | |
| A-Square 250 SP boat-tail | velocity, fps: | 2820 | 2684 | 2552 | 2424 | 2299 |
| | energy, ft-lb: | 4414 | 3999 | 3615 | 3261 | 2935 |
| | arc, inches: | | +4.0 | +4.6 | 0 | -10.6 |
| A-Square 250 Triad | velocity, fps: | 2820 | 2520 | 2238 | 1976 | 1741 |
| | energy, ft-lb: | 4414 | 3524 | 2781 | 2166 | 1683 |
| | arc, inches: | | +2.0 | 0 | -9.0 | -26.8 |
| Federal 225 Trophy Bonded | velocity, fps: | 3100 | 2840 | 2600 | 2370 | 2150 |
| | energy, ft-lb: | 4800 | 4035 | 3375 | 2800 | 2310 |
| | arc, inches: | | +1.4 | 0 | -6.5 | -19.4 |

| CARTRIDGE BULLET | RANGE, YARDS: | 0 | 100 | 200 | 300 | 400 |
|---|---|---|---|---|---|---|
| Wby. 200 Pointed Expanding | velocity, fps: | 3221 | 2946 | 2688 | 2444 | 2213 |
| | energy, ft-lb: | 4607 | 3854 | 3208 | 2652 | 2174 |
| | arc, inches: | | +3.3 | +4.0 | 0 | -9.9 |
| Wby. 200 Nosler Bal. Tip | velocity, fps: | 3221 | 2980 | 2753 | 2536 | 2329 |
| | energy, ft-lb: | 4607 | 3944 | 3364 | 2856 | 2409 |
| | arc, inches: | | +3.1 | +3.9 | 0 | -9.2 |
| Wby. 210 Nosler Partition | velocity, fps: | 3211 | 2963 | 2728 | 2505 | 2293 |
| | energy, ft-lb: | 4807 | 4093 | 3470 | 2927 | 2452 |
| | arc, inches: | | +3.2 | +3.9 | 0 | -9.5 |
| Wby. 225 Pointed Expanding | velocity, fps: | 3066 | 2824 | 2595 | 2377 | 2170 |
| | energy, ft-lb: | 4696 | 3984 | 3364 | 2822 | 2352 |
| | arc, inches: | | +3.6 | +4.4 | 0 | -10.7 |
| Wby. 225 Barnes X | velocity, fps: | 3001 | 2804 | 2615 | 2434 | 2260 |
| | energy, ft-lb: | 4499 | 3927 | 3416 | 2959 | 2551 |
| | arc, inches: | | +3.6 | +4.3 | 0 | -10.3 |
| Wby. 250 Pointed Expanding | velocity, fps: | 2963 | 2745 | 2537 | 2338 | 2149 |
| | energy, ft-lb: | 4873 | 4182 | 3572 | 3035 | 2563 |
| | arc, inches: | | +3.9 | +4.6 | 0 | -11.1 |
| Wby. 250 Nosler Partition | velocity, fps: | 2941 | 2743 | 2553 | 2371 | 2197 |
| | energy, ft-lb: | 4801 | 4176 | 3618 | 3120 | 2678 |
| | arc, inches: | | +3.9 | +4.6 | 0 | -10.9 |

## .330 DAKOTA

| CARTRIDGE BULLET | RANGE, YARDS: | 0 | 100 | 200 | 300 | 400 |
|---|---|---|---|---|---|---|
| Dakota 200 Barnes X | velocity, fps: | 3200 | 2971 | 2754 | 2548 | 2350 |
| | energy, ft-lb: | 4547 | 3920 | 3369 | 2882 | 2452 |
| | arc, inches: | | +2.1 | +1.8 | -3.1 | -13.4 |
| Dakota 250 Barnes X | velocity, fps: | 2900 | 2719 | 2545 | 2378 | 2217 |
| | energy, ft-lb: | 4668 | 4103 | 3595 | 3138 | 2727 |
| | arc, inches: | | +2.3 | +1.3 | -5.0 | -17.5 |

## .338 REMINGTON ULTRA MAGNUM

| CARTRIDGE BULLET | RANGE, YARDS: | 0 | 100 | 200 | 300 | 400 |
|---|---|---|---|---|---|---|
| Federal 210 Nosler Partition | velocity, fps: | 3025 | 2800 | 2585 | 2385 | 2190 |
| | energy, ft-lb: | 4270 | 3655 | 3120 | 2645 | 2230 |
| | arc, inches: | | +1.5 | 0 | -6.7 | -19.5 |
| Federal 250 Trophy Bonded | velocity, fps: | 2860 | 2630 | 2420 | 2210 | 2020 |
| | energy, ft-lb: | 4540 | 3850 | 3245 | 2715 | 2260. |
| | arc, inches: | | +0.8 | 0 | -7.7 | -22.6 |
| Rem. 250 Swift A-Frame | velocity, fps: | 2860 | 2645 | 2440 | 2244 | 2057 |
| | energy, ft-lb: | 4540 | 3882 | 3303 | 2794 | 2347 |
| | arc, inches: | | +1.7 | 0 | -7.6 | -22.1 |
| Rem. 250 PSP Core-Lokt | velocity, fps: | 2860 | 2647 | 2443 | 2249 | 2064 |
| | energy, ft-lb: | 4540 | 3888 | 3314 | 2807 | 2363 |
| | arc, inches: | | +1.7 | 0 | -7.6 | -22.0 |

## .338 LAPUA

| CARTRIDGE BULLET | RANGE, YARDS: | 0 | 100 | 200 | 300 | 400 |
|---|---|---|---|---|---|---|
| Black Hills 250 Sierra MKing | velocity, fps: | 2950 | | | | |
| | energy, ft-lb: | 4831 | | | | |
| | arc, inches: | | | | | |
| Black Hills 300 Sierra MKing | velocity, fps: | 2800 | | | | |
| | energy, ft-lb: | 5223 | | | | |
| | arc, inches: | | | | | |
| Hornady 285 BTHP | velocity, fps: | 2745 | 2616 | 2491 | 2369 | 2251 |
| | energy, ft-lb: | 4768 | 4331 | 3926 | 3552 | 3206 |
| | arc, inches: | -1.5 | +1.8 | 0 | -7.4 | -21.0 |

| CARTRIDGE BULLET | RANGE, YARDS: | 0 | 100 | 200 | 300 | 600 |
|---|---|---|---|---|---|---|
| Lapua 250 Scenar | velocity, fps: | 2970 | 2823 | 2680 | 2539 | 2141 |
| | energy, ft-lb: | 4896 | 4424 | 3985 | 3579 | 2545 |
| | arc, inches: | -1.5 | +3.0 | +4.0 | 0 | -47.0 |
| Lapua 300 Scenar | velocity, fps: | 2723 | 2600 | 2482 | 2367 | 2042 |
| | energy, ft-lb: | 4938 | 4504 | 4102 | 3731 | 2778 |
| | arc, inches: | -1.5 | +4.0 | +5.0 | 0 | -54.0 |

| CARTRIDGE BULLET | RANGE, YARDS: | 0 | 100 | 200 | 300 | 400 |
|---|---|---|---|---|---|---|
| Nosler 225 AB | velocity, fps: | 3000 | 2826 | 2659 | 2498 | 2342 |
| | energy, ft-lb: | 4495 | 3990 | 3532 | 3117 | 2741 |
| | arc, inches: | -1.5 | +1.4 | 0 | -6.3 | -18.3 |

## .338-378 WEATHERBY MAGNUM

| CARTRIDGE BULLET | RANGE, YARDS: | 0 | 100 | 200 | 300 | 400 |
|---|---|---|---|---|---|---|
| Wby. 200 Nosler Bal. Tip | velocity, fps: | 3350 | 3102 | 2868 | 2646 | 2434 |
| | energy, ft-lb: | 4983 | 4273 | 3652 | 3109 | 2631 |
| | arc, inches: | 0 | +2.8 | +3.5 | 0 | -8.4 |
| Wby. 225 Barnes X | velocity, fps: | 3180 | 2974 | 2778 | 2591 | 2410. |
| | energy, ft-lb: | 5052 | 4420 | 3856 | 3353 | 2902 |
| | arc, inches: | 0 | +3.1 | +3.8 | 0 | -8.9 |
| Wby. 250 Nosler Partition | velocity, fps: | 3060 | 2856 | 2662 | 2475 | 2297 |
| | energy, ft-lb: | 5197 | 4528 | 3933 | 3401 | 2927 |
| | arc, inches: | 0 | +3.5 | +4.2 | 0 | -9.8 |

## 8.59 (.338) TITAN

| CARTRIDGE BULLET | RANGE, YARDS: | 0 | 100 | 200 | 300 | 400 |
|---|---|---|---|---|---|---|
| Lazzeroni 200 Nos. Bal. Tip | velocity, fps: | 3430 | 3211 | 3002 | 2803 | 2613 |
| | energy, ft-lb: | 5226 | 4579 | 4004 | 3491 | 3033 |
| | arc, inches: | | +2.5 | +3.2 | 0 | -7.6 |
| Lazzeroni 225 Nos. Partition | velocity, fps: | 3235 | 3031 | 2836 | 2650 | 2471 |
| | energy, ft-lb: | 5229 | 4591 | 4021 | 3510 | 3052 |
| | arc, inches: | | +3.0 | +3.6 | 0 | -8.6 |
| Lazzeroni 250 Swift A-Fr. | velocity, fps: | 3100 | 2908 | 2725 | 2549 | 2379 |
| | energy, ft-lb: | 5336 | 4697 | 4123 | 3607 | 3143 |
| | arc, inches: | | +3.3 | +4.0 | 0 | -9.3 |

## .338 A-SQUARE

| CARTRIDGE BULLET | RANGE, YARDS: | 0 | 100 | 200 | 300 | 400 |
|---|---|---|---|---|---|---|
| A-Square 200 Nos. Bal. Tip | velocity, fps: | 3500 | 3266 | 3045 | 2835 | 2634 |
| | energy, ft-lb: | 5440 | 4737 | 4117 | 3568 | 3081 |
| | arc, inches: | | +2.4 | +3.1 | 0 | -7.5 |
| A-Square 250 SP boat-tail | velocity, fps: | 3120 | 2974 | 2834 | 2697 | 2565. |
| | energy, ft-lb: | 5403 | 4911 | 4457 | 4038 | 3652 |
| | arc, inches: | | +3.1 | +3.7 | 0 | -8.5 |
| A-Square 250 Triad | velocity, fps: | 3120 | 2799 | 2500 | 2220 | 1958 |
| | energy, ft-lb: | 5403 | 4348 | 3469 | 2736 | 2128 |
| | arc, inches: | | +1.5 | 0 | -7.1 | -20.4. |

## .338 EXCALIBER

| CARTRIDGE BULLET | RANGE, YARDS: | 0 | 100 | 200 | 300 | 400 |
|---|---|---|---|---|---|---|
| A-Square 200 Nos. Bal. Tip | velocity, fps: | 3600 | 3361 | 3134 | 2920 | 2715 |
| | energy, ft-lb: | 5755 | 5015 | 4363 | 3785 | 3274 |
| | arc, inches: | | +2.2 | +2.9 | 0 | -6.7 |
| A-Square 250 SP boat-tail | velocity, fps: | 3250 | 3101 | 2958 | 2684 | 2553 |
| | energy, ft-lb: | 5863 | 5339 | 4855 | 4410 | 3998 |
| | arc, inches: | | +2.7 | +3.4 | 0 | -7.8 |
| A-Square 250 Triad | velocity, fps: | 3250 | 2922 | 2618 | 2333 | 2066 |
| | energy, ft-lb: | 5863 | 4740 | 3804 | 3021 | 2370 |
| | arc, inches: | | +1.3 | 0 | -6.4 | -19.2 |

## .348 WINCHESTER

| CARTRIDGE BULLET | RANGE, YARDS: | 0 | 100 | 200 | 300 | 400 |
|---|---|---|---|---|---|---|
| Win. 200 Silvertip | velocity, fps: | 2520 | 2215 | 1931 | 1672 | 1443. |
| | energy, ft-lb: | 2820 | 2178 | 1656 | 1241 | 925 |
| | arc, inches: | | 0 | -6.2 | -21.9 | |

## .357 MAGNUM

| CARTRIDGE BULLET | RANGE, YARDS: | 0 | 100 | 200 | 300 | 400 |
|---|---|---|---|---|---|---|
| Federal 180 Hi-Shok HP Hollow Point | velocity, fps: | 1550 | 1160 | 980 | 860 | 770 |
| | energy, ft-lb: | 960 | 535 | 385 | 295 | 235 |
| | arc, inches: | | 0 | -22.8 | -77.9 | -173.8 |
| Win. 158 Jacketed SP | velocity, fps: | 1830 | 1427 | 1138 | 980 | 883 |
| | energy, ft-lb: | 1175 | 715 | 454 | 337 | 274 |
| | arc, inches: | | 0 | -16.2 | -57.0 | -128.3 |

## .35 REMINGTON

| CARTRIDGE BULLET | RANGE, YARDS: | 0 | 100 | 200 | 300 | 400 |
|---|---|---|---|---|---|---|
| Federal 200 Hi-Shok | velocity, fps: | 2080 | 1700 | 1380 | 1140 | 1000 |
| | energy, ft-lb: | 1920 | 1280 | 840 | 575 | 445 |
| | arc, inches: | | 0 | -10.7 | -39.3 | |

# Centerfire Rifle Ballistics

## .35 REMINGTON TO 9.3X74 R

**Hornady 200 Evolution**

| | 0 | 100 | 200 | 300 | 400 |
|---|---|---|---|---|---|
| velocity, fps: | 2225 | 1963 | 1721 | 1503 | |
| energy, ft-lb: | 2198 | 1711 | 1315 | 1003 | |
| arc, inches: | | +3.0 | -1.3 | -17.5 | |

**Rem. 150 PSP Core-Lokt**

| | 0 | 100 | 200 | 300 | 400 |
|---|---|---|---|---|---|
| velocity, fps: | 2300 | 1874 | 1506 | 1218 | 1039 |
| energy, ft-lb: | 1762 | 1169 | 755 | 494 | 359 |
| arc, inches: | | 0 | -8.6 | -32.6 | |

**Rem. 200 SP Core-Lokt**

| | 0 | 100 | 200 | 300 | 400 |
|---|---|---|---|---|---|
| velocity, fps: | 2080 | 1698 | 1376 | 1140 | 1001 |
| energy, ft-lb: | 1921 | 1280 | 841 | 577 | 445 |
| arc, inches: | | 0 | -10.7 | -40.1 | |

**Win. 200 Power-Point**

| | 0 | 100 | 200 | 300 | 400 |
|---|---|---|---|---|---|
| velocity, fps: | 2020 | 1646 | 1335 | 1114 | 985 |
| energy, ft-lb: | 1812 | 1203 | 791 | 551 | 431 |
| arc, inches: | | 0 | -12.1 | -43.9 | |

### .356 WINCHESTER

**Win. 200 Power-Point**

| | 0 | 100 | 200 | 300 | 400 |
|---|---|---|---|---|---|
| velocity, fps: | 2460 | 2114 | 1797 | 1517 | 1284 |
| energy, ft-lb: | 2688 | 1985 | 1434 | 1022 | 732 |
| arc, inches: | | +1.6 | -3.8 | -20.1 | -51.2 |

### .358 WINCHESTER

**Hornady 200 SP**

| | 0 | 100 | 200 | 300 | 400 |
|---|---|---|---|---|---|
| velocity, fps: | 2475 | 2180 | 1906 | 1655 | 1434 |
| energy, ft-lb: | 2720 | 2110 | 1612 | 1217 | 913 |
| arc, inches: | -1.5 | +2.9 | 0 | -12.6 | -37.9 |

**Win. 200 Silvertip**

| | 0 | 100 | 200 | 300 | 400 |
|---|---|---|---|---|---|
| velocity, fps: | 2490 | 2171 | 1876 | 1610 | 1379 |
| energy, ft-lb: | 2753 | 2093 | 1563 | 1151 | 844 |
| arc, inches: | | +1.5 | -3.6 | -18.6 | -47.2 |

### .35 WHELEN

**Federal 225 Trophy Bonded**

| | 0 | 100 | 200 | 300 | 400 |
|---|---|---|---|---|---|
| velocity, fps: | 2600 | 2400 | 2200 | 2020 | 1840 |
| energy, ft-lb: | 3375 | 2865 | 2520 | 2030 | 1690. |
| arc, inches: | | +2.3 | 0 | -9.4 | -27.3 |

**Hornady 200 SP**

| | 0 | 100 | 200 | 300 | 400 |
|---|---|---|---|---|---|
| velocity, fps: | 2910 | 2585 | 2283 | 2001 | 1742 |
| energy, ft-lb: | 3760 | 2968 | 2314 | 1778 | 1347 |
| arc, inches: | -1.5 | +1.9 | 0 | -8.6 | -25.9 |

**Rem. 200 Pointed Soft Point**

| | 0 | 100 | 200 | 300 | 400 |
|---|---|---|---|---|---|
| velocity, fps: | 2675 | 2378 | 2100 | 1842 | 1606 |
| energy, ft-lb: | 3177 | 2510 | 1958 | 1506 | 1145 |
| arc, inches: | | +2.3 | 0 | -10.3 | -30.8 |

**Rem. 250 Pointed Soft Point**

| | 0 | 100 | 200 | 300 | 400 |
|---|---|---|---|---|---|
| velocity, fps: | 2400 | 2197 | 2005 | 1823 | 1652 |
| energy, ft-lb: | 3197 | 2680 | 2230 | 1844 | 1515 |
| arc, inches: | | +1.3 | -3.2 | -16.6 | -40.0 |

### .350 REMINGTON MAGNUM

**Nosler 225 PT**

| | 0 | 100 | 200 | 300 | 400 |
|---|---|---|---|---|---|
| velocity, fps: | 2550 | 2349 | 2158 | 1976 | 1804 |
| energy, ft-lb: | 3248 | 2758 | 2327 | 1951 | 1626 |
| arc, inches: | -1.5 | +2.4 | 0 | -9.9 | -28.7 |

### .358 NORMA MAGNUM

**A-Square 275 Triad**

| | 0 | 100 | 200 | 300 | 400 |
|---|---|---|---|---|---|
| velocity, fps: | 2700 | 2394 | 2108 | 1842 | 1653 |
| energy, ft-lb: | 4451 | 3498 | 2713 | 2072 | 1668 |
| arc, inches: | | +2.3 | 0 | -10.1 | -29.8 |

**Norma 250 TXP Swift A-Fr.**

| | 0 | 100 | 200 | 300 | 400 |
|---|---|---|---|---|---|
| velocity, fps: | 2723 | 2467 | 2225 | 1996 | |
| energy, ft-lb: | 4117 | 3379 | 2748 | 2213 | |
| arc, inches: | | +2.1 | 0 | -9.1 | |

**Norma 250 Woodleigh**

| | 0 | 100 | 200 | 300 | 400 |
|---|---|---|---|---|---|
| velocity, fps: | 2799 | 2442 | 2112 | 1810 | |
| energy, ft-lb: | 4350 | 3312 | 2478 | 1819 | |
| arc, inches: | | +2.2 | 0 | -10.0 | |

**Norma 250 Oryx**

| | 0 | 100 | 200 | 300 | 400 |
|---|---|---|---|---|---|
| velocity, fps: | 2756 | 2493 | 2245 | 2011 | |
| energy, ft-lb: | 4217 | 3451 | 2798 | 2245 | |
| arc, inches: | | +2.1 | 0 | -9.0 | |

### .358 STA

**A-Square 275 Triad**

| | 0 | 100 | 200 | 300 | 400 |
|---|---|---|---|---|---|
| velocity, fps: | 2850 | 2562 | 2292 | 2039 | 1764 |
| energy, ft-lb: | 4959 | 4009 | 3208 | 2539 | 1899. |
| arc, inches: | | +1.9 | 0 | -8.6 | -26.1 |

### 9.3x57

**Norma 232 Vulkan**

| | 0 | 100 | 200 | 300 | 400 |
|---|---|---|---|---|---|
| velocity, fps: | 2329 | 2031 | 1757 | 1512 | |
| energy, ft-lb: | 2795 | 2126 | 1591 | 1178 | |
| arc, inches: | | +3.5 | 0 | -14.9 | |

**Norma 232 Oryx**

| | 0 | 100 | 200 | 300 | 400 |
|---|---|---|---|---|---|
| velocity, fps: | 2362 | 2058 | 1778 | 1528 | |
| energy, ft-lb: | 2875 | 2182 | 1630 | 1203 | |
| arc, inches: | | +3.4 | 0 | -14.5 | |

**Norma 285 Oryx**

| | 0 | 100 | 200 | 300 | 400 |
|---|---|---|---|---|---|
| velocity, fps: | 2067 | 1859 | 1666 | 1490 | |
| energy, ft-lb: | 2704 | 2188 | 1756 | 1404 | |
| arc, inches: | | +4.3 | 0 | -16.8 | |

**Norma 286 Alaska**

| | 0 | 100 | 200 | 300 | 400 |
|---|---|---|---|---|---|
| velocity, fps: | 2067 | 1857 | 1662 | 1484 | |
| energy, ft-lb: | 2714 | 2190 | 1754 | 1399 | |
| arc, inches: | | +4.3 | 0 | -17.0 | |

### 9.3x62

**Federal 286 TSX**

| | 0 | 100 | 200 | 300 | 400 |
|---|---|---|---|---|---|
| velocity, fps: | 2360 | 2160 | 1970 | 1790 | |
| energy, ft-lb: | 3535 | 2965 | 2465 | 2035 | |
| arc, inches: | -1.5 | +3.0 | 0 | -12.0 | |

**Federal 286 Woodleigh Hydro**

| | 0 | 100 | 200 | 300 | 400 |
|---|---|---|---|---|---|
| velocity, fps: | 2360 | 2050 | 1760 | 1510 | |
| energy, ft-lb: | 3535 | 2665 | 1975 | 1445 | |
| arc, inches:: | -1.5 | +3.4 | 0 | -14.7 | |

**Hornady 286 SP-HP**

| | 0 | 100 | 200 | 300 | 400 |
|---|---|---|---|---|---|
| velocity, fps: | 2350 | 2155 | 1961 | 1778 | |
| energy, ft-lb: | 3537 | 2949 | 2442 | 2008 | |
| arc, inches: | -1.5 | +3.0 | 0 | -12.1 | |

**Norma 232 Oryx**

| | 0 | 100 | 200 | 300 | 400 |
|---|---|---|---|---|---|
| velocity, fps: | 2625 | 2294 | 1988 | 1708 | |
| energy, ft-lb: | 3535 | 2700 | 2028 | 1497 | |
| arc, inches: | -1.5 | +2.5 | 0 | -11.4 | |

**Norma 250 A-Frame**

| | 0 | 100 | 200 | 300 | 400 |
|---|---|---|---|---|---|
| velocity, fps: | 2625 | 2322 | 2039 | 1778 | |
| energy, ft-lb: | 3826 | 2993 | 2309 | 1755 | |
| arc, inches: | -1.5 | +2.5 | 0 | -10.9 | |

**Norma 286 Plastic Point**

| | 0 | 100 | 200 | 300 | 400 |
|---|---|---|---|---|---|
| velocity, fps: | 2362 | 2141 | 1931 | 1736 | |
| energy, ft-lb: | 3544 | 2911 | 2370 | 1914 | |
| arc, inches: | -1.5 | +3.1 | 0 | -12.4 | |

**Nosler 250 AccuBond**

| | 0 | 100 | 200 | 300 | 400 |
|---|---|---|---|---|---|
| velocity, fps: | 2550 | 2376 | 2208 | 2048 | 1894 |
| energy, ft-lb: | 3609 | 3133 | 2707 | 2328 | 1992 |
| arc, inches: | -1.5 | +2.3 | 0 | -9.5 | -27.2 |

**Nosler 286 Partition**

| | 0 | 100 | 200 | 300 | 400 |
|---|---|---|---|---|---|
| velocity, fps: | 2350 | 2179 | 2015 | 1859 | 1711 |
| energy, ft-lb: | 3506 | 3014 | 2578 | 2194 | 1859 |
| arc, inches: | -1.5 | +2.9 | 0 | -11.5 | -33.1 |

### 9.3x64

**A-Square 286 Triad**

| | 0 | 100 | 200 | 300 | 400 |
|---|---|---|---|---|---|
| velocity, fps: | 2700 | 2391 | 2103 | 1835 | 1602 |
| energy, ft-lb: | 4629 | 3630 | 2808 | 2139 | 1631 |
| arc, inches: | | +2.3 | 0 | -10.1 | -30.8 |

### .370 SAKO

**Federal 286 TSX**

| | 0 | 100 | 200 | 300 | 400 |
|---|---|---|---|---|---|
| velocity, fps: | 2550 | 2370 | 2190 | 2020 | 1860 |
| energy, ft-lb: | 4130 | 3555 | 3045 | 2595 | 2195 |
| arc, inches: | -1.5 | +2.4 | 0 | -9.6 | -27.5 |

### 9.3x74 R

**A-Square 286 Triad**

| | 0 | 100 | 200 | 300 | 400 |
|---|---|---|---|---|---|
| velocity, fps: | 2360 | 2089 | 1844 | 1623 | |
| energy, ft-lb: | 3538 | 2771 | 2157 | 1670 | |
| arc, inches: | | +3.6 | 0 | -14.0 | |

**Hornady 286**

| | 0 | 100 | 200 | 300 | 400 |
|---|---|---|---|---|---|
| velocity, fps | 2360 | 2136 | 1924 | 1727 | 1545 |
| energy, ft-lb | 3536 | 2896 | 2351 | 1893 | 1516 |
| arc, inches | -1.5 | 0 | -6.1 | -21.7 | -49.0 |

**Norma 232 Vulkan**

| | 0 | 100 | 200 | 300 | 400 |
|---|---|---|---|---|---|
| velocity, fps: | 2625 | 2327 | 2049 | 1792 | |
| energy, ft-lb: | 3551 | 2791 | 2164 | 1655 | |
| arc, inches: | | +2.5 | 0 | -10.8 | |

**Norma 232 Oryx**

| | 0 | 100 | 200 | 300 | 400 |
|---|---|---|---|---|---|
| velocity, fps: | 2526 | 2191 | 1883 | 1605 | |
| energy, ft-lb: | 3274 | 2463 | 1819 | 1322 | |
| arc, inches: | | +2.9 | 0 | -12.8 | |

BALLISTICS

| CARTRIDGE BULLET | RANGE, YARDS: | 0 | 100 | 200 | 300 | 400 |
|---|---|---|---|---|---|---|
| Norma 285 Oryx | velocity, fps: | 2362 | 2114 | 1881 | 1667 | |
| | energy, ft-lb: | 3532 | 2829 | 2241 | 1758 | |
| | arc, inches: | | +3.1 | 0 | -13.0 | |
| Norma 286 Alaska | velocity, fps: | 2362 | 2135 | 1920 | 1720 | |
| | energy, ft-lb: | 3544 | 2894 | 2342 | 1879 | |
| | arc, inches: | | +3.1 | 0 | -12.5 | |
| Norma 286 Plastic Point | velocity, fps: | 2362 | 2135 | 1920 | 1720 | |
| | energy, ft-lb: | 3544 | 2894 | 2342 | 1879 | |
| | arc, inches: | | +3.1 | 0 | -12.5 | |

## .375 WINCHESTER

| CARTRIDGE BULLET | RANGE, YARDS: | 0 | 100 | 200 | 300 | 400 |
|---|---|---|---|---|---|---|
| Win. 200 Power-Point | velocity, fps: | 2200 | 1841 | 1526 | 1268 | 1089 |
| | energy, ft-lb: | 2150 | 1506 | 1034 | 714 | |
| | arc, inches: | | 0 | -9.5 | -33.8 | |

## .375 FLANGED

| CARTRIDGE BULLET | RANGE, YARDS: | 0 | 100 | 200 | 300 | 400 |
|---|---|---|---|---|---|---|
| Nosler 300 PT | velocity, fps: | 2400 | 2191 | 1993 | 1806 | 1632 |
| | energy, ft-lb: | 3836 | 3198 | 2646 | 2173 | 1775 |
| | arc, inches: | -1.5 | +2.9 | 0 | -11.7 | -34.0 |

## .375 H&H MAGNUM

| CARTRIDGE BULLET | RANGE, YARDS: | 0 | 100 | 200 | 300 | 400 |
|---|---|---|---|---|---|---|
| A-Square 300 SP boat-tail | velocity, fps: | 2550 | 2415 | 2284 | 2157 | 2034 |
| | energy, ft-lb: | 4331 | 3884 | 3474 | 3098 | 2755 |
| | arc, inches: | | +5.2 | +6.0 | 0 | -13.3 |
| A-Square 300 Triad | velocity, fps: | 2550 | 2251 | 1973 | 1717 | 1496 |
| | energy, ft-lb: | 4331 | 3375 | 2592 | 1964 | 1491 |
| | arc, inches: | | +2.7 | 0 | -11.7 | -35.1 |
| Federal 250 Trophy Bonded | velocity, fps: | 2670 | 2360 | 2080 | 1820 | 1580 |
| | energy, ft-lb: | 3955 | 3100 | 2400 | 1830 | 1380 |
| | arc, inches: | | +2.4 | 0 | -10.4 | -31.7 |
| Federal 270 Hi-Shok | velocity, fps: | 2690 | 2420 | 2170 | 1920 | 1700 |
| | energy, ft-lb: | 4340 | 3510 | 2810 | 2220 | 1740 |
| | arc, inches: | | +2.4 | 0 | -10.9 | -33.3 |
| Federal 300 Hi-Shok | velocity, fps: | 2530 | 2270 | 2020 | 1790 | 1580 |
| | energy, ft-lb: | 4265 | 3425 | 2720 | 2135 | 1665 |
| | arc, inches: | | +2.6 | 0 | -11.2 | -33.3 |
| Federal 300 Nosler Partition | velocity, fps: | 2530 | 2320 | 2120 | 1930 | 1750 |
| | energy, ft-lb: | 4265 | 3585 | 2995 | 2475 | 2040 |
| | arc, inches: | | +2.5 | 0 | -10.3 | -29.9 |
| Federal 300 Trophy Bonded | velocity, fps: | 2530 | 2280 | 2040 | 1810 | 1610 |
| | energy, ft-lb: | 4265 | 3450 | 2765 | 2190 | 1725 |
| | arc, inches: | | +2.6 | 0 | -10.9 | -32.8 |
| Federal 300 Tr. Bonded HE | velocity, fps: | 2700 | 2440 | 2190 | 1960 | 1740 |
| | energy, ft-lb: | 4855 | 3960 | 3195 | 2550 | 2020 |
| | arc, inches: | | +2.2 | 0 | -9.4 | -28.0 |
| Federal 300 Trophy Bonded Sledgehammer Solid | velocity, fps: | 2530 | 2160 | 1820 | 1520 | 1280. |
| | energy, ft-lb: | 4265 | 3105 | 2210 | 1550 | 1090 |
| | arc, inches, s: | | 0 | -6.0 | -22.7 | -54.6 |
| Hornady 270 SP HM | velocity, fps: | 2870 | 2620 | 2385 | 2162 | 1957 |
| | energy, ft-lb: | 4937 | 4116 | 3408 | 2802 | 2296 |
| | arc, inches: | | +2.2 | 0 | -8.4 | -23.9 |
| Hornady 300 FMJ RN HM | velocity, fps: | 2705 | 2376 | 2072 | 1804 | 1560 |
| | energy, ft-lb: | 4873 | 3760 | 2861 | 2167 | 1621 |
| | arc, inches: | | +2.7 | 0 | -10.8 | -32.1 |
| Norma 300 Soft Point | velocity, fps: | 2549 | 2211 | 1900 | 1619 | |
| | energy, ft-lb: | 4329 | 3258 | 2406 | 1747 | |
| | arc, inches: | | +2.8 | 0 | -12.6 | |
| Norma 300 TXP Swift A-Fr. | velocity, fps: | 2559 | 2296 | 2049 | 1818 | |
| | energy, ft-lb: | 4363 | 3513 | 2798 | 2203 | |
| | arc, inches: | | +2.6 | 0 | -10.9 | |
| Norma 300 Oryx | velocity, fps: | 2559 | 2292 | 2041 | 1807 | |
| | energy, ft-lb: | 4363 | 3500 | 2775 | 2176 | |
| | arc, inches: | | +2.6 | 0 | -11.0 | |

| CARTRIDGE BULLET | RANGE, YARDS: | 0 | 100 | 200 | 300 | 400 |
|---|---|---|---|---|---|---|
| Norma 300 Barnes Solid | velocity, fps: | 2493 | 2061 | 1677 | 1356 | |
| | energy, ft-lb: | 4141 | 2829 | 1873 | 1234 | |
| | arc, inches: | | +3.4 | 0 | -16.0 | |
| PMC 270 PSP | velocity, fps: | | | | | |
| | energy, ft-lb: | | | | | |
| | arc, inches: | | | | | |
| PMC 270 Barnes X | velocity, fps: | 2690 | 2528 | 2372 | 2221 | 2076 |
| | energy, ft-lb: | 4337 | 3831 | 3371 | 2957 | 2582 |
| | arc, inches: | | +2.0 | 0 | -8.2 | -23.4 |
| PMC 300 Barnes X | velocity, fps: | 2530 | 2389 | 2252 | 2120 | 1993 |
| | energy, ft-lb: | 4263 | 3801 | 3378 | 2994 | 2644 |
| | arc, inches: | | +2.3 | 0 | -9.2 | -26.1 |
| Rem. 270 Soft Point | velocity, fps: | 2690 | 2420 | 2166 | 1928 | 1707 |
| | energy, ft-lb: | 4337 | 3510 | 2812 | 2228 | 1747 |
| | arc, inches: | | +2.2 | 0 | -9.7 | -28.7 |
| Rem. 300 Swift A-Frame | velocity, fps: | 2530 | 2245 | 1979 | 1733 | 1512 |
| | energy, ft-lb: | 4262 | 3357 | 2608 | 2001 | 1523 |
| | arc, inches: | | +2.7 | 0 | -11.7 | -35.0 |
| Speer 285 Grand Slam | velocity, fps: | 2610 | 2365 | 2134 | 1916 | |
| | energy, ft-lb: | 4310 | 3540 | 2883 | 2323 | |
| | arc, inches: | | +2.4 | 0 | -9.9 | |
| Speer 300 African GS Tungsten Solid | velocity, fps: | 2609 | 2277 | 1970 | 1690 | |
| | energy, ft-lb: | 4534 | 3453 | 2585 | 1903 | |
| | arc, inches: | | +2.6 | 0 | -11.7 | -35.6 |
| Win. 270 Fail Safe | velocity, fps: | 2670 | 2447 | 2234 | 2033 | 1842 |
| | energy, ft-lb: | 4275 | 3590 | 2994 | 2478 | 2035 |
| | arc, inches: | | +2.2 | 0 | -9.1 | -28.7 |
| Win. 300 Fail Safe | velocity, fps: | 2530 | 2336 | 2151 | 1974 | 1806 |
| | energy, ft-lb: | 4265 | 3636 | 3082 | 2596 | 2173 |
| | arc, inches: | | +2.4 | 0 | -10.0 | -26.9 |

## .375 DAKOTA

| CARTRIDGE BULLET | RANGE, YARDS: | 0 | 100 | 200 | 300 | 400 |
|---|---|---|---|---|---|---|
| Dakota 270 Barnes X | velocity, fps: | 2800 | 2617 | 2441 | 2272 | 2109 |
| | energy, ft-lb: | 4699 | 4104 | 3571 | 3093 | 2666 |
| | arc, inches: | | +2.3 | +1.0 | -6.1 | -19.9 |
| Dakota 300 Barnes X | velocity, fps: | 2600 | 2316 | 2051 | 1804 | 1579 |
| | energy, ft-lb: | 4502 | 3573 | 2800 | 2167 | 1661 |
| | arc, inches: | | +2.4 | -0.1 | -11.0 | -32.7 |

## .375 RUGER

| CARTRIDGE BULLET | RANGE, YARDS: | 0 | 100 | 200 | 300 | 400 |
|---|---|---|---|---|---|---|
| Hornady 270 SP | velocity, fps: | 2840 | 2600 | 2372 | 2156 | 1951 |
| | energy, ft-lb: | 4835 | 4052 | 3373 | 2786 | 2283 |
| | arc, inches: | -1.5 | +1.8 | 0 | -8.0 | -23.6 |
| Hornady 300 Solid | velocity, fps | 2660 | 2344 | 2050 | 1780 | 1536 |
| | energy, ft-lb | 4713 | 3660 | 2800 | 2110 | 1572 |
| | arc, inches | -1.5 | +2.4 | 0 | -10.8 | -32.6 |
| Nosler 260 AB | velocity, fps: | 2900 | 2703 | 2514 | 2333 | 2160 |
| | energy, ft-lb: | 4854 | 4217 | 3649 | 3143 | 2693 |
| | arc, inches: | -1.5 | +1.6 | 0 | -7.1 | -20.7 |

## .375 WEATHERBY MAGNUM

| CARTRIDGE BULLET | RANGE, YARDS: | 0 | 100 | 200 | 300 | 400 |
|---|---|---|---|---|---|---|
| A-Square 300 SP boat-tail | velocity, fps: | 2700 | 2560 | 2425 | 2293 | 2166 |
| | energy, ft-lb: | 4856 | 4366 | 3916 | 3503 | 3125 |
| | arc, inches: | | +4.5 | +5.2 | 0 | -11.9 |
| A-Square 300 Triad | velocity, fps: | 2700 | 2391 | 2103 | 1835 | 1602 |
| | energy, ft-lb: | 4856 | 3808 | 2946 | 2243 | 1710 |
| | arc, inches: | | +2.3 | 0 | -10.1 | -30.8 |
| Wby. 300 Nosler Part. | velocity, fps: | 2800 | 2572 | 2366 | 2140 | 1963 |
| | energy, ft-lb: | 5224 | 4408 | 3696 | 3076 | 2541 |
| | arc, inches: | | +1.9 | 0 | -8.2 | -23.9 |

BALLISTICS

## .375 JRS TO .416 REMINGTON MAGNUM

**BALLISTICS** (side tab)

### .375 JRS

| CARTRIDGE BULLET | RANGE, YARDS: | 0 | 100 | 200 | 300 | 400 |
|---|---|---|---|---|---|---|
| A-Square 300 SP boat-tail | velocity, fps: | 2700 | 2560 | 2425 | 2293 | 2166. |
| | energy, ft-lb: | 4856 | 4366 | 3916 | 3503 | 3125 |
| | arc, inches: | | +4.5 | +5.2 | 0 | -11.9 |
| A-Square 300 Triad | velocity, fps: | 2700 | 2391 | 2103 | 1835 | 1602 |
| | energy, ft-lb: | 4856 | 3808 | 2946 | 2243 | 1710 |
| | arc, inches: | | +2.3 | 0 | -10.1 | -30.8 |

### .375 REMINGTON ULTRA MAGNUM

| CARTRIDGE BULLET | RANGE, YARDS: | 0 | 100 | 200 | 300 | 400 |
|---|---|---|---|---|---|---|
| Nosler 260 AB | velocity, fps: | 2950 | 2750 | 2560 | 2377 | 2202 |
| | energy, ft-lb: | 5023 | 4367 | 3783 | 3262 | 2799 |
| | arc, inches: | -1.5 | +1.6 | 0 | -6.9 | -19.9 |
| Nosler 300 PT | velocity, fps: | 2750 | 2524 | 2309 | 2105 | 1912 |
| | energy, ft-lb: | 5036 | 4244 | 3553 | 2953 | 2435 |
| | arc, inches: | -1.5 | +2.0 | 0 | -8.5 | -24.9 |
| Rem. 270 Soft Point | velocity, fps: | 2900 | 2558 | 2241 | 1947 | 1678 |
| | energy, fps: | 5041 | 3922 | 3010 | 2272 | 1689 |
| | arc, inches: | | +1.9 | 0 | -9.2 | -27.8 |
| Rem. 300 Swift A-Frame | velocity, fps: | 2760 | 2505 | 2263 | 2035 | 1822 |
| | energy, ft-lb: | 5073 | 4178 | 3412 | 2759 | 2210 |
| | arc, inches: | | +2.0 | 0 | -8.8 | -26.1 |

### .375 A-SQUARE

| CARTRIDGE BULLET | RANGE, YARDS: | 0 | 100 | 200 | 300 | 400 |
|---|---|---|---|---|---|---|
| A-Square 300 SP boat-tail | velocity, fps: | 2920 | 2773 | 2631 | 2494 | 2360 |
| | energy, ft-lb: | 5679 | 5123 | 4611 | 4142 | 3710 |
| | arc, inches: | | +3.7 | +4.4 | 0 | -9.8 |
| A-Square 300 Triad | velocity, fps: | 2920 | 2596 | 2294 | 2012 | 1762 |
| | energy, ft-lb: | 5679 | 4488 | 3505 | 2698 | 2068 |
| | arc, inches: | | +1.8 | 0 | -8.5 | -25.5 |

### .376 STEYR

| CARTRIDGE BULLET | RANGE, YARDS: | 0 | 100 | 200 | 300 | 400 |
|---|---|---|---|---|---|---|
| Hornady 225 SP | velocity, fps: | 2600 | 2331 | 2078 | 1842 | 1625 |
| | energy, ft-lb: | 3377 | 2714 | 2157 | 1694 | 1319 |
| | arc, inches: | | +2.5 | 0 | -10.6 | -31.4 |
| Hornady 270 SP | velocity, fps: | 2600 | 2372 | 2156 | 1951 | 1759 |
| | energy, ft-lb: | 4052 | 3373 | 2787 | 2283 | 1855 |
| | arc, inches: | | +2.3 | 0 | -9.9 | -28.9 |

### .378 WEATHERBY MAGNUM

| CARTRIDGE BULLET | RANGE, YARDS: | 0 | 100 | 200 | 300 | 400 |
|---|---|---|---|---|---|---|
| A-Square 300 SP boat-tail | velocity, fps: | 2900 | 2754 | 2612 | 2475 | 2342 |
| | energy, ft-lb: | 5602 | 5051 | 4546 | 4081 | 3655 |
| | arc, inches: | | +3.8 | +4.4 | 0 | -10.0 |
| A-Square 300 Triad | velocity, fps: | 2900 | 2577 | 2276 | 1997 | 1747 |
| | energy, ft-lb: | 5602 | 4424 | 3452 | 2656 | 2034 |
| | arc, inches: | | +1.9 | 0 | -8.7 | -25.9 |
| Wby. 270 Pointed Expanding | velocity, fps: | 3180 | 2921 | 2677 | 2445 | 2225 |
| | energy, ft-lb: | 6062 | 5115 | 4295 | 3583 | 2968 |
| | arc, inches: | | +1.3 | 0 | -6.1 | -18.1 |
| Wby. 270 Barnes X | velocity, fps: | 3150 | 2954 | 2767 | 2587 | 2415 |
| | energy, ft-lb: | 5948 | 5232 | 4589 | 4013 | 3495 |
| | arc, inches: | | +1.2 | 0 | -5.8 | -16.7 |
| Wby. 300 RN Expanding | velocity, fps: | 2925 | 2558 | 2220 | 1908 | 1627. |
| | energy, ft-lb: | 5699 | 4360 | 3283 | 2424 | 1764 |
| | arc, inches: | | +1.9 | 0 | -9.0 | -27.8 |
| Wby. 300 FMJ | velocity, fps: | 2925 | 2591 | 2280 | 1991 | 1725 |
| | energy, ft-lb: | 5699 | 4470 | 3461 | 2640 | 1983 |
| | arc, inches: | | +1.8 | 0 | -8.6 | -26.1 |

### .38-40 WINCHESTER

| CARTRIDGE BULLET | RANGE, YARDS: | 0 | 100 | 200 | 300 | 400 |
|---|---|---|---|---|---|---|
| Win. 180 Soft Point | velocity, fps: | 1160 | 999 | 901 | 827 | |
| | energy, ft-lb: | 538 | 399 | 324 | 273 | |
| | arc, inches: | | 0 | -23.4 | -75.2 | |

### .38-55 WINCHESTER

| CARTRIDGE BULLET | RANGE, YARDS: | 0 | 100 | 200 | 300 | 400 |
|---|---|---|---|---|---|---|
| Black Hills 255 FN Lead | velocity, fps: | 1250 | | | | |
| | energy, ft-lb: | 925 | | | | |
| | arc, inches: | | | | | |
| Win. 255 Soft Point | velocity, fps: | 1320 | 1190 | 1091 | 1018 | |
| | energy, ft-lb: | 987 | 802 | 674 | 587 | |
| | arc, inches: | | 0 | -33.9 | -110.6 | |

### .41 MAGNUM

| CARTRIDGE BULLET | RANGE, YARDS: | 0 | 100 | 200 | 300 | 400 |
|---|---|---|---|---|---|---|
| Win. 240 Platinum Tip | velocity, fps: | 1830 | 1488 | 1220 | 1048 | |
| | energy, ft-lb: | 1784 | 1180 | 792 | 585 | |
| | arc inches: | | 0 | -15.0 | -53.4 | |

### .450/.400 NITRO EXPRESS

| CARTRIDGE BULLET | RANGE, YARDS: | 0 | 100 | 200 | 300 | 400 |
|---|---|---|---|---|---|---|
| A-Square 400 Triad | velocity, fps: | 2150 | 1910 | 1690 | 1490 | |
| | energy, ft-lb: | 4105 | 3241 | 2537 | 1972 | |
| | arc, inches: | | +4.4 | 0 | -16.5 | |
| Hornady 400 DGS, DGX | velocity, fps: | 2050 | 1820 | 1609 | 1420 | |
| | energy, ft-lb: | 3732 | 2940 | 2298 | 1791 | |
| | arc, inches: | -0.9 | 0 | -9.7 | -32.8 | |

### .404 JEFFERY

| CARTRIDGE BULLET | RANGE, YARDS: | 0 | 100 | 200 | 300 | 400 |
|---|---|---|---|---|---|---|
| A-Square 400 Triad | velocity, fps: | 2150 | 1901 | 1674 | 1468 | 1299 |
| | energy, ft-lb: | 4105 | 3211 | 2489 | 1915 | 1499 |
| | arc, inches: | | +4.1 | 0 | -16.4 | -49.1 |
| Hornady 400 DGS, DGX | velocity, fps: | 2300 | 2046 | 1809 | 1592 | |
| | energy, ft-lb: | 4698 | 3717 | 2906 | 2251 | |
| | arc, inches: | -1.5 | 0 | -6.9 | -24.4 | |
| Norma 450 Woodleigh SP | velocity, fps: | 2150 | 2048 | 1949 | 1853 | 1760 |
| | energy, ft-lb: | 4620 | 4191 | 3795 | 3430 | 3096 |
| | arc, inches: | -1.5 | +.2 | 0 | -2.5 | -7.6 |

### .405 WINCHESTER

| CARTRIDGE BULLET | RANGE, YARDS: | 0 | 100 | 200 | 300 | 400 |
|---|---|---|---|---|---|---|
| Hornady 300 Flatpoint | velocity, fps: | 2200 | 1851 | 1545 | 1296 | |
| | energy, ft-lb: | 3224 | 2282 | 1589 | 1119 | |
| | arc, inches: | | 0 | -8.7 | -31.9 | |
| Hornady 300 SP Interlock | velocity, fps: | 2200 | 1890 | 1610 | 1370 | |
| | energy, ft-lb: | 3224 | 2379 | 1727 | 1250 | |
| | arc, inches: | | 0 | -8.3 | -30.2 | |

### .416 TAYLOR

| CARTRIDGE BULLET | RANGE, YARDS: | 0 | 100 | 200 | 300 | 400 |
|---|---|---|---|---|---|---|
| A-Square 400 Triad | velocity, fps: | 2350 | 2093 | 1853 | 1634 | 1443 |
| | energy, ft-lb: | 4905 | 3892 | 3049 | 2371 | 1849 |
| | arc, inches: | | +3.2 | 0 | -13.6 | -39.8 |

### .416 HOFFMAN

| CARTRIDGE BULLET | RANGE, YARDS: | 0 | 100 | 200 | 300 | 400 |
|---|---|---|---|---|---|---|
| A-Square 400 Triad | velocity, fps: | 2380 | 2122 | 1879 | 1658 | 1464 |
| | energy, ft-lb: | 5031 | 3998 | 3136 | 2440 | 1903 |
| | arc, inches: | | +3.1 | 0 | -13.1 | -38.7 |

### .416 REMINGTON MAGNUM

| CARTRIDGE BULLET | RANGE, YARDS: | 0 | 100 | 200 | 300 | 400 |
|---|---|---|---|---|---|---|
| A-Square 400 Triad | velocity, fps: | 2380 | 2122 | 1879 | 1658 | 1464 |
| | energy, ft-lb: | 5031 | 3998 | 3136 | 2440 | 1903 |
| | arc, inches: | | +3.1 | 0 | -13.2 | -38.7 |
| Federal 400 Trophy Bonded Sledgehammer Solid | velocity, fps: | 2400 | 2150 | 1920 | 1700 | 1500 |
| | energy, ft-lb: | 5115 | 4110 | 3260 | 2565 | 2005 |
| | arc, inches: | | 0 | -6.0 | -21.6 | -49.2 |
| Federal 400 Trophy Bonded | velocity, fps: | 2400 | 2180 | 1970 | 1770 | 1590 |
| | energy, ft-lb: | 5115 | 4215 | 3440 | 2785 | 2245 |
| | arc, inches: | | 0 | -5.8 | -20.6 | -46.9 |
| Rem. 400 Swift A-Frame | velocity, fps: | 2400 | 2175 | 1962 | 1763 | 1579 |
| | energy, ft-lb: | 5115 | 4201 | 3419 | 2760 | 2214 |
| | arc, inches: | | 0 | -5.9 | -20.8 | |

# Centerfire Rifle Ballistics

| CARTRIDGE BULLET | RANGE, YARDS: | 0 | 100 | 200 | 300 | 400 |
|---|---|---|---|---|---|---|
| **.416 RIGBY** | | | | | | |
| A-Square 400 Triad | velocity, fps: | 2400 | 2140 | 1897 | 1673 | 1478 |
| | energy, ft-lb: | 5115 | 4069 | 3194 | 2487 | 1940 |
| | arc, inches: | | +3.0 | 0 | -12.9 | -38.0 |
| Federal 400 Trophy Bonded | velocity, fps: | 2370 | 2150 | 1940 | 1750 | 1570 |
| | energy, ft-lb: | 4990 | 4110 | 3350 | 2715 | 2190 |
| | arc, inches: | | 0 | -6.0 | -21.3 | -48.1 |
| Federal 400 Trophy Bonded Sledgehammer Solid | velocity, fps: | 2370 | 2120 | 1890 | 1660 | 1460 |
| | energy, ft-lb: | 4990 | 3975 | 3130 | 2440 | 1895 |
| | arc, inches: | | 0 | -6.3 | -22.5 | -51.5 |
| Federal 410 Woodleigh Weldcore | velocity, fps: | 2370 | 2110 | 1870 | 1640 | 1440 |
| | energy, ft-lb: | 5115 | 4050 | 3165 | 2455 | 1895 |
| | arc, inches: | | 0 | -7.4 | -24.8 | -55.0 |
| Federal 410 Solid | velocity, fps: | 2370 | 2110 | 2870 | 1640 | 1440 |
| | energy, ft-lb: | 5115 | 4050 | 3165 | 2455 | 1895 |
| | arc, inches: | | 0 | -7.4 | -24.8 | -55.0 |
| Hornady 400 DGX, DGS | velocity, fps: | 2415 | 2156 | 1915 | 1691 | |
| | energy, ft-lb: | 5180 | 4130 | 3256 | 2540 | |
| | arc, inches: | -1.5 | 0 | -6.0 | -21.6 | |
| Norma 400 TXP Swift A-Fr. | velocity, fps: | 2350 | 2127 | 1917 | 1721 | |
| | energy, ft-lb: | 4906 | 4021 | 3266 | 2632 | |
| | arc, inches: | | +3.1 | 0 | -12.5 | |
| Norma 400 Barnes Solid | velocity, fps: | 2297 | 1930 | 1604 | 1330 | |
| | energy, ft-lb: | 4687 | 3310 | 2284 | 1571 | |
| | arc, inches: | | +3.9 | 0 | -17.7 | |
| **.416 RUGER** | | | | | | |
| Hornady 400 DGS, DGX | velocity, fps: | 2400 | 2151 | 1917 | 1700 | |
| | energy, ft-lb: | 5116 | 4109 | 3264 | 2568 | |
| | arc, inches: | -1.5 | 0 | -6.0 | -21.6 | |

| **.500/416 NITRO EXPRESS** | | | | | | |
|---|---|---|---|---|---|---|
| CARTRIDGE BULLET | RANGE, YARDS: | 0 | 50 | 100 | 150 | 200 |
| Norma 450 Woodleigh SP | velocity, fps: | 2100 | 1991 | 1886 | 1785 | 1688 |
| | energy, ft-lb: | 4408 | 3963 | 3556 | 3185 | 2849 |
| | arc, inches: | -1.5 | +.3 | 0 | -2.7 | -8.2 |

| **.416 DAKOTA** | | | | | | |
|---|---|---|---|---|---|---|
| CARTRIDGE BULLET | RANGE, YARDS: | 0 | 100 | 200 | 300 | 400 |
| Dakota 400 Barnes X | velocity, fps: | 2450 | 2294 | 2143 | 1998 | 1859 |
| | energy, ft-lb: | 5330 | 4671 | 4077 | 3544 | 3068 |
| | arc, inches: | | +2.5 | -0.2 | -10.5 | -29.4 |

| **.416 WEATHERBY** | | | | | | |
|---|---|---|---|---|---|---|
| A-Square 400 Triad | velocity, fps: | 2600 | 2328 | 2073 | 1834 | 1624 |
| | energy, ft-lb: | 6004 | 4813 | 3816 | 2986 | 2343 |
| | arc, inches: | | +2.5 | 0 | -10.5 | -31.6 |
| Wby. 350 Barnes X | velocity, fps: | 2850 | 2673 | 2503 | 2340 | 2182 |
| | energy, ft-lb: | 6312 | 5553 | 4870 | 4253 | 3700 |
| | arc, inches: | | +1.7 | 0 | -7.2 | -20.9 |
| Wby. 400 Swift A-Fr. | velocity, fps: | 2650 | 2426 | 2213 | 2011 | 1820 |
| | energy, ft-lb: | 6237 | 5227 | 4350 | 3592 | 2941 |
| | arc, inches: | | +2.2 | 0 | -9.3 | -27.1 |
| Wby. 400 RN Expanding | velocity, fps: | 2700 | 2417 | 2152 | 1903 | 1676 |
| | energy, ft-lb: | 6474 | 5189 | 4113 | 3216 | 2493 |
| | arc, inches: | | +2.3 | 0 | -9.7 | -29.3 |
| Wby. 400 Monolithic Solid | velocity, fps: | 2700 | 2411 | 2140 | 1887 | 1656 |
| | energy, ft-lb: | 6474 | 5162 | 4068 | 3161 | 2435 |
| | arc, inches: | | +2.3 | 0 | -9.8 | -29.7 |

| **10.57 (.416) METEOR** | | | | | | |
|---|---|---|---|---|---|---|
| Lazzeroni 400 Swift A-Fr. | velocity, fps: | 2730 | 2532 | 2342 | 2161 | 1987 |
| | energy, ft-lb: | 6621 | 5695 | 4874 | 4147 | 3508 |
| | arc, inches: | | +1.9 | 0 | -8.3 | -24.0 |

| CARTRIDGE BULLET | RANGE, YARDS: | 0 | 100 | 200 | 300 | 400 |
|---|---|---|---|---|---|---|
| **.425 EXPRESS** | | | | | | |
| A-Square 400 Triad | velocity, fps: | 2400 | 2136 | 1888 | 1662 | 1465 |
| | energy, ft-lb: | 5115 | 4052 | 3167 | 2454 | 1906 |
| | arc, inches: | | +3.0 | 0 | -13.1 | -38.3 |
| **.44-40 WINCHESTER** | | | | | | |
| Rem. 200 Soft Point | velocity, fps: | 1190 | 1006 | 900 | 822 | 756 |
| | energy, ft-lb: | 629 | 449 | 360 | 300 | 254 |
| | arc, inches: | | 0 | -33.1 | -108.7 | -235.2 |
| Win. 200 Soft Point | velocity, fps: | 1190 | 1006 | 900 | 822 | 756 |
| | energy, ft-lb: | 629 | 449 | 360 | 300 | 254 |
| | arc, inches: | | 0 | -33.3 | -109.5 | -237.4 |
| **.44 REMINGTON MAGNUM** | | | | | | |
| Federal 240 Hi-Shok HP | velocity, fps: | 1760 | 1380 | 1090 | 950 | 860 |
| | energy, ft-lb: | 1650 | 1015 | 640 | 485 | 395 |
| | arc, inches: | | 0 | -17.4 | -60.7 | -136.0 |
| Rem. 210 Semi-Jacketed HP | velocity, fps: | 1920 | 1477 | 1155 | 982 | 880 |
| | energy, ft-lb: | 1719 | 1017 | 622 | 450 | 361 |
| | arc, inches: | | 0 | -14.7 | -55.5 | -131.3 |
| Rem. 240 Soft Point | velocity, fps: | 1760 | 1380 | 1114 | 970 | 878 |
| | energy, ft-lb: | 1650 | 1015 | 661 | 501 | 411 |
| | arc, inches: | | 0 | -17.0 | -61.4 | -143.0 |
| Rem. 240 Semi-Jacketed Hollow Point | velocity, fps: | 1760 | 1380 | 1114 | 970 | 878 |
| | energy, ft-lb: | 1650 | 1015 | 661 | 501 | 411 |
| | arc, inches: | | 0 | -17.0 | -61.4 | -143.0 |
| Rem. 275 JHP Core-Lokt | velocity, fps: | 1580 | 1293 | 1093 | 976 | 896 |
| | energy, ft-lb: | 1524 | 1020 | 730 | 582 | 490 |
| | arc, inches: | | 0 | -19.4 | -67.5 | -210.8 |
| Win. 210 Silvertip HP | velocity, fps: | 1580 | 1198 | 993 | 879 | 795 |
| | energy, ft-lb: | 1164 | 670 | 460 | 361 | 295 |
| | arc, inches: | | 0 | -22.4 | -76.1 | -168.0 |
| Win. 240 Hollow Soft Point | velocity, fps: | 1760 | 1362 | 1094 | 953 | 861 |
| | energy, ft-lb: | 1650 | 988 | 638 | 484 | 395 |
| | arc, inches: | | 0 | -18.1 | -65.1 | -150.3 |
| Win. 250 Platinum Tip | velocity, fps: | 1830 | 1475 | 1201 | 1032 | 931 |
| | energy, ft-lb: | 1859 | 1208 | 801 | 591 | 481 |
| | arc, inches: | | 0 | -15.3 | -54.7 | -126.6 |
| **.444 MARLIN** | | | | | | |
| Rem. 240 Soft Point | velocity, fps: | 2350 | 1815 | 1377 | 1087 | 941 |
| | energy, ft-lb: | 2942 | 1755 | 1010 | 630 | 472 |
| | arc, inches: | | +2.2 | -5.4 | -31.4 | -86.7 |
| Hornady 265 Evolution | velocity, fps: | 2325 | 1971 | 1652 | 1380 | |
| | energy, ft-lb: | 3180 | 2285 | 1606 | 1120 | |
| | arc, inches: | | +3.0 | -1.4 | -18.6 | |
| Hornady 265 FP LM | velocity, fps: | 2335 | 1913 | 1551 | 1266 | |
| | energy, ft-lb: | 3208 | 2153 | 1415 | 943 | |
| | arc, inches: | | + 2.0 | -4.9 | -26.5 | |
| **.45-70 GOVERNMENT** | | | | | | |
| Black Hills 405 FPL | velocity, fps: | 1250 | | | | |
| | energy, ft-lb: | | | | | |
| | arc, inches: | | | | | |
| Federal 300 Sierra Pro-Hunt. HP FN | velocity, fps: | 1880 | 1650 | 1430 | 1240 | 1110 |
| | energy, ft-lb: | 2355 | 1815 | 1355 | 1015 | 810 |
| | arc, inches: | | 0 | -11.5 | -39.7 | -89.1 |
| PMC 350 FNSP | velocity, fps: | | | | | |
| | energy, ft-lb: | | | | | |
| | arc, inches: | | | | | |
| Rem. 300 Jacketed HP | velocity, fps: | 1810 | 1497 | 1244 | 1073 | 969 |
| | energy, ft-lb: | 2182 | 1492 | 1031 | 767 | 625 |
| | arc, inches: | | 0 | -13.8 | -50.1 | -115.7 |

**BALLISTICS**

# Centerfire Rifle Ballistics

## .45-70 GOVERNMENT TO .460 WEATHERBY MAGNUM

| CARTRIDGE BULLET | RANGE, YARDS: | 0 | 100 | 200 | 300 | 400 |
|---|---|---|---|---|---|---|
| Rem. 405 Soft Point | velocity, fps: | 1330 | 1168 | 1055 | 977 | 918 |
| | energy, ft-lb: | 1590 | 1227 | 1001 | 858 | 758 |
| | arc, inches: | | 0 | -24.0 | -78.6 | -169.4 |
| Win. 300 Jacketed HP | velocity, fps: | 1880 | 1650 | 1425 | 1235 | 1105 |
| | energy, ft-lb: | 2355 | 1815 | 1355 | 1015 | 810 |
| | arc, inches: | | 0 | -12.8 | -44.3 | -95.5 |
| Win. 300 Partition Gold | velocity, fps: | 1880 | 1558 | 1292 | 1103 | 988 |
| | energy, ft-lb: | 2355 | 1616 | 1112 | 811 | 651 |
| | arc, inches: | | 0 | -12.9 | -46.0 | -104.9. |

### .450 BUSHMASTER

| CARTRIDGE BULLET | RANGE, YARDS: | 0 | 100 | 200 | 300 | 400 |
|---|---|---|---|---|---|---|
| Hornady 250 SST-ML | velocity, fps: | 2200 | 1840 | 1524 | 1268 | |
| | energy, ft-lb: | 2686 | 1879 | 1289 | 893 | |
| | arc, inches: | -2.0 | +2.5 | -3.5 | -24.5 | |

### .450 MARLIN

| CARTRIDGE BULLET | RANGE, YARDS: | 0 | 100 | 200 | 300 | 400 |
|---|---|---|---|---|---|---|
| Hornady 325 FTX | velocity, fps: | 2225 | 1887 | 1585 | 1331 | |
| | energy, ft-lb: | 3572 | 2569 | 1813 | 1278 | |
| | arc, inches: | -1.5 | +3.0 | -2.2 | -21.3 | |
| Hornady 350 FP | velocity, fps: | 2100 | 1720 | 1397 | 1156 | |
| | energy, ft-lb: | 3427 | 2298 | 1516 | 1039 | |
| | arc, inches: | | 0 | -10.4 | -38.9 | |

### .450 NITRO EXPRESS (3¼")

| CARTRIDGE BULLET | RANGE, YARDS: | 0 | 100 | 200 | 300 | 400 |
|---|---|---|---|---|---|---|
| A-Square 465 Triad | velocity, fps: | 2190 | 1970 | 1765 | 1577 | |
| | energy, ft-lb: | 4952 | 4009 | 3216 | 2567 | |
| | arc, inches: | | +4.3 | 0 | -15.4 | |
| Hornady 480 DGS, DGX | velocity, fps: | 2150 | 1881 | 1635 | 1418 | |
| | energy, ft-lb: | 4927 | 3769 | 2850 | 2144 | |
| | arc, inches: | -1.5 | 0 | -8.4 | -29.9 | |

### .450 #2

| CARTRIDGE BULLET | RANGE, YARDS: | 0 | 100 | 200 | 300 | 400 |
|---|---|---|---|---|---|---|
| A-Square 465 Triad | velocity, fps: | 2190 | 1970 | 1765 | 1577 | |
| | energy, ft-lb: | 4952 | 4009 | 3216 | 2567 | |
| | arc, inches: | | +4.3 | 0 | -15.4 | |

### .458 WINCHESTER MAGNUM

| CARTRIDGE BULLET | RANGE, YARDS: | 0 | 100 | 200 | 300 | 400 |
|---|---|---|---|---|---|---|
| A-Square 465 Triad | velocity, fps: | 2220 | 1999 | 1791 | 1601 | 1433 |
| | energy, ft-lb: | 5088 | 4127 | 3312 | 2646 | 2121 |
| | arc, inches: | | +3.6 | 0 | -14.7 | -42.5 |
| Federal 350 Soft Point | velocity, fps: | 2470 | 1990 | 1570 | 1250 | 1060 |
| | energy, ft-lb: | 4740 | 3065 | 1915 | 1205 | 870 |
| | arc, inches: | | 0 | -7.5 | -29.1 | -71.1 |
| Federal 400 Trophy Bonded | velocity, fps: | 2380 | 2170 | 1960 | 1770 | 1590 |
| | energy, ft-lb: | 5030 | 4165 | 3415 | 2785 | 2255 |
| | arc, inches: | | 0 | -5.9 | -20.9 | -47.1 |
| Federal 500 Solid | velocity, fps: | 2090 | 1870 | 1670 | 1480 | 1320 |
| | energy, ft-lb: | 4850 | 3880 | 3085 | 2440 | 1945 |
| | arc, inches: | | 0 | -8.5 | -29.5 | -66.2 |
| Federal 500 Trophy Bonded | velocity, fps: | 2090 | 1870 | 1660 | 1480 | 1310 |
| | energy, ft-lb: | 4850 | 3870 | 3065 | 2420 | 1915 |
| | arc, inches: | | 0 | -8.5 | -29.7 | -66.8 |
| Federal 500 Trophy Bonded Sledgehammer Solid | velocity, fps: | 2090 | 1860 | 1650 | 1460 | 1300 |
| | energy, ft-lb: | 4850 | 3845 | 3025 | 2365 | 1865 |
| | arc, inches: | | 0 | -8.6 | -30.0 | -67.8 |
| Federal 510 Soft Point | velocity, fps: | 2090 | 1820 | 1570 | 1360 | 1190 |
| | energy, ft-lb: | 4945 | 3730 | 2790 | 2080 | 1605 |
| | arc, inches: | | 0 | -9.1 | -32.3 | -73.9 |
| Hornady 500 FMJ-RN HM | velocity, fps: | 2260 | 1984 | 1735 | 1512 | |
| | energy, ft-lb: | 5670 | 4368 | 3341 | 2538 | |
| | arc, inches: | | 0 | -7.4 | -26.4 | |
| Norma 500 TXP Swift A-Fr. | velocity, fps: | 2116 | 1903 | 1705 | 1524 | |
| | energy, ft-lb: | 4972 | 4023 | 3228 | 2578 | |
| | arc, inches: | | +4.1 | 0 | -16.1 | |

| CARTRIDGE BULLET | RANGE, YARDS: | 0 | 100 | 200 | 300 | 400 |
|---|---|---|---|---|---|---|
| Norma 500 Barnes Solid | velocity, fps: | 2067 | 1750 | 1472 | 1245 | |
| | energy, ft-lb: | 4745 | 3401 | 2405 | 1721 | |
| | arc, inches: | | +4.9 | 0 | -21.2 | |
| Rem. 450 Swift A-Frame PSP | velocity, fps: | 2150 | 1901 | 1671 | 1465 | 1289 |
| | energy, ft-lb: | 4618 | 3609 | 2789 | 2144 | 1659 |
| | arc, inches: | | 0 | -8.2 | -28.9 | |
| Speer 500 African GS Tungsten Solid | velocity, fps: | 2120 | 1845 | 1596 | 1379 | |
| | energy, ft-lb: | 4989 | 3780 | 2828 | 2111 | |
| | arc, inches: | | 0 | -8.8 | -31.3 | |
| Speer African Grand Slam | velocity, fps: | 2120 | 1853 | 1609 | 1396 | |
| | energy, ft-lb: | 4989 | 3810 | 2875 | 2163 | |
| | arc, inches: | | 0 | -8.7 | -30.8 | |
| Win. 510 Soft Point | velocity, fps: | 2040 | 1770 | 1527 | 1319 | 1157 |
| | energy, ft-lb: | 4712 | 3547 | 2640 | 1970 | 1516 |
| | arc, inches: | | 0 | -10.3 | -35.6 | |

### .458 LOTT

| CARTRIDGE BULLET | RANGE, YARDS: | 0 | 100 | 200 | 300 | 400 |
|---|---|---|---|---|---|---|
| A-Square 465 Triad | velocity, fps: | 2380 | 2150 | 1932 | 1730 | 1551 |
| | energy, ft-lb: | 5848 | 4773 | 3855 | 3091 | 2485 |
| | arc, inches: | | +3.0 | 0 | -12.5 | -36.4 |
| Federal 500 TSX | velocity, fps: | 2280 | 2090 | 1900 | 1730 | 1560 |
| | energy, ft-lb: | 5770 | 4825 | 4000 | 3305 | 2715 |
| | arc, inches: | | 0 | -6.4 | -22.7 | -50.7 |
| Hornady 500 RNSP or solid | velocity, fps: | 2300 | 2022 | 1776 | 1551 | |
| | energy, ft-lb: | 5872 | 4537 | 3502 | 2671 | |
| | arc, inches: | | +3.4 | 0 | -14.3 | |
| Hornady 500 InterBond | velocity, fps: | 2300 | 2028 | 1777 | 1549 | |
| | energy, ft-lb: | 5872 | 4535 | 3453 | 2604 | |
| | arc, inches: | | 0 | -7.0 | -25.1 | |

| CARTRIDGE BULLET | RANGE, YARDS: | 0 | 50 | 100 | 150 | 200 |
|---|---|---|---|---|---|---|
| Norma 500 Woodleigh SP | velocity, fps: | 2100 | 1982 | 1868 | 1758 | 1654 |
| | energy, ft-lb: | 4897 | 4361 | 3874 | 3434 | 3039 |
| | arc, inches: | -1.5 | +.3 | 0 | -2.8 | -8.4 |

### .450 ACKLEY

| CARTRIDGE BULLET | RANGE, YARDS: | 0 | 100 | 200 | 300 | 400 |
|---|---|---|---|---|---|---|
| A-Square 465 Triad | velocity, fps: | 2400 | 2169 | 1950 | 1747 | 1567 |
| | energy, ft-lb: | 5947 | 4857 | 3927 | 3150 | 2534 |
| | arc, inches: | | +2.9 | 0 | -12.2 | -35.8 |

### .450 RIGBY

| CARTRIDGE BULLET | RANGE, YARDS: | 0 | 50 | 100 | 150 | 200 |
|---|---|---|---|---|---|---|
| Norma 550 Woodleigh SP | velocity, fps: | 2100 | 1992 | 1887 | 1787 | 1690 |
| | energy, ft-lb: | 5387 | 4847 | 4352 | 3900 | 3491 |
| | arc, inches: | -1.5 | +.3 | 0 | -2.7 | -8.2 |

### .460 SHORT A-SQUARE

| CARTRIDGE BULLET | RANGE, YARDS: | 0 | 100 | 200 | 300 | 400 |
|---|---|---|---|---|---|---|
| A-Square 500 Triad | velocity, fps: | 2420 | 2198 | 1987 | 1789 | 1613 |
| | energy, ft-lb: | 6501 | 5362 | 4385 | 3553 | 2890 |
| | arc, inches: | | +2.9 | 0 | -11.6 | -34.2 |

### .450 DAKOTA

| CARTRIDGE BULLET | RANGE, YARDS: | 0 | 100 | 200 | 300 | 400 |
|---|---|---|---|---|---|---|
| Dakota 500 Barnes Solid | velocity, fps: | 2450 | 2235 | 2030 | 1838 | 1658 |
| | energy, ft-lb: | 6663 | 5544 | 4576 | 3748 | 3051 |
| | arc, inches: | | +2.5 | -0.6 | -12.0 | -33.8 |

### .460 WEATHERBY MAGNUM

| CARTRIDGE BULLET | RANGE, YARDS: | 0 | 100 | 200 | 300 | 400 |
|---|---|---|---|---|---|---|
| A-Square 500 Triad | velocity, fps: | 2580 | 2349 | 2131 | 1923 | 1737 |
| | energy, ft-lb: | 7389 | 6126 | 5040 | 4107 | 3351 |
| | arc, inches: | | +2.4 | 0 | -10.0 | -29.4 |
| Wby. 450 Barnes X | velocity, fps: | 2700 | 2518 | 2343 | 2175 | 2013 |
| | energy, ft-lb: | 7284 | 6333 | 5482 | 4725 | 4050 |
| | arc, inches: | | +2.0 | 0 | -8.4 | -24.1 |

## .460 WEATHERBY MAGNUM TO .700 NITRO EXPRESS

| CARTRIDGE BULLET | RANGE, YARDS: | 0 | 100 | 200 | 300 | 400 |
|---|---|---|---|---|---|---|
| Wby. 500 RN Expanding | velocity, fps: | 2600 | 2301 | 2022 | 1764 | 1533. |
| | energy, ft-lb: | 7504 | 5877 | 4539 | 3456 | 2608 |
| | arc, inches: | | +2.6 | 0 | -11.1 | -33.5 |
| Wby. 500 FMJ | velocity, fps: | 2600 | 2309 | 2037 | 1784 | 1557 |
| | energy, ft-lb: | 7504 | 5917 | 4605 | 3534 | 2690 |
| | arc, inches: | | +2.5 | 0 | -10.9 | -33.0 |

### .500/.465

| CARTRIDGE BULLET | RANGE, YARDS: | 0 | 100 | 200 | 300 | 400 |
|---|---|---|---|---|---|---|
| A-Square 480 Triad | velocity, fps: | 2150 | 1928 | 1722 | 1533 | |
| | energy, ft-lb: | 4926 | 3960 | 3160 | 2505 | |
| | arc, inches: | | +4.3 | 0 | -16.0 | |

### .470 NITRO EXPRESS

| CARTRIDGE BULLET | RANGE, YARDS: | 0 | 100 | 200 | 300 | 400 |
|---|---|---|---|---|---|---|
| A-Square 500 Triad | velocity, fps: | 2150 | 1912 | 1693 | 1494 | |
| | energy, ft-lb: | 5132 | 4058 | 3182 | 2478 | |
| | arc, inches: | | +4.4 | 0 | -16.5 | |
| Federal 500 Trophy Bond (and Sledgehammer solid) | velocity, fps: | 2150 | 1890 | 1660 | 1450 | |
| | energy, ft-lb: | 5130 | 3975 | 3045 | 2320 | |
| | arc, inches: | -1.5 | 0 | -9.4 | -29.3 | |
| Hornady 500 DGX, DGS | velocity, fps: | 2150 | 1885 | 1643 | 1429 | |
| | energy, ft-lb: | 5132 | 3946 | 2998 | 2267 | |
| | arc, inches: | -1.5 | 0 | -8.9 | -30.9 | |

| CARTRIDGE BULLET | RANGE, YARDS: | 0 | 50 | 100 | 150 | 200 |
|---|---|---|---|---|---|---|
| Norma 500 Woodleigh (soft and solid) | velocity, fps: | 2100 | 2002 | 1906 | 1814 | 1725 |
| | energy, ft-lb: | 4897 | 4449 | 4035 | 3654 | 3304 |
| | arc, inches: | -1.5 | +.3 | 0 | -2.7 | -8.0 |

### .470 CAPSTICK

| CARTRIDGE BULLET | RANGE, YARDS: | 0 | 100 | 200 | 300 | 400 |
|---|---|---|---|---|---|---|
| A-Square 500 Triad | velocity, fps: | 2400 | 2172 | 1958 | 1761 | 1553 |
| | energy, ft-lb: | 6394 | 5236 | 4255 | 3445 | 2678 |
| | arc, inches: | | +2.9 | 0 | -11.9 | -36.1 |

### .475 #2

| CARTRIDGE BULLET | RANGE, YARDS: | 0 | 100 | 200 | 300 | 400 |
|---|---|---|---|---|---|---|
| A-Square 480 Triad | velocity, fps: | 2200 | 1964 | 1744 | 1544 | |
| | energy, ft-lb: | 5158 | 4109 | 3240 | 2539 | |
| | arc, inches: | | +4.1 | 0 | -15.6 | |

### .475 #2 JEFFERY

| CARTRIDGE BULLET | RANGE, YARDS: | 0 | 100 | 200 | 300 | 400 |
|---|---|---|---|---|---|---|
| A-Square 500 Triad | velocity, fps: | 2200 | 1966 | 1748 | 1550 | |
| | energy, ft-lb: | 5373 | 4291 | 3392 | 2666 | |
| | arc, inches: | | +4.1 | 0 | -15.6 | |

### .495 A-SQUARE

| CARTRIDGE BULLET | RANGE, YARDS: | 0 | 100 | 200 | 300 | 400 |
|---|---|---|---|---|---|---|
| A-Square 570 Triad | velocity, fps: | 2350 | 2117 | 1896 | 1693 | 1513 |
| | energy, ft-lb: | 6989 | 5671 | 4552 | 3629 | 2899 |
| | arc, inches: | | +3.1 | 0 | -13.0 | -37.8 |

### .500 NITRO EXPRESS (3")

| CARTRIDGE BULLET | RANGE, YARDS: | 0 | 100 | 200 | 300 | 400 |
|---|---|---|---|---|---|---|
| A-Square 570 Triad | velocity, fps: | 2150 | 1928 | 1722 | 1533 | |
| | energy, ft-lb: | 5850 | 4703 | 3752 | 2975 | |
| | arc, inches: | | +4.3 | 0 | -16.1 | |
| Federal 570 TSX | velocity, fps: | 2100 | 1890 | 1700 | 1520 | 1370 |
| | energy, ft-lb: | 5580 | 4530 | 3655 | 2935 | 2355 |
| | arc, inches: | 0 | -8.4 | -28.7 | -64.2 | |

| CARTRIDGE BULLET | RANGE, YARDS: | 0 | 100 | 200 | 300 | 400 |
|---|---|---|---|---|---|---|
| Hornady 570 DGX, DGS | velocity, fps: | 2150 | 1881 | 1635 | 1419 | |
| | energy, ft-lb: | 5850 | 4477 | 3384 | 2547 | |
| | arc, inches: | -.9 | 0 | -9.0 | -31.1 | |

| CARTRIDGE BULLET | RANGE, YARDS: | 0 | 50 | 100 | 150 | 200 |
|---|---|---|---|---|---|---|
| Norma 570 Woodleigh SP | velocity, fps: | 2100 | 2000 | 1903 | 1809 | 1719 |
| | energy, ft-lb: | 5583 | 5064 | 4585 | 4145 | 3742 |
| | arc, inches: | -1.5 | +.3 | 0 | -2.7 | -8.0 |

### 50 BMG

| | RANGE, YARDS: | 0 | 50 | 100 | 150 | 200 |
|---|---|---|---|---|---|---|
| Hornady 750 A-MAX | velocity, fps: | 2815 | 2727 | 2641 | 2557 | 2474 |
| | energy, ft-lb: | 13196 | 12386 | 11619 | 10889 | 10196 |
| | arc, inches: | -1.8 | +1.4 | 0 | -6.4 | -18.2 |

### .500 JEFFERY

| CARTRIDGE BULLET | RANGE, YARDS: | 0 | 50 | 100 | 150 | 200 |
|---|---|---|---|---|---|---|
| Norma 570 Woodleigh SP | velocity, fps: | 2200 | 2097 | 1997 | 1901 | 1807 |
| | energy, ft-lb: | 6127 | 5568 | 5050 | 4573 | 4134 |
| | arc, inches: | -1.5 | +.2 | 0 | -2.4 | -7.1 |

### .500 A-SQUARE

| CARTRIDGE BULLET | RANGE, YARDS: | 0 | 100 | 200 | 300 | 400 |
|---|---|---|---|---|---|---|
| A-Square 600 Triad | velocity, fps: | 2470 | 2235 | 2013 | 1804 | 1620 |
| | energy, ft-lb: | 8127 | 6654 | 5397 | 4336 | 3495 |
| | arc, inches: | | +2.7 | 0 | -11.3 | -33.5 |

### .505 GIBBS

| | RANGE, YARDS: | 0 | 100 | 200 | 300 | 400 |
|---|---|---|---|---|---|---|
| A-Square 525 Triad | velocity, fps: | 2300 | 2063 | 1840 | 1637 | |
| | energy, ft-lb: | 6166 | 4962 | 3948 | 3122 | |
| | arc, inches: | | +3.6 | 0 | -14.2 | |

| CARTRIDGE BULLET | RANGE, YARDS: | 0 | 50 | 100 | 150 | 200 |
|---|---|---|---|---|---|---|
| Norma 600 Woodleigh SP | velocity, fps: | 2100 | 1998 | 1899 | 1803 | 1711 |
| | energy, ft-lb: | 5877 | 5319 | 4805 | 4334 | 3904 |
| | arc, inches: | -1.5 | +.3 | 0 | -2.7 | -8.1 |

### .577 NITRO EXPRESS

| CARTRIDGE BULLET | RANGE, YARDS: | 0 | 100 | 200 | 300 | 400 |
|---|---|---|---|---|---|---|
| A-Square 750 Triad | velocity, fps: | 2050 | 1811 | 1595 | 1401 | |
| | energy, ft-lb: | 6998 | 5463 | 4234 | 3267 | |
| | arc, inches: | | +4.9 | 0 | -18.5 | |

### .577 TYRANNOSAUR

| | RANGE, YARDS: | 0 | 100 | 200 | 300 | 400 |
|---|---|---|---|---|---|---|
| A-Square 750 Triad | velocity, fps: | 2460 | 2197 | 1950 | 1723 | 1516 |
| | energy, ft-lb: | 10077 | 8039 | 6335 | 4941 | 3825 |
| | arc, inches: | | +2.8 | 0 | -12.1 | -36.0 |

### .600 NITRO EXPRESS

| | RANGE, YARDS: | 0 | 100 | 200 | 300 | 400 |
|---|---|---|---|---|---|---|
| A-Square 900 Triad | velocity, fps: | 1950 | 1680 | 1452 | 1336 | |
| | energy, ft-lb: | 7596 | 5634 | 4212 | 3564 | |
| | arc, inches: | | +5.6 | 0 | -20.7 | |

### .700 NITRO EXPRESS

| | RANGE, YARDS: | 0 | 100 | 200 | 300 | 400 |
|---|---|---|---|---|---|---|
| A-Square 1000 Monolithic Solid | velocity, fps: | 1900 | 1669 | 1461 | 1288 | |
| | energy, ft-lb: | 8015 | 6188 | 4740 | 3685 | |
| | arc, inches: | | +5.8 | 0 | -22.2 | |

BALLISTICS

# Long Range Rifle

## 6.6 CREEDMOOR TO .338 LAPUA

### 6.6 CREEDMOOR

| CARTRIDGE BULLET | RANGE, YARDS: | 0 | 400 | 600 | 800 | 1000 |
|---|---|---|---|---|---|---|
| Nosler 140 HPBT | velocity, fps: | 2550 | 2229 | 1932 | 1662 | 1426 |
| | energy, ft-lb: | 2021 | 1544 | 1160 | 859 | 632 |
| | arc, inches: | -1.5 | 0 | -26.7 | -90.9 | -205.9 |

### .264 WINCHESTER MAGNUM

| CARTRIDGE BULLET | RANGE, YARDS: | 0 | 400 | 600 | 800 | 1000 |
|---|---|---|---|---|---|---|
| Nosler 130 AccuBond | velocity, fps: | 3100 | 2709 | 2350 | 2019 | 1718 |
| | energy, ft-lb: | 2773 | 2118 | 1594 | 1176 | 852 |
| | arc, inches: | -1.5 | 0 | -17.6 | -60.6 | -137.9 |

### 6.5/284 NORMA

| CARTRIDGE BULLET | RANGE, YARDS: | 0 | 400 | 600 | 800 | 1000 |
|---|---|---|---|---|---|---|
| Nosler 129 AccuBond | velocity, fps: | 2965 | 2633 | 2324 | 2036 | 1771 |
| Long Range | energy, ft-lb: | 2517 | 1985 | 1547 | 1188 | 899 |
| | arc, inches: | -1.5 | 0 | -18.7 | -63.2 | -141.6 |

### .270 WSM

| CARTRIDGE BULLET | RANGE, YARDS: | 0 | 400 | 600 | 800 | 1000 |
|---|---|---|---|---|---|---|
| Nosler 150 AccuBond | velocity, fps: | 2960 | 2661 | 2381 | 2118 | 1873 |
| Long Range | energy, ft-lb: | 2917 | 2358 | 1888 | 1495 | 1169 |
| | arc, inches: | -1.5 | 0 | -18.2 | -61.1 | -135.1 |

### 7MM REMINGTON MAGNUM

| CARTRIDGE BULLET | RANGE, YARDS: | 0 | 400 | 600 | 800 | 1000 |
|---|---|---|---|---|---|---|
| Nosler 168 AccuBond | velocity, fps: | 2880 | 2598 | 2333 | 2084 | 1851 |
| Long Range | energy, ft-lb: | 3093 | 2518 | 2030 | 1620 | 1278 |
| | arc, inches: | -1.5 | 0 | -19.2 | -64.0 | -141.0 |

### 7MM STW

| CARTRIDGE BULLET | RANGE, YARDS: | 0 | 400 | 600 | 800 | 1000 |
|---|---|---|---|---|---|---|
| Nosler 175 AccuBond | velocity, fps: | 2900 | 2625 | 2366 | 2122 | 1893 |
| Long Range | energy, ft-lb: | 3267 | 2677 | 2175 | 1750 | 1393 |
| | arc, inches: | -1.5 | 0 | -18.8 | -62.4 | -137.1 |

### 7MM REMINGTON ULTRA MAG

| CARTRIDGE BULLET | RANGE, YARDS: | 0 | 400 | 600 | 800 | 1000 |
|---|---|---|---|---|---|---|
| Nosler 175 AccuBond | velocity, fps: | 3040 | 2756 | 2490 | 2239 | 2002 |
| Long Range | energy, ft-lb: | 3590 | 2952 | 2409 | 1948 | 1558 |
| | arc, inches: | -1.5 | 0 | -16.9 | -56.2 | -123.5 |

### .308 WINCHESTER

| CARTRIDGE BULLET | RANGE, YARDS: | 0 | 400 | 600 | 800 | 1000 |
|---|---|---|---|---|---|---|
| Barnes 175 OTM | | | | | | |
| velocity, fps: | | 2650 | 2318 | 2011 | 1730 | 1480 | 1272 |
| energy, ft-lb: | | 2730 | 2089 | 1571 | 1163 | 852 | 629 |
| arc, inches: | | -1.5 | 0 | -24.6 | -83.8 | -189.9 | -360.0 |

### .300 WSM

| CARTRIDGE BULLET | RANGE, YARDS: | 0 | 400 | 600 | 800 | 1000 |
|---|---|---|---|---|---|---|
| Nosler 190 AccuBond | velocity, fps: | 2875 | 2588 | 2319 | 2066 | 1830 |
| Long Range | energy, ft-lb: | 3486 | 2826 | 2269 | 1801 | 1413 |
| | arc, inches: | -1.5 | 0 | -19.3 | -64.7 | -142.7 |

### .300 WINCHESTER MAGNUM

| CARTRIDGE BULLET | RANGE, YARDS: | 0 | 400 | 600 | 800 | 1000 |
|---|---|---|---|---|---|---|
| Barnes 220 OTM | | | | | | |
| | velocity, fps: | 2700 | 2420 | 2158 | 1912 | 1685 | 1481 |
| | energy, ft-lb: | 3562 | 2862 | 2275 | 1786 | 1387 | 1072 |
| | arc, inches: | -1.5 | 0 | -22.4 | -74.7 | -165.4 | -305.3 |
| Nosler 190 AccuBond | velocity, fps: | 2870 | 2583 | 2314 | 2062 | 1826 |
| Long Range | energy, ft-lb: | 3474 | 2816 | 2260 | 1794 | 1407 |
| | arc, inches: | -1.5 | 0 | -19.4 | -64.9 | -143.3 |

### .300 WEATHERBY MAGNUM

| CARTRIDGE BULLET | RANGE, YARDS: | 0 | 400 | 600 | 800 | 1000 |
|---|---|---|---|---|---|---|
| Nosler 210 AccuBond | velocity, fps: | 2825 | 2575 | 2339 | 2115 | 1905 |
| Long Range | energy, ft-lb: | 3720 | 3092 | 2551 | 2087 | 1691 |
| | arc, inches: | -1.5 | 0 | -19.5 | -64.6 | -140.8 |

### .300 REMINGTON ULTRA MAG

| CARTRIDGE BULLET | RANGE, YARDS: | 0 | 400 | 600 | 800 | 1000 |
|---|---|---|---|---|---|---|
| Nosler 210 AccuBond | velocity, fps: | 2920 | 2665 | 2424 | 2196 | 1980 |
| Long Range | energy, ft-lb: | 3975 | 3311 | 2740 | 2248 | 1828 |
| | arc, inches: | -1.5 | 0 | -18.1 | -60.0 | -130.8 |

### .30-378 WEATHERBY MAGNUM

| CARTRIDGE BULLET | RANGE, YARDS: | 0 | 400 | 600 | 800 | 1000 |
|---|---|---|---|---|---|---|
| Nosler 210 AccuBond | velocity, fps: | 3040 | 2778 | 2531 | 2297 | 2076 |
| Long Range | energy, ft-lb: | 4308 | 3599 | 2987 | 2461 | 2009 |
| | arc, inches: | -1.5 | 0 | -16.6 | -54.9 | -119.7 |

### .338 REMINGTON ULTRA MAG

| CARTRIDGE BULLET | RANGE, YARDS: | 0 | 400 | 600 | 800 | 1000 |
|---|---|---|---|---|---|---|
| Nosler 300 AccuBond | velocity, fps: | 2600 | 2359 | 2131 | 1916 | 1716 |
| | energy, ft-lb: | 4502 | 3707 | 3026 | 2447 | 1963 |
| | arc, inches: | -1.5 | 0 | -23.6 | -77.9 | -170.2 |

### .338 LAPUA

| CARTRIDGE BULLET | RANGE, YARDS: | 0 | 400 | 600 | 800 | 1000 |
|---|---|---|---|---|---|---|
| Barnes 300 OTM | | | | | | |
| velocity, fps: | | 2600 | 2375 | 2161 | 1958 | 1767 | 1591 |
| energy, ft-lb: | | 4504 | 3757 | 3110 | 2554 | 2081 | 1687 |
| arc, inches: | | -1.5 | 0 | -23.2 | -76.4 | -165.9 | -300.1 |
| Nosler 300 AccuBond | velocity, fps: | 2650 | 2406 | 2176 | 1959 | 1755 |
| | energy, ft-lb: | 4677 | 3857 | 3154 | 2555 | 2053 |
| | arc, inches: | -1.5 | 0 | -22.6 | -74.7 | -163.1 |

Data shown here is taken from manufacturers' charts; your chronograph readings may vary. Barrel lengths for pistol data vary, and depend in part on which pistols are typically chambered in a given cartridge. Velocity variations due to barrel length depend on the baseline bullet speed and the load. Velocity for the .30 Carbine, normally a rifle cartridge, was determined in a pistol barrel.

Listings are current as of February the year *Shooter's Bible* appears (not the cover year). Listings are not intended as recommendations. For example, the data for the .25 Auto gives velocity and energy readings to 100 yards. Few handgunners would call the little .25 a 100-yard cartridge.

Abbreviations: Bullets are designated by loading company, weight (in grains) and type, with these abbreviations for shape and construction: BJHP=brass-jacketed hollowpoint; FN=Flat Nose; FMC=Full Metal Case; FMJ=Full Metal Jacket; HP=Hollowpoint; L=Lead; LF=Lead-Free; +P=a more powerful load than traditionally manufactured for that round; RN=Round Nose; SFHP=Starfire (PMC) Hollowpoint; SP=Softpoint; SWC=Semi Wadcutter; TMJ=Total Metal Jacket; WC=Wadcutter; CEPP, SXT and XTP are trademarked designations of Lapua, Winchester and Hornady, respectively.

## .25 AUTO TO .32 S&W LONG

**BALLISTICS**

| CARTRIDGE BULLET | RANGE, YARDS: | 0 | 25 | 50 | 75 | 100 |
|---|---|---|---|---|---|---|
| **.25 AUTO** | | | | | | |
| Federal 50 FMJ | velocity, fps: | 760 | 750 | 730 | 720 | 700 |
| | energy, ft-lb: | 65 | 60 | 60 | 55 | 55 |
| Hornady 35 JHP/XTP | velocity, fps: | 900 | | 813 | | 742 |
| | energy, ft-lb: | 63 | | 51 | | 43 |
| Magtech 50 FMC | velocity, fps: | 760 | | 707 | | 659 |
| | energy, ft-lb: | 64 | | 56 | | 48 |
| PMC 50 FMJ | velocity, fps: | 754 | 730 | 707 | 685 | 663 |
| | energy, ft-lb: | 62 | | | | |
| Rem. 50 Metal Case | velocity, fps: | 760 | | 707 | | 659 |
| | energy, ft-lb: | 64 | | 56 | | 48 |
| Speer 35 Gold Dot | velocity, fps: | 900 | | 816 | | 747 |
| | energy, ft-lb: | 63 | | 52 | | 43 |
| Speer 50 TMJ (and Blazer) | velocity, fps: | 760 | | 717 | | 677 |
| | energy, ft-lb: | 64 | | 57 | | 51 |
| Win. 45 Expanding Point | velocity, fps: | 815 | | 729 | | 655 |
| | energy, ft-lb | 66 | | 53 | | 42 |
| Win. 50 FMJ | velocity, fps: | 760 | | 707 | | |
| | energy, ft-lb | 64 | | 56 | | |
| **.30 LUGER** | | | | | | |
| Win. 93 FMJ | velocity, fps: | 1220 | | 1110 | | 1040 |
| | energy, ft-lb | 305 | | 255 | | 225 |
| **7.62x25 TOKAREV** | | | | | | |
| PMC 93 FMJ | velocity and energy figures not available | | | | | |
| **.30 CARBINE** | | | | | | |
| Win. 110 Hollow SP | velocity, fps: | 1790 | | 1601 | | 1430 |
| | energy, ft-lb | 783 | | 626 | | 500 |
| **.32 AUTO** | | | | | | |
| Federal 65 Hydra-Shok JHP | velocity, fps: | 950 | 920 | 890 | 860 | 830 |
| | energy, ft-lb: | 130 | 120 | 115 | 105 | 100 |
| Federal 71 FMJ | velocity, fps: | 910 | 880 | 860 | 830 | 810 |
| | energy, ft-lb: | 130 | 120 | 115 | 110 | 105 |
| Hornady 60 JHP/XTP | velocity, fps: | 1000 | | 917 | | 849 |
| | energy, ft-lb: | 133 | | 112 | | 96 |
| Hornady 71 FMJ-RN | velocity, fps: | 900 | | 845 | | 797 |
| | energy, ft-lb: | 128 | | 112 | | 100 |
| Magtech 71 FMC | velocity, fps: | 905 | | 855 | | 810 |
| | energy, ft-lb: | 129 | | 115 | | 103 |
| Magtech 71 JHP | velocity, fps: | 905 | | 855 | | 810 |
| | energy, ft-lb: | 129 | | 115 | | 103 |

| CARTRIDGE BULLET | RANGE, YARDS: | 0 | 25 | 50 | 75 | 100 |
|---|---|---|---|---|---|---|
| PMC 60 JHP | velocity, fps: | 980 | 849 | 820 | 791 | 763 |
| | energy, ft-lb: | 117 | | | | |
| PMC 70 SFHP | velocity, fps: | velocity and energy figures not available | | | | |
| PMC 71 FMJ | velocity, fps: | 870 | 841 | 814 | 791 | 763 |
| | energy, ft-lb: | 119 | | | | |
| Rem. 71 Metal Case | velocity, fps: | 905 | | 855 | | 810 |
| | energy, ft-lb: | 129 | | 115 | | 97 |
| Speer 60 Gold Dot | velocity, fps: | 960 | | 868 | | 796 |
| | energy, ft-lb: | 123 | | 100 | | 84 |
| Speer 71 TMJ (and Blazer) | velocity, fps: | 900 | | 855 | | 810 |
| | energy, ft-lb: | 129 | | 115 | | 97 |
| Win. 60 Silvertip HP | velocity, fps: | 970 | | 895 | | 835 |
| | energy, ft-lb | 125 | | 107 | | 93 |
| Win. 71 FMJ | velocity, fps: | 905 | | 855 | | |
| | energy, ft-lb | 129 | | 115 | | |
| **.32 S&W** | | | | | | |
| Rem. 88 LRN | velocity, fps: | 680 | | 645 | | 610 |
| | energy, ft-lb: | 90 | | 81 | | 73 |
| Win. 85 LRN | velocity, fps: | 680 | | 645 | | 610 |
| | energy, ft-lb: | 90 | | 81 | | 73 |
| **.32 S&W LONG** | | | | | | |
| Federal 98 LWC | velocity, fps: | 780 | 700 | 630 | 560 | 500 |
| | energy, ft-lb: | 130 | 105 | 85 | 70 | 55 |
| Federal 98 LRN | velocity, fps: | 710 | 690 | 670 | 650 | 640 |
| | energy, ft-lb: | 115 | 105 | 100 | 95 | 90 |
| Lapua 83 LWC | velocity, fps: | 240 | | 189* | | 149* |
| | energy, ft-lb: | 154 | | 95* | | 59* |
| Lapua 98 LWC | velocity, fps: | 240 | | 202* | | 171* |
| | energy, ft-lb: | 183 | | 130* | | 93* |
| Magtech 98 LRN | velocity, fps: | 705 | | 670 | | 635 |
| | energy, ft-lb: | 108 | | 98 | | 88 |
| Magtech 98 LWC | velocity, fps: | 682 | | 579 | | 491 |
| | energy, ft-lb: | 102 | | 73 | | 52 |
| Norma 98 LWC | velocity, fps: | 787 | 759 | 732 | | 683 |
| | energy, ft-lb: | 136 | 126 | 118 | | 102 |
| PMC 98 LRN | velocity, fps: | 789 | 770 | 751 | 733 | 716 |
| | energy, ft-lb: | 135 | | | | |
| PMC 100 LWC | velocity, fps: | 683 | 652 | 623 | 595 | 569 |
| | energy, ft-lb: | 102 | | | | |
| Rem. 98 LRN | velocity, fps: | 705 | | 670 | | 635 |
| | energy, ft-lb: | 115 | | 98 | | 88 |

# Centerfire Handgun Ballistics

## .32 S&W LONG TO 9MM LUGER

| CARTRIDGE BULLET | RANGE, YARDS: | 0 | 25 | 50 | 75 | 100 |
|---|---|---|---|---|---|---|
| Win. 98 LRN | velocity, fps: | 705 | | 670 | | 635 |
| | energy, ft-lb: | 115 | | 98 | | 88 |

### .32 SHORT COLT

| CARTRIDGE BULLET | RANGE, YARDS: | 0 | 25 | 50 | 75 | 100 |
|---|---|---|---|---|---|---|
| Win. 80 LRN | velocity, fps: | 745 | | 665 | | 590 |
| | energy, ft-lb: | 100 | | 79 | | 62 |

### .32-20

| CARTRIDGE BULLET | RANGE, YARDS: | 0 | 25 | 50 | 75 | 100 |
|---|---|---|---|---|---|---|
| Black Hills 115 FPL | velocity, fps: | 800 | | | | |
| | energy, ft-lb: | | | | | |

### .32 H&R MAG

| CARTRIDGE BULLET | RANGE, YARDS: | 0 | 25 | 50 | 75 | 100 |
|---|---|---|---|---|---|---|
| Black Hills 85 JHP | velocity, fps | 1100 | | | | |
| | energy, ft-lb | 228 | | | | |
| Black Hills 90 FPL | velocity, fps | 750 | | | | |
| | energy, ft-lb | | | | | |
| Black Hills 115 FPL | velocity, fps | 800 | | | | |
| | energy, ft-lb | | | | | |
| Federal 85 Hi-Shok JHP | velocity, fps: | 1100 | 1050 | 1020 | 970 | 930 |
| | energy, ft-lb: | 230 | 210 | 195 | 175 | 165 |
| Federal 95 LSWC | velocity, fps: | 1030 | 1000 | 940 | 930 | 900 |
| | energy, ft-lb: | 225 | 210 | 195 | 185 | 170 |
| Hornady 80 FTX | | 0 | | 50 yds. | | 100. |
| | velocity, fps: | 1150 | | 1039 | | 963 |
| | energy, ft-lb: | 235 | | 192 | | 165 |

### .38 SPECIAL LITE, 4"BBL

| CARTRIDGE BULLET | RANGE, YARDS: | 0 | 25 | 50 | 75 | 100 |
|---|---|---|---|---|---|---|
| Hornady 90 FTX | velocity, fps: | 1200 | | 1037 | | 938 |
| | energy, ft-lb: | 288 | | 215 | | 176 |

### 9MM MAKAROV

| CARTRIDGE BULLET | RANGE, YARDS: | 0 | 25 | 50 | 75 | 100 |
|---|---|---|---|---|---|---|
| Federal 90 Hi-Shok JHP | velocity, fps: | 990 | 950 | 910 | 880 | 850 |
| | energy, ft-lb: | 195 | 180 | 165 | 155 | 145 |
| Federal 90 FMJ | velocity, fps: | 990 | 960 | 920 | 900 | 870 |
| | energy, ft-lb: | 205 | 190 | 180 | 170 | 160 |
| Hornady 95 JHP/XTP | velocity, fps: | 1000 | | 930 | | 874 |
| | energy, ft-lb: | 211 | | 182 | | 161 |
| PMC 100 FMJ-TC | velocity, fps: | velocity and energy figures not available | | | | |
| Speer 95 TMJ Blazer | velocity, fps: | 1000 | | 928 | | 872 |
| | energy, ft-lb: | 211 | | 182 | | 161 |

### 9x21 IMI

| CARTRIDGE BULLET | RANGE, YARDS: | 0 | 25 | 50 | 75 | 100 |
|---|---|---|---|---|---|---|
| PMC 123 FMJ | velocity, fps: | 1150 | 1093 | 1046 | 1007 | 973 |
| | energy, ft-lb: | 364 | | | | |

### 9MM LUGER

| CARTRIDGE BULLET | RANGE, YARDS: | 0 | 25 | 50 | 75 | 100 |
|---|---|---|---|---|---|---|
| Black Hills 115 JHP | velocity, fps: | 1150 | | | | |
| | energy, ft-lb: | 336 | | | | |
| Black Hills 115 FMJ | velocity, fps: | 1150 | | | | |
| | energy, ft-lb: | 336 | | | | |
| Black Hills 115 JHP +P | velocity, fps: | 1300 | | | | |
| | energy, ft-lb: | 431 | | | | |
| Black Hills 115 EXP JHP | velocity, fps: | 1250 | | | | |
| | energy, ft-lb: | 400 | | | | |
| Black Hills 124 JHP +P | velocity, fps: | 1250 | | | | |
| | energy, ft-lb: | 430 | | | | |
| Black Hills 124 JHP | velocity, fps: | 1150 | | | | |
| | energy, ft-lb: | 363 | | | | |
| Black Hills 124 FMJ | velocity, fps: | 1150 | | | | |
| | energy, ft-lb: | 363 | | | | |
| Black Hills 147 JHP subsonic | velocity, fps: | 975 | | | | |
| | energy, ft-lb: | 309 | | | | |
| Black Hills 147 FMJ subsonic | velocity, fps: | 975 | | | | |
| | energy, ft-lb: | 309 | | | | |
| Federal 105 EFMJ | velocity, fps: | 1225 | 1160 | 1105 | 1060 | 1025 |
| | energy, ft-lb: | 350 | 315 | 285 | 265 | 245 |
| Federal 115 Hi-Shok JHP | velocity, fps: | 1160 | 1100 | 1060 | 1020 | 990 |
| | energy, ft-lb: | 345 | 310 | 285 | 270 | 250 |
| Federal 115 FMJ | velocity, fps: | 1160 | 1100 | 1060 | 1020 | 990 |
| | energy, ft-lb: | 345 | 310 | 285 | 270 | 250 |
| Federal 124 FMJ | velocity, fps: | 1120 | 1070 | 1030 | 990 | 960 |
| | energy, ft-lb: | 345 | 315 | 290 | 270 | 255 |
| Federal 124 Hydra-Shok JHP | velocity, fps: | 1120 | 1070 | 1030 | 990 | 960 |
| | energy, ft-lb: | 345 | 315 | 290 | 270 | 255 |
| Federal 124 TMJ TMF Primer | velocity, fps: | 1120 | 1070 | 1030 | 990 | 960 |
| | energy, ft-lb: | 345 | 315 | 290 | 270 | 255 |
| Federal 124 Truncated FMJ Match | velocity, fps: | 1120 | 1070 | 1030 | 990 | 960 |
| | energy, ft-lb: | 345 | 315 | 290 | 270 | 255 |
| Federal 124 Nyclad HP | velocity, fps: | 1120 | 1070 | 1030 | 990 | 960 |
| | energy, ft-lb: | 345 | 315 | 290 | 270 | 255 |
| Federal 124 FMJ +P | velocity, fps: | 1120 | 1070 | 1030 | 990 | 960 |
| | energy, ft-lb: | 345 | 315 | 290 | 270 | 255 |
| Federal 135 Hydra-Shok JHP | velocity, fps: | 1050 | 1030 | 1010 | 980 | 970 |
| | energy, ft-lb: | 330 | 315 | 300 | 290 | 280 |
| Federal 147 Hydra-Shok JHP | velocity, fps: | 1000 | 960 | 920 | 890 | 860 |
| | energy, ft-lb: | 325 | 300 | 275 | 260 | 240 |
| Federal 147 Hi-Shok JHP | velocity, fps: | 980 | 950 | 930 | 900 | 880 |
| | energy, ft-lb: | 310 | 295 | 285 | 265 | 255 |
| Federal 147 FMJ FN | velocity, fps: | 960 | 930 | 910 | 890 | 870 |
| | energy, ft-lb: | 295 | 280 | 270 | 260 | 250 |
| Federal 147 TMJ TMF Primer | velocity, fps: | 960 | 940 | 910 | 890 | 870 |
| | energy, ft-lb: | 300 | 285 | 270 | 260 | 245 |
| Hornady 115 JHP/XTP | velocity, fps: | 1155 | | 1047 | | 971 |
| | energy, ft-lb: | 341 | | 280 | | 241 |
| Hornady 124 JHP/XTP | velocity, fps: | 1110 | | 1030 | | 971 |
| | energy, ft-lb: | 339 | | 292 | | 259 |
| Hornady 124 TAP-FPD | velocity, fps: | 1100 | | 1028 | | 967 |
| | energy, ft-lb: | 339 | | 291 | | 257 |
| Hornady 147 JHP/XTP | velocity, fps: | 975 | | 935 | | 899 |
| | energy, ft-lb: | 310 | | 285 | | 264 |
| Hornady 147 TAP-FPD | velocity, fps: | 975 | | 935 | | 899 |
| | energy, ft-lb: | 310 | | 285 | | 264 |
| Lapua 116 FMJ | velocity, fps: | 365 | | 319* | | 290* |
| | energy, ft-lb: | 500 | | 381* | | 315* |
| Lapua 120 FMJ CEPP Super | velocity, fps: | 360 | | 316* | | 288* |
| | energy, ft-lb: | 505 | | 390* | | 324* |
| Lapua 120 FMJ CEPP Extra | velocity, fps: | 360 | | 316* | | 288* |
| | energy, ft-lb: | 505 | | 390* | | 324* |
| Lapua 123 HP Megashock | velocity, fps: | 355 | | 311* | | 284* |
| | energy, ft-lb: | 504 | | 388* | | 322* |
| Lapua 123 FMJ | velocity, fps: | 320 | | 292* | | 272* |
| | energy, ft-lb: | 410 | | 342* | | 295* |
| Lapua 123 FMJ Combat | velocity, fps: | 355 | | 315* | | 289* |
| | energy, ft-lb: | 504 | | 397* | | 333* |
| Magtech 115 JHP +P | velocity, fps: | 1246 | | 1137 | | 1056 |
| | energy, ft-lb: | 397 | | 330 | | 285 |
| Magtech 115 FMC | velocity, fps: | 1135 | | 1027 | | 961 |
| | energy, ft-lb: | 330 | | 270 | | 235 |
| Magtech 115 JHP | velocity, fps: | 1155 | | 1047 | | 971 |
| | energy, ft-lb: | 340 | | 280 | | 240 |
| Magtech 124 FMC | velocity, fps: | 1109 | | 1030 | | 971 |
| | energy, ft-lb: | 339 | | 292 | | 259 |
| Norma 84 Lead Free Frangible (Geco brand) | velocity, fps: | 1411 | | | | |
| | energy, ft-lb: | 371 | | | | |
| Norma 124 FMJ (Geco brand) | velocity, fps: | 1120 | | | | |
| | energy, fps: | 341 | | | | |
| Norma 123 FMJ | velocity, fps: | 1099 | 1032 | 980 | | 899 |
| | energy, ft-lb: | 331 | 292 | 263 | | 221 |
| Norma 123 FMJ | velocity, fps: | 1280 | 1170 | 1086 | | 972 |
| | energy, ft-lb: | 449 | 375 | 323 | | 259 |

# Centerfire Handgun Ballistics

## 9MM LUGER TO .380 AUTO

| CARTRIDGE BULLET | RANGE, YARDS: | 0 | 25 | 50 | 75 | 100 |
|---|---|---|---|---|---|---|
| PMC 75 Non-Toxic Frangible | velocity, fps: | 1350 | 1240 | 1154 | 1088 | 1035 |
| | energy, ft-lb: | 303 | | | | |
| PMC 95 SFHP | velocity, fps: | 1250 | 1239 | 1228 | 1217 | 1207 |
| | energy, ft-lb: | 330 | | | | |
| PMC 115 FMJ | velocity, fps: | 1157 | 1100 | 1053 | 1013 | 979 |
| | energy, ft-lb: | 344 | | | | |
| PMC 115 JHP | velocity, fps: | 1167 | 1098 | 1044 | 999 | 961 |
| | energy, ft-lb: | 350 | | | | |
| PMC 124 SFHP | velocity, fps: | 1090 | 1043 | 1003 | 969 | 939 |
| | energy, ft-lb: | 327 | | | | |
| PMC 124 FMJ | velocity, fps: | 1110 | 1059 | 1017 | 980 | 949 |
| | energy, ft-lb: | 339 | | | | |
| PMC 124 LRN | velocity, fps: | 1050 | 1006 | 969 | 937 | 908 |
| | energy, ft-lb: | 304 | | | | |
| PMC 147 FMJ | velocity, fps: | 980 | 965 | 941 | 919 | 900 |
| | enerby, ft-lb: | 310 | | | | |
| PMC 147 SFHP | velocity, fps: | velocity and energy figures not available | | | | |
| Rem. 101 Lead Free Frangible | velocity, fps: | 1220 | | 1092 | | 1004 |
| | energy, ft-lb: | 334 | | 267 | | 226 |
| Rem. 115 FN Enclosed Base | velocity, fps: | 1135 | | 1041 | | 973 |
| | energy, ft-lb: | 329 | | 277 | | 242 |
| Rem. 115 Metal Case | velocity, fps: | 1135 | | 1041 | | 973 |
| | energy, ft-lb: | 329 | | 277 | | 242 |
| Rem. 115 JHP | velocity, fps: | 1155 | | 1047 | | 971 |
| | energy, ft-lb: | 341 | | 280 | | 241 |
| Rem. 115 JHP +P | velocity, fps: | 1250 | | 1113 | | 1019 |
| | energy, ft-lb: | 399 | | 316 | | 265 |
| Rem. 124 JHP | velocity, fps: | 1120 | | 1028 | | 960 |
| | energy, ft-lb: | 346 | | 291 | | 254 |
| Rem. 124 FNEB | velocity, fps: | 1100 | | 1030 | | 971 |
| | energy, ft-lb: | 339 | | 292 | | 252 |
| Rem. 124 BJHP | velocity, fps: | 1125 | | 1031 | | 963 |
| | energy, ft-lb: | 349 | | 293 | | 255 |
| Rem. 124 BJHP +P | velocity, fps: | 1180 | | 1089 | | 1021 |
| | energy, ft-lb: | 384 | | 327 | | 287 |
| Rem. 124 Metal Case | velocity, fps: | 1110 | | 1030 | | 971 |
| | energy, ft-lb: | 339 | | 292 | | 259 |
| Rem. 147 JHP subsonic | velocity, fps: | 990 | | 941 | | 900 |
| | energy, ft-lb: | 320 | | 289 | | 264 |
| Rem. 147 BJHP | velocity, fps: | 990 | | 941 | | 900 |
| | energy, ft-lb: | 320 | | 289 | | 264 |
| Speer 90 Frangible | velocity, fps: | 1350 | | 1132 | | 1001 |
| | energy, ft-lb: | 364 | | 256 | | 200 |
| Speer 115 JHP Blazer | velocity, fps: | 1145 | | 1024 | | 943 |
| | energy, ft-lb: | 335 | | 268 | | 227 |
| Speer 115 FMJ Blazer | velocity, fps: | 1145 | | 1047 | | 971 |
| | energy, ft-lb: | 341 | | 280 | | 241 |
| Speer 115 FMJ | velocity, fps: | 1200 | | 1060 | | 970 |
| | energy, ft-lb: | 368 | | 287 | | 240 |
| Speer 115 Gold Dot HP | velocity, fps: | 1200 | | 1047 | | 971 |
| | energy, ft-lb: | 341 | | 280 | | 241 |
| Speer 124 FMJ Blazer | velocity, fps: | 1090 | | 989 | | 917 |
| | energy, ft-lb: | 327 | | 269 | | 231 |
| Speer 124 FMJ | velocity, fps: | 1090 | | 987 | | 913 |
| | energy, ft-lb: | 327 | | 268 | | 230 |
| Speer 124 TMJ-CF (and Blazer) | velocity, fps: | 1090 | | 989 | | 917 |
| | energy, ft-lb: | 327 | | 269 | | 231 |
| Speer 124 Gold Dot HP | velocity, fps: | 1150 | | 1030 | | 948 |
| | energy, ft-lb: | 367 | | 292 | | 247 |
| Speer 124 Gold Dot HP+P | velocity, ft-lb: | 1220 | | 1085 | | 996 |
| | energy, ft-lb: | 410 | | 324 | | 273 |
| Speer 147 TMJ Blazer | velocity, fps: | 950 | | 912 | | 879 |
| | energy, ft-lb: | 295 | | 272 | | 252 |

| CARTRIDGE BULLET | RANGE, YARDS: | 0 | 25 | 50 | 75 | 100 |
|---|---|---|---|---|---|---|
| Speer 147 TMJ | velocity, fps: | 985 | | 943 | | 906 |
| | energy, ft-lb: | 317 | | 290 | | 268 |
| Speer 147 TMJ-CF (and Blazer) | velocity, fps: | 985 | | 960 | | 924 |
| | energy, ft-lb: | 326 | | 300 | | 279 |
| Speer 147 Gold Dot | velocity, fps: | 985 | | 960 | | 924 |
| | energy, ft-lb: | 326 | | 300 | | 279 |
| Win. 105 Jacketed FP | velocity, fps: | 1200 | | 1074 | | 989 |
| | energy, ft-lb: | 336 | | 269 | | 228 |
| Win. 115 Silvertip HP | velocity, fps: | 1225 | | 1095 | | 1007 |
| | energy, ft-lb: | 383 | | 306 | | 259 |
| Win. 115 Jacketed HP | velocity, fps: | 1225 | | 1095 | | |
| | energy, ft-lb: | 383 | | 306 | | |
| Win. 115 FMJ | velocity, fps: | 1190 | | 1071 | | |
| | energy, ft-lb: | 362 | | 293 | | |
| Win. 115 EB WinClean | velocity, fps: | 1190 | | 1088 | | |
| | energy, ft-lb: | 362 | | 302 | | |
| Win. 124 FMJ | velocity, fps: | 1140 | | 1050 | | |
| | energy, ft-lb: | 358 | | 303 | | |
| Win. 124 EB WinClean | velocity, fps: | 1130 | | 1049 | | |
| | energy, ft-lb: | 352 | | 303 | | |
| Win. 147 FMJ FN | velocity, fps: | 990 | | 945 | | |
| | energy, ft-lb: | 320 | | 292 | | |
| Win. 147 SXT | velocity, fps: | 990 | | 947 | | 909 |
| | energy, ft-lb: | 320 | | 293 | | 270 |
| Win. 147 Silvertip HP | velocity, fps: | 1010 | | 962 | | 921 |
| | energy, ft-lb: | 333 | | 302 | | 277 |
| Win. 147 JHP | velocity, fps: | 990 | | 945 | | |
| | energy, ft-lb: | 320 | | 291 | | |
| Win. 147 EB WinClean | velocity, fps: | 990 | | 945 | | |
| | energy, ft-lb: | 320 | | 291 | | |

### 9 x 23 WINCHESTER

| CARTRIDGE BULLET | RANGE, YARDS: | 0 | 25 | 50 | 75 | 100 |
|---|---|---|---|---|---|---|
| Win. 124 Jacketed FP | velocity, fps: | 1460 | | 1308 | | |
| | energy, ft-lb: | 587 | | 471 | | |
| Win. 125 Silvertip HP | velocity, fps: | 1450 | | 1249 | | 1103 |
| | energy, ft-lb: | 583 | | 433 | | 338 |

### .38 S&W

| CARTRIDGE BULLET | RANGE, YARDS: | 0 | 25 | 50 | 75 | 100 |
|---|---|---|---|---|---|---|
| Rem. 146 LRN | velocity, fps: | 685 | | 650 | | 620 |
| | energy, ft-lb: | 150 | | 135 | | 125 |
| Win. 145 LRN | velocity, fps: | 685 | | 650 | | 620 |
| | energy, ft-lb: | 150 | | 135 | | 125 |

### .38 SHORT COLT

| CARTRIDGE BULLET | RANGE, YARDS: | 0 | 25 | 50 | 75 | 100 |
|---|---|---|---|---|---|---|
| Rem. 125 LRN | velocity, fps: | 730 | | 685 | | 645 |
| | energy, ft-lb: | 150 | | 130 | | 115 |

### .38 LONG COLT

| CARTRIDGE BULLET | RANGE, YARDS: | 0 | 25 | 50 | 75 | 100 |
|---|---|---|---|---|---|---|
| Black Hills 158 RNL | velocity, fps: | 650 | | | | |
| | energy, ft-lb: | | | | | |

### .380 AUTO

| CARTRIDGE BULLET | RANGE, YARDS: | 0 | 25 | 50 | 75 | 100 |
|---|---|---|---|---|---|---|
| Black Hills 90 JHP | velocity, fps: | 1000 | | | | |
| | energy, ft-lb: | 200 | | | | |
| Black Hills 95 FMJ | velocity, fps: | 950 | | | | |
| | energy, ft-lb: | 190 | | | | |
| Federal 90 Hi-Shok JHP | velocity, fps: | 1000 | 940 | 890 | 840 | 800 |
| | energy, ft-lb: | 200 | 175 | 160 | 140 | 130 |
| Federal 90 Hydra-Shok JHP | velocity, fps: | 1000 | 940 | 890 | 840 | 800 |
| | energy, ft-lb: | 200 | 175 | 160 | 140 | 130 |
| Federal 95 FMJ | velocity, fps: | 960 | 910 | 870 | 830 | 790 |
| | energy, ft-lb: | 190 | 175 | 160 | 145 | 130 |
| Hornady 90 JHP/XTP | velocity, fps: | 1000 | | 902 | | 823 |
| | energy, ft-lb: | 200 | | 163 | | 135 |

# Centerfire Handgun Ballistics

## .380 AUTO TO .38 SPECIAL

| CARTRIDGE BULLET | RANGE, YARDS: | 0 | 25 | 50 | 75 | 100 |
|---|---|---|---|---|---|---|
| Magtech 85 JHP + P | velocity, fps: | 1082 | | 999 | | 936 |
| | energy, ft-lb: | 221 | | 188 | | 166 |
| Magtech 95 FMC | velocity, fps: | 951 | | 861 | | 781 |
| | energy, ft-lb: | 190 | | 156 | | 128 |
| Magtech 95 JHP | velocity, fps: | 951 | | 861 | | 781 |
| | energy, ft-lb: | 190 | | 156 | | 128 |
| PMC 77 NT/FR | velocity, fps: | 1200 | 1095 | 1012 | 932 | 874 |
| | energy, ft-lb: | 223 | | | | |
| PMC 90 FMJ | velocity, fps: | 910 | 872 | 838 | 807 | 778 |
| | energy, ft-lb: | 165 | | | | |
| PMC 90 JHP | velocity, fps: | 917 | 878 | 844 | 812 | 782 |
| | energy, ft-lb: | 168 | | | | |
| PMC 95 SFHP | velocity, fps: | 925 | 884 | 847 | 813 | 783 |
| | energy, ft-lb: | 180 | | | | |
| Rem. 88 JHP | velocity, fps: | 990 | | 920 | | 868 |
| | energy, ft-lb: | 191 | | 165 | | 146 |
| Rem. 95 FNEB | velocity, fps: | 955 | | 865 | | 785 |
| | energy, ft-lb: | 190 | | 160 | | 130 |
| Rem. 95 Metal Case | velocity, fps: | 955 | | 865 | | 785 |
| | energy, ft-lb: | 190 | | 160 | | 130 |
| Rem. 102 BJHP | velocity, fps: | 940 | | 901 | | 866 |
| | energy, ft-lb: | 200 | | 184 | | 170 |
| Speer 88 JHP Blazer | velocity, fps: | 950 | | 920 | | 870 |
| | energy, ft-lb: | 195 | | 164 | | 148 |
| Speer 90 Gold Dot | velocity, fps: | 990 | | 907 | | 842 |
| | energy, ft-lb: | 196 | | 164 | | 142 |
| Speer 95 TMJ Blazer | velocity, fps: | 945 | | 865 | | 785 |
| | energy, ft-lb: | 190 | | 160 | | 130 |
| Speer 95 TMJ | velocity, fps: | 950 | | 877 | | 817 |
| | energy, ft-lb: | 180 | | 154 | | 133 |
| Win. 85 Silvertip HP | velocity, fps: | 1000 | | 921 | | 860 |
| | energy, ft-lb: | 189 | | 160 | | 140 |
| Win. 95 SXT | velocity, fps: | 955 | | 889 | | 835 |
| | energy, ft-lb: | 192 | | 167 | | 147 |
| Win. 95 FMJ | velocity, fps: | 955 | | 865 | | |
| | energy, ft-lb: | 190 | | 160 | | |
| Win. 95 EB WinClean | velocity, fps: | 955 | | 881 | | |
| | energy, ft-lb: | 192 | | 164 | | |

### .38 SPECIAL

| CARTRIDGE BULLET | RANGE, YARDS: | 0 | 25 | 50 | 75 | 100 |
|---|---|---|---|---|---|---|
| Black Hills 125 JHP +P | velocity, fps: | 1050 | | | | |
| | energy, ft-lb: | 306 | | | | |
| Black Hills 148 HBWC | velocity, fps: | 700 | | | | |
| | energy, ft-lb: | | | | | |
| Black Hills 158 SWC | velocity, fps: | 850 | | | | |
| | energy, ft-lb: | | | | | |
| Black Hills 158 CNL | velocity, fps: | 800 | | | | |
| | energy, ft-lb: | | | | | |
| Federal 110 Hydra-Shok JHP | velocity, fps: | 1000 | 970 | 930 | 910 | 880 |
| | energy, ft-lb: | 245 | 225 | 215 | 200 | 190 |
| Federal 110 Hi-Shok JHP +P | velocity, fps: | 1000 | 960 | 930 | 900 | 870 |
| | energy, ft-lb: | 240 | 225 | 210 | 195 | 185 |
| Federal 125 Nyclad HP | velocity, fps: | 830 | 780 | 730 | 690 | 650 |
| | energy, ft-lb: | 190 | 170 | 150 | 130 | 115 |
| Federal 125 Hi-Shok JSP +P | velocity, fps: | 950 | 920 | 900 | 880 | 860 |
| | energy, ft-lb: | 250 | 235 | 225 | 215 | 205 |
| Federal 125 Hi-Shok JHP +P | velocity, fps: | 950 | 920 | 900 | 880 | 860 |
| | energy, ft-lb: | 250 | 235 | 225 | 215 | 205 |
| Federal 125 Nyclad HP +P | velocity, fps: | 950 | 920 | 900 | 880 | 860 |
| | energy, ft-lb: | 250 | 235 | 225 | 215 | 205 |
| Federal 129 Hydra-Shok JHP+P | velocity, fps: | 950 | 930 | 910 | 890 | 870 |
| | energy, ft-lb: | 255 | 245 | 235 | 225 | 215 |
| Federal 130 FMJ | velocity, fps: | 950 | 920 | 890 | 870 | 840 |
| | energy, ft-lb: | 260 | 245 | 230 | 215 | 205 |

| CARTRIDGE BULLET | RANGE, YARDS: | 0 | 25 | 50 | 75 | 100 |
|---|---|---|---|---|---|---|
| Federal 148 LWC Match | velocity, fps: | 710 | 670 | 630 | 600 | 560 |
| | energy, ft-lb: | 165 | 150 | 130 | 115 | 105 |
| Federal 158 LRN | velocity, fps: | 760 | 740 | 720 | 710 | 690 |
| | energy, ft-lb: | 200 | 190 | 185 | 175 | 170 |
| Federal 158 LSWC | velocity, fps: | 760 | 740 | 720 | 710 | 690 |
| | energy, ft-lb: | 200 | 190 | 185 | 175 | 170 |
| Federal 158 Nyclad RN | velocity, fps: | 760 | 740 | 720 | 710 | 690 |
| | energy, ft-lb: | 200 | 190 | 185 | 175 | 170 |
| Federal 158 SWC HP +P | velocity, fps: | 890 | 870 | 860 | 840 | 820 |
| | energy, ft-lb: | 280 | 265 | 260 | 245 | 235 |
| Federal 158 LSWC +P | velocity, fps: | 890 | 870 | 860 | 840 | 820 |
| | energy, ft-lb: | 270 | 265 | 260 | 245 | 235 |
| Federal 158 Nyclad SWC-HP+P | velocity, fps: | 890 | 870 | 860 | 840 | 820 |
| | energy, ft-lb: | 270 | 265 | 260 | 245 | 235 |
| Hornady 125 JHP/XTP | velocity, fps: | 900 | | 856 | | 817 |
| | energy, ft-lb: | 225 | | 203 | | 185 |
| Hornady 140 JHP/XTP | velocity, fps: | 825 | | 790 | | 757 |
| | energy, ft-lb: | 212 | | 194 | | 178 |
| Hornady 140 Cowboy | velocity, fps: | 800 | | 767 | | 735 |
| | energy, ft-lb: | 199 | | 183 | | 168 |
| Hornady 148 HBWC | velocity, fps: | 800 | | 697 | | 610 |
| | energy, ft-lb: | 210 | | 160 | | 122 |
| Hornady 158 JHP/XPT | velocity, fps: | 800 | | 765 | | 731 |
| | energy, ft-lb: | 225 | | 205 | | 188 |
| Lapua 123 HP Megashock | velocity, fps: | 355 | | 311* | | 284* |
| | energy, ft-lb: | 504 | | 388* | | 322* |
| Lapua 148 LWC | velocity, fps: | 230 | | 203* | | 181* |
| | energy, ft-lb: | 254 | | 199* | | 157* |
| Lapua 150 SJFN | velocity, fps: | 325 | | 301* | | 283* |
| | energy, ft-lb: | 512 | | 439* | | 388* |
| Lapua 158 FMJLF | velocity, fps: | 255 | | 243* | | 232* |
| | energy, ft-lb: | 332 | | 301* | | 275* |
| Lapua 158 LRN | velocity, fps: | 255 | | 243* | | 232* |
| | energy, ft-lb: | 332 | | 301* | | 275* |
| Magtech 125 JHP +P | velocity, fps: | 1017 | | 971 | | 931 |
| | energy, ft-lb: | 287 | | 262 | | 241 |
| Magtech 148 LWC | velocity, fps: | 710 | | 634 | | 566 |
| | energy, ft-lb: | 166 | | 132 | | 105 |
| Magtech 158 LRN | velocity, fps: | 755 | | 728 | | 693 |
| | energy, ft-lb: | 200 | | 183 | | 168 |
| Magtech 158 LFN | velocity, fps: | 800 | | 776 | | 753 |
| | energy, ft-lb: | 225 | | 211 | | 199 |
| Magtech 158 SJHP | velocity, fps: | 807 | | 779 | | 753 |
| | energy, ft-lb: | 230 | | 213 | | 199 |
| Magtech 158 LSWC | velocity, fps: | 755 | | 721 | | 689 |
| | energy, ft-lb: | 200 | | 182 | | 167 |
| Magtech 158 FMC-Flat | velocity, fps: | 807 | | 779 | | 753 |
| | energy, ft-lb: | 230 | | 213 | | 199 |
| PMC 85 Non-Toxic Frangible | velocity, fps: | 1275 | 1181 | 1109 | 1052 | 1006 |
| | energy, ft-lb: | 307 | | | | |
| PMC 110 SFHP +P | velocity, fps: | velocity and energy figures not available | | | | |
| PMC 125 SFHP +P | velocity, fps: | 950 | 918 | 889 | 863 | 838 |
| | energy, ft-lb: | 251 | | | | |
| PMC 125 JHP +P | velocity, fps: | 974 | 938 | 906 | 878 | 851 |
| | energy, ft-lb: | 266 | | | | |
| PMC 132 FMJ | velocity, fps: | 841 | 820 | 799 | 780 | 761 |
| | energy, ft-lb: | 206 | | | | |
| PMC 148 LWC | velocity, fps: | 728 | 694 | 662 | 631 | 602 |
| | energy, ft-lb: | 175 | | | | |
| PMC 158 LRN | velocity, fps: | 820 | 801 | 783 | 765 | 749 |
| | energy, ft-lb: | 235 | | | | |
| PMC 158 JSP | velocity, fps: | 835 | 816 | 797 | 779 | 762 |
| | energy, ft-lb: | 245 | | | | |

| CARTRIDGE BULLET | RANGE, YARDS: | 0 | 25 | 50 | 75 | 100 |
|---|---|---|---|---|---|---|
| PMC 158 LFP | velocity, fps: | 800 | | 761 | | 725 |
| | energy, ft-lb: | 225 | | 203 | | 185 |
| Rem. 101 Lead Free Frangible | velocity, fps: | 950 | | 896 | | 850 |
| | energy, ft-lb: | 202 | | 180 | | 162 |
| Rem. 110 SJHP | velocity, fps: | 950 | | 890 | | 840 |
| | energy, ft-lb: | 220 | | 194 | | 172 |
| Rem. 110 SJHP +P | velocity, fps: | 995 | | 926 | | 871 |
| | energy, ft-lb: | 242 | | 210 | | 185 |
| Rem. 125 SJHP +P | velocity, ft-lb: | 945 | | 898 | | 858 |
| | energy, ft-lb: | 248 | | 224 | | 204 |
| Rem. 125 BJHP | velocity, fps: | 975 | | 929 | | 885 |
| | energy, ft-lb: | 264 | | 238 | | 218 |
| Rem. 125 FNEB | velocity, fps: | 850 | | 822 | | 796 |
| | energy, ft-lb: | 201 | | 188 | | 176 |
| Rem. 125 FNEB +P | velocity, fps: | 975 | | 935 | | 899 |
| | energy, ft-lb: | 264 | | 242 | | 224 |
| Rem. 130 Metal Case | velocity, fps: | 950 | | 913 | | 879 |
| | energy, ft-lb: | 261 | | 240 | | 223 |
| Rem. 148 LWC Match | velocity, fps: | 710 | | 634 | | 566 |
| | energy, ft-lb: | 166 | | 132 | | 105 |
| Rem. 158 LRN | velocity, fps: | 755 | | 723 | | 692 |
| | energy, ft-lb: | 200 | | 183 | | 168 |
| Rem. 158 SWC +P | velocity, fps: | 890 | | 855 | | 823 |
| | energy, ft-lb: | 278 | | 257 | | 238 |
| Rem. 158 SWC | velocity, fps: | 755 | | 723 | | 692 |
| | energy, ft-lb: | 200 | | 183 | | 168 |
| Rem. 158 LHP +P | velocity, fps: | 890 | | 855 | | 823 |
| | energy, ft-lb: | 278 | | 257 | | 238 |
| Speer 125 JHP +P Blazer | velocity, fps: | 945 | | 898 | | 858 |
| | energy, ft-lb: | 248 | | 224 | | 204 |
| Speer 125 Gold Dot +P | velocity, fps: | 945 | | 898 | | 858 |
| | energy, ft-lb: | 248 | | 224 | | 204 |
| Speer 158 TMJ +P (and Blazer) | velocity, fps: | 900 | | 852 | | 818 |
| | energy, ft-lb: | 278 | | 255 | | 235 |
| Speer 158 LRN Blazer | velocity, fps: | 755 | | 723 | | 692 |
| | energy, ft-lb: | 200 | | 183 | | 168 |
| Speer 158 Trail Blazer LFN | velocity, fps: | 800 | | 761 | | 725 |
| | energy, ft-lb: | 225 | | 203 | | 184 |
| Speer 158 TMJ-CF +P (and Blazer) | velocity, fps: | 900 | | 852 | | 818 |
| | energy, ft-lb: | 278 | | 255 | | 235 |
| Win. 110 Silvertip HP | velocity, fps: | 945 | | 894 | | 850 |
| | energy, ft-lb: | 218 | | 195 | | 176 |
| Win. 110 Jacketed FP | velocity, fps: | 975 | | 906 | | 849 |
| | energy, ft-lb: | 232 | | 201 | | 176 |
| Win. 125 Jacketed HP | velocity, fps: | 945 | | 898 | | |
| | energy, ft-lb: | 248 | | 224 | | |
| Win. 125 Jacketed HP +P | velocity, fps: | 945 | | 898 | | 858 |
| | energy, ft-lb: | 248 | | 224 | | 204 |
| Win. 125 Jacketed FP | velocity, fps: | 850 | | 804 | | |
| | energy, ft-lb: | 201 | | 179 | | |
| Win. 125 Silvertip HP + P | velocity, fps: | 945 | | 898 | | 858 |
| | energy, ft-lb: | 248 | | 224 | | 204 |
| Win. 125 JFP WinClean | velocity, fps: | 775 | | 742 | | |
| | energy, ft-lb: | 167 | | 153 | | |
| Win. 130 FMJ | velocity, fps: | 800 | | 765 | | |
| | energy, ft-lb: | 185 | | 169 | | |
| Win. 130 SXT +P | velocity, fps: | 925 | | 887 | | 852 |
| | energy, ft-lb: | 247 | | 227 | | 210 |
| Win. 148 LWC Super Match | velocity, fps: | 710 | | 634 | | 566 |
| | energy, ft-lb: | 166 | | 132 | | 105 |
| Win. 150 Lead | velocity, fps: | 845 | | 812 | | |
| | energy, ft-lb: | 238 | | 219 | | |
| Win. 158 Lead | velocity, fps: | 800 | | 761 | | 725 |
| | energy, ft-lb: | 225 | | 203 | | 185 |

| CARTRIDGE BULLET | RANGE, YARDS: | 0 | 25 | 50 | 75 | 100 |
|---|---|---|---|---|---|---|
| Win. 158 LRN | velocity, fps: | 755 | | 723 | | 693 |
| | energy, ft-lb: | 200 | | 183 | | 168 |
| Win. 158 LSWC | velocity, fps: | 755 | | 721 | | 689 |
| | energy, ft-lb: | 200 | | 182 | | 167 |
| Win. 158 LSWC HP +P | velocity, fps: | 890 | | 855 | | 823 |
| | energy, ft-lb: | 278 | | 257 | | 238 |

### .38-40

| CARTRIDGE BULLET | RANGE, YARDS: | 0 | 25 | 50 | 75 | 100 |
|---|---|---|---|---|---|---|
| Black Hills 180 FPL | velocity, fps: | 800 | | | | |
| | energy, ft-lb: | | | | | |

### .38 SUPER

| CARTRIDGE BULLET | RANGE, YARDS: | 0 | 25 | 50 | 75 | 100 |
|---|---|---|---|---|---|---|
| Federal 130 FMJ +P | velocity, fps: | 1200 | 1140 | 1100 | 1050 | 1020 |
| | energy, ft-lb: | 415 | 380 | 350 | 320 | 300 |
| PMC 115 JHP | velocity, fps: | 1116 | 1052 | 1001 | 959 | 923 |
| | energy, ft-lb: | 318 | | | | |
| PMC 130 FMJ | velocity, fps: | 1092 | 1038 | 994 | 957 | 924 |
| | energy, ft-lb: | 348 | | | | |
| Rem. 130 Metal Case | velocity, fps: | 1215 | | 1099 | | 1017 |
| | energy, ft-lb: | 426 | | 348 | | 298 |
| Win. 125 Silvertip HP +P | velocity, fps: | 1240 | | 1130 | | 1050 |
| | energy, ft-lb: | 427 | | 354 | | 306 |
| Win. 130 FMJ +P | velocity, fps: | 1215 | | 1099 | | |
| | energy, ft-lb: | 426 | | 348 | | |

### .357 SIG

| CARTRIDGE BULLET | RANGE, YARDS: | 0 | 25 | 50 | 75 | 100 |
|---|---|---|---|---|---|---|
| Federal 125 FMJ | velocity, fps: | 1350 | 1270 | 1190 | 1130 | 1080 |
| | energy, ft-lb: | 510 | 445 | 395 | 355 | 325 |
| Federal 125 JHP | velocity, fps: | 1350 | 1270 | 1190 | 1130 | 1080 |
| | energy, ft-lb: | 510 | 445 | 395 | 355 | 325 |
| Federal 150 JHP | velocity, fps: | 1130 | 1080 | 1030 | 1000 | 970 |
| | energy, ft-lb: | 420 | 385 | 355 | 330 | 310 |
| Hornady 124 JHP/XTP | velocity, fps: | 1350 | | 1208 | | 1108 |
| | energy, ft-lb: | 502 | | 405 | | 338 |
| Hornady 147 JHP/XTP | velocity, fps: | 1225 | | 1138 | | 1072 |
| | energy, ft-lb: | 490 | | 422 | | 375 |
| PMC 85 Non-Toxic Frangible | velocity, fps: | 1480 | 1356 | 1245 | 1158 | 1092 |
| | energy, ft-lb: | 413 | | | | |
| PMC 124 SFHP | velocity, fps: | 1350 | 1263 | 1190 | 1132 | 1083 |
| | energy, ft-lb: | 502 | | | | |
| PMC 124 FMJ/FP | velocity, fps: | 1350 | 1242 | 1158 | 1093 | 1040 |
| | energy, ft-lb: | 512 | | | | |
| Rem. 104 Lead Free Frangible | velocity, fps: | 1400 | | 1223 | | 1094 |
| | energy, ft-lb: | 453 | | 345 | | 276 |
| Rem. 125 Metal Case | velocity, fps: | 1350 | | 1146 | | 1018 |
| | energy, ft-lb: | 506 | | 422 | | 359 |
| Rem. 125 JHP | velocity, fps: | 1350 | | 1157 | | 1032 |
| | energy, ft-lb: | 506 | | 372 | | 296 |
| Speer 125 TMJ (and Blazer) | velocity, fps: | 1350 | | 1177 | | 1057 |
| | energy, ft-lb: | 502 | | 381 | | 307 |
| Speer 125 TMJ-CF | velocity, fps: | 1350 | | 1177 | | 1057 |
| | energy, ft-lb: | 502 | | 381 | | 307 |
| Speer 125 Gold Dot | velocity, fps: | 1375 | | 1203 | | 1079 |
| | energy, ft-lb: | 525 | | 402 | | 323 |
| Win. 105 JFP | velocity, fps: | 1370 | | 1179 | | 1050 |
| | energy, ft-lb | 438 | | 324 | | 257 |
| Win. 125 FMJ FN | velocity, fps: | 1350 | | 1185 | | |
| | energy, ft-lb | 506 | | 390 | | |

### .357 MAGNUM

| CARTRIDGE BULLET | RANGE, YARDS: | 0 | 25 | 50 | 75 | 100 |
|---|---|---|---|---|---|---|
| Black Hills 125 JHP | velocity, fps: | 1500 | | | | |
| | energy, ft-lb: | 625 | | | | |
| Black Hills 158 CNL | velocity, fps: | 800 | | | | |
| | energy, ft-lb: | | | | | |
| Black Hills 158 SWC | velocity, fps: | 1050 | | | | |
| | energy, ft-lb: | | | | | |

# Centerfire Handgun Ballistics

## .357 MAGNUM TO .40 S&W

| CARTRIDGE BULLET | RANGE, YARDS: | 0 | 25 | 50 | 75 | 100 |
|---|---|---|---|---|---|---|
| Black Hills 158 JHP | velocity, fps: | 1250 | | | | |
| | energy, ft-lb: | | | | | |
| Federal 110 Hi-Shok JHP | velocity, fps: | 1300 | 1180 | 1090 | 1040 | 990 |
| | energy, ft-lb: | 410 | 340 | 290 | 260 | 235 |
| Federal 125 Hi-Shok JHP | velocity, fps: | 1450 | 1350 | 1240 | 1160 | 1100 |
| | energy, ft-lb: | 580 | 495 | 430 | 370 | 335 |
| Federal 130 Hydra-Shok JHP | velocity, fps: | 1300 | 1210 | 1130 | 1070 | 1020 |
| | energy, ft-lb: | 490 | 420 | 370 | 330 | 300 |
| Federal 158 Hi-Shok JSP | velocity, fps: | 1240 | 1160 | 1100 | 1060 | 1020 |
| | energy, ft-lb: | 535 | 475 | 430 | 395 | 365 |
| Federal 158 JSP | velocity, fps: | 1240 | 1160 | 1100 | 1060 | 1020 |
| | energy, ft-lb: | 535 | 475 | 430 | 395 | 365 |
| Federal 158 LSWC | velocity, fps: | 1240 | 1160 | 1100 | 1060 | 1020 |
| | energy, ft-lb: | 535 | 475 | 430 | 395 | 365 |
| Federal 158 Hi-Shok JHP | velocity, fps: | 1240 | 1160 | 1100 | 1060 | 1020 |
| | energy, ft-lb: | 535 | 475 | 430 | 395 | 365 |
| Federal 158 Hydra-Shok JHP | velocity, fps: | 1240 | 1160 | 1100 | 1060 | 1020 |
| | energy, ft-lb: | 535 | 475 | 430 | 395 | 365 |
| Federal 180 Hi-Shok JHP | velocity, fps: | 1090 | 1030 | 980 | 930 | 890 |
| | energy, ft-lb: | 475 | 425 | 385 | 350 | 320 |
| Federal 180 Castcore | velocity, fps: | 1250 | 1200 | 1160 | 1120 | 1080 |
| | energy, ft-lb: | 625 | 575 | 535 | 495 | 465 |
| Hornady 125 JHP/XTP | velocity, fps: | 1500 | | 1314 | | 1166 |
| | energy, ft-lb: | 624 | | 479 | | 377 |
| Hornady 125 JFP/XTP | velocity, fps: | 1500 | | 1311 | | 1161 |
| | energy, ft-lb: | 624 | | 477 | | 374 |
| Hornady 140 Cowboy | velocity, fps: | 800 | | 767 | | 735 |
| | energy, ft-lb: | 199 | | 183 | | 168 |
| Hornady 140 JHP/XTP | velocity, fps: | 1400 | | 1249 | | 1130 |
| | energy, ft-lb: | 609 | | 485 | | 397 |
| Hornady 158 JHP/XTP | velocity, fps: | 1250 | | 1150 | | 1073 |
| | energy, ft-lb: | 548 | | 464 | | 404 |
| Hornady 158 JFP/XTP | velocity, fps: | 1250 | | 1147 | | 1068 |
| | energy, ft-lb: | 548 | | 461 | | 400 |
| Lapua 150 FMJ CEPP Super | velocity, fps: | 370 | | 527* | | 303* |
| | energy, ft-lb: | 664 | | 527* | | 445* |
| Lapua 150 SJFN | velocity, fps: | 385 | | 342* | | 313* |
| | energy, ft-lb: | 719 | | 569* | | 476* |
| Lapua 158 SJHP | velocity, fps: | 470 | | 408* | | 359* |
| | energy, ft-lb: | 1127 | | 850* | | 657* |
| Magtech 158 SJSP | velocity, fps: | 1235 | | 1104 | | 1015 |
| | energy, ft-lb: | 535 | | 428 | | 361 |
| Magtech 158 SJHP | velocity, fps: | 1235 | | 1104 | | 1015 |
| | energy, ft-lb: | 535 | | 428 | | 361 |
| PMC 85 Non-Toxic Frangible | velocity, fps: | 1325 | 1219 | 1139 | 1076 | 1025 |
| | energy, ft-lb: | 331 | | | | |
| PMC 125 JHP | velocity, fps: | 1194 | 1117 | 1057 | 1008 | 967 |
| | energy, ft-lb: | 399 | | | | |
| PMC 150 JHP | velocity, fps: | 1234 | 1156 | 1093 | 1042 | 1000 |
| | energy, ft-lb: | 512 | | | | |
| PMC 150 SFHP | velocity, fps: | 1205 | 1129 | 1069 | 1020 | 980 |
| | energy, ft-lb: | 484 | | | | |
| PMC 158 JSP | velocity, fps: | 1194 | 1122 | 1063 | 1016 | 977 |
| | energy, ft-lb: | 504 | | | | |
| PMC 158 LFP | velocity, fps: | 800 | | 761 | | 725 |
| | energy, ft-lb: | 225 | | 203 | | 185 |
| Rem. 110 SJHP | velocity, fps: | 1295 | | 1094 | | 975 |
| | energy, ft-lb: | 410 | | 292 | | 232 |
| Rem. 125 SJHP | velocity, fps: | 1450 | | 1240 | | 1090 |
| | energy, ft-lb: | 583 | | 427 | | 330 |
| Rem. 125 BJHP | velocity, fps: | 1220 | | 1095 | | 1009 |
| | energy, ft-lb: | 413 | | 333 | | 283 |
| Rem. 125 FNEB | velocity, fps: | 1450 | | 1240 | | 1090 |
| | energy, ft-lb: | 583 | | 427 | | 330 |
| Rem. 158 SJHP | velocity, fps: | 1235 | | 1104 | | 1015 |
| | energy, ft-lb: | 535 | | 428 | | 361 |
| Rem. 158 SP | velocity, fps: | 1235 | | 1104 | | 1015 |
| | energy, ft-lb: | 535 | | 428 | | 361 |
| Rem. 158 SWC | velocity, fps: | 1235 | | 1104 | | 1015 |
| | energy, ft-lb: | 535 | | 428 | | 361 |
| Rem. 165 JHP Core-Lokt | velocity, fps: | 1290 | | 1189 | | 1108 |
| | energy, ft-lb: | 610 | | 518 | | 450 |
| Rem. 180 SJHP | velocity, fps: | 1145 | | 1053 | | 985 |
| | energy, ft-lb: | 542 | | 443 | | 388 |
| Speer 125 Gold Dot | velocity, fps: | 1450 | | 1240 | | 1090 |
| | energy, ft-lb: | 583 | | 427 | | 330 |
| Speer 158 JHP Blazer | velocity, fps: | 1150 | | 1104 | | 1015 |
| | energy, ft-lb: | 535 | | 428 | | 361 |
| Speer 158 Gold Dot | velocity, fps: | 1235 | | 1104 | | 1015 |
| | energy, ft-lb: | 535 | | 428 | | 361 |
| Speer 170 Gold Dot SP | velocity, fps: | 1180 | | 1089 | | 1019 |
| | energy, ft-lb: | 525 | | 447 | | 392 |
| Win. 110 JFP | velocity, fps: | 1275 | | 1105 | | 998 |
| | energy, ft-lb: | 397 | | 298 | | 243 |
| Win. 110 JHP | velocity, fps: | 1295 | | 1095 | | |
| | energy, ft-lb: | 410 | | 292 | | |
| Win. 125 JFP WinClean | velocity, fps: | 1370 | | 1183 | | |
| | energy, ft-lb: | 521 | | 389 | | |
| Win. 145 Silvertip HP | velocity, fps: | 1290 | | 1155 | | 1060 |
| | energy, ft-lb: | 535 | | 428 | | 361 |
| Win. 158 JHP | velocity, fps: | 1235 | | 1104 | | 1015 |
| | energy, ft-lb: | 535 | | 428 | | 361 |
| Win. 158 JSP | velocity, fps: | 1235 | | 1104 | | 1015 |
| | energy, ft-lb: | 535 | | 428 | | 361 |
| Win. 180 Partition Gold | velocity, fps: | 1180 | | 1088 | | 1020 |
| | energy, ft-lb: | 557 | | 473 | | 416 |

## .40 S&W

| CARTRIDGE BULLET | RANGE, YARDS: | 0 | 25 | 50 | 75 | 100 |
|---|---|---|---|---|---|---|
| Black Hills 155 JHP | velocity, fps: | 1150 | | | | |
| | energy, ft-lb: | 450 | | | | |
| Black Hills 165 EXP JHP | velocity, fps: | 1150 (2005: 1100) | | | | |
| | energy, ft-lb: | 483 | | | | |
| Black Hills 180 JHP | velocity, fps: | 1000 | | | | |
| | energy, ft-lb: | 400 | | | | |
| Black Hills 180 JHP | velocity, fps: | 1000 | | | | |
| | energy, ft-lb: | 400 | | | | |
| Federal 135 Hydra-Shok JHP | velocity, fps: | 1190 | 1050 | 970 | 900 | 850 |
| | energy, ft-lb: | 420 | 330 | 280 | 245 | 215 |
| Federal 155 FMJ Ball | velocity, fps: | 1140 | 1080 | 1030 | 990 | 960 |
| | energy, ft-lb: | 445 | 400 | 365 | 335 | 315 |
| Federal 155 Hi-Shok JHP | velocity, fps: | 1140 | 1080 | 1030 | 990 | 950 |
| | energy, ft-lb: | 445 | 400 | 365 | 335 | 315 |
| Federal 155 Hydra-Shok JHP | velocity, fps: | 1140 | 1080 | 1030 | 990 | 950 |
| | energy, ft-lb: | 445 | 400 | 365 | 335 | 315 |
| Federal 165 EFMJ | velocity, fps: | 1190 | 1060 | 970 | 905 | 850 |
| | energy, ft-lb: | 520 | 410 | 345 | 300 | 265 |
| Federal 165 FMJ | velocity, fps: | 1050 | 1020 | 990 | 960 | 935 |
| | energy, ft-lb: | 405 | 380 | 355 | 335 | 320 |
| Federal 165 FMJ Ball | velocity, fps: | 980 | 950 | 920 | 900 | 880 |
| | energy, ft-lb: | 350 | 330 | 310 | 295 | 280 |
| Federal 165 Hydra-Shok JHP | velocity, fps: | 980 | 950 | 930 | 910 | 890 |
| | energy, ft-lb: | 350 | 330 | 315 | 300 | 290 |
| Federal 180 High Antim. Lead | velocity, fps: | 990 | 960 | 930 | 910 | 890 |
| | energy, ft-lb: | 390 | 365 | 345 | 330 | 315 |
| Federal 180 TMJ TMF Primer | velocity, fps: | 990 | 960 | 940 | 910 | 890 |
| | energy, ft-lb: | 390 | 370 | 350 | 330 | 315 |
| Federal 180 FMJ Ball | velocity, fps: | 990 | 960 | 940 | 910 | 890 |
| | energy, ft-lb: | 390 | 370 | 350 | 330 | 315 |

# Centerfire Handgun Ballistics

## .40 S&W TO .41 REMINGTON MAGNUM

| CARTRIDGE BULLET | RANGE, YARDS: | 0 | 25 | 50 | 75 | 100 |
|---|---|---|---|---|---|---|
| Federal 180 Hi-Shok JHP | velocity, fps: | 990 | 960 | 930 | 910 | 890 |
| | energy, ft-lb: | 390 | 365 | 345 | 330 | 315 |
| Federal 180 Hydra-Shok JHP | velocity, fps: | 990 | 960 | 930 | 910 | 890 |
| | energy, ft-lb: | 390 | 365 | 345 | 330 | 315 |
| Hornady 155 JHP/XTP | velocity, fps: | 1180 | | 1061 | | 980 |
| | energy, ft-lb: | 479 | | 387 | | 331 |
| Hornady 155 TAP-FPD | velocity, fps: | 1180 | | 1061 | | 980 |
| | energy, ft-lb: | 470 | | 387 | | 331 |
| Hornady 180 JHP/XTP | velocity, fps: | 950 | | 903 | | 862 |
| | energy, ft-lb: | 361 | | 326 | | 297 |
| Hornady 180 TAP-FPD | velocity, fps: | 950 | | 903 | | 862 |
| | energy, ft-lb: | 361 | | 326 | | 297 |
| Magtech 155 JHP | velocity, fps: | 1025 | | 1118 | | 1052 |
| | energy, ft-lb: | 500 | | 430 | | 381 |
| Magtech 180 JHP | velocity, fps: | 990 | | 933 | | 886 |
| | energy, ft-lb: | 390 | | 348 | | 314 |
| Magtech 180 FMC | velocity, fps: | 990 | | 933 | | 886 |
| | energy, ft-lb: | 390 | | 348 | | 314 |
| PMC 115 Non-Toxic Frangible | velocity, fps: | 1350 | 1240 | 1154 | 1088 | 1035 |
| | energy, ft-lb: | 465 | | | | |
| PMC 155 SFHP | velocity, fps: | 1160 | 1092 | 1039 | 994 | 957 |
| | energy, ft-lb: | 463 | | | | |
| PMC 165 JHP | velocity, fps: | 1040 | 1002 | 970 | 941 | 915 |
| | energy, ft-lb: | 396 | | | | |
| PMC 165 FMJ | velocity, fps: | 1010 | 977 | 948 | 922 | 899 |
| | energy, ft-lb: | 374 | | | | |
| PMC 180 FMJ/FP | velocity, fps: | 985 | 957 | 931 | 908 | 885 |
| | energy, ft-lb: | 388 | | | | |
| PMC 180 SFHP | velocity, fps: | 985 | 958 | 933 | 910 | 889 |
| | energy, ft-lb: | 388 | | | | |
| Rem. 141 Lead Free Frangible | velocity, fps: | 1135 | | 1056 | | 996 |
| | energy, ft-lb: | 403 | | 349 | | 311 |
| Rem. 155 JHP | velocity, fps: | 1205 | | 1095 | | 1017 |
| | energy, ft-lb: | 499 | | 413 | | 356 |
| Rem. 165 BJHP | velocity, fps: | 1150 | | 1040 | | 964 |
| | energy, ft-lb: | 485 | | 396 | | 340 |
| Rem. 180 JHP | velocity, fps: | 1015 | | 960 | | 914 |
| | energy, ft-lb: | 412 | | 368 | | 334 |
| Rem. 180 FN Enclosed Base | velocity, fps: | 985 | | 936 | | 893 |
| | energy, ft-lb: | 388 | | 350 | | 319 |
| Rem. 180 Metal Case | velocity, fps: | 985 | | 936 | | 893 |
| | energy, ft-lb: | 388 | | 350 | | 319 |
| Rem. 180 BJHP | velocity, fps: | 1015 | | 960 | | 914 |
| | energy, ft-lb: | 412 | | 368 | | 334 |
| Speer 105 Frangible | velocity, fps: | 1380 | | 1128 | | 985 |
| | energy, ft-lb: | 444 | | 297 | | 226 |
| Speer 155 TMJ Blazer | velocity, fps: | 1175 | | 1047 | | 963 |
| | energy, ft-lb: | 475 | | 377 | | 319 |
| Speer 155 TMJ | velocity, fps: | 1200 | | 1065 | | 976 |
| | energy, ft-lb: | 496 | | 390 | | 328 |
| Speer 155 Gold Dot | velocity, fps: | 1200 | | 1063 | | 974 |
| | energy, ft-lb: | 496 | | 389 | | 326 |
| Speer 165 TMJ Blazer | velocity, fps: | 1100 | | 1006 | | 938 |
| | energy, ft-lb: | 443 | | 371 | | 321 |
| Speer 165 TMJ | velocity, fps: | 1150 | | 1040 | | 964 |
| | energy, ft-lb: | 484 | | 396 | | 340 |
| Speer 165 Gold Dot | velocity, fps: | 1150 | | 1043 | | 966 |
| | energy, ft-lb: | 485 | | 399 | | 342 |
| Speer 180 HP Blazer | velocity, fps: | 985 | | 951 | | 909 |
| | energy, ft-lb: | 400 | | 361 | | 330 |
| Speer 180 FMJ Blazer | velocity, fps: | 1000 | | 937 | | 886 |
| | energy, ft-lb: | 400 | | 351 | | 313 |
| Speer 180 FMJ | velocity, fps: | 1000 | | 951 | | 909 |
| | energy, ft-lb: | 400 | | 361 | | 330 |

| CARTRIDGE BULLET | RANGE, YARDS: | 0 | 25 | 50 | 75 | 100 |
|---|---|---|---|---|---|---|
| Speer 180 TMJ-CF (and Blazer) | velocity, fps: | 1000 | | 951 | | 909 |
| | energy, ft-lb: | 400 | | 361 | | 330 |
| Speer 180 Gold Dot | velocity, fps: | 1025 | | 957 | | 902 |
| | energy, ft-lb: | 420 | | 366 | | 325 |
| Win. 140 JFP | velocity, fps: | 1155 | | 1039 | | 960 |
| | energy, ft-lb: | 415 | | 336 | | 286 |
| Win. 155 Silvertip HP | velocity, fps: | 1205 | | 1096 | | 1018 |
| | energy, ft-lb | 500 | | 414 | | 357 |
| Win. 165 SXT | velocity, fps: | 1130 | | 1041 | | 977 |
| | energy, ft-lb: | 468 | | 397 | | 349 |
| Win. 165 FMJ FN | velocity, fps: | 1060 | | 1001 | | |
| | energy, ft-lb: | 412 | | 367 | | |
| Win. 165 EB WinClean | velocity, fps: | 1130 | | 1054 | | |
| | energy, ft-lb: | 468 | | 407 | | |
| Win. 180 JHP | velocity, fps: | 1010 | | 954 | | |
| | energy, ft-lb: | 408 | | 364 | | |
| Win. 180 FMJ | velocity, fps: | 990 | | 936 | | |
| | energy, ft-lb: | 390 | | 350 | | |
| Win. 180 SXT | velocity, fps: | 1010 | | 954 | | 909 |
| | energy, ft-lb: | 408 | | 364 | | 330 |
| Win. 180 EB WinClean | velocity, fps: | 990 | | 943 | | |
| | energy, ft-lb: | 392 | | 356 | | |

## 10 MM AUTO

| CARTRIDGE BULLET | RANGE, YARDS: | 0 | 25 | 50 | 75 | 100 |
|---|---|---|---|---|---|---|
| Federal 155 Hi-Shok JHP | velocity, fps: | 1330 | 1230 | 1140 | 1080 | 1030 |
| | energy, ft-lb: | 605 | 515 | 450 | 400 | 360 |
| Federal 180 Hi-Shok JHP | velocity, fps: | 1030 | 1000 | 970 | 950 | 920 |
| | energy, ft-lb: | 425 | 400 | 375 | 355 | 340 |
| Federal 180 Hydra-Shok JHP | velocity, fps: | 1030 | 1000 | 970 | 950 | 920 |
| | energy, ft-lb: | 425 | 400 | 375 | 355 | 340 |
| Federal 180 High Antim. Lead | velocity, fps: | 1030 | 1000 | 970 | 950 | 920 |
| | energy, ft-lb: | 425 | 400 | 375 | 355 | 340 |
| Federal 180 FMJ | velocity, fps: | 1060 | 1025 | 990 | 965 | 940 |
| | energy, ft-lb: | 400 | 370 | 350 | 330 | 310 |
| Hornady 155 JHP/XTP | velocity, fps: | 1265 | | 1119 | | 1020 |
| | energy, ft-lb: | 551 | | 431 | | 358 |
| Hornady 180 JHP/XTP | velocity, fps: | 1180 | | 1077 | | 1004 |
| | energy, ft-lb: | 556 | | 464 | | 403 |
| Hornady 200 JHP/XTP | velocity, fps: | 1050 | | 994 | | 948 |
| | energy, ft-lb: | 490 | | 439 | | 399 |
| PMC 115 Non-Toxic Frangible | velocity, fps: | 1350 | 1240 | 1154 | 1088 | 1035 |
| | energy, ft-lb: | 465 | | | | |
| PMC 170 JHP | velocity, fps: | 1200 | 1117 | 1052 | 1000 | 958 |
| | energy, ft-lb: | 543 | | | | |
| PMC 180 SFHP | velocity, fps: | 950 | 926 | 903 | 882 | 862 |
| | energy, ft-lb: | 361 | | | | |
| PMC 200 TC-FMJ | velocity, fps: | 1050 | 1008 | 972 | 941 | 912 |
| | energy, ft-lb: | 490 | | | | |
| Rem. 180 Metal Case | velocity, fps: | 1150 | | 1063 | | 998 |
| | energy, ft-lb: | 529 | | 452 | | 398 |
| Speer 200 TMJ Blazer | velocity, fps: | 1050 | | 966 | | 952 |
| | energy, ft-lb: | 490 | | 440 | | 402 |
| Win. 175 Silvertip HP | velocity, fps: | 1290 | | 1141 | | 1037 |
| | energy, ft-lb: | 649 | | 506 | | 418 |

## .41 REMINGTON MAGNUM

| CARTRIDGE BULLET | RANGE, YARDS: | 0 | 25 | 50 | 75 | 100 |
|---|---|---|---|---|---|---|
| Federal 210 Hi-Shok JHP | velocity, fps: | 1300 | 1210 | 1130 | 1070 | 1030 |
| | energy, ft-lb: | 790 | 680 | 595 | 540 | 495 |
| PMC 210 TCSP | velocity, fps: | 1290 | 1201 | 1128 | 1069 | 1021 |
| | energy, ft-lb: | 774 | | | | |
| PMC 210 JHP | velocity, fps: | 1289 | 1200 | 1127 | 1068 | 1020 |
| | energy, ft-lb: | 774 | | | | |
| Rem. 210 SP | velocity, fps: | 1300 | | 1162 | | 1062 |
| | energy, ft-lb: | 788 | | 630 | | 526 |

# Centerfire Handgun Ballistics

## .41 REMINGTON MAGNUM TO .45 AUTOMATIC (ACP)

| CARTRIDGE BULLET | RANGE, YARDS: | 0 | 25 | 50 | 75 | 100 |
|---|---|---|---|---|---|---|
| Win. 175 Silvertip HP | velocity, fps: | 1250 | | 1120 | | 1029 |
| | energy, ft-lb: | 607 | | 488 | | 412 |
| Win. 240 Platinum Tip | velocity, ft-lb: | 1250 | | 1151 | | 1075 |
| | energy, ft-lb: | 833 | | 706 | | 616 |

### .44 COLT

| CARTRIDGE BULLET | RANGE, YARDS: | 0 | 25 | 50 | 75 | 100 |
|---|---|---|---|---|---|---|
| Black Hills 230 FPL | velocity, fps: | 730 | | | | |
| | energy, ft-lb: | | | | | |

### .44 RUSSIAN

| CARTRIDGE BULLET | RANGE, YARDS: | 0 | 25 | 50 | 75 | 100 |
|---|---|---|---|---|---|---|
| Black Hills 210 FPL | velocity, fps: | 650 | | | | |
| | energy, ft-lb: | | | | | |

### .44 SPECIAL

| CARTRIDGE BULLET | RANGE, YARDS: | 0 | 25 | 50 | 75 | 100 |
|---|---|---|---|---|---|---|
| Black Hills 210 FPL | velocity, fps: | 700 | | | | |
| | energy, ft-lb: | | | | | |
| Federal 200 SWC HP | velocity, fps: | 900 | 860 | 830 | 800 | 770 |
| | energy, ft-lb: | 360 | 330 | 305 | 285 | 260 |
| Federal 250 CastCore | velocity, fps: | 1250 | 1200 | 1150 | 1110 | 1080 |
| | energy, ft-lb: | 865 | 795 | 735 | 685 | 645 |
| Hornady 180 JHP/XTP | velocity, fps: | 1000 | | 935 | | 882 |
| | energy, ft-lb: | 400 | | 350 | | 311 |
| Magtech 240 LFN | velocity, fps: | 750 | | 722 | | 696 |
| | energy, ft-lb: | 300 | | 278 | | 258 |
| PMC 180 JHP | velocity, fps: | 980 | 938 | 902 | 869 | 839 |
| | energy, ft-lb: | 383 | | | | |
| PMC 240 SWC-CP | velocity, fps: | 764 | 744 | 724 | 706 | 687 |
| | energy, ft-lb: | 311 | | | | |
| PMC 240 LFP | velocity, fps: | 750 | | 719 | | 690 |
| | energy, ft-lb: | 300 | | 275 | | 253 |
| Rem. 246 LRN | velocity, fps: | 755 | | 725 | | 695 |
| | energy, ft-lb: | 310 | | 285 | | 265 |
| Speer 200 HP Blazer | velocity, fps: | 875 | | 825 | | 780 |
| | energy, ft-lb: | 340 | | 302 | | 270 |
| Speer 200 Trail Blazer LFN | velocity, fps: | 750 | | 714 | | 680 |
| | energy, ft-lb: | 250 | | 226 | | 205 |
| Speer 200 Gold Dot | velocity, fps: | 875 | | 825 | | 780 |
| | energy, ft-lb: | 340 | | 302 | | 270 |
| Win. 200 Silvertip HP | velocity, fps: | 900 | | 860 | | 822 |
| | energy, ft-lb: | 360 | | 328 | | 300 |
| Win. 240 Lead | velocity, fps: | 750 | | 719 | | 690 |
| | energy, ft-lb | 300 | | 275 | | 253 |
| Win. 246 LRN | velocity, fps: | 755 | | 725 | | 695 |
| | energy, ft-lb: | 310 | | 285 | | 265 |

### .44 REMINGTON MAGNUM

| CARTRIDGE BULLET | RANGE, YARDS: | 0 | 25 | 50 | 75 | 100 |
|---|---|---|---|---|---|---|
| Black Hills 240 JHP | velocity, fps: | 1260 | | | | |
| | energy, ft-lb: | 848 | | | | |
| Black Hills 300 JHP | velocity, fps: | 1150 | | | | |
| | energy, ft-lb: | 879 | | | | |
| Federal 180 Hi-Shok JHP | velocity, fps: | 1610 | 1480 | 1370 | 1270 | 1180 |
| | energy, ft-lb: | 1035 | 875 | 750 | 640 | 555 |
| Federal 240 Hi-Shok JHP | velocity, fps: | 1180 | 1130 | 1080 | 1050 | 1010 |
| | energy, ft-lb: | 740 | 675 | 625 | 580 | 550 |
| Federal 240 Hydra-Shok JHP | velocity, fps: | 1180 | 1130 | 1080 | 1050 | 1010 |
| | energy, ft-lb: | 740 | 675 | 625 | 580 | 550 |
| Federal 240 JHP | velocity, fps: | 1180 | 1130 | 1080 | 1050 | 1010 |
| | energy, ft-lb: | 740 | 675 | 625 | 580 | 550 |
| Federal 300 CastCore | velocity, fps: | 1250 | 1200 | 1160 | 1120 | 1080 |
| | energy, ft-lb: | 1040 | 960 | 885 | 825 | 775 |
| Hornady 180 JHP/XTP | velocity, fps: | 1550 | | 1340 | | 1173 |
| | energy, ft-lb: | 960 | | 717 | | 550 |
| Hornady 200 JHP/XTP | velocity, fps: | 1500 | | 1284 | | 1128 |
| | energy, ft-lb: | 999 | | 732 | | 565 |

| CARTRIDGE BULLET | RANGE, YARDS: | 0 | 25 | 50 | 75 | 100 |
|---|---|---|---|---|---|---|
| Hornady 240 JHP/XTP | velocity, fps: | 1350 | | 1188 | | 1078 |
| | energy, ft-lb: | 971 | | 753 | | 619 |
| Hornady 300 JHP/XTP | velocity, ft-lb: | 1150 | | 1084 | | 1031 |
| | energy, ft-lb: | 881 | | 782 | | 708 |
| Magtech 240 SJSP | velocity, fps: | 1180 | | 1081 | | 1010 |
| | energy, ft-lb: | 741 | | 632 | | 623 |
| PMC 180 JHP | velocity, fps: | 1392 | 1263 | 1157 | 1076 | 1015 |
| | energy, ft-lb: | 772 | | | | |
| PMC 240 JHP | velocity, fps: | 1301 | 1218 | 1147 | 1088 | 1041 |
| | energy, ft-lb: | 900 | | | | |
| PMC 240 TC-SP | velocity, fps: | 1300 | 1216 | 1144 | 1086 | 1038 |
| | energy, ft-lb: | 900 | | | | |
| PMC 240 SFHP | velocity, fps: | 1300 | 1212 | 1138 | 1079 | 1030 |
| | energy, ft-lb: | 900 | | | | |
| PMC 240 LSWC-GCK | velocity, fps: | 1225 | 1143 | 1077 | 1025 | 982 |
| | energy, ft-lb: | 806 | | | | |
| Rem. 180 JSP | velocity, fps: | 1610 | | 1365 | | 1175 |
| | energy, ft-lb: | 1036 | | 745 | | 551 |
| Rem. 210 Gold Dot HP | velocity, fps: | 1450 | | 1276 | | 1140 |
| | energy, ft-lb: | 980 | | 759 | | 606 |
| Rem. 240 SP | velocity, fps: | 1180 | | 1081 | | 1010 |
| | energy, ft-lb: | 721 | | 623 | | 543 |
| Rem. 240 SJHP | velocity, fps: | 1180 | | 1081 | | 1010 |
| | energy, ft-lb: | 721 | | 623 | | 543 |
| Rem. 275 JHP Core-Lokt | velocity, fps: | 1235 | | 1142 | | 1070 |
| | energy, ft-lb: | 931 | | 797 | | 699 |
| Speer 240 JHP Blazer | velocity, fps: | 1200 | | 1092 | | 1015 |
| | energy, ft-lb: | 767 | | 636 | | 549 |
| Speer 240 Gold Dot HP | velocity, fps: | 1400 | | 1255 | | 1139 |
| | energy, ft-lb: | 1044 | | 839 | | 691 |
| Speer 270 Gold Dot SP | velocity, fps: | 1250 | | 1142 | | 1060 |
| | energy, ft-lb: | 937 | | 781 | | 674 |
| Win. 210 Silvertip HP | velocity, fps: | 1250 | | 1106 | | 1010 |
| | energy, ft-lb: | 729 | | 570 | | 475 |
| Win. 240 Hollow SP | velocity, fps: | 1180 | | 1081 | | 1010 |
| | energy, ft-lb: | 741 | | 623 | | 543 |
| Win. 240 JSP | velocity, fps: | 1180 | | 1081 | | |
| | energy, ft-lb: | 741 | | 623 | | |
| Win. 250 Partition Gold | velocity, fps: | 1230 | | 1132 | | 1057 |
| | energy, ft-lb: | 840 | | 711 | | 620 |
| Win. 250 Platinum Tip | velocity, fps: | 1250 | | 1148 | | 1070 |
| | energy, ft-lb: | 867 | | 732 | | 635 |

### .44-40

| CARTRIDGE BULLET | RANGE, YARDS: | 0 | 25 | 50 | 75 | 100 |
|---|---|---|---|---|---|---|
| Black Hills 200 RNFP | velocity, fps: | 800 | | | | |
| | energy, ft-lb: | | | | | |
| Hornady 205 Cowboy | velocity, fps: | 725 | | 697 | | 670 |
| | energy, ft-lb: | 239 | | 221 | | 204 |
| Magtech 225 LFN | velocity, fps: | 725 | | 703 | | 681 |
| | energy, ft-lb: | 281 | | 247 | | 232 |
| PMC 225 LFP | velocity, fps: | 725 | | 723 | | 695 |
| | energy, ft-lb: | 281 | | 261 | | 242 |
| Win. 225 Lead | velocity, fps: | 750 | | 723 | | 695 |
| | energy, ft-lb: | 281 | | 261 | | 242 |

### .45 AUTOMATIC (ACP)

| CARTRIDGE BULLET | RANGE, YARDS: | 0 | 25 | 50 | 75 | 100 |
|---|---|---|---|---|---|---|
| Black Hills 185 JHP | velocity, fps: | 1000 | | | | |
| | energy, ft-lb: | 411 | | | | |
| Black Hills 200 Match SWC | velocity, fps: | 875 | | | | |
| | energy, ft-lb: | 340 | | | | |
| Black Hills 230 FMJ | velocity, fps: | 850 | | | | |
| | energy, ft-lb: | 368 | | | | |

BALLISTICS

## .45 AUTOMATIC (ACP) TO .45 GAP

| CARTRIDGE BULLET | RANGE, YARDS: | 0 | 25 | 50 | 75 | 100 |
|---|---|---|---|---|---|---|
| Black Hills 230 JHP | velocity, fps: | 850 | | | | |
| | energy, ft-lb: | 368 | | | | |
| Black Hills 230 JHP +P | velocity, fps: | 950 | | | | |
| | energy, ft-lb: | 460 | | | | |
| Federal 165 Hydra-Shok JHP | velocity, fps: | 1060 | 1020 | 980 | 950 | 920 |
| | energy, ft-lb: | 410 | 375 | 350 | 330 | 310 |
| Federal 165 EFMJ | velocity, fps: | 1090 | 1045 | 1005 | 975 | 942 |
| | energy, ft-lb: | 435 | 400 | 370 | 345 | 325 |
| Federal 185 Hi-Shok JHP | velocity, fps: | 950 | 920 | 900 | 880 | 860 |
| | energy, ft-lb: | 370 | 350 | 335 | 315 | 300 |
| Federal 185 FMJ-SWC Match | velocity, fps: | 780 | 730 | 700 | 660 | 620 |
| | energy, ft-lb: | 245 | 220 | 200 | 175 | 160 |
| Federal 200 Exp. FMJ | velocity, fps: | 1030 | 1000 | 970 | 940 | 920 |
| | energy, ft-lb: | 470 | 440 | 415 | 395 | 375 |
| Federal 230 FMJ | velocity, fps: | 850 | 830 | 810 | 790 | 770 |
| | energy, ft-lb: | 370 | 350 | 335 | 320 | 305 |
| Federal 230 FMJ Match | velocity, fps: | 855 | 835 | 815 | 795 | 775 |
| | energy, ft-lb: | 375 | 355 | 340 | 325 | 305 |
| Federal 230 Hi-Shok JHP | velocity, fps: | 850 | 830 | 810 | 790 | 770 |
| | energy, ft-lb: | 370 | 350 | 335 | 320 | 300 |
| Federal 230 Hydra-Shok JHP | velocity, fps: | 850 | 830 | 810 | 790 | 770 |
| | energy, ft-lb: | 370 | 350 | 335 | 320 | 305 |
| Federal 230 FMJ | velocity, fps: | 850 | 830 | 810 | 790 | 770 |
| | energy, ft-lb: | 370 | 350 | 335 | 320 | 305 |
| Federal 230 TMJ TMF Primer | velocity, fps: | 850 | 830 | 810 | 790 | 770 |
| | energy, ft-lb: | 370 | 350 | 335 | 315 | 305 |
| Hornady 185 JHP/XTP | velocity, fps: | 950 | | 880 | | 819 |
| | energy, ft-lb: | 371 | | 318 | | 276 |
| Hornady 200 JHP/XTP | velocity, fps: | 900 | | 855 | | 815 |
| | energy, ft-lb: | 358 | | 325 | | 295 |
| Hornady 200 HP/XTP +P | velocity, fps: | 1055 | | 982 | | 925 |
| | energy, ft-lb: | 494 | | 428 | | 380 |
| Hornady 200 TAP-FPD | velocity, fps: | 1055 | | 982 | | 926 |
| | energy, ft-lbs: | 494 | | 428 | | 380 |
| Hornady 230 FMJ/RN | velocity, fps: | 850 | | 809 | | 771 |
| | energy, ft-lb: | 369 | | 334 | | 304 |
| Hornady 230 FMJ/FP | velocity, fps: | 850 | | 809 | | 771 |
| | energy, ft-lb: | 369 | | 334 | | 304 |
| Hornady 230 HP/XTP +P | velocity, fps: | 950 | | 904 | | 865 |
| | energy, ft-lb: | 462 | | 418 | | 382 |
| Hornady 230 TAP-FPD | velocity, fps: | 950 | | 908 | | 872 |
| | energy, ft-lb: | 461 | | 421 | | 388 |
| Magtech 185 JHP +P | velocity, fps: | 1148 | | 1066 | | 1055 |
| | energy, ft-lb: | 540 | | 467 | | 415 |
| Magtech 200 LSWC | velocity, fps: | 950 | | 910 | | 874 |
| | energy, ft-lb: | 401 | | 368 | | 339 |
| Magtech 230 FMC | veloctiy, fps: | 837 | | 800 | | 767 |
| | energy, ft-lb: | 356 | | 326 | | 300 |
| Magtech 230 FMC-SWC | velocity, fps: | 780 | | 720 | | 660 |
| | energy, ft-lb: | 310 | | 265 | | 222 |
| PMC 145 Non-Toxic Frangible | velocity, fps: | 1100 | 1045 | 999 | 961 | 928 |
| | energy, ft-lb: | 390 | | | | |
| PMC 185 JHP | velocity, fps: | 903 | 870 | 839 | 811 | 785 |
| | energy, ft-lb: | 339 | | | | |
| PMC 200 FMJ-SWC | velocity, fps: | 850 | 818 | 788 | 761 | 734 |
| | energy, ft-lb: | 321 | | | | |
| PMC 230 SFHP | velocity, fps: | 850 | 830 | 811 | 792 | 775 |
| | energy, ft-lb: | 369 | | | | |
| PMC 230 FMJ | velocity, fps: | 830 | 809 | 789 | 769 | 749 |
| | energy, ft-lb: | 352 | | | | |
| Rem. 175 Lead Free Frangible | velocity, fps: | 1020 | | 923 | | 851 |
| | energy, ft-lb: | 404 | | 331 | | 281 |

| CARTRIDGE BULLET | RANGE, YARDS: | 0 | 25 | 50 | 75 | 100 |
|---|---|---|---|---|---|---|
| Rem. 185 JHP | velocity, fps: | 1000 | | 939 | | 889 |
| | energy, ft-lb: | 411 | | 362 | | 324 |
| Rem. 185 BJHP | velocity, fps: | 1015 | | 951 | | 899 |
| | energy, ft-lb: | 423 | | 372 | | 332 |
| Rem. 185 BJHP +P | velocity, fps: | 1140 | | 1042 | | 971 |
| | energy, ft-lb: | 534 | | 446 | | 388 |
| Rem. 185 MC | velocity, fps: | 1015 | | 955 | | 907 |
| | energy, ft-lb: | 423 | | 375 | | 338 |
| Rem. 230 FN Enclosed Base | velocity, fps: | 835 | | 800 | | 767 |
| | energy, ft-lb: | 356 | | 326 | | 300 |
| Rem. 230 Metal Case | velocity, fps: | 835 | | 800 | | 767 |
| | energy, ft-lb: | 356 | | 326 | | 300 |
| Rem. 230 JHP | velocity, fps: | 835 | | 800 | | 767 |
| | energy, ft-lb: | 356 | | 326 | | 300 |
| Rem. 230 BJHP | velocity, fps: | 875 | | 833 | | 795 |
| | energy, ft-lb: | 391 | | 355 | | 323 |
| Speer 140 Frangible | velocity, fps: | 1200 | | 1029 | | 928 |
| | energy, ft-lb: | 448 | | 329 | | 268 |
| Speer 185 Gold Dot | velocity, fps: | 1050 | | 956 | | 886 |
| | energy, ft-lb: | 453 | | 375 | | 322 |
| Speer 185 TMJ/FN | velocity, fps: | 1000 | | 909 | | 839 |
| | energy, ft-lb: | 411 | | 339 | | 289 |
| Speer 200 JHP Blazer | velocity, fps: | 975 | | 917 | | 860 |
| | energy, ft-lb: | 421 | | 372 | | 328 |
| Speer 200 Gold Dot +P | velocity, fps: | 1080 | | 994 | | 930 |
| | energy, ft-lb: | 518 | | 439 | | 384 |
| Speer 200 TMJ/FN | velocity, fps: | 975 | | 897 | | 834 |
| | energy, ft-lb: | 422 | | 357 | | 309 |
| Speer 230 FMJ (and Blazer) | velocity, fps: | 845 | | 804 | | 775 |
| | energy, ft-lb: | 363 | | 329 | | 304 |
| Speer 230 TMJ-CF (and Blazer) | velocity, fps: | 845 | | 804 | | 775 |
| | energy, ft-lb: | 363 | | 329 | | 304 |
| Speer 230 Gold Dot | velocity, fps: | 890 | | 845 | | 805 |
| | energy, ft-lb: | 405 | | 365 | | 331 |
| Win. 170 JFP | velocity, fps: | 1050 | | 982 | | 928 |
| | energy, ft-lb: | 416 | | 364 | | 325 |
| Win. 185 Silvertip HP | velocity, fps: | 1000 | | 938 | | 888 |
| | energy, ft-lb: | 411 | | 362 | | 324 |
| Win. 185 FMJ FN | velocity, fps: | 910 | | 861 | | |
| | energy, ft-lb: | 340 | | 304 | | |
| Win. 185 EB WinClean | velocity, fps: | 910 | | 835 | | |
| | energy, ft-lb: | 340 | | 286 | | |
| Win. 230 JHP | velocity, fps: | 880 | | 842 | | |
| | energy, ft-lb: | 396 | | 363 | | |
| Win. 230 FMJ | velocity, fps: | 835 | | 800 | | |
| | energy, ft-lb: | 356 | | 326 | | |
| Win. 230 SXT | velocity, fps: | 880 | | 846 | | 816 |
| | energy, ft-lb: | 396 | | 366 | | 340 |
| Win. 230 JHP subsonic | velocity, fps: | 880 | | 842 | | 808 |
| | energy, ft-lb: | 396 | | 363 | | 334 |
| Win. 230 EB WinClean | velocity, fps: | 835 | | 802 | | |
| | energy, ft-lb: | 356 | | 329 | | |

## .45 GAP

| CARTRIDGE BULLET | RANGE, YARDS: | 0 | 25 | 50 | 75 | 100 |
|---|---|---|---|---|---|---|
| Federal 185 Hydra-Shok JHP | velocity, fps: | 1090 | 1020 | 970 | 920 | 890 |
| And Federal TMJ | energy, ft-lb: | 490 | 430 | 385 | 350 | 320 |
| Federal 230 Hydra-Shok | velocity, fps: | 880 | 870 | 850 | 840 | 820 |
| And Federal FMJ | energy, ft-lb: | 395 | 380 | 3760 | 355 | 345 |
| Win. 185 STHP | velocity, fps: | 1000 | | 938 | | 887 |
| | energy, ft-lb: | 411 | | 361 | | 323 |
| Win. 230 JHP | velocity, fps: | 880 | | 842 | | |
| | energy, ft-lb: | 396 | | 363 | | |

BALLISTICS

# Centerfire Handgun Ballistics

## .45 GAP TO .500 SMITH & WESSON

| CARTRIDGE BULLET | RANGE, YARDS: | 0 | 25 | 50 | 75 | 100 |
|---|---|---|---|---|---|---|
| Win. 230 EB WinClean | velocity, fps: | 875 | | 840 | | |
| | energy, ft-lb: | 391 | | 360 | | |
| Win. 230 FMJ | velocity, fps: | 850 | | 814 | | |
| | energy, ft-lb: | 369 | | 338 | | |

### .45 WINCHESTER MAGNUM

| CARTRIDGE BULLET | RANGE, YARDS: | 0 | 25 | 50 | 75 | 100 |
|---|---|---|---|---|---|---|
| Win. 260 Partition Gold | velocity, fps: | 1200 | | 1105 | | 1033 |
| | energy, ft-lb: | 832 | | 705 | | 616 |
| Win. 260 JHP | velocity, fps: | 1200 | | 1099 | | 1026 |
| | energy, ft-lb: | 831 | | 698 | | 607 |

### .45 SCHOFIELD

| CARTRIDGE BULLET | RANGE, YARDS: | 0 | 25 | 50 | 75 | 100 |
|---|---|---|---|---|---|---|
| Black Hills 180 FNL | velocity, fps: | 730 | | | | |
| | energy, ft-lb: | | | | | |
| Black Hills 230 RNFP | velocity, fps: | 730 | | | | |
| | energy, ft-lb: | | | | | |

### .45 COLT

| CARTRIDGE BULLET | RANGE, YARDS: | 0 | 25 | 50 | 75 | 100 |
|---|---|---|---|---|---|---|
| Black Hills 250 RNFP | velocity, fps: | 725 | | | | |
| | energy, ft-lb: | | | | | |
| Federal 225 SWC HP | velocity, fps: | 900 | 880 | 860 | 840 | 820 |
| | energy, ft-lb: | 405 | 385 | 370 | 355 | 340 |
| Hornady 255 Cowboy | velocity, fps: | 725 | | 692 | | 660 |
| | energy, ft-lb: | 298 | | 271 | | 247 |
| Magtech 250 LFN | velocity, fps: | 750 | | 726 | | 702 |
| | energy, ft-lb: | 312 | | 293 | | 274 |
| PMC 250 LFP | velocity, fps: | 800 | | 767 | | 736 |
| | energy, ft-lb: | 355 | | 331 | | 309 |
| PMC 300 +P+ | velocity, fps: | 1250 | 1192 | 1144 | 1102 | 1066 |
| | energy, ft-lb: | 1041 | | | | |
| Rem. 225 SWC | velocity, fps: | 960 | | 890 | | 832 |
| | energy, ft-lb: | 460 | | 395 | | 346 |
| Rem. 250 RLN | velocity, fps: | 860 | | 820 | | 780 |
| | energy, ft-lb: | 410 | | 375 | | 340 |
| Speer 200 FMJ Blazer | velocity, fps: | 1000 | | 938 | | 889 |
| | energy, ft-lb: | 444 | | 391 | | 351 |
| Speer 230 Trail Blazer LFN | velocity, fps: | 750 | | 716 | | 684 |
| | energy, ft-lb: | 287 | | 262 | | 239 |
| Speer 250 Gold Dot | velocity, fps: | 900 | | 860 | | 823 |
| | energy, ft-lb: | 450 | | 410 | | 376 |
| Win. 225 Silvertip HP | velocity, fps: | 920 | | 877 | | 839 |
| | energy, ft-lb: | 423 | | 384 | | 352 |
| Win. 255 LRN | velocity, fps: | 860 | | 820 | | 780 |
| | energy, ft-lb: | 420 | | 380 | | 345 |
| Win. 250 Lead | velocity, fps: | 750 | | 720 | | 692 |
| | energy, ft-lb: | 312 | | 288 | | 266 |

### .454 CASULL

| CARTRIDGE BULLET | RANGE, YARDS: | 0 | 25 | 50 | 75 | 100 |
|---|---|---|---|---|---|---|
| Federal 300 Trophy Bonded | velocity, fps: | 1630 | 1540 | 1450 | 1380 | 1300 |
| | energy, ft-lb: | 1760 | 1570 | 1405 | 1260 | 1130 |
| Federal 360 CastCore | velocity, fps: | 1500 | 1435 | 1370 | 1310 | 1255 |
| | energy, ft-lb: | 1800 | 1640 | 1500 | 1310 | 1260 |
| Hornady 240 XTP-MAG | velocity, fps: | 1900 | | 1679 | | 1483 |
| | energy, ft-lb: | 1923 | | 1502 | | 1172 |
| Hornady 300 XTP-MAG | velocity, fps: | 1650 | | 1478 | | 1328 |
| | energy, ft-lb: | 1813 | | 1455 | | 1175 |
| Magtech 260 SJSP | velocity, fps: | 1800 | | 1577 | | 1383 |
| | energy, ft-lb: | 1871 | | 1437 | | 1104 |
| Rem. 300 Core-Lokt Ultra | velocity, fps: | 1625 | | 1472 | | 1335 |
| | energy, ft-lb: | 1759 | | 1442 | | 1187 |

| CARTRIDGE BULLET | RANGE, YARDS: | 0 | 25 | 50 | 75 | 100 |
|---|---|---|---|---|---|---|
| Speer 300 Gold Dot HP | velocity, fps: | 1625 | | 1477 | | 1343 |
| | energy, ft-lb: | 1758 | | 1452 | | 1201 |
| Win. 250 JHP | velocity, fps: | 1300 | | 1151 | | 1047 |
| | energy, ft-lb: | 938 | | 735 | | 608 |
| Win. 260 Partition Gold | velocity, fps: | 1800 | | 1605 | | 1427 |
| | energy, ft-lb: | 1871 | | 1485 | | 1176 |
| Win. 260 Platinum Tip | velocity, fps: | 1800 | | 1596 | | 1414 |
| | eneryg, ft-lb: | 1870 | | 1470 | | 1154 |
| Win. 300 JFP | velocity, fps: | 1625 | | 1451 | | 1308 |
| | energy, ft-lb: | 1759 | | 1413 | | 1141 |

### .460 SMITH & WESSON

| CARTRIDGE BULLET | RANGE, YARDS: | 0 | 25 | 50 | 75 | 100 |
|---|---|---|---|---|---|---|
| Federal 275 Expander | velocity, fps: | 1800 | | 1640 | | 1500 |
| | energy, ft-lb: | 1980 | | 1650 | | 1370 |
| Federal 300 A-Frame | velocity, fps: | 1750 | | 1510 | | 1300 |
| | energy, ft-lb: | 2040 | | 1510 | | 1125 |
| Hornady 200 SST | velocity, fps: | 2250 | | 2003 | | 1772 |
| | energy, ft-lb: | 2248 | | 1395 | | 1081 |
| Win. 260 Supreme Part. Gold | velocity, fps | 2000 | | 1788 | | 1592 |
| | energy, ft-lb | 2309 | | 1845 | | 2012 |

### .475 LINEBAUGH

| CARTRIDGE BULLET | RANGE, YARDS: | 0 | 25 | 50 | 75 | 100 |
|---|---|---|---|---|---|---|
| Hornady 400 XTP-MAG | velocity, fps: | 1300 | | 1179 | | 1093 |
| | energy, ft-lb: | 1501 | | 1235 | | 1060 |

### .480 RUGER

| CARTRIDGE BULLET | RANGE, YARDS: | 0 | 25 | 50 | 75 | 100 |
|---|---|---|---|---|---|---|
| Federal 275 Expander | velocity, fps: | 1350 | | 1190 | | 1080 |
| | energy, ft-lb: | 1115 | | 870 | | 710 |
| Hornady 325 XTP-MAG | velocity, fps: | 1350 | | 1191 | | 1076 |
| | energy, ft-lb: | 1315 | | 1023 | | 835 |
| Hornady 400 XTP-MAG | velocity, fps: | 1100 | | 1027 | | 971 |
| | energy, ft-lb: | 1075 | | 937 | | 838 |
| Speer 275 Gold Dot HP | velocity, fps: | 1450 | | 1284 | | 1152 |
| | energy, ft-lb: | 1284 | | 1007 | | 810 |
| Speer 325 SP | velocity, fps: | 1350 | | 1224 | | 1124 |
| | energy, ft-lb: | 1315 | | 1082 | | 912 |

### .50 ACTION EXPRESS

| CARTRIDGE BULLET | RANGE, YARDS: | 0 | 25 | 50 | 75 | 100 |
|---|---|---|---|---|---|---|
| Hornady 300 XTP/HP | velocity, fps: | 1475 | | 1251 | | 1092 |
| | energy, ft-lb: | 1449 | | 1043 | | 795 |
| Speer 300 Gold Dot HP | velocity, fps: | 1550 | | 1361 | | 1207 |
| | energy, ft-lb: | 1600 | | 1234 | | 970 |
| Speer 325 UCHP | velocity, fps: | 1400 | | 1232 | | 1106 |
| | energy, ft-lb: | 1414 | | 1095 | | 883 |

### .500 SMITH & WESSON

| CARTRIDGE BULLET | RANGE, YARDS: | 0 | 25 | 50 | 75 | 100 |
|---|---|---|---|---|---|---|
| Federal 275 Expander | velocity, fps: | 1660 | | 1440 | | 1250 |
| | energy, ft-lb: | 1680 | | 1255 | | 950 |
| Federal 325 A-Frame | velocity, fps: | 1800 | | 1560 | | 1350 |
| | energy, ft-lb: | 2340 | | 1755 | | 1315 |
| Hornady 350 XTP Mag | velocity, fps: | 1900 | | 1656 | | 1439 |
| | energy, ft-lb: | 2805 | | 2131 | | 1610 |
| Hornady 500 FP-XTP | velocity, fps: | 1425 | | 1281 | | 1164 |
| | energy, ft-lb: | 2254 | | 1823 | | 1505 |
| Win. 350 Super-X | velocity, fps | 1400 | | 1231 | | 1106 |
| | energy, ft-lb | 1523 | | 1178 | | 951 |
| Win. 400 Platinum Tip | velocity, fps: | 1800 | | 1647 | | 1505 |
| | energy, ft-lb: | 2877 | | 2409 | | 2012 |

BALLISTICS

# Directory of Manufacturers & Suppliers

**Accu-Tek Firearms**
Ontario, CA
www.accu-tekfirearms.com

**Accurate Powder**
Miles City, MT
www.accuratepowder.com

**Advanced Armament**
Lawrenceville, GA
www.advanced-armament.com

**Aimpoint**
Chantilly, VA
www.aimpoint.com

**Airforce Airguns**
Fort Worth, TX
www.airforceairguns.com

**Alliant Powder**
Radford, VA
www.alliantpowder.com

**Alpen Optics**
Rancho Cucamonga, CA
www.alpenoptics.com

**American Derringer**
Waco, TX
www.amderringer.com

**American Tactical Imports**
Rochester, NY
www.americantactical.us

**ArmaLite, Inc.**
Geneso, IL
www.armalite.com

**Arsenal Firearms**
Gardone val Trompia, Italy
www.arsenalfirearms.com

**Arsenal Inc.**
Las Vegas, NV
www.arsenalinc.com

**Auto-Ordnance**
Worcester, MA
www.auto-ordnance.com

**AYA**
Eibar, Spain
www.aya-fineguns.com

**Barnes Bullets**
Mona, UT
www.barnesbullets.com

**Barrett**
Murfreesboro, TN
www.barrett.net

**Beeman Precision Airguns**
Santa Fe Springs, CA
www.beeman.com

**Benelli USA**
Pocomoke, MD
www.benelliusa.com

**Beretta**
Brescia, Italy
www.berettausa.com

**Berger Bullets**
Fullerton, CA
www.bergerbullets.com

**Bernardelli**
Brescia, Italy
www.bernardelli.com

**Bersa**
Wanamassa, NJ
www.bersa.com

**Black Hills**
Rapid City, SD
www.black-hills.com

**Blaser**
San Antonio , TX
www.blaser-usa.com

**Bond Arms**
Granbury, TX
www.bondarms.com

**Brenneke USA**
Clinton, IA
www.brennekeusa.com

**Browning**
Morgan, UT
www.browning.com

**Brunton**
Riverton, WY
www.bruntonhunting.com

**BSA Optics**
Ft. Lauderdale, FL
www.bsaoptics.com

**Burris**
Greeley , CO
www.burrisoptics.com

**Bushmaster**
Madison, NC
www.bushmaster.com

**Bushnell Outdoor Products**
Overland Park, KS
www.bushnell.com

**Cabela's, Inc.**
Sidney, NE
www.cabelas.com

**Cabot Gun Company**
Cabot, PA
www.cabotgun.com

**Caesar Guerini USA, Inc.**
Cambridge, MD
www.gueriniusa.com

**Carl Zeiss Sports Optics**
North Chesterfield, VA
www.sportsoptics.zeiss.com

**CCI Ammunition**
Lewiston, ID
www.cci-ammunition.com

**Century International Arms, Inc.**
Delray Beach, FL
www.centuryarms.com

**Ceska Zbrojovka Arms (CZ)**
Kansas City, KS
www.cz-usa.com

**Charter Arms**
Shelton, CT
www.charterfirearms.com

**Chiappa Firearms**
Dayton, OH
www.chiappafirearms.com

**Chipmunk Rifles**
Milton, PA
www.chipmunkrifles.com

**Cimarron Firearms Co.**
Fredericksburg, TX
www.cimarron-firearms.com

**Citadel by Legacy Sports**
see Legacy Sports

**Colt Competition Rifle**
Breckenridge, TX
www.coltcompetitionrifle.com

**Colt's Manufacturing Company**
Hartford, CT
www.coltsmfg.com

**Connecticut Shotguns
Mfg. Co.**
New Britain, CT
www.connecticutshotgun.com

**Connecticut Valley Arms (CVA)**
Duluth, GA
www.cva.com

**Coonan Inc.**
Blaine, MN
www.coonaninc.com

**Cooper Firearms**
Stevensville, MT
www.cooperfirearms.com

**CorBon / Glaser**
Sturgis, SD
www.corbon.com

**Crosman**
Bloomfield, NY
www.crosman.com

**Daisy**
Rogers, AR
www.daisy.com

**Dakota Arms**
Sturgis, SD
www.dakotaarms.com

**Dan Wesson Firearms Co.**
Norwich, NY
www.cz-usa.com/products/by-brand/
dan-wesson

**Del-Ton, Inc.**
Elizabethtown, NC
www.del-ton.com

**Dillon Precision Reloaders**
Scottsdale, AZ
www.dillonprecision.com

**Dixie Gun Works**
Union City, TN
www.dixiegunworks.com

**DoubleTap Defense LLC**
St. Louis, MO
www.doubletapdefense.com

**DPMS Firearms**
St. Cloud, MN
www.dpmsinc.com

**Eagle Imports**
Wanamassa, NJ
www.eagleimportsinc.com

**E.R. Shaw, Inc.**
Bridgeville, PA
www.ershawbarrels.com

**Ed Brown Products, Inc.**
Perry, MO
www.edbrown.com

**EMF Company, Inc.**
Santa Ana, CA
www.emf-company.com

**Enterprise Arms**
Irwindale, CA
www.entreprise.com

**ENVIRON-Metal, Inc.**
Sweet Home, OR
www.hevishot.com

**EOTech**
Ann Arbor, MI
www.eotech-inc.com

**Escort by Legacy Sports**
Reno, NV
www.legacysports.com

**European American Armory**
Rockledge, FL
www.eaacorp.com

**Excel Arms**
Ontario, CA
www.excelarms.com

**Fabarm**
Brescia, Italy
www.fabarm.com

**Fausti USA**
Fredericksburg, VA
www.faustiusa.com

**Federal Premium Ammunition**
Anoka, MN
www.federalpremium.com

**Fiocchi**
Ozark, MO
www.fiocchiusa.com

**Flodman**
Jarsta, Sweden
www.flodman.com

**FNH USA**
McLean, VA
www.fnhusa.com

**Forster Products**
Lanark, IL
www.forsterproducts.com

**Franchi USA**
Pocomoke, MD
www.franchiusa.com

**Frankford Arsenal**
Columbia, MO
www.frankfordarsenal.com

**Freedom Arms**
Freedom, WY
www.freedomarms.com

**Gamo USA**
Ft. Lauderdale, FL
www.gamousa.com

**Glock, Inc.**
Smyrna, GA
www.glock.com

**Hammerli**
Ulm, Germany
www.haemmerli.info

**Harrington & Richardson**
Madison, NC
www.hr1871.com

**Harvester Muzzleloading**
Henderson, KY
www.harvestermuzzleloading.com

**Heckler & Koch**
Columbus, GA
www.hk-usa.com

**Henry Repeating Arms**
Bayonne, NJ
www.henryrepeating.com

**Heritage Mfg., Inc.**
Miami, FL
www.heritagemfg.com

**High Standard**
Houston, TX
www.highstandard.com

**Hi-Point**
Dayton, OH
www.hi-pointfirearms.com

**Hodgdon Powder Company**
Shawnee Mission, KS
www.hodgdon.com

**Hornady Mfg., Co.**
Grand Island, NE
www.hornady.com

**Howa by Legacy Sports**
Reno, NV
wwww.legacysports.com

**H-S Precision**
Rapid City, SD
www.hsprecision.com

**IMR Powder Company**
Shawnee, KS
www.imrpowder.com

**ISSC by Legacy Sports**
Reno, NV
www.legacysports.com

**Ithaca Gun Company**
Upper Sandusky, OH
www.ithacagun.com

**IWI US, Inc.**
Harrisburg, PA
www.iwi.us

**J. P. Sauer & Sohn Rifles**
San Antonio, TX
www.jpsauer.us/firearms

**J.G. Anschutz**
Ulm, Germany
www.jga.anscheutz-sport.com

**Jarrett Rifles**
Jackson, SC
www.jarrettrifles.com

**K-Var Corp.**
Las Vegas, NV
www.k-var.com

**Kahr Arms**
Worcester, MA
www.kahr.com

**Kel-Tec CNC Industries, Inc.**
Cocoa, FL
www.keltecweapons.com

**Kimber Mfg. Inc.**
Elmsford, NY
www.kimberamerica.com

**Knight Rifles**
Athens, TN
www.knightrifles.com

# Directory of Manufacturers & Suppliers

**Krieghoff International, Inc.**
Ottsville, PA
www.krieghoff.com

**Kriss USA**
Virginia Beach, VA
www.kriss-usa.com

**Kruger Optical**
Sisters, OR
www.krugeroptical.com

**Kynoch Ammunition**
Englewood, CO
www.kynochusa.com

**L.A.R. Mfg., Inc (Grizzly Firearms)**
West Jordan, UT
www.largrizzly.com

**LWRC International, LLC**
Cambridge, MD
www.lwrci.com

**Lapua Bullets**
Lapua, Finland
www.lapua.com

**Lazzeroni Arms, Inc.**
Tuscon, AZ
www.lazzeroni.com

**Leatherwood/Hi-Lux Optics**
Torrance, CA
www.hi-luxoptics.com
www.leatherwoodoptics.com

**Legacy Sports International**
Reno, NV
www.legacysports.com

**Leica**
Allendale, NJ
www.us.leica-camera.com/sport_optics

**Les Baer Custom**
LeClaire, IA
www.lesbaer.com

**Leupold and Stevens**
Beaverton, OR
www.leupold.com

**Ljutic LLC**
Yakima, Washington
www.Ljuticgun.com

**LUCID**
Riverton, WY
www.mylucidgear.com

**Lyman Products**
Middletown , CT
www.lymanproducts.com

**M.O.A. Corporation**
Sundance, WY
www.moaguns.com

**Magnum Research**
Pillager, MN
www.magnumresearch.com

**Magtech Ammunition Company, Inc.**
Lino Lakes, MN
www.magtechammunition.com

**Marlin**
Madison, NC
www.marlinfirearms.com

**Marocchi Arms**
Sarezzo, Italy
www.marocchiarms.com

**MasterPiece Arms**
Carrollton, GA
www.masterpiecearms.com

**Mauser**
Isny, Germany
www.mauser.com

**McMillian**
Phoenix, AZ
www.mcmfamily.com

**MEC Reloading**
Mayville, Wisconsin
www.mecreloaders.com

**Merkel**
Trussville, AL
www.merkel-usa.com

**MG Arms**
Spring, TX
www.mgarmsinc.com

**Millet Sights**
Overland Park, KS
www.millettsights.com

**Minox**
Germany
www.minox.com

**Montana Rifle Company**
Kalispell, MT
www.montanarifleco.com

**Mossberg**
North Haven, CT
www.mossberg.com

**MTM Molded Products Co.**
Dayton, Ohio
www.mtmcase-gard.com

**New Ultra Light Arms**
Granville, WV
www.newultralight.com

**Nightforce Optics, Inc.**
Orofino, ID
www.nightforceoptics.com

**Nighthawk Custom**
Berryville, AR
www.nighthawkcustom.com

**Nikon Sport Optics**
Melville, NY
www.nikonsportoptics.com

**Norma**
Amotfors, Sweden
www.norma-usa.com

**North American Arms**
Provo, UT
www.naaminis.com

**Nosler**
Bend, OR
www.nosler.com

**Olympic Arms**
Olympia, WA
www.olyarms.com

**P.M.C. Ammunition**
Conroe, TX
www.pmcammo.com

**PARA USA, LLC**
Pineville, NC
www.para-usa.com

**Pedersoli & C.**
Brescia, Italy
www.davide-pedersoli.com

**Pentax Ricoh Imaging Americas Corp.**
Denver, CO
www.pentaximaging.com/sports-optics

**Perazzi**
Azusa, CA
www.perazzi.it

**Powerbelt Bullets**
Nampa, ID
www.powerbeltbullets.com

**Puma by Legacy Sports**
Reno, NV
www.legacysports.com

**Purdey**
London, England
www.purdey.com

**Ramshot Powders**
Miles City, MT
www.ramshot.com/powders

**RCBS**
Oroville, CA
www.rcbs.com

**Redding Reloading Equipment**
Cortland, NY
www.redding-reloading.com

**Redfield**
Beaverton, OR
www.redfield.com

**Remington Arms**
Madison, NC
www.remington.com

**Rifles, Inc.**
Pleasanton, TX
www.riflesinc.com

**Rock River Arms**
Colona, IL
www.rockriverarms.com

**Rossi**
Miami, FL
www.rossiusa.com

**Ruger**
Newport, NH
www.ruger.com

**RWS**
Furth, Germany
www.rws-munition.de/en

**Sako**
Riihimaki, Finland
www.sako.fi

**Savage Arms**
Westfield, MA
www.Savagearms.com

**Schmidt & Bender**
Claremont, NH
www.schmidtundbender.de/en

**Shiloh**
Big Timber, MT
www.shilohrifle.com

**Sierra Bullets**
Sedalia, MO
www.sierrabullets.com

**Sig Sauer**
Exeter, NH
www.sigsauer.com

**Simmons Optics**
Overland Park, KS
www.simmonsoptics.com

**Smith & Wesson**
Springfield, MA
www.smith-wesson.com

**Speer Bullets**
Lewiston, ID
www.speer-bullets.com

**Springfield Armory**
Geneso, IL
www.springfield-armory.com

**Stag Arms**
New Britain, CT
www.stagarms.com

**Steiner Division**
Greeley, CO
www.steiner-binoculars.com

**Steyr Arms**
Trussville, AL
www.steyrarms.com

**STI International, Inc.**
Georgetown, TX
www.stiguns.com

**Stoeger Industries**
Pocomoke, MD
www.stoegerindustries.com

**Swarovski Optik**
Cranston, RI
www.swarovskioptik.com

**Swift Bullets**
Quinter, KS
www.swiftbullets.com

**Szecsei & Fuchs**
Windsor, Ontario, Canada
www.fuchs-fine-guns.com or
www.szceseidoubleboltrepeater.ca

**Tactical Rifles**
Zephyrhills, FL
www.tacticalrifles.net

**Taurus**
Miami, FL
www.taurususa.com

**Taylor's & Co.**
Winchester , VA
www.taylorsfirearms.com

**Thompson/Center**
Springfield, MA
www.tcarms.com

**Traditions Firearms**
Old Saybrook, CT
www.traditionsfirearms.com

**Tikka T3**
Riihimaki, Finland
www.tikka.fi

**Trijicon**
Wixom, Michigan
www.trijicon.com

**Tristar Sporting Arms**
North Kansas City, MO
www.tristarsportingarms.com

**Turnbull Mfg. Co.**
Bloomfield, NY
www.turnbullmfg.com

**Uberti**
Pocomoke, MD
www.uberti.com

**U.S. Firearms**
Hartford, CT
www.usfirearms.com

**UTAS USA**
Des Plaines, IL
www.utas-usa.com

**VihtaVuori**
Bensenville, IL
www.vihtavuori-lapua.com

**Volquartsen Custom**
Carroll, IA
www.volquartsen.com

**Walther Arms, Inc.**
Fort Smith, AR
www.waltherarms.com

**Weatherby**
Paso Robles, CA
www.weatherby.com

**Weaver Optics**
Anoka, MN
www.weaveroptics.com

**Western Powders, Inc.**
Miles City, MT
www.accuratepowder.com

**Wild West Guns**
Anchorage, AK
www.wildwestguns.com

**Wilson Combat**
Berryville, AR
www.wilsoncombat.com

**Winchester Repeating Arms & Ammunition**
East Alton, IL
www.winchester.com

**Woodleigh Bullets**
Murrabit, Australia
www.woodleighbullets.com.au

# Gunfinder Index

# Gunfinder Index

# Gunfinder Index